Teachers' Edition

ALGEBRA TWO

and TRIGONOMETRY

Mervin L. Keedy

Marvin L. Bittinger

Stanley A. Smith

Addison-Wesley Publishing Company
Menlo Park, California   Reading, Massachusetts   London
Amsterdam   Don Mills, Ontario   Sydney

ISBN 0-201-03852-8
ABCDEFGHIJK-VH-82107987

Contents

Answers

Answers are found in several places.

1. In the student text, Selected Answers begin on page 692. In the Selected Answers, many graphs are described rather than drawn. This technique calls attention to aspects of the graphs that students may not readily observe from drawings.

2. This Teachers' Edition contains overprinted answers for all problems, including **TRY THIS** Exercises, Chapter Reviews, and Chapter Tests. When answers are too long to be included on the page, they appear along with graph answers in the Additional Answers section which begins on page 692. (In the student text, Selected Answers begin on this page. The Selected Answers do not appear in this Teachers' Edition.)

3. The Solutions Manual for **TRY THIS** Exercises, a separate supplement, contains step-by-step solutions for all **TRY THIS** Exercises, with reasons for each step when appropriate.

4. The Student Answer Book contains answers to all exercises and problems.

Features of the Student Text

"Ready for" Exercises.   Determine student readiness for the coming chapter.

Chapter Opening photos.   Relate to some problem in the chapters or to uses of mathematics in careers.

Lessons.   Offer topics sufficient for a class period.

Lesson Labels.   Use a system of double numbering. Lesson 7–4 means the fourth lesson in Chapter 7.

Lesson Objectives.   Appear with color marks after each lesson title. The parts of the lesson are keyed to the objectives.

Instruction.   Gives brief and direct presentation of the lesson content, keyed to the objectives.

Examples.   Provide prototypes of the exercises that follow.

TRY THIS Exercises.   Follow each example to provide immediate reinforcement. They are boxed in color.

Exercise Sets.   Follow each lesson. Exercise instructions refer students to appropriate examples. Each pair of odd and even numbered exercises are exactly parallel in difficulty.

Calculator Exercises.   Appear at the end of many exercise sets. These are appropriate for hand-held calculators.

Challenge Exercises.   Extend the content of many exercise sets. They are appropriate for special assignments.

Chapter Reviews.   Test the terminal objectives listed in the Teachers' Edition. These objectives begin on page T15.

Chapter Tests.   Correspond item by item to the Chapter Reviews.

Cumulative Reviews.   Occur at the ends of chapters 4, 8, 11, 15, and 19.

Computer Activities.   Present relevant problems to be solved by means of flow charts and BASIC programming language.

Career Features.   Give overviews of the world of work.

Program Management

The various components of *Algebra Two with Trigonometry* have been carefully designed to interact with each other and support the teacher in the goal of making each student successful. The complete program consists of the

> Student Text
> Teachers' Edition
> Test Booklet
> Solutions Manual for **TRY THIS** Exercises
> Answer Book for all problems

These components interact to provide for sound planning, testing, diagnosing, and individualizing.

Planning

To plan the course for one year or for three semesters, use:

> Suggested Time Schedules, pages T10 through T13
> Table of Contents, pages v to x

To plan each chapter, use:

> Table of Contents, pages v to x
> Objectives and Comments for Each Chapter, beginning on page T15

To plan a particular lesson, look at:

> Lesson objectives indicated by marks like these, **▎** , **▊▊** , **▊▊▊** , at
>   the beginning of each lesson
> Lesson examples
> Comments for that chapter and lesson (see pages T15 and following)

Testing

In the student text use:

> Chapter Review and Chapter Test at the end of each chapter
> Cumulative Reviews following chapters 4, 8, 11, 15, and 19

In the Test Booklet supplement, use:

> Weekly Quizzes
> Cumulative Tests
> Chapter Tests (for either Pre- or Post-testing)
> Midterm Test
> Final Test

Diagnosing

To diagnose student needs in Chapters 2 through 21, use:

"Ready for ..." (at the beginning of each chapter)

Chapter Tests in TEST BOOKLET

Individualizing

To prescribe individual student assignments, use:

Color lesson reference numbers on the "Ready for" pages, and the Chapter Review. Chapter Review problems parallel the problems in the Chapter Test.

To instruct individual students or small groups, use:

Self-teaching examples in student text

SOLUTIONS MANUAL for step-by-step solutions to **TRY THIS** Exercises.

Student ANSWER BOOK for all answers in student text.

Evaluation

To evaluate student progress, use:

Chapter Tests in student text

Cumulative Reviews in student text

Chapter Tests in TEST BOOKLET

Cumulative Tests in TEST BOOKLET

Midterm and Final Tests in TEST BOOKLET

Weekly Quizzes in TEST BOOKLET

Test Booklet

38 Weekly Quizzes

21 Chapter Tests

5 Cumulative Tests

Midterm and Final Examinations

Order Number: 3853

Solutions Manual

Solutions for all **TRY THIS** Exercises

Step-by-step solutions

Reasons for many steps

Order Number: 3854

Student Answer Book

Answers for all exercises, even and odd

Includes Calculator Problems

TRY THIS Exercises

Exercise Sets

Order Number: 3855

Teachers' Edition

The Teachers' Edition includes management procedures, suggested time schedules, chapter objectives, and notes from the authors about each chapter.

Student pages are printed full size in full color. Notice that answers to all exercises are annotated in color. The sample below, taken from page 197 of the Teachers' Edition, includes answers and—at the bottom of the page—a reference to a supplement.

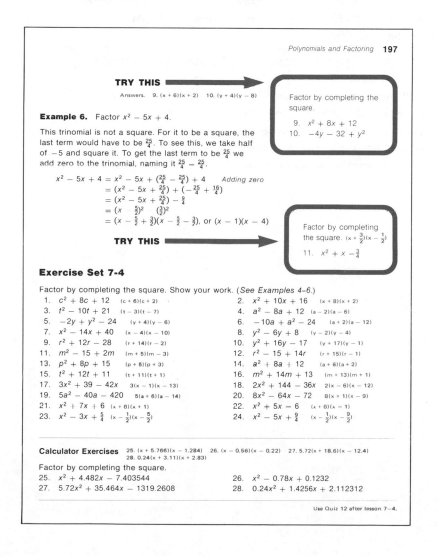

TRY THIS ➡

Answers.   9. $(x + 6)(x + 2)$ 10. $(y + 4)(y - 8)$

Factor by completing the square.

9. $x^2 + 8x + 12$
10. $-4y - 32 + y^2$

Example 6. Factor $x^2 - 5x + 4$.

This trinomial is not a square. For it to be a square, the last term would have to be $\frac{25}{4}$. To see this, we take half of -5 and square it. To get the last term to be $\frac{25}{4}$ we add zero to the trinomial, naming it $\frac{25}{4} - \frac{25}{4}$.

$$x^2 - 5x + 4 = x^2 - 5x + \left(\frac{25}{4} - \frac{25}{4}\right) + 4 \quad \text{Adding zero}$$
$$= \left(x^2 - 5x + \frac{25}{4}\right) + \left(-\frac{25}{4} + \frac{16}{4}\right)$$
$$= \left(x^2 - 5x + \frac{25}{4}\right) - \frac{9}{4}$$
$$= \left(x - \frac{5}{2}\right)^2 - \left(\frac{3}{2}\right)^2$$
$$= \left(x - \frac{5}{2} + \frac{3}{2}\right)\left(x - \frac{5}{2} - \frac{3}{2}\right), \text{ or } (x - 1)(x - 4)$$

Factor by completing the square. $(x + \frac{3}{2})(x - \frac{1}{2})$

11. $x^2 + x - \frac{3}{4}$

TRY THIS ➡

Exercise Set 7-4

Factor by completing the square. Show your work. (*See Examples 4–6.*)

1. $c^2 + 8c + 12$ $(c + 6)(c + 2)$
2. $x^2 + 10x + 16$ $(x + 8)(x + 2)$
3. $t^2 - 10t + 21$ $(t - 3)(t - 7)$
4. $a^2 - 8a + 12$ $(a - 2)(a - 6)$
5. $-2y + y^2 - 24$ $(y + 4)(y - 6)$
6. $-10a + a^2 - 24$ $(a + 2)(a - 12)$
7. $x^2 - 14x + 40$ $(x - 4)(x - 10)$
8. $y^2 - 6y + 8$ $(y - 2)(y - 4)$
9. $r^2 + 12r - 28$ $(r + 14)(r - 2)$
10. $y^2 + 16y - 17$ $(y + 17)(y - 1)$
11. $m^2 - 15 + 2m$ $(m + 5)(m - 3)$
12. $r^2 - 15 + 14r$ $(r + 15)(r - 1)$
13. $p^2 + 8p + 15$ $(p + 5)(p + 3)$
14. $a^2 + 8a + 12$ $(a + 6)(a + 2)$
15. $t^2 + 12t + 11$ $(t + 11)(t + 1)$
16. $m^2 + 14m + 13$ $(m + 13)(m + 1)$
17. $3x^2 + 39 - 42x$ $3(x - 1)(x - 13)$
18. $2x^2 + 144 - 36x$ $2(x - 6)(x - 12)$
19. $5a^2 - 40a - 420$ $5(a + 6)(a - 14)$
20. $8x^2 - 64x - 72$ $8(x + 1)(x - 9)$
21. $x^2 + 7x + 6$ $(x + 6)(x + 1)$
22. $x^2 + 5x - 6$ $(x + 6)(x - 1)$
23. $x^2 - 3x + \frac{5}{4}$ $(x - \frac{1}{2})(x - \frac{5}{2})$
24. $x^2 - 5x + \frac{9}{4}$ $(x - \frac{1}{2})(x - \frac{9}{2})$

Calculator Exercises   25. $(x + 5.766)(x - 1.284)$ 26. $(x - 0.56)(x - 0.22)$ 27. $5.72(x + 18.6)(x - 12.4)$
28. $0.24(x + 3.11)(x + 2.83)$

Factor by completing the square.

25. $x^2 + 4.482x - 7.403544$
26. $x^2 - 0.78x + 0.1232$
27. $5.72x^2 + 35.464x - 1319.2608$
28. $0.24x^2 + 1.4256x + 2.112312$

Use Quiz 12 after lesson 7–4.

Time Schedules

Suggested Time Schedule: Algebra Two and Trigonometry in One Year

This text contains 146 lessons in 21 chapters. Each lesson is designed to take one 50-minute instructional period. The suggested time schedule provides a plan for a school year of 170 instructional periods. It also provides instructional time for the following:

Beginning of the school year activities such as making the students familiar with the text and administering entry skill check-ups.

Ongoing review and testing such as are provided in the five cumulative reviews and tests, and in the midterm and final reviews and tests.

Chapter preparation activities and chapter-end testing as provided in the 20 "Ready fors" and the 21 chapter reviews and tests.

Supplements such as weekly quizzes from the test booklet.

Chapter	Instructional Periods	Reference Points for Pacing		
		Months	Quarters	Semesters
1	10	September		
2	5	September		
3	6	October		
4	7	October	1st	
5	6	October		
6	6	November		1st
7	8	November		
8	10	Nov/Dec		
9	10	December	2nd	
10	10	Dec/Jan		
11	7	January		
Total Ch 1–11	85	4 months/ 3 weeks	2 quarters	1 semester
12	9	January		
13	8	February		
14	8	February	3rd	
15	8	March		
16	9	March		2nd
17	7	April		
18	7	April		
19	7	Apr/May	4th	
20	10	May		
21	12	June		
Total Ch 12–21	85	4 months/ 2 weeks	2 quarters	1 semester
Total Ch 1–21	170	9 months 1 week	4 quarters	2 semesters

Suggested Time Schedule: Algebra Two and Trigonometry in Three Semesters

This text contains 146 lessons in 21 chapters. Each lesson is designed to take one 50-minute instructional period. The following suggested time schedule completes the 255 instructional periods of three semesters by providing instructional time for the following:

Beginning of the school year activities such as making the students familiar with the text and administering entry skill check-ups.

Ongoing review and testing such as are provided in the five cumulative reviews and tests, and in the midterm and final reviews and tests.

Chapter preparation activities and chapter-end testing as provided in the 20 "Ready fors" and the 21 chapters reviews and tests.

Supplements such as weekly quizzes from the test booklet.

Chapter	Instructional Periods	Reference Points for Pacing		
		Months	Quarters	Semesters
1	14	September		
2	7	September	1st	
3	9	October		
4	11	October		1st
5	9	November		
6	10	November	2nd	
7	11	December		
8	14	Dec/Jan		
Total Ch 1–8	85	4 months/ 3 weeks	2 quarters	1 semester
9	14	Jan/Feb		
10	14	Feb/Mar	3rd	
11	11	March		
12	12	April		2nd
13	11	Apr/May		
14	12	May/June	4th	
15	11	June		
Total Ch 9–15	85	4 months/ 2 weeks	2 quarters	1 semester
16	14	September		
17	14	Sep/Oct	5th	
18	13	Oct/Nov		3rd
19	12	November		
20	15	December	6th	
21	17	Dec/Jan		
Total Ch 16–21	85	4 months/ 3 weeks	2 quarters	1 semester
Total Ch 1–21	255	14 months	6 quarters	3 semesters

Authors' Notes to Teachers

Comments for each chapter of this book appear in the following pages. Here are some general comments about the book's important features.

TRY THIS Exercises.   In the student pages, these exercises are marked by red arrows and frames. They follow explanation and examples of particular concepts and skills.

The **TRY THIS** Exercises can be used in a variety of ways, but teachers have found greatest success from using them as follows: After the explanation and the examples, the class comes to the **TRY THIS** Exercises. Students should work these exercises individually, then check their answers (the answers are given in the back of the book). The teacher can answer any questions that arise. When the teacher is sure that students understand the concept or have acquired the necessary skill, the class proceeds with the lesson.

This way of teaching has proved successful because students become involved and have their questions answered as they arise, rather than having to wait. Moreover, the students learn just what they are expected to do on homework. They have experienced the exercises themselves, as opposed to watching someone else do the work.

Lesson Objectives.   The text proceeds through cycles of explanation, examples, and **TRY THIS** Exercises. They are keyed to lesson objectives by marks like these: $\blacksquare$, $\blacksquare\blacksquare$, $\blacksquare\blacksquare\blacksquare$, etc. The objectives are listed at the beginning of each lesson.

At the end of each lesson is an exercise set. The exercises are grouped according to the objectives they cover, and they are keyed by the same marks.

Chapter Objectives.   Chapter objectives which are listed in the following pages, correspond to the exercises in both the Chapter Review and the Chapter Test at the end of each chapter. Hence the chapter objectives are terminal objectives for the chapter.

These objectives are compiled from the lesson objectives.

"Ready for" Exercises.   At the beginning of each chapter except the first there are exercises titled "Ready for . . .?" These exercises incorporate the key skills and ideas that students will need as they work through the chapter. The exercises can be used as a diagnostic tool. If students are weak in any of the prerequisite skills, they should go back and brush up according to their needs. All the "Ready for" exercises are referenced to earlier lessons so students can easily find the review they need.

Exercise Sets: Basic Exercises.   An exercise set appears at the end of each lesson. The exercises are presented in two columns. The odd-numbered exercises in the left-hand column match in difficulty the even-numbered exercises in the right-hand column. Exercise 1 is like Exercise 2, Exercise 3 is like Exercise 4, and so on. Thus the basic exercises can be assigned as separate groups, odd or even. The answers to selected odd-numbered exercises appear in the back of the student text; the answers to even-numbered do not.

The directions for basic exercises include references to examples in the lesson. If students have difficulty with a group of exercises, they can use the references to go back to the text examples and review the procedure there.

Exercise Sets: Calculator Exercises.   Calculator exercises are a unique feature of this text. In many exercise sets there are several exercises designed to be worked using a calculator. Note the following about these exercises: 1) They are like the others in the lesson except that the numbers are not set up so that the answers come out even. 2) These exercises tend to fix the algebraic ideas in a way that the others do not. 3) The exercises are optional. 4) It is very easy to make up other calculator exercises because the answers need not come out even. Simply change the numbers in the printed exercises. 5) Answers to calculator exercises are given to 8 digits. It is important to realize that calculators are different. Some round differently than others. Some give answers to more or fewer than 8 digits. Answers will have to be graded flexibly, accordingly.

It would be a mistake to let students work all the exercises and/or take tests with calculators. It is too easy to become overly dependent on them.

Exercise Sets: Challenge Exercises. A number of exercise sets include Challenge Exercises. These exercises, which extend the objectives of the lesson, may be used as special assignments.

Chapter Reviews and Chapter Tests. The Chapter Review and the Chapter Test for any chapter are very much alike. Exercise 1 in the Chapter Review is like Exercise 1 in the Chapter Test, and so on. Note that the review exercises have references to lessons in the chapter. Thus if students have trouble doing any review exercises, they can easily find the appropriate lesson to review. Answers to the review exercises are in the back of the student text.

Cumulative Reviews. Cumulative Reviews occur following chapters 4, 8, 11, 15, and 19. References are included to earlier lessons so that appropriate review material is easy to find.

Proofs. For students going on in mathematically related endeavors, proofs and rigor are important and should be emphasized. For others, proofs are not so important and may be omitted. This text contains numerous proofs and remarks of a formal nature, aimed at the former kind of student. However, all of these are optional, and can be omitted for other students.

Careers. Five career features appear in the book following chapters 3, 7, 10, 13, and 16. Note the circle graph in each feature. Other graphs vary from feature to feature.

Objectives and Comments for Each Chapter

Chapter 1. REAL NUMBERS AND THEIR PROPERTIES

After finishing Chapter 1, students should be able to
- convert between fractional and decimal notation for rational numbers.
- distinguish between rational and irrational numbers.
- find the absolute value and additive inverse of a number.
- add, subtract, multiply, and divide real numbers.
- tell which laws are illustrated by certain sentences.
- recognize impossible divisions (by zero).
- use the distributive law to factor and multiply expressions.
- collect like terms.

- rename additive inverses without parentheses.
- simplify expressions with and without exponents.
- rewrite expressions with and without exponents.
- use exponents in multiplication and division.
- use exponents in raising a power to a power.
- simplify expressions with absolute values.

Chapter 1 contains material on the properties of real numbers and algebra, and constitutes a review of the fundamental parts of first year algebra.

Lesson 1—1, page 3. In this book we make a distinction between numbers and numerals. This does not make the presentation difficult or stilted. One reason for this is that we use the word "notation" liberally, as opposed to the word "numeral."

We work with the set of real numbers or the set of rational numbers, and we use different kinds of *notation* in different circumstances. Rational numbers, for example, can be named by decimal notation, fractional notation, percent notation, scientific notation, etc. We have found that the use of the word "notation" helps to clarify the distinction without making it difficult.

Lesson 1—2, page 6.   The precise definition of absolute value comes later. At this point, students are given an intuitive review of the idea. The concept of *definition* is often difficult for students in mathematics, because definitions in mathematics are quite different from those outside of mathematics.

In Math	*Outside of Math*
We don't define things until we know what they are.	We don't bother to define a term if we know what it means.
Once a definition is made, we use it and keep referring to it.	Once the meaning of a term is known, we don't bother with the definition. It has served its purpose.

Absolute value provides an example of this. Intuitively we know what the concept means, and this is discussed here. Later, we shall make a precise definition because we will want to prove the properties. We will *use* the definition in establishing that $|ab| = |a| \cdot |b|$, for example. Without the definition to use, we would not be able to do such a proof. Numbers may have additive inverses and also multiplicative inverses. To simplify reading and speaking, we suggest that the words "additive inverse" be shortened to "inverse." Later, when it comes up, "multiplicative inverse" can be called "reciprocal."

Page 9.   A word about reading mathematical symbolism: A symbol such as $-x$ might be read "minus x," or "negative x," or "the inverse of x," and may-

be even other ways. Once the concept has been grasped, it is not important how one reads the symbol. For purposes of learning the concepts, however, some attention to precision in speaking is in order. When an expression contains a variable and could take on negative values, and it is preceded by the symbol $-$, it should be read as "the inverse of." If the expression can take nothing but positive values, or is a constant, it is correct to read $-$ as "negative."

We suggest that this distinction be made, but that you not make too much of it.

Lesson 1—3, page 11.   Students may ask whether commutative, associative, and distributive laws are definitions or theorems. The best answer is that they are neither. They are usually axioms, depending upon the author's treatment.

Page 12.   Throughout the text you will find remarks such as this one. They are designed to add to the interest and knowledge of students, without placing a burden on them to master these ideas. All of these remarks are optional.

Some writers define subtraction in terms of additive inverses. We prefer this definition, because it is general. This definition holds in the system of natural numbers, for example, where there are no additive inverses. Also, this definition is believable, and, it is usable in situations such as Example 7.

Page 13.   Student activity can be used here. Half the class could do subtractions as in Column A and the other half the additions in Column B, putting their answers on the board in tabular form. Before long, students will discover and be able to describe the pattern. This sets the stage for accepting the theorem. Throughout the text we state important generalizations, calling them theorems, as we do here.

Page 14.   Proofs are occasionally given in the text, but not too often, since we do not wish to make the book heavy. Proofs of additional theorems will be given in the *Teacher's Edition,* so that they will be available if you wish to use them with better students. You will note that when proofs are given, they do not ordinarily follow immediately the statement of the theorem. Rather, the theorem is followed by some examples and some **TRY THIS** activity. Only then may a proof be given. Thus students have some experience with the theorem's ideas and applications before studying its proof.

Note that the proofs in this book are written in narrative style. We avoid the two-column format commonly used in geometry books for several reasons. Such proofs are not written in that style anywhere else. Also, writing proofs can be the means by which students begin to learn to write mathematical English.

Lesson 1—4, page 16. It should be noted how the definition of division is exactly parallel to that for subtraction. Division is defined to be the operation opposite to multiplication, like subtraction is defined to be the operation opposite to addition.

Page 17. Note that the definition of reciprocal is exactly parallel to that for additive inverse. Two numbers are additive inverses if their sum is the additive identity, and two numbers are reciprocals if their product is the multiplicative identity.

Theorem 1—2 exactly parallels Theorem 1—1. We can subtract by adding an inverse, and we can divide by multiplying by a reciprocal.

A Proof of Theorem 1—2. By the definition of division, $(a/b) \div (c/d)$ is the number which, when multiplied by c/d, gives a/b. Consider what happens when we multiply $(a/b)(d/c)$ by (c/d): $((a/b)(d/c)) \cdot (c/d) = (a/b) \cdot (d \cdot c/c \cdot d) = a/b$. We have shown that $(a/b)(d/c)$ when multiplied by c/d gives a/b. Thus $(a/b)(d/c) = (a/b) \div (c/d)$ by the definition of division.

Note that this proof exactly parallels the one for Theorem 1—1. If we consider group structure in an abstract sense, these theorems are really the same. The operations are different, but the proofs depend upon the *group structure,* and in terms of group structure, they are identical.

Lesson 1—5, page 20. You will note that there is no lesson in this text titled "order of operations." The reason is that such a treatment is time consuming, unnecessary, and confusing. What we do here is to make an *agreement* concerning omitting parentheses. Everything else comes naturally if it is not mentioned. Since we use fractional notation to indicate division almost entirely in algebra, students will very naturally do any divisions before adding or subtracting. They will also quite naturally do additions and subtractions in order from left to right when there are no parentheses.

Page 22. The definition of *field* (in the Remark) is of interest because it is precisely the properties listed in the definition that enable us to proceed in elementary algebra. There are other fields besides the real numbers. The rational numbers form a field, and so do the complex numbers. The clock arithmetics, where the number of elements is a prime number, are also fields.

Page 23, A Proof. Using Theorem 1—3, we can prove the distributive law of multiplication over subtraction. We know that subtraction can be done by adding an additive inverse. So, $b - c = b + (-c)$. Also, we know that $-1 \cdot a = -a$.

Thus $a(b - c) = a[b + (-c)] = ab + a \cdot (-c) = ab + a(-1 \cdot c) = ab + (-1 \cdot ac) = ab + (-ac) = ab - ac$.

Page 23. *Terms* can also be defined as follows: If an expression is rewritten with only plus signs between the parts, then the parts separated by the plus signs are the terms.

Page 24. It can be noted that factoring and collecting like terms both depend upon the same property of real numbers, the distributive law. In this sense, they are not basically different procedures.

Lesson 1—6, page 26. Some activity is in order in connection with Theorem 1—3. Have someone choose any positive number. Then have the class multiply it by −1. Then have them add the result to the original number, noting that the result is 0. Hence the numbers are additive inverses of each other. Repeat this for some other positive numbers. Repeat for some negative numbers. Repeat for 0. Then conclude (although this is not a proof) with the statement of Theorem 1–3.

A Proof of Theorem 1–3. We know that $(-1 + 1) = 0$. Thus $(-1 + 1) \cdot a = 0 \cdot a$; $-1 \cdot a + 1 \cdot a = 0$; $-1 \cdot a + a = 0$. Now, since $-1 \cdot a + a = 0$, $-1 \cdot a$ must be the additive inverse of a. Thus $-1 \cdot a = -a$.

Page 27. Examples 8 and 9 demonstrate the rule, stated just before Example 10. To find the additive inverse of an expression with several terms, we can change the sign of every term. "Changing the sign" means to replace an expression with its additive inverse.

Lesson 1–7, page 32. Sometimes it is not understood that a^1 must be defined separately from a^n, where n is greater than 1. It would not make sense to say "to use a as a factor one time." Thus the expression a^1 is meaningless until we assign a meaning to it. It is clearer that a separate definition is needed for a^0. 0^0 is not defined. The reason will become apparent later.

Page 33. The definitions of a^1, a^0, and negative exponents make patterns, e. g., in expanded notation. $621.562 = (6 \times 10^2) + (2 \times 10^1) + (1 \times 10^0) + (5 \times 10^{-1})$ etc. To keep the laws of exponents, we will naturally define x^1 to be x and x^0 to be 1.

Lesson 1–8, page 35. It can be pointed out that definitions are *agreements* about how we are going to use certain words or symbols. The definition here can help to make this clear.

Page 36. The development before the statement of Theorem 1–4 is a kind of proof of that theorem. For the mathematician, a rigorous proof would be done by induction. The explanation before Theorem 1–5 is scarcely a proof, since only one case has been considered, namely the one where both exponents are positive and the one in the numerator is greater. Again, a rigorous proof would be done by induction.

Page 37. A rigorous proof of Theorem 1–6 would involve induction.

Lesson 1–9, page 39. If b is a number between a and c, we can write $a < b < c$, or $c < b < a$.

Page 40. The use of the word "inverse" is most important. Consider, for example, how confusing it would be to say "the absolute value of a negative number is its negative," or "the absolute value of x, when x is negative, is negative x."

The *definition* of absolute value is *not* "the distance from 0 on a number line." The latter is merely an intuitive idea. This illustrates an important point. In mathematics, we make definitions only *after* we know what something is intuitively. Once we make a definition we *use* it in proving theorems, etc. (For example, see proof of Theorem 6, page 1, which leans heavily on the definition of $|x|$, and could not be done without it.) Outside of mathematics, once we know what something is, we rarely need to bother with a definition of it again. This, too, is the opposite of the way definitions are used in mathematics. For students with mathematical aptitude, it is good to point this out.

In this development of absolute value, examples are given to illustrate the various parts of the theorem (Theorem 1–7) and then the theorem is stated. These examples, of course, do not constitute a proof. The proof is given below. For better students who wish to study the proof, it can be pointed out that in this proof we proceed by considering various cases. This sort of proof is fairly common.

Page 41, A Proof of Theorem 1–7, Part a). To prove that $|a \cdot b| = |a| \cdot |b|$ for any real numbers a and b, we consider several cases.

Case I. If both a and $b \geqslant 0$, $|ab| = ab$ (since $ab \geqslant 0$) $= |a| \cdot |b|$.

Case II. If $a < 0$ and $b < 0$, $|a| = -a$ and $|b| = -b$. Thus $|ab| = ab$ (since $ab > 0$) $= 1 \cdot ab = (-1)(-1) \cdot ab = (-a)(-b) = |a| \cdot |b|$.

Case III. If $a > 0$ and $b < 0$, $|a| = a$, $|b| = -b$ and $ab < 0$. Thus, $|ab| = -(ab)$ (since $ab < 0$) $= -1 \cdot (ab) = a \cdot (-b) = |a| \cdot |b|$.

Chapter 2. SOLVING EQUATIONS

After finishing Chapter 2, students should be able to

- solve equations using the addition and multiplication principles.
- solve equations containing parentheses.
- use the principle of zero products to solve equations.
- solve problems by translating to equations and solving the equations.
- solve a formula for a specified letter.

Lesson 2–1, page 48. Some equations with variables are true (or false). For example: "For any x, y, $x + y = y + x$." When a variable is quantified, substitution is neither permitted nor contemplated. Variables not quantified are called "free variables." They are "free" for substitution.

Page 49. The addition principle is taken as an axiom is some texts, but is easy to prove as a theorem. In fact, the paragraph above the statement of the theorem is almost a proof.

The proof depends upon two things: the definition of "equals" and the meaning of "operation." For any operation the principle given here as the addition principle holds.

Suppose $*$ represents any operation. By binary operation we mean a relation in which, given elements a and c, there corresponds *only* one element called $a*c$. If $a = b$, a and b are the same element by definition of $=$. Then for any c, $a*c$ is a unique element. It can also be called $b*c$, since a and b are the same. Thus if $a = b$, then $a*c = b*c$.

Page 50. The logic of solving equations will be brought out in this chapter. This is done gradually, without making it seems difficult. Basically, the idea is this:

1. We establish that solving an equation in the ordinary way is a proof. We write down the equation to be solved and we accept it as true (hypothesis).
2. We use theorems to derive a sequence of other statements from this one. The idea is to get another equation so simple that we can see its solution set at a glance.
3. We have now proved that *IF* the original equation is true *THEN* the last one is true. Thus anything that makes the first one true must make the last one true. In other words, *if* the original equation has solutions they are to be found among those of the last equation.
4. We find whether the solutions of the last equation are solutions of the first one, by substituting them into the first one.

Page 51. When a conditional sentence *"if A then B"* is true, the solution set of A is a subset of the solution set of B (but not necessarily conversely).

Example: If $x < 7$, then $x < 9$.

This sentence is true, because if a number is less than 7 it is certainly less than 9.

Solution set of the antecedent: The set of numbers less than 7.

Solution set of the consequent: The set of numbers less than 9.

The solution sets look like this:

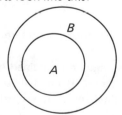

A is a subset of B

The converse would also be true if B were a subset of A.

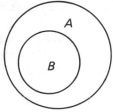

(Then A and B would be the same set), but that is not the case here.

When we solve an equation in the ordinary way, we establish a conditional sentence, " if A then B," where A is the equation to be solved, and B is a simpler equation, or equations. Then we know that the solution set of A is a subset of the solution set of B. Thus all the solutions of A are among the solutions of B. The converse of what is proved is, " if B then A." We can prove this converse in various ways, but in simple situations, the easiest way is to substitute the solutions of B into A and see whether they fit.

Students often get the impression that checking an equation is done only to determine if a mistake has been made. This is indeed one reason for doing it, but there is also a logical reason. In simple linear equations, the usual procedures do not produce answers that are not solutions of the original equation, but in other situations this can happen (answers thus obtained are often called "extraneous roots").

Here is a simple example to show how this can happen. Consider the equation $x = 1$, having just one solution.

$$x = 1$$
$$x^2 = x \quad \text{Multiplying on both sides by } x$$

This time the equation obtained has more solutions than the first one. It has two solutions, 0 and 1, while the original equation has just the number 1.

Lesson 2—2, page 55, A Proof of Theorem 2—3. Half of the principle of zero products really needs no proof. If one factor of any product is 0 then the product is 0. Here is a proof of the other half:

Consider two numbers a and b such that $ab = 0$, and assume that one of the numbers is not 0, say b. Then b has a reciprocal $1/b$. Since $ab = 0$, $ab(1/b) = 0(1/b)$, $a(b \cdot 1/b) = 0$, $a \cdot 1 = 0$, $a = 0$. Therefore, if the product of two numbers is 0 and one of the factors is not 0, then the other factor *is* 0. At least one factor must be 0.

Since the principle of zero products consists of a statement and its converse, the use of it does not produce any answers that are not solutions. Thus logically a check is not necessary for any procedure that uses only this principle.

Lesson 2—3, page 57. The importance of drawing a picture in problem solving cannot be overemphasized. In Example 1, you can use a picture of a rope (a straight line) cut in two unequal parts, x and $x + 3$. The length of the uncut rope is 8 m, and this is the source of the equation. When checking the answer to a problem, we check the conditions of the problem itself to detect errors in translating as well as errors in solving an equation.

Lesson 2—4, page 60. Skill in manipulating formulas is a very important one. Technicians of various kinds must often deal with formulas, and it is easy to see that more students should learn this skill in their high school math courses.

Chapter 3. LINEAR EQUATIONS
After finishing Chapter 3, students should be able to
- decide whether a given ordered pair is a solution of an equation.
- draw graphs of simple equations.
- recognize linear equations.
- find standard form for linear equations.
- graph linear equations using intercepts.
- graph linear equations with a missing variable.
- find the slope of a line containing a given pair of points.

- given a point on a line and its slope, find an equation for the line.
- given two points, find an equation of the line containing them.
- given the slope-intercept equation for a line, find the slope and y-intercept.
- tell, without graphing, whether the graphs of a pair of equations are parallel.
- given an equation of a line and a point, write an equation of the line parallel to the given line through the given point.
- given an equation of a line and a point, write an equation of the line perpendicular to the given line through the given point.
- find a linear equation which fits two data points and use the equation to make predictions.

Lesson 3—1, page 66. The terminology "first axis" and "second axis" is temporary. We establish that the *first* coordinate of a point gives its distance in the direction of the *first axis* and the *second* coordinate gives its distance in the direction of the *second axis*. Then later we assign letters to identify the axes. Note that they need not be x and y. The first coordinate of a point is called its *abscissa* and the second coordinate is called its *ordinate*. This terminology is disappearing from high school books, but is still very much in books at the college level. Therefore, college bound students should be exposed to it.

Page 67. We *usually* take variables in alphabetical order. In math classes this is almost invariably so, but it may be helpful to students if they know that this may very well *not* be the case outside the math classroom.

Page 68. An ordered pair of numbers identifies a point, and conversely, a point has a unique pair of numbers. It is common in speaking or writing to use terms "point" and "ordered pair" somewhat interchangeably. We are not recommending this in the algebra class, although language such as "this point satisfies the equation" is common. We suggest that students be exposed, somewhere in the course, to this kind of loose language.

Page 69. Students often fail to realize that if we plot enough points (say 1,000 per centimeter), the dots we draw would overlap, and there would be no need to draw a line or curve to connect the plotted points. In other words, the set of *all* points satisfying the equation *is* the line. Since we do not wish to plot points for days on end, we select a few representative points and draw a curve to show where the rest of the points would be if we plotted them.

Lesson 3—2, page 72. Some equations with variables in denominators have graphs which come close to being lines. For example

$$3 + 2y/x + 4/x = 0$$

If we multiply by x on both sides, we get

$$3x + 2y + 4 = 0$$

This is standard form of a linear equation. The point $(0, -2)$ is not in the graph of the first equation because x cannot equal 0, so its graph is not an entire line.

To put a linear equation into standard form, we use the addition and multiplication principles. A word about the logic here: When we do this, we know that all solutions of the original equation will be solutions of the equation in standard form. We would hope that the converse is also true, that all solutions of the equation in standard form will be solutions of the original equation. Since we have ruled out variables in denominators, we can start with the standard form and, using the addition and multiplication principles, arrive at the original equation. Hence the converse *is* true, and the equations are equivalent.

Page 74. Graphing linear equations using intercepts is rather easy. Just have students cover up the x-term in an equation. Then they can easily determine the value of y. This is the y-intercept. Similarly, covering up the y-term and determining x gives the x-intercept.

The term *intercept* is another one that is not always used precisely. We may speak of the point $(0, 4)$ as being the y-intercept. We may also say that "the y-intercept is 4." The former is strictly correct; the latter is more convenient.

Lesson 3–4, page 82. Since a line has many equations, it's best not to speak of *the* equation of a line.

The proof of Theorem 3–5 follows very quickly from Theorem 3–4. You might point out that this manner of proceeding is common in mathematics. That is, we *use* theorems already proved in proving other theorems.

A Proof of Theorem 3–5. Suppose a nonvertical line contains the points P_1, with coordinates (x_1, y_1), and P_2, with coordinates (x_2, y_2). The slope of the line is $(y_2 - y_1)/(x_2 - x_1)$. We substitute $(y_2 - y_1)/(x_2 - x_1)$ for m in the point-slope equation (Theorem 3–4), to obtain the desired expression.

For students going on in mathematics, it is very important that they learn to write mathematical explanations or arguments IN ENGLISH! It is very common for otherwise good students going to college to write only a sequence of equations when they write a proof—no words, no explanations, just mathematical symbols. You might explain to students that when we write a proof, we must set the stage, explain what we are doing, tell where things come from, and so on. In writing mathematical arguments, we need to say what the symbolism means, if it is not of a universally understood nature. We need to say when a certain statement is taken as an assumption, or hypothesis. If we use a variable, we should say what it represents, etc. Here are some sample wordings, to illustrate:

Consider any point (x, y) . . .

Let (x_1, y_1) be the point where the two lines intersect . . .

Suppose l_1 and l_2 are any two nonvertical parallel lines . . .

Let p represent the price of each item. Then, according to our hypothesis, . . .

To be mathematically literate, a student must be able to write a mathematical argument *in English.*

Page 83. To prove Theorem 3–6, simply solve Theorem 3–4 for y and substitute $(0, b)$ for (x_1, y_1).

Lesson 3–5, page 85, A Proof of Theorem 3–7. Suppose l_1 and l_2 have the same slope and different y-intercepts, but intersect at point $A(x_2, y_2)$ as shown. Then the slope of l_1 is $(y_2 - y_1)/(x_2 - 0)$, and the slope of l_2 is $(y_2 - y_3)/(x_2 - 0)$. Since $y_1 \neq y_3$, it follows that the two slopes are different. But this contradicts the hypothesis that the slopes are the same. Thus our assumption that the lines intersect is false. Therefore the lines must be parallel.

Page 87. Theorem 3–8 is a good example of a theorem consisting of a statement and its converse. The first part of it tells us that the set of pairs of lines having −1 as a product of slopes is a subset of the set of perpendicular lines (no lines vertical). The second part tells us that the set of perpendicular lines is a subset of the set having −1 as product of slopes. Thus these are the same set.

Such theorems are often expressed more concisely using the words "if and only if," as follows: Two nonvertical lines are perpendicular *if and only if* the product of the slopes is −1.

Lesson 3–6, page 90. If you feel that students can recall how to solve systems of equations (not yet considered in this book) you can alternatively have them solve this problem by solving the system of equations

$$10 = 40m + b$$
$$20 = 112m + b$$

Chapter 4. SYSTEMS OF EQUATIONS

After finishing Chapter 4, students should be able to

- solve systems of equations graphically.
- solve systems of equations using the substitution method.
- solve systems of equations using the addition method.
- determine whether a system of equations is inconsistent or dependent.
- solve systems of three equations in three variables.
- solve problems by translating them to systems of equations.
- solve motion problems.

Lesson 4–1, page 101. Solving linear systems by graphing is not efficient. It does illustrate graphically what the possibilities are. Two lines can intersect in either one point, no points, or all points. Thus the section on graphical solving is optional.

Lesson 4–2, page 103. When a system of two linear equations is quite simple, the substitution method is usually the easiest way to solve. However, for non-simple systems or for systems of more than two equations, the addition method is far better.

Page 104. When a system of linear equations is solved using the addition method, all answers obtained are actually solutions. Thus, checking by substituting into the original equations is only for detecting errors in this case.

Lesson 4–3, page 107. In referring to the lesson on solving by graphing, we see that for two linear equations to be inconsistent, the graphs must be parallel lines (for equations in two variables). Thus if a system is consistent, the graphs must intersect in one point or the two equations must have the same graph. The definition of dependent systems of equations is given in such a way that it holds for systems with any number of variables. For the case of two variables, a system of two equations is consistent in case the equations have the same graph, or in case one equation can be obtained from the other (by multiplying by constants and rearranging).

Lesson 4–5, page 114. In Example 1, note that we translate, putting in letters, and then afterward state precisely what the letters represent. This is much easier than trying to state in advance what letters we are going to use and what they are to represent. Translating applied problems is almost always easier if we can translate to a system of equations, rather than to a single equation.

Page 115. A hint that is often helpful in translating mixture problems is as follows: The amount of an ingredient in one mixture plus the amount of that ingredient in the other mixture is the amount in the total mixture.

Lesson 4–6, page 119. The definition of speed (or *rate* of speed, to be redundant) is easy to remember, so it is preferable to memorize it, if it is indeed necessary to memorize. Then the other two forms can easily be obtained from this definition.

It should be emphasized, again and again, that one should make sketches when solving problems. Students can also be given the hint to look for two things that are the same. This very often allows for translation directly. In Example 1, the trains go the same distance, for example.

Note the use of subscripts in Example 1. Students may show some resistance to using them at first, but subscripts are convenient and help to keep work orderly. For example, d_1 is the distance traveled by the first train, while d_2 is the distance traveled by the second train. Subscripts are used a great deal in most mathematically related activities.

Keeping data in charts, as is done here, is very often a good idea. Solving a problem is something like putting together a jigsaw puzzle. We lay out all the pieces. Then we put them into bunches, and then try to fit them together. Listing data in a table corresponds to bunching the pieces.

Page 121. Solving problems is the hardest thing the student will have to try to learn in a high school algebra course. One thing required is a *lot of practice!* Therefore, it is good teaching technique to assign problems on a regular basis, a few at a time along with other material, rather than considering them only in bunches on relatively rare occasions.

Chapter 5. INEQUALITIES

After finishing Chapter 5, students should be able to
- graph inequalities in one variable on a line.
- solve inequalities using the addition principle.
- solve and graph conjunctions of inequalities in one variable.
- solve and graph disjunctions of inequalities in one variable.
- solve inequalities using the multiplication principle.
- solve inequalities using both the addition and multiplication principles.
- solve inequalities involving absolute value.
- graph inequalities in two variables on a plane.
- graph systems of linear inequalities in two variables.
- solve linear programming problems.

For students going on in mathematics the material of this chapter is important. For those not going on, it can be considered optional.

Lesson 5–1, page 130. This definition provides another example to illustrate that in mathematics we already know what something means before we define it. We have the intuitive notion that $a < b$ means "a is to the left of b." This intuitive notion does not enable us to prove the properties of inequalities however, so we need a formal definition.

Once we make the formal definition, we must keep it in mind (students should memorize definitions!) and use it.

Page 131, A Proof of Part of Theorem 5–1. Let us prove that the Addition Principle (Theorem 5–1) is true for the inequality $a < b$.

If $a < b$, then $b - a$ is a positive number by definition of $<$. Since $c - c = 0$, we can add $c - c$ and still have a positive number. Thus $b - a + (c - c)$ is positive. We can rename this positive number $(b + c) - (a + c)$. But this means that $a + c < b + c$ by the definition of $<$.

Theorem 5–1 applies to inequalities containing $<$, $\leq$, $>$ or $\geq$. Inequalities having the verb $>$ can be proved very much like this. For $a > b$, we can write $b < a$ and then use this theorem, after which we reverse again. The equality parts of $\leq$ and $\geq$ do not need separate proof, because they follow at once from the addition principle for equations.

Page 132. It can be proved that the use of the addition principle with inequalities always produces *equivalent* inequalities, as follows: Consider an inequality $a < b$. By the addition principle, it follows that for any number c, $a + c < b + c$. Thus $a < b$ implies $a + c < b + c$.

Now consider $a + c < b + c$. Let us use the addition principle again, adding $-c$. We obtain $a < b$. Thus $a + c < b + c$ implies $a < b$. We now know that the two inequalities are equivalent, having the same solution set.

In the text treatment, this theorem is omitted for brevity. The proof is easy, however, and you may wish to have better students try it.

Lesson 5–2, page 134. The word *and* corresponds to set intersection. If A and B are sentences and we know how to graph both A and B, then we can graph the conjunction "A and B" by finding the intersection of the graphs of the two parts. That is what we do in these examples.

Page 135. The word *or* corresponds to set union. If we know how to graph a sentence A and a sentence B, we can graph the disjunction "A or B" by finding the union of the graphs of the parts. Note that a disjunction cannot be abbreviated the way a conjunction can. This should be emphasized, since it is common for students to try to do it.

Page 136, A Proof of Part of Theorem 5–2. We prove Theorem 5–2 for the inequality $a < b$.

Case I, $c > 0$: If $a < b$, then $b - a$ is positive by the definition of $<$. Thus $c(b - a)$ is positive, since the product of two positive numbers is positive. But $c(b - a) = cb - ca$. So, $ac < bc$ by definition of $<$.

Case II, $c < 0$: If $a < b$, then $b - a$ is positive by the definition of $<$. Now $-c$ is positive because c is negative. Thus $-c(b - a)$ is positive and equals $-bc + ac$, or $ac - bc$. Therefore $bc < ac$ by definition of $<$.

Proving Theroem 5–2 for the verb $>$ can be done as follows: For $a < b$, reverse the sentence to read $b > a$. Then apply Theorem 5–2 and then reverse again. The equality parts of this theorem follow from the multiplication principle for equations.

When the multiplication principle for inequalities is used, an equivalent inequality is obtained (they have the same solution set), if we multiply by a non-zero constant. It is not true if we multiply by an expression with a variable that could be 0.

This can be proved as follows: Consider an inequality $a < b$. Let us multiply by a positive constant c, obtaining $ac < bc$. We know that the solution set of $a < b$ is a subset of $ac < bc$.

Now consider $ac < bc$, (where of course c is a positive constant). The reciprocal of c is $1/c$ and is also a positive constant. Let us multiply by $1/c$ to obtain $a < b$. Now we know that the solution set of $ac < bc$ is a subset of $a < b$. Therefore $a < b$ and $ac < bc$ have the same solution set.

This is one case. The case of multiplying by a negative constant can be proved in a similar way.

Lesson 5–3, page 139. Many students will have studied geometry in which there is a so-called "ruler postulate." This postulate says: There is a one–one correspondence between the points of a line and the set of real numbers such that: if the number a corresponds to point P and the number b corresponds to point Q, then the distance from P to Q is $|a - b|$.

The statement here, therefore, is not a theorem, but essentially that postulate.

Lesson 5–4, page 143. It is a good idea, when graphing inequalities like these always to begin by drawing a dashed line. It can be made solid later, if that is required.

Lesson 5–5, page 148. This lesson is essential if you are going to teach the following one on linear programming. Otherwise, it is optional.

Lesson 5–6, page 151. Linear programming is an example of mathematics developed recently. It was developed around the time of World War II. This is unusual, because most of the mathematics taught in high school is centuries old.

Trying to find maximum values for $T = 10x + 15y$ can also be done graphically. Graph $10x + 15y = 0$. Then find the line parallel to it that intersects the polygon at just one point—or just one line. Such points or lines give the greatest or least values possible for T.

Chapter 6. POLYNOMIALS

After finishing Chapter 6, students should be able to
- collect like terms.
- arrange a polynomial in ascending or descending powers of a given variable.
- add, subtract and multiply polynomials.
- find special products of polynomials.
- solve certain problems using the compound interest formula.

Lesson 6–1, page 161. In Example 4, we have rewritten the polynomial using only plus signs. The student is not expected to do this, but rather to proceed mentally.

If a polynomial is a constant other than 0, it has degree 0. The polynomial 0 is not given a degree, because statements of certain theorems are simplified if the zero polynomial is not given a degree.

Page 162. Collecting like terms is based upon the distributive law of multiplication over addition. This should be reviewed or pointed out, and it should be emphasized that this procedure therefore gives equivalent expressions.

Equivalent expressions are expressions that have the same value for *all* sensible replacements, and it is important to know when we have equivalent expressions. The expressions x/x and $(x-1)/(x-1)$ are equivalent. They have the value 1 for all replacements except the nonsensible replacements 0 for the first and 1 for the second.

Page 163. This definition is not difficult to memorize, and students should be required to learn it and be able to reproduce it. In fact, serious students should be required to memorize all definitions. This does not mean memorization word-for-word, but rather the learning of the gist, *precisely!* Many students going on to college do not realize the necessity for this kind of memory work.

Lesson 6–2, page 166. Skill in calculating with polynomials *mentally* is an important one. A good teaching technique is to use oral drills and contests at appropriate times to develop this skill. One useful device in mental addition is the use of check marks. In Example 3, for instance, when we add the x^3y terms we could mark each of them with a check. This shows that we have used them and that we need no longer consider them.

Oral drill in subtracting polynomials is also in order. The use of check marks is also useful here.

A Proof of Theorem 6–1. Consider any polynomial $a_nx^n + a_{n-1}x^{n-1} + \ldots + a_1x + a_0$. We multiply each term by -1 and add this to the original polynomial. We get 0, the additive identity. Thus the polynomials are additive inverses of each other.

Lesson 6–3, page 171. Two polynomials can be multiplied without going through all the steps of Example 5 or Example 6, and students should learn to do this, proceeding mentally as much as possible. In the **TRY THIS** Exercise 8, for example, one can do the following:

$$(p-3)(p^3 + 4p^2 - 5)$$

Multiply every term in the second polynomial by p and write the results.

$$\text{(A)} \quad p^4 + 4p^3 - 5p$$

Then multiply every term in the second polynomial by -3 and write the results.

$$\text{(B)} \quad -3p^3 - 12p^2 + 15$$

Then collect like terms.

$$p^4 + p^3 - 12p^2 - 5p + 15$$

After some practice, some of this can be telescoped. For example, in (B) instead of writing $-3p^3$, go back to (A) and mark out the 4, replacing it by 1. In (A) leave spaces for missing terms and when they are obtained in (B) write them in those spaces.

Lesson 6–4, page 173. These products are actually just special cases of what was done in the last lesson. They occur often enough that they deserve special mention. Also, a good deal of drill, especially oral drill, is very much in order on all of them.

The rule stated here can be of a great deal of help to some students. If they will memorize the rule, then when they go to square a binomial, they can apply it and know exactly what to do.

Lesson 6–5, page 175. This rule can be shortened for memorizing: "Square the first, square the second, write a minus sign between the squares."

Lesson 6–6, page 178. This lesson provides a good application of elementary algebra. It is optional, however.

A Proof of Theorem 6–3. Suppose we invest P dollars at an interest rate r. At the end of a year we will have an amount A_1 given by $A_1 = P + Pr$ or $A_1 = P(1 + r)$. For the second year we have $P(1 + r)$ dollars to invest. At the end of that year we will have a total of A_2 dollars given by

$$A_2 = A_1 \cdot (1 + r)$$
$$= P(1 + r)(1 + r)$$
$$= P(1 + r)^2$$

Similarly at the end of t years we will have an amount $P(1 + r)^t$.

Page 179, A Proof of Theorem 6–4.   Let us consider compounding four times a year, or *quarterly*. Then we consider one-fourth of a year to be an *interest period.* The rate of interest for such a period is then $r/4$. The number of periods will be four times the number years. Now suppose that the number of interest periods per year is any number n. For one period the interest rate will be r/n, and the number of times interest is compounded is nt. Thus we have $A = P[1 + (r/n)]^{nt}$.

Chapter 7. POLYNOMIALS AND FACTORING
After finishing Chapter 7, students should be able to
- factor polynomials where the terms have a common factor.
- factor polynomials which are differences of squares.
- factor polynomials which are squares of binomials.
- factor polynomials of the type $ax^2 + bx + c$.
- factor polynomials by completing the square.
- factor polynomials that are sums or differences of two cubes.
- solve equations by factoring and using the principle of zero products.
- solve problems by translating to equations and solving the equations.

Lesson 7–1, page 187.   Remind students that factoring by grouping works only for certain polynomials with four terms, not all of them. This method of factoring is the basis of a method of factoring general trinomials which we consider as an optional method in Lesson 5–3. Factoring by grouping will be needed if that lesson is to be covered.

Lesson 7–2, page 189.   It is usual, and helpful, to write the terms that are squares as the first and last terms. Then, once it has been determined that an expression is a trinomial square (or square of a binomial) we can proceed as follows. Again, memorizing the wording and reciting to oneself when factoring can be helpful to many students: "Write the square root of the first term, the sign of the middle term and the square root of the last term. Then write an exponent of 2."

Page 191.   Oral drill is important on many kinds of manipulations with polynomials. This is certainly true of factoring. Always stress that one should look first for a common factor.

Lesson 7–3, page 193.   This method can be helpful to students who are having difficulty. It obviously takes more time than the other method, and need not be stressed, especially for better students.

Lesson 7–4, page 195.   The technique of completing the square is an important one in later mathematics, although it is not often used in factoring. It is used in finding standard form of a quadratic equation, in one or two variables, for example. Most students seem to find this procedure somewhat sophisticated, so they need to see it several times.

Lesson 7–5, page 198.   To learn factoring of sums or differences of cubes, the patterns shown here must be learned. It may be helpful to think of the pattern in comparison with trinomial squares, for example,

$$a^3 + b^3 = (a + b)(a^2 - ab + b^2)$$

cube roots and   like $(a + b)^2$ except sign is
same sign   different and there is no 2 in
                                  middle term

An expression like $a^6 - b^6$ can be thought of as a difference of two squares or the difference of two cubes. The latter factorization causes no difficulty. But the factorization as the difference of cubes creates the factor $a^4 + a^2b^2 + b^4$, which students will not recognize as being factorable. It factors as $(a^2 + ab + b^2)(a^2 - ab + b^2)$.

Lesson 7–7, page 202. Now that a general strategy has been described, students should get lots of practice in factoring, much of it oral.

Chapter 8. RELATIONS, FUNCTIONS, TRANSFORMATIONS

After finishing Chapter 8, students should be able to
- list the domain and range of a given relation.
- graph relations which are the solution sets of sentences in two variables.
- test for symmetry with respect to the x-axis, y-axis, and origin.
- write equations of inverses of relations.
- recognize graphs of functions.
- find function values for a given function.
- find equations for inverses of functions.
- sketch graphs which are either vertical or horizontal stretchings or shrinkings of given graphs.
- show that certain functions are either even or odd.

The concepts of relation, function and transformation in this chapter are of fundamental importance, both in this text and mathematics courses. The transformation idea clarifies and simplifies a number of topics, especially graphing.

Lesson 8–1, page 214. It is assumed that students have had some experience with set notation. If that is not the case, the only thing necessary to know is that braces indicate that a set is being denoted. The ideas of relations and functions are easier to grasp if one begins by using finite sets.

The material in the next few pages establishes a motive for the definition of relation. Since there is such a close connection between relations and sets of ordered pairs, we eventually define a relation to be any set of ordered pairs. (We are considering only binary relations, of course. For a ternary relation we would use a set of ordered triples, and so on.)

Page 216. It often helps to consider some non-mathematical relations. For example, within a certain set of people, we have the relation "is a brother of." This also gives rise to a set of ordered pairs (a, b), in which a is the brother of b. The relation "is older than" can be demonstrated for the members of a class. Choose any two class members and write the name of the older one first in an ordered pair. This makes a set of ordered pairs in which the first member is always older than the second.

Lesson 8–2, page 218. With Example 1 and others like it, the point should be made that when we take *all* of the ordered pairs in the relation we get the solid line. When we graph the relation, we cannot of course plot an infinite number of points, but if we did we would get the solid line.

The wording in Example 2 and others like it is often shortened. Instead of saying "graph the relation which is the solution set of $y \geqslant x^2 - 5$" we can say "graph the relation $y \geqslant x^2 - 5$." We could also say "graph $y \geqslant x^2 - 5$." The wording in the text is designed to make a certain point, and should probably not be shortened too soon. Sometimes, in graphing inequalities (when the verb is $\leqslant$ or $\geqslant$) the boundary curve itself is included. When it is not, we draw the curve with dashed lines to indicate this. Therefore, whenever we graph inequalities, it is convenient to first graph the curve in question, drawing it with *dashed* lines. If later we decide that it is to be included in the graph, we can make it a solid line. If not, we leave it dashed.

Lesson 8–3, page 220. The notions of symmetry are very helpful in graphing, and are therefore very important.

In the first definition, P_1 is said to be the image of P. It is also true that P is the image of P_1. You may also find it helpful in having students gain an intuitive feel for line symmetry by pointing out that when a figure is symmetric with respect to a line, the halves would match if it were folded along that line. Also, if a mirror were placed on the line, we would see the same thing as if the mirror were not there.

For line symmetry one can think of finding the image of a point as follows: Start at the given point *P*. Travel in a direction perpendicular to the line. When you reach the line, note the distance you have gone. Go that much farther and in the same direction. The point where you stop will be the image.

Page 221. In Example 3, you might ask how far the upper point (2, 5) is from the *x*-axis. This must, of course, be measured along a line perpendicular to the *x*-axis. Hence the distance we are looking for is the distance between the points (2, 5) and (2, 0). This distance is certainly 5. (It could be shown with the distance formula, but that is not necessary for this development.) Similarly we can see that the distance of (2, −5) from the *x*-axis is 5. Hence the points are symmetric with respect to the *x*-axis. You may wish to choose more points as examples. For example, you could have one student choose any point not on the *x*-axis and have another determine the point symmetric to it. Students can then see the pattern described in Theorem 8—1.

Page 223. Theorem 8—2 follows at once from 8—1. The importance of this theorem in graphing is brought out in Examples 7 and 8. Students should learn, in graphing any equation, to look for symmetries before beginning to plot points in order to save a great deal of time.

Lesson 8—4, page 225. This same idea for point symmetry is as follows. Start at the given point *P*. Travel to the point of symmetry. Note the distance. Then go that much farther and in the same direction. The point where you stop will be the image.

Page 226. In connection with Example 3, you

may wish to have students find points symmetric with each other, with respect to the origin. Have a student select any point, writing it on the board, locate its image and write its coordinates. Then have students look for the pattern.

Page 227. Theorem 8—4 is important in graphing. Students should be encouraged to test any equation for symmetry with respect to the origin when graphing. In connection with this definition, you may wish to have students go back and look at some of the finite relations they looked at earlier. The relation $<$ consists of a set of ordered pairs in which the first coordinate is always less than the second, for example. If the first and second members are interchanged, we will have a set of ordered pairs in which the first coordinate is greater than the second in each ordered pair. Thus, the inverse of the relation $<$ is $>$. You can also have students look at the graphs of inverse relations and compare them. It is easy to see a pattern if the two relations just mentioned are graphed together.

Page 228. To help in seeing what happens when the *x*- and *y*-axes are interchanged, you can have students trace axes on a thin piece of paper and draw some relation. Then have them interchange the *x*- and *y*-axes by turning the paper over. By looking through the paper they can see more clearly what is illustrated here. If the line $y = x$ is also drawn, it will be clear that this line remains unchanged, and thus what happens is a reflection across this line.

We could state a theorem here, if desired: When a relation is described by an equation, if interchanging *x* and *y* produces an equivalent equation, the graph is symmetric with respect to the line $y = x$. This fact is quite helpful in graphing, and students should be encouraged to make this test when graphing any equation.

Lesson 8—5, page 231. The function concept is described and illustrated emphatically and in several ways in this lesson:

a) A function is a set of ordered pairs (a relation) in which for any first coordinate there is only one second coordinate.
b) A function is a rule that assigns a unique value to any member of the domain.
c) A *function machine* illustrates how an *input* (member of the domain) goes into the machine and an *output* (member of the range that corresponds to the input) comes out.

The function idea is an important one, although it is sometimes difficult for students. Students should grasp the function concept if they can go back to some of the finite relations and pick out those that are functions.

Page 232. The ordered pairs in a relation which is a function can be denoted *(x, f(x))*. Thus *x* is the symbol we use for the first coordinate and *f(x)* is the symbol we use for the second coordinate, or *function value*. Later, we refer to *x* as the *input* and *f(x)* as the *output.* We refer to a formula like $f(x) = x^2 + 3$ as a *rule* for assigning function values. This rule says to take any input *x*, square it and then add 3. An effective activity which can be used from time to time, is having students play a function guessing game. One student acts as the function machine, assigning outputs, according to some fixed but undisclosed rule. Students give inputs and are told the outputs, and the object is to guess the rule.

For Example 3, you might describe this function as the function that takes each input, squares it and then adds 3. Give students a few inputs and have them square and add 3 to tell you what the output is. Then have them write notation such as $f(2) = 7$, *after* they have gotten the idea.

Page 233. Example 5 can be described as the function that takes each input, doubles it, and adds 3.

Page 234. Example 6 is the function that takes the reciprocal of each input. Guessing games are good, with the function machines, in which a student acts

as a function machine and other students are to guess how the machine (student) is programmed, i.e., what is the rule.

Page 235. In Exercises 7–14, you might have students state in words what each function does. In 7, for example, the function adds 1 to each input. In 13, the function takes the absolute value and doubles, then adds 3 times the input.

Lesson 8–6, page 237. It needs to be emphasized that the notation f^{-1} does not mean $1/f$. The first few examples here are to get across the idea that if we interchange variables and solve we get an equation of a function that does the reverse of what the function itself does. This new function is the inverse of the given function. Example 1 is a function that adds 1 to every input. Before doing any algebra, we know that the function that does the opposite (inverse) must be the function that subtracts 1 from each input. You might bring this out in discussion, before having students work through Example 1.

Page 238. Example 2 is a function that takes the nonnegative square root of each input. The function that does the opposite must square each input.

Theorem 8–6 is an important one, and students should be drilled so that they can *immediately* simplify such expressions. This is very easy of course, but the drill and practice is still necessary. Here is an example that comes up frequently in later mathematics: $e^{\ln x}$ or $\ln e^x$. The exponential function e^x and the log function $\ln x$ are inverses of each other. Therefore, $e^{\ln x} = x$ and $\ln e^x = x$. Similarly sin Arcsin $x = x$, and so on.

A Proof of Theroem 8–6. Consider a function *f* and let *a* be an element in the domain of *f*. Then *(a, f(a))* is in *f*. By the definition of f^{-1}, if *(a, f(a))* is in *f*, then *(f(a), a)* is in f^{-1}. But this means that $f^{-1}(f(a)) = a$, which was to be proved. A similar argument shows that $f(f^{-1}(a)) = a$ for any *a* in the domain of f^{-1}.

An additional explanation in the proof of Theorem 8–6 may help. We know that *(a, f(a))* is in *f* and then *(f(a), a)* is in f^{-1}. Then when we take f^{-1} *(f(a))* we use *f(a)* as an input in f^{-1}. In other words, we look for the ordered pair in f^{-1} having *f(a)* as the first coordinate. When we find it, we see that the second coordinate (the function value) is *a*.

Lesson 8–7, page 240.   Here we begin to use the notation *f(x)* in a slightly different, but very common, way. We have already written such things as $f(x) = x^2$ and $y = x^2$. Function values are thus indicated by *y* or by *f(x)* or by expressions such as x^2. When we do not have any specific expression we may simply write *y = f(x)*. In this explanation, we have outputs given by *f(x)*. If we add 1, to get *y* = 1 + *f(x)*, each output is increased by 1, moving the graph upward.

Theorem 8–7 could have been stated by saying that a constant is added to *f(x)*. The wording used in the text simplifies the wording of similar statements later in the text.

Note: If we *subtract* a *positive* constant from *y*, this translates in the positive direction. This is what should be remembered. Of course if we subtract a *negative* constant, this translates in the *negative* direction (downward in this case).

Page 241.   It is important to stress that when we replace a variable *x* by *x — a*, to translate, the replacement must be made everywhere the variable occurs. The translation theorems are very important in graphing. If, for example, we know what the graph of $y = x^2$ looks like, and we see an equation *y* = 3 + x^2, we can figure out immediately what the graph looks like, even though we have never seen it. Similarly, we would know immediately what the graph of $y = (x - 2)^2$ looks like.

Lesson 8–8, page 244.   The stretching and shrinking transformations are also important in graphing. The theorems will be stated in a way analogous to the translation theorems, so that there will be a minimum of memorization and so that there will be some carry-over.

When we say that we stretch both ways from the horizontal axis, this means that *each point* will be twice as far from that axis as it was before the stretching.

Note that Theorem 8–9 is stated to be analogous to the translation theorems. Before, we subtracted; here we divide. Before, we talked about a positive constant and the positive direction; here we talk about a constant whose absolute value is greater than 1 and stretching.

Lesson 8–9, page 248.   It should be noted that all constant functions are linear.

Page 249.   In working through Example 4, students should do three things.
a) Find *f(—x)*. This of course means to replace *x* by —*x* wherever it occurs.
b) Find —*f(x)*. This means to find the additive inverse of *f(x)*.
c) See whether the two expressions are equivalent.

Chapter 9. FRACTIONAL EXPRESSIONS AND EQUATIONS

After finishing Chapter 9, students should be able to
- multiply, divide, and simplify fractional expressions.
- add and subtract fractional expressions.
- simplify complex fractional expressions.
- divide a polynomial by a divisor which is not a monomial.
- solve fractional equations.
- solve a formula for a given letter.
- solve problems using fractional equations.
- solve problems involving direct or inverse variation.

The idea of multiplying an expression by 1 is the key to understanding in this chapter and should be emphasized.

Lesson 9—1, page 260. The idea of multiplying by 1 provides the rationale for canceling. We suggest that simplification be done, initially, by factoring an expression and removing a factor of 1, and later, if at all, by allowing students to use the shortcut called canceling.

Page 261. The statement that we can divide fractional expressions by multiplying by the reciprocal of the divisor can be proved during Lesson 9—4. Consider the divisor fraction to be the denominator of a complex fraction. Multiply both numerator and denominator by 1 in the form of the reciprocal of this denominator over itself. The numerator expression shows the source of this rule.

Lesson 9—2, page 264. It can be pointed out that the LCM of several expressions may be one of the expressions itself.

Page 265. Students may need to be reminded that an expression like $3 - x$ is the additive inverse of $x - 3$.

Lesson 9—3, page 266. The use of parentheses in numerators when subtracting, as in Example 3, is very important and should be emphasized.

Lesson 9—4, page 272. There is another way to do Example 1. The entire expression can be multiplied by x^2/x^2, obtaining $(x^2 + x)/(x^2 - 1)$. After factoring and canceling, $x/(x - 1)$ is the result. In this example the result was obtained more quickly by this method, but such is not always the case.

Lesson 9—8, page 284. Although there is a complete lesson here devoted to solving problems it is preferable not to teach all of this at one time. It is far better to assign a few problems to be solved from time to time along with other homework assignments. Problem solving is a skill that takes time and practice to develop, and it is difficult for students to develop this skill if they are asked to work such problems only occasionally in concentrated bunches.

Lesson 9—9, page 290. The applications of direct variation provide an example illustrating mathematical models. A mathematical model is mathematics developed to provide a description of a real world situation, hopefully good enough that it allows one to predict what will happen in a given situation. The mathematical model of Example 2 gives very precise results and, hence, allows for accurate prediction. The model of **TRY THIS** Exercise 3, concerning amounts of garbage produced, gives only approximate results. In a rural area, for example, different amounts of garbage per person are produced. Hence this model might have to be altered in various situations.

Chapter 10. EXPONENTS, POWERS, AND ROOTS

After finishing Chapter 10, students should be able to
- convert to scientific notation and to decimal notation.
- simplify radical expressions with perfect square radicands.
- simplify expressions of the form $\sqrt[k]{a^k}$.
- multiply, divide, and simplify radical expressions.
- find roots of powers.
- add or subtract with radical notation.
- multiply expressions involving radicals.
- rationalize denominators or numerators of a radical expression.
- write expressions with and without fractional exponents.
- use fractional exponents to simplify radical expressions.
- solve radical equations.

Lesson 10—1, page 299. A common error in working with scientific notation is to move the decimal point the wrong way or the wrong distance. The idea of multiplying by 1, used here, largely eliminates this problem. A question that often arises is as follows: "Do we have to put our answer into scientific notation?" Clearly, for purposes of comparing answers in mathematics class it is a good idea. However, it is not always essential that this be done, and in many situations, people using mathematics daily do not consistently use scientific notation.

Lesson 10—2, page 303. There is an opportunity here to tell students about complex numbers and to introduce the notion that a new number system can be devised in which negative numbers have square roots. A *brief* introduction is all that is warranted at this point. The definition here is important and should be emphasized. That is, the radical symbol without a minus sign in front represents the principal (nonnegative) square root of a number.

Page 304. It has been common in the past to say that $\sqrt{a^2} = a$ rather than $\sqrt{a^2} = |a|$. This is, of course, incorrect, and students should never get the impression that the old way is correct.

Page 305. In connection with Theorem 10—4, note that every nonzero real number has three cube roots in the system of complex numbers, but only one of them is a real number.

Lesson 10—3, page 308. It should be noted carefully in Theorem 10—6 that the radicands a and b must be nonnegative. Otherwise, this theorem is not true. For example, consider $\sqrt{-2} \cdot \sqrt{-2} = \sqrt{(-2)(-2)} = \sqrt{4}$. This is false because $\sqrt{4} = 2$, and $\sqrt{-2} \cdot \sqrt{-2}$ does not exist in real numbers.

Page 309. Using absolute value notation to simplify radicals is essential unless we assume that radicands and variables in radicands are all nonnegative. The use of absolute value notation can become very cumbersome for students at this level. Therefore, we assume in the **TRY THIS** Exercises here and in many of the other exercises that all variables

represent nonnegative real numbers.

Lesson 10—4, page 313. Note that in connection with Theorem 10—7 the theorem is not true unless we assume that the radicands are nonnegative.

Lesson 10—6, page 319. Students should be encouraged to learn to do exercises like these mentally. Oral drill is most appropriate.

Lesson 10—7, page 320. The idea illustrated in Example 1 is to multiply by 1 in such a way that the denominator becomes a perfect square. In Example 2 the idea is to make the denominator a perfect cube.

Page 321. It is sometimes easier to multiply by 1 under the radical, and it is sometimes easier to multiply by 1 outside the radical, as in in Example 3. Students should be encouraged to use whichever procedure is easier. Again, students should be encouraged to do as many of these calculations as possible mentally.

Page 322. In Example 7 the denominator is $\sqrt{5} - \sqrt{2}$. The number $\sqrt{5} + \sqrt{2}$ is sometimes called the *conjugate* of that denominator. In other words, given an expression with two terms, changing the sign between them produces the conjugate.

Lesson 10—8, page 326. The motivation for the definitions given to fractional exponents is the preservation of the properties of exponents. The demonstration here shows that *if* we wish to have the usual properties of exponents hold, *then* we *must* make the definition in a certain way. Does this guarantee that the properties of exponents will hold? The answer is that it does not! The converse of what we have established is as follows: *If* we make the definition in this way, *then* the properties will hold. We have not established this, and in fact it is very difficult and time consuming to do so. It is good to point this out to students.

Page 328. When using rational exponents it is essential that the base be a nonnegative number.

Page 329. The assumption that the variables stand for nonnegative numbers is essential here since we are using rational exponents.

Chapter 11. COMPLEX NUMBERS

After finishing Chapter 11, students should be able to
- add, subtract, multiply, and divide complex numbers.
- solve equations involving complex numbers for x and y.
- find conjugates of complex numbers.
- find the reciprocal of a complex number and name in the form $a + bi$.
- find an equation having given complex numbers as solutions.
- solve first-degree equations having complex numbers as solutions.
- graph complex numbers in the plane.
- find absolute values of complex numbers.
- find a polynomial in $\bar{z}$ that is the conjugate of a polynomial in z.

Lesson 11–1, page 342. Students should realize that the word *imaginary* is misleading. It suggests that this kind of number cannot represent anything in the real world and is not useful. In fact, imaginary numbers have important applications.

Page 343. Students may need to be reminded that $-\sqrt{-3}\sqrt{-7} \neq -\sqrt{(-3)(-7)}$.

It is possible to *construct* the system of complex numbers using ordered pairs of real numbers. It can then be proved that the properties of a field hold in that system. Since we are not proceeding that way, we assume that the number i acts like a real number with the usual properties. This conforms to the historical development of this number system.

The system of complex numbers is not *ordered*. This means that it is not possible to select a positive and a negative set of complex numbers in the usual way. Thus, it is misleading and incorrect to read the symbol $-i$ as "negative i." Rather, this should be read "the inverse of i."

Lesson 11–2, page 348. This method of dividing complex numbers is very much like the procedure for rationalizing denominators having two terms.

Page 349. How do we know that two fractional expressions in complex numbers can be multiplied by finding the products of numerators and denominators, as is true in arithmetic? Because $(a/b)(c/d) = (a \cdot c)/(b \cdot d)$ is a field theorem, it tells us that this kind of multiplication can be done in *any* field.

Does the principle of zero products hold for complex numbers? Again the answer is *yes*, because this must hold in *any* field.

Whenever we work in any field, we can do the same kinds of things we do in solving equations in rational numbers. We can always add, subtract, and multiply. We can always divide, except by 0, and the principle of zero products holds. In many fields we cannot always take square roots, but in the field of complex numbers we can.

Lesson 11–3, page 352. The statement of the Fundamental Theorem of Algebra, given here, is somewhat different from the usual statement. It is often said that every equation of degree n with complex coefficients has n solutions. This is confusing, however, because some of the solutions may be the same, i.e., have multiplicities greater than 1.

Page 353, A Proof of Theorem 11–4. To find square roots of a nonzero complex number z, we solve the equation $x^2 = z$, or $x^2 - z = 0$. Thus, we have $x^2 - z = (x + a)(x + b)$ (fundamental theorem of algebra) $= x^2 + ax + bx + ab$. Since there is no x-term in $x^2 - z$, we know that $ax + bx$ must be 0, so $a = -b$. Thus the factors of $x^2 - z$ are of the form $x + r$ and $x - r$. Thus $x^2 - z = (x + r)(x - r) = 0$. Then $x + r = 0$ or $x - r = 0$ (principle of zero products) and $x = -r$ or $x = r$. Thus there are two square roots of z, r and $-r$, additive inverses of each other.

Page 357, A Proof of Theorem 11–6. We have also said that for any complex number z, $z + \bar{z}$ is a real number. Let us prove this. Let $z = a + bi$. Then $(a - bi)$ is $\bar{z}$, and $z + \bar{z} = (a + bi) + (a - bi) = 2a$. Since a is a real number, so is $2a$. Thus $z + \bar{z}$ is a real number.

Page 358, A Proof of Theorem 11–8. Let $z = a + bi$ and $w = c + di$.

$$\overline{z \cdot w} = \overline{(a + bi)(c + di)}$$
$$= \overline{(ac - bd) + (bc + ad)i}$$
$$= (ac - bd) - (bc + ad)i$$

$$\bar{z} \cdot \bar{w} = \overline{(a + bi)} \cdot \overline{(c + di)}$$
$$= (a - bi)(c - di)$$
$$= (ac - bd) - (bc + ad)i$$

Since the same result is obtained, $\overline{z \cdot w} = \bar{z} \cdot \bar{w}$.

Page 359. Example 4 and the development following it provides a spectacular discovery activity. Students will very easily discover that, given a polynomial in a complex variable z, the conjugate of that expression can be found by replacing z by its conjugate every place it appears.

Chapter 12. QUADRATIC EQUATIONS
After finishing Chapter 12, students should be able to
- solve equations of the type $ax^2 = k$, where $k \neq 0$.
- solve quadratic equations by factoring.
- solve quadratic equations using the quadratic formula.
- find approximate solutions using a square root table.
- determine the nature of the solutions of a quadratic equation with real coefficients, without solving it.
- find, without solving, the sum and product of the solutions of a quadratic equation.
- find an equation having specified numbers as solutions.
- solve a formula for a given letter.
- use quadratic equations to solve interest and motion problems.
- solve equations which are quadratic in form.

Lesson 12–1, page 368. In the definition of the standard form of a quadratic equation we require that a should not be zero. Since we ordinarily arrange an equation so that a is positive, b and c might be negative.

An alternate method for Example 1 follows:

$$3x^2 = 6$$
$$x^2 = 2$$
$$x^2 - 2 = 0$$
$$(x + \sqrt{2})(x - \sqrt{2}) = 0$$

$$x + \sqrt{2} = 0 \quad \text{or} \quad x - \sqrt{2} = 0$$
$$x = -\sqrt{2} \quad \text{or} \quad x = \sqrt{2}$$

That is, $x = \pm\sqrt{2}$.

Lesson 12–3, page 375. Note that this proof of the quadratic formula is not the usual one, in which we proceed by completing the square. This proof is simpler. It should be pointed out that the coefficients a, b, and c can be any complex numbers except that a is not zero.

Lesson 12–4, page 379. It should be emphasized in connection with Theorem 12–2 that the coefficients must be real numbers.

Lesson 12–8, page 389. This lesson, we feel, is a very important one for almost all students. Therefore, it should be taught and emphasized.

Chapter 13. QUADRATIC FUNCTIONS

After finishing Chapter 13, students should be able to

- graph functions and determine the vertex, the line of symmetry, and the maximum or minimum value.
- given a function, find an equation of the type $f(x) = a(x - h)^2 + k$, the vertex, line of symmetry, and the maximum or minimum value.
- find the x-intercepts of a quadratic function.
- find the quadratic function that fits certain data points.
- solve problems involving quadratic functions and variation.

Lesson 13—1, page 396. It should be pointed out in connection with this definition that a must not be 0. Otherwise, the expression is not quadratic. A short review of the essential parts of transformations is in order before proceeding. Note how the ideas of transformations are extremely useful here and simplify ideas greatly.

Lesson 13—5, page 409. It should be pointed out that the data given in the table is not sufficient to determine that a quadratic function is a good mathematical model. It is true that a quadratic function will fit the three data points, but further experience and information is needed before we can reasonably conclude that a quadratic function will give correct answers.

Page 410. This is an example of a mathematical model derived from theoretical considerations. The assumption made in the derivation of this quadratic function is that there is no friction or air resistance. Since, in the real world, there is air resistance, this model is incorrect in that sense and will give only approximately correct answers.

Lesson 13—6, page 414. Remind students that constant, linear, and quadratic functions are all polynomial functions.

Page 415. We often say that any physical situation which fits an equation like this obeys an *inverse square law.*

Page 416. In solving problems involving variation it is sometimes simpler to find the variation constant. It is also sometimes simpler to use a proportion and bypass finding the constant. Students should learn both methods and be encouraged to use the one that gives the simplest results.

Chapter 14. EQUATIONS OF SECOND DEGREE

After finishing Chapter 14, students should be able to

- use the distance formula to find the distance between any two points in the plane.
- find the coordinates of the midpoint of a segment, given the endpoints.
- find an equation for a circle, given the center and radius.
- find the center and radius of a circle.
- find the center, vertices, and foci of an ellipse and graph the ellipse.
- find the center, vertices, foci, and asymptotes of a hyperbola and graph the hyperbola.
- find the vertex, focus, and directrix of a parabola and graph the parabola.
- solve systems of first-degree and second-degree equations.
- solve problems involving systems of first-degree and second-degree equations.

Lesson 14—1, page 426. It is easy to verify that the distance formula also holds when two points are on a horizontal or vertical line. You might have students check this.

Lesson 14—2, page 429. Note carefully that the proof of Theorem 14—3 has two parts. We show that *if* a point is on the circle *then* it satisfies the equation. We must then show the converse, that *if* a point satisfies the equation, *then* it is on the circle. Many books omit the important second half of this proof.

Note once again how the transformation theorems can be applied to get results that would otherwise be more difficult to obtain.

Lesson 14-3, page 432. Ellipses have many applications in space mathematics. Satellites travel in elliptical orbits. Planets travel around the sun in elliptical orbits with the sun being at one of the foci.

There are two parts to the proof of Theorem 14-5. Here is a proof that if $P(x, y)$ is on the ellipse, then it satisfies an equation of the type $x^2/a^2 + y^2/b^2 = 1$. Suppose we have an ellipse placed so that the foci, F_1 and F_2, are on the x-axis, each a distance c from the origin. If $P(x, y)$ is a point on the ellipse, then $F_1P + F_2P$ is the given constant distance. We call the constant distance $2a$. Then $F_1P + F_2P = 2a$. By the distance formula,

$$\sqrt{(x + c)^2 + y^2} + \sqrt{(x - c)^2 + y^2} = 2a$$

or

$$\sqrt{(x + c)^2 + y^2} = 2a - \sqrt{(x - c)^2 + y^2}.$$

Squaring, we get $x^2 + 2cx + c^2 + y^2 = 4a^2 - 4a\sqrt{(x - c)^2 + y^2} + x^2 - 2cx + c^2 + y^2$, or $-a^2 + cx = -a\sqrt{(x - c)^2 + y^2}$. Squaring again, we get $a^4 - 2a^2cx + c^2x^2 = a^2[(x - c)^2 + y^2]$ or $x^2(c^2 - a^2) - a^2y^2 = a^2(c^2 - a^2)$. Multiply by -1: $x^2(a^2 - c^2) + a^2y^2 = a^2(a^2 - c^2)$. Since $a > c$, $a^2 > c^2$, so $a^2 - c^2 > 0$. We represent $a^2 - c^2$ by b^2: $x^2b^2 + a^2y^2 = a^2b^2$. Divide by a^2b^2: $x^2/a^2 + y^2/b^2 = 1$.

Page 433, A Proof of Theorem 14-6. If in the equation of Theorem 14-5, we interchange x and y, we know that we reflect the graph across the line $y = x$. The foci will then be on the y-axis. To make remembering easier we also rename the constants a

and b, so that a goes with x and b goes with y.

Page 434, A Proof That an Ellipse Is a Stretched Circle. Consider the unit circle $x^2 + y^2 = 1$. If we replace x by x/a and y by y/b, this stretches or shrinks the graph, according to Theorems 8-9 and 8-10. When we replace x by x/a and y by y/b we get the standard form for the equation of an ellipse. Therefore an ellipse is a circle transformed by a stretch or shrink in the x-direction and a stretch or shrink in the y-direction.

Lesson 14-4, page 436. Hyperbolas also have many applications. A jet breaking the sound barrier creates a sonic boom in the shape of a cone. This cone intersects the ground in one branch of the hyperbola. Some comets travel in hyperbolic orbits.

The equation $x^2 - y^2 = 1$ represents an equilateral hyperbola that has perpendicular asymptotes. By interchanging x and y we reflect across the line $y = x$. By multiplying x by $1/a$ and y by $1/b$ we get other hyperbolas by stretching or by shrinking.

A common misconception is that a curve never crosses its asymptote. Although it is true that hyperbolas never cross their asymptotes, many curves do. Consider, for example, $y = (\sin x)/x$. This curve is asymptotic to the x-axis but crosses it an infinite number of times.

A Proof of Theorem 14-8. Place the hyperbola so that both foci are on the x-axis, with the origin halfway between them. The coordinates of the foci will be F_2: $(c, 0)$ and F_1: $(-c, 0)$, where c is some positive number. Now we must prove that $P(x, y)$ is on the hyperbola if and only if it satisfies an equation of the type $x^2/a^2 - y^2/b^2 = 1$. There are two parts to the proof.

i) We first prove that if $P(x, y)$ is on the hyperbola, then $x^2/a^2 - y^2/b^2 = 1$. Suppose that $P(x, y)$ is on the hyperbola in the first quadrant. (The proof for the second, third, and fourth quadrants is similar to this). We know that $PF_2 > PF_1$, thus $PF_2 - PF_1 > 0$ and $|PF_2 - PF_1| = PF_2 - PF_1 = 2a$, the constant difference. In the triangle F_2PF_1, $PF_2 - PF_1 < F_1F_2$, or $2a < 2c$; therefore $a < c$. Using the distance formula, we have

$$\sqrt{(x+c)^2 + y^2} - \sqrt{(x-c)^2 + y^2} = 2a$$

or

$$\sqrt{(x+c)^2 + y^2} = 2a + \sqrt{(x-c)^2 + y^2}.$$

Squaring, we get

$$x^2 + 2xc + c^2 + y^2 = 4a^2 + 4a\sqrt{(x-c)^2 + y^2}$$
$$+ x^2 - 2xc + c^2 + y^2,$$

which simplifies to

$$4cx - 4a^2 = 4a\sqrt{(x-c)^2 + y^2},$$

or

$$cx - a^2 = \sqrt{(x-c)^2 + y^2}.$$

Squaring again, we get

$$c^2x^2 - 2a^2cx + a^4 = a^2x^2 - 2a^2cx + a^2c^2 + a^2y^2,$$

or

$$x^2(c^2 - a^2) - a^2y^2 = a^2(c^2 - a^2).$$

Since $c > a$, $c^2 > a^2$, so $c^2 - a^2$ is positive. We represent $c^2 - a^2$ by b^2. The previous equation then becomes

$$x^2b^2 - a^2y^2 = a^2b^2.$$

Multiplying on both sides by $1/a^2b^2$, we get the equation $x^2/a^2 - y^2/b^2 = 1$.

ii) The second part of the proof is to prove that if $P(x, y)$ satisfies the equation $x^2/a^2 - y^2/b^2 = 1$, then it is on the hyperbola. We will not consider that proof here.

Page 437, A Proof of Theorem 14—9. In Theorem 14—8, we interchange x and y. This reflects the graph across the line $y = x$. To make remembering easier we rename the constants so that a goes with x and b goes with y.

Page 439, A Proof That Hyperbolas Have Asymptotes. Why are $y = (b/a)x$ and $y = -(b/a)x$ asymptotes? To answer this we solve $x^2/16 - y^2/9 = 1$ for y^2:

$$-16y^2 = 144 - 9x^2 \text{ (multiplying by 144)}$$
$$y^2 = (9x^2 - 144)/16.$$

From this last equation, we see that as $|x|$ gets larger the term -144 is very small compared to $9x^2$, so y^2 gets closer to $9x^2/16$. That is, when $|x|$ is large,

$$y^2 \approx 9x^2/16 \approx |(3/4)x| \approx \pm(3/4)x.$$

Thus the lines $y = (3/4)x$ and $y = -(3/4)x$ are asymptotes.

Lesson 14—5, page 441. It should be pointed out that although parabolas have shapes reminiscent of hyperbolas the curves are different. For one thing, parabolas do not have asymptotes.

Parabolas have many applications. Cross sections of headlights are parabolas. The bulb is located at the focus. All light from this point is reflected outward, parallel to the axis of symmetry. Radar and radio antennas may have cross sections that are parabolas. Incoming radio waves are reflected and concentrated at the focus.

Page 442, A Proof of Part of Theorem 14—12.
Given a point F and a line l, we place the y-axis through F and perpendicular to l. We place the x-axis halfway between F and l. The distance from F to l we shall call $2p$. F then has coordinates $(0, p)$ and l has an equation $y = -p$. We must prove that $P(x, y)$ is on the parabola if and only if it satisfies the equation $x^2 = 4py$. There are two parts to the

proof, but we prove only that if $P(x, y)$ is on the parabola, then it satisfies $x^2 = 4py$. Let $P(x, y)$ be any point of the parabola and consider $\overline{PG}$ perpendicular to the line $y = -p$. The coordinates of G are $(x, -p)$. By definition of a parabola,

$$PF = PG.$$

Then using the distance formula, we have

$$\sqrt{(x-0)^2 + (y-p)^2} = \sqrt{(x-x)^2 + (y+p)^2}.$$

Squaring, we get

$$x^2 + y^2 - 2py + p^2 = y^2 + 2py + p^2$$
$$x^2 = 4py.$$

Lesson 14–7, page 450.   It is a good idea to remind students once again to make drawings when solving problems.

Chapter 15. POLYNOMIAL FUNCTIONS
After finishing Chapter 15, students should be able to
- determine whether a number is a root of a polynomial.
- find the remainder when a polynomial is divided by $x - r$.
- determine whether $x - r$ is a factor of a polynomial.
- use synthetic division to find the quotient and remainder when a polynomial is divided by a binomial $x - r$.
- use synthetic division to find function values of a polynomial.
- find a polynomial with roots of given multiplicities.
- given a polynomial with rational coefficients and some of its roots, find the other roots.
- find the rational roots and the other roots of a polynomial with integer coefficients.

Lesson 15–1, page 456.   Do not discourage the use of a calculator for evaluating polynomials.

Lesson 15–2, page 459, A Proof of Theorem 15–1.
If we divide $P(x)$ by $x - r$, we obtain a quotient $Q(x)$ and a remainder $R(x)$ related as follows:

$$P(x) = (x - r) \cdot Q(x) + R(x).$$

The remainder $R(x)$ must either be 0 or have degree less than $x - r$. Thus $R(x)$ must be a constant. Let us call this constant R. In the above expression we get a true sentence whenever we replace x by any number. Let us replace x by r. We get

$$P(r) = (r - r) \cdot Q(r) + R$$
$$= 0 \cdot Q(r) + R$$
$$= R.$$

This tells us that the function value $P(r)$ is the remainder obtained when we divide $P(x)$ by $x - r$.

Lesson 15–4, page 467, A Proof of Theorem 15–3.
Let $P(x) = a_n x^n + a_{n-1} x^{n-1} + \ldots + a_1 x + a_0$, where the coefficients are real numbers. Suppose z is a complex root of $P(x)$. Then $P(z) = 0$, or

$$a_n z^n + \ldots + a_1 z + a_0 = 0.$$

Now let us find the conjugate of each side of the equation. First note that $\overline{0} = 0$, since 0 is a real number. Then we have the following.

$$0 = \overline{0}$$
$$= \overline{a_n z^n + \ldots + a_1 z + a_0}$$
$$= \overline{a_n z^n} + \ldots + \overline{a_1 z} + \overline{a_0} \text{ (The conjugate of a sum)}$$
$$= \overline{a_n} \cdot \overline{z^n} + \ldots + \overline{a_1} \cdot \overline{z} + \overline{a_0} \text{ (The conjugate of a product)}$$
$$= a_n \overline{z^n} + \ldots + a_1 \overline{z} + a_0 \text{ (Every real number is its own conjugate)}$$
$$= a_n \overline{z}^n + \ldots + a_1 \overline{z} + a_0 \text{ (The conjugate of a power)}$$

Thus $P(\overline{z}) = 0$, so $\overline{z}$ is a root of the polynomial.

Page 468. In order for Theorem 15–4 to hold the coefficients must be *rational* numbers.

Lesson 15–5, page 471, A Proof of Theorem 15–5.
Suppose that c/d, where c and d have no common factor other than 1 or -1, is a root of $P(x)$. Then

$$a_n (c/d)^n + a_{n-1} (c/d)^{n-1} + \ldots + a_1 (c/d) + a_0 = 0$$

We multiply by d^n and solve for $a_n c^n$:

$$a_n c^n = (-a_{n-1} c^{n-1} - \ldots - a_1 cd^{n-2} - a_0 d^{n-1})d,$$

so d is a factor of $a_n c^n$. Now d is not a factor of c because c and d have no common factor besides 1 and -1. Thus d is not a factor of c^n, so d is a factor of a_n. In a similar way we can show that

$$a_0 d^n = (-a_n c^{n-1} - a_{n-1} c^{n-2} d - \ldots - a_1 d^{n-1})c.$$

Thus c is a factor of $a_0 d^n$. Again, c is not a factor of d^n, so it must be a factor of a_0.

Chapter 16. EXPONENTIAL AND LOGARITHM FUNCTIONS

After finishing Chapter 16, students should be able to
- graph exponential and logarithmic functions.
- convert to logarithmic or exponential equations.
- solve certain logarithmic equations.
- simplify logarithmic expressions.
- convert from logarithms of sums or differences to single logarithms, and convert from single logarithms to logarithms of sums and differences.
- given logarithms of some numbers, find logarithms of other numbers, using properties of logarithms.
- use a table to find logarithms and antilogarithms.
- use logarithms for certain calculations.
- use linear interpolation to find logarithms and antilogarithms with four-digit precision.

- solve exponential and logarithmic equations.
- solve problems involving exponential and logarithmic functions and equations.

Lesson 16–2, page 485. The lesson on logarithms in computation should be considered optional because, with the advent of small calculators, the use of logarithms for computing is obsolete. However, this lesson is still useful because it helps to emphasize to the students the properties of logarithmic functions.

Lesson 16–4, page 498. It is interesting to point out to students that only base 10 logarithms have characteristic and mantissa.

Chapter 17. SEQUENCES AND SERIES

After finishing Chapter 17, students should be able to
- given a formula for the general term of a sequence, find the nth term.
- write sigma notation for a series.
- given any two terms of an arithmetic sequence, find a_1 and d.
- find the sum of the first n terms of an arithmetic sequence.
- find the nth term of a geometric sequence.
- find the sum of the first n terms of a geometric series.
- find the sum of an infinite geometric series when $|r| < 1$.
- convert from repeating decimal notation to fractional notation.

Lesson 17–1, page 520. A sequence can also be defined to be a function whose domain is the set of all natural numbers. If the sequence is finite there will be only a finite set of function values not zero.

Page 521. Students should verify that these general terms fit.

Lesson 17–2, page 522. You might wish to point out that the greek letter Σ (sigma) corresponds to the latin letter S (for sum).

Again, you should have students verify that the general terms fit in these examples.

Lesson 17–4, page 528, A Proof of Theorem 17–3. By Theorem 17–2, we have $S_n = (n/2)(a_1 + a_n)$. From Theorem 17–1, we see that $a_n = a_1 + (n - 1)d$. We substitute this in the formula for Theorem 17–2, obtaining the desired result. Note that in the form

$$a_4 = 600 \cdot (1.07)^3,$$

the equation fits the compound interest formula,

$$A = P(1 + r)^t$$

which was developed in Chapter 6. Note that the numbers A_1, A_2, A_3, and so on, form a geometric sequence where $A_1 = P(1 + r)$, $n - 1 = t$, and the common ratio is $1 + r$.

Lesson 17–7, page 538. It should be pointed out that any repeating decimal represents an infinite geometric series.

Chapter 18. MATRICES AND DETERMINANTS
After finishing Chapter 18, students should be able to
- solve systems of two linear equations in two variables using matrices.
- solve systems of three linear equations in three variables using matrices.
- evaluate determinants of second order.
- solve systems of two equations in two variables using Cramer's Rule.
- evaluate determinants of third order.
- solve systems of three equations in three variables using Cramer's Rule.

- add, subtract, or multiply matrices of the same dimensions.
- find the scalar product of a number k and a matrix.

This chapter is optional. The material on determinants is not as important as it was once considered to be, since determinants do not provide an efficient way for solving systems of equations. However, there are still many theoretical questions that are handled in mathematics (including things pertaining to matrices) for which determinants are essential. Therefore, students planning to go on in mathematics should learn what determinants are.

Lesson 18–3, page 549, A Proof of Theorem 18–1. We use the addition method to solve the system

$$a_1 x + b_1 y = c_1$$
$$a_2 x + b_2 y = c_2$$

We multiply equation 1 by $-a_2$ and equation 2 by a_1. Adding and solving for y, we obtain the desired expression.

Lesson 18–5, page 556, A Proof of Theorem 18–5. Consider two matrices A and B of the same dimensions, and construct a new matrix by subtracting corresponding elements. Thus for a in A and b in B, in the corresponding position, the new matrix will have $a - b$ in that position. Now consider adding the new matrix to B. When we do, we will add $a - b$ from our new matrix to b in the matrix B, obtaining a. Since the same thing happens in every position, the new matrix is the matrix which when added to B gives A.

Page 557, A Proof of Theorem 18–6. Consider two matrices A and B of the same dimension, in which corresponding elements are additive inverses of each other. When these matrices are added, 0 will be obtained in each position.

Theorem 18–7 is actually a group theorem so is, in effect, already proved. The proof is the same as the corresponding theorem for numbers.

Lesson 18—6, page 560. The following can be used to further develop matrix multiplication. Consider a system of equations.

$$3x + 2y - 2z = 4$$
$$2x - y + 5z = 3$$
$$-x + y + 4z = 7$$

Now consider the following matrices.

$$\begin{bmatrix} 3 & 2 & -2 \\ 2 & -1 & 5 \\ -1 & 1 & 4 \end{bmatrix} \begin{bmatrix} x \\ y \\ z \end{bmatrix} \begin{bmatrix} 4 \\ 3 \\ 7 \end{bmatrix}$$

$$A \qquad X \quad B$$

If we multiply A by X and set this column matrix equal to B, we obtain

$$\begin{bmatrix} 3x + 2y - 2z \\ 2x - y + 5z \\ -x + y + 4z \end{bmatrix} = \begin{bmatrix} 4 \\ 3 \\ 7 \end{bmatrix}$$

Equality for matrices is the same as for numbers, i.e., the "two" matrices are really the same one. This means that $3x + 2y - 2z$ is 4, $2x - y + 5z$ is 3, and $-x + y + 4z$ is 7, which is equivalent to the given system of equations.

Chapter 19. COMBINATORIAL ALGEBRA; PROBABILITY

After finishing Chapter 19, students should be able to

- evaluate a factorial.
- find the total number of permutations of a set of n objects.
- find the number of permutations of n objects taken r at a time.
- find the number of distinct arrangements of a set

of n objects taken r at a time with replacements or with repetition.
- evaluate $\binom{n}{r}$.
- find the number of combinations of n objects taken r at a time.
- find the rth term of the binomial expansion of $(a + b)^n$.
- use the Binomial Theorem to expand binomial expressions.
- compute the probability of a simple event, using Principle P.

Lesson 19—2, page 571, A Proof of Theorem 19—4. Consider a set of n objects and the selecting of an ordered subset of r objects. The total number, $_nP_r$, is

$$n(n-1)(n-2)(n-3) \cdots [n-(r-1)].$$

We now multiply this by 1, in the form

$$\frac{(n-r)!}{(n-r)!}.$$

By Theorem 19—3, the numerator is $n!$ We now have

$$_nP_r = \frac{n!}{(n-r)!}$$

Lesson 19—3, page 575, A Proof of Theorem 19—6. Consider a set of n objects. The number of subsets with r members we call $_nC_r$. For each unordered subset with r members there are $r!$ ordered subsets, by Theorem 19—2. We have $_nC_r \cdot r!$ ordered subsets with r members. This gives us

$$_nP_r = {_nC_r} \cdot r!$$

We solve for $_nC_r$ and substitute for $_nP_r$ to obtain

$$_nC_r = \frac{n!}{r!(n-r)!}$$

$$= \binom{n}{r}.$$

Chapter 20. TRIGONOMETRIC FUNCTIONS

After finishing Chapter 20, students should be able to

- use trigonometric functions to find missing parts of right triangles.
- convert from degree to radian measure and from radian to degree measure.
- find the values of the six trigonometric functions of an angle or rotation.
- find the function values for any angle whose terminal side makes an angle of 30°, 45°, or 60° with the x-axis.
- sketch graphs of the sine and cosine functions.
- sketch graphs of the tangent, cotangent, secant, and cosecant functions.
- derive variations of the Pythagorean identities.
- derive variations of the cofunction identities.
- find the function values for the complement of an acute angle, given the function values for the angle.
- sketch graphs of $y = A \sin B\theta$ and $y = A \cos B\theta$ and determine the amplitude and period of the function.
- find function values for angles of any size.
- compute with and simplify expressions containing trigonometric expressions.
- solve equations containing trigonometric expressions.

Lesson 20–1, page 592. It is important to point out that for similar triangles, the ratios of corresponding sides are proportional. Thus we can use these ratios to assign function values to the various angle sizes.

Relate the trigonometric functions to previous experiences with functions. Functions like the sine, cosine, and tangent take angle sizes as inputs and assign function values as outputs.

When using trigonometric functions to solve problems, we generalize the real situation into a mathematical model—in this case, the model is the triangle. Then we solve the problem using mathematics. Finally, we translate back into the real situa-tion.

It can be explained that the sine function has for its domain a set of angles and for its range a set of all real numbers from −1 to 1 inclusive. Similar remarks could be made about the other trigonometric functions.

Page 593. It is important to tell students in solving problems such as the one in Example 3 to make drawings. It is difficult to overemphasize their importance.

Lesson 20–2, page 596. Most students will probably be accustomed to thinking of an angle in terms of the union of two rays with a common endpoint. In this lesson the angle concept is extended to include the notion of a rotation. In like fashion the measures of angles in degrees are extended to the rotation concept.

Radian measure provides a convenient and consistent link between the measure of angles and the measure of length on the x- and y-axes. In effect, the circle is coordinatized in the same units used to measure a radius of the circle. Be sure to stress the importance of memorizing the relationships between radian and degree measure as shown on page 598.

Page 597. In converting from degrees to radians, or radians to degrees, the best procedure is to multiply by 1 in the form of $\pi/180$ or $180/\pi$, as illustrated in Examples 5 and 6.

Lesson 20–3, page 599. With the angle concept extended to include rotations it is now possible to extend the trigonometric functions to rotations. Once again, the input—output idea of a function should be stressed. Thus, for example, the sine function consists of all ordered pairs of the form $(\theta, \sin \theta)$ where θ is a measure of a rotation.

Stress the importance of memorizing the sine, cosine, and tangent function values for 30°, 60°, and 45°.

Page 602.   Students should be required to memorize function values for 45°, 30°, and 60°. They should also be required to memorize the approximate square roots of 2, 3, 5, and a few more numbers. The square roots of 2 and 3 are especially important in finding decimal approximations for function values of 30°, 45°, and 60°.

Page 603.   It helps to emphasize that the reference angle is the smallest angle that the terminal side of an angle makes with the *x*-axis.

Lesson 20–4, page 606.   The graphing of the trigonometric functions should be related to earlier experiences with graphing functions. In this case we plot the inputs (rotation sizes) on the first axis and the outputs (function values) on the second axis. As with any function, it is appropriate to consider the questions of domain and range, even or odd, and periodicity. Comparisons of the graphs of tangent and cotangent; cosine and secant; and sine and cosecant should help to clarify the reciprocal relationship.

Students have been gradually led to using any variable for sin *s*, cos *θ*, or tan *x*. Some word of caution may be in order to avoid having them think of *x* in this context as the first coordinate of a point on a unit circle.

Page 607.   Theorem 20–1 could also be visualized as follows: The graph of sin $(\theta + 2\pi)$ is the same as that of sin *θ* but translated a distance of 2π to the right. Translating in this manner gives us a graph equivalent to the original one, hence the function is periodic. To see that sin $(-\theta) = -\sin \theta$, note that if we start with the graph of sin *θ*, and reflect across the *y*-axis, we will get a graph of sin $(-\theta)$. If we start with the graph of sin *θ* and reflect across the *x*-axis, we get the graph of $-\sin \theta$. The two results are the same.

Page 608.   Theorem 20–2 can be visualized by using transformations in a manner similar to that

described for Theorem 20–1.

Lesson 20–6, page 619.   It is important to stress in this lesson the fact that the trigonometric functions behave as all functions do with respect to transformations.

It may be good to review the role of certain constants in stretching and shrinking in Chapter 8.

Lesson 20–7, page 623.   Be sure to relate the work on interpolation to that previously discussed in the logarithms section. Students can examine successive values of the sine function in the table and observe that it is approximately linear over short intervals. Hence, linear interpolation is appropriate.

Page 624.   The material on interpolation will not be important for students who have calculators containing the trigonometric functions values, except that you may wish to teach this material to illustrate what is meant by interpolation in general.

Lesson 20–8, page 627.   This lesson is important since it shows the algebraic development of trigonometric expressions.

It is important to point out that expressions containing trigonometric functions can be handled like algebraic expressions in computing and simplifying, but that we can sometimes do further simplification by using trigonometric identities.

Chapter 21. TRIGONOMETRIC IDENTITIES AND EQUATIONS

After finishing Chapter 21, students should be able to

• use the sum and difference identities to simplify trigonometric expressions.

• use the double-angle identities to find function values of twice an angle when one function value is known for that angle.

• use the half-angle identities to find the function

values of half an angle when one function value is known for that angle.
- prove trigonometric identities.
- find principal values of the inverses of the trigonometric functions.
- find all values of arcsin a, arccos a, and arctan a, in degrees and radians, given a number a.
- solve trigonometric equations requiring the use of identities.
- solve triangles using three-digit precision.
- solve applied problems involving triangles.
- use the law of sines to solve any triangle, given a side and two angles.
- use the law of cosines, with the law of sines, to solve any triangle, given two sides and the included angle.
- find polar notation when given rectangular notation for a complex number, and conversely.
- use polar notation to multiply and divide complex numbers.
- find the nth roots of a complex number.
- use De Moivre's theorem to raise complex numbers to powers.

Lesson 21—1, page 634. When we consider the cosine of a sum we employ a technique used frequently in mathematics. To determine $\cos (\alpha + \beta)$ we change the problem into one for which have a solution, i.e., the cosine of a difference. Similarly, to find the tangent of a sum we translate this situation into one which is familiar, i.e., $\tan (\alpha + \beta) = [\sin (\alpha + \beta)]/[\cos (\alpha + \beta)]$. Encourage students to memorize the identities stated in Theorem 21—1.

Page 638. The sum and difference formulas given in Theorem 21—1 are basic and important. Students should be required to memorize them. This is particularly true for students who plan to go on in mathematics. It is not ususual for students to come to a calculus course, for example, feeling that they can always "look up" trigonometry identities. They find that this does not work; there is too much "looking up" needed.

Lesson 21—2, page 640. Once again we employ the technique described above. That is, to find $\sin 2\theta$, we change the problem into a familiar one; $\sin 2\theta \equiv \sin (\theta + \theta)$. Encourage students to memorize the identities in Theorem 21—2. In developing the half-angle identities, be sure students understand the relationship between θ and ϕ as illustrated on page 642. Since we know an identity in 2θ we may use it to derive an identity in θ or $\phi/2$.

Lesson 21—3, page 645. Proving identities is a skill that frequently requires considerable practice. It might be wise to use the exercise set for this lesson over several assignments. Another good technique is to allow some time for students to work in pairs. It is important for students to realize that in proving identities we really need to show that each member of the equation can be transformed into the other. It is important to use steps that are reversible. The reversibility of each step guarantees that the right member can also be transformed into the left.

Lesson 21—4, page 648. Relate the idea of inverses of trigonometric functions to previous experiences with inverses of relations. Make sure that students recall that all functions have inverses but that these inverses may or may not be functions. This will lead naturally to the need to distinguish between the inverse of the function and finding principal values by restricting ranges.

Lesson 21—5, page 653. It is important in solving trigonometric equations to substitute possible answers into the original equation to make sure that they are actually solutions. It sometimes turns out that they are not.

Lesson 21—6, page 658. Since the main concern here is the ability to set up and solve problems, rather than obtain a high degree of precision in answers, we shall give answers only to three-digit precision from this point on. Emphasize again that students should make drawings when solving.

Lesson 21—7, page 662. Students might be encouraged to build some type of model to illustrate the ambiguous case.

Lesson 21—8, page 667. Point out that the law of cosines does, in effect, extend the idea of the Pythagorean theorem to any triangle.

Teachers' Edition

ALGEBRA TWO

and TRIGONOMETRY

Mervin L. Keedy

Marvin L. Bittinger

Stanley A. Smith

Addison-Wesley Publishing Company
Menlo Park, California   Reading, Massachusetts   London
Amsterdam   Don Mills, Ontario   Sydney

ii

AUTHORS

Mervin L. Keedy is Professor of Mathematics at Purdue University. He received his Ph.D. degree at the University of Nebraska, and formerly taught at the University of Maryland. He has also taught mathematics and science in junior and senior high schools. Professor Keedy is the author of many books on mathematics, including *A Modern Introduction to Basic Mathematics* (Addison-Wesley, 1969), and he is co-author with Charles W. Nelson of *Geometry: A Modern Introduction* (Addison-Wesley, 1973).

Marvin L. Bittinger is Professor of Mathematics Education at Indiana University-Purdue University at Indianapolis. He earned his Ph.D. degree at Purdue University. He is the author of *Logic and Proof* (Addison-Wesley, 1970), and is co-author with Professor Keedy of several college textbooks published by Addison-Wesley.

Stanley A. Smith is Coordinator, Office of Mathematics (K-12), for Baltimore County Public Schools, Maryland. He has taught junior high school mathematics and science and senior high school mathematics. He earned his M.A. degree at the University of Maryland. He is co-author with Professor Keedy of *Exploring Modern Mathematics,* Books 1 and 2 (Holt, Rinehart & Winston, 1976).

Photographs: Opening photograph for Chapter 1 by NASA; for Chapter 2 ⓒ William Rosenthal, Jeroboam, Inc.; for Chapter 3 by M. W. S. Tweedie, National Audubon Society Collection, Photo Researchers, Inc.; for Chapter 12 by Fred J. Maroon, Photo Researchers, Inc.; for Chapter 14 by William Liller; for Chapter 20 by Lynda Gordon*; for Chapter 21 by Daniel DeWilde.* All other photographs by Betty Medsger.*

ISBN 0-201-03851-X
ABCDEFGHIJK-VH-82107987

*Photographs provided expressly for the publisher. Special thanks to Weatherly Aviation, Hollister, California, for their cooperation.

To the Students

Why are you studying second-year algebra? You may be planning a career in business, the arts, or the sciences, and you know that a mathematical background can be very useful. Or you may be planning to go to college and you have learned that second-year algebra is important for getting into a good college or university. It may be that you are taking this course because your counselor advised you to or because most of your friends are taking it. Or you may find mathematics interesting and challenging, the way puzzles are interesting.

No matter why you are studying second-year algebra, we want you to have success and we want you to enjoy the course as much as possible. So, we have written this book accordingly. If you will read it carefully and put forth some effort, you will succeed. When you come to exercises marked "Try This," you should stop and work those exercises. They are very much like the examples in the text and very much like the homework exercises. The homework will be relatively easy and your understanding of the material will be good. If you have been leery of math in the past, perhaps you will now find that it is not so bad after all.

We hope that you will attack the subject with an inquiring attitude. This is a subject that can be fun just because it is interesting. Yes, algebra is very useful in many careers, but if you will study it just to see how the ideas are developed and how they fit together, this is enough. The career aspects will take care of themselves.

Enjoy yourself as much as possible as you study. Then, no matter what your career objective, you will be further down the road. Moreover, your life will be more pleasant in the process.

The Authors

Special Thanks

To Judy Beecher, formerly of Southport High School, Indianapolis, Indiana, for her careful checking of the manuscript and preparation of the answers.

To all the students who participated in learner verification studies.

To all the teachers who aided in reviewing this text:

L. A. Abert
Livermore, California

Flora Berry
Union County Schools
Union, South Carolina

Mildred H. Davis
Kansas City, Missouri

Terry Haug
Sacramento, California

Stephen L. Johnson
Jewell School District
Seaside, Oregon

Gaye P. Lindsey
Greenway, Virginia

Calvin Miller
Midland Public Schools
Midland, Michigan

Donavon Nagel
John Marshall High School
Rochester, Minnesota

Joann E. Roller
Saginaw Public Schools
Saginaw, Michigan

Ed Rykowski
Springfield, Missouri

J. Norman C. Sharp
Borough of Etobicoke
Etobicoke, Ontario

Louise M. Smith
Charleston County School District
Charleston, South Carolina

John Walton
Denver Public Schools
Denver, Colorado

Contents

Chapter **10** EXPONENTS, POWERS, AND ROOTS, 297

Chapter **11** COMPLEX NUMBERS, 341

Chapter **12** QUADRATIC EQUATIONS, 367

Chapter **13** QUADRATIC FUNCTIONS, 395

In the Teachers' Edition, pages 692 through the end of the book provide additional answers to supplement the answers overprinted on the student pages. The "Selected Answers" appear in the student edition only.

Chapter 1
Real Numbers and Their Properties

What is the volume of the earth?

1-1 Real Numbers

After finishing Lesson 1-1, you should be able to
- **I** give examples of natural numbers, whole numbers, integers, and rational numbers.
- **II** convert fractional to decimal notation for rational numbers.
- **III** distinguish between rational and irrational numbers.

I Some Subsets of Real Numbers

There is only one real number for each point of a line.

The *positive* real numbers are those shown to the right of 0. The *negative* real numbers are those to the left of 0. Zero is neither negative nor positive. There are various kinds of real numbers. The *natural numbers* are those used for counting.

The *natural numbers* are 1, 2, 3, 4, 5, 6, 7, 8, 9, 10, 11, and so on.

When we include 0, we then have the set of *whole numbers*.

The *whole numbers* are 0, 1, 2, 3, 4, 5, 6, 7, 8, 9, 10, 11, and so on.

TRY THIS ▬▬▶

> 1. Name four natural numbers.
> 2. Name four whole numbers.
> **Answers may vary.**

We extend the set of whole numbers to the integers by including some *negative* numbers. The negative integers are those pictured to the left of 0.

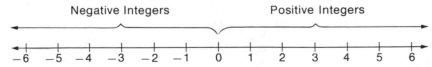

The *integers* are 0, −1, 1, −2, 2, −3, 3, −4, 4, and so on.

TRY THIS ▬▬▶

> 3. Name four integers.
> **Answers may vary.**

The set of *rational* numbers includes not only the integers, but all quotients of integers (excluding division by zero).

Any rational number can be named by a fractional symbol having integers for numerator and denominator.

Example 1. The following are rational numbers.

$$\frac{4}{5}, \frac{-4}{7}, \frac{9}{1}, 9, \frac{234}{1}, 234, \frac{-78}{1}, -78, \frac{78}{-4}, -\frac{2}{3}$$

TRY THIS

4. Name six rational numbers.
Answers may vary.

ⅠⅠ Decimal Notation

Rational numbers can also be named using decimal notation.

Example 2. Find decimal notation for $\frac{5}{8}$.

$\frac{5}{8}$ means $5 \div 8$, so we divide:

$$
\begin{array}{r}
0.625 \\
8\overline{)5.000} \\
\underline{4\,8} \\
20 \\
\underline{16} \\
40 \\
\underline{40}
\end{array}
$$

Thus $\frac{5}{8} = 0.625$. We call 0.625 a *decimal*. We call it a *terminating decimal* because it ends.

Sometimes we get a repeating decimal when we divide.

Example 3. Find decimal notation for $\frac{6}{11}$.

$\frac{6}{11}$ means $6 \div 11$, so we divide:

$$
\begin{array}{r}
0.5454\ldots \\
11\overline{)6.0000} \\
\underline{5\,5} \\
50 \\
\underline{44} \\
60 \\
\underline{55} \\
50 \\
\underline{44} \\
6
\end{array}
$$

4 *Chapter 1*

Such decimals are often abbreviated by putting a bar over the repeating part. Thus $\frac{6}{11} = 0.\overline{54}$. When such repeating decimals occur in problems, we round them.

Decimal notation for rational numbers either ends or repeats.

TRY THIS ➡

Find decimal notation for each of the following.

5. $\frac{7}{8}$ 0.875

6. $\frac{7}{11}$ $0.\overline{63}$

7. $\frac{17}{15}$ $1.1\overline{3}$

ɪɪɪ Irrational Numbers

Any rational number can be named by fractional notation, $\frac{a}{b}$, where both numerator and denominator are integers. Rational numbers can be named in other ways, but they can all be named *this* way. Is there a rational number that is a square root of 2; that is, a number $\frac{a}{b}$ for which $\frac{a}{b} \cdot \frac{a}{b} = 2$? We can find rational numbers whose squares are close to 2, but we can never find one whose square is exactly 2. Thus $\sqrt{2}$ is not a rational number. It is *irrational*. There are many irrational numbers. Unless a whole number is a perfect square, its square root is irrational.

Example 4. $\sqrt{3}$, $\sqrt{8}$, and $\sqrt{45}$ are irrational numbers.

Decimal notation for rational numbers either terminates or repeats. Thus decimal notation for irrational numbers never terminates or repeats.

Examples.

5. 8.97979797 . . . is rational since the numeral repeats.

6. 3.121121112 . . . is irrational since the numeral does not repeat or terminate.

7. 0.984 is rational since the numeral terminates.

TRY THIS ➡

Which of the following are rational? Which are irrational?

8. $\frac{-4}{5}$ Rational

9. $\frac{59}{37}$ Rational

10. 7.42   Rational

11. 0.047474747 . . . (numeral repeats   Rational

12. 2.573410756631 . . . (numeral does not repeat)   Irrational

13. $\sqrt{7}$ Irrational

Exercise Set 1-1

▮ (*See page 2.*) 1.–6. Answers may vary.

1. Name four natural numbers.
2. Name four whole numbers.
3. Name four positive integers.
4. Name four negative integers.
5. Name four positive rational numbers.
6. Name four negative rational numbers.

▮▮ Find decimal notation for each of the following. (*See Examples 2 and 3.*)

7. $\dfrac{5}{8}$ 0.625

8. $\dfrac{1}{8}$ 0.125

9. $\dfrac{3}{7}$ $0.\overline{428571}$

10. $\dfrac{4}{7}$ $0.\overline{571428}$

11. $\dfrac{9}{16}$ 0. 5625

12. $\dfrac{7}{16}$ 0.4375

13. $\dfrac{5}{12}$ $0.41\overline{6}$

14. $\dfrac{11}{12}$ $0.91\overline{6}$

15. $\dfrac{7}{11}$ $0.\overline{63}$

16. $\dfrac{5}{11}$ $0.\overline{45}$

▮▮▮ Which of the following are rational? Which are irrational? (*See Examples 4–7.*)

17. $\dfrac{-5}{6}$ Rational

18. $\dfrac{-2}{7}$ Rational

19. 8.93   Rational

20. 7.604   Rational

21. $3.579\overline{579}$ Rational

22. $8.23\overline{23}$ Rational

23. 2.1010010001 . . . (numeral does not repeat)   Irrational

24. 5.2121121112 . . . (numeral does not repeat)   Irrational

25. $\sqrt{6}$ Irrational

26. $\sqrt{5}$ Irrational

27. $\sqrt{13}$ Irrational

28. $\sqrt{15}$ Irrational

29. $\sqrt{16}$ Rational

30. $\sqrt{36}$ Rational

Challenge Exercises

31. $\dfrac{1}{13} = 0.\overline{076923}$, $\dfrac{2}{13} = 0.\overline{153846}$, $\dfrac{3}{13} = 0.\overline{230769}$, $\dfrac{4}{13} = 0.\overline{307692}$, $\dfrac{5}{13} = 0.\overline{384615}$, $\dfrac{6}{13} = 0.\overline{461538}$, $\dfrac{7}{13} = 0.\overline{538461}$, $\dfrac{8}{13} = 0.\overline{615384}$, $\dfrac{9}{13} = 0.\overline{692307}$, $\dfrac{10}{13} = 0.\overline{769230}$, $\dfrac{11}{13} = 0.\overline{846153}$, $\dfrac{12}{13} = 0.\overline{923076}$

31. Find decimal notation for $\frac{1}{13}$, $\frac{2}{13}$, $\frac{3}{13}$, . . . , $\frac{12}{13}$. Study the repeating portion of the numerals. What pattern do you find?

32. Suppose $n = 0.88\overline{8}$. Find fractional notation for n. (*Hint:* Find $10n$ and then $10n - n$.) $\frac{8}{9}$

33. Make up a name for an irrational number using only the digits 0 and 9.   Answers may vary, an example is 0.09009000900009. . .

1-2 Addition

After finishing Lesson 1-2, you should be able to
▮   find the absolute value and additive inverse of a number.
▮▮ add real numbers.
▮▮▮ simplify expressions like $-(-9)$.

▮ Absolute Value and Additive Inverses

The absolute value of a number can be thought of as its distance from 0 on the number line. The absolute value of any number a can be named $|a|$.

Example 1. Simplify $|-7|$.

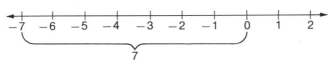

The distance from -7 to 0 is 7. Thus $|-7| = 7$.

Example 2. Simplify $|0|$.

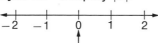

The distance from 0 to 0 is 0. Thus $|0| = 0$.

TRY THIS ▬▬▶

Simplify. Think of distance on a number line.

1. $|-2|$ **2**
2. $|\sqrt{3}|$ **$\sqrt{3}$**
3. $|0|$ **0**
4. $\left|-\dfrac{1}{4}\right|$ **$\dfrac{1}{4}$**

Every real number has an *additive inverse*.

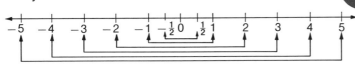

Additive Inverses

Examples.

3. The additive inverse of -3 is 3.

4. The additive inverse of $\dfrac{1}{2}$ is $-\dfrac{1}{2}$.

5. The additive inverse of 0 is 0.

TRY THIS ▬▬▶

Find the additive inverse of each number.

5. 9   **−9**
6. -23 **23**
7. -14 **14**
8. 0   **0**

The additive inverse of *a* can be named −*a*.

Examples.　Simplify, if possible.

6.　$-(-8.4) = 8.4$ (The additive inverse of -8.4 is 8.4.)

7.　$-0 = 0$ (The additive inverse of 0 is 0.)

8.　-4 *can't be simplified* (This tells us that -4 can be read two ways: as "the additive inverse of 4" or as "negative 4.")

TRY THIS

Simplify, if possible.

9.　$-(-9)$　9
10.　$-(-7)$　7
11.　-0　0
12.　-8.4　−8.4
13.　$-\left(-\dfrac{1}{2}\right)$　$\frac{1}{2}$
14.　$-(-9.8)$　9.8

ıı Addition of Real Numbers

The number line can help explain addition of real numbers. To find $a + b$, we start at *a* and move according to *b*. If *b* is positive, we move to the right. If *b* is negative, we move to the left.

Examples.　Add, using a number line.

9.　$6 + (-4) = 2$

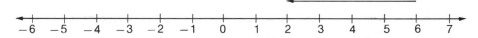

10.　$-6 + 9 = 3$

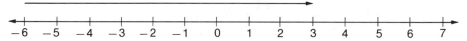

11.　$-3 + (-2) = -5$

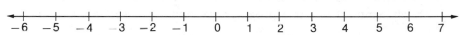

TRY THIS

Add, using a number line.

15.　$3 + (-5)$　−2
16.　$-3 + 8$　5
17.　$-5 + 0$　−5
18.　$-9 + (-5)$　−14

The sum of two negative real numbers is negative. We add their absolute values and then take the additive inverse. The result is negative.

Examples. Add.

12. $-5 + (-9) = -14$

13. $-10 + (-21) = -31$

14. $-9.4 + (-3.2) = -12.6$

15. $-\dfrac{9}{6} + \left(-\dfrac{11}{6}\right) = -\dfrac{20}{6}$, or $-\dfrac{10}{3}$

TRY THIS

Add.

19. $-7 + (-11)$
20. $-8 + (-9)$
21. $-20 + (-9)$
22. $-8.9 + (-9.7)$
23. $-\dfrac{6}{5} + \left(-\dfrac{23}{5}\right)$

Answers. 19. -18 20. -17
21. -29 22. -18.6
23. $-\dfrac{29}{5}$

To add a positive and a negative number with different absolute values, find the difference of their absolute values. If the negative number has the greater absolute value, the answer is negative. If the positive number has the greater absolute value, the answer is positive.

Examples. Add.

16. $3 + (-5) = -2$

17. $14 + (-9) = 5$

18. $-9.2 + 3.1 = -6.1$

19. $-\dfrac{5}{4} + \dfrac{1}{7} = -\dfrac{35}{28} + \dfrac{4}{28} = -\dfrac{31}{28}$

When we add 0 and any real number, the result is the number itself. Since 0 has this property, we call it the *additive identity*.

TRY THIS

Answers.   24. -3 25. 12
26. -3.3 27. $-\dfrac{7}{3}$ 28. $-\dfrac{11}{24}$

Add.

24. $4 + (-7)$
25. $23 + (-11)$
26. $-7.8 + 4.5$
27. $-\dfrac{7}{3} + 0$
28. $\dfrac{3}{8} + \left(-\dfrac{5}{6}\right)$

⦙⦙⦙ Additive Inverses

DEFINITION

The additive inverse of a number a is the number which when added to a gives 0. The additive inverse of a is $-a$.

Thus for any real number a, $a + (-a) = (-a) + a = 0$.

Examples.

20. $-8 + 8 = 0$

21. $0 + 0 = 0$

22. $4.2 + (-4.2) = 0$

TRY THIS ➡

> Add.
>
> 29. $-5 + 5$ **0**
> 30. $10 + (-10)$ **0**
> 31. $-\dfrac{1}{4} + \dfrac{1}{4}$ **0**

Note that the symbol $-a$ refers to the number we add to a to get 0. We cannot know whether $-a$ is positive, negative, or 0 unless we know what a stands for.

Example 23. Find $-a$ when a stands for -8.

$$-a = -(-8) = 8$$

Example 24. Find $-a$ when a stands for 0.

$$-a = -0 = 0$$

Example 25. Find $-a$ when a stands for 7.

$$-a = -(7) = -7$$

TRY THIS ➡

> Find $-x$ when x stands for
>
> 32. 4 **−4**
> 33. -14 **14**
> 34. -8.6 **8.6**
> 35. 0 **0**

Exercise Set 1-2

▌Simplify. (*See Examples 1 and 2.*)

1. $|-4|$ **4**
2. $|-6|$ **6**
3. $|9|$ **9**
4. $|11|$ **11**
5. $|\sqrt{5}|$ **$\sqrt{5}$**
6. $|\sqrt{6}|$ **$\sqrt{6}$**
7. $\left|-\dfrac{1}{9}\right|$ **$\dfrac{1}{9}$**
8. $\left|-\dfrac{5}{8}\right|$ **$\dfrac{5}{8}$**
9. $|0|$ **0**
10. $|3|$ **3**
11. $|-19|$ **19**
12. $|-23|$ **23**
13. $|-4.7|$ **4.7**
14. $|-6.3|$ **6.3**

Find the additive inverse of each number. (*See Examples 3–5.*)

15. 12 **−12**
16. 18 **−18**
17. -31 **31**
18. -43 **43**
19. 5 **−5**
20. 0 **0**

21. $-\dfrac{1}{6}$ $\frac{1}{6}$

22. $-\dfrac{7}{8}$ $\frac{7}{8}$

23. -7.6 7.6

24. -8.3 8.3

25. 9.03 −9.03

26. 5.72 −5.72

Simplify, if possible. (*See Examples 6–8.*)

27. $-(-8)$ 8

28. $-(-7)$ 7

29. -5 −5

30. -9 −9

31. $-(-7.5)$ 7.5

32. $-(-6.4)$ 6.4

33. -0 0

34. -7 −7

■■ Add. (*See Examples 9–19.*)

35. $5 + (-4)$ 1

36. $9 + (-6)$ 3

37. $-8 + (-10)$ −18

38. $-4 + (-8)$ −12

39. $-12 + (-16)$ −28

40. $-11 + (-18)$ −29

41. $-8 + (-8)$ −16

42. $-6 + (-6)$ −12

43. $8 + (-3)$ 5

44. $9 + (-4)$ 5

45. $11 + (-7)$ 4

46. $12 + (-8)$ 4

47. $-16 + 9$ −7

48. $-23 + 8$ −15

49. $-24 + 0$ −24

50. $-34 + 0$ −34

51. $-8.4 + 9.6$ 1.2

52. $-6.3 + 8.2$ 1.9

53. $-2.62 + (-6.24)$ −8.86

54. $-5.83 + (-7.43)$ −13.26

55. $-\dfrac{2}{7} + \dfrac{3}{7}$ $\frac{1}{7}$

56. $-\dfrac{5}{6} + \dfrac{1}{6}$ $-\frac{2}{3}$

57. $-\dfrac{11}{12} + \left(-\dfrac{5}{12}\right)$ $-\frac{4}{3}$

58. $-\dfrac{3}{8} + \left(-\dfrac{7}{8}\right)$ $-\frac{5}{4}$

59. $-\dfrac{8}{3} + \dfrac{3}{4}$ $-\frac{23}{12}$

60. $-\dfrac{4}{5} + \dfrac{5}{6}$ $\frac{1}{30}$

■■■ Find $-a$ when a stands for: (*See Examples 23–25.*)

61. 8 −8

62. 11 −11

63. -18 18

64. -19 19

65. $-\sqrt{11}$ $\sqrt{11}$

66. $-\sqrt{7}$ $\sqrt{7}$

67. $\dfrac{5}{6}$ $-\frac{5}{6}$

68. $\dfrac{3}{4}$ $-\frac{3}{4}$

Challenge Exercises

Simplify.

69. 4   70. 2   71. −9   72. −10   73. 11   74. 15   75. 6   76. 3

69. $|-8 - 4|$

70. $|6| + |-8|$

71. $-|-9|$

72. $-|-7 + (-3)|$

73. $|-4| + |-7|$

74. $|-|17| + |-2||$

75. $-|0| + |6|$

76. $|-(-3)|$

1-3 Properties of Addition and Subtraction

After finishing Lesson 1-3, you should be able to
I   simplify expressions involving parentheses.
II   tell which laws are illustrated by certain sentences.
III   subtract real numbers.

I Parentheses, Symbols of Grouping

What does $4 + 5 \times 3$ mean? If we add 4 and 5 and then multiply by 3, we get 60. If we multiply 5 and 3 and add the result to 4, we get 19. To tell which operation to do first, we use parentheses. Calculations shown in parentheses are to be done first.

Example 1.

$(3 \times 7) + 10$ means $21 + 10$, or 31.
$3 \times (7 + 10)$ means 3×17, or 51.

TRY THIS ➡

Do these calculations.

1. $(4 \times 10) + 13$ **53**
2. $6(10 + 14)$ **144**
3. $(-13 + 9) + 2$ **–2**
4. $-13 + (9 + 2)$ **–2**

II Order and Grouping in Addition

A basic property of real numbers is that they can be added in any order.

Examples.

2. $4 + 7 = 7 + 4 = 11$

3. $-3.2 + 5.6 = 5.6 + (-3.2) = 2.4$

The Commutative Law of Addition

For any numbers a and b, $a + b = b + a$.

TRY THIS ➡

5. Add and compare.

a) $-9 + 4$; $4 + (-9)$
b) $-6 + (-8)$; $-8 + (-6)$
c) $-4.7 + (-5.2)$;
    $-5.2 + (-4.7)$

**a) –5; –5 b) –14; –14
c) –9.9; –9.9**

If we write $10 + 14 + 15$, what does it mean? Does it mean $(10 + 14) + 15$ or $10 + (14 + 15)$? Either way we get 39. If we are doing only addition, we can omit parentheses.

Example 4.

$-4 + (9 + 8) = -4 + 17$, or 13
$(-4 + 9) + 8 = 5 + 8$, or 13

The Associative Law of Addition

For any real numbers a, b, and c,
$a + (b + c) = (a + b) + c$.

TRY THIS ➡

6. Add and compare.

a) $(5 + 8) + 3$; $5 + (8 + 3)$
b) $(-9 + 4) + (-6)$; $-9 + (4 + (-6))$
c) $(4.3 + 7.2) + 6.8$; $4.3 + (7.2 + 6.8)$

a) 16; 16   b) −11; −11   c) 18.3; 18.3

Examples. Tell which property of real numbers is illustrated by each sentence.

5. $4.5 + \left(9 + \dfrac{1}{2}\right) = (4.5 + 9) + \dfrac{1}{2}$

Associative law of addition

6. $7.8 + \dfrac{1}{4} = \dfrac{1}{4} + 7.8$

Commutative law of addition

TRY THIS ➡

Tell which property of real numbers is illustrated by each sentence.

7. $4 + \left(9 + \dfrac{1}{4}\right) = (4 + 9) + \dfrac{1}{4}$
8. $4.5 + 9.67 = 9.67 + 4.5$
9. $\left(9 + \dfrac{1}{2}\right) + \dfrac{1}{2} = 9 + \left(\dfrac{1}{2} + \dfrac{1}{2}\right)$

Answers.   7. Associative law, addition   8. Commutative law, addition
9. Associative law, addition

Remark. We have seen that the real numbers with respect to addition are associative. Also, we know that 0 is the additive identity and each real number has an additive inverse. Any mathematical system with one operation which has these properties is called a *group*. Do the integers form a group with respect to addition?

ııı Subtraction of Real Numbers

DEFINITION

The difference $a - b$ is the number which when added to b gives a.

Example 7. Subtract: $-3 - 5$.

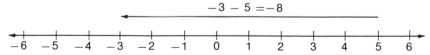

$$-3 - 5 = -8$$

To subtract 5 from -3 we find the number which when added to 5 gives -3. Thus we start at 5. We move 8 units to the left (negative direction) to get to -3. Since adding -8 to 5 gives -3, we know that $-3 - 5 = -8$.

TRY THIS

Draw a number line. Then do these subtractions. Check by adding.

10. $-2 - 3$ ₋₅
11. $5 - 8$ ₋₃
12. $-2 - (-5)$ ₃

To see how to subtract without a number line compare column A and column B and look for a pattern.

Column A	**Column B**
a) $3 - 8 = -5$	a) $3 + (-8) = -5$
b) $-2 - (-9) = 7$	b) $-2 + 9 = 7$
c) $-6 - 4 = -10$	c) $-6 + (-4) = -10$
d) $0 - (-3) = 3$	d) $0 + 3 = 3$
e) $-11 - (-4) = -7$	e) $-11 + 4 = -7$

The pattern suggests that we can always subtract by adding an additive inverse. This can be proved, so we call it a *theorem*. Anything that can be proved is called a theorem. In this book, we will prove theorems occasionally. We will not prove all of them because there isn't room, and because we don't have the necessary mathematics to prove some of them.

THEOREM 1-1
For any real numbers a and b, $a - b = a + (-b)$. (We can subtract by adding the additive inverse of the subtrahend.)

Examples. Subtract.

8. $5 - (-4) = 5 + 4 = 9$

9. $-7 - 4 = -7 + (-4) = -11$

10. $-19.4 - 5.6 = -19.4 + (-5.6) = -25$

11. $-\dfrac{4}{3} - \left(-\dfrac{2}{5}\right) = -\dfrac{4}{3} + \dfrac{2}{5} = -\dfrac{20}{15} + \dfrac{6}{15} = -\dfrac{14}{15}$

TRY THIS

Subtract by adding an inverse.

13. $8 - (-9)$ ₁₇
14. $-10 - 6$ ₋₁₆
15. $-23.7 - 5.9$ _{-29.6}
16. $-\dfrac{11}{16} - \left(-\dfrac{23}{12}\right)$ _{59/48}

A Proof of Theorem 1-1

We have seen that $a - b = a + (-b)$. Let us prove this, where a and b are real numbers.

By the definition of subtraction, $a - b$ is the number which, when added to b, gives a. If we can show that $a + (-b)$ is the number which when added to b gives a, then we will have proved that $a - b = a + (-b)$. Consider what happens when we add $a + (-b)$ to b.

$$[a + (-b)] + b = a + [(-b) + b] \qquad \text{Adding } a + (-b) \text{ to b and}$$
$$\text{using the associative property}$$
$$= a + 0 \qquad \text{Property of additive inverses}$$
$$= a$$

We have shown that $a + (-b)$ is a number which when added to b gives a. Thus $a + (-b) = a - b$ by the definition of subtraction.

Exercise Set 1-3

▌ Do these calculations. (*See Example 1.*)

1. $(5 \times 8) + 9$ 49
2. $(6 \times 3) + 11$ 29
3. $(8 \times 12) + (-3)$ 93
4. $(7 \times 13) + (-4)$ 87
5. $(9 \times 9) + (9 \times 6)$ 135
6. $(10 \times 12) + (7 \times 9)$ 183
7. $(2 - 8) + (8 - 2)$ 0
8. $(7 - 11) + (11 - 7)$ 0

▌▌ Tell which property of real numbers is illustrated by each sentence. (*See Examples 5 and 6.*)   See answer section

9. $1.9 + 7.3 = 7.3 + 1.9$
10. $1.23 + 3.21 = 3.21 + 1.23$
11. $8 + (2 + 5) = (8 + 2) + 5$
12. $14 + (9 + 16) = (14 + 9) + 16$
13. $(2.6 + 5.2) + 3.4 =$
    $2.6 + (5.2 + 3.4)$
14. $(6.8 + 9.6) + 3.1 =$
    $6.8 + (9.6 + 3.1)$
15. $-8 + (-4) = -4 + (-8)$
16. $-16 + (-2) = -2 + (-16)$

▌▌▌ Subtract by adding an inverse. (*See Examples 8–11.*)

17. $5 - 7$ −2
18. $9 - 12$ −3
19. $-5 - 7$ −12
20. $-9 - 12$ −21
21. $-6 - (-11)$ 5
22. $-7 - (-12)$ 5
23. $10 - (-5)$ 15
24. $28 - (-16)$ 44
25. $15.8 - 27.4$ −11.6
26. $17.2 - 34.9$ −17.7
27. $-18.01 - 11.24$ −29.25
28. $-19.04 - 15.76$ −34.8
29. $-\dfrac{21}{4} - \left(-\dfrac{7}{2}\right)$ $-\dfrac{7}{4}$
30. $-\dfrac{16}{5} - \left(-\dfrac{5}{3}\right)$ $-\dfrac{23}{15}$

1-4 *Multiplication and Division*

After finishing Lesson 1-4, you should be able to
- **▌** multiply real numbers.
- **▌▌** tell which laws are illustrated by certain sentences.
- **▌▌▌** divide real numbers.
- **▌▌▌▌** divide by multiplying by a reciprocal.
- **▌▌▌▌▌** recognize impossible divisions (divisions by 0).

▌Multiplication of Real Numbers

When we multiply a positive and negative number we multiply their absolute values. The answer is negative.

Examples. Multiply.

1. $-3 \cdot 5 = -15$

2. $6 \cdot (-7) = -42$

3. $-5.2 \times 10 = -52$

4. $4 \cdot \left(-\dfrac{1}{5}\right) = -\dfrac{4}{5}$

TRY THIS ➤

Multiply.
1. $-4 \cdot 6$ **−24**
2. $8(-9)$ **−72**
3. $-7.4 \cdot (10)$ **−74**
4. $8\left(-\dfrac{1}{4}\right)$ **−2**

When we multiply two negative numbers we multiply their absolute values. The answer is positive.

Examples. Multiply.

5. $-3 \cdot (-5) = 15$

6. $-6 \cdot (-7) = 42$

7. $-5.2 \cdot (-10) = 52$

8. $-7 \cdot \left(-\dfrac{2}{3}\right) = \dfrac{14}{3}$

When we multiply 1 and any real number the result is the number itself. Since 1 has this property, we call it the *multiplicative identity*.

TRY THIS ➤

Multiply.
5. $-8 \cdot (-9)$ **72**
6. $-1 \cdot (-5)$ **5**
7. $-20 \cdot (-6.4)$ **128**
8. $-5\left(-\dfrac{2}{3}\right)$ **$\dfrac{10}{3}$**

Properties of Multiplication

Our experience with real numbers tells us that multiplication is both commutative and associative.

For any real numbers a, b, c,
$a \cdot b = b \cdot a$,   *Commutative law of multiplication*
$a \cdot (b \cdot c) = (a \cdot b) \cdot c$.   *Associative law of multiplication*

Examples. Which laws are illustrated by these sentences?

9. $3 \times 9 = 9 \times 3$ Commutative law of multiplication

10. $-4 + 4.2 = 4.2 + (-4)$ Commutative law of addition

11. $-9 + (10 + 5) = (-9 + 10) + 5$ Associative law of addition

12. $\frac{1}{2} \times \left(\frac{1}{4} \times 58\right) = \left(\frac{1}{2} \times \frac{1}{4}\right) \times 58$ Associative law of multiplication

TRY THIS ➤

Answers. 9. Commutative law, addition   10. Associative law, multiplication   11. Commutative law, multiplication   12. Associative law, addition

Which laws are illustrated by these sentences?

9. $4 + 9 = 9 + 4$
10. $67 \times (9 \times 11) = (67 \times 9) \times 11$
11. $-6.7 \times 89 = 89 \times (-6.7)$
12. $5.6 + (89 + 4) = (5.6 + 89) + 4$

Division of Real Numbers

DEFINITION

The quotient $\frac{p}{q}$ is the number which when multiplied by q gives p.

Examples.

13. $\frac{10}{-2} = -5$ because $-5 \cdot (-2) = 10$.

14. $\frac{-32}{4} = -8$ because $-8 \cdot (4) = -32$.

15. $\frac{-56}{-7} = 8$ because $8 \cdot (-7) = -56$.

When we divide a positive number by a negative or a negative by a positive, the answer is negative. When we divide a negative number by a negative number, the answer is positive.

TRY THIS ➤

Divide.

13. $\frac{24}{-8}$ -3
14. $\frac{-125}{5}$ -25
15. $\frac{-75}{-25}$ 3
16. $\frac{-42}{-21}$ 2

▸▸▸▸ Reciprocals and Division

DEFINITION
Two numbers whose product is 1 are called *reciprocals* of each other. They are also called *multiplicative inverses* of each other.

Examples.

16. The reciprocal of $\frac{4}{5}$ is $\frac{5}{4}$ because $\frac{4}{5} \cdot \frac{5}{4} = \frac{20}{20} = 1$.

17. The reciprocal of 8 is $\frac{1}{8}$ because $8 \cdot \frac{1}{8} = \frac{8}{8} = 1$.

18. The reciprocal of $-\frac{2}{3}$ is $-\frac{3}{2}$ because $-\frac{2}{3} \cdot \left(-\frac{3}{2}\right) = \frac{6}{6} = 1$.

Any nonzero real number a has a reciprocal $\frac{1}{a}$. The reciprocal of a negative number is negative. The reciprocal of a positive number is positive.

TRY THIS ➡

Name the reciprocal of each number.

17. $\frac{3}{8}$ $\frac{8}{3}$

18. 18 $\frac{1}{18}$

19. $-\frac{112}{234}$ $-\frac{234}{112}$

20. -43 $-\frac{1}{43}$

To subtract we can add an inverse. To divide we can multiply by a reciprocal.

THEOREM 1-2
To do the division $\frac{a}{b} \div \frac{c}{d}$, we can do the multiplication $\frac{a}{b} \times \frac{d}{c}$.
(We can multiply by the reciprocal of the divisor.)

Examples. Divide by multiplying by the reciprocal of the divisor.

19. $\frac{1}{4} \div \frac{3}{5} = \frac{1}{4} \times \frac{5}{3} = \frac{5}{12}$

20. $-\frac{5}{6} \div \frac{4}{3} = -\frac{5}{6} \times \frac{3}{4} = -\frac{15}{24}$, or $-\frac{5}{8}$

21. $\frac{2}{3} \div \left(-\frac{4}{9}\right) = \frac{2}{3} \times \left(-\frac{9}{4}\right) = -\frac{18}{12}$, or $-\frac{3}{2}$

TRY THIS ➡

Divide by multiplying by a reciprocal.

21. $\left(-\frac{3}{4}\right) \div \frac{7}{5}$ $-\frac{15}{28}$

22. $\left(-\frac{11}{5}\right) \div \left(-\frac{7}{8}\right)$ $\frac{88}{35}$

‖‖‖ Division by Zero

Why do we not divide by zero? Recall the definition of division.

$\frac{n}{0}$ would be some number c such that $c \cdot 0 = n$. But $c \cdot 0 = 0$, so

the only possible number n which could be divided by 0 is 0.

Let's consider what $\frac{0}{0}$ might be.

    a) $\frac{0}{0} = 5$ because $0 = 0 \cdot 5$.

    b) $\frac{0}{0} = 567$ because $0 = 0 \cdot 567$.

    c) $\frac{0}{0} = -8$ because $0 = 0 \cdot (-8)$.

    d) $\frac{0}{0} = \frac{1}{4}$ because $0 = 0 \cdot \frac{1}{4}$.

It looks as if $\frac{0}{0}$ could be any number at all. Thus we

agree to exclude division by zero.

Division by 0 is not defined. We never divide by 0.

We cannot divide by 0, but we can divide 0 by any

nonzero number a. The result is 0. That is, $\frac{0}{a} = 0$,

because $a \cdot 0 = 0$.

TRY THIS ■■■■➤

Which of these divisions are possible?
23. $\frac{7}{0}$ Not possible
24. $\frac{0}{7}$ 0
25. $\frac{4}{x - x}$ Not possible
26. $\frac{-9}{15 - (3 \cdot 4)}$ -3

Exercise Set 1-4   Use Quiz 1 after lesson 1—4.

■ Multiply. (*See Examples 1–8.*)

1. $3(-7)$ −21
2. $5(-8)$ −40
3. $-2 \cdot 4$ −8
4. $-5 \cdot 9$ −45
5. $(-8)(-2)$ 16
6. $(-7)(-3)$ 21
7. $(-9)(-14)$ 126
8. $(-8)(-17)$ 136
9. $(-6)(-5.7)$ 34.2
10. $(-7)(-6.1)$ 42.7
11. $-4.2(-6.3)$ 26.46
12. $-7.4(-9.6)$ 71.04
13. $-3\left(-\frac{2}{3}\right)$ 2
14. $-5\left(-\frac{3}{5}\right)$ 3
15. $-3(-4)(5)$ 60
16. $-6(-8)(9)$ 432
17. $4(-3) \cdot (-2)(1)$ 24
18. $-3 \cdot (-6)(8)(0)$ 0

▌▌ Which laws are illustrated by these sentences? (*See Examples 9–12.*)

19. $5 + (4 + 23) = (5 + 4) + 23$

20. $5.2 \times 3.6 = 3.6 \times 5.2$

21. $-6 + 5 = 5 + (-6)$

See answer section

22. $\left(\dfrac{2}{3} \times \dfrac{3}{8}\right) \times \dfrac{5}{6} = \dfrac{2}{3} \times \left(\dfrac{3}{8} \times \dfrac{5}{6}\right)$

▌▌▌ Divide. (*See Examples 13–15.*)

23. $\dfrac{-8}{4}$ −2

24. $\dfrac{-16}{2}$ −8

25. $\dfrac{56}{-8}$ −7

26. $\dfrac{63}{-7}$ −9

27. $\dfrac{-77}{-11}$ 7

28. $\dfrac{-48}{-6}$ 8

29. $\dfrac{-5.4}{-18}$ 0.3

30. $\dfrac{-8.4}{-12}$ 0.7

▌▌▌▌ Name the reciprocal of each. (*See Examples 16–18.*)

31. $\dfrac{3}{4}$ $\frac{4}{3}$

32. $\dfrac{9}{10}$ $\frac{10}{9}$

33. $-\dfrac{7}{8}$ $-\frac{8}{7}$

34. $-\dfrac{5}{6}$ $-\frac{6}{5}$

35. 26 $\frac{1}{26}$

36. 38 $\frac{1}{38}$

37. -56 $-\frac{1}{56}$

38. -97 $-\frac{1}{97}$

Divide by multiplying by a reciprocal. (*See Examples 19–21.*)

39. $\dfrac{2}{7} \div \left(-\dfrac{11}{3}\right)$ $-\frac{6}{77}$

40. $\dfrac{3}{5} \div \left(-\dfrac{6}{7}\right)$ $-\frac{7}{10}$

41. $-\dfrac{10}{3} \div \left(-\dfrac{2}{15}\right)$ 25

42. $-\dfrac{12}{5} \div \left(-\dfrac{3}{10}\right)$ 8

▌▌▌▌▌ Which of these divisions are possible? (*See page 18.*)

43. $\dfrac{9}{0}$ Not possible

44. $\dfrac{8}{0}$ Not possible

45. $\dfrac{0}{16}$ 0

46. $\dfrac{0}{28}$ 0

47. $\dfrac{9}{y - y}$ Not possible

48. $\dfrac{3}{2x - 2x}$ Not possible

Calculator Exercises   49. 46,871,451   50. 398,871   51. −0.00168012   52. −0.00002155

Compute.

49. $-80{,}397 \times (-583)$

50. $-14{,}773 \times (-27)$

51. -0.56004×0.003

52. -0.00431×0.005

1-5 The Distributive Laws and Their Use

After finishing Lesson 1-5, you should be able to
> **I**   evaluate expressions when numbers are specified for the letters.
> **II**   evaluate expressions involving the distributive law.
> **III** use the distributive law to factor and multiply expressions.
> **IIII** collect like terms.

▪ Some Agreements

When a letter can represent various numbers, we call it a *variable*. When we write two or more variables together we agree that this means multiplication. We have the same agreement when variables and numerals occur.

Examples. What does each of the following mean?

1. *pqr* means $p \cdot q \cdot r$

2. *mmm* means $m \cdot m \cdot m$

3. 5*xy* means $5 \cdot x \cdot y$

TRY THIS ➡

> What does each of the following mean?
>
> 1. *abc* $a \cdot b \cdot c$
> 2. *bbb* $b \cdot b \cdot b$
> 3. 8*ab* $8 \cdot a \cdot b$

We also agree that in an expression like $(4 \cdot 10) + (9 \cdot 2)$, we can omit the parentheses. Thus $4 \cdot 10 + 9 \cdot 2$ means $(4 \cdot 10) + (9 \cdot 2)$. In other words, do the multiplications first. We have a similar agreement for subtraction. That is, $4 \cdot 10 - 9 \cdot 2$ means $(4 \cdot 10) - (9 \cdot 2)$. The multiplications are still to be done first.

Example 4. Evaluate and simplify.

$$8 \cdot 4 + 3 \cdot 6 = 32 + 18 \quad \textit{Multiplying first}$$
$$= 50 \quad \textit{Adding}$$

TRY THIS ➡

> Evaluate and simplify.
>
> 4. $10 \cdot 5 + 4 \cdot 2$ **58**
> 5. $-4 \cdot 7 - 8 \cdot 9$ **−100**

In expressions like $ab + cd$ and $ab - cd$ it is understood that parentheses belong around *ab* and *cd*. In other words, the multiplications are to be done first.

Example 5. Evaluate $xy + z$ when $x = 2$, $y = -3$, and $z = -4$.

$$xy + z = 2 \cdot (-3) + (-4)$$
$$= -6 + (-4)$$
$$= -10$$

TRY THIS ━━▶

Evaluate each expression when $a = 5$, $b = -2$, $c = 4$, and $d = 10$.

6. $ab + cd$ 30
7. $ab - cd$ −50

ⅡThe Distributive Laws

Compare.

a) $5(4 + 8) = 5 \cdot 12$
$\qquad = 60$
$\quad 5 \cdot 4 + 5 \cdot 8 = 20 + 40$
$\qquad\qquad\quad = 60$

b) $-4(9 + 5) = -4 \cdot 14$
$\qquad\qquad = -56$
$\quad -4 \cdot 9 + (-4)5 = -36 + (-20)$
$\qquad\qquad\qquad\quad = -56$

We can either add and then multiply, or we can multiply and then add. The results are the same.

The Distributive Law of Multiplication over Addition

For any numbers a, b, and c, $a(b + c) = ab + ac$.

Note that we cannot omit the parentheses in $a(b + c)$. If we did, we would have $ab + c$, which by our agreement means $(ab) + c$. Compare.

a) $5(4 - 8) = 5(-4)$
$\qquad\qquad = -20$
$\quad 5 \cdot 4 - 5 \cdot 8 = 20 - 40$
$\qquad\qquad\qquad = -20$

b) $10(7 - 4) = 10 \cdot 3$
$\qquad\qquad\quad = 30$
$\quad 10 \cdot 7 - 10 \cdot 4 = 70 - 40$
$\qquad\qquad\qquad\quad = 30$

When we multiply a number by a difference, we can either subtract and then multiply, or multiply and then subtract.

The Distributive Law of Multiplication over Subtraction

For any numbers a, b, and c, $a(b - c) = ab - ac$.

Note again that we cannot omit the parentheses on the left. If we did, we would have $ab - c$, which would mean $(ab) - c$.

Examples. Evaluate each expression when $x = 2$, $y = 3$, and $z = 8$.

6. $x(y + z) = 2(3 + 8)$
$\qquad\qquad = 2 \cdot 11$
$\qquad\qquad = 22$

7. $xy + xz = 2 \cdot 3 + 2 \cdot 8$
$\qquad\qquad\ = 6 + 16$
$\qquad\qquad\ = 22$

8. $x(y - z) = 2(3 - 8)$
$\qquad\qquad = 2(-5)$
$\qquad\qquad = -10$

9. $xy - xz = 2 \cdot 3 - 2 \cdot 8$
$\qquad\qquad\ = 6 - 16$
$\qquad\qquad\ = -10$

TRY THIS ➡

Evaluate each expression when $a = -4$, $b = -10$, and $c = 5$.

8. $a(b + c)$ **20**
9. $ab + ac$ **20**

Evaluate each expression when $a = 6$, $b = 10$, and $c = -2$.

10. $a(b - c)$ **72**
11. $ab - ac$ **72**

Remark   We have seen that the real numbers have the following properties.

Addition	Multiplication
1. Commutative	1. Commutative
2. Associative	2. Associative
3. Additive Identity (0)	3. Multiplicative Identity (1)
4. Each number has an additive inverse.	4. Each number except 0 has a reciprocal (multiplicative inverse).

Multiplication is distributive over addition.

Any system with two operations having these properties is called a *field*.

ⅲ Factoring and Multiplying

Any equation can be reversed without changing its meaning. Thus the distributive laws could be written as follows.

$$ab + ac = a(b + c) \text{ and}$$
$$ab - ac = a(b - c)$$

When we write the distributive laws like this, they show more clearly the basis of *factoring*.

Examples. Factor.

10. $8x + 8y = 8(x + y)$ *By a distributive law*

11. $cx - cy = c(x - y)$ *By a distributive law*

The parts of an expression, such as $3x$, $+ 4y$, $-2z$, are called *terms*. Notice that we take the $+$ or the $-$ as part of the term. When all the terms of an expression contain a common factor, we can ''remove'' it, using the distributive laws.

Examples. Factor.

12. $4x + 8 = 4x + 4 \cdot 2$
$\qquad\qquad = 4(x + 2)$

13. $5x - 10 = 5x - 5 \cdot 2$
$\qquad\qquad = 5(x - 2)$

14. $P + Prt = P(1 + rt)$

15. $9x + 27y - 9 = 9x + 9(3y) - 9 \cdot 1$
$\qquad\qquad\qquad = 9(x + 3y - 1)$

TRY THIS

> Factor.
>
> 12. $9x + 9y$
> 13. $ac - ay$
> 14. $6x + 12$
> 15. $4y - 16$
> 16. $bs + bt - bw$
> 17. $35x - 25y + 15$

Answers.   12. $9(x + y)$ 13. $a(c - y)$ 14. $6(x + 2)$ 15. $4(y - 4)$ 16. $b(s + t - w)$
17. $5(7x - 5y + 3)$

One kind of multiplying is the reverse of the factoring process above.

Examples. Multiply.

16. $4(x - 2) = 4x - 4 \cdot 2$
$\qquad\qquad = 4x - 8$

17. $3(x + 10) = 3x + 3 \cdot 10$
$\qquad\qquad = 3x + 30$

18. $b(s - t + f) = bs - bt + bf$

In Examples 16, 17, and 18, we used the distributive laws. We multiplied each term inside the parentheses by the factor outside.

> Multiply.
>
> 18. $5(x - 9)$
> 19. $8(y + 10)$
> 20. $a(x + y - z)$

Answers.   18. $5x - 45$ 19. $8y + 80$ 20. $ax + ay - az$

TRY THIS

ⅠⅠⅠⅠ Collecting Like Terms

If two terms have the same variable, we say they are *like* terms, or *similar* terms. We can often simplify expressions by a process called *collecting like terms* or *combining like terms*. This also depends on the distributive laws.

Examples. Collect like terms.

19. $4x - 7x = (4 - 7)x$
$$= -3x$$

20. $y - 3y = 1 \cdot y - 3 \cdot y$
$$= (1 - 3)y$$
$$= -2y$$

21. $2x + 3y - 5x - 2y = 2x + 3y + (-5x) + (-2y)$ *Using Theorem 1-1*
$$= 2x + (-5x) + 3y + (-2y)$$
$$= (2 - 5)x + (3 - 2)y$$
$$= -3x + y$$

It is not necessry to write all the steps.

Example 22. $5t - 8x - 10t + 11x = -5t + 3x$

TRY THIS ▮▬▬▬▬▶

> Collect like terms.
>
> 21. $9x - 11x$ −2x
> 22. $5x + 12x$ 17x
> 23. $5y + y$ 6y
> 24. $t - 7t$ −6t
> 25. $22x - 25y + 14x + 6y$
>
>   36x − 19y

Exercise Set 1-5

▮ What does each of the following mean? (*See Examples 1–3.*)

1. xyz x · y · z
2. rst r · s · t
3. xxx x · x · x
4. yyy y · y · y
5. $9xy$ 9 · x · y
6. $12ab$ 12 · a · b

Evaluate and simplify. (*See Example 4.*)

7. $7 \cdot 3 + 4 \cdot 6$ 45
8. $2 \cdot 5 + 6 \cdot 3$ 28
9. $-8 \cdot 7 + 7 \cdot 4$ −28
10. $-5 \cdot 9 + 8 \cdot 2$ −29
11. $-6 \cdot 9 - 5 \cdot (-7)$ −19
12. $-3 \cdot 8 - 4 \cdot (-7)$ 4

Evaluate each expression when $x = -2$, $y = 3$, and $z = -4$. (*See Example 5.*)

13. $xy + x$ −8
14. $xy - y$ −9
15. $xz + yz$ −4
16. $xy - xz$ −14
17. $yz + xy$ −18
18. $xz + xy$ 2

∎∎ Evaluate each expression when $r = 8$, $s = 7$, and $t = -5$. (*See Examples 6–9.*)

19. $rs + rt$ 16
20. $r(s + t)$ 16
21. $rs - rt$ 96
22. $r(s - t)$ 96

∎∎∎ Factor. (*See Examples 10–15.*)

23. $8x + 8y$ 8(x + y)
24. $7a + 7b$ 7(a + b)
25. $9p - 9q$ 9(p − q)
26. $12x - 12y$ 12(x − y)
27. $7x - 21$ 7(x − 3)
28. $6y - 36$ 6(y − 6)
29. $xy + xz$ x(y + z)
30. $ab + ac$ a(b + c)
31. $2x - 2y + 2z$ 2(x − y + z)
32. $3x + 3y - 3z$ 3(x + y − z)
33. $3x + 6y - 9z$ 3(x + 2y − 3z)
34. $4a + 8b - 16c$ 4(a + 2b − 4c)
35. $ab + ac - ad$ a(b + c − d)
36. $xy - xz + xw$ x(y − z + w)
37. $P + Prt$ P(1 + rt)
38. $2\pi rh + 2\pi rr$ 2πr(h + r)
39. $\pi rr + \pi rs$ πr(r + s)
40. $\frac{1}{2}ah + \frac{1}{2}bh$ $\frac{1}{2}$h(a + b)

Multiply. (*See Examples 16–18.*)

41. $3(a + 2)$ 3a + 6
42. $8(x + 5)$ 8x + 40
43. $4(x - y)$ 4x − 4y
44. $9(a - b)$ 9a − 9b
45. $-5(2a + 3b)$ −10a − 15b
46. $-2(3c + 5d)$ −6c − 10d
47. $2a(b - c + d)$ 2ab − 2ac + 2ad
48. $5x(y - z + w)$ 5xy − 5xz + 5xw
49. $2\pi r(h + r)$ 2πrh + 2πrr
50. $P(1 + rt)$ P + Prt
51. $\frac{1}{2}h(a + b)$ $\frac{1}{2}$ha + $\frac{1}{2}$hb
52. $\pi r(r + s)$ πrr + πrs

∎∎∎∎ Collect like terms. (*See Examples 19–21.*)

53. $4a + 5a$ 9a
54. $9x + 3x$ 12x
55. $8b - 11b$ −3b
56. $9c - 12c$ −3c
57. $14y + y$ 15y
58. $13x + x$ 14x
59. $12a - a$ 11a
60. $15x - x$ 14x
61. $t - 9t$ −8t
62. $x - 6x$ −5x
63. $5x - 3x + 8x$ 10x
64. $3x - 11x + 2x$ −6x
65. $5x - 8y + 3x$ 8x − 8y
66. $9a - 10b + 4a$ 13a − 10b
67. $7c + 8d - 5c + 2d$ 2c + 10d
68. $12a + 3b - 5a + 6b$ 7a + 9b

Calculator Exercises

Collect like terms.

69. $830{,}979x + 15{,}007y - 947{,}864x + 833{,}609y$ −116,885x + 848,616y
70. $438{,}909a + 76{,}503b - 880{,}479a + 606{,}422b$ −441,570a + 682,925b
71. $0.00897x - 0.109743y + 0.00042x - 0.001048y$ 0.00939x − 0.110791y
72. $0.994107x - 0.001349y + 0.008049x - 0.001005y$ 1.002156x − 0.002354y

1-6 Multiplying by –1 and Simplifying

After finishing Lesson 1-6, you should be able to
- **I** rename an additive inverse without parentheses.
- **II** identify the terms of an expression.
- **III** simplify expressions by removing parentheses.
- **IIII** simplify expressions by removing parentheses within parentheses.

I Multiplying by –1

What happens when we multiply a number by -1?

Examples.

1. $-1 \cdot 9 = -9$

2. $-1 \cdot 0 = 0$

3. $-1 \cdot (-6) = 6$

TRY THIS

> Multiply.
>
> 1. $-1 \cdot 24$ **–24**
> 2. $-1 \cdot 0$ **0**
> 3. $-1 \cdot (-10)$ **10**

THEOREM 1-3

For any number a, $-1 \cdot a = -a$. Negative 1 times a is the additive inverse of a.

Whenever we see something like $-(\ )$ in an expression, we can replace the "$-$" by "$-1 \cdot$" if we wish. Whenever we see $-1 \cdot (\ )$, we can replace "$-1 \cdot$" by "$-$".
We can use Theorem 1-3 to rename additive inverses.

Examples. Rename each additive inverse without parentheses.

4. $-(3x) = -1(3x)$
$ = (-1 \cdot 3)x$
$ = -3x$

5. $-(-9y) = -1(-9y)$
$ = -1 \cdot (-9)y$
$ = 9y$

TRY THIS

> Rename each additive inverse without parentheses.
>
> 4. $-(9x)$ **–9x**
> 5. $-(-24t)$ **24t**

Examples.   Rename each additive inverse without parentheses.

6. $-(4 + x) = -1 \cdot (4 + x)$ *Replacing* − *by* −1 · *(Theorem 1-3)*
$= -1 \cdot 4 + (-1) \cdot x$ *Using a distributive law*
$= -4 + (-x)$ *Replacing* −1 · x *by* −x *(Theorem 1-3)*
$= -4 - x$ *Adding an inverse is the same as subtracting (Theorem 1-1)*

7. $-(a - b) = -1(a - b)$
$= (-1)a - (-1)b$
$= -a + [-(-1)b]$
$= -a + b$
$= b - a$
Note that $-(a - b)$, or $-1(a - b)$, is just $b - a$.

TRY THIS
Answers.   6. y − 7   7. y − x   8. −9x − 6y − 11
9. −23x + 7y + 2

> Rename each additive inverse without parentheses.
>
> 6. $-(7 - y)$
> 7. $-(x - y)$
> 8. $-(9x + 6y + 11)$
> 9. $-(23x - 7y - 2)$

We can rename an additive inverse by multiplying every term by −1. We could also say that we "change the sign" of every term inside the parentheses.

Examples.

8. $-(-9t + 7z - \frac{1}{4}w) = 9t - 7z + \frac{1}{4}w$ *Changing the sign of every term*

9. $-(-x) = x$

TRY THIS
Answers.   10. 2x + 5z − 24   11. t

> Rename each additive inverse without parentheses.
>
> 10. $-(-2x - 5z + 24)$
> 11. $-(-t)$

ıı Terms

We have already said what we mean by the terms of an expression. When there are only addition signs, the terms are easy to identify. They are the parts separated by addition signs. If there are subtraction signs, we can rename using addition signs.

Example 10.   What are the terms of $3x - 4y + 2z$?

$3x - 4y + 2z = 3x + (-4y) + 2z$

Thus the terms are: $3x$, $-4y$, and $2z$.

TRY THIS
Answers.   12. −5x, −7y, 67t, and −$\frac{4}{5}$ 13. −9a, −4b, 17c, and −24

> What are the terms of
>
> 12. $-5x - 7y + 67t - \frac{4}{5}$?
> 13. $-9a - 4b + 17c - 24$?

ⅡⅠ **Removing Certain Parentheses**

In some expressions there are parentheses preceded by subtraction signs. These parentheses can be removed.

Examples. Remove parentheses and simplify.

11. $6x - (4x + 2) = 6x + [-(4x + 2)]$ *Subtracting is adding the additive inverse (Theorem 1-1)*

$$= 6x + (-4x) + (-2)$$
$$= 6x - 4x - 2$$
$$= 2x - 2$$

12. $3y - 4 - (9y - 7) = 3y - 4 - 9y + 7$
$$= -6y + 3$$

When removing parentheses preceded by a subtraction sign, or additive inverse sign, the sign of each term inside the parentheses is changed. If parentheses are preceded by an addition sign, no signs are changed.

TRY THIS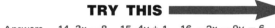

Answers.   14. $3x - 8$ 15. $4y + 1$ 16. $-2x - 9y - 6$

Remove parentheses and simplify.

14. $6x - (3x + 8)$
15. $6y - 4 - (2y - 5)$
16. $6x - (9y - 4) - (8x + 10)$

ⅡⅡⅠ **Parentheses Within Parentheses**

When parentheses occur within parentheses, we may use parentheses of different shapes, such as [ ] (also called "brackets") and { } (usually called "braces"). In mathematics, these all have the same meaning. The computations in the innermost parentheses are to be done first.

Example 13. Simplify.

$$\{3(2 - 5) - 4(2 + 3)\} - \{6 - [3 - (7 + 3)]\} = \{3(-3) - 4 \cdot 5\} - \{6 - [3 - 10]\}$$
$$= \{-9 - 20\} - \{6 - (-7)\}$$
$$= -29 - 13$$
$$= -42$$

TRY THIS ➡

When expressions within parentheses contain variables we may simplify by removing parentheses. We still work from the inside out.

Simplify.

17. $\{4(5 - 6) - 3(4 + 5)\}$
18. $-\{7 - [9 - (7 + 8)]\}$
19. $\{\frac{3}{2}(8 - 4) - \frac{2}{3}(8 + 4)\}$
20. $-\{-7 - [-6 - (5 - 12)]\}$

Example 14. Simplify.

$$[5(x + 2) - 3x] - \{4[3(y - 2) - 4(y + 2)] - 3\}$$
$$= [5x + 10 - 3x] - \{4[3y - 6 - 4y - 8] - 3\}$$
$$= 2x + 10 - \{4[-y - 14] - 3\} \quad \textit{Collecting like terms}$$
$$= 2x + 10 - \{-4y - 56 - 3\}$$
$$= 2x + 10 - \{-4y - 59\}$$
$$= 2x + 10 + 4y + 59$$
$$= 2x + 4y + 69$$

TRY THIS ➡

Simplify.

21. $[4(x - 3) + 4x]$
22. $-\{8[2(3y - 4) - (9y + 4)] + 7\}$
23. $2(x + 4) - 7[4(x - 5) + 3y]$

Exercise Set 1-6

▮ Rename each additive inverse without parentheses. (*See Examples 4–9.*)

1. $-(5)$ −5
2. $-(9)$ −9
3. $-(-19)$ 19
4. $-(-34)$ 34
5. $-(-4b)$ 4b
6. $-(-5x)$ 5x
7. $-(a + 2)$ −a − 2
8. $-(b + 9)$ −b − 9
9. $-(b - 3)$ −b + 3
10. $-(x - 8)$ −x + 8
11. $-(t - y)$ −t + y
12. $-(r - s)$ −r + s
13. $-(a + b + c)$ −a − b − c
14. $-(x + y + z)$ −x − y − z
15. $-(8x - 6y + 13)$ −8x + 6y − 13
16. $-(9a - 7b + 24)$ −9a + 7b − 24
17. $-(m - n - s)$ −m + n + s
18. $-(x - y - z)$ −x + y + z
19. $-(-2c + 5d - 3e + 4f)$ 2c − 5d + 3e − 4f
20. $-(-4x + 8y - 5w + 9z)$ 4x − 8y + 5w − 9z

▮▮ What are the terms of the following? (*See Example 10.*)

21. $4a - 5b + 6$ 4a, −5b, 6
22. $5x - 9y + 12$ 5x, −9y, 12
23. $8m - 5n + \frac{1}{2}p$ 8m, −5n, $\frac{1}{2}$p
24. $4a - 21b + \frac{3}{4}c$ 4a, −21b, $\frac{3}{4}$c
25. $\sqrt{2}x - \sqrt{3}y - 2z$ $\sqrt{2}$x, −$\sqrt{3}$y, −2z
26. $\sqrt{5}a - \sqrt{7}b - 9c$ $\sqrt{5}$a, −$\sqrt{7}$b, −9c

III Remove parentheses and simplify. (*See Examples 11 and 12.*)

27. $a + (2a + 5)$ ₃ₐ ₊ ₅
28. $x + (5x + 9)$ ₆ₓ ₊ ₉
29. $b - (b + 2)$ ₋₂
30. $x - (x + 7)$ ₋₇
31. $4m - (3m - 1)$ ₘ ₊ ₁
32. $5a - (4a - 3)$ ₐ ₊ ₃
33. $3d - 7 - (5 - 2d)$ ₅d ₋ ₁₂
34. $8x - 9 - (7 - 5x)$ ₁₃ₓ ₋ ₁₆
35. $-(p - q) + (p - q)$ ₀
36. $-(x - y) + (x - y)$ ₀
37. $(2a - 3b) + (-3a + 4b)$ ₋ₐ ₊ b
38. $(3x - 5y) + (-8x + 7y)$ ₋₅ₓ ₊ ₂y
39. $-2(x + 3) - 5(x - 4)$ ₋₇ₓ ₊ ₁₄
40. $-9(y + 7) - 6(y - 3)$ ₋₁₅y ₋ ₄₅

IIII Remove parentheses and simplify. (*See Examples 13 and 14.*)

41. $2x + [4 - 3(4x - 5)]$ ₋₁₀ₓ ₊ ₁₉
42. $5y + [8 - 9(3y - 7)]$ ₋₂₂y ₊ ₇₁
43. $9a - [7 - 5(7a - 3)]$ ₄₄ₐ ₋ ₂₂
44. $12b - [9 - 7(5b - 6)]$ ₄₇b ₋ ₅₁
45. $5\{-2 + 3[4 - 2(3 + 5)] - (8 - 3)\}$ ₋₂₁₅
46. $7\{-7 + 8[5 - 3(4 + 6)] - (9 - 4)\}$
47. $[8(x - 2) + 9x] - \{7[3(2y - 5) - (8y + 7)] + 9\}$ ₁₇ₓ ₊ ₁₄y ₊ ₁₂₉
48. $[11(a - 3) + 12a] - \{6[4(3b - 7) - (9b + 10)] + 11\}$ ₋₁₄₈₄ ... ₂₃ₐ ₋ ₁₈b ₊ ₁₈₄
49. $-3[9(x - 4) + 5x] - 8\{3[5(3y + 4)] - 12\}$ ₋₄₂ₓ ₋ ₃₆₀z ₋ ₂₇₆
50. $-6[8(y - 7) + 9y] - 7\{5[7(4z + 3)] - 14\}$ ₋₁₀₂y ₋ ₉₈₀z ₋ ₃₀₁

Calculator Exercises

Remove parentheses and simplify.

51. $(87{,}573a - 47{,}924b) + (-578{,}563a + 903{,}408b)$ ₋₄₉₀,₉₉₀ₐ ₊ ₈₅₅,₄₈₄b
52. $-348(107{,}324x + 57{,}820) - 927(33{,}429x - 88{,}007)$ ₋₆₈,₃₃₇,₄₃₅ₓ ₊ ₆₁,₄₆₁,₁₂₉
53. $(0.00079x - 0.000843y) - (-0.007943x - 0.000059y)$ ₀.₀₀₈₇₃₃ₓ ₋ ₀.₀₀₀₇₈₄y

Challenge Exercises

Simplify.

54. 9   55. ₋₁₀   56. 8

54. $-[-(-(-9))]$
55. $-\{-[-(-(-10))]\}$
56. $-\{-[-(-(-(-8)))]\}$

COMPUTER NOTE: Software and Hardware

Hardware in a computer system is the solid part of the system. It includes all the electronic and mechanical parts. Software is organized information. It includes programs telling the computer what to do and data for the computer to work on. Software information is usually kept on punched paper tape or magnetic tape.

1-7 *Exponential Notation*

After finishing Lesson 1-7, you should be able to
I rewrite expressions with and without exponents.
II rewrite expressions involving negative exponents.

I Whole Number Exponents

Exponential notation is like shorthand. For $3 \cdot 3 \cdot 3 \cdot 3$ we can write 3^4. The latter is called *exponential notation*. In 3^4 the number 3 is called a *base* and the number 4 is called an *exponent*.

DEFINITION

Exponential notation a^n, where *n* is an integer greater than 1, means

$$\underbrace{a \cdot a \cdot \cdots \cdot a \cdot a}_{n \; factors}$$

Examples. Write exponential notation for the following.

1. $7 \cdot 7 \cdot 7$ 7^3

2. xxx x^3

3. $2x \cdot 2x \cdot 2x$ $(2x)^3$

TRY THIS ➡

Write exponential notation.

1. $8 \cdot 8 \cdot 8 \cdot 8$ 8^4
2. mmm m^3
3. $4y \cdot 4y \cdot 4y \cdot 4y \cdot 4y$ $(4y)^5$

Examples. Rewrite without exponents.

4. 5^2 $5 \cdot 5$, or 25

5. $(4y)^3$ $4y \cdot 4y \cdot 4y$

TRY THIS ➡

Rewrite without exponents.

4. 3^4 5. y^2 6. $(5x)^4$

Answers.   4. $3 \cdot 3 \cdot 3 \cdot 3$ or 81   5. $y \cdot y$ 6. $5x \cdot 5x \cdot 5x \cdot 5x$

Example 6. Simplify.

$$(4x)^2 = 4x \cdot 4x$$
$$= 4 \cdot 4 \cdot x \cdot x \quad \textit{Using associative and commutative laws}$$
$$= 16x^2$$

TRY THIS ➡

Simplify.

7. $(5y)^2$ $25y^2$
8. $(-2x)^3$ $-8x^3$

In general, the exponent tells how many times the base occurs as a factor. What happens when the exponent is 1? Look for a pattern.

$$10^3 = 10 \cdot 10 \cdot 10 = 1000$$
$$10^2 = 10 \cdot 10 \qquad = 100$$
$$10^1 = ? \qquad\qquad = ?$$

For the pattern to continue, 10^1 would have to be 10. We shall make a definition (agreement) accordingly. An exponent of 1 makes no change in the meaning of an expression.

DEFINITION
For any number a, $a^1 = a$.

Examples. Rename each of the following without an exponent.

7. $4^1 = 4$

8. $(-5)^1 = -5$

9. $(-9y)^1 = -9y$

Answers. 9. 8   10. 31   11. −7.89   12. $23\frac{1}{4}$

TRY THIS ➤

How should we define an exponent of 0? Look for a pattern.

$$10^3 = 10 \cdot 10 \cdot 10 = 1000$$
$$10^2 = 10 \cdot 10 \qquad = 100$$
$$10^1 = 10 \qquad\qquad = 10$$
$$10^0 = ? \qquad\qquad = ?$$

For the pattern to continue, 10^0 would have to be 1. We shall make a definition (agreement) accordingly. When 0 occurs as the exponent of a nonzero base a, we agree that a^0 means 1.

DEFINITION
For any nonzero a, $a^0 = 1$.

Examples. Rename each of the following without exponents.

10. $6^0 = 1$

11. $6789^0 = 1$

12. $(-34.7)^0 = 1$

13. $(-9zt)^0 = 1$, when z and t stand for nonzero numbers

> Rename each without an exponent.
>
> 9. 8^1
> 10. $(31)^1$
> 11. $(-7.89)^1$
> 12. $(23\frac{1}{4})^1$

TRY THIS ➡️

▮ Negative Exponents

How should we define negative exponents? Look for a pattern.

$$10^3 = 1000$$
$$10^2 = 100$$
$$10^1 = 10$$
$$10^0 = 1$$
$$10^{-1} = ?$$
$$10^{-2} = ?$$

> Rename without exponents.
>
> 13. 3^0 1
> 14. $(-7)^0$ 1
> 15. y^0, y stands for a nonzero number. 1
> 16. $(\frac{1}{4}xy)^0$, x and y stand for nonzero numbers. 1

For the pattern to continue, 10^{-1} would have to be $\frac{1}{10}$ and 10^{-2} would have to be $\frac{1}{100}$. This leads us to make the definition.

DEFINITION

If n is any integer and a is not zero, a^{-n} means $\frac{1}{a^n}$.

In other words a^n and a^{-n} are reciprocals.

Examples.   Rename without using a negative exponent.

14. $7^{-3} = \frac{1}{7^3}$

15. $8^{-5} = \frac{1}{8^5}$

> Rename without using a negative exponent.
>
> 17. 10^{-4} $\frac{1}{10^4}$
> 18. 12^{-7} $\frac{1}{12^7}$

TRY THIS ➡️

Examples.   Rename using a negative exponent.

16. $\frac{1}{5^2} = 5^{-2}$

17. $\frac{1}{9^6} = 9^{-6}$

> Rename using a negative exponent.
>
> 19. $\frac{1}{4^3}$ 4^{-3} 20. $\frac{1}{9^8}$ 9^{-8}

TRY THIS ➡️

Example 18. Write three other symbols for 5^{-4}.

$$5^{-4} = \frac{1}{5^4} = \frac{1}{5 \cdot 5 \cdot 5 \cdot 5} = \frac{1}{625}$$

TRY THIS ➡

> 21. Write three other symbols for 4^{-3}. $4^{-3} = \frac{1}{4^3} = \frac{1}{4 \cdot 4 \cdot 4} = \frac{1}{64}$

Exercise Set 1-7

▮ Write exponential notation. (*See Examples 1–3.*)

1. $4 \cdot 4 \cdot 4 \cdot 4 \cdot 4$ 4^5
2. $6 \cdot 6 \cdot 6$ 6^3
3. $5 \cdot 5 \cdot 5 \cdot 5 \cdot 5 \cdot 5$ 5^6
4. $x \cdot x \cdot x \cdot x$ x^4
5. $mmmm$ m^4
6. $ttttt$ t^5
7. $3a \cdot 3a \cdot 3a \cdot 3a$ $(3a)^4$
8. $5x \cdot 5x \cdot 5x \cdot 5x \cdot 5x$ $(5x)^5$
9. $5 \cdot 5 \cdot c \cdot c \cdot c \cdot d \cdot d \cdot d \cdot d$ $5^2 c^3 d^4$
10. $2 \cdot 2 \cdot 2 \cdot r \cdot r \cdot r \cdot r \cdot t \cdot t$ $2^3 r^4 t^2$

Rename without exponents. (*See Examples 4–6.*)

11. 2^5 $2 \cdot 2 \cdot 2 \cdot 2 \cdot 2$ or 32
12. 3^4 $3 \cdot 3 \cdot 3 \cdot 3$ or 81
13. $(-3)^4$ $(-3) \cdot (-3) \cdot (-3) \cdot (-3)$ or 81
14. $(-8)^2$ $-8 \cdot (-8)$ or 64
15. x^4 $x \cdot x \cdot x \cdot x$
16. y^6 $y \cdot y \cdot y \cdot y \cdot y \cdot y$
17. $(4b)^3$ $4b \cdot 4b \cdot 4b$
18. $(3x)^4$ $3x \cdot 3x \cdot 3x \cdot 3x$
19. $(ab)^4$ $ab \cdot ab \cdot ab \cdot ab$
20. $(xyz)^3$ $xyz \cdot xyz \cdot xyz$

Rename each without an exponent. (*See Examples 7–13.*)

21. 5^1 5
22. $(\sqrt{6})^1$ $\sqrt{6}$
23. $(\frac{7}{8})^1$ $\frac{7}{8}$
24. $(\frac{9}{7})^1$ $\frac{9}{7}$
25. $(\sqrt{8})^0$ 1
26. $(-4)^0$ 1
27. $(3z)^0$ 1
28. $(5xy)^0$ 1

▮▮ Rename without using a negative exponent. (*See Examples 14 and 15.*)

29. 6^{-3} $\frac{1}{6^3}$
30. 8^{-4} $\frac{1}{8^4}$
31. 9^{-5} $\frac{1}{9^5}$
32. 16^{-2} $\frac{1}{16^2}$
33. 11^{-1} $\frac{1}{11^1}$
34. 40^{-4} $\frac{1}{40^4}$

Rename using a negative exponent. (*See Examples 16 and 17.*)

35. $\frac{1}{3^4}$ 3^{-4}
36. $\frac{1}{9^2}$ 9^{-2}
37. $\frac{1}{10^3}$ 10^{-3}
38. $\frac{1}{12^5}$ 12^{-5}
39. $\frac{1}{16^2}$ 16^{-2}
40. $\frac{1}{8^6}$ 8^{-6}

1-8 Properties of Exponents

After finishing Lesson 1-8, you should be able to
I use exponential notation in multiplication and division.
II use exponential notation in raising a power to a power.

I Multiplication and Division

Consider an expression like $a^3 \cdot a^2$. To see how to simplify, recall the definition of exponents.

DEFINITION

$$a^n = \overbrace{a \cdot a \cdot \cdots \cdot a}^{n \text{ factors}}, \text{ if } n > 1$$
$$a^n = a, \text{ if } n = 1$$
$$a^n = 1, \text{ if } n = 0, a \neq 0$$
$$a^{-n} = \frac{1}{a^n} \text{ if } a \neq 0$$

$a^3 \cdot a^2$ means $(a \cdot a \cdot a)(a \cdot a)$ and $(a \cdot a \cdot a)(a \cdot a) = a^5$. The exponent in a^5 is the sum of the exponents in $a^3 \cdot a^2$. In general, when we multiply like this, the exponents are added. The base must be the same in both parts. Let's consider a case where one exponent is positive and one is negative.

$$b^5 \cdot b^{-2} = (b \cdot b \cdot b \cdot b \cdot b) \cdot \frac{1}{b \cdot b} \qquad \textit{Definition of exponents}$$
$$= \frac{b \cdot b}{b \cdot b} \cdot b \cdot b \cdot b$$
$$= b \cdot b \cdot b, \text{ or } b^3 \qquad \textit{Simplifying}$$

If we add exponents, we again get the correct result. Now let's consider a case where both exponents are negative.

$$c^{-3} \cdot c^{-2} = \frac{1}{c \cdot c \cdot c} \cdot \frac{1}{c \cdot c} \qquad \textit{Definition of exponents}$$
$$= \frac{1}{c \cdot c \cdot c \cdot c \cdot c} \qquad \textit{Multiplying}$$
$$= \frac{1}{c^5}, \text{ or } c^{-5} \qquad \textit{Simplifying}$$

Again, adding the exponents gives the correct result.

THEOREM 1-4

In multiplication with exponential notation, we can add exponents if the bases are the same.

$$a^m a^n = a^{m+n}$$

Examples. Multiply and simplify.

1. $x^4 \cdot x^3 = x^{4+3} = x^7$

2. $4^5 \cdot 4^{-3} = 4^{5+(-3)} = 4^2$

3. $(8x^4 y^{-2})(3x^{-3} y) = 8 \cdot 3 \cdot x^4 \cdot x^{-3} \cdot y^{-2} \cdot y^1 = 24x^{4+(-3)} y^{-2+1} = 24xy^{-1}$

TRY THIS ➡

Multiply and simplify.

1. $8^9 \cdot 8^4$ 8^{13}
2. $7^{-3} \cdot 7^5$ 7^2
3. $y^7 \cdot y^{-2}$ 7^5
4. $x^{-7} \cdot x^{-3}$ x^{-10} $10x^{-12} y^2$
5. $(5x^{-3} y^4)(2x^{-9} y^{-2})$
6. $(-4x^{-2} y^4)(15x^2 y^{-3})$
           $-60y$

Consider division with exponential notation.

$\dfrac{8^5}{8^3}$ means $\dfrac{8 \cdot 8 \cdot 8 \cdot 8 \cdot 8}{8 \cdot 8 \cdot 8}$, which simplifies to $8 \cdot 8$, or 8^2.

The results can be obtained by subtracting exponents. This holds in general.

THEOREM 1-5

In division with exponential notation, we can subtract exponents if the bases are the same.

$$\frac{a^m}{a^n} = a^{m-n}$$

Examples. Divide.

4. $\dfrac{5^7}{5^3} = 5^{7-3} = 5^4$

5. $\dfrac{5^7}{5^{-3}} = 5^{7-(-3)} = 5^{10}$

6. $\dfrac{9^{-2}}{9^5} = 9^{-2-5} = 9^{-7}$

7. $\dfrac{7^{-4}}{7^{-5}} = 7^{-4-(-5)} = 7^1 = 7$

Divide and simplify.

7. $\dfrac{4^8}{4^5}$ 4^3

8. $\dfrac{5^4}{5^{-2}}$ 5^6

9. $\dfrac{10^{-5}}{10^9}$ 10^{-14}

10. $\dfrac{9^{-8}}{9^{-2}}$ 9^{-6}

TRY THIS ➡

Examples. Divide and simplify.

8. $\dfrac{x^3}{x^5} = x^{3-5} = x^{-2}$

9. $\dfrac{16x^4y^7}{-8x^3y^9} = \dfrac{16}{-8} \cdot \dfrac{x^4}{x^3} \cdot \dfrac{y^7}{y^9}$

$\qquad\qquad = -2x^{4-3} \cdot y^{7-9}$

$\qquad\qquad = -2xy^{-2}$

TRY THIS

> Divide and simplify.
>
> **11.** $\dfrac{y^6}{y^{-5}}$ $\quad y^{11}$
>
> **12.** $\dfrac{10y^2}{2y^3}$ $\quad 5y^{-1}$
>
> **13.** $\dfrac{42y^7x^6}{-21y^{-3}x^{10}}$
> $\qquad\qquad -2y^{10}x^{-4}$

Remark. We said that 0^0 was not defined. To see why, consider the following: $0^0 = 0^{1-1} = \dfrac{0^1}{0^1} = \dfrac{0}{0}$. But we cannot divide by 0. To avoid this difficulty, we leave 0^0 undefined.

ıı Raising Powers to Powers

Consider an expression like $(5^2)^4$.

$\qquad(5^2)^4$ means $5^2 \cdot 5^2 \cdot 5^2 \cdot 5^2$, and this is equal to 5^8.

In this case we could have multiplied the exponents in $(5^2)^4$. Suppose the exponents are not both positive, as in the following example.

$(8^{-2})^3$ means $\dfrac{1}{8^2} \cdot \dfrac{1}{8^2} \cdot \dfrac{1}{8^2}$, which is $\dfrac{1}{8^6}$, or 8^{-6}.

Again we could have multiplied exponents.

THEOREM 1-6

To raise a power to a power we can multiply exponents.
$(a^m)^n = a^{mn}$

Examples. Simplify.

10. $(3^5)^7 = 3^{5 \cdot 7} = 3^{35}$

11. $(x^{-5})^4 = x^{-5 \cdot 4} = x^{-20}$

TRY THIS

> Simplify.
>
> **14.** $(5^6)^4$ $\quad 5^{24}$
> **15.** $(8^2)^{-4}$ $\quad 8^{-8}$
> **16.** $(9^{-3})^{-5}$ $\quad 9^{15}$

There may be several factors inside parentheses as in the following.

Examples. Simplify.

12. $(3x^2y^{-2})^3 = 3^3(x^2)^3(y^{-2})^3$
$\qquad\qquad = 3^3x^6y^{-6}$, or $27x^6y^{-6}$

13. $(5x^3y^{-5}z^2)^4 = 5^4(x^3)^4(y^{-5})^4(z^2)^4$
$\qquad\qquad\quad = 5^4x^{12}y^{-20}z^8$, or $625x^{12}y^{-20}z^8$

TRY THIS ➡

Answers.   17. $8x^3y^3$ 18. $16x^{-4}y^{14}$ 19. $-243x^{20}y^{10}$ 20. $1000x^{-12}y^{21}z^{-6}$

Simplify.

17. $(2xy)^3$
18. $(4x^{-2}y^7)^2$
19. $(-3x^4y^2)^5$
20. $(10x^{-4}y^7z^{-2})^3$

Exercise Set 1-8

❚ Multiply and simplify. (*See Examples 1–3.*)

1. $5^6 \cdot 5^3$ 5^9
2. $6^2 \cdot 6^6$ 6^8
3. $8^{-6} \cdot 8^2$ 8^{-4}
4. $9^{-5} \cdot 9^3$ 9^{-2}
5. $8^{-2} \cdot 8^{-4}$ 8^{-6}
6. $9^{-1} \cdot 9^{-6}$ 9^{-7}
7. $b^2 \cdot b^{-5}$ b^{-3}
8. $a^4 \cdot a^{-3}$ a
9. $a^{-3} \cdot a^4 \cdot a^2$ a^3
10. $x^{-8} \cdot x^5 \cdot x^3$ 1
11. $(2x)^3(3x)^2$ $72x^5$
12. $(9y)^2(2y)^3$ $648y^5$
13. $(14m^2n^3)(-2m^3n^2)$ $-28m^5n^5$
14. $(6x^5y^{-2})(-3x^2y^3)$ $-18x^7y$

Divide and simplify. (*See Examples 4–9.*)

15. $\dfrac{6^8}{6^3}$ 6^5
16. $\dfrac{7^9}{7^4}$ 7^5
17. $\dfrac{4^3}{4^{-2}}$ 4^5
18. $\dfrac{5^8}{5^{-3}}$ 5^{11}
19. $\dfrac{10^{-3}}{10^6}$ 10^{-9}
20. $\dfrac{12^{-4}}{12^8}$ 12^{-12}
21. $\dfrac{9^{-4}}{9^{-6}}$ 9^2
22. $\dfrac{2^{-7}}{2^{-5}}$ 2^{-2}
23. $\dfrac{a^3}{a^{-2}}$ a^5
24. $\dfrac{y^4}{y^{-5}}$ y^9
25. $\dfrac{9a^2}{(-3a)^2}$ 1
26. $\dfrac{24a^5b^3}{-8a^4b}$ $-3ab^2$

❚❚ Simplify. (*See Examples 10–13.*)

27. $(4^3)^2$ 4^6
28. $(5^4)^5$ 5^{20}
29. $(8^4)^{-3}$ 8^{-12}
30. $(9^3)^{-4}$ 9^{-12}
31. $(6^{-4})^{-3}$ 6^{12}
32. $(7^{-8})^{-5}$ 7^{40}
33. $(3x^2y^2)^3$ $3^3x^6y^6$ or $27x^6y^6$
34. $(2a^3b^4)^5$ $2^5a^{15}b^{20}$ or $32a^{15}b^{20}$
35. $(-2x^3y^{-4})^{-2}$ $(-2)^{-2}x^{-6}y^8$ or $\frac{1}{4}x^{-6}y^8$
36. $(-3a^2b^{-5})^{-3}$ $(-3)^{-3}a^{-6}b^{15}$ or $-\frac{1}{27}a^{-6}b^{15}$
37. $(-6a^{-2}b^3c)^{-2}$ $(-6)^{-2}a^4b^{-6}c^{-2}$ or $\frac{1}{36}a^4b^{-6}c^{-2}$
38. $(-8x^{-4}y^5z^2)^{-4}$ $(-8)^{-4}x^{16}y^{-20}z^{-8}$ or $\frac{1}{4096}x^{16}y^{-20}z^{-8}$

1-9 Order and Properties of Absolute Value

After finishing Lesson 1-9, you should be able to
I determine whether an inequality is true or false.
II simplify expressions with absolute values.

I Inequalities

Sentences like those in the following definition are called *inequalities*.

DEFINITION
$a \neq b$ means a is not equal to b.
$a < b$ means a is less than b.
$a \leq b$ means a is less than or equal to b.
$a > b$ means a is greater than b.
$a \geq b$ means a is greater than or equal to b.

Examples. Determine whether each sentence is true or false.

1. $3 < -4$ This sentence says that 3 is less than -4. It is false.

2. $-3 \leq 5$ This sentence says that $-3 < 5$ is true or $-3 = 5$ is true. It is true since $-3 < 5$ is true.

3. $5 \leq 5$ True, since $5 = 5$ is true.

4. $9 \leq 5$ False, since both $9 < 5$ and $9 = 5$ are false.

TRY THIS

> Determine whether each sentence is true or false.
>
> 1. $-3 > -1$ False
> 2. $-8 \leq -2$ True
> 3. $-4 > 7$ False

A sentence like

$$-4 \leq 5 < 8 \qquad \textbf{(1)}$$

is an abbreviation for

$$-4 \leq 5 \text{ and } 5 < 8 \qquad \textbf{(2)}$$

For the sentence **(1)** to be true, both parts of **(2)** must be true. Both parts are true, so **(1)** is true.

Examples. Determine whether each sentence is true or false.

5. $-3 < 5 < 0$ False, since $5 < 0$ is false.

6. $-3 < -4 \leq 0$ False, since $-3 < -4$ is false.

7. $-10 < -5 < 0$ True, since $-10 < -5$ and $-5 < 0$ are
                both true.

TRY THIS

Determine whether each sentence is true or false.

4. $2 \leq 5 < 7$ True
5. $-4 < 0 \leq 8$ True
6. $5 \leq 2 < -3$ False

▪ Properties of Absolute Value

The absolute value of a nonnegative number is that number itself. The absolute value of a negative number is its additive inverse. We can formalize this definition as follows.

DEFINITION
For any number x,
$|x| = x$ if $x \geq 0$;
$|x| = -x$ if $x < 0$.

Examples. Simplify.

8. $|8| = 8$

9. $|-3| = -(-3) = 3$

10. $|0| = 0$

TRY THIS

Simplify.

7. $|19|$ 19
8. $|-9|$ 9
9. $|-15|$ 15

Certain properties of absolute value notation follow at once. For example, the absolute value of a product is the product of the absolute values.

Example 11. $|-2 \cdot 5| = |-10| = 10$, and
                $|-2| \cdot |5| = 2 \cdot 5 = 10$, so
                $|-2 \cdot 5| = |-2| \cdot |5|$.

Similarly, the absolute value of a quotient is the quotient of the absolute values.

Example 12. $\left|\dfrac{-42}{7}\right| = |-6| = 6$, and

$$\dfrac{|-42|}{|7|} = \dfrac{42}{7} = 6, \text{ so}$$

$$\left|\dfrac{-42}{7}\right| = \dfrac{|-42|}{|7|}.$$

The absolute value of an even power can be simplified by leaving off the absolute value signs, because no even power can be negative.

Example 13. $|(-5)^2| = |25| = 25$, and
$$(-5)^2 = 25, \text{ so}$$
$$|(-5)^2| = (-5)^2.$$

THEOREM 1-7

For any real numbers a and b,

a) $|ab| = |a| \cdot |b|$

b) $\left|\dfrac{a}{b}\right| = \dfrac{|a|}{|b|}$, assuming $b \neq 0$

c) $|a^n| = a^n$ if n is an even integer.

Examples. Simplify, leaving as little as possible inside absolute value signs.

14. $|5x| = |5| \cdot |x| = 5|x|$

15. $|x^2| = x^2$

16. $|x^2 y^3| = |x^2 \cdot y^2 \cdot y| = |x^2| \cdot |y^2| \cdot |y| = x^2 y^2 |y|$

17. $\left|\dfrac{x^2}{y}\right| = \dfrac{|x^2|}{|y|} = \dfrac{x^2}{|y|}$

18. $|-5x| = |-5| \cdot |x| = 5|x|$

TRY THIS ➡

Simplify, leaving as little as possible inside absolute value signs.

10. $|7x|$ $7|x|$
11. $|x^8|$ x^8
12. $|5a^2 b|$ $5a^2 |b|$
13. $\left|\dfrac{7a}{b^2}\right|$ $\dfrac{7|a|}{b^2}$
14. $|-9x|$ $9|x|$

Exercise Set 1-9 Use Quiz 2 after lesson 1–9.

▮ Determine whether each sentence is true or false. (*See Examples 1–7.*)

1. $-9 \geq -2$ False
2. $-11 \geq -7$ False
3. $-6 \leq -5$ True
4. $-5 \leq -2$ True
5. $11 > 12$ False
6. $9 > 11$ False
7. $6 + 3 \neq 5 - 13$ True
8. $9 + 4 \neq 6 - 10$ True
9. $-2 < -1 \leq 0$ True
10. $6 \leq 9 < 11$ True
11. $-2 \leq 2 \leq 8$ True
12. $6 \leq 6 < 5$ False
13. $-3 < -5 \leq 0$ False
14. $9 \leq 8 < 10$ False

▮▮ Simplify, leaving as little as possible inside absolute value signs. (*See Examples 14–18.*)

15. $|3x|$ $3|x|$
16. $|4x|$ $4|x|$
17. $|x^6|$ x^6
18. $|x^8|$ x^8
19. $|7x^2y^3|$ $7x^2y^2|y|$
20. $|9a^4b^5|$ $9a^4b^4|b|$
21. $\left|\dfrac{a^2}{b}\right|$ $\dfrac{a^2}{|b|}$
22. $\left|\dfrac{x^4}{y}\right|$ $\dfrac{x^4}{|y|}$
23. $|-4t|$ $4|t|$
24. $|-8b|$ $8|b|$
25. $|-5a^4b|$ $5a^4|b|$
26. $|-10x^6y|$ $10x^6|y|$
27. $|t^3|$ $t^2|t|$
28. $|p^5|$ $p^4|p|$
29. $|a^8|$ a^8
30. $|y^6|$ y^6

Challenge Exercises

31. We have seen that $|a \cdot b| = |a| \cdot |b|$. Experiment and determine the relationship between $|a + b|$ and $|a| + |b|$. $|a + b| \leq |a| + |b|$

SCIENCE NOTE: Photographing Distant Stars

Some telescopes can turn to keep pointed at a certain star for hours at a time. The light from these telescopes is directed to photographic film. The light accumulates on the film. That is, the telescope provides a time exposure of the star. Using such a telescope, astronomers have recorded light from stars more than 1,000,000,000 light-years away. That means the film image shows how these stars looked 1,000,000,000 years ago.

COMPUTER ACTIVITY

Finding the Absolute Value of Any Number

PROBLEM: Find the absolute value of N.

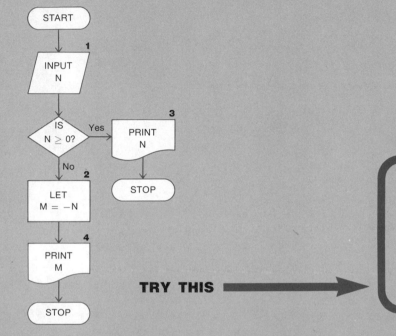

Examples using the flowchart:

1	2	3,4
N	M	|N|
5.6		5.6
$-3\frac{1}{5}$	$-(-3\frac{1}{5})$	$3\frac{1}{5}$

TRY THIS

1. Suppose the number is 95.6. What is |95.6|?
2. Suppose the number is 0. What is |0|?
3. Suppose the number is $-89\frac{1}{3}$. What is $|-89\frac{1}{3}|$?

Note: A flowchart will be used in many activities to follow. Flowchart symbols are defined below:

1. ◻ Input operation—brings data from keyboard, punched cards, magnetic tape, disc memory

2. ◇ Decision operation—indicates which alternative path to follow

3. ◻ Processing operation—"M = −N" means that M takes on the value of −N

4. ◻ Output operation—sends data to printer, video display, punched cards, magnetic tape, disc memory

CHAPTER 1 REVIEW

Review the material in the chapter. Then see how you have done by trying these review exercises. If you miss an exercise, restudy the indicated lesson.

1-1   1. Find decimal notation for $\frac{5}{8}$. 0.625

1-1   Which of the following are rational and which are irrational?
2. $\sqrt{7}$ Irrational
3. $\frac{-5}{7}$ Rational
4. 2.113111311113. . . (numeral does not repeat) Irrational

1-2   Simplify.
5. $|4|$ 4
6. $\left|-\frac{3}{4}\right|$ $\frac{3}{4}$
7. $|0|$ 0

1-2   Find the additive inverse of each.
8. 7 $_{-7}$ 9. $-\frac{9}{10}$ $\frac{9}{10}$ 10. 0 $_0$

1-2   Add.
11. $7 + (-9)$ $_{-2}$
12. $-11 + 4$ $_{-7}$
13. $-16 + (-9)$ $_{-25}$

1-3,   Tell which property of real numbers
1-4,   is illustrated by each sentence.
1-5   14. $5 + 6 = 6 + 5$ See answer section
15. $(3 + 2) + 6 = 3 + (2 + 6)$
16. $(5 \cdot 6) \cdot 7 = 5 \cdot (6 \cdot 7)$
17. $-9(3 + 5) = (-9)(3) + (-9)(5)$

1-3   Subtract.
18. $8 - (-3)$ $_{11}$
19. $-6 - (-5)$ $_{-1}$
20. $-17 - 8$ $_{-25}$

1-4   Multiply.
21. $-4(8)$ $_{-32}$
22. $(-7)(-3)$ $_{21}$
23. $9(-6)$ $_{-54}$

1-4   Divide.
24. $\frac{-18}{3}$ $_{-6}$
25. $\frac{-24}{-6}$ 4
26. $\frac{2}{3} \div \left(-\frac{8}{5}\right)$ $-\frac{5}{12}$

1-4   Which of these divisions are possible?
27. $\frac{10}{0}$ 28. $\frac{0}{56}$ 29. $\frac{10}{x - x}$
27. Not possible 28. 0 29. Not possible

1-5   Factor.
30. $3m + 6n$ 3(m + 2n)
31. $5a - 15$ 5(a − 3)
32. $2ab + 6ac - 8ad$ 2a(b + 3c − 4d)

1-5   Multiply.
33. $6(x - 5)$ 6x − 30
34. $-3(s - 2t)$ −3s + 6t
35. $12\left(\frac{a}{2} - \frac{b}{3} + \frac{c}{4}\right)$ 6a − 4b + 3c

1-5   Collect like terms.
36. $6y - 8y - 4y + 3y$ −3y
37. $2.3y - 8 - 4y + 7.6x - 5.8x$
0.1x − 8

1-6   Rename each additive inverse without parentheses.
38. $-(-6x)$ 6x
39. $-(r - s)$ −r + s

1-6   Remove parentheses and simplify.
40. $2a - (3a - 4)$ −a + 4
41. $5x - [2x + (3x - 2)]$ 2

1-7,   Simplify.
1-8   42. 8^{-3} $\frac{1}{8^3}$
43. $7^2 \cdot 7^{-3} \cdot 7^{-1}$ 7^{-2}
44. $(10^2)^3$ 10^6
45. $\frac{a^4}{a^{-2}}$ a^6
46. $(4r^2)(-8r^6)$ $-32r^8$
47. $\frac{54x^5y^4}{18x^3y^{-1}}$ $3x^2y^5$

1-9   Simplify, leaving as little as possible inside absolute value signs.
48. $|-8t|$ 8|t|
49. $|20t^2m^3|$ $20t^2m^2|m|$

CHAPTER 1 TEST

1. Find decimal notation for $\frac{3}{8}$. 0.375

Which of the following are rational and which are irrational?

2. $\sqrt{5}$ Irrational
3. $-\frac{8}{9}$ Rational
4. 3.221222122221... (numeral does not repeat) Irrational

Simplify.

5. $|5|$ 5
6. $\left|-\frac{2}{3}\right|$ $\frac{2}{3}$
7. $|0|$ 0

Find the additive inverse of each.

8. 19   9. $-\frac{3}{10}$ 10. 0

8. -19 9. $\frac{3}{10}$ 10. 0

Add.

11. $9 + (-11)$ -2
12. $-14 + 6$ -8
13. $-18 + (-6)$ -24

Tell which property of real numbers is illustrated by each sentence.

14. $9 + 7 = 7 + 9$ See answer section
15. $(8 + 6) + 9 = 8 + (6 + 9)$
16. $(4 \cdot 3) \cdot 9 = 4 \cdot (3 \cdot 9)$
17. $-6(8 + 9) = (-6)(8) + (-6)(9)$

Subtract.

18. $9 - (-4)$ 13
19. $-7 - (-6)$ -1
20. $-14 - 6$ -20

Multiply.

21. $-9(7)$ -63
22. $(-6)(-8)$ 48
23. $4(-3)$ -12

Divide.

24. $\dfrac{-27}{3}$ -9

25. $\dfrac{-16}{-4}$ 4

26. $\dfrac{3}{5} \div \left(-\dfrac{6}{5}\right)$ $-\frac{1}{2}$

Which of these divisions are possible?

27. $\dfrac{19}{0}$ 28. $\dfrac{0}{53}$ 29. $\dfrac{11}{y - y}$

27. Not possible   28. 0   29. Not possible

Factor.

30. $8x + 16y$ 8(x + 2y)
31. $6b - 18$ 6(b − 3)
32. $3xy + 12xz - 15xw$ 3x(y + 4z − 5w)

Multiply.

33. $9(y - 4)$ 9y − 36
34. $-8(a - 4b)$ −8a + 32b
35. $12\left(\dfrac{x}{6} - \dfrac{y}{2} + \dfrac{z}{4}\right)$ 2x − 6y + 3z

Collect like terms.

36. $9x - 5x - 6x + 7x$ 5x
37. $3.2y - 9 - 5y + 4.8x - 5.7x$

−1.8y − 9 − 0.9x

Rename each additive inverse without parentheses.

38. $-(-9y)$ 9y
39. $-(x - t)$ −x + t

Remove parentheses and simplify.

40. $3t - (5t - 6)$ −2t + 6
41. $9y - [4y - (2y - 5)]$ 7y − 5

Simplify.

42. 9^{-4} $\frac{1}{9^4}$
43. $8^3 \cdot 8^{-5} \cdot 8^{-2}$ 8^{-4}
44. $(11^4)^3$ 11^{12}
45. $\dfrac{x^5}{x^{-3}}$ x^8
46. $(5x^3)(-6x^5)$ $-30x^8$
47. $\dfrac{63y^4z^9}{9y^2z^{-3}}$ $7y^2z^{12}$

Simplify, leaving as little as possible inside absolute value signs.

48. $|-7y|$ 7|y|
49. $|36x^2y^5|$ $36x^2y^4|y|$

Ready for Solving Equations?

1-2   Add.

     1. $5 + (-3)$ 2   2. $-8 + (-4)$ −12

     3. $-6 + 0$ −6   4. $-8.2 + 3.6$ −4.6

     5. $-\frac{4}{5} + \frac{1}{2}$ $-\frac{3}{10}$ 6. $3.8 + (-3.8)$ 0

1-2   Find $-a$ when a stands for

     7. -7 7

     8. 0 0

     9. 8 −8

1-3   Subtract.

     10. $8 - (-5)$ 13

     11. $-11 - 9$ −20

     12. $-18.2 - 4.7$ −22.9

     13. $-\frac{2}{3} - (-\frac{4}{7})$ $-\frac{2}{21}$

1-4   Multiply.

     14. $-5 \cdot 2$ −10   15. $3 \cdot (-8)$ −24

     16. $-4.7 \cdot 10$ −47   17. $3 \cdot (-\frac{1}{4})$ $-\frac{3}{4}$

     18. $-2.3 \cdot -20$ 46   19. $-8 \cdot (-\frac{3}{4})$ 6

1-4   Find the reciprocal of

     20. $\frac{2}{3}$ $\frac{3}{2}$

     21. 5 $\frac{1}{5}$

     22. $-\frac{4}{5}$ $-\frac{5}{4}$

1-5   23.   Factor: $5x - 10y + 15$.   5(x − 2y + 3)

1-5   Multiply.

     24. $5(y - 4)$ 5y − 20

     25. $c(x + y - z)$ cx + cy − cz

1-5   26.   Collect like terms: $x + 3x - 5x$.   −x

Chapter 2
Solving Equations

We can solve equations to predict future running records.

2-1 Solving Equations

After finishing Lesson 2-1, you should be able to
I tell what an equation means.
II solve equations using the addition principle.
III solve equations using the multiplication principle.

I Equations

The most common kind of sentence we use in algebra is an equation. An equation is a number sentence with = for its verb. Some equations are true. Some are false. Some are neither true nor false.

Examples.

1. The equation $1 + 10 = 11$ is true.

2. The equation $7 - 8 = 9 - 13$ is false.

3. The equation $x - 9 = 3$ is neither true nor false because we do not know what x represents.

TRY THIS

1. Write three true equations.
2. Write three false equations.
3. Write three equations that are neither true nor false.
   Answers may vary.

An equation says that the symbols on either side of the equals sign name the same number. For example, $7 - 8 = 9 - 13$ says that $7 - 8$ and $9 - 13$ name the same number. In this case, the equation is false.

TRY THIS

Answers. 4. The equation $89 + 2 = 3 + 4$ says that $89 + 2$ and $3 + 4$ name the same number. 5. The equation $6 - 7 + \frac{1}{2} = 14$ says that $6 - 7 + \frac{1}{2}$ and 14 name the same number.

Tell what each equation means.
4. $89 + 2 = 3 + 4$
5. $6 - 7 + \frac{1}{2} = 14$

If an equation contains a variable it may be neither true nor false. Some replacements for the variable may make it true. Some may make it false. When we find the solution we say that we have *solved* the equation.

DEFINITION

The replacements that make an equation true are called its *solutions*.

Example 4.

a) Find three replacements that make $3x + 6 = 12$ false.

    0, 1, and 8, because
    $3 \cdot 0 + 6 = 12$ is false;
    $3 \cdot 1 + 6 = 12$ is false; and
    $3 \cdot 8 + 6 = 12$ is false.

b) Find the replacement that makes $3x + 6 = 12$ true.

    2, because $3 \cdot 2 + 6 = 12$ is true.

TRY THIS

> 6. Find three replacements that make $2x + 3 = 11$ false.   **Answers may vary.**
> 7. Find the replacement that makes $2x + 3 = 11$ true. **4**

ıı The Addition Principle

The equation $a = b$ says that a and b represent the same number. Suppose this is true. Then add a number c to the number a. We will get the same answer as if we add c to b, because a and b are the same number.

THEOREM 2-1 (The Addition Principle)

If an equation $a = b$ is true, then $a + c = b + c$ is true for any number c.

When we use the addition principle we sometimes say that we "add the same number on both sides of an equation." Let's use this principle to solve an equation.

Example 5. Solve: $x + 6 = -15$.

$$x + 6 + (-6) = -15 + (-6) \qquad \text{Using the addition principle;}$$
$$x + 0 = -15 + (-6) \qquad \text{adding } -6 \text{ on both sides}$$
$$x = -21 \qquad \text{Simplifying}$$

Check:
$$\begin{array}{c|c} x + 6 = -15 \\ \hline -21 + 6 & -15 \\ -15 & \end{array}$$

The solution is -21.

In Example 5, to get x alone, we added the inverse of 6. This "got rid of" the 6 on the left.

TRY THIS ⟶

> Solve, using the addition principle.
>
> 8. $x + 9 = 2$ **−7**
> 9. $13 = -25 + y$ **38**
> 10. $x + \dfrac{1}{4} = -\dfrac{3}{4}$ **−1**
> 11. $y - 61.4 = 78.9$ **140.3**

Remark. When we solve an equation such as $x + 6 = -15$ using the addition principle we have really proved "If $x + 6 = -15$, then $x = -21$." Such an if-then sentence is called a *conditional sentence*. The conditional sentence is made up of two sentences. The sentence following the *if*, in this case "$x + 6 = -15$," is called the *antecedent* of the conditional. The sentence following the *then*, in this case "$x = -21$," is called the *consequent* of the conditional. To prove "if $x + 6 = -15$, then $x = -21$" we assume the antecedent is true. We then use theorems to try to get the consequent. Any solution of the antecedent (the *if* sentence) must be a solution of the consequent (the *then* sentence).

ɪɪɪ The Multiplication Principle

Suppose the equation $a = b$ is true and we multiply the number a by some number c. We will get the same answer as if we multiply b by c. This must be so because a and b are the same number.

THEOREM 2-2 (The Multiplication Principle)

If an equation $a = b$ is true, then $a \cdot c = b \cdot c$ is true for any number c.

Example 6. Solve: $4x = 9$.

$$\frac{1}{4} \cdot 4x = \frac{1}{4} \cdot 9 \qquad \text{\textit{Using the multiplication principle;}}$$
$$\text{\textit{multiplying by } } \tfrac{1}{4}$$
$$1 \cdot x = \frac{9}{4}$$
$$\qquad \text{\textit{Simplifying}}$$
$$x = \frac{9}{4}$$

Check:

$$
\begin{array}{c|c}
\multicolumn{2}{c}{4x = 9} \\
\hline
4 \cdot \dfrac{9}{4} & 9 \\
9 &
\end{array}
$$

The solution is $\frac{9}{4}$.

Checking by substituting in the original equation is an important part of solving.

In Example 6 we multiplied by the reciprocal of 4. When we multiplied we got $1 \cdot x$, which simplified to x. This enabled us to "get rid of" the 4 on the left.

Example 7. Solve: $-\dfrac{4}{5}x = 22$.

$$\left(-\frac{5}{4}\right)\left(-\frac{4}{5}x\right) = \left(-\frac{5}{4}\right) \cdot 22$$

$$1 \cdot x = -\frac{55}{2}$$

$$x = -\frac{55}{2}$$

This checks, so the solution is $-\dfrac{55}{2}$.

TRY THIS ➡

Solve, using the multiplication principle.

12. $8x = 10$ $\frac{5}{4}$
13. $-4x = 64$ **−16**
14. $-3x = -\dfrac{6}{7}$ $\frac{2}{7}$
15. $-12.6 = 4.2y$ **−3**

Remark. When we solve an equation such as that of Example 7 we have proved "If $-\frac{4}{5}x = 22$, then $x = -\frac{55}{2}$." This means that whenever $-\frac{4}{5}x = 22$ is true, $x = -\frac{55}{2}$ is also true. Thus *if* there is a solution, it is $-\frac{55}{2}$. The *converse* of this conditional sentence is formed by interchanging the antecedent and consequent: "If $x = -\frac{55}{2}$, then $-\frac{4}{5}x = 22$." The converse of a conditional sentence is not necessarily true. If the converse is true, this will tell us that $-\frac{55}{2}$ is a solution. The check shows that the converse is true. Thus, $-\frac{55}{2}$ is a solution.

Exercise Set 2-1

▌ Tell what each equation means. (*See Examples 1–4.*)   See answer section

1. $91 + 4 = 7 - 9$ See answer section
2. $18 \times 4 = 144 \div 2$
3. Find three replacements that make $5x + 4 = 19$ false. Answers may vary.
4. Find three replacements that make $7x - 3 = 11$ false. Answers may vary.
5. Find the replacement that makes $3x + 4 = 22$ true.   6
6. Find the replacement that makes $8x - 2 = 62$ true.   8

52 *Chapter 2*

▌▌ Solve using the addition principle. Check. (*See Example 5.*)

7. $x + 5 = 14$ ₉
8. $y + 7 = 19$ ₁₂
9. $y + 11 = 8$ ₋₃
10. $t + 13 = 4$ ₋₉
11. $x - 18 = 22$ ₄₀
12. $y - 19 = 26$ ₄₅
13. $t - 12 = 9$ ₂₁
14. $p - 15 = 11$ ₂₆
15. $x + 9 = -6$ ₋₁₅
16. $x + 11 = -8$ ₋₁₉
17. $t + 11 = -30$ ₋₄₁
18. $p + 14 = -42$ ₋₅₆
19. $x - 6 = -4$ ₂
20. $y - 7 = -3$ ₄
21. $t - 9 = -23$ ₋₁₄
22. $r - 8 = -19$ ₋₁₁
23. $-8 + y = 15$ ₂₃
24. $-9 + t = 17$ ₂₆
25. $r + \dfrac{2}{5} = \dfrac{8}{5}$ $\frac{6}{5}$
26. $x + \dfrac{5}{9} = \dfrac{8}{9}$ $\frac{1}{3}$
27. $t + \dfrac{5}{6} = -\dfrac{7}{12}$ $-\frac{17}{12}$
28. $p + \dfrac{1}{3} = -\dfrac{5}{6}$ $-\frac{7}{6}$
29. $-\dfrac{1}{6} + z = -\dfrac{1}{4}$ $-\frac{1}{12}$
30. $-\dfrac{3}{4} + x = -\dfrac{7}{16}$ $\frac{5}{16}$
31. $x + 14.2 = 7.14$ ₋₇.₀₆
32. $y + 62.8 = 37.3$ ₋₂₅.₅
33. $p - 29.6 = 83.9$ ₁₁₃.₅
34. $z - 14.9 = 57.3$ ₇₂.₂

▌▌▌ Solve using the multiplication principle. Check. (*See Examples 6 and 7.*)

35. $5x = 20$ ₄
36. $3x = 21$ ₇
37. $56 = 7x$ ₈
38. $48 = 8y$ ₆
39. $8y = -72$ ₋₉
40. $9t = -81$ ₋₉
41. $-24x = -192$ ₈
42. $-13y = -117$ ₉
43. $\dfrac{1}{5}y = 8$ ₄₀
44. $\dfrac{1}{4}x = 9$ ₃₆
45. $\dfrac{2}{3}x = 27$ $\frac{81}{2}$
46. $\dfrac{4}{5}x = 35$ $\frac{175}{4}$
47. $\dfrac{1}{6} = \dfrac{1}{4}t$ $\frac{2}{3}$
48. $\dfrac{1}{8} = \dfrac{1}{5}y$ $\frac{5}{8}$
49. $-\dfrac{3}{4}x = -\dfrac{3}{10}$ $\frac{2}{5}$
50. $-\dfrac{2}{3}y = -\dfrac{3}{8}$ $\frac{9}{16}$
51. $0.5x = 1.5$ ₃
52. $0.4x = 2.8$ ₇
53. $26.2y = 209.6$ ₈
54. $34.7t = 312.3$ ₉

Calculator Exercises

Solve. Remember that you must check.

55. $0.0008x = 0.0000056$ ₀.₀₀₇
56. $-0.015y = -0.0001821$ ₀.₀₁₂₁₄
57. $-34.324y = -0.07756$ ₀.₀₀₂₂₅₉₆
58. $43.008z = 1.201135$ ₀.₀₂₇₉₂₈₁

2-2 More on Solving Equations

After finishing Lesson 2-2, you should be able to
- **I** solve equations using both the addition and multiplication principles.
- **II** solve equations containing parentheses.
- **III** use the principle of zero products to solve equations (already factored).

I Using the Principles Together

Let's see how to use the addition and multiplication principles together.

Example 1. Solve: $3x - 4 = 13$.

$$3x - 4 + 4 = 13 + 4 \qquad \textit{Using the addition principle, adding 4}$$

$$3x + (-4) + 4 = 13 + 4$$
$$\qquad\qquad\qquad \textit{Simplifying}$$

$$3x = 17$$

$$\frac{1}{3} \cdot 3x = \frac{1}{3} \cdot 17 \qquad \textit{Using the multiplication principle,}$$
$$\qquad\qquad\qquad\qquad \textit{multiplying by } \tfrac{1}{3}$$

$$x = \frac{17}{3} \qquad \textit{Simplifying}$$

This checks, so the solution is $\frac{17}{3}$, or $5\frac{2}{3}$.

TRY THIS

Solve.
1. $9x - 4 = 8 \quad \frac{4}{3}$
2. $-\frac{1}{4}y + \frac{3}{2} = \frac{1}{2} \quad 4$

In Example 1, we used the addition principle first. This is usually best.

If there are like terms in an equation, they should be collected first.

Example 2. Solve: $7x - 3x = 32$.

$$4x = 32 \qquad \textit{Collecting like terms}$$

$$\frac{1}{4} \cdot 4x = \frac{1}{4} \cdot 32 \qquad \textit{Using the multiplication principle}$$

$$x = 8$$

This checks, so the solution is 8.

Solve.
3. $5x + 9x = 42 \quad 3$
4. $14x - 9x + 7 = -22 \quad -\frac{29}{5}$

TRY THIS

If there are like terms on opposite sides of an equation, we can get them on the same side using the addition principle, and then "combine" them.

Example 3. Solve: $8x + 6 - 2x = -12 - 4x + 5$.

$$8x - 2x = -12 - 4x + 5 - 6 \qquad \text{\textit{Adding} } -6 \text{ \textit{and simplifying}}$$

$$8x - 2x + 4x = -12 + 5 - 6 \qquad \text{\textit{Adding 4x and simplifying}}$$

$$10x = -13 \qquad \text{\textit{Collecting like terms and simplifying}}$$

$$\frac{1}{10} \cdot 10x = \frac{1}{10} \cdot (-13) \qquad \text{\textit{Multiplying by } } \tfrac{1}{10}$$

$$x = \frac{-13}{10}, \text{ or } -1.3 \qquad \text{\textit{Simplifying}}$$

Check:

$$8x + 6 - 2x = -12 - 4x + 5$$

$8\left(\dfrac{-13}{10}\right) + 6 - 2\left(\dfrac{-13}{10}\right)$	$-12 - 4\left(\dfrac{-13}{10}\right) + 5$
$\dfrac{-52}{5} + 6 - \dfrac{-13}{5}$	$-12 - \dfrac{-26}{5} + 5$
$\dfrac{-39}{5} + 6$	$-7 + \dfrac{26}{5}$
$\dfrac{-9}{5}$	$\dfrac{-9}{5}$

In Example 3 we used the addition principle to get all terms with the variable on one side of the equation and all other terms on the other side. Then we combined like terms and proceeded as before.

TRY THIS ➡️

Solve.

5. $30 + 7(x - 1) = 3(2x + 7)$

$_{-2}$

ıı Equations with Parentheses

Certain equations with parentheses can be solved by first removing the parentheses and then proceeding as before.

Example 4. Solve: $3(7 - 2x) = 14 - 8(x - 1)$.

$$21 - 6x = 14 - 8x + 8 \qquad \text{\textit{Removing parentheses}}$$

$$21 - 6x = 22 - 8x \qquad \text{\textit{Simplifying}}$$

$$8x - 6x = 22 + (-21) \qquad \text{\textit{Using the addition principle}}$$

$$2x = 1 \qquad \text{\textit{Collecting like terms and simplifying}}$$

$$x = \frac{1}{2} \qquad \text{\textit{Using the multiplication principle}}$$

This checks, so the solution is $\frac{1}{2}$.

TRY THIS ━━━▶

Solve.

6. $3(y - 1) - 1 = 2 - 5(y + 5) - \frac{19}{8}$

III The Principle of Zero Products

When we multiply two numbers, the product will be zero if one of the factors is zero. Furthermore, if a product is zero, then at least one of the factors must be zero.

THEOREM 2-3   (The Principle of Zero Products)

For any numbers a and b,
if $ab = 0$, then $a = 0$ or $b = 0$, and
if $a = 0$ or $b = 0$, then $ab = 0$.

Example 5.   Solve: $(x + 4)(x - 2) = 0$.

Here we have a product which is zero. This equation will become true when either factor is zero. Hence it is true when $x + 4 = 0$ or $x - 2 = 0$. We have applied the principle of zero products. Solving each equation separately we get:

$x = -4$ or $x = 2$.

There are two solutions, -4 and 2.

The check is not necessary when we use the principle of zero products, except to detect errors.

Example 6.   Solve: $7x(4x + 2) = 0$.

$7x = 0$ or $4x + 2 = 0$ *Using the principle of zero products*
$x = 0$ or $4x = -2$
$x = 0$ $x = -\frac{1}{2}$ *Solving each equation separately*

The solutions are 0 and $-\frac{1}{2}$.

TRY THIS ━━━▶

Solve.

7. $(x - 19)(x + 5) = 0$
8. $x(3x - 17) = 0$
9. $(9x + 2)(-6x + 3) = 0$

Answers.   7. $19, -5$ 8. $0, \frac{17}{3}$ 9. $-\frac{2}{9}, \frac{1}{2}$

Exercise Set 2-2

▌Solve. (*See Example 1.*)

1. $4x - 12 = 60$ 18
3. $5y + 3 = 28$ 5
5. $2y - 11 = 37$ 24
7. $5x - 10 = 45$ 11
9. $9t + 4 = -104$ −12
11. $-7x + 2 = -54$ 8
13. $-4x - 7 = -35$ 7

2. $4x - 6 = 70$ 19
4. $7t + 11 = 74$ 9
6. $3x - 13 = 29$ 14
8. $6z - 7 = 11$ 3
10. $5x + 7 = -108$ −23
12. $-9y + 8 = -91$ 11
14. $-8y - 83 = -5$ $-\frac{39}{4}$

Solve. (*See Examples 2 and 3.*)

15. $6x + 2x = 16$ 2
17. $5x + 2x = 56$ 8
19. $9y - 7y = 42$ 21
21. $-8x - 4x = 60$ −5
23. $-6y - 10y = -32$ 2
25. $8x + 48 = 3x - 12$ −12
27. $7y - 1 = 23 - 5y$ 2
29. $4x - 3 = 5 + 12x$ −1
31. $5 - 4a = a - 13$ $\frac{18}{5}$
33. $3m - 7 = -7 - 4m - m$ 0
35. $5r - 2 + 3r = 2r + 6 - 4r$ $\frac{4}{5}$

16. $9y + 2y = 33$ 3
18. $3x + 7x = 120$ 12
20. $8t - 3t = 65$ 13
22. $-9y - 5y = 28$ −2
24. $-8t - 12t = -80$ 4
26. $15x + 20 = 8x - 22$ −6
28. $3z - 15 = 15 - 3z$ 5
30. $9t - 4 = 14 + 15t$ −3
32. $8 - 5x = x - 16$ 4
34. $5x - 8 = -8 + 3x - x$ 0
36. $5m - 17 - 2m = 6m - 1 - m$ −8

▌▌Solve. (*See Example 4.*)

37. $2(x + 6) = 8x$ 2
39. $80 = 10(3t + 2)$ 2
41. $180(n - 2) = 900$ 7
43. $5y - (2y - 10) = 25$ 5
45. $7(3x + 6) = 11 - (x + 2)$ $-\frac{3}{2}$
47. $\frac{1}{8}(16y + 8) - 17 = -\frac{1}{4}(8y - 16)$ 5
49. $a + (a - 3) = (a + 2) - (a + 1)$ 2

38. $3(y + 5) = 8y$ 3
40. $27 = 9(5y - 2)$ 1
42. $210(x - 3) = 840$ 7
44. $8x - (3x - 5) = 40$ 7
46. $9(2x + 8) = 20 - (x + 5)$ −3
48. $\frac{1}{6}(12t + 48) - 20 = -\frac{1}{8}(24t - 144)$ 6
50. $8 - 4(b - 1) = 2 + 3(4 - b)$ −2

▌▌▌Solve. (*See Examples 5 and 6.*)

51. $(x + 2)(x - 5) = 0$ −2, 5
53. $(y - 8)(y - 9) = 0$ 8, 9
55. $(2x - 3)(3x - 2) = 0$ $\frac{3}{2}, \frac{2}{3}$
57. $m(m - 8) = 0$ 0, 8
59. $0 = (2x + 8)(3x - 9)$ −4, 3
61. $x(x - 1)(x + 2) = 0$ 0, 1, −2

52. $(x + 4)(x - 8) = 0$ −4, 8
54. $(t - 3)(t - 7) = 0$ 3, 7
56. $(3y - 4)(4y - 1) = 0$ $\frac{4}{3}, \frac{1}{4}$
58. $p(p - 5) = 0$ 0, 5
60. $0 = (4x + 16)(5x - 10)$ −4, 2
62. $y(y - 4)(y + 2) = 0$ 0, 4, −2

2-3 Solving Problems

After finishing Lesson 2-3, you should be able to
▌ solve problems by translating to equations.

▌ The first step in solving a problem is to translate to mathematical language. Very often this means translating to an equation. Drawing a picture sometimes helps. We solve the equation. Then we check to see if we have a solution to the problem.

Example 1. A 8-meter rope is cut into two pieces. One piece is 3 meters longer than the other. How long are the pieces?

One way to translate is this:

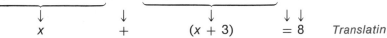

Length of one piece plus length of other piece = 8

$$x \quad + \quad (x + 3) \quad = 8 \qquad \textit{Translating}$$

(We use x for the length of one piece and $x + 3$ for the length of the other because we know one is 3 m longer than the other.)
Now we solve: $x + (x + 3) = 8$

$$2x + 3 = 8 \qquad \textit{Combining like terms}$$
$$2x = 5$$
$$x = \tfrac{5}{2}, \text{ or } 2\tfrac{1}{2}$$

Do we have an answer to the problem itself? If one piece is $2\tfrac{1}{2}$ m long and the other is 3 m longer, it must be $5\tfrac{1}{2}$ m long. Then the lengths of the pieces add up to 8 m. This checks, so the answer is that the pieces are $2\tfrac{1}{2}$ m and $5\tfrac{1}{2}$ m long.

TRY THIS

> 1. A 12-cm rod is cut into two pieces, one three times as long as the other. How long are the pieces?
>
> 9 cm; 3 cm

Example 2. It has been found that the world record for the 10,000-meter run has been decreasing steadily since 1940. The record is 30.18 minutes minus 0.12 times the number of years since 1940. If the record continues to decrease this way, what will the record be in 1980?

Record is <u>30.18 minutes</u> minus 0.12 times <u>the number of years since 1940</u>

$$R = 30.18 - 0.12 \cdot t \qquad \textit{Translating}$$

$$R = 30.18 - 0.12t$$
$$= 30.18 - 0.12(40) \qquad \textit{1980 is 40 years from}$$
$$= 30.18 - 4.8 \qquad \textit{1940}$$
$$= 25.38$$

The number 25.38 checks in the problem, so the world record in the 10,000-meter run in 1980 will be 25.38 minutes (a prediction).

TRY THIS ➡

Example 3. On December 17, 1974 the pilots of Pan American Airlines shocked the business world by taking a pay *cut* of 11% to a new salary of $48,950 per year. What was their former salary?

(Former salary) − 11%(Former salary) = New salary

$$x \qquad - 11\% \cdot x \qquad = \qquad 48,950 \qquad \textit{Translating}$$

We have used x to represent the former salary.

$$x - 11\%x = 48,950 \qquad \textit{Solving}$$
$$1x - 0.11x = 48,950$$
$$(1 - 0.11)x = 48,950$$
$$0.89x = 48,950$$
$$x = \frac{48,950}{0.89}$$
$$x = 55,000$$

Check: 11% of 55,000 is 6050. Subtracting from 55,000 we get 48,950. This checks, so the former salary was $55,000

TRY THIS ➡

2. It has been found that the world record for the 800-meter run has been decreasing steadily since 1930. The record is 1.82 minutes minus 0.0035 times the number of years since 1930. Predict what the record will be in 1980. **1.645 min.**

3. The County Cab Company charges sixty cents plus eleven cents per km as the fare. What will be the total cost of a 12 km ride? **$1.92**

4. A clothing store drops the price of suits 25% to a sale price of $93. What was the former price? **$124**

5. An investment is made at 8% simple interest. It grows to $783 at the end of 1 year. How much was invested originally? (*Hint:* Recall the expression $P + Prt$ regarding the return on a principal of P dollars.) **$725**

Exercise Set 2-3

▌Solve. (*See Examples 1–3.*)

1. A 12-cm piece of tubing is cut into two pieces. One piece is 4 cm longer than the other. How long are the pieces? 8 cm; 4 cm

2. A 10 meter piece of wire is cut into two pieces. One piece is 2 meters longer than the other. How long are the pieces? 6 m; 4 m

3. A piece of wire four meters long is cut into two pieces so that one piece is two-thirds as long as the other. Find the length of each piece. $1\frac{3}{5}$ m; $2\frac{2}{5}$ m

4. A piece of rope five meters long is cut into two pieces so that one piece is three-fifths as long as the other. Find the length of each piece. $1\frac{7}{8}$ m; $3\frac{1}{8}$ m

5. Tony's baby-sitting service charges $2.50 per day plus $1.75 per hour. What is the cost of a seven hour baby-sitting job? $14.75

6. The cost of renting a rug shampooer is $3.25 per hour plus $2.75 for the shampoo. Find the cost of shampooing if the time involved is 3.5 hours. $14.13

7. The Klunker car rental charges $16 per day plus 15¢ per kilometer. Find the cost of renting a car for a one day trip of 290 kilometers. $59.50

8. A phone company charges 30¢ per long distance call plus 20¢ per minute. Find the cost of an 18-minute long distance call. $3.90

9. Eight plus five times a number is seven times the number. What is the number? 4

10. Six plus three times a number is four times the number. What is the number? 6

11. Five more than three times a number is the same as ten less than six times the number. What is the number? 5

12. Six more than nine times a number is the same as two less than ten times the number. What is the number? 8

13. A pro shop in a bowling alley drops the price of bowling balls 24% to a sale price of $34.20. What was the former price? $45

14. An appliance store drops the price of a certain type of TV 18% to a sale price of $410. What was the former price? $500

15. Money is borrowed at 9% simple interest. After 1 year $708.50 pays off the loan. How much was originally borrowed? $650

16. Money is borrowed at 7% simple interest. After 1 year $856 pays off the loan. How much was originally borrowed? $800

17. The second angle of a triangle is three times the first and the third is 12° less than twice the first. Find the measures of the angles. 32°, 96°, 52°

18. The second angle of a triangle is four times the first and the third is 5° more than twice the first. Find the measures of the angles. 25°, 100°, 55°

19. The perimeter of a college basketball court is 96 m and the length is 14 m more than the width. What are the dimensions? Length is 31 m; width is 17 m

20. The perimeter of a certain soccer field is 310 m. The length is 65 m more than the width. What are the dimensions? Length is 110 m; width is 45 m

2-4 Formulas

After finishing Lesson 2-4, you should be able to
▌ solve a formula for a specified letter.

▌A formula is a kind of recipe for doing a certain kind of calculation. Formulas are often given by equations. Here is a formula we have considered.

$$A = P + Prt$$

This formula tells us the amount *A* we will have if we invest principal *P* at simple interest, at rate *r* for *t* years. Suppose we know *A*, *r*, and *t*, and want to find *P*. To do this, we get *P* alone on one side, or "solve" the formula for *P*.

Example 1. Solve for *P*.

$$A = P + Prt$$
$$A = P(1 + rt) \qquad \textit{Factoring}$$
$$\frac{1}{1 + rt} \cdot A = P(1 + rt) \cdot \frac{1}{1 + rt} \qquad \textit{Multiplying by } \frac{1}{1 + rt}, \textit{ to get P}$$
$$\frac{A}{1 + rt} = P \qquad\qquad\qquad \textit{alone on one side}$$

TRY THIS ➤

> 1. Solve for *Q*.
> $$T = Q + Qiy$$
> $$Q = \frac{T}{1 + iy}$$

Example 2. Solve for *D*.

$$C = \pi D$$
$$\frac{1}{\pi} \cdot C = \frac{1}{\pi} \cdot \pi D \qquad \textit{Multiplying by } \frac{1}{\pi}$$
$$\frac{C}{\pi} = D \qquad \textit{Simplifying}$$

TRY THIS ➤

> 2. A formula for the area of a triangle is $A = \frac{1}{2}bh$. Solve for *b*. $b = \frac{2A}{h}$

Example 3. Solve for r.

$$H = 2r + 3m$$
$$H - 3m = 2r \qquad \textit{Adding } -3m$$
$$\tfrac{1}{2}(H - 3m) = r \qquad \textit{Multiplying by } \tfrac{1}{2}$$

TRY THIS ━━━━━━━━━▶

> 3. Solve for m.
> $$H = 2r + 3m$$
> $$m = \frac{h - 2r}{3}$$

Exercise Set 2-4 Use Quiz 3 after lesson 2—4.

▌ Solve for the indicated letter. (*See Examples 1–3.*)

1. $A = lw$, for l $l = \frac{A}{w}$
2. $A = lw$, for w $w = \frac{A}{l}$
3. $W = EI$, for I $I = \frac{W}{E}$
4. $W = EI$, for E $E = \frac{W}{I}$
5. $F = ma$, for m $m = \frac{F}{a}$
6. $F = ma$, for a $a = \frac{F}{m}$
7. $I = Prt$, for t $t = \frac{I}{pr}$
8. $I = Prt$, for P $p = \frac{I}{rt}$
9. $E = mc^2$, for m $m = \frac{E}{c^2}$
10. $E = mc^2$, for c^2 $c^2 = \frac{E}{m}$
11. $P = 2l + 2w$, for l $l = \frac{1}{2}(P - 2w)$
12. $P = 2l + 2w$, for w $w = \frac{1}{2}(P - 2l)$
13. $C^2 = a^2 + b^2$, for a^2 $a^2 = C^2 - b^2$
14. $C^2 = a^2 + b^2$, for b^2 $b^2 = C^2 - a^2$
15. $A = \pi r^2$, for r^2 $r^2 = \frac{A}{\pi}$
16. $A = \pi r^2$, for π $\pi = \frac{A}{r^2}$
17. $W = \frac{11}{2}(h - 40)$, for h $h = \frac{2}{11}W + 40$
18. $C = \frac{5}{9}(F - 32)$, for F $F = \frac{9}{5}C + 32$
19. $V = \frac{4}{3}\pi r^3$, for r^3 $r^3 = \frac{3V}{4\pi}$
20. $V = \frac{4}{3}\pi r^3$, for π $\pi = \frac{3V}{4r^3}$
21. $A = \frac{1}{2}h(a + b)$, for h $h = \frac{2A}{a + b}$
22. $A = \frac{1}{2}h(a + b)$, for b $b = \frac{1}{h}(2A - ha)$
23. $\frac{P_1 V_1}{T_1} = \frac{P_2 V_2}{T_2}$, for V_1 $V_1 = \frac{T_1 P_2 V_2}{P_1 T_2}$
24. $\frac{P_1 V_1}{T_1} = \frac{P_2 V_2}{T_2}$, for T_2 $T_2 = \frac{T_1 P_2 V_2}{P_1 V_1}$
25. $F = \frac{Wr^2}{gr}$, for r $r = \frac{gF}{W}$
26. $F = \frac{Wr^2}{gr}$, for W $w = \frac{Fg}{r}$

CONSUMER NOTE: Balloon Payments

Installment buying usually requires monthly payments that are all about the same. Sometimes, though, an installment contract calls for a "balloon" payment at the end. This is a final payment much larger than any of the others. If the buyer cannot pay it, the item being bought can be repossessed—taken away by the credit company. All the buyer has left is some hard-won knowledge about installment contracts.

Installment buyers should watch out for balloon payments. They can be a trap.

CHAPTER 2 REVIEW

Review the material in the chapter. Then see how you have done by trying these review exercises. If you miss an exercise, restudy the indicated lesson.

2-1   Solve using the addition principle.
  1. $x + 13 = 27$ 14
  2. $p - 17 = 9$ 26

2-1   Solve using the multiplication principle.
  3. $7y = -56$ −8
  4. $-14y = -126$ 9

2-2   Solve.
  5. $8x - 19 = 53$ 9
  6. $-9t - 74 = -2$ −8
  7. $3(x + 7) = 63$ 14
  8. $9y - (4y - 7) = -33$ −8
  9. $(x + 4)(x - 3) = 0$ −4, 3
  10. $(2x - 5)(3x - 4) = 0$ $\frac{5}{2}, \frac{4}{3}$

2-3   Solve.
  11. A 12-meter piece of wire is cut into two pieces. One piece is 3 meters longer than the other. How long are the pieces? $4\frac{1}{2}$ m; $7\frac{1}{2}$ m
  12. The cost of renting a lawn thatcher is $4.75 per hour plus $1.50 for gasoline. Find the cost of thatching a lawn if the time involved is 3.5 hours. $18.13

2-4   Solve for the indicated letter.
  13. $A = \frac{1}{2}bh$, for b $b = \frac{2A}{h}$
  14. $V = ah + at$, for a $a = \frac{V}{h + t}$

CHAPTER 2 TEST

Solve using the addition principle.
1. $x + 18 = 32$ ₁₄
2. $t - 19 = 6$ ₂₅

Solve using the multiplication principle.
3. $-8y = 72$ ₋₉
4. $15y = -225$ ₋₁₅

Solve.
5. $9x + 14 = -67$ ₋₉
6. $-3p - 75 = -3$ ₋₂₄
7. $8(x + 9) = 112$ ₅
8. $8y - (5y - 9) = -160$ $-\frac{169}{3}$
9. $(x + 7)(x - 8) = 0$ _{-7, 8}
10. $(3x + 5)(2x - 6) = 0$ $-\frac{5}{3}, 3$

Solve.
11. A 14-meter piece of cable is cut into two pieces. One piece is 4 meters longer than the other. How long are the pieces?   _{9 m; 5 m}
12. The cost of renting a floor sander is $5.25 per hour plus $2 for sandpaper. Find the cost of sanding a floor if the time involved is 4.5 hours.   _{$25.63}

Solve for the indicated letter.
13. $E = \dfrac{I}{R}$, for I _{I = RE}
14. $Q = P - Prt$, for P $P = \dfrac{Q}{1 - rt}$

Ready for Linear Equations?

1-5   1.   Evaluate $y - xz$ when $x = -2$, $y = 3$, $z = -4$.   −5

1-2   Add.

      2. $-4 + 0$ −4
      3. $-2 + (-7)$ −9
      4. $-2.7 + (-3.5)$ −6.2
      5. $15 + (-8)$ 7
      6. $-8.1 + 2.4$ −5.7
      7. $\frac{2}{3} + \left(-\frac{3}{5}\right)$ $\frac{1}{15}$

1-2   Find $-a$ when a stands for

      8. -10 10
      9. 0 0
    10. $\frac{1}{2}$ $-\frac{1}{2}$

      Solve.

2-1   11. $x + 8 = -12$ −20
2-1   12. $3x = 21$ 7
2-2   13. $4x - 5 = 11$ 4
2-2   14. $9x - 2x = 21$ 3
2-2   15. $7x - 4 + 2x = -8 - 3x + 6$ $\frac{1}{6}$

Chapter 3
Linear Equations

Temperature is related to cricket chirps by a linear
equation.

3-1 Graphs and Equations

After finishing Lesson 3-1, you should be able to
I   plot points given their coordinates.
II   decide whether a given point is a solution of an equation.
III   draw graphs of simple equations.

On a number line each point is the graph of a number. On a plane each point is the graph of a number pair. Two perpendicular number lines called *axes* are used. The point where they cross is called the *origin* and is labeled 0. The arrows show the positive directions.

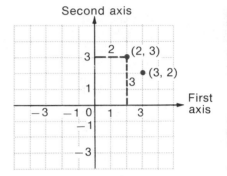

I Plotting Points

Notice that (2, 3) and (3, 2) give different points. They are called *ordered pairs* of numbers since it makes a difference which number comes first.

Example 1. Plot the point (−4, 3).

The first number, −4, tells us the distance in the first direction.
We go 4 units *left*. The second number, 3, tells us the distance in the second direction. We go 3 units *up*.
The numbers in an ordered pair are called *coordinates*. In (−4, 3), −4 is the *first coordinate* and 3 is the *second coordinate*.

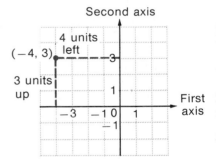

TRY THIS ➡

Use graph paper. Draw and label the first and second axes. Then plot these points.
  See answer section
1.   (6, 4)
2.   (−3, 5)
3.   (4, 6)
4.   (−4, −3)
5.   (0, 2)

When plotting a point, the first coordinate of the ordered pair tells us the distance in the first direction. The second coordinate tells us the distance in the second direction.

When finding the coordinates of a point, we see how far to the right or left it is located and how far up or down.

Example 2. Find the coordinates of point *A*.

Point *A* is 4 units to the right and 3 units up. Its coordinates are (4, 3).

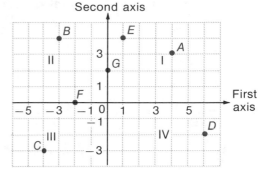

TRY THIS ➡

Answer.   6. B(−3, 4); C(−4, −3); D(6, −2); E(1, 4); F(−2, 0); G(0, 2)

6. Find the coordinates of points *B, C, D, E, F,* and *G* in the drawing of Example 2.

Note that in region I (called the first *quadrant*) both coordinates of a point are positive. In region II (second quadrant) the first coordinate is negative and the second is positive.

TRY THIS ➡

Answers.   7. Both coordinates are negative.   8. The first coordinate is positive and the second negative.

7. What can you say about the coordinates of a point in the third quadrant?
8. What can you say about the coordinates of a point in the fourth quadrant?

▪ Solutions of Equations

If an equation has two variables, its solutions must be pairs of numbers. We usually take the variables in alphabetical order. We get ordered pairs of numbers for solutions.

Example 3. Determine whether (−1, −4) is a solution of $y = 3x − 1$.

We replace *x* by −1 and *y* by −4.

$$
\begin{array}{c|l}
\multicolumn{2}{l}{y = 3x - 1} \\
\hline
-4 & 3 \cdot (-1) - 1 \\
& -3 - 1 \\
& -4
\end{array}
$$

(−1, −4) is a solution.

Example 4. Determine whether (7, 5) is a solution of
$q = 3p - 1$.

We take the variables in alphabetical order, so $p = 7$ and $q = 5$.

$$
\begin{array}{c|l}
q = 3p - 1 \\
\hline
5 & 3 \cdot 7 - 1 \\
& 21 - 1 \\
& 20
\end{array}
$$

(7, 5) is not a solution.

TRY THIS ➡

> 9. Determine whether
>   (9, −2) is a solution of
> $y = 4x + 17$. No
> 10. Determine whether (0, 23)
>   is a solution of
> $q = 4p + 17$. No
> 11. Determine whether
>   (2, −2) is a solution of
> $2s + 6r = 8$. Yes

ⅢGraphs of Equations

To *graph an equation* we plot enough points to see a pattern and then draw a line or curve.

Example 5. Graph the equation $y - 2x = 1$.

We use alphabetical order for the variables. The first axis will be the *x*-axis and the second axis will be the *y*-axis.
First solve the equation for *y*.

$$y = 2x + 1$$

Next, find some solutions (ordered pairs), keeping the results in a table. To find an ordered pair we choose *any* number for *x*, substitute it in the equation, and then find *y*. Suppose we choose 0 for *x*. Then

$$
\begin{aligned}
y &= 2x + 1 \\
  &= 2 \cdot 0 + 1 \\
  &= 0 + 1 \\
  &= 1
\end{aligned}
$$

When $x = 0$, $y = 1$. This gives us an ordered pair (0, 1). We continue to find ordered pairs, filling in the table.

x	y
0	1
−1	−1
−2	−3
1	3
2	5

We choose these numbers.   *We find these numbers by substituting in the equation.*

Now we plot these points. (See the graph to the left below.)

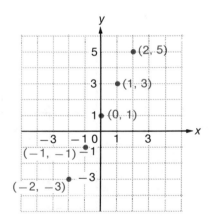
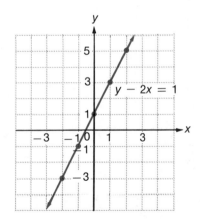

In this case the points seem to lie on a straight line. In fact, they do. If we take all the solutions of the equation we get the entire line, so the graph of this equation is a straight line containing the points we plotted. We can draw the line with a ruler. The graph is shown above to the right.

TRY THIS

12. Graph $y = 2x - 1$.
13. Graph $y = -x + 1$.
See answer section

Exercise Set 3-1

▮Use graph paper. Draw a first and a second axis. Then plot these points. You may plot several points on the same piece of paper. (*See Example 1.*)

1. (3, 4)
   See answer section
2. (6, 3)
3. (−2, 3)
4. (−3, 5)
5. (2, −4)
6. (3, −4)
7. (−3, −5)
8. (−7, −4)
9. (0, 3)
10. (0, 7)
11. (0, −2)
12. (0, −5)
13. (6, 0)
14. (4, 0)
15. (−6, 0)
16. (−7, 0)

(*See Example 2.*)

17. Find the coordinates of points *A*, *B*, *C*, *D*, and *E*.

18. Find the coordinates of points *A*, *B*, *C*, *D*, and *E*.

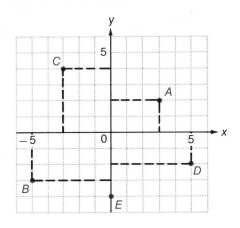

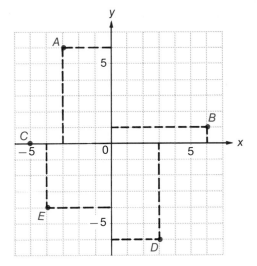

17. A(3, 2); B(−5, −3); C(−3, 4); D(5, −2); E(0, −4)
18. A(−3, 6); B(6, 1); C(−5, 0); D(3, −6); E(−4, −4)

▮▮Decide whether the given point is a solution of the indicated equation. (*See Examples 3 and 4.*)

19. (1, −1); $y = 2x − 3$ Yes
20. (2, 5); $y = 3x − 1$ Yes
21. (3, 4); $3s + t = 4$ No
22. (2, 3); $2p + q = 5$ No
23. (3, 5); $4x − y = 7$ Yes
24. (2, 7); $5x − y = 3$ Yes
25. $(0, \frac{3}{5})$; $2a + 5b = 3$ Yes
26. $(0, \frac{3}{2})$; $3f + 4g = 6$ Yes
27. (2, −1); $4r + 3s = 5$ Yes
28. (2, −4); $5w + 2z = 2$ Yes
29. (3, 2); $3x − 2y = −4$ No
30. (1, 2); $2x − 5y = −6$ No

■■■Graph the following equations. (*See Example 5.*)

31. $y = x$ See answer section
32. $y = -x$
33. $y = -3x$
34. $y = 3x$
35. $q = p + 2$
36. $q = p - 2$
37. $y = 3x + 1$
38. $y = 2x - 1$
39. $t = -4s + 1$
40. $t = -3s + 2$
41. $3x = 2y + 1$
42. $2x = 3y + 1$
43. $2x + 5y = 10$
44. $3x + 9y = 12$
45. $3p - 2q = 6$
46. $4r - 3s = 12$
47. $y = \frac{1}{2}x + 2$
48. $y = \frac{1}{3}x - 2$

Calculator Exercises

Decide whether the given point is a solution of the indicated equation.   49. Yes   50. Yes

49. $(3.721, -3.058)$; $4x - 2y = 21$
50. $(-1.072, 1.592)$; $2x + 7y = 9$

Challenge Exercises

Devise a coordinate system in which the axes are not perpendicular. Graph the following equations using your coordinate system.

51. $y = x$ 52. $y = x + 2$

See answer section   Answers may vary.

HISTORICAL NOTE: Let a Machine Do It

Anyone who has done a difficult calculation experiences two feelings. One is impatience. The work seems to take a long time. The other feeling is worry. An error in any part of the calculation will mean an error in the result. These two feelings prompted the invention of calculating machines.

Blaise Pascal invented a calculating machine in France in 1642. Gottfried Wilhelm von Leibniz, a great German mathematician, invented one in 1671. Charles Babbage of England designed several calculating machines in the 1800s. None of these inventions was produced for public sale, but their principles of operation led to modern calculating machines.

3-2 *Linear Equations*

After finishing Lesson 3-2, you should be able to
  ▮   identify linear equations.
  ▮▮   find the standard form of a linear equation.
  ▮▮▮ graph linear equations.
  ▮▮▮▮ graph linear equations using intercepts.
  ▮▮▮▮▮ graph linear equations with a missing variable (single variable).

▮ Recognizing Linear Equations

Equations which have straight lines for their graphs are called *linear* equations. An equation is linear if the variables occur to the first power only. There must be no products of variables or variables in denominators.

Example 1. Which of the following equations are linear?

  a) $xy = 9$ b) $2r + 7 = 4s$ c) $4x^3 = 7y$

  d) $8x - 17y = y$ e) $q = \dfrac{3}{p}$ f) $4x = -3$

Equations b), d), and f) are linear equations.

Since in linear equations the variables occur to the first power only, they are also called *first degree equations*.

TRY THIS ➡️

Which of these equations are linear (first degree)?

1. $5y + 8x = 9$ Yes
2. $7y = 11$ Yes
3. $5y^2x = 13$ No
4. $x = 4 + \dfrac{7}{y}$ No
5. $xy = 0$ No
6. $3x - 2y + 5 = 0$ Yes

▮▮ Finding the Standard Form

DEFINITION
The *standard form* for a linear equation is $Ax + By + C = 0$, where A and B are not both zero.

Example 2. Find standard form for the equation $4x + y = 2$.

  $4x + y - 2 = 0$ *Using the addition principle, adding* -2

This equation is of the form $Ax + By + C = 0$, where $A = 4$, $B = 1$, and $C = -2$.

Example 3. Find standard form for the equation $7x = \frac{1}{4} - 5x$.

$$7x = \frac{1}{4} - 5x$$
$$7x + 5x - \frac{1}{4} = 0 \qquad \textit{Using the addition principle, adding } 5x - \frac{1}{4}$$
$$12x + 0y - \frac{1}{4} = 0$$

This equation is of the form $Ax + By + C = 0$, where $A = 12$, $B = 0$, and $C = -\frac{1}{4}$.

TRY THIS

Answers.   7. $-5x + 5y - \frac{1}{2} = 0$ 8. $0x + 3y - 10 = 0$

Find standard form for each equation.

7. $5y = \frac{1}{2} + 5x$
8. $8y = 10 + 5y$

ⅠⅠⅠ Graphing Linear Equations

THEOREM 3-1

The graph of any linear equation is a straight line.

From Theorem 3-1, we know that the graph of a first degree equation will be a straight line. Plotting two points is sufficient, but we usually use at least one more point, as a check.

Example 4. Graph the equation $3y + 3 = 2x$.

We solve for y.

$$y = \tfrac{2}{3}x - 1.$$

We find two points.

If $x = 0$, $y = \frac{2}{3} \cdot 0 - 1$
$\qquad = -1$

If $x = -2$, $y = \frac{2}{3} \cdot (-2) - 1$
$\qquad = -\frac{7}{3}$

We plot the points $(0, -1)$ and $(-2, -\frac{7}{3})$ and draw the line.
We find a third point as a check.

If $x = 3$, $y = \frac{2}{3} \cdot 3 - 1$
$\qquad = 2 - 1$
$\qquad = 1$

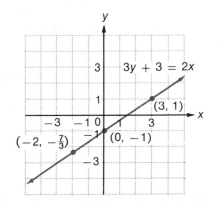

We plot the point $(3, 1)$ as a check. It lies on the line, so our graph is probably correct.

TRY THIS

9.   Graph $2x - 6y = -2$
10.   Graph $3y = 2x - 6$
See answer section

ⅠⅠⅠⅠ Graphing Using Intercepts

DEFINITION

The points where a line crosses the axes are called the *intercepts*.

We can usually find intercepts easily, so we often use them in graphing. To find an intercept, we give one variable the value 0.

Example 5. Graph $4x + 5y = 20$.

To find the *y*-intercept, we let $x = 0$.

Then
$$4 \cdot 0 + 5y = 20$$
$$5y = 20$$
$$y = 4$$

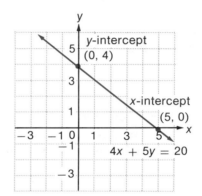

Thus (0, 4) is the *y*-intercept.

To find the *x*-intercept, we let $y = 0$.

Then
$$4x + 5 \cdot 0 = 20$$
$$4x = 20$$
$$x = 5$$

Thus (5, 0) is the *x*-intercept.

We plot the points (0, 4) and (5, 0) and draw the graph. If a line goes through the origin (0, 0), we must use another point. A third point should be used as a check.

TRY THIS

Graph using intercepts.

11. $3y = 2x - 6$
12. $4x + 7y = 28$
13. $9x + 2y = 18$

See answer section

ⅠⅠⅠⅠⅠ Equations with a Missing Variable

Consider the equation $y = 4$. We can think of it as $y = 0 \cdot x + 4$. No matter what number we choose for *x*, we find *y* is 4. Thus (*x*, 4) is a solution no matter what *x* is.

THEOREM 3-2

If *x* is missing in a linear equation the graph is a line parallel to the *x*-axis. If *y* is missing the graph is a line parallel to the *y*-axis.

Example 6. Graph $y = 4$.

Any ordered pair $(x, 4)$ is a solution. So the line is parallel to the x-axis with y-intercept $(0, 4)$.

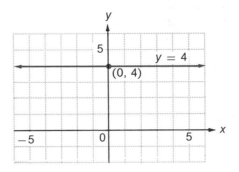

Example 7. Graph $x = -2$.

Any ordered pair $(-2, y)$ is a solution. So the line is parallel to the y-axis with x-intercept $(-2, 0)$.

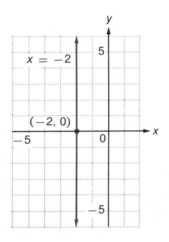

TRY THIS ➡

Graph these equations, using the same axes.

14. $x = 4$
15. $y = -3$
16. $y = 0$

See answer section

Exercise Set 3-2

▮ Which of the following equations are linear? If an equation is not linear, give the reason. (*See Example 1.*)

1. $3x - 4 = y$ Yes
2. $x = 9$ Yes
3. $4r^2 = 2r + 1$ No, second degree term
4. $2 + 3pq = -9$ No, product of variables
5. $y = 7$ Yes
6. $3x^2 + 4y^2 = 16$ No, second degree terms
7. $4x - 5y = 20$ Yes
8. $5 = \dfrac{1}{x}$ No, variable in denominator
9. $3p - 4 = q - 1$ Yes
10. $5 = r + 4t$ Yes

∎∎ Find standard form. (*See Examples 2 and 3.*)

11. $4x - 8 = y$ $\quad$ 4x − y − 8 = 0

12. $x = 2y - 1$ $\quad$ x − 2y + 1 = 0

13. $y = 2x + 3$ $\quad$ −2x + y − 3 = 0

14. $y = 6x - 2$ $\quad$ −6x + y + 2 = 0

15. $y + 4 = 4x + 8$ $\quad$ −4x + y − 4 = 0

16. $3x - 8 = x - 2$ $\quad$ 2x + 0y − 6 = 0

17. $x = 6$ $\quad$ x + 0y − 6 = 0

18. $y = 9$ $\quad$ 0x + y − 9 = 0

19. $\sqrt{2}y = 3x$ $\quad$ −3x + √2y + 0 = 0

20. $\sqrt{3}x = 5y$ $\quad$ √3x − 5y + 0 = 0

∎∎∎ Use graph paper. Graph these linear equations. Use a different set of axes for each. (*See Example 4.*)

21. $x + 2y = 4$ $\qquad$ See answer section

22. $x + 3y = 9$

23. $-x + 4y = 8$

24. $-x + 2y = 6$

25. $4x + y = 8$

26. $3x + y = 6$

27. $3y - 3 = 6x$

28. $2y - 6 = 4x$

29. $y = 3x$

30. $y = 4x$

31. $3x + 6y = 18$

32. $4x + 5y = 20$

∎∎∎∎ Find the intercepts of each equation. (*See Example 5.*)

33. $x - 2 = y$ $\quad$ (0, −2), (2, 0)

34. $x - 4 = y$ $\quad$ (0, −4), (4, 0)

35. $3a - 1 = b$ $\quad$ (0, −1), ($\frac{1}{3}$, 0)

36. $3a - 4 = b$ $\quad$ (0, −4), ($\frac{4}{3}$, 0)

37. $5x - 4y = 20$ $\quad$ (0, −5), (4, 0)

38. $3x - 5y = 15$ $\quad$ (0, −3), (5, 0)

39. $y = -5 - 5x$ $\quad$ (0, −5), (−1, 0)

40. $y = -2 - 2x$ $\quad$ (0, −2), (−1, 0)

41. $2p + 7q = 14$ $\quad$ (0, 2), (7, 0)

42. $3p + 6q = 12$ $\quad$ (0, 2), (4, 0)

Use graph paper and different axes for each equation. Label the intercepts and a third point used as a check. (*See Example 5.*) $\quad$ See answer section

43. Graph the equation in Exercise 33.

44. Graph the equation in Exercise 34.

45. Graph the equation in Exercise 35.

46. Graph the equation in Exercise 36.

47. Graph the equation in Exercise 37.

48. Graph the equation in Exercise 38.

49. Graph the equation in Exercise 39.

50. Graph the equation in Exercise 40.

51. Graph the equation in Exercise 41.

52. Graph the equation in Exercise 42.

∎∎∎∎∎ Graph the following equations. (*See Examples 6 and 7.*)

53. $x = 2$ $\qquad$ See answer section

54. $x = 4$

55. $y = -6$

56. $y = -3$

57. $x = -5$

58. $x = -3$

59. $y = 7$

60. $y = 5$

Calculator Exercises

Find the intercepts of each equation. $\quad$ 61. (0, −3.07), (0.6239837, 0) $\quad$ 62. (0, −2.0922148), (4.2690504, 0)

61. $4.92x - 3.07 = y$

62. $1.706x - 3.481y = 7.283$

3-3 Slope

After finishing Lesson 3-3, you should be able to
I find the slope of a line containing a given pair of points.
II find the slope, if it exists, of lines such as $y = 6$ or $x = 5$.
III given a point on a line and its slope, use the point-slope equation of a line to find an equation for the line.

I Finding the Slope of a Line

Graphs of some linear equations slant upward from left to right. Others slant downward. Some slant more steeply than others. Here is a line with two points marked. As we go from P_1 to P_2 the change in x is $x_2 - x_1$. The change in y is $y_2 - y_1$.

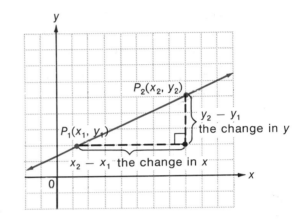

DEFINITION

The slope m of a line is $\dfrac{y_2 - y_1}{x_2 - x_1} \left(\dfrac{\text{change in } y}{\text{change in } x}\right)$, where (x_1, y_1) and (x_2, y_2) are any two points on the line.

To find the slope of a line, we find two points on it. We find the change in y and the change in x and divide.

Example 1. The points $(1, 2)$ and $(3, 6)$ are on a line. Find its slope.

The slope, $m = \dfrac{y_2 - y_1}{x_2 - x_1}, \dfrac{\text{change in } y}{\text{change in } x}$

$$= \frac{6 - 2}{3 - 1}$$

$$= \frac{4}{2}, \text{ or } 2$$

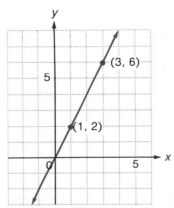

If we use the points $(1, 2)$ and $(3, 6)$ in opposite order, we find that the change in y is negative and the change in x is negative. We get the same number for the slope.

$$m = \frac{2 - 6}{1 - 3} = \frac{-4}{-2}, \text{ or } 2$$

To compute slope the order of the points does not matter as long as we take the same order for finding the differences.

TRY THIS

Find the slope of the line containing these points.

1. (1, 1) and (12, 14) $\frac{13}{11}$
2. (3, 9) and (4, 10)   1

If a line slants up from left to right, it has positive slope. See Example 1. The line in the example below has negative slope. It slants down from left to right.

Example 2. Graph the line containing the points (1, −1) and (3, −4) and find its slope.

$$m = \frac{-4 - (-1)}{3 - 1}$$
$$= \frac{-4 + 1}{2}$$
$$= -\frac{3}{2}$$

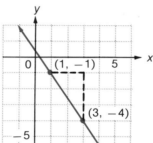

TRY THIS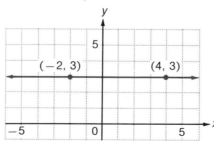

Graph the lines containing these points and find their slopes.

3. (−1, −1) and (2, −4) −1
4. (0, 2) and (3, 1) $-\frac{1}{3}$

▪ Horizontal and Vertical Lines

What about the slopes of vertical and horizontal lines?

Example 3. Find the slope of the line $y = 3$.

$$y_2 - y_1 = 3 - 3$$
$$= 0$$
$$x_2 - x_1 = -2 - 4$$
$$= -6$$
$$\text{slope} = \frac{0}{-6} = 0$$

Any two points on a horizontal line have the same second coordinate. Thus the change in y is 0, so the slope is 0.

Example 4. Find the slope of the line $x = -4$.

$$y_2 - y_1 = -2 - 3$$
$$= -5$$
$$x_2 - x_1 = -4 - (-4)$$
$$= 0$$
$$\text{slope} = \frac{-5}{0}$$

Since division by 0 is not defined, we say that this line has no slope.

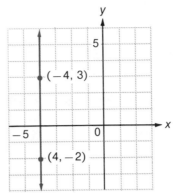

Any two points on a vertical line have the same first coordinates. Thus the change in x is 0, so the denominator in the formula for slope would be 0. Since we cannot divide by 0, the line has no slope.

THEOREM 3-3

A horizontal line has slope 0. A vertical line has *no* slope.

TRY THIS

Find the slopes, if they exist, of the lines containing these points.

5. $(4, 6)$ and $(-2, 6)$ **o**
6. $(-7, 3)$ and $(-7, 2)$ No slope

ᴵᴵᴵ Point-Slope Equations of Lines

If we know the slope of a line and the coordinates of a point on the line, we can find an equation of the line.

THEOREM 3-4   (The Point-Slope Equation)

A line containing a point (x_1, y_1) with slope m has an equation $(y - y_1) = m(x - x_1)$.

Example 5. Find an equation of the line containing the point $(\frac{1}{2}, -1)$ with slope 5.

$$(y - y_1) = m(x - x_1)$$
$$y - (-1) = 5(x - \tfrac{1}{2}) \qquad \textit{Substituting}$$
$$y + 1 = 5(x - \tfrac{1}{2})$$
$$y = 5x - \tfrac{7}{2} \qquad \textit{Simplifying}$$

Example 6. Find an equation of the line with y-intercept $(0, 4)$ and slope $\frac{3}{5}$.

$$(y - y_1) = m(x - x_1)$$
$$y - 4 = \tfrac{3}{5}(x - 0) \quad \textit{Substituting}$$
$$y = \tfrac{3}{5}x + 4 \quad \textit{Simplifying}$$

TRY THIS ➡

Answers. 7. $y = -3x - 2$ 8. $y = \frac{1}{4}x - 9$ 9. $y = -\frac{1}{2}x + \frac{5}{2}$

7. Find an equation of the line containing the point $(-2, 4)$ with slope -3.
8. Find an equation of the line containing the point $(-4, -10)$ with slope $\frac{1}{4}$.
9. Find an equation of the line with x-intercept $(5, 0)$ and slope $-\frac{1}{2}$.

A Proof of Theorem 3-4

We have seen that a line containing a point (x_1, y_1) with slope m has an equation $(y - y_1) = m(x - x_1)$. Let us prove this.

Think of a fixed point P, with coordinates (x_1, y_1), on a nonvertical line. Suppose we have a movable point P on the line with coordinates (x, y). The slope m is

$$\frac{y - y_1}{x - x_1}.$$

This is true only when (x, y) is a point different from (x_1, y_1). Now we can use the multiplication principle.

$$\frac{y - y_1}{x - x_1} = m \quad \textit{Definition of slope}$$
$$\frac{(y - y_1)}{(x - x_1)} \cdot (x - x_1) = m(x - x_1) \quad \textit{Multiplication principle}$$
$$(y - y_1) \cdot \frac{(x - x_1)}{(x - x_1)} = m(x - x_1) \quad \textit{Simplifying}$$
$$(y - y_1) = m(x - x_1)$$

This equation holds even when $(x, y) = (x_1, y_1)$.

Use Quiz 4 after lesson 3–3.

Exercise Set 3-3

I Find the slopes of the lines containing these points. (*See Examples 1 and 2.*)

1. (5, 0) and (6, 8) 8
2. (4, 0) and (7, 3) 1
3. (0, 7) and (−2, 9) −1
4. (0, 8) and (3, 8) 0
5. (4, −3) and (6, −4) $-\frac{1}{2}$
6. (5, −7) and (8, −3) $\frac{4}{3}$
7. (0, 0) and (−4, −8) 2
8. (0, 0) and (−5, −6) $\frac{6}{5}$
9. (−2, −4) and (−9, −7) $\frac{3}{7}$
10. (−3, −7) and (−8, −5) $-\frac{2}{5}$
11. $(\frac{1}{2}, \frac{1}{4})$ and $(\frac{3}{2}, \frac{3}{4})$ $\frac{1}{2}$
12. $(\frac{3}{5}, \frac{1}{2})$ and $(\frac{1}{5}, -\frac{1}{2})$ $\frac{5}{2}$
13. $(\frac{1}{8}, \frac{1}{4})$ and $(\frac{3}{4}, \frac{1}{2})$ $\frac{2}{5}$
14. $(\frac{1}{3}, -\frac{1}{8})$ and $(\frac{5}{6}, -\frac{1}{4})$ $-\frac{1}{4}$

II Find the slope, if it exists, of each of these lines. (*See Examples 3 and 4.*)

15. $x = 7$ No slope
16. $x = -4$ No slope
17. $y = -3$ 0
18. $y = 18$ 0
19. $x = 6$ No slope
20. $x = -17$ No slope
21. $y = 20$ 0
22. $y = -31$ 0

III Find equations of the lines containing the given points with the indicated slopes. (*See Examples 5 and 6.*)

23. (3, 2); $m = 4$ y = 4x − 10
24. (4, 7); $m = -2$ y = −2x + 15
25. (−5, −2); $m = -1$ y = −x − 7
26. (−2, −4); $m = 3$ y = 3x + 2
27. (−6, 4); $m = \frac{1}{2}$ y = $\frac{1}{2}$x + 7
28. (3, −1); $m = -\frac{4}{3}$ y = $-\frac{4}{3}$x + 3
29. (0, −7); $m = 0$ y = −7
30. (3, 0); $m = 0$ y = 0

Calculator Exercises

Find the slopes of the lines containing these points.

31. (0.04, 0.08) and (0.47, 0.83) 1.7441860
32. (0.02, 0.8) and (−0.2, −0.04) 3.8181818
33. (46,592, 86,874) and (−56,729, −83,497) 1.6489484
34. (54,706, −73,082) and (−93,349, −75,876) 0.0188713

Challenge Exercises

35. $\overline{AB}$ $\frac{1}{4}$; $\overline{BC}$ $\frac{4}{3}$; $\overline{CD}$ $\frac{4}{3}$; $\overline{DA}$ $\frac{4}{3}$ 36. $\overline{EG}$ $\frac{1}{3}$; $\overline{FH}$ −3
See answer section

35. Use graph paper. Plot the points $A(0, 0)$, $B(8, 2)$, $C(11, 6)$ and $D(3, 4)$. Draw $\overline{AB}$, $\overline{BC}$, $\overline{CD}$, and $\overline{DA}$. Find the slopes of each of these four segments. Compare the slopes of $\overline{AB}$ and $\overline{CD}$. Compare the slopes of $\overline{BC}$ and $\overline{DA}$.

36. Use graph paper. Plot the points $E(-2, -5)$, $F(2, -2)$, $G(7, -2)$ and $H(3, -5)$. Draw $\overline{EF}$, $\overline{FG}$, $\overline{GH}$, $\overline{HE}$, $\overline{EG}$, and $\overline{FH}$. Compare the slopes of $\overline{EG}$ and $\overline{FH}$.

3-4 More Equations of Lines

After finishing Lesson 3-4, you should be able to
∎ given two points, find the two-point equation of the line.
∎∎ given the slope-intercept equation for a line, find the slope and *y*-intercept.

∎ Two-Point Equations of Lines

Given two points, we can find an equation of the line containing them.

THEOREM 3-5 (The Two-Point Equation)

Any nonvertical line containing the points (x_1, y_1) and (x_2, y_2) has

an equation $y - y_1 = \dfrac{y_2 - y_1}{x_2 - x_1}(x - x_1)$.

Example 1. Find an equation of the line containing the points $(2, 3)$ and $(1, -4)$.

a) We take $(2, 3)$ as P_1 and $(1, -4)$ as P_2. Then substitute in the two-point equation.

$$y - 3 = \frac{-4 - 3}{1 - 2}(x - 2)$$
$$y - 3 = \frac{-7}{-1}(x - 2)$$
$$y - 3 = 7(x - 2) \qquad \textit{Simplifying}$$
$$y - 3 = 7x - 14 \qquad \textit{Removing parentheses}$$
$$y = 7x - 11 \qquad \textit{Using the addition principle}$$

b) It doesn't matter which point we take as P_1 and which we take as P_2. If we take $(1, -4)$ as P_1 and $(2, 3)$ as P_2, we get the same equation.

$$y - (-4) = \frac{3 - (-4)}{2 - 1}(x - 1)$$
$$y = 7x - 11 \qquad \textit{Simplifying}$$

TRY THIS

Answers. 1. y = −3x + 7   2. $y = -\dfrac{10}{3}x + 4$

Find an equation of the line containing the points

1. $(1, 4)$ and $(3, -2)$
2. $(3, -6)$ and $(0, 4)$

▪ Slope-Intercept Equations of Lines

Given the slope and y-intercept of a line, we can find an equation of the line.

THEOREM 3-6   (The Slope-Intercept Equation)
A nonvertical line with slope m and y-intercept $(0, b)$ has an equation $y = mx + b$.

For brevity, we often refer to the number b as the intercept.

Example 2. Find the slope and y-intercept of $y = 5x - \frac{1}{4}$.

We can read the numbers from the equation directly.

$$y = 5x - \tfrac{1}{4}$$

slope 5   intercept $-\frac{1}{4}$

Example 3. Find the slope and y-intercept of $y = 8$.

We can first write this equation as

$$y = 0x + 8.$$

Then   slope 0   intercept 8

TRY THIS

Answers.   **3.** m = −7, b = 11   **4.** m = 0, b = −4

From any equation for a nonvertical line we can find the slope-intercept equation by solving for y.

3.   Find the slope and y-intercept of $y = -7x + 11$.
4.   Find the slope and y-intercept of $y = -4$.

Example 4. Find the slope and y-intercept of the line whose equation is $3x - 6y - 7 = 0$.

First solve for y.

$$-6y = -3x + 7$$
$$-\tfrac{1}{6} \cdot (-6y) = -\tfrac{1}{6} \cdot (-3x) + (-\tfrac{1}{6}) \cdot 7$$
$$y = \tfrac{1}{2}x - \tfrac{7}{6}$$

slope $\frac{1}{2}$ y-intercept $-\frac{7}{6}$

There is no slope-intercept equation for a vertical line because such a line has no slope.

TRY THIS

5.   a)   Find the slope-intercept equation of the line whose equation is $-2x + 3y - 6 = 0$.
     b)   Find the slope and y-intercept of this line.

a) $y = \frac{2}{3}x + 2$ b) $m = \frac{2}{3}$, b = 2

Exercise Set 3-4

I Find an equation of the line containing each of the following pairs of points. (*See Example 1.*)

1. $(1, 4)$ and $(5, 6)$ $y = \frac{1}{2}x + \frac{7}{2}$
2. $(2, 6)$ and $(4, 1)$ $y = -\frac{5}{2}x + 11$
3. $(-1, -1)$ and $(2, 2)$ $y = x$
4. $(-3, -3)$ and $(6, 6)$ $y = x$
5. $(-2, 0)$ and $(0, 5)$ $y = \frac{5}{2}x + 5$
6. $(6, 0)$ and $(0, -3)$ $y = \frac{1}{2}x - 3$
7. $(3, 5)$ and $(-5, 3)$ $y = \frac{1}{4}x + \frac{17}{4}$
8. $(4, 6)$ and $(-6, 4)$ $y = \frac{1}{5}x + \frac{26}{5}$
9. $(0, 0)$ and $(5, 2)$ $y = \frac{2}{5}x$
10. $(0, 0)$ and $(7, 3)$ $y = \frac{3}{7}x$
11. $(-4, -7)$ and $(-2, -1)$ $y = 3x + 5$
12. $(-2, -3)$ and $(-4, -6)$ $y = \frac{3}{2}x$

II Find the slope and *y*-intercept of each of the following lines. (*See Examples 2–4.*)

13. $y = 2x + 3$ $m = 2, b = 3$
14. $y = 3x + 4$ $m = 3, b = 4$
15. $y = -4x + 9$ $m = -4, b = 9$
16. $y = -5x - 7$ $m = -5, b = -7$
17. $y = 6 - x$ $m = -1, b = 6$
18. $y = 7 - x$ $m = -1, b = 7$
19. $2y = -6x + 10$ $m = -3, b = 5$
20. $-3y = -12x + 6$ $m = 4, b = -2$
21. $3x - 4y = 12$ $m = \frac{3}{4}, b = -3$
22. $5x + 2y = -7$ $m = -\frac{5}{2}, b = -\frac{7}{2}$
23. $6x + 2y - 8 = 0$ $m = -3, b = 4$
24. $3y - 2x + 5 = 0$ $m = \frac{2}{3}, b = -\frac{5}{3}$
25. $-7x - 3y - 9 = 0$ $m = -\frac{7}{3}, b = -3$
26. $-8x - 5y - 7 = 0$ $m = -\frac{8}{5}, b = -\frac{7}{5}$
27. $y = 7$ $m = 0, b = 7$
28. $y = 9$ $m = 0, b = 9$
29. $3y + 10 = 0$ $m = 0, b = -\frac{10}{3}$
30. $4y + 11 = 0$ $m = 0, b = -\frac{11}{4}$

Calculator Exercises

Find the slope and *y*-intercept of each of the following lines.

31. $2.735x - 1.379y - 6.084 = 0$
32. $-4.005x + 2.057y + 8.316 = 0$

31. $m = 1.9833212, b = -4.4118926$ 32. $m = 1.9470102, b = -4.0427807$

Challenge Exercises

33. Find an equation of the line containing $(2, -3)$ and having the same slope as the line $3x + 4y = 10$. $y = -\frac{3}{4}x - \frac{3}{2}$
34. Find an equation of the line containing $(3, -4)$ and having slope -2. If this line contains the points $(a, 8)$ and $(5, b)$, find a and b. $y = -2x + 2, a = -3, b = -8$

3-5 Parallel and Perpendicular Lines

After finishing Lesson 3-5, you should be able to
I tell, without graphing, whether the graphs of a pair of equations are parallel.
II given an equation of a line and a point, write an equation of the line parallel to the given line through the given point.
III given an equation of a line and a point, write an equation of the line perpendicular to the given line through the given point.

I Parallel Lines

When we graph a pair of linear equations, there are three possibilities.

 1. The equations have the same graph.
 2. The graphs intersect at exactly one point.
 3. The graphs are parallel lines.

THEOREM 3-7
If nonvertical lines have the same slope but different y-intercepts, they are parallel. Also, if nonvertical lines are parallel they have the same slope and different y-intercepts.

Example 1. Determine whether the graphs of $y = -3x + 5$ and $4y = -12x + 20$ are parallel.

These equations have the same graph, so the lines are not parallel. We can determine this without looking at the graphs. We find the slope-intercept equations by solving for y.

$$y = -3x + 5$$
$$y = -3x + 5$$

The slope-intercept equations are the same. This tells us that the graphs are the same line.

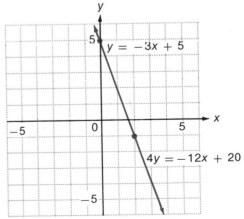

Example 2. Determine whether the graphs of $y - 3x = 1$ and $-2y = 3x + 2$ are parallel.

These graphs intersect. We can determine this without looking at the graphs. We find the slope-intercept equations by solving for y.

$$y = 3x + 1$$
$$y = -\tfrac{3}{2}x - 1$$

The slopes are different, so the lines are not parallel.

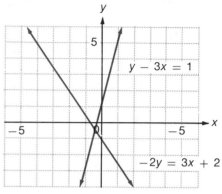

Example 3. Determine whether the graphs of $3x - y = -5$ and $y - 3x = -2$ are parallel.

We can determine this without looking at the graphs. We find the slope-intercept equations by solving for y.

$$y = 3x + 5$$
$$y = 3x - 2$$

The slopes are the same, but the y-intercepts are different, so the lines are parallel.

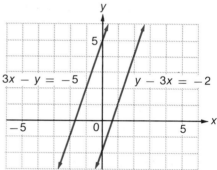

TRY THIS ➡

Without graphing, tell whether the graphs of each pair of equations are parallel. (*Hint:* First find the slope-intercept equation.)

1. $x + 4 = y$
    $y - x = -3$ Yes
2. $y + 4 = 3x$
    $4x - y = -7$ No
3. $y = 4x + 5$
    $2y = 8x + 10$ No

▪▪ Finding Equations of Parallel Lines

Example 4. Write an equation of the line parallel to the line $2x + y - 10 = 0$ and containing the point $(-1, 3)$.

a) We first find the slope-intercept equation. It is

$$y = -2x + 10.$$

Now we see that the parallel line must have slope -2.

b) We find the point-slope equation of the line with slope -2 and containing the point $(-1, 3)$.

$$y - y_1 = m(x - x_1) \qquad \text{\textit{Theorem 3-4}}$$
$$y - 3 = -2[x - (-1)] \qquad \text{\textit{Substituting}}$$
$$y = -2x + 1 \qquad \text{\textit{Simplifying}}$$

The equations $y = -2x + 10$ and $y = -2x + 1$ have the same slope and different y-intercepts. Hence their graphs are parallel.

TRY THIS

> 4. Write an equation of the line parallel to the line $2y + 8x = 6$ and containing the point $(-2, -4)$.
> $y = -4x - 12$

▪▪▪ Perpendicular Lines

If two lines meet at right angles, they are called perpendicular.

THEOREM 3-8
If for two nonvertical lines, the product of the slopes is -1, the lines are perpendicular. Also, if two lines are perpendicular, the product of the slopes is -1.

Example 5. Determine whether the lines $5y = 4x + 10$ and $4y = -5x + 4$ are perpendicular.

We find the slope-intercept equations by solving for y.

$$y = \tfrac{4}{5}x + 2$$
$$y = -\tfrac{5}{4}x + 1$$

The product of the slopes is -1; that is,

$$\tfrac{4}{5} \cdot \left(-\tfrac{5}{4}\right) = -1.$$

The lines are perpendicular.

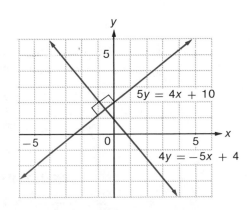

TRY THIS

Answers.   5. a) $-\frac{1}{2}$ b) 4   c) $-\frac{6}{7}$ d) $\frac{5}{2}$

6. a) Yes   b) No

5. Complete.

	Slope of a line	Slope of any perpendicular
a)	2	
b)	$-\frac{1}{4}$	
c)	$\frac{7}{6}$	
d)	$-\frac{2}{5}$	

6. Without graphing, tell whether the graphs of each pair of equations are perpendicular.

   a) $2y - x = 2$
   $\quad\ y + 2x = 4$
   b) $3y = 2x + 15$
   $\quad\ 2y = 3x + 10$

Example 6. Write an equation of the line perpendicular to $4y - x = 20$ and containing the point $(2, -3)$.

a) We find the slope-intercept equation for $4y - x = 20$.

$$y = \tfrac{1}{4}x + 5$$

We know that the slope of the perpendicular line is -4, because

$$\tfrac{1}{4} \cdot (-4) = -1.$$

b) We find the point-slope equation of the line having slope -4 and containing the point $(2, -3)$.

$$\begin{aligned} y - y_1 &= m(x - x_1) && \textit{Theorem 3-4} \\ y - (-3) &= -4(x - 2) && \textit{Substituting} \\ y &= -4x + 5 && \textit{Simplifying} \end{aligned}$$

7. Write an equation of the line perpendicular to the line $y = \frac{7}{8}x - 3$ and containing the point $(-1, 2)$.

8. Write an equation of the line perpendicular to the line $4 - y = 2x$ and containing the point $(3, 4)$.

TRY THIS

Answers.   7. $y = -\frac{8}{7}x + \frac{6}{7}$ 8. $y = \frac{1}{2}x + \frac{5}{2}$

Exercise Set 3-5

❚ Without graphing, tell whether the graphs of each pair of equations are parallel. (*See Examples 1–3.*)

1. $x + 6 = y$
   $y - x = -2$ Yes

2. $2x - 7 = y$
   $y - 2x = 8$ Yes

3. $y + 3 = 5x$
   $3x - y = -2$ No

4. $y + 8 = -6x$
   $-2x + y = 5$ No

5. $y = 3x + 9$
   $2y = 6x - 2$ Yes

6. $y = -7x - 9$
   $-3y = 21x + 7$ Yes

❚❚ Write an equation of the line containing the given point and parallel to the given line. (*See Example 4.*)

7. $(3, 7)$, $x + 2y = 6$ $y = -\frac{1}{2}x + \frac{17}{2}$

8. $(0, 3)$, $3x - y = 7$ $y = 3x + 3$

9. $(2, -1)$, $5x - 7y = 8$ $y = \frac{5}{7}x - \frac{17}{7}$

10. $(-4, -5)$, $2x + y = -3$ $y = -2x - 13$

11. $(-6, 2)$, $3x - 9y = 2$ $y = \frac{1}{3}x + 4$

12. $(-7, 0)$, $5x + 2y = 6$ $y = -\frac{5}{2}x - \frac{35}{2}$

❚❚❚ Write an equation of the line containing the given point and perpendicular to the given line. (*See Example 6.*)

13. $(2, 5)$, $2x + y = -3$ $y = \frac{1}{2}x + 4$

14. $(4, 0)$, $x - 3y = 0$ $y = -3x + 12$

15. $(3, 2)$, $3x + 4y = 5$ $y = \frac{4}{3}x - 6$

16. $(-3, -5)$, $5x - 2y = 4$ $y = -\frac{2}{5}x - \frac{31}{5}$

17. $(0, 9)$, $2x + 5y = 7$ $y = \frac{5}{2}x + 9$

18. $(-3, -4)$, $-3x + 6y = 2$ $y = -2x - 10$

Challenge Exercises

19. Find an equation of the line containing $(4, -2)$ and parallel to the line containing $(-1, 4)$ and $(2, -3)$. $y = -\frac{7}{3}x + \frac{22}{3}$

20. Find an equation of the line containing $(-1, 3)$ and perpendicular to the line containing $(3, -5)$ and $(-2, -7)$. $y = -\frac{5}{2}x + \frac{1}{2}$

21. Use the slope relationship to show that the triangle with vertices $(-2, 7)$, $(6, 9)$, and $(3, 4)$ is a right triangle.   See answer section

CONSUMER NOTE: Inflation

During inflation, earnings go up, and people have more money to spend. But prices go up, also. If prices rise faster than earnings, people lose buying power. If earnings rise faster than prices, peoples' buying power increases.

3-6 Applications of Linear Equations

After finishing Lesson 3-6, you should be able to
■ find a linear equation which fits two data points and use the equation to make predictions.

■ Mathematics is often constructed to fit certain situations. Suppose some experience indicates that a linear equation would fit the situation. In the following diagram, data have been plotted on a graph. It looks as if the points lie more or less on a straight line.

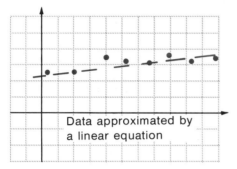

Data approximated by
a linear equation

We can find an equation that fits the situation and use it to make predictions.

Example. (*Temperature and Cricket Chirps*). It has been shown experimentally that the temperature in degrees Celsius is related to the number of cricket chirps per minute by a linear equation. When crickets chirp 40 times per minute, the temperature is 10° and when they chirp 112 times per minute, the temperature is 20°.

a) Find a linear equation which fits the data.
b) From your equation, find the temperature when there are 76 chirps per minute; 100 chirps per minute.

a) To find a linear equation which fits the data we use the two-point equation. Let us use T for temperature and N for the number of chirps per minute. We know two ordered pairs that the equation must fit. They are (40, 10°) and (112, 20°). We call these *data points*. The equation is

$$T - T_1 = \frac{T_2 - T_1}{N_2 - N_1}(N - N_1).$$

We substitute and simplify.

$$T - 10 = \frac{20 - 10}{112 - 40}(N - 40)$$

$$T - 10 = \frac{10}{72}(N - 40)$$

$$T - 10 = \frac{10}{72}N - \frac{10}{72} \cdot 40$$

$$T = \frac{5}{36}N - \frac{400}{72} + 10$$

$$T = \frac{5}{36}N + \frac{40}{9}, \text{ or } \frac{5N + 160}{36}$$

b)   Using this formula, we find that when $N = 76$,

$$T = \frac{5(76) + 160}{36}$$

$$= 15°$$

When $N = 100$,

$$T = \frac{5(100) + 160}{36}$$

$$\approx 18.3° \qquad (\approx \textit{means approximately equal})$$

TRY THIS ▬▬▶

Answer.   1. a) R = −0.01t + 10.43   b) 9.83; 9.73
c) 2063

1.   (*Records in the 100-meter dash*). It has been found experimentally that running records follow linear equations. In 1920 the record for the 100-meter dash was 10.43 seconds. In 1970 it was 9.93 seconds. Let R represent the record in the 100-meter dash and t the number of years since 1920.
   a)   Fit a linear equation to the data points.
   b)   Use the equation of a) to predict the record in 1980; in 1990.
   c)   In what year will the record be 9.0 seconds?

Use Quiz 5 after lesson 3—6.

Exercise Set 3-6

▌Solve. (*See the Example.*)

1. (*Life expectancy of females in the United States*). In 1950, the life expectancy of females was 72 years. In 1970, it was 75 years. Let *E* represent the life expectancy and *t* the number of years since 1950. ($t = 0$ gives 1950 and $t = 20$ gives 1970).
   a) Fit a linear equation to the data points. [They are (0, 72) and (20, 75).] $E = 0.15t + 72$
   b) Use the equation of a) to predict the life expectancy of females in 1980; in 1985.   **76.5; 77.25**

2. (*Life expectancy of males in the United States*). In 1950, the life expectancy of males was 65 years. In 1970, it was 68 years. Let *E* represent life expectancy and *t* the number of years since 1950.
   a) Fit a linear equation to the data points. $E = 0.15t + 65$
   b) Use the equation of a) to predict the life expectancy of males in 1980; in 1985.   **69.5; 70.25**

3. (*Weight versus Height*). It has been shown experimentally that the height *H* of a person is related to that person's weight *W* by a linear equation. A person 180 cm tall weighs 76.4 kg, and a person 170 cm tall weighs 66.6 kg.
   a) Fit a linear equation to the data points. $H = \frac{50}{49}W + \frac{5000}{49}$ or $H = \frac{50W + 5000}{49}$
   b) Use the equation of a) to estimate the weight of a person 160 cm tall. (This equation is valid only for heights above 102 cm.)   **56.8 kg**

4. (*Natural gas demand*). In 1950, natural gas demand in the United States was 20 quadrillion joules. In 1960, the demand was 22 quadrillion joules. Let *D* represent the demand for natural gas *t* years after 1950.
   a) Fit a linear equation to the data points. $D = 0.2t + 20$
   b) Use the equation of a) to predict the natural gas demand in 1980; in 2000.   **26; 30**

5. (*Records in the 1500-meter Run*). In 1930, the record for the 1500-meter run was 3.85 minutes. In 1950, it was 3.70 minutes. Let *R* represent the record in the 1500-meter run and *t* the number of years since 1930.
   a) Fit a linear equation to the data points. $R = -0.0075t + 3.85$
   b) Use the equation of a) to predict the record in 1980; in 1984.   **3.475; 3.445**
   c) When will the record be 3.3 minutes?   **2004**

6. (*Records in the 400-meter Run*). In 1930, the record for the 400-meter run was 46.8 seconds. In 1970, it was 43.8 seconds. Let *R* represent the record in the 400-meter run and *t* the number of years since 1930.
   a) Fit a linear equation to the data points. $R = -0.075t + 46.8$
   b) Use the equation of a) to predict the record in 1980; in 1990.   **43.05; 42**
   c) When will the record be 40 seconds?   **2020**

COMPUTER ACTIVITY

Finding the Slope and Y-Intercept of Linear Equations

PROBLEM: Find the slope and Y-intercept of $AX + BY + C = 0$.

Examples using the flowchart:

	1		2	3
A	B	C	SLOPE M	Y-INTERCEPT (0,K)
4	5	−2	−0.8	(0, 0.4)
2.21	−3.14	3	0.70382	(0, 0.95541)
−0.7	4.2	0.25	0.16667	(0, −0.05952)
2	6	−3		
1.5	−3	−4		

START

1 INPUT A,B,C

DOES B = 0? Yes No

2 LET M = −A/B

3 LET K = −C/B

PRINT M

PRINT (0,K)

STOP

TRY THIS ➡ Find the numbers to complete the examples.

BASIC PROGRAM (Optional)
```
10   INPUT A,B,C
20   IF B = 0 THEN 70
30   LET M = −A/B
40   PRINT K = −C/B
50   PRINT "THE SLOPE ="M
60   PRINT "THE Y-INTERCEPT =
       (0,";K;")"
70   STOP
```

CHAPTER 3 REVIEW

Review the material in the chapter. Then see how you have done by trying these review exercises. If you miss an exercise, restudy the indicated lesson.

3-1   1.   Decide whether (2, 4) is a solution to $2x + 3y = 16$.   Yes

3-1   2.   Graph $-8x + 4y = -4$. Use a table of values.   See answer section

3-2   3.   Which of these are linear equations?
     a) $x - 5y = 8$ Yes
     b) $3xy + y^2 = 0$ No
     c) $2x = 5y - 9$ Yes
     d) $x^2 - 7 = 9y$ No

3-2   4.   Find standard form for $2x = 9y - 7$. $2x - 9y + 7 = 0$

3-2   5.   Graph $-5x + 2y = 10$ using intercepts.   See answer section

3-2   6.   Graph $x = 9$.

3-2   7.   Graph $y = -2$.

3-3   8.   Find the slope of the line containing (8, 2) and $(-4, -3)$. $\frac{5}{12}$

3-3   9.   Find an equation for the line with slope of -3 and containing (2, 1). $y = -3x + 7$

3-4   10.   Find an equation of the line containing (3, 5) and $(-2, -4)$. $y = \frac{9}{5}x - \frac{2}{5}$

3-4   11.   Find the slope and y-intercept of the equation $-5x + 2y = -4$. $m = \frac{5}{2}, b = -2$

3-5   12.   Determine, without graphing, whether the graphs of the following pairs of equations are parallel.   12. a) Yes   b) No   c) Yes
     a) $y + 3 = x$ b) $7x + 3y = 11$ c) $2x - y = 8$
        $x - 5 = y$ $3x + 7y = 12$ $2y = 6 + 4x$

3-5   13.   Find an equation of the line containing $(-3, 7)$ which is
     a)   parallel to the line $5x + 3y = 8$. $y = -\frac{5}{3}x + 2$
     b)   perpendicular to the line $5x + 3y = 8$. $y = \frac{3}{5}x + \frac{44}{5}$

3-6   14.   (*Records in the 200-meter Dash*). In 1920 the record for the 200-meter dash was 20.8 seconds. In 1945 it was 20.1 seconds. Let R represent the record in the 200-meter dash and t the number of years since 1920.
     a)   Fit a linear equation to the data points. $R = -0.028t + 20.8$
     b)   Use the equation of a) to predict the record in 1980; in 1984.   19.12; 19.008
     c)   When will the record be 19.0?   1984

CHAPTER 3 TEST

1. Determine whether (3, 2) is a solution to $x + 3y = 10$. No
2. Graph $-4x + 2y = 2$. Use a table of values. See answer section
3. Which of these are linear equations?
   a) $xy + 3y^2 = 0$ No
   b) $2x - 4y + 9 = 0$ Yes
   c) $y = 3x + 2$ Yes
   d) $x^2 - y^2 = 16$ No
4. Find standard form for $8y = 42x - 9$. $-42x + 8y + 9 = 0$
5. Graph $-3x + 4y = 12$ using intercepts. See answer section
6. Graph $x = -3$.
7. Graph $y = 4$.
8. Find the slope of the line containing (9, 1) and (−5, −6). $\frac{1}{2}$
9. Find an equation for the line with slope of −4 and containing (3, 2). $y = -4x + 14$
10. Find an equation of the line containing (2, 8) and (−3, −6). $y = \frac{14}{5}x + \frac{12}{5}$
11. Determine the slope and y-intercept of the equation $-3x + 5y = 10$. $m = \frac{3}{5}, b = 2$
12. Tell, without graphing, whether the graphs of the following pairs of equations are parallel. 12. a) No b) Yes c) Yes
    a) $18x + 3y = 16$ b) $x - 3 = y$ c) $3x - y = 9$
       $y = -9x + 2$ $y + 9 = x$ $4y - 8 = 12x$
13. Find an equation of the line containing (−5, 8) which is
    a) parallel to the line $3x + 5y = 15$. $y = -\frac{3}{5}x + 5$
    b) perpendicular to the line $3x + 5y = 15$. $y = \frac{5}{3}x + \frac{49}{3}$
14. (*Records in the 1000-meter Run*). In 1920 the record for the 1000-meter run was 2.47 minutes. In 1940 it was 2.38 minutes. Let R represent the record in the 1000-meter run and t the number of years since 1920.
    a) Fit a linear equation to the data points. $R = -0.0045t + 2.47$
    b) Use the equation of a) to predict the record in 1980; in 1990. 2.20, 2.155
    c) When will the record be 2.20 minutes? 1980

Television and radio service technicians fix communication equipment. This equipment may include stereo components and tape recorders as well as other products.

Advertising copywriters prepare slogans and text used in ads. Copywriters try to describe a product in a way that appeals to a certain group of buyers.

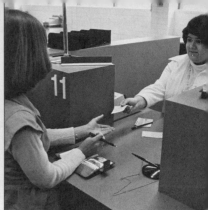

Bank tellers receive and pay out money. During banking hours tellers deal directly with customers. Afterward, tellers count cash and keep records.

Cooks or chefs meet the cooking needs of a dining place. Coffee shops need simple meals prepared quickly. Fine restaurants need a variety of excellent dishes.

CAREERS IN VARIOUS SERVICES

Careers in various services can be divided into two main groups. One includes careers in finance, insurance, and real estate services. The other includes careers in health, repair, advertising, and hotel services.

The line graph below shows the projected growth of both groups of careers. The graph is based on data gathered by the United States Bureau of Labor Statistics. Note that careers in health, repair, advertising, hotel, and other services are likely to increase more rapidly than careers in the other group. Some of the people who follow careers in various services are pictured here, and their work is described briefly.

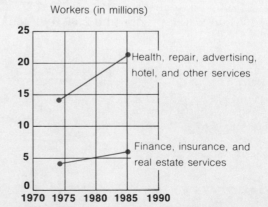

Numbers of Workers Producing Various Services

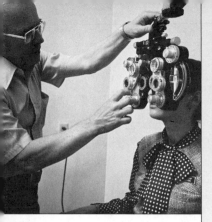

ptometrists measure vision and
escribe lenses or treatments, if
eded. Optometrists' prescriptions
 glasses or contact lenses are
ed by opticians.

Veterinarians provide health care for
animals. In cities, veterinarians usually treat pets. In rural areas, veterinarians usually provide health care
for farm animals.

Systems analysts decide how to
handle information for an entire operation. In business, analysts try to
make the operation more efficient
and profitable.

Insurance underwriters
decide what policies a
company should issue.
Underwriters judge insur-
ance applications in relation to customer pay-
ments and company risks.

   Altogether, careers in various services are likely to increase
more rapidly than other sorts of service careers, such as trade,
government, and transportation. And service careers in general
are likely to increase more rapidly than goods-producing careers
such as manufacturing and construction.
   The growth of service careers in general follows a long trend.
These careers have increased steadily since 1947. Goods-producing careers have not increased in that time. Analysts at the Bureau of Labor Statistics expect the long-term trend to continue.
They project that the United States labor force in the mid-1980s
will have the proportions shown in the circle graph. The graph
shows that in the mid-1980s careers in various services are likely
to be greater in number than careers in
trade or in government (including state and
local governments) or in manufacturing.
   The black shading around the graph indicates service careers, and the color shading
indicates goods-producing careers. The gap
between the black and color represents un-
employment. (Two kinds of goods-producing
careers, mining and agriculture, are part of
the "Other" area in the graph.)

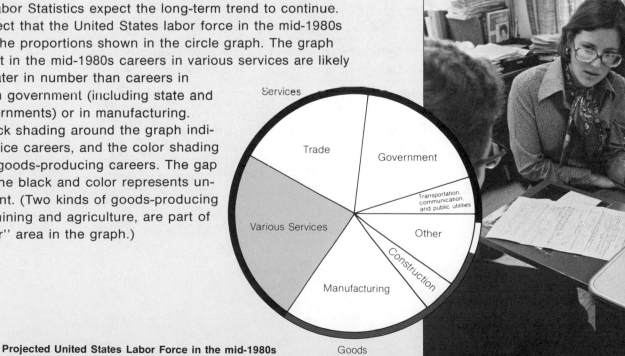

Services

Trade

Government

Transportation,
communication,
and public utilities

Various Services

Other

Construction

Manufacturing

Goods

Projected United States Labor Force in the mid-1980s

? Ready for Systems of Equations?

1-2   Find the additive inverse of each number.
1. -8 8
2. 7 -7
3. $\frac{3}{4}$ $-\frac{3}{4}$
4. 0 0

1-2   Add.
5. $-\frac{3}{4} + \frac{1}{6}$ $-\frac{7}{12}$
6. $9.7 + (-2.8)$ 6.9
7. $\frac{4}{5} + (-\frac{4}{5})$ 0
8. $-8.6 + (-3.4)$ -12
9. $-8 + 10$ 2
10. $-\frac{1}{4} + (-\frac{2}{5})$ $-\frac{13}{20}$

1-3   Subtract.
11. $8 - (-2)$ 10
12. $-4 - 8$ -12
13. $-\frac{2}{3} - \frac{4}{5}$ $-\frac{22}{15}$
14. $-3.2 - (-8.1)$ 4.9

3-1   15. Determine whether $(1, -3)$ is a solution of $y = 2x - 5$. Yes
3-1   16. Determine whether $(2, -1)$ is a solution of $4r + 3s = 7$. No

Graph.
3-1   17. $y - 4x = 3$ Line through $(-1, -1)$ and $(0, 3)$
3-2   18. $4y - 4 = 2x$ Line through $(-2, 0)$ and $(0, 1)$
3-2   19. $y = 2$ Horizontal line through $(0, 2)$

Chapter 4
Systems of Equations

Chemists use systems of equations in mixing solutions.

4-1 Systems of Equations in Two Variables

After finishing Lesson 4-1, you should be able to
▮ identify solutions of a system of two equations.
▮▮ solve systems of two equations graphically.

▮ Identifying Solutions

A pair of linear equations is called a *system* of equations. A solution of a system of two equations is an ordered pair that makes both equations true.

Example 1. Determine whether (4, 7) is a solution of this system: $x + y = 11$
$3x - y = 5$

We use alphabetical order of the variables. Thus we replace x by 4 and y by 7, and check:

$$
\begin{array}{c|c}
x + y = 11 & \\\hline
4 + 7 & 11 \\
11 &
\end{array}
\qquad
\begin{array}{c|c}
3x - y = 5 & \\\hline
3 \cdot 4 - 7 & 5 \\
12 - 7 & \\
5 &
\end{array}
$$

The pair (4, 7) checks, so it is a solution of the system. We could describe such a solution by saying that $x = 4$ and $y = 7$.

Example 2. Determine whether (4, 2) is a solution of this system: $y - x = -2$
$y + 5x = -1$

$$
\begin{array}{c|c}
y - x = -2 & \\\hline
2 - 4 & -2 \\
-2 &
\end{array}
\qquad
\begin{array}{c|c}
y + 5x = -1 & \\\hline
2 + 5 \cdot 4 & -1 \\
2 + 20 & \\
22 &
\end{array}
$$

(4, 2) is not a solution of $y + 5x = -1$, so it is not a solution of the system.

TRY THIS ➡

1. Determine whether (20, 40) is a solution of this system:
    $x = \frac{1}{2}y$
    $y + \frac{1}{4}x = 45$ Yes
2. Determine whether (−2, 3) is a solution of this system:
    $2a - 5b = 7$
    $5b + 3a = -4$ No

▪ Solving Systems of Equations by Graphing

We can solve some systems of two equations by graphing.

Example 3. Solve this system graphically: $y - x = 1$
$$y + x = 3$$

We graph the two equations using the same axes.
The point of intersection has coordinates which
satisfy both equations. The solution seems to be
(1, 2). Because graphing can be inaccurate, we
should always check.

Check:

$y - x = 1$		$y + x = 3$	
$2 - 1$	1	$2 + 1$	3
	1		3

(1, 2) checks, so it is the solution.

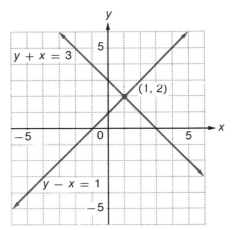

TRY THIS

See answer section

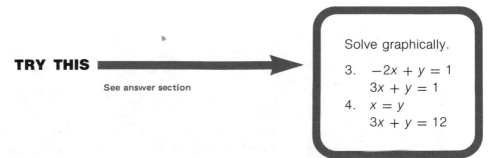

Solve graphically.

3. $-2x + y = 1$
   $3x + y = 1$
4. $x = y$
   $3x + y = 12$

Exercise Set 4-1

▪ Determine whether the given ordered pair is a solution of the system of
equations. Remember to use alphabetical order of variables. (*See Examples 1 and 2.*)

1. (1, 2); $-4x - y = 2$
   $10x - 3y = 4$ No

2. (−1, −2); $2x + y = -4$
   $x - y = 1$ Yes

3. (2, 5); $y = 3x - 1$
   $2x + y = 4$ No

4. (−1, −2); $3x - 2y = 12$
   $x + 3y = -7$ No

5. (1, 5); $x + y = 6$
   $y = 2x + 3$ Yes

6. (5, 2); $a + b = 7$
   $2a - 8 = b$ Yes

7. (2, −7); $3a + b = -1$
   $2a - 3b = -8$ No

8. (2, 1); $3p + 2q = 5$
   $4p + 5q = 2$ No

∎∎ Use graph paper. Solve each system graphically and check. (*See Example 3.*)

9. $x + y = 4$ See answer section
   $x - y = 2$

10. $x - y = 3$
    $x + y = 5$

11. $2x - y = 4$
    $5x - y = 13$

12. $3x + y = 5$
    $x - 2y = 4$

13. $4x - y = 9$
    $x - 3y = 16$

14. $2y = 6 - x$
    $3x - 2y = 6$

15. $a = 1 + b$
    $b = -2a + 5$

16. $x = y - 1$
    $2x = 3y$

17. $2u + v = 3$
    $2u = v + 7$

18. $2b + a = 11$
    $a - b = 5$

19. $y = -\frac{1}{3}x - 1$
    $4x - 3y = 18$

20. $y = -\frac{1}{4}x + 1$
    $2y = x - 4$

HISTORICAL NOTE: Mathematical Problems in Ancient Egypt

In Egypt 4000 years ago, students of mathematics solved problems written entirely in words. At that time, all mathematical problems were written like this. Symbols for quantities were mixed with symbols that we would call words.

Most problems of ancient Egypt involved fractions. We could translate these problems to first degree equations with one variable. A papyrus from about 2000 B.C. has a quadratic problem. We could translate it to a system of equations.

$$x^2 + y^2 = 100$$
$$y = \frac{3}{4}x$$

The papyrus has the correct answer: one quantity is 8, the other is 6.

4-2 Other Methods for Solving

After finishing Lesson 4-2, you should be able to
- **I** solve systems of equations using the substitution method.
- **II** solve systems of equations using the addition method.

We can solve systems of equations without graphing. One method is called the *substitution method*.

I The Substitution Method

Example 1. Solve this system: $x + y = 5$
$$x = y + 1$$

The second equation says that x and $y + 1$ name the same thing. In the first equation we can substitute $y + 1$ for x.

$$x + y = 5$$
$$(y + 1) + y = 5 \quad \text{Substituting } y + 1 \text{ for } x$$

Solve this last equation.

$$(y + 1) + y = 5$$
$$2y + 1 = 5$$
$$2y = 4$$
$$y = 2$$

We return to the original pair of equations. Substitute 2 for y in either of them. We use the first equation.

$$x + y = 5$$
$$x + 2 = 5$$
$$x = 3$$

The ordered pair (3, 2) may be a solution.

Check:

$x + y = 5$		$x = y + 1$	
$3 + 2$	5	3	$2 + 1$
5			3

Since (3, 2) checks, it is the solution.

TRY THIS ➡️

Solve by the substitution method.

1. $x + y = 6$
   $y = x + 2$ **(2, 4)**
2. $y = 7 - x$
   $2x - y = 8$ **(5, 2)**

Suppose neither equation of a pair has a variable alone on one side. We then solve one equation for one of the variables.

Example 2. Solve this system: $2x + y = 6$
$$3x + 4y = 4$$

First solve one equation for one variable. We solve the first equation for *y*.

$$y = 6 - 2x$$

Then substitute $6 - 2x$ for *y* in the second equation and solve for *x*.

$$3x + 4(6 - 2x) = 4 \qquad \textit{Substituting } 6 - 2x \textit{ for y}$$
$$3x + 24 - 8x = 4 \qquad \textit{Solving}$$
$$3x - 8x = 4 - 24$$
$$-5x = -20$$
$$x = 4$$

Now substitute 4 for *x* in either equation and solve for *y*. We use the first equation.

$$2 \cdot 4 + y = 6$$
$$y = -2$$

We obtain $(4, -2)$. This checks, so it is the solution.

TRY THIS ➡

Solve. Use the substitution method.

3. $2y + x = 1$
   $y = 2x + 8$ **(−3, 2)**
4. $8x + 5y = 184$
   $x - y = -3$ **(13, 16)**

▮ The Addition Method

The *addition method* for solving systems of equations makes use of the *addition principle*.

Consider this system: $x + y = 2$
$$3x = 2y$$

The first equation says that $x + y$ and 2 represent the same number. We use the addition principle with the second equation. We add the "same thing" on both sides. On the left we call it $x + y$. On the right we call it 2.

$$3x + (x + y) = 2y + 2.$$

Using this method we try to get an equation with only one variable. We often say that we have eliminated a variable.

Example 3. Solve this system: $2x - 3y = 0$
$$-4x + 3y = -1$$

$$
\begin{array}{l}
2x - 3y = 0 \\
\underline{-4x + 3y = -1} \\
-2x + 0 = -1 \quad \textit{Adding}
\end{array}
$$

We have made one variable "disappear."

$$
\begin{array}{l}
-2x = -1 \\
x = \tfrac{1}{2} \quad \textit{Solving for x} \\
2 \cdot \tfrac{1}{2} - 3y = 0 \quad \textit{Substituting } \tfrac{1}{2} \textit{ for x in the first equation} \\
\phantom{2 \cdot \tfrac{1}{2}}1 - 3y = 0 \\
\phantom{2 \cdot \tfrac{1}{2} 1 -}y = \tfrac{1}{3}
\end{array}
$$

We obtain $(\tfrac{1}{2}, \tfrac{1}{3})$. This checks, so it is the solution.

TRY THIS ➡️

Solve. Use the addition method.

5. $5x + 3y = 17$
   $-5x + 2y = 3$ **(1, 4)**
6. $-3a + 2b = 0$
   $3a - 4b = -1$ $(\tfrac{1}{3}, \tfrac{1}{2})$

Note in Example 3 that a term in one equation and a term in the other were additive inverses of each other. Thus their sum was 0. This enabled us to eliminate a variable.

In order to eliminate a variable we sometimes have to multiply one or both of the equations by something before adding.

Example 4. Solve this system: $3x + 3y = 15$
$$2x + 6y = 22$$

If we add, we do not eliminate a variable. However, if the $3y$ in the first equation were $-6y$, we could. So, we multiply by -2 in the first equation.

$$
\begin{array}{l}
-6x - 6y = -30 \quad \textit{Multiplying by } -2 \\
\underline{2x + 6y = 22} \\
-4x + 0 = -8 \quad \textit{Adding} \\
x = 2 \quad \textit{Solving for x} \\
2 \cdot 2 + 6y = 22 \quad \textit{Substituting 2 for x in second equation} \\
4 + 6y = 22 \\
y = 3 \quad \textit{Solving for y}
\end{array}
$$

We obtain (2, 3). This checks, so it is the solution.

TRY THIS ➡️

Solve. Use the addition method.

7. $2y + 3x = 12$
   $-4y + 5x = -2$
   (2, 3)

Sometimes we have to multiply twice.

Example 5. Solve this system: $2x + 3y = 12$
$$5x + 7y = 29$$

From first equation: $10x + 15y = 60$ *Multiplying by 5*
From second equation: $\underline{-10x - 14y = -58}$ *Multiplying by −2*
$$0 + \quad y = 2 \quad \text{Adding}$$
$$y = 2 \quad \text{Solving for y}$$

$2x + 3 \cdot 2 = 12$ *Substituting 2 for y in first equation*
$$2x = 6$$
$$x = 3 \quad \text{Solving for x}$$

We obtain (3, 2). This checks, so it is the solution.

TRY THIS ▐▬▬▬▬▶

> Solve. Use the addition method.
>
> 8. $3x + 5y = 30$
> $5x + 3y = 34$ (5, 3)

Exercise Set 4-2

▌Solve using the substitution method. (*See Examples 1 and 2.*)

1. $3x + 5y = 3$ (−4, 3)
    $x = 8 - 4y$

2. $2x - 3y = 13$ (2, −3)
    $y = 5 - 4x$

3. $9x - 2y = 3$ (−3, −15)
    $3x - 6 = y$

4. $x = 3y - 3$ $(\frac{21}{5}, \frac{12}{5})$
    $x + 2y = 9$

5. $5m + n = 8$ (2, −2)
    $3m - 4n = 14$

6. $4x + y = 1$ (2, −7)
    $x - 2y = 16$

7. $4x + 12y = 4$ (−2, 1)
    $5x - y = -11$

8. $3b - a = -7$ (4, −1)
    $5a + 6b = 14$

▌▌Solve using the addition method. (*See Examples 3–5.*)

9. $x + 3y = 7$ (1, 2)
    $-x + 4y = y$

10. $x + y = 9$ (2, 7)
     $2x - y = -3$

11. $2x + y = 6$ (3, 0)
     $x - y = 3$

12. $x - 2y = 6$ (10, 2)
     $-x + 3y = -4$

13. $9x + 3y = -3$ (−1, 2)
     $2x - 3y = -8$

14. $6x - 3y = 18$ $(\frac{1}{2}, -5)$
     $6x + 3y = -12$

15. $5x + 3y = 19$ $(\frac{128}{31}, -\frac{17}{31})$
     $2x - 5y = 11$

16. $3x + 2y = 3$ $(\frac{10}{21}, \frac{11}{14})$
     $9x - 8y = -2$

17. $5r - 3s = 24$ (6, 2)
     $3r + 5s = 28$

18. $5x - 7y = -16$ (1, 3)
     $2x + 8y = 26$

19. $0.3x - 0.2y = 4$ $(\frac{140}{13}, -\frac{50}{13})$
     $0.2x + 0.3y = 1$

20. $0.7x - 0.3y = 0.5$ (2, 3)
     $-0.4x + 0.7y = 1.3$

21. $\frac{1}{2}x + \frac{1}{3}y = 4$ (4, 6)
     $\frac{1}{4}x + \frac{1}{3}y = 3$

22. $\frac{2}{3}x + \frac{1}{7}y = -11$ (−21, 21)
     $\frac{1}{7}x - \frac{1}{3}y = -10$

4-3 Inconsistent and Dependent Equations

After finishing Lesson 4-3, you should be able to
▮   determine whether a system of equations is inconsistent or dependent.

▮ Some systems of equations have no solution.

DEFINITION
A system of equations that has no solution is called *inconsistent*.
If a system has one or more solutions it is called *consistent*.

For a system of two linear equations to be inconsistent, their
graphs must be parallel lines.

Example 1.   Determine whether this system is inconsistent: $x - 3y = 1$
$$-2x + 6y = 5$$

We multiply on both sides of the first equation by 2 and then
add. This gives us

$$x - 3y = 1$$
$$0 = 7$$

The second equation says that $0 \cdot x + 0 \cdot y = 7$. There are no
numbers x and y for which this is true, so there is no solution.
The system of equations is inconsistent.

Whenever we obtain a statement such as $0 = 7$,
which is clearly false, we know that the system we
are trying to solve is inconsistent.

TRY THIS

> 1.   Determine whether this sys-
> tem of equations is incon-
> sistent.
>
> $3y - 9x = 12$
> $y - 3x = 9$ Yes

Consider this system: $3x + 4y = 1$
$$6x + 8y = 2$$

If we multiply on both sides of the first equation by 2 we get the
second equation. Thus, the two equations are *equivalent,* meaning that they have exactly the same solution set.

DEFINITION
If a system of n linear equations is equivalent to a system of
fewer than n of them, then the system is called *dependent*.

Example 2. Determine whether this system is dependent: $2x + 3y = 1$
$$4x + 6y = 2$$

Multiplying on both sides of the first equation by 2, we get

$$4x + 6y = 2$$
$$4x + 6y = 2$$

The two equations are equivalent to just one of them, so the system is dependent.

In Example 2, suppose we had multiplied the first equation by -2 and then added.

$$-4x - 6y = -2 \qquad \textit{Multiplying by } -2$$
$$\underline{4x + 6y = 0}$$
$$0 + 0 = 0 \qquad \textit{Adding}$$

The last equation says that $0 \cdot x + 0 \cdot y = 0$. This is true for all numbers x and y. Whenever we get an obviously true sentence like this, we know that the system we are trying to solve is dependent.

TRY THIS

> 2. Determine whether this system of equations is dependent.
>
> $y = 5x + 2$
> $2y = 10x + 4$ Yes

Exercise Set 4-3

▌ Determine which systems are inconsistent and which are dependent. (*See Examples 1 and 2.*)

1. $y - x = 4$ Inconsistent
    $-2x + 2y = 5$

2. $y + x = 5$ Inconsistent
    $-y = x - 3$

3. $x - 3 = y$ Dependent
    $2x - 2y = 6$

4. $3y = x - 2$ Dependent
    $3x = 6 + 9y$

5. $x + 2y = 6$ Inconsistent
    $2x = 8 - 4y$

6. $y - 2x = 1$ Inconsistent
    $2x - 3 = y$

7. $y = x$ Inconsistent
    $x = y - 1$

8. $y = 2x$ Inconsistent
    $2x = y + 3$

9. $2x + 3y = 1$ Dependent
    $x + 1.5y = 0.5$

10. $15x + 6y = 20$ Dependent
    $7.5x - 10 = -3y$

Use Quiz 6 after lesson 4–3.

4-4 Systems of Equations in Three Variables

After finishing Lesson 4-4, you should be able to
I identify solutions of systems of three equations in three variables.
II solve systems of three equations in three variables.

I Identifying Solutions

A solution of a system of equations in three variables is an ordered triple which makes all three sentences true.

Example 1. Determine whether $(\frac{3}{2}, -4, 3)$ is a solution of this system: $4x - 2y - 3z = 5$
$$-8x - y + z = -5$$
$$2x + y + 2z = 5$$

$4x - 2y - 3z = 5$		$-8x - y + z = -5$		$2x + y + 2z = 5$	
$4 \cdot \frac{3}{2} - 2 \cdot (-4) - 3 \cdot 3$	5	$-8 \cdot \frac{3}{2} - (-4) + 3$	-5	$2 \cdot \frac{3}{2} + (-4) + 2 \cdot 3$	5
$6 + 8 - 9$		$-12 + 4 + 3$		$3 - 4 + 6$	
5		-5		5	

The triple $(\frac{3}{2}, -4, 3)$ checks, so it is a solution of
the system.

TRY THIS ➡

> 1. Consider this system:
> $$4x + 2y + 5z = 6$$
> $$2x - y + z = 5$$
> $$x + 2y - z = 0$$
>   a) Determine whether
> $(1, 2, 3)$ is a solution of
>   this system.   No
>   b) Determine whether
> $(2, -1, 0)$ is a solution
>   of this system.   Yes

II The Addition Method

The substitution method is not convenient for solving systems with three variables. We will consider
only the addition method.

The procedure for using the addition method is
as follows.
a) Use *any* two of the three equations to get an
    equation in two variables.
b) Use a different pair of equations and get another equation in
    the same two variables. That is, eliminate the same variable
    as in a).
c) Solve the resulting system (pair) of equations. This will give
    two of the numbers.
d) Use any of the original three equations to find the third number.

Example 2.   Solve: $x + y + z = 4$ **(1)**
$$x - 2y - z = 1 \qquad \textbf{(2)}$$
$$2x - y - 2z = -1 \qquad \textbf{(3)}$$

a)   We first use *any* two of the three equations to get an equation in two variables. Using equations **(1)** and **(2),** we add to eliminate z.

$$
\begin{array}{ll}
x + y + z = 4 & \textbf{(1)} \\
\underline{x - 2y - z = 1} & \textbf{(2)} \\
2x - y \phantom{{}- z} = 5 & \textbf{(4)}
\end{array}
$$

b)   Using a different pair of equations we get another equation in the same two variables. We eliminate the same variable as in a). Using equations **(1)** and **(3)** we can eliminate z.

$$
\begin{array}{ll}
x + y + z = 4 & \textbf{(1)} \\
2x - y - 2z = -1 & \textbf{(3)}
\end{array}
$$

$$
\begin{array}{lll}
2x + 2y + 2z = 8 & & \textit{Multiplying equation \textbf{(1)} by 2} \\
\underline{2x - y - 2z = -1} & & \\
4x + y \phantom{{}- 2z} = 7 & \textbf{(5)} & \textit{Adding}
\end{array}
$$

c)   We solve the resulting system of equations **(4)** and **(5).** This will give us two of the numbers.

$$
\begin{array}{lll}
2x - y = 5 & \textbf{(4)} & \\
\underline{4x + y = 7} & \textbf{(5)} & \\
6x \phantom{{}- y} = 12 & & \textit{Adding} \\
x = 2 & &
\end{array}
$$

We use either equation **(4)** or **(5)** to find y. From **(5)** we get

$$
\begin{array}{l}
4x + y = 7 \\
4 \cdot 2 + y = 7 \\
8 + y = 7 \\
y = -1
\end{array}
$$

d)   Using any of the original three equations we substitute to find the third number, z. Let us use equation **(1).**

$$
\begin{array}{ll}
x + y + z = 4 & \\
2 + (-1) + z = 4 & \textit{Substituting 2 for x and -1 for y} \\
1 + z = 4 & \\
z = 3 &
\end{array}
$$

We obtain $(2, -1, 3)$.

Check:
$$\begin{array}{c|c} x + y + z = 4 \\ \hline 2 + (-1) + 3 & 4 \\ 4 & \end{array} \qquad \begin{array}{c|c} x - 2y - z = 1 \\ \hline 2 - 2(-1) - 3 & 1 \\ 1 & \end{array} \qquad \begin{array}{c|c} 2x - y - 2z = -1 \\ \hline 2 \cdot 2 - (-1) - 2 \cdot 3 & -1 \\ -1 & \end{array}$$

The solution is $(2, -1, 3)$.

TRY THIS

Answers.   2. $(2, 1, -1)$ 3. $(2, -2, \frac{1}{2})$

2. Solve: $4x - y + z = 6$
    $$-3x + 2y - z = -3$$
    $$2x + y + 2z = 3$$
    Don't forget to check.

3. Solve: $2x + y - 4z = 0$
    $$x - y + 2z = 5$$
    $$3x + 2y + 2z = 3$$

Example 3.   Solve:
$$\begin{array}{ll} x + y + z = 180 & \textbf{(1)} \\ x - z = -70 & \textbf{(2)} \\ 2y - z = 0 & \textbf{(3)} \end{array}$$

a)   There is no y in equation **(2),** so
b)   we use equations **(1)** and **(3)** and eliminate y.

$$\begin{array}{ll} x + y + z = 180 & \textbf{(1)} \\ 2y - z = 0 & \textbf{(3)} \end{array}$$

$$\begin{array}{ll} -2x - 2y - 2z = -360 & \text{\emph{Multiplying by}} -2 \\ 2y - z = 0 \\ \hline -2x - 3z = -360 & \textbf{(4)} \end{array}$$

c)   We use equations **(2)** and **(4).**

$$\begin{array}{ll} x - z = -70 & \textbf{(2)} \\ -2x - 3z = -360 & \textbf{(4)} \end{array}$$

$$\begin{array}{ll} 2x - 2z = -140 & \text{\emph{Multiplying by}} 2 \\ -2x - 3z = -360 \\ \hline -5z = -500 \\ z = 100 \end{array}$$

We use equation **(2)** to find x.

$$\begin{array}{l} x - 100 = -70 \\ x = 30 \end{array}$$

d)   Using any of the original equations, we substitute to find the third number, y. From equation **(3)** we get

$$\begin{array}{l} 2y - 100 = 0 \\ 2y = 100 \\ y = 50 \end{array}$$

We obtain $(30, 50, 100)$. This checks so it is the solution.

TRY THIS ➤

4. Solve: $x + y + z = 100$
$x - y\ \ \ \ \ \ \ = -10$
$x\ \ \ \ \ \ - z = -30$
(20, 30, 50)

Exercise Set 4-4

▌(*See Example 1.*)

1. Determine whether $(1, -2, 3)$ is a solution of the system
$x + y + z = 2$
$x - 2y - z = 2$
$3x + 2y + z = 2$ Yes

2. Determine whether $(2, -1, -2)$ is a solution of the system
$x + y - 2z = 5$
$2x - y - z = 7$
$-x - 2y + 3z = 6$ No

▌▌Solve. (*See Examples 2 and 3.*)

3. $x + y + z = 6$ (1, 2, 3)
$2x - y + 3z = 9$
$-x + 2y + 2z = 9$

4. $2x - y + z = 10$ (4, 0, 2)
$4x + 2y - 3z = 10$
$x - 3y + 2z = 8$

5. $2x - y - 3z = -1$ (−1, 5, −2)
$2x - y + z = -9$
$x + 2y - 4z = 17$

6. $x - y + z = 6$ (2, −2, 2)
$2x + 3y + 2z = 2$
$3x + 5y + 4z = 4$

7. $2x - 3y + z = 5$ (3, 1, 2)
$x + 3y + 8z = 22$
$3x - y + 2z = 12$

8. $6x - 4y + 5z = 31$ (3, −2, 1)
$5x + 2y + 2z = 13$
$x + y + z = 2$

9. $3a - 2b + 7c = 13$ (−3, −4, 2)
$a + 8b - 6c = -47$
$7a - 9b - 9c = -3$

10. $x + y + z = 0$ (7, −3, −4)
$2x + 3y + 2z = -3$
$-x + 2y - 3z = -1$

11. $2x + 3y + z = 17$ (2, 4, 1)
$x - 3y + 2z = -8$
$5x - 2y + 3z = 5$

12. $2x + y - 3z = -4$ (2, 1, 3)
$4x - 2y + z = 9$
$3x + 5y - 2z = 5$

13. $2x + y + z = -2$ (−3, 0, 4)
$2x - y + 3z = 6$
$3x - 5y + 4z = 7$

14. $2x + y + 2z = 11$ (2, −5, 6)
$3x + 2y + 2z = 8$
$x + 4y + 3z = 0$

15. $x - y + z = 4$ (2, 2, 4)
$5x + 2y - 3z = 2$
$3x - 7y + 4z = 8$

16. $2x + y + 2z = 3$ (−2, −1, 4)
$x + 6y + 3z = 4$
$3x - 2y + z = 0$

17. $4x - y - z = 4$ ($\frac{1}{2}$, 4, −6)
$2x + y + z = -1$
$6x - 3y - 2z = 3$

18. $a + 2b + c = 1$ (3, −5, 8)
$7a + 3b - c = -2$
$a + 5b + 3c = 2$

19. $2r + 3s + 12t = 4$ ($\frac{1}{2}$, $\frac{1}{3}$, $\frac{1}{6}$)
$4r - 6s + 6t = 1$
$r + s + t = 1$

20. $10x + 6y + z = 7$ ($\frac{3}{5}$, $\frac{2}{3}$, −3)
$5x - 9y - 2z = 3$
$15x - 12y + 2z = -5$

Challenge Exercises

Solve.

21. $\dfrac{x}{5} - \dfrac{y}{2} + \dfrac{z}{3} = -1$ $(\frac{645}{19}, \frac{16}{19}, -\frac{420}{19})$

      $\dfrac{x}{3} + \dfrac{y}{4} + \dfrac{z}{4} = 6$

      $\dfrac{x}{5} - \dfrac{y}{8} + \dfrac{z}{6} = 3$

      $\left(\text{Hint: } \dfrac{x}{5} = \dfrac{1}{5} \cdot x.\right)$

22. $L + m = 7$ $(2, 5, -3)$

      $3m + 2n = 9$

      $4L + n = 5$

23. $x + y + z + w = 2$ $(-2, 4, -1, 1)$

      $2x + 2y + 4z + w = 1$

      $x - y - z - w = -6$

      $3x + y - z - w = -2$

24. $x - y + z + w = 0$ $(-1, 0, 4, -3)$

      $2x + 2y + z - w = 5$

      $3x + y - z - w = -4$

      $x + y - 3z - 2w = -7$

Determine whether each system is inconsistent or dependent.

25. $-2x + 8y + 12z = -8$ Dependent

      $3x + 2y + z = 2$

      $x - 4y - 6z = 4$

26. $-2x - y - z = 1$ Inconsistent

      $6x + 5y + 3z = 2$

      $8x + y + 4z = -4$

BIOGRAPHICAL NOTE: Sonya Kovalesky

When Sonya Kovalesky was a young woman, in the 1860s, Russian universities were closed to women. Her father did not want her to go to a foreign university. By marrying, she was able to travel to Germany. There she distinguished herself as a student of advanced mathematics. She gained a doctoral degree in 1874, but she could not find a teaching position in a university in Germany or in Russia.

Eventually she was accepted as a member of the faculty at the University of Stockholm, Sweden. Even there she faced opposition from scholars who did not think a woman should be a university professor. In time her researches in mathematics earned her honors in France, Russia, Sweden, and other countries.

4-5 Solving Problems

After finishing Lesson 4-5, you should be able to
▮ solve problems by translating them to systems of two equations in two variables.

▮ To solve problems we often translate to a system of two equations in two variables.

Example 1. 8 times a certain number added to 5 times a second number is 184. The first number minus the second number is -3. Find the numbers.

There are two statements in the problem. We translate the first one.

$$\underbrace{\text{8 times a certain number}}_{8x} \underbrace{\text{added to}}_{+} \underbrace{\text{5 times a second number}}_{5y} \underbrace{\text{is 184.}}_{= 184}$$

Here x represents the first number and y represents the second. Now we translate the second statement, remembering to use x and y.

$$\underbrace{\text{The first number}}_{x} \underbrace{\text{minus}}_{-} \underbrace{\text{the second number}}_{y} \underbrace{\text{is } -3.}_{= -3}$$

We have the system of equations

$$8x + 5y = 184$$
$$x - y = -3$$

The solution of this system is $x = 13$ and $y = 16$.

We check in the original problem. Since $8 \cdot 13 = 104$ and $5 \cdot 16 = 80$, the sum is 184. The difference of 13 and 16 is -3, so the answer checks.

TRY THIS

1. One number is 4 times another number. The sum of the numbers is 175. Find the numbers. **35 and 140**

Example 2. One day Glovers, Inc., sold 20 pairs of gloves. Cloth gloves sold for $4.95 a pair and pigskin gloves sold for $7.50 a pair. They sold $137.25 worth of gloves. How many pairs of each were sold?

We let x = the number of cloth gloves sold and y = the number of pigskin gloves.

a) We first consider the number of pairs sold. The total is 20 pairs, so $x + y = 20$.

b) Second, we consider the amount of money. The amount taken in for cloth gloves was $4.95x$, since each pair sold for $4.95. This amount is *in dollars*. In cents the amount is $495x$. The amount taken in for pigskin gloves is $7.50y$ in dollars, or $750y$ in cents. Then we have the equation $495x + 750y = 13725$.

c) We solve the system of equations

$$x + y = 20$$
$$495x + 750y = 13725$$

The solution is $x = 5$ and $y = 15$. This checks in the original problem, so the company sold 5 pairs of cloth gloves and 15 pairs of pigskin gloves.

TRY THIS

2. One day a store sold 30 sweatshirts. White ones cost $8.95 and red ones cost $9.50. They sold $272.90 worth of sweatshirts. How many of each color were sold?

    22 white ones and 8 red ones

Example 3. *Mixture Problem.* Solution A is 2% alcohol. Solution B is 6% alcohol. A service station attendant wants to mix the two to get 60 liters of a solution which is 3.2% alcohol. How many liters of each should he use?

Let us assume he uses x liters of A and y liters of B.

a) First, consider the amount of liquid.
    He wants 60 liters in all, so we have the equation
    $x + y = 60$.

b)   Second, consider the amount of alcohol.
The amount of alcohol in the new mixture is to be 3.2% of
60 liters, or 1.92 liters. This is to be made up of the alcohol
in the two solutions to be mixed. These amounts are 2%x
and 6%y. Thus we have another equation.

$$2\%x + 6\%y = 1.92, \text{ or } 0.02x + 0.06y = 1.92$$

We can eliminate decimals by multiplying on both sides
by 100.

$$100(0.02x + 0.06y) = 100(1.92)$$
$$2x + 6y = 192$$

c)   Now we solve the system

$$x + y = 60$$
$$2x + 6y = 192$$

and get $x = 42$ and $y = 18$. Thus the attendant
should use 42 liters of A and 18 liters of B.

TRY THIS

> 3.   A gardener has two kinds
> of solutions containing
> weedkiller and water. One
> is 5% weedkiller and the
> other is 15% weedkiller.
> She needs 100 liters of
> 12% solution and wants to
> make it from the solutions
> she has by mixing the two.
> How much should she use
> of each?
>
> 30 liters of 5% and 70 liters of 15%

Example 4.   *Interest Problem*. Two investments are made which
total $4800. For a certain year these investments yield $412 in
simple interest. Part of the $4800 is invested at 8% and the rest
at 9%. Find the amount invested at each rate.

Recall the formula for simple interest.

$$I = Prt$$

Interest I is the principal P times rate r times time t.

a)   Let x represent the amount invested at 8% and y the amount
invested at 9%. Then the interest from x is 8%x, and the interest from y is 9%y. Thus the $412 total interest is given by

$$8\%x + 9\%y = 412,$$
$$\text{or } 0.08x + 0.09y = 412.$$

b)   Considering the total amount invested we have

$$x + y = 4800.$$

c)   We now have a system of equations

$$0.08x + 0.09y = 412$$
$$x + y = 4800$$

Multiplying the first equation by 100 to clear of decimals, we get

$$8x + 9y = 41{,}200$$
$$x + y = 4800$$

Solving we get $x = 2000$ and $y = 2800$. This checks, so $2000 is invested at 8% and $2800 is invested at 9%.

TRY THIS

> 4.   Two investments are made which total $3700. For a certain year these investments yield $297 in simple interest. Part of the $3700 is invested at 7% and the other part at 9%. Find the amount invested at each rate. $1800 at 7% and $1900 at 9%

Exercise Set 4-5

■ Solve. (*See Examples 1–4.*)

1.   The sum of a certain number and a second number is -42. The first number minus the second is 52. Find the numbers.   5 and −47

2.   The sum of two numbers is -63. The first number minus the second is -41. Find the numbers.   −52 and −11

3.   The difference between two numbers is 16. Three times the larger number is nine times the smaller. What are the numbers?   24 and 8

4.   The difference between two numbers is 11. Twice the smaller number plus three times the larger is 123. What are the numbers?   29 and 18

5.   The perimeter of a rectangular field is 628 m. The length of the field exceeds its width by 6 m. Find the dimensions.   l = 160 m; w = 154 m

6.   The perimeter of a rectangular lot is 190 m. The width is one-fourth the length. Find the dimensions.   l = 76 m; w = 19 m

7.   One day a store sold 30 sweatshirts. White ones cost $9.95 and yellow ones cost $10.50. In dollars, $310.60 worth of sweatshirts were sold. How many of each color were sold?   8 white, 22 yellow

8.   One week a business sold 40 scarves. White ones cost $4.95 and printed ones cost $7.95. In dollars, $282 worth of scarves were sold. How many of each kind were sold?   12 white, 28 printed

9.   Soybean meal is 16% protein; corn meal is 9% protein. How many pounds of each should be mixed together to get a 350 pound mixture which is 12% protein?   150 lbs of soybean meal, 200 lbs of corn meal

10.   A chemist has one solution of acid and water which is 25% acid and a second which is 50% acid. How many liters of each should be mixed together to get 10 liters of a solution which is 40% acid?   4 liters of 25%, 6 liters of 50%

11. Two investments are made which total $8800. For a certain year these investments yield $663 in simple interest. Part of the $8800 is invested at 7% and part at 8%. Find the amount invested at each rate. $4100 at 7%, $4700 at 8%

12. Two investments are made which total $15,000. For a certain year these investments yield $1432 in simple interest. Part of the $15,000 is invested at 9% and part at 10%. Find the amount invested at each rate. $6800 at 9%, $8200 at 10%

13. For a certain year $3900 is received in interest from two investments. A certain amount is invested at 5%, and $10,000 more than this is invested at 6%. Find the amount invested at each rate. (*Hint:* Express each equation in standard form $ax + by = c$.) $30,000 at 5%, $40,000 at 6%

14. For a certain year $876 is received from two investments. A certain amount is invested at 7%, and $1200 more than this is invested at 8%. Find the amount invested at each rate. $5200 at 7%, $6400 at 8%

15. Ann Teak is twice as old as her son. Ten years ago Ann was three times as old as her son. What are their present ages? Ann 40, son 20

16. Gerry Atric is twice as old as his youngest daughter. In eight years Gerry's age will be three times what his daughter's age was six years ago. How old is each at present? Gerry 52, daughter 26

17. The Melody Mart music store averages monthly expenses of $3800 and pays the sales people a 5% commission. The store begins to make a profit when costs equal sales. Find the amount of sales at which the store begins to profit. $4000

18. The Hobby House averages monthly expenses of $4200 and pays the sales people a 4% commission. The store begins to make a profit when costs equal sales. Find the amount of sales at which the store begins to profit. $4375

Calculator Exercises

19. The perimeter of a rectangle is 86.21 cm. The length is 19.31 cm greater than the width. Find the length and the width. l = 31.2075 cm; w = 11.8975 cm

20. The perimeter of a rectangle is 385.9 m. The length is 82.46 m greater than the width. Find the length and the width. l = 137.705 m; w = 55.245 m

Challenge Exercises

21. An automobile radiator contains 16 liters of antifreeze and water. This mixture is 30% antifreeze. How much of this mixture should be drained and replaced with pure antifreeze so there will be 50% antifreeze? $4\frac{4}{7}$ liters

---

4-6 Motion Problems

After finishing Lesson 4-6, you should be able to
▌ solve motion problems.

▌ Many problems deal with distance, time, and speed. To translate such problems we usually use the definition of speed.

DEFINITION

$$\text{Speed} = \frac{\text{distance}}{\text{time}}$$

$$r = \frac{d}{t}$$

From the equation $r = \frac{d}{t}$ we can easily obtain $d = rt$ or $t = \frac{d}{r}$.

Example 1. A train leaves Soul City traveling east at 30 km/h. Two hours later another train leaves Soul City traveling east on a parallel track at 45 km/h. How far from Soul City will the trains meet?

We first make a drawing.

From the drawing we see that the distances are the same,

$$d_1 = d_2.$$

Now the slow train travels 2 hours longer than the other, so

$$t_1 = t_2 + 2.$$

Soul City   30 km/h
t_1 hours d_1 kilometers

Soul City   45 km/h
t_2 hours d_2 kilometers

Trains
meet here

We can summarize in a chart.

	r	t	d
Slow train	30	$t_2 + 2$	d_1
Fast train	45	t_2	d_1

Using $d = rt$ in each row of the chart, we get an equation. We have the system of equations

$$30(t_2 + 2) = d_1 \qquad \text{or} \qquad 30t_2 + 60 = d_1$$
$$45t_2 = d_1 \qquad\qquad\qquad\qquad 45t_2 = d_1$$

We find that $t_1 = 6$ hours and $t_2 = 4$ hours. The problem asks for distance, however. We find it using $d = rt$. So $d = 30 \cdot 6$ or $45 \cdot 4$. The distance is 180 km. This checks in the original problem.

TRY THIS ➡️

1. A train leaves Gigville traveling east at 35 km/h. An hour later another train leaves Gigville traveling east on a parallel track at 40 km/h. How far from Gigville will the trains meet?

   280 km

Example 2. A canoeist paddled for 4 hours with a 5 km/h current to reach a campsite. The return trip, against the current, took 9 hours. Find the speed of the canoe in still water.

Make a drawing.

The drawing shows that the distances are the same, $d_1 = d_2$. The rates are $r + 5$ and $r - 5$ where r is the speed in still water.

Downstream $r + 5$
4 hours d_1 kilometers

Upstream $r - 5$
9 hours d_2 kilometers

We can summarize in a chart.

	r	t	d
Downstream	$r + 5$	4	d_1
Upstream	$r - 5$	9	d_1

Using $d = rt$ in each row of the chart we get an equation. This gives us a system of equations.

$$(r + 5) \cdot 4 = d_1 \qquad \text{or} \qquad 4r + 20 = d_1$$
$$(r - 5) \cdot 9 = d_1 \qquad\qquad\qquad 9r - 45 = d_1$$

We find that $d = 72$ and $r = 13$. The speed in still water is 13 km/h. This checks in the problem.

TRY THIS ➡️

2. An airplane flew for 3 hours with an 18 km/h tailwind. The return flight against the same wind took 4 hours. Find the speed of the plane in still air. 126 km/h

Example 3. Two bicycles leave town traveling in opposite directions. One travels 20 km/h and the other 28 km/h. In how many hours will they be 120 kilometers apart?

Make a drawing.

The time is the same, $t_1 = t_2$. The sum of the distances is 120, so $d_1 + d_2 = 120$ and $d_2 = 120 - d_1$.

We summarize in a chart.

	r	t	d
First bicycle	20	t_1	d_1
Second bicycle	28	t_1	$120 - d_1$

Using $d = rt$ in each row of the chart we get an equation. This gives us a system of equations.

$$20t_1 = d_1$$
$$28t_1 = 120 - d_1$$

We find that $t_1 = 2\frac{1}{2}$. In $2\frac{1}{2}$ hours, the bicycles will be 120 km apart. This checks in the problem.

TRY THIS ➡

3. Two cars leave the center of town at the same time. One travels north at 64 km/h and the other travels south at 56 km/h. In how many hours will they be 480 km apart?   **4**

Exercise Set 4-6

❚ Solve. (*See Examples 1–3.*)

1. A train leaves a station and travels north at 75 km/h. Two hours later a second train leaves on a parallel track and travels north at 125 km/h. How far from the station will they meet?   **375 km**

2. A private plane leaves an airport and flies due east at 180 km/h. Two hours later a jet leaves the same airport and flies due east at 900 km/h. How far from the airport will they meet?   **450 km**

3. Two cars leave town traveling in opposite directions. One travels 80 km/h and the other 96 km/h. In how many hours will they be 528 kilometers apart?   **3 hours**

4. A passenger train and a freight train leave Union Station at the same time. The passenger train travels west at 55 km/h, and the freight train travels east at 45 km/h. In how many hours will they be 350 kilometers apart? $3\frac{1}{2}$ **hours**

5. Two motorcycles travel toward each other from Chicago and Indianapolis, which are about 350 km apart, at rates of 110 and 90 km/h. They started at the same time. In how many hours will they meet? $1\frac{3}{4}$ hours

6. Two planes travel toward each other from cities which are 780 km apart at rates of 190 and 200 km/h. They started at the same time. In how many hours will they meet?   2 hours

7. Fly High Airlines flies from Podunk to Swampville in 5 hours with a tailwind. The return trip, against the same wind, takes 6 hours. Podunk is about 5550 km from Swampville. Find the speed of the plane and the velocity of the wind.   Plane $1017\frac{1}{2}$ km/h; wind $92\frac{1}{2}$ km/h

8. Hopeweland Airlines flies from Plunketville to Seedytown in 4 hours with a tailwind. The return trip, against the same wind, takes 5 hours. Plunketville is about 4000 km from Seedytown. Find the speed of the plane and the velocity of the wind.   Plane 900 km/h; wind 100 km/h

9. G. Otrotrot jogs and walks to school each day. He averages 4 km/h walking and 8 km/h jogging. The distance from home to school is 6 km and he makes the trip in 1 hour. How far does he jog in a trip?   4 km

10. R. U. Fastre rides a motorbike to work. She had to walk part of the way because of a flat tire. The motorbike averages 40 km/h and she walks 5 km/h. The distance from home to work is 30 km and she made the trip in 3 hours. How far did she ride on the motorbike? $17\frac{1}{7}$ km

---

Calculator Exercises

11. A boat travels 3.15 hours downstream, where the current is 5.82 km/h. It returns in 9.97 hours. Find the speed of the boat in still water.   11.196246 km/h

12. An airplane flies for 4.18 hours with a 28.6 km/h tailwind. The return trip against the same wind takes 4.93 hours. Find the speed of the plane in still air.   347.39466 km/h

Challenge Exercises

13. A train leaves Koolsville for Groovetown, 216 km away, at 9 A.M. One hour later, a train leaves Groovetown for Koolsville. They meet at noon. If the second train had started at 9 A.M. and the first train at 10:30 A.M., they would still have met at noon. Find the speed of each train.   First train 36 km/h; second train 54 km/h

14. When Jupiter and Mars are on the same side of the sun and in line with it, the distance between them is 549,908,000 km. When they are on opposite sides of the sun and in line with it, the distance between them is 1,005,393,000 km. How far is each planet from the sun?   Jupiter 777,650,500 km; Mars 227,742,500 km

---

COMPUTER ACTIVITY

Solving Simultaneous Equations by Cramer's Rule

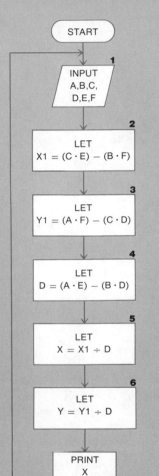

PROBLEM: Find the solution (X, Y) of a system of two equations in two unknowns.

Equations:

$$AX + BY = C$$
$$DX + EY = F$$

Solutions:

$$X = \frac{\begin{pmatrix} C & B \\ F & E \end{pmatrix}}{\begin{pmatrix} A & B \\ D & E \end{pmatrix}} = \frac{X1}{D} \qquad Y = \frac{\begin{pmatrix} A & C \\ D & F \end{pmatrix}}{\begin{pmatrix} A & B \\ D & E \end{pmatrix}} = \frac{Y1}{D}$$

Examples using the flowchart:

1			2	3	4	5	6
ABC DEF			X1	Y1	D	X	Y
2	1	4					
3	1	7	−3	?	−1	3	−2
4	3	7					
2	−7	5	−64	6	−34	1.882353	−0.176471
3	4	2					
−1	6	3					
5	−2	.5					
6	9	1					

TRY THIS ➡ Find the numbers to complete the examples.

BASIC PROGRAM (Optional)

```
10   READ A,B,C,D,E,F
20   LET X1 = (C*E) − (B*F)
30   LET Y1 = (A*F) − (C*D)
40   LET D = (A*E) − (B*D)
50   LET X = X1/D
60   LET Y = Y1/D
70   PRINT "X="X, "Y="Y
80   GO TO 10
90   DATA 2,1,4,3,1,7
100  DATA 4,3,7,2,−7,5
```

CHAPTER 4 REVIEW

Review the material in the chapter. Then see how you have done by trying these review exercises. If you miss an exercise, restudy the indicated lesson.

4-1   Solve graphically.   See answer section
          1. $x + y = 3$ 2. $x + 2y = 5$
              $x - y = 5$ $3x - y = -6$

4-2   3. Solve, using the substitution method: $2x - y = -9$
                                             $3x - 8y = -7$ $(-5, -1)$

4-2   4. Solve, using the addition method: $2x + 7y = 2$
                                         $3x + 5y = -8$ $(-6, 2)$

4-3   Which of the following systems of equations are inconsistent and which are dependent?   5. Inconsistent   6. Inconsistent   7. Dependent
          5. $2x - y = 4$ 6. $2x - y = 4$ 7. $x - 2y = 3$
              $2x - y = 6$ $4x = 2y - 5$ $4x - 8y = 12$

4-4   8. Solve: $2a - b + c = 7$
                        $a + 2b + 2c = 3$ $(1, -2, 3)$
                        $7a - 3b - 3c = 4$

4-5   Solve.
          9. The perimeter of a rectangular lot is 504 meters. The length is 36 meters more than twice the width. Find the dimensions.   l = 180 m; w = 72 m

4-6   10. On a recent trip Allie Gator drove 372 km in the same length of time that Crockie Dial required to drive 270 km. Gator's speed was 17 km/h greater than Dial's speed. Find the rate of each.

                                         Gator 62 km/h; Dial 45 km/h

CHAPTER 4 TEST

Solve graphically. See answer section
1. $x + y = 2$ 2. $7x - 4y = 2$
   $x - y = 4$ $5x + y = 13$

3. Solve, using the substitution method: $x + y = 7$ (5, 2)
   $2x - y = 8$

4. Solve, using the addition method: $3x + 2y = 5$ (3, −2)
   $4x + 5y = 2$

Which of the following systems are inconsistent and which are dependent? 5. Dependent 6. Inconsistent 7. Inconsistent
5. $x - 3y = 2$ 6. $3x - y = 8$ 7. $-3x + 2y = 7$
   $5x - 15y = 10$ $3x - y = 10$ $4y = 6x - 3$

8. Solve: $x + y - 3z = 8$
   $2x - 3y + z = -6$ (2, 3, −1)
   $3x + 4y - 2z = 20$

Solve.
9. The perimeter of a rectangular field is 608 meters. The length is 42 meters more than twice the width. Find the dimensions. $l = 216\frac{2}{3}$ m; $w = 87\frac{1}{3}$ m

10. Rocky drove his trail bike into the country at the rate of 50 km/h. He returned over the same route at 40 km/h. The total trip took 9 hours. How far did he drive into the country? 200 km

Use Cumulative Test 1 after Cumulative Review below.

CUMULATIVE REVIEW FOR CHAPTERS 1–4

1-1   1.   Find decimal notation for $\frac{11}{20}$.   0.55

1-1   Which of the following are rational and which are irrational?   2. Rational   3. Irrational   4. Rational
  2. $5.134343\overline{34}$ 3. $\sqrt{19}$ 4. $-\frac{5}{6}$

1-2   5.   Simplify: $|-20|$.   20
1-2   6.   Find the additive inverse of -4.21.   4.21
1-2   7.   Add: $-18 + (-2)$.   −20

1-3, 1-4   Tell which property of real numbers is illustrated by each sentence.
  8. $14 + 2 = 2 + 14$ Commutative law, addition
  9. $(3 \cdot 4) \cdot 6 = 3 \cdot (4 \cdot 6)$ Associative law, multiplication

1-3   10.   Subtract: $15 - (-4)$.   19
1-4   11.   Multiply: $6(-5)$.   −30
1-4   12.   Divide: $\dfrac{-40}{-5}$.   8

1-4   Which of these divisions are possible?
  13. $\frac{0}{11}$ 14. $\frac{23}{0}$ 13. Possible   14. Not possible

1-5   15.   Factor: $10x - 14y$.   2(5x − 7y)
1-5   16.   Multiply: $-2(-x + 7)$.   2x − 14
1-5   17.   Collect like terms: $-2w + 7 - 3 - 10w$.   −12w + 4

1-6   Remove parentheses and simplify.
  18. $-(-14y)$ 19. $-(7x + 2) - x$
  20. $3w - [w - (3w + 6)]$ 18. 14y   19. −8x − 2   20. 5w + 6

1-7, 1-8   Simplify.
  21. 3^{-2} 22. $5^3 \cdot 5^{-6}$ 23. $\dfrac{x^{-3}}{x^5}$ 24. $(3^{-4})^{-2}$
  21. $\frac{1}{3^2}$ 22. 5^{-3} 23. x^{-8} 24. 3^8

1-9   25.   Simplify: $|-4w^2z^5|$.   4w² z⁴ |z|

Solve.
2-1   26. $5 - y = 10$ 27. $-3w = 54$
2-2   28. $-7t + 23 = -33$ 29. $-2(4 - y) = 18$
  30. $(x - 7)(2x + 1) = 0$ 26. 15   27. −18   28. 8   29. 13   30. 7, $-\frac{1}{2}$

2-3   31.   Solve: An 8-meter plank is cut into two pieces. One piece is 3 times as long as the other. How long are the pieces?   2 m, 6 m

2-4   32.   Solve for s: $Fs = wh$. $s = \frac{wh}{F}$

3-1   33.   Determine whether $(7, -2)$ is a solution of $2x - 3y = -20$. No

3-1   34.   Graph $-x + 2y = 1$. Line through $(0, \frac{1}{2})$ and $(-1, 0)$

3-2   35.   Is $3y - x^2 = x - x^2$ a linear equation? Yes

3-2   36.   Find standard form for $3y = -2x + 9$. $2x + 3y - 9 = 0$

3-2   37.   Graph $5x - 3y = 15$ using intercepts. Line through $(0, -5)$ and $(3, 0)$

3-2   38.   Graph $-y = 7$. Horizontal line through $(0, -7)$

3-3   39.   Find the slope of the line containing $(-3, 5)$ and $(2, -1)$. $-\frac{6}{5}$

3-3   40.   Find an equation for the line with slope of $-\frac{1}{2}$ and containing $(-8, 0)$. $y = -\frac{1}{2}x - 4$

3-4   41.   Find an equation for the line containing $(-2, -1)$ and $(-3, 7)$. $y + 1 = -8x - 16$

3-4   42.   Find the slope and y-intercept of the equation $-2x + 1 = 2y$. $-1, \frac{1}{2}$

3-5   43.   Without graphing, tell whether the graphs of $x + 8 = y$ and $-y - 3 = x$ are parallel.   No

3-5   Find an equation of the line containing $(-5, -1)$ which is
      44.   parallel to the line $-2x - y = 10$. $y = -2x - 11$
      45.   perpendicular to the line $-2x - y = 10$. $y = \frac{1}{2}x + \frac{3}{2}$ or $2y = x + 3$

4-1   46.   Solve this system graphically: $2x - y = 8$ Line through $(4, 0)$ and $(5, 2)$;
                                             $-x + 3y = 1$ line through $(-1, 0)$ and $(5, 2)$

4-2   47.   Solve, using the substitution method: $x - 3y = 2$ $(-7, -3)$
                                                          $2x + 3y = -23$

4-2   48.   Solve, using the addition method: $-4x + y = -8$ $(3, 4)$
                                                   $2x + 3y = 18$

4-3   49.   Is this system inconsistent or dependent: $3x + y = 2$ Inconsistent
                                                        $y = -3x + 1$

4-4   50.   Solve: $2x - y - z = -11$
                    $x + 2y - 3z = -13$ $(-1, 3, 6)$
                    $-x - y + 4z = 22$

Solve.

4-5   51.   One canned juice drink is 15% orange juice; another is 5% orange juice. How many liters of each should be mixed together to get 10 liters which is 10% orange juice?   5 liters of each

4-6   52.   Two trucks leave town traveling in opposite directions. One travels 75 km/h and the other 60 km/h. In how many hours will they be 324 km apart?   2.4 h

Ready for Inequalities?

1-2   Simplify.
  1. $|-8|$ 8
  2. $|0|$ 0
  3. $|\sqrt{4}|$ $\sqrt{4}$

1-2   Add.
  4. $-8 + (-1.2)$ −9.2
  5. $\frac{3}{4} + \left(-\frac{2}{5}\right)$ $\frac{7}{20}$
  6. $-4.8 + 1.2$ −3.6

Solve.
2-1   7. $r + \frac{5}{6} = -\frac{3}{12}$ $-\frac{13}{12}$
2-1   8. $5t = -12$ $-\frac{12}{5}$
2-1   9. $\frac{2}{3}x = 16$ 24
2-2   10. $-4y - 3y = 28$ −4
2-2   11. $8 - 5x = x - 14$ $\frac{11}{3}$
2-2   12. $8a = 3(a + 5)$ 3

Graph.
3-1   13. $y - 3x = 6$ Line through (−2, 0) and (0, 6)
3-2   14. $5y + 2 = x$ Line through (−3, −1) and (2, 0)

3-2   15. Find the intercepts of $3x - 4y = 15$.   y-intercept: $\left(0, -\frac{15}{4}\right)$; x-intercept: (5, 0)

3-2   Graph.
  16. $y = -2$ Horizontal line through (0, −2)
  17. $x = 4$ Vertical line through (4, 0)

4-1   18. Solve graphically: $2x - y = 4$
                                  $x - y = 3$
          Line through (0, −4) and (1, −2); line through (0, −3) and (1, −2)

Chapter 5
Inequalities

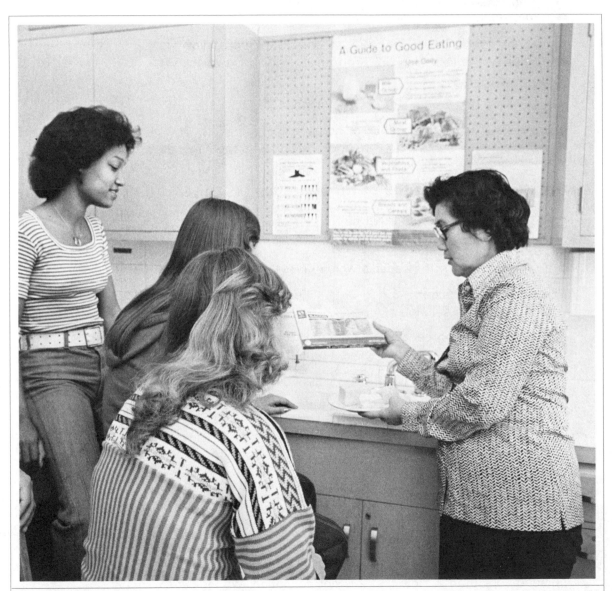

How can the minimum daily requirements of calcium and protein be obtained at the least cost by eating certain foods?

5-1 Solving Inequalities

After finishing Lesson 5-1, you should be able to
I graph inequalities in one variable on a line.
II solve inequalities using the addition principle.

Sentences containing $<$, $>$, $\leq$, or $\geq$ are called inequalities.
$a < b$ read "*a* is less than *b*." The formal definition is as follows.

DEFINITION

$a < b$ means that $b - a$ is a positive number.

$a \leq b$ means that *a* is less than or equal to *b*.
$a > b$ means the same as $b < a$, and $a \geq b$ means the same as $b \leq a$.

I Solutions and Graphs of Inequalities

A *solution* of an inequality such as

$$-3 \leq x$$

is a replacement for the variable which makes the sentence true.

Example 1. Consider $-3 \leq x$. Determine whether each number is a solution.

a) -2 is a solution because $-3 \leq -2$ is true.
b) -3 is a solution because $-3 \leq -3$ is true.
c) -5 is not a solution because $-3 \leq -5$ is false.

TRY THIS

1. Consider $x > -7$. Determine whether each number is a solution.

   a) -5 b) -7
   c) 4 d) 0

2. Consider $x \geq -7$. Determine whether each number is a solution.

   a) -8 b) -6
   c) -7 d) 0
   1. a) Yes b) No c) Yes d) Yes
   2. a) No b) Yes c) Yes d) Yes

The *graph* of an inequality shows all its solutions on a number line.

Example 2. Graph $x < 2$ on a number line.

The solutions consist of all numbers less than 2, so we shade all numbers less than 2. Note that 2 is not a solution. We indicate this by using an open circle at 2.

Example 3. Graph $x \le 2$ on a number line.

This time 2 and all numbers less than 2 are solutions. We shade all numbers less than 2 and use a solid circle at 2 to indicate that it is a solution.

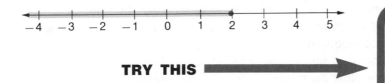

TRY THIS

Graph on a number line.

3. $x < -2$
4. $x \le -2$
See answer section

‖ The Addition Principle

Consider the true inequality

$4 < 9$.

If we add 3 to both numbers we get another true inequality,

$7 < 12$.

Similarly if we add -6 to both numbers we get another true inequality,

$-2 < 3$.

THEOREM 5-1 (The Addition Principle for Inequalities)
If any number is added to both members of a true inequality, another true inequality is obtained. For example, for any numbers a, b, and c, if $a < b$, then $a + c < b + c$.

Example 4. Solve $x + 3 > 6$. Then graph.

Using Theorem 5-1, we add -3.

$x + 3 + (-3) > 6 + (-3)$
$x > 3$

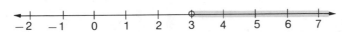

Any number greater than 3 makes the last sentence true, and hence is a solution of that sentence. Any such number is also a solution of the original sentence.

See answer section

TRY THIS

Solve and graph.

5. $x + 6 > 9$
6. $x + 4 \le 7$

Remark. We cannot check all the solutions of an inequality by substitution as we can check solutions of equations. There are too many. However, we really do not need to check. Let us see why. Consider the first and last inequalities, $x + 3 > 6$ and $x > 3$.

We have proved "If $x + 3 > 6$, then $x > 3$." The solution set of the antecedent of a conditional sentence is always a subset of the solution set of the consequent.

Thus any number that makes the first inequality true must make the last inequality true. Now the question is, will any number that makes the last one true also be a solution of the first one? Let us use the addition principle again, adding 3:

$$x > 3$$
$$x + 3 > 6$$

This proves the converse, that is, "If $x > 3$, then $x + 3 > 6$."

Now we know that any number that makes $x > 3$ true also makes $x + 3 > 6$ true. Thus the sentences $x > 3$ and $x + 3 > 6$ have the same solutions. Now we know that when we use Theorem 5-1, the first and last sentences will have the same solutions.

Example 5. Solve $5x - 2 \le 4x - 1$.
$$5x - 2 + 2 \le 4x - 1 + 2 \qquad \textit{Adding 2}$$
$$5x \le 4x + 1 \qquad \textit{Simplifying}$$
$$5x - 4x \le 4x + 1 - 4x \qquad \textit{Adding} -4x$$
$$x \le 1$$

Now we know that any number less than or equal to 1 is a solution.

TRY THIS ➡

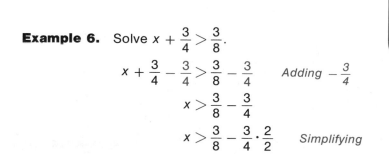

Solve. You need not graph.

7. $3x + 1 > 2x - 5$
8. $1 + 4y \le 5y + 2$

7. $x > -6$ 8. $y \ge -1$

Example 6. Solve $x + \dfrac{3}{4} > \dfrac{3}{8}$.
$$x + \frac{3}{4} - \frac{3}{4} > \frac{3}{8} - \frac{3}{4} \qquad \textit{Adding} -\frac{3}{4}$$
$$x > \frac{3}{8} - \frac{3}{4}$$
$$x > \frac{3}{8} - \frac{3}{4} \cdot \frac{2}{2} \qquad \textit{Simplifying}$$

$$x > \frac{3}{8} - \frac{6}{8}$$

$$x > -\frac{3}{8}$$

TRY THIS

Solve. You need not graph.

9. $x - \frac{1}{3} > \frac{5}{4}$ $x > \frac{19}{12}$

Exercise Set 5-1

▌ Graph on a number line. (*See Examples 2 and 3.*)

1. $x \leq 4$ See answer section
2. $y \leq -1$
3. $x > 5$
4. $x > 3$
5. $y < 10$
6. $x < -4$
7. $x \geq -5$
8. $y \geq -1$
9. $x < 0$
10. $y < -8$

▌▌ Solve using the addition principle. (*See Examples 4–6.*)

11. $x + 8 > 3$ $x > -5$
12. $x + 5 > 2$ $x > -3$
13. $y + 3 < 9$ $y < 6$
14. $y + 4 < 10$ $y < 6$
15. $a + 9 \leq -12$ $a \leq -21$
16. $a + 7 \leq -13$ $a \leq -20$
17. $t + 14 \geq 9$ $t \geq -5$
18. $t + 16 \geq 6$ $t \geq -10$
19. $x - 9 \leq 10$ $x \leq 19$
20. $x - 4 \leq 15$ $x \leq 19$
21. $y - 8 > -14$ $y > -6$
22. $y - 9 > -18$ $y > -9$
23. $x - 11 \leq -2$ $x \leq 9$
24. $y - 18 \leq -4$ $y \leq 14$
25. $y - \frac{1}{8} \leq \frac{1}{4}$ $y \leq \frac{3}{8}$
26. $y - \frac{1}{4} \leq \frac{1}{2}$ $y \leq \frac{3}{4}$
27. $x - \frac{1}{4} \geq -\frac{1}{3}$ $x \geq -\frac{1}{12}$
28. $x + \frac{1}{3} \leq -\frac{1}{6}$ $x \leq -\frac{1}{2}$
29. $x + 2.6 \leq 5.3$ $x \leq 2.7$
30. $x + 3.9 \leq 8.2$ $x \leq 4.3$
31. $5x - 1 > 4x + 7$ $x > 8$
32. $6x - 3 > 5x + 9$ $x > 12$
33. $1 + 2x < 3x + 5$ $x > -4$
34. $2 + 5x < 6x + 7$ $x > -5$
35. $11 - 3x \geq -4x - 3$ $x \geq -14$
36. $12 - 2x \geq -3x - 7$ $x \geq -19$
37. $8x + \frac{2}{3} \leq 7x - \frac{7}{8}$ $x \leq -\frac{37}{24}$
38. $5x + \frac{1}{4} \leq 4x - \frac{1}{5}$ $x \leq -\frac{9}{20}$
39. $9x + 2.7 > 8x - 9.7$ $x > -12.4$
40. $10x + 3.8 > 9x - 7.8$ $x > -11.6$

Calculator Exercises   41. $x \leq -0.010658$ 42. $y \geq -0.006888$ 43. $x \leq 0.01805$ 44. $y < -0.000114$

41. $x + 0.000894 \leq -0.009764$
42. $y + 0.001096 \geq -0.005792$
43. $8x - 0.00962 \leq 7x + 0.00843$
44. $6y - 0.000834 < 5y - 0.000948$

5-2 More About Solving Inequalities

After finishing Lesson 5-2, you should be able to
▮ solve and graph conjunctions of inequalities in one variable.
▮▮ solve and graph disjunctions of inequalities in one variable.
▮▮▮ solve inequalities using the multiplication principle.
▮▮▮▮ solve inequalities using both the addition and multiplication principles.

▮Conjunctions

Consider the sentence $-2 \le x < 3$. This is an abbreviation for
the conjunction $-2 \le x$ and $x < 3$. Thus any solution of
$-2 \le x < 3$ must be a solution of *both* $-2 \le x$ and $x < 3$.

Example 1. Graph $-2 \le x < 3$.

Example 2. Graph $-7 < x \le 5$.

Example 3. Graph $-4 \le x \le 2$.

TRY THIS ➡️

See answer section

Graph.

1. $-1 \le x < 4$
2. $-1 < x \le 4$
3. $-1 \le x \le 4$

Example 4. Solve $-3 < x + 5 < 7$.

Method 1. We first express this conjunction with the word *and*.
Then we solve the inequalities separately.

$$
\begin{array}{ccc}
-3 < x + 5 & and & x + 5 < 7 \\
-3 + (-5) < x + 5 + (-5) & and & x + 5 + (-5) < 7 + (-5) \\
-8 < x & and & x < 2
\end{array}
$$

Now we translate back.

$$-8 < x < 2$$

Method 2. In Method 1 we did the same thing to both inequalities. We can abbreviate as follows.

$$-3 + (-5) < x + 5 + (-5) < 7 + (-5) \qquad \textit{Adding } -5$$
$$-8 < x < 2$$

Method 2 is more efficient.

TRY THIS

> 4. Consider $-2 < x + 4 < 7$.
>   a) Solve using *Method 1*.
>   b) Solve using *Method 2*.
> 5. Solve $-4 < x - 6 < 9$.
>   4. $-6 < x < 3$ 5. $2 < x < 15$

ıı Disjunctions

Consider the disjunction $x < -3$ *or* $x > 3$. A disjunction is true when one or both parts are true. There is no number that is both less than -3 and greater than 3. Thus the solutions are those numbers which are either less than -3 *or* greater than 3.

Examples. Graph these disjunctions of inequalities.

5. $x < -3$ *or* $x > 3$

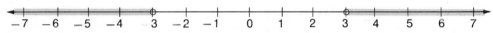

6. $x < -1$ *or* $x \geq 4$

7. $x \leq 2$ *or* $x \geq 5$

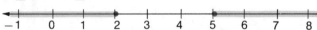

TRY THIS

> Graph.
>
> 6. $x \leq -2$ or $x > 2$
> 7. $x < -2$ or $x \geq 2$
> 8. $x \leq -2$ or $x \geq 2$
> See answer section

Example 8. Solve: $x - 5 < -2$ or $x - 5 > 2$.

We solve the inequalities separately, but we keep writing the word *or*.

$$x - 5 + 5 < -2 + 5 \qquad or \qquad x - 5 + 5 > 2 + 5$$
$$x < 3 \qquad\qquad or \qquad\qquad x > 7$$

TRY THIS

Answers.   9. $x < 1$ or $x > 7$ 10. $x < -7$ or $x > -1$

> Solve.
>
> 9. $x - 4 < -3$
>   or $x - 4 > 3$
> 10. $x + 4 < -3$
>   or $x + 4 > 3$

▮▮▮ The Multiplication Principle

Consider the true inequality

$$4 < 9.$$

If we multiply both numbers by 2 we get another true inequality,

$$8 < 18.$$

If we multiply both numbers by -3 we get a false inequality,

$$-12 < -27.$$

However, if we reverse the inequality symbol we get a true inequality,

$$-12 > -27.$$

THEOREM 5-2   (The Multiplication Principle for Inequalities)
If both members of a true inequality are multiplied by a positive number, another true inequality is obtained.
If both members are multiplied by a *negative* number and the inequality sign is reversed, another true inequality is obtained.

When we solve an inequality using the multiplication principle, we do not need to check, provided that we do not multiply by an expression containing a variable.

Examples.   Solve these inequalities.

9. $3y < \dfrac{3}{4}$

$\quad\dfrac{1}{3} \cdot 3y < \dfrac{1}{3} \cdot \dfrac{3}{4}$ *Using Theorem 5-2, multiplying by $\dfrac{1}{3}$*

$\qquad y < \dfrac{1}{4}$

Any number less than $\dfrac{1}{4}$ is a solution.

10. $-4x < \dfrac{4}{5}$

$\quad -\dfrac{1}{4} \cdot -4x > -\dfrac{1}{4} \cdot \dfrac{4}{5}$ *Multiplying by $-\dfrac{1}{4}$ and reversing the inequality sign*

$\qquad x > -\dfrac{1}{5}$

Any number greater than $-\dfrac{1}{5}$ is a solution.

TRY THIS

Answers. 11. $y \leqslant \frac{3}{10}$ 12. $y < -\frac{5}{12}$

> Solve.
>
> 11. $5y \leq \frac{3}{2}$
>
> 12. $-2y > \frac{5}{6}$

IIII Using the Principles Together

We use the addition and multiplication principles together in solving inequalities in much the same way as for equations.

Example 11. Solve: $7 - 4y > 8$.

$$-7 + 7 - 4y > -7 + 8 \qquad \textit{Adding } -7$$
$$-4y > 1 \qquad \textit{Simplifying}$$
$$-\frac{1}{4} \cdot -4y < -\frac{1}{4} \cdot 1 \qquad \textit{Multiplying by } -\frac{1}{4} \textit{ and}$$
$$\textit{reversing the inequality sign}$$
$$y < -\frac{1}{4} \qquad \textit{Simplifying}$$

TRY THIS

Answers. 13. $y \leqslant -\frac{1}{5}$ 14. $x < \frac{1}{2}$

> Solve.
>
> 13. $6 - 5y \geq 7$
> 14. $3x + 5x < 4$

Example 12. Solve: $16 - 7y \geq 10y - 4$.

$$-16 + 16 - 7y \geq -16 + 10y - 4 \qquad \textit{Adding } -16$$
$$-7y \geq 10y - 20 \qquad \textit{Simplifying}$$
$$-10y - 7y \geq -10y + 10y - 20 \qquad \textit{Adding } -10y$$
$$-17y \geq -20 \qquad \textit{Simplifying}$$
$$-\frac{1}{17} \cdot (-17y) \leq -\frac{1}{17} \cdot (-20) \qquad \textit{Multiplying by } -\frac{1}{17} \textit{ and}$$
$$\textit{reversing the inequality sign}$$
$$y \leq \frac{20}{17}$$

Example 13. Solve this conjunction of inequalities.

$$-1 < 2x + 3 \leq 11$$
$$-1 + (-3) < 2x + 3 + (-3) \leq 11 + (-3) \qquad \textit{Adding } -3$$
$$-4 < 2x \leq 8 \qquad \textit{Simplifying}$$
$$\frac{1}{2} \cdot (-4) < \frac{1}{2} \cdot 2x \leq \frac{1}{2} \cdot 8 \qquad \textit{Multiplying by } \frac{1}{2}$$
$$-2 < x \leq 4 \qquad \textit{Simplifying}$$

> Solve.
>
> 15. $17 - 5y \leq 8y - 5$
> 16. $7 \leq 4x - 5 < 11$

TRY THIS

Answers. 15. $y \geqslant \frac{22}{13}$ 16. $3 \leqslant x < 4$

Exercise Set 5-2

▌Graph. (*See Examples 1–3.*)

1. $-2 < x < 4$ See answer section
3. $-2 \leq x < 4$
5. $1 < x < 6$
7. $-7 \leq y \leq -3$

2. $-2 < x \leq 4$
4. $-2 \leq x \leq 4$
6. $0 \leq y \leq 3$
8. $-9 \leq x < -5$

Solve. (*See Example 4.*)

9. $-2 < x + 2 < 8$ $-4 < x < 6$
11. $2 \leq y + 5 \leq 9$ $-3 \leq y \leq 4$
13. $-5 < x + 8 < 12$ $-13 < x < 4$
15. $-10 \leq x - 5 \leq -1$ $-5 \leq x \leq 4$

10. $-1 < x + 1 \leq 6$ $-2 < x \leq 5$
12. $3 \leq x + 3 \leq 8$ $0 \leq x \leq 5$
14. $-6 < x + 6 \leq 2$ $-12 < x \leq -4$
16. $-18 \leq x - 7 < 0$ $-11 \leq x < 7$

▌▌Graph. (*See Examples 5–7.*)

17. $x < -1$ or $x > 2$ See answer section
19. $x \leq -3$ or $x > 1$
21. $x < -8$ or $x > -2$
23. $t < 1$ or $t \geq 5$

18. $x < -2$ or $x > 0$
20. $x \leq -1$ or $x > 3$
22. $t \leq -10$ or $t \geq -5$
24. $p \leq 3$ or $p \geq 9$

Solve. (*See Example 8.*)   See answer section

25. $x + 7 < -2$ or $x + 7 > 2$
27. $x - 8 \leq -3$ or $x - 8 \geq 3$
29. $x - 9 < -5$ or $x - 9 > 6$

26. $x + 9 < -4$ or $x + 9 > 4$
28. $x - 7 \leq -2$ or $x - 7 \geq 2$
30. $x - 4 < -8$ or $x - 4 > 12$

▌▌▌Solve. (*See Examples 9 and 10.*)

31. $3x < 18$ $x < 6$
33. $-5x \geq 10$ $x \leq -2$
35. $-9x \geq -81$ $x \leq 9$
37. $-5y \leq 3$ $y \geq -\frac{3}{5}$
39. $-8y < -\frac{1}{9}$ $y > \frac{1}{72}$
41. $-\frac{3}{4}x \geq -\frac{5}{8}$ $x \leq \frac{5}{6}$

32. $5x < 25$ $x < 5$
34. $-6y \geq 30$ $y \leq -5$
36. $-8y \leq -32$ $y \geq 4$
38. $-9x < 7$ $x > -\frac{7}{9}$
40. $-7x \leq -\frac{1}{4}$ $x \geq \frac{1}{28}$
42. $-\frac{5}{6}y \leq -\frac{3}{4}$ $y \geq \frac{9}{10}$

▌▌▌▌Solve. (*See Examples 11–13.*)

43. $8 + 5x \leq 38$ $x \leq 6$
45. $2x - 6 > 8$ $x > 7$
47. $5y + 2y \leq -21$ $y \leq -3$
49. $2y - 7 < 5y - 9$ $y > \frac{2}{3}$
51. $11x - 2 \geq 15x - 7$ $x \leq \frac{5}{4}$
53. $8 < 3x + 2 < 14$ $2 < x < 4$
55. $3 \leq 4x - 3 \leq 19$ $\frac{3}{2} \leq x \leq \frac{11}{2}$
57. $-7 \leq 5x - 2 \leq 12$ $-1 \leq x \leq \frac{14}{5}$

44. $7 + 4y \geq 39$ $y \geq 8$
46. $5y - 9 > 16$ $y > 5$
48. $9x + 3x \geq -24$ $x \geq -2$
50. $8x - 9 < 3x - 11$ $x < -\frac{2}{5}$
52. $10y - 3 \geq 13y - 8$ $y \leq \frac{5}{3}$
54. $9 \leq 5x + 3 < 19$ $\frac{6}{5} \leq x < \frac{16}{5}$
56. $2 < 5x - 8 \leq 12$ $2 < x \leq 4$
58. $-11 \leq 2x - 1 < -5$ $-5 \leq x < -2$

5-3 Absolute Value

After finishing Lesson 5-3, you should be able to
I find the distance between a pair of numbers on a number line.
II solve inequalities involving absolute value.

I Distance

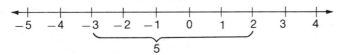

The number line above shows that the distance between -3 and
2 is 5. Another way to find the distance between two numbers
on a number line is to subtract and take the absolute value.

$$|-3 - 2| = |-5| = 5, \text{ or } |2 - (-3)| = |5| = 5$$

Note that the order in which we subtract does not matter.

For any numbers a and b, $|a - b|$ is the
distance between the two numbers a and b.

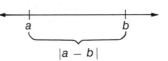

Example 1. Find the distance between -8 and -92.

$$|-8 - (-92)| = |84| = 84$$

Example 2. Find the distance between x and 0.

$$|x - 0| = |x|$$

TRY THIS ➡

> Find the distance
> between each
> pair of numbers.
>
> 1. $-7, -35$ 28
> 2. $19, 14$ 5
> 3. $a, 0$ |a|

II Equations and Inequalities with Absolute Value

Example 3. Solve $|x| = 4$.

Note that $|x| = |x - 0|$. So $|x - 0|$ is the distance from x to 0.
Thus the solutions of the equation are those numbers x whose
distance from 0 is 4. The solutions are -4 and 4.

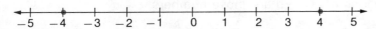

TRY THIS ➤

Solve, using a number line.

4. $|x| = 6$

5. $|x| = \frac{1}{2}$

Example 4. Solve $|x| < 4$.

Again, note that $|x| = |x - 0|$. So $|x - 0|$ is the distance from x to 0. Thus the solutions of $|x - 0| < 4$ are those numbers x whose distance from 0 is less than 4. The solutions are those numbers x such that $-4 < x < 4$.

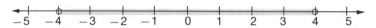

TRY THIS ➤

Solve, using a number line.

6. $|x| < 6$

7. $|x| \leq \frac{1}{2}$

Example 5. Solve $|x| \geq 4$.

Since $|x| = |x - 0|$, the solutions of $|x - 0| \geq 4$ are those numbers x whose distance from 0 is greater than or equal to 4. In other words, those numbers x such that $x \leq -4$ *or* $x \geq 4$.

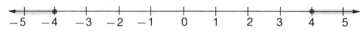

TRY THIS ➤

Solve. Use a number line.

8. $|x| \geq 6$

9. $|x| > \frac{1}{2}$

Examples 4 and 5 illustrate solving inequalities involving absolute value. We can prove that they work for any inequalities, so we state the following theorem.

THEOREM 5-3

For any number $b > 0$ and any expression X,
1. The solutions of $|X| = b$ are those numbers that satisfy $X = -b$ or $X = b$.
2. The solutions of $|X| < b$ are those numbers that satisfy $-b < X < b$.
3. The solutions of $|X| > b$ are those numbers that satisfy $X < -b$ or $X > b$.

Parts 1 and 2 of Theorem 5-3 show that the solutions of $|X| \leq b$ are those numbers that satisfy $-b \leq X \leq b$. Parts 1 and 3 together tell us that the solutions of $|X| \geq b$ are those numbers that satisfy $X \leq -b$ or $X \geq b$.

To solve inequalities with absolute value, we can use graphing or Theorem 5-3.

Example 6.   Solve $|x - 2| < 4$.

(Using Theorem 5-3). We use part 2, replacing b by 4 and X by $x - 2$.

$$-|X| < b$$
$$|x - 2| < 4$$
$$-4 < x - 2 < 4$$
$$-2 < x < 6 \quad \textit{Adding 2}$$

TRY THIS

10.   Solve $|x - 3| < 7$ using Theorem 5-3.

−4 < x < 10

Example 7.   Solve $|x + 2| \geq 5$.

(Graphing). We can rewrite this as $|x - (-2)| \geq 5$, and then think of distance. The solutions are those numbers x whose distance from -2 is greater than or equal to 5. Thus the solutions are those numbers x such that $x \leq -7$ or $x \geq 3$.

TRY THIS

Answers.   11. $x \leqslant -7$ or $x \geqslant 1$ 12. $-8 \leqslant x \leqslant 3$

Solve.

11. $|x + 3| \geq 4$
12. $|2x + 5| \leq 11$

Example 8.   Solve $\left|\dfrac{3x - 1}{5}\right| > 2$.

We use Theorem 5-3, part 3, replacing b by 2 and X by $\dfrac{3x - 1}{5}$.

$$\left|\frac{3x - 1}{5}\right| > 2$$

$$\frac{3x - 1}{5} < -2 \qquad \textit{or} \qquad \frac{3x - 1}{5} > 2$$
$$3x - 1 < -10 \qquad \textit{or} \qquad 3x - 1 > 10 \qquad \textit{Multiplying by 5}$$
$$3x < -9 \qquad \textit{or} \qquad 3x > 11 \qquad \textit{Adding 1}$$
$$x < -3 \qquad \textit{or} \qquad x > \frac{11}{3} \qquad \textit{Multiplying by } \tfrac{1}{3}$$

TRY THIS ━━━▶

13. Solve $\left|\dfrac{4x + 2}{3}\right| > 1$.

$x < -\dfrac{5}{4}$ or $x > \dfrac{1}{4}$

Exercise Set 5-3

▌Find the distance between each pair of numbers. (*See Examples 1 and 2.*)

1. $-8, -42$ ₃₄ 2. $-9, -36$ ₂₇
3. $26, 15$ ₁₁ 4. $54, 18$ ₃₆
5. $-26, -35$ ₉ 6. $-58, -96$ ₃₈
7. $-9, 24$ ₃₃ 8. $-18, 37$ ₅₅
9. $-\dfrac{1}{2}, -\dfrac{1}{4}$ $\frac14$ 10. $-\dfrac{1}{3}, -\dfrac{1}{6}$ $\frac16$
11. $h, 0$ $|h|$ 12. $b, 0$ $|b|$

▌▌Solve. (*See Examples 3–8.*)

13. $|x| = 3$ ₋₃, ₃ 14. $|x| = 5$ ₋₅, ₅
15. $|y| = 9$ ₋₉, ₉ 16. $|y| = 12$ ₋₁₂, ₁₂
17. $|x| < 3$ ₋₃<x<₃ 18. $|x| \le 5$ ₋₅≤x≤₅
19. $|y| \le 6$ ₋₆≤y≤₆ 20. $|y| < 10$ ₋₁₀<y<₁₀
21. $|x| > 2$ x<₋₂ or x>₂ 22. $|x| > 5$ x<₋₅ or x>₅
23. $|y| \ge 4$ y≤₋₄ or y≥₄ 24. $|y| \ge 8$ y≤₋₈ or y≥₈
25. $|x - 3| < 12$ ₋₉<x<₁₅ 26. $|x - 2| < 6$ ₋₄<x<₈
27. $|x + 5| \le 19$ ₋₂₄≤x≤₁₄ 28. $|x + 3| \le 12$ ₋₁₅≤x≤₉
29. $|2x + 3| \le 4$ $-\frac72\le x\le\frac12$ 30. $|5x + 2| \le 3$ $-1\le x\le\frac15$
31. $|4x - 9| < 8$ $\frac14<x<\frac{17}{4}$ 32. $|5x - 8| < 7$ $\frac15<x<3$
33. $|2y - 7| > 5$ y<1 or y>6 34. $|3y - 4| > 8$ $y<-\frac43$ or y>4
35. $|4x - 9| \ge 14$ $x\le-\frac54$ or $x\ge\frac{23}{4}$ 36. $|9y - 2| \ge 17$ $y\le-\frac53$ or $y\ge\frac{19}{9}$
37. $\left|\dfrac{2x - 1}{3}\right| \le 1$ ₋₁≤x≤₂ 38. $\left|\dfrac{5x - 2}{6}\right| \le 2$ $-2\le x\le\frac{14}{5}$
39. $\left|\dfrac{3x - 1}{4}\right| \ge 2$ $x\le-\frac73$ or x≥3 40. $\left|\dfrac{3x - 2}{5}\right| \ge 1$ x≤₋₁ or $x\ge\frac73$

Calculator Exercises

Solve. 41. 0.79494 ≤ x ≤ 0.80506 42. y ≤ 0.1466 or y ≥ 0.1534

41. $\left|\dfrac{0.005x - 0.004}{0.0059}\right| \le 0.0043$ 42. $\left|\dfrac{0.006y - 0.0009}{0.0023}\right| \ge 0.0089$

5-4 *Inequalities in Two Variables*

After finishing Lesson 5-4, you should be able to
▌ graph inequalities in two variables on a plane.

▌ The solutions of inequalities in two variables are ordered pairs.

Example 1. Determine whether $(-3, 2)$ is a solution of
$5x - 4y > 13$.

We replace x by -3 and y by 2.

$$
\begin{array}{c|c}
5x - 4y > 13 & \\
\hline
5(-3) - 4 \cdot 2 & 13 \\
-15 - 8 & \\
-23 & \\
\end{array}
$$

Since $-23 > 13$ is false, $(-3, 2)$ is not a solution.

TRY THIS ➡

1. Determine whether $(4, -3)$
    is a solution of
    $-2x + 3y \leq 6$. Yes

Inequalities in two variables are graphed on a plane.

Example 2. Graph $y < x$.

For comparison we first graph the line $y = x$ as shown below. We draw it dashed. Every solution of $y = x$ is an ordered pair having the same first and second coordinates.

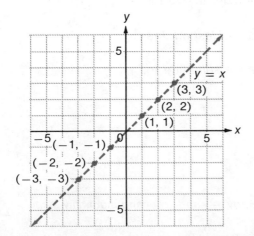

Now look at the vertical line through (2, 2) and some ordered pairs on it as shown below on the left.

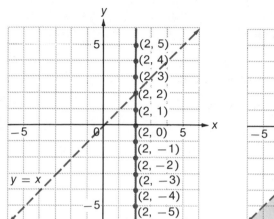
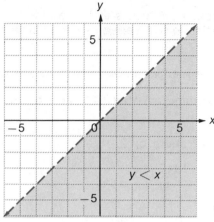

For all points below $y = x$, the second coordinate is less than the first ($y < x$). For all points above the line, $y > x$. The same thing happens for any vertical line. Then for all points below $y = x$ the ordered pairs are solutions. We shade the half-plane below $y = x$. The graph of $y < x$ is shown above on the right. The points on the line $y = x$ are not in the graph; that is why we drew it dashed.

TRY THIS

See answer section

2. Graph $y > x$.

In general,

> the graph of $y < mx + b$ consists of all pairs below the line $y = mx + b$.
> the graph of $y > mx + b$ consists of all pairs above the line $y = mx + b$.
> for $y < mx + b$, or $y > mx + b$, we draw a *dashed* line for $y = mx + b$.
> for $y \leq mx + b$, or $y \geq mx + b$, we draw a *solid* line for $y = mx + b$.

Example 3. Graph $6x - 2y < 10$.

a) We first solve for y.

$$6x - 2y < 10$$
$$-2y < -6x + 10 \qquad \textit{Adding } -6x$$
$$y > -\tfrac{1}{2}(-6x + 10) \qquad \textit{Multiplying by } -\tfrac{1}{2} \textit{ and reversing inequality sign}$$
$$y > 3x - 5 \qquad \textit{Simplifying}$$

b) We graph $y = 3x - 5$ using a dashed line, and shade the region above the line.

x	y
0	-5
1	-2
2	1

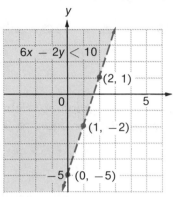

TRY THIS

See answer section

Graph.

3. $6x - 2y \leq 10$
4. $5y - 2x > -10$

Here is an example of a method in which we do not need to solve for *y*.

Example 4. Graph $3x - 2y \geq 6$.

a) Graph $3x - 2y = 6$ using a solid line. The *y*-intercept is $(0, -3)$ and the *x*-intercept is $(2, 0)$.

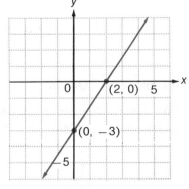

b) We try a checkpoint off the line to see which side of the line to shade. The origin $(0, 0)$ is usually an easy one to try. $3 \cdot 0 - 2 \cdot 0 \geq 6$ is false, so the origin is not in the graph. We shade the other half-plane.

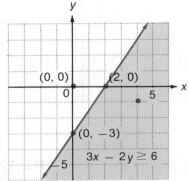

If the line contains the origin then we try another point not on the line. The point (1, 1) is often a good one to try.

TRY THIS

See answer section

> Graph.
>
> 5. $3x - 2y > 6$
> 6. $2x + 3y \leq 6$

Example 5. Graph $x \leq 3$.

We can think of this as $x + 0y \leq 3$. The graph consists of all pairs whose first coordinate x is less than or equal to 3.

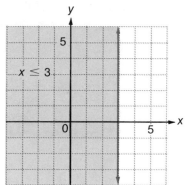

TRY THIS

See answer section

> Graph.
>
> 7. $x \leq -1$
> 8. $x > 2$
> 9. $y > -2$

Example 6. Graph $-1 < y \leq 2$.

The graph consists of all pairs whose second coordinate y is greater than -1 and less than or equal to 2.

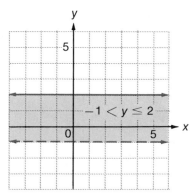

See answer section

TRY THIS

> Graph.
>
> 10. $1 \leq y \leq 3$
> 11. $-4 \leq x < 1$

Exercise Set 5-4

▌Use graph paper. Graph these inequalities. (*See Examples 2–6.*)

1. $y > 2x$ See answer section   2. $y > 3x$
3. $y \leq x + 1$ 4. $y \leq x + 3$
5. $y > x + 2$ 6. $y > x + 4$
7. $y \leq x - 2$ 8. $y < x - 3$
9. $y > x - 1$ 10. $y \geq x - 2$
11. $x + y < 4$ 12. $x + y \leq 5$
13. $x - y > 8$ 14. $x - y \geq 3$
15. $3x + 4y \leq 12$ 16. $2x + 3y < 6$
17. $7x + 3y < 21$ 18. $5x + 4y \geq 20$
19. $2y - 3x > 6$ 20. $2y - x \leq 4$
21. $x < -4$ 22. $x \geq 1$
23. $y \geq 5$ 24. $y < 2$
25. $x \geq 0$ 26. $y \geq 0$
27. $-4 < y < -1$ 28. $-2 < y < 3$
29. $-3 \leq x \leq 3$ 30. $-4 \leq x \leq 4$

Challenge Exercises

Graph.   See answer section

31. $y > |x|$ 32. $y \leq |x|$ 33. $y > |x| + 3$
34. $|x| + |y| = 2$ 35. $|x| + |y| > 2$ 36. $|x| + |y| < 2$

COMPUTER NOTE: Number Crunching

Computers can solve problems that require many thousands or millions of calculations. Dealing with so many calculations is called number crunching. A classic number-crunching problem is the relation of three bodies in space. How do their gravitational fields interact? About 300 years ago, Sir Issac Newton solved the problem for two bodies such as the earth and the moon. It was not until 1950 that the three-body problem was solved. It was done by mathematicians and a number-crunching computer.

5-5 Systems of Linear Inequalities

After finishing Lesson 5-5, you should be able to
∎ graph systems of linear inequalities in two variables.
∎∎ graph systems of linear inequalities in two variables and find vertices if a polygon is formed.

∎ Graphs

A pair of linear inequalities is called a *system* of inequalities. The solutions of the system are the ordered pairs that make both inequalities true.

Example 1. Graph this system: $y < x$
$$y < -2x - 1$$

The graphs of the separate inequalities are shown below on the left. The intersection of these graphs is shown on the right. This is the graph of the system.

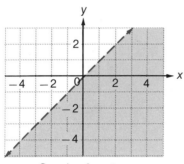
Graph of $y < x$

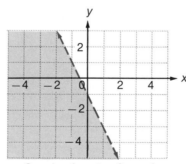
Graph of $y < -2x - 1$

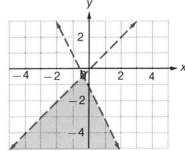
This is the graph of the system.

Example 2. Graph this system: $y \leq -2$
$$x < -1$$

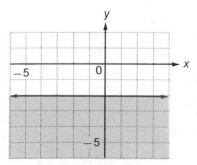
Graph of $y \leq -2$

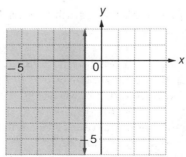
Graph of $x \leq -1$

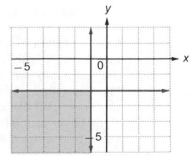
This is the graph of the system.

TRY THIS

See answer section

ıı Graphs and Vertices

Example 3.   Graph this system. If a polygon is formed, find the vertices.

$$2x + y \geq 2$$
$$4x + 3y \leq 12$$
$$\tfrac{1}{2} \leq x \leq 2$$
$$y \geq 0$$

> Graph these systems.
>
> 1. $y > x$
> $y < -2x + 1$
> 2. $y \geq 2$
> $x > -3$

The separate graphs are shown at the left and the graph of the intersection, which is the graph of the system, is shown at the right.

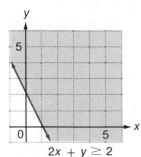

$$2x + y \geq 2$$

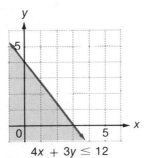

$$4x + 3y \leq 12$$

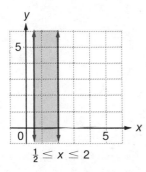

$$\tfrac{1}{2} \leq x \leq 2$$

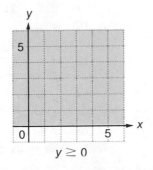

$$y \geq 0$$

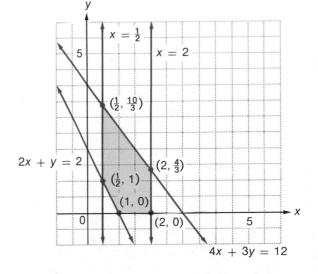

We find the vertex $(\tfrac{1}{2}, 1)$ by solving the system

$$2x + y = 2$$
$$x = \tfrac{1}{2}$$

We find the vertex $(1, 0)$ by solving the system

$$2x + y = 2$$
$$y = 0$$

We find the vertex (2, 0) from the system

$$x = 2$$
$$y = 0$$

The vertices $(2, \frac{4}{3})$ and $(\frac{1}{2}, \frac{10}{3})$ were found by solving, respectively, the systems

$$x = 2 \qquad \text{and} \qquad x = \frac{1}{2}$$
$$4x + 3y = 12 \qquad\qquad 4x + 3y = 12$$

TRY THIS ➡

Graph. If a polygon is formed, find the vertices.

3. $y \le 2x + 2$
   $y \ge -\frac{1}{3}x + 2$
   $1 \le y \le 3$
   $x \le 5$

See answer section

Exercise Set 5-5

▌Graph (*See Examples 1 and 2.*)

1. $y < x$ See answer section
   $y > -x + 3$

2. $y > x$
   $y < -x + 1$

3. $y \ge x$
   $y < -x + 4$

4. $y \ge x$
   $y < -x + 2$

5. $y \ge -2$
   $x > 1$

6. $y \le -2$
   $x > 2$

7. $x < 3$
   $y \ge -3x + 2$

8. $x > -2$
   $y \le -2x + 3$

9. $y \ge -2$
   $y \ge x + 3$

10. $y \le 4$
    $y \ge -x + 2$

11. $x + y \le 1$
    $x - y \le 2$

12. $x + y \le 3$
    $x - y \le 4$

13. $y - 2x > 1$
    $y - 2x < 3$

14. $y + 3x > 0$
    $y + 3x < 2$

15. $2y - x \le 2$
    $y - 3x \ge -1$

16. $x + 3y \ge 9$
    $3x - 2y \le 5$

▌▌Graph. If a polygon is formed, find the vertices. (*See Example 3.*)

17. $x + 2y \le 12$ See answer section
    $2x + y \le 12$
    $x \ge 0$
    $y \ge 0$

18. $8x + 5y \le 40$
    $x + 2y \le 8$
    $x \ge 0$
    $y \ge 0$

19. $3x + 4y \ge 12$
    $5x + 6y \le 30$
    $1 \le x \le 3$

20. $y - 2x \ge 3$
    $y - 2x \le 5$
    $6 \le y \le 8$

5-6 *Linear Programming*

After finishing Lesson 5-6, you should be able to
▮ find the maximum and minimum values, if they exist, of a linear function subject to a system of constraints.
▮▮ solve linear programming problems.

▮Linear Programming

You are taking a test in which items of type A are worth 10 points and items of type B are worth 15 points. It takes 3 minutes for each item of type A and 6 minutes for each item of type B. Total time allowed is 60 minutes and you may not answer more than 16 questions. Assuming all of your answers are correct, how many items of each type should you answer to get the best score?

A kind of mathematics called *linear programming* provides the answer.

Let $x =$ the number of items of type A, and
  $y =$ the number of items of type B.

The total score T is given by $T = 10x + 15y$. The set of ordered pairs (x, y) for which this equation makes sense is determined by the following inequalities, called *constraints*.

Total number of questions allowed, not more than 16:	$x + y \leq 16$
Time, not more than 60 minutes:	$3x + 6y \leq 60$
Number of items of type A, not negative:	$x \geq 0$
Number of items of type B, not negative:	$y \geq 0$

We now graph the system of inequalities and determine the vertices, if any are formed.

The graph consists of a polygon and its interior. Under this condition, T does have a maximum value and a minimum value. Moreover, the maximum and minimum values occur at the vertices of the polygon. All we need do is find the vertices and substitute the coordinates in $T = 10x + 15y$.

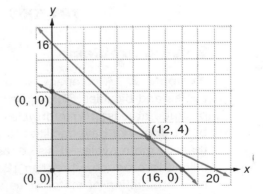

Vertices: (x, y)	Score: $T = 10x + 15y$	
(0, 0)	0	*Minimum*
(16, 0)	160	
(12, 4)	180	*Maximum*
(0, 10)	150	

Thus the maximum score is 180. To get this you would answer 12 items of type A and 4 items of type B.

The following is the main theorem used to solve linear programming problems.

THEOREM 5-4

Suppose a quantity F is given by a linear equation $F = ax + by + c$, and that the set of ordered pairs (x, y) for which the equation makes sense can be described by a system of linear inequalities (called *constraints*). If the graph of this system consists of a polygon and its interior, then F has a maximum and a minimum value, and they occur at the vertices.

Example 1. Find the maximum and minimum values of $F = 9x + 40y$, subject to the constraints

$$y - x \geq 1$$
$$y - x \leq 3$$
$$2 \leq x \leq 5$$

We graph the system of inequalities, determine the vertices, and find the function value for those ordered pairs.

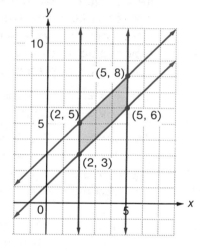

Vertices: (x, y)	$F = 9x + 40y$	
(2, 3)	138	*Minimum*
(2, 5)	218	
(5, 6)	285	
(5, 8)	365	*Maximum*

The maximum value of F occurs when $x = 5$ and $y = 8$.
The minimum value of F occurs when $x = 2$ and $y = 3$.

TRY THIS ➤

ıı Solving Problems

Example 2. A company manufactures motorcycles and bicycles. To stay in business it must produce at least 10 motorcycles each month, but it does not have facilities to produce more than 60 motorcycles. It also does not have facilities to produce more than 120 bicycles. The total production of motorcycles and bicycles cannot exceed 160. The profit on a motorcycle is $134 and on a bicycle is $20. Find the number of each that should be manufactured to maximize profit.

Find maximum and minimum values of the following.

1. $F = 34x + 6y$ subject to:
   $x + y \leq 6$
   $x + y \geq 1$
   $1 \leq x \leq 3$
2. $G = 3x - 5y + 27$ subject to:
   $x + 2y \leq 8$
   $0 \leq y \leq 3$
   $0 \leq x \leq 6$
   See answer section

Let x = the number of motorcycles to be produced, and y = the number of bicycles to be produced.

The profit P is given by $P = 134x + 20y$, subject to the constraints

$10 \leq x \leq 60$
$0 \leq y \leq 120$
$x + y \leq 160$

Vertices: (x, y)	Profit $P = 134x + 20y$	
(10, 0)	1340	
(60, 0)	8040	
(60, 100)	10,040	*Maximum*
(40, 120)	7760	
(10, 120)	3740	

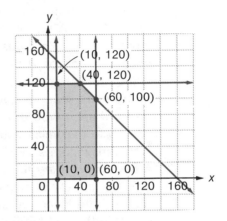

Thus the company will make a maximum profit of $10,040 by producing 60 motorcycles and 100 bicycles.

TRY THIS

Answer. 3. The snack bar will make a maximum profit of $23.70 by selling 40 hamburgers and 50 hot dogs.

3. A college snack bar cooks and sells hamburgers and hot dogs during the lunch hour. To stay in business it must sell at least 10 hamburgers but cannot cook more than 40. It must also sell at least 30 hot dogs but cannot cook more than 70. It cannot cook more than 90 sandwiches all together. The profit on a hamburger is $0.33 and on a hot dog it is $0.21. How many of each kind of sandwich should the snack bar sell to make the maximum profit?

Exercise Set 5-6

Find the maximum and minimum values, and where they occur. (*See Example 1.*)

1. $F = 4x + 28y$ subject to:
   $5x + 9 \leq 34$
   $3x + 5y \leq 30$
   $x \geq 0$ Max of F is 168 when x = 0 and y = 6.
   $y \geq 0$ Min of F is 0 when x = 0 and y = 0.

2. $G = 14x + 16y$ subject to:
   $2y + 9 \leq 16$ Max of G is 84 when x = 2 and y
   $7x + 4y \leq 28$ $= \frac{7}{2}$. Min of G is 0 when x = 0 and
   $x \geq 0$ y = 0.
   $y \geq 0$

3. $P = 16x - 2y + 40$ subject to:
   $6x + 8y \leq 48$
   $0 \leq y \leq 4$ Max of P is 152 when x = 7 and y = 0.
   $0 \leq x \leq 7$ Min of P is 32 when x = 0 and y = 4.

4. $Q = 24x - 3y + 52$ subject to:
   $5x + 4y \geq 20$
   $0 \leq y \leq 4$ Max of Q is 124 when x = 3 and
   $0 \leq x \leq 3$ y = 0. Min of Q is 40 when x = 0
   and y = 4.

▐▌ Solve. (*See Example 2.*)   See answer section

5. You are about to take a test that contains questions of type A worth 4 points and questions of type B worth 7 points. You must do at least 5 questions of type A but time restricts doing more than 10. You must do at least 3 questions of type B but time restricts doing more than 10. In total, you can do no more than 18 questions. How many of each type of question must you do to maximize your score? What is this maximum score?

6. You are about to take a test that contains questions of type A worth 10 points and questions of type B worth 25 points. You must do at least 3 questions of type A but time restricts doing more than 12. You must do at least 4 questions of type B but time restricts doing more than 15. In total you can do no more than 20 questions. How many of each type of question must you do to maximize your score? What is this maximum score?

7. A man is planning to invest up to $22,000 in bank X or bank Y or both. He wants to invest at least $2000 but no more than $14,000 in bank X. Bank Y does not insure more than a $15,000 investment so he will invest no more than that in bank Y. The interest in bank X is 6% and in bank Y it is $6\frac{1}{2}$% and this will be simple interest for one year. How much should he invest in each bank to maximize his income? What is the maximum income?

8. A woman is planning to invest up to $40,000 in corporate or municipal bonds or both. The least she is allowed to invest in corporate bonds is $6000 and she does not want to invest more than $22,000 in corporate bonds. She also does not want to invest more than $30,000 in municipal bonds. The interest on corporate bonds is 8% and on municipal bonds it is $7\frac{1}{2}$%. This is simple interest for one year. How much should she invest in each type of bond to maximize her income? What is the maximum income?

Challenge Exercises

9. The minimal daily nutritional requirement of protein is 50 g. For calcium it is 0.75 g. Every gram of beef contains 0.007 g of calcium and 0.186 g of protein, and costs 0.36¢. Every gram of cheddar cheese contains 0.57 g of calcium and 0.205 g of protein, and costs 0.32¢. To avoid gaining weight one should eat no more than 2000 g of beef and 1100 g of cheddar cheese. Assuming only beef and cheddar cheese are eaten, how many grams of each should be eaten to minimize the cost of obtaining the minimal daily requirements?   9. 0 g of beef and 243.90243 g of cheese to minimize cost at 78.05 ¢ per day.

COMPUTER ACTIVITY
Linear Programming

PROBLEM: Maximize $Q = 24X - 3Y + 52$ subject to the constraints that X and Y are integers,
$$0 \leq X \leq 3,$$
$$0 \leq Y \leq 4,$$
$$5X + 4Y \geq 20.$$

Example using the flowchart:

1	2	3	4		
X	Y	Q	A	X1	Y1
0	0	0			
⋮	⋮	⋮			
1	4	64	64	1	4
2	0	64	64	1	4
⋮	⋮	⋮	⋮	⋮	⋮
2	3	91	91	2	3
2	4	88	91	2	3

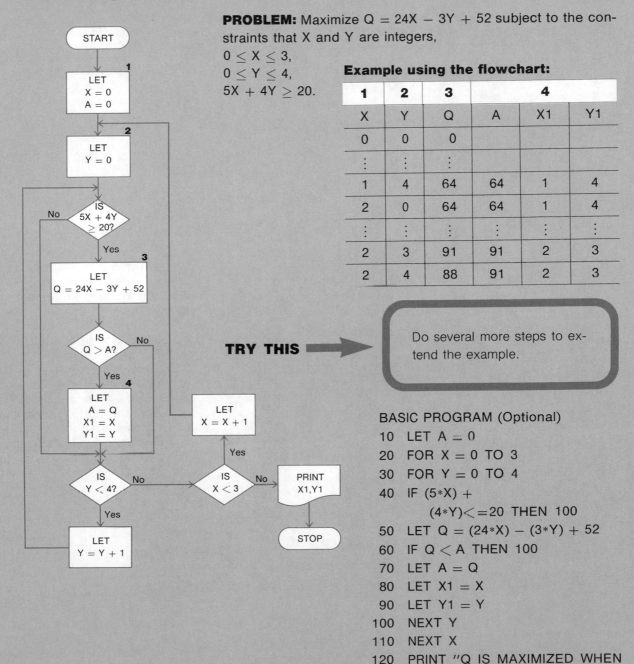

TRY THIS

Do several more steps to extend the example.

BASIC PROGRAM (Optional)

```
10   LET A = 0
20   FOR X = 0 TO 3
30   FOR Y = 0 TO 4
40   IF (5*X) +
        (4*Y)<=20 THEN 100
50   LET Q = (24*X) - (3*Y) + 52
60   IF Q < A THEN 100
70   LET A = Q
80   LET X1 = X
90   LET Y1 = Y
100  NEXT Y
110  NEXT X
120  PRINT "Q IS MAXIMIZED WHEN
        X ="X1" AND Y ="Y1
```

CHAPTER 5 REVIEW

Review the material in the chapter. Then see how you have done by trying these review exercises. If you miss an exercise, restudy the indicated lesson.

5-1   Graph on a line.
   1. $x > -1$ See answer section
   2. $x \leq 4$

5-1   Solve using the addition principle.
   3. $y + 3 \geq 4$ $y \geq 1$
   4. $2x + 7 > x - 9$ $x > -16$

5-2   Graph.   See answer section in
   5. $-3 < x < 2$
   6. $x < -2$ or $x > 5$

5-2   Solve.
   7. $-7 < 2x - 1 < 9$ $-3 < x < 5$
   8. $x + 1 < -4$ or $x + 1 > 4$
                          $x < -5$ or $x > 3$

5-2   Solve using the multiplication principle.
   9. $3x \geq 27$ $x \geq 9$
   10. $-9y \geq -45$ $y \leq 5$

5-2   Solve using the addition and multiplication principles.
   11. $3 + 8y \leq 27$ $y \leq 3$
   12. $3x - 8 \leq 7x + 5$ $x \geq -\frac{13}{4}$

5-3   Solve.
   13. $|y| < 4$ $-4 < y < 4$
   14. $|x| \geq 10$ $x \leq -10$ or $x \geq 10$
   15. $|x - 3| \leq 5$ $-2 \leq x \leq 8$
   16. $|3x + 5| < 7$ $-4 < x < \frac{2}{3}$

5-4   Graph on a plane.
   17. $y > x + 2$ See answer section
   18. $3x - 5y \geq 15$

5-5   Graph these systems.
   19. $y > x$ See answer section
        $y \leq -2x - 2$
   20. $y \geq 2$
        $x \leq -4$

5-5   21. Graph. If a polygon is formed, find the vertices.
        $5x + 10y \leq 50$
        $x + y \leq 8$
        $x \geq 0$
        $y \geq 0$ See answer section

5-6   Solve.
   22. You are about to take a test that contains questions of type A worth 4 points and questions of type B worth 8 points. You must do a total of at least 8 questions, and you must do at least 5 type A questions and 3 type B questions. You know that type A questions take 3 minutes and type B questions take 5 minutes, and that the total time cannot exceed 45 minutes. How many of each type of question must you do to maximize your score? What is this maximum score?
        5 of A and 6 of B to maximize score at 68.

CHAPTER 5 TEST

Graph on a line.
1. $x > -2$ <small>See answer section</small>
2. $x \leq 5$

Solve using the addition principle.
3. $y + 5 \geq 8$ <small>$y \geqslant 3$</small>
4. $3x + 5 > 2x - 7$ <small>$x > -12$</small>

Graph.
5. $-2 < x < 4$ <small>See answer section</small>
6. $x < -3$ or $x > 4$

Solve.
7. $-6 < 3x - 1 < 10$ <small>$-\frac{5}{3} < x < \frac{11}{3}$</small>
8. $x + 2 < -3$ or $x + 4 > 8$ <small>$x < -5$ or $x > 4$</small>

Solve using the multiplication principle.
9. $4x \geq 28$ <small>$x \geqslant 7$</small>
10. $-8y \leq -40$ <small>$y \geqslant 5$</small>

Solve using the addition and multiplication principles.
11. $4 + 7y \leq 39$ <small>$y \leqslant 5$</small>
12. $2x - 9 \leq 9x + 4$ <small>$x \geqslant -\frac{13}{7}$</small>

Solve.
13. $|x| < 3$ <small>$-3 < x < 3$</small>
14. $|y| \geq 8$ <small>$y \leqslant -8$ or $y \geqslant 8$</small>
15. $|x - 2| \leq 6$ <small>$-4 \leqslant x \leqslant 8$</small>
16. $|2x + 7| < 9$ <small>$-8 < x < 1$</small>

Graph on a plane.
17. $y < -x + 3$ <small>See answer section</small>
18. $3x + 2y \leq 18$

Solve these systems.
19. $y \geq 2x$ <small>See answer section</small>
    $y < -x + 3$
20. $y \leq 3$
    $x \geq -5$

21. Graph. If a polygon is formed, find the vertices.
    $5x + 10y \leq 50$
    $x + y \leq 8$
    $x \geq 2$ <small>See answer section</small>
    $y \geq 0$

Solve.
22. You are about to take a test which contains questions of type A worth 7 points and questions of type B worth 12 points. The total number of questions worked must be at least 8. You know that type A questions take 10 minutes and type B questions take 8 minutes, and that the maximum time for the test is 80 minutes. How many of each type of question must you do to maximize your score? What is this maximum score?
    <small>0 of A and 10 of B to maximize score at 120.</small>

Ready for Polynomials?

1-2 Find the additive inverse of each number.
  1. 6   2. −8.3   3. −$\frac{7}{8}$ 4. 0

  1. −6   2. 8.3   3. $\frac{7}{8}$ 4. 0

1-2 Add.
  5. 10 + (−4)   6   6. −6.3 + 8.2   1.9
  7. −$\frac{3}{8}$ + (−$\frac{3}{24}$)   −$\frac{1}{2}$ 8. 0 + (−2.2)   −2.2

1-3 Subtract.
  9. 4 − 8   −4   10. −4 − 8   −12
  11. $\frac{21}{5}$ − (−$\frac{5}{2}$) $\frac{67}{10}$ 12. 17.9 − 32.4   −14.5

1-4 Multiply.
  13. −2 · 6   −12   14. 3 · (−4)   −12
  15. −3.4 · (−10)   34   16. −7 · (−$\frac{4}{5}$) $\frac{28}{5}$

1-5 17. Factor: 10x + 15y − 5.   5(2x + 3y − 1)

1-5 Multiply.
  18. 3(y − 2)   19. 4(x + 12)   20. c(t + s − f)

  18. 3y − 6   19. 4x + 48   20. ct + cs − cf

1-5 Collect like terms.
  21. 3y + 2y   22. a + 4a   23. b − 4b + 3b

  21. 5y   22. 5a   23. 0

1-6 Rename each additive inverse without parentheses.
  24. −(4x)   25. −(−3a)   26. −(−1)y

  24. −4x   25. 3a   26. y

1-6 27. What are the terms of −5y + 4x − t − 4?   −5y, 4x, −t, −4

1-6 Remove parentheses and simplify.
  28. 3x − (2x + 4)   29. 7y − 2 − (8y − 4)

  28. x − 4   29. −y + 2

1-7 30. Simplify: (−2y)³.   −8y³

1-8 Multiply and simplify.
  31. y² · y⁵   32. 3⁻² · 3⁵   33. (4a⁷b⁻²)(2a²b³)

  31. y⁷   32. 3³   33. 8a⁹b

1-8 Simplify.
  34. (4³)⁴   35. (y⁻³)³

  34. 4¹²   35. y⁻⁹

Chapter 6
Polynomials

The $8.00, $8.16, $8.24, and $8.30 are the amounts of interest received on $100.00 at 8% compounded annually, semiannually, quarterly, and monthly. How can we find them?

6-1 Some Properties of Polynomials

After finishing Lesson 6-1, you should be able to
- **I** rewrite a polynomial with plus signs.
- **II** identify the terms and coefficients of a polynomial.
- **III** determine the degree of each term of a polynomial and the degree of the polynomial.
- **IIII** collect like terms.
- **IIIII** arrange a polynomial in ascending or descending powers of a given variable.
- **IIIIII** tell whether a polynomial is a monomial, binomial, trinomial, or none of these.

I Polynomials

Expressions like these are called *polynomials in one variable*.

$$2x + 3, \qquad -7x + 5, \qquad 2y^2 + 5y - 3,$$
$$5a^4 - 3a^2 + \tfrac{1}{4}a - 8, \qquad b^6 + 3b^5 - 8b + 7b^4 + \tfrac{1}{2}$$

They show additions and subtractions. Each part to be added or subtracted is a number or a number times a variable to some whole number power. A polynomial can also consist of just one of the parts. Thus the following are also polynomials in one variable.

$$5x^2, \qquad -8a, \qquad \tfrac{1}{4}y^5, \qquad 8t^4, \qquad x, \qquad a, \qquad t, \qquad 5, \qquad -2, \qquad \tfrac{1}{4}, \qquad 0$$

Expressions like these are called *polynomials in several variables*.

$$5x - xy^2 + 7y + 2, \qquad 9xy^2z - 4x^3z + (-14x^4y^2) + 9, \qquad 15x^3y^2$$

Recall that we can subtract by adding an additive inverse. So any polynomial can be rewritten with plus signs.

Examples.

1. $4x - 3 = 4x + (-3)$

2. $7xy - 4x^2 = 7xy + (-4x^2)$

3. $-9x^3z - 7xyz^2 + y - 6x^4y^2$
$\qquad = -9x^3z + (-7xyz^2) + y + (-6x^4y^2)$

TRY THIS

Rewrite each polynomial with plus signs.

1. $9xy - 5x^3 - y + 4$
2. $8pq - 7pqr^2 - 34xyz^6$

Answers.   1. $9xy + (-5x^3) + (-y) + 4$ 2. $8pq + (-7pqr^2) + (-34xyz^6)$

II Terms and Coefficients

When a polynomial is written with plus signs, the parts separated by the plus signs are its *terms,* and the numbers in the terms (other than exponents) are the *coefficients.*

Example 4. Identify the terms and the coefficients in $-3x^2 - 4x^3z + 14x^4y^3 - 9$.

We rewrite with only plus signs between the parts.

$$-3x^2 + (-4x^3z) + 14x^4y^3 + (-9)$$

The terms are $-3x^2$, $-4x^3z$, $14x^4y^3$, and -9. The coefficients are -3, -4, 14, and -9.

Answers. 3. $9xy, -5x^3, -y, 10$ 4. $-92x^5, -8x^4, x^2, \frac{1}{4}$ 5. 5, $-4, -2, 1, -1, -7$

TRY THIS

Identify the terms.

3. $9xy - 5x^3 - y + 10$
4. $-92x^5 - 8x^4 + x^2 + \frac{1}{4}$
5. What is the coefficient of each term? $5x^2y - 4xy^2 - 2y^3 + xy - y - 7$

If a coefficient is 0, we usually do not write the term. We say that we have a *missing* term.

Example 5. In $9x^5 - 2x^3 + 5x - 9$ there is no term with x^4. We say "the x^4 term is missing."

TRY THIS

Answers. 6. x^3, x^2, x 7. x^2, x 8. y^3, y^2, y, y^0

III Degrees

The *degree* of a term is the sum of the exponents of the variables. The degree of a polynomial is the same as its term of highest degree.

Identify the missing terms in each polynomial.

6. $-2x^4 + 7$
7. $x^3 - 1$
8. $-2y^4$

Example 6. Determine the degree of each term and the degree of the polynomial: $6x^2 + 8x^2y^3 - 17xy - 24xy^2z^4 + 2y + 3$.

Term	Degree
$6x^2$	2
$8x^2y^3$	5
$-17xy$	2
$-24xy^2z^4$	7
$2y$	1
3	0

The degree of the polynomial is 7.

TRY THIS

9. Determine the degree of each term and the degree of the polynomial.
    $2y + 4 - 5x + 7x^2y^3z^2 + 5xy^2$
    1, 0, 1, 7, 3; 7

ⅢⅢ Collecting Like Terms

Terms that have the same variables with the same exponents are called *like* terms.

Example 7.   **Like Terms**   **Unlike Terms**

$4x^2$ and $-2x^2$ $4x^2$ and $4x$

$7y^6z^9$ and $23y^6z^9$ $5xyz^2$ and $-5xy$

We can often simplify expressions by collecting like terms. The process is based on the distributive laws. Thus we know that the simplified expression and the original expression will name the same number for all replacements. That is, they are *equivalent*.

Examples.   Collect like terms.

8. $4x - 5x = (4 - 5)x$

$\qquad\qquad = -1 \cdot x$

$\qquad\qquad = -x$

9. $4x^3 + 5x - 4x^2 - 2x^3 + 5x^2$

$\qquad = (4 - 2)x^3 + (-4 + 5)x^2 + 5x$

$\qquad = 2x^3 + x^2 + 5x$

Answers.   10. $3x^2$ 11. $-x^3 + x^4$ 12. $3x^2 + 2x^4$

TRY THIS ➡️

> Collect like terms.
>
> 10. $5x^2 - 2x^2$
> 11. $5x^3 - 6x^3 + x^4$
> 12. $5x^2 + 3x^4 - 2x^2 - x^4$

Example 10.   Collect like terms.

$3x^2y + 5xy^2 - 3x^2y - xy^2 = (3 - 3)x^2y + (5 - 1)xy^2$

$\qquad\qquad\qquad\qquad\qquad\qquad = 4xy^2$

TRY THIS ➡️

> Collect like terms.
>
> 13. $5x^2y + 6xy^2 - 7x^2y +$ $2xy$ $-2x^2y + 6xy^2 + 2xy$
> 14. $-9pq + 8pqr^3 + 4pq +$ $3pqr^3 - 1$ $-5pq + 11pqr^3 - 1$

ⅢⅢ Ascending and Descending Order

We usually arrange polynomials in one variable so that the exponents decrease (descending order) or so that they increase (ascending order).

Examples.

11.   Arrange $-2x + x^2 + 5x^7 + 6x^5$ in descending order.

$\qquad 5x^7 + 6x^5 + x^2 - 2x$

12. Arrange $9x^{10} - 2 + 4x - 8x^2$ in ascending order.

$-2 + 4x - 8x^2 + 9x^{10}$

We will usually write polynomials in one variable in descending order although it is not incorrect to use ascending or any other order.

TRY THIS

Answers. 15. $-6x^7 + 3x^5 - 7x^4 + 6x^3 - 5x^2 + x$ 16. $9 + 4y^2 - 2y^3 - 5y^4 - 7y^5$

15. Arrange $3x^5 + x + 6x^3 - 5x^2 - 6x^7 - 7x^4$ in descending order.
16. Arrange $4y^2 + 9 - 7y^5 - 2y^3 - 5y^4$ in ascending order.

For polynomials in several variables we choose one of the variables and arrange the terms with respect to it.

Examples.

13. Arrange $y^4 + 2 - 5x^3 + 3x^3y + 7xy$ in descending powers of x.

$3x^3y - 5x^3 + 7xy + y^4 + 2$

14. Arrange $-17x^3y^2 + 4xy^3 + 13xy + 8$ in ascending powers of y.

$8 + 13xy - 17x^3y^2 + 4xy^3$

17. Arrange $-8xy^2 + 3xy + 7xy^4 - 2xy^3$ in descending powers of y.
18. Arrange $4x^2yz + 5xy^2 + 5x^3yz^2 - 4$ in ascending powers of x.

TRY THIS

Answers. 17. $7xy^4 - 2xy^3 - 8xy^2 + 3xy$ 18. $-4 + 5xy^2 + 4x^2yz + 5x^3yz^2$

We now give a precise definition of polynomials in one variable.

DEFINITION

A polynomial in x is any expression equivalent to one of this form,

$a_nx^n + a_{n-1}x^{n-1} + a_{n-2}x^{n-2} + \cdots + a_1x + a_0,$

where n is a natural number and the a's are taken from some number system.

In the standard form of a polynomial used in the definition, we have used descending order. The degree of the polynomial is of course n. The a's are the coefficients. Some or all of them can be 0.

In this chapter and the next we consider mainly polynomials with integer coefficients. Later we consider polynomials with rational coefficients. In some situations, polynomials with real number coefficients are important.

ꟷꟷꟷMonomials, Binomials, and Trinomials

Polynomials with just one term are called *monomials*. Polynomials with just two terms are called *binomials*. Those with just three terms are called *trinomials*.

Example 15.

Monomials	**Binomials**	**Trinomials**
$5x^2$	$3x - 5$	$5x^2 - 6x + \frac{1}{4}$
-1	$-2x^5 + 8x$	$3xy - 4x^2 - 10$
$-23xyz^3$	$7x^3y^4 + 91z^4$	$6x^2y^2 + \frac{1}{2}x^3 - 3$

TRY THIS

Answers.   19. None of these   20. Monomial   21. Trinomial   22. Binomial

Tell whether each polynomial is a monomial, binomial, trinomial, or none of these.

19. $9y^4 - 8y^3 - 10y + 8$
20. $-8x^5$
21. $4x^3y - 5x^2y^2 + 8xy^3$
22. $P + Prt$

Exercise Set 6-1

▎Rewrite each polynomial with plus signs. (*See Examples 1–3.*)

1. $8x^2 - 2x - 5$ See answer section
2. $9y^3 - 3y^2 + 6$
3. $18xy - 8x^3 - y + 50$
4. $24y^3 - 9y^2 - y - 21$
5. $4xy - 5xy^2 + 6x^2y - 7x^2y^2$
6. $8ab - 9ab^3 + 11a^3b - 12a^2b^2$
7. $2x^5 - 7x^4 - 6x^3 + 3x^2 - 8x - 9$
8. $5y^5 - 9y^4 - 8y^3 - 3y^2 + 9y - 11$

▎▎Identify the terms and coefficients. (*See Example 4.*)   See answer section

9. $5x^3 + 7x^2 - 3x - 9$
10. $8y^3 - 9y^2 + 12y + 11$
11. $-3xyz + 7x^2y^2 - 5xy^2z + 4xyz^2$
12. $-9abc + 19a^2bc - 8ab^2c + 12abc^2$

Identify the missing terms in each polynomial. (*See Example 5.*)

13. $x^3 + 1$ x^2, x
14. $y^3 - 2$ y^2, y
15. $-3y^4 + 8$ y^3, y^2, y
16. $-5x^4$ x^3, x^2, x, x^0

▎▎▎Determine the degree of each term and the degree of the polynomial. (*See Example 6.*)

17. $x^2 + 3y^5 - x^3y^4 - 7$ 2, 5, 7, 0; 7
18. $y^3 + 2y^6 + x^2y - 9$ 3, 6, 3, 0; 6
19. $x^5 + 3x^2y^4 - 5xy + 4x - 3$ 5, 6, 2, 1, 0; 6
20. $9y^6 + 2x^4y^4 - 8x^3y + 5x^2 - 9$ 6, 8, 4, 2, 0; 8

▮▮▮▮ Collect like terms. (*See Examples 8–10.*)

21. $6x^2 - 7x^2 + 3x^2$ $2x^2$
22. $-2y^2 - 7y^2 + 5y^2$ $-4y^2$
23. $5x - 4y - 2x + 5y$ $3x + y$
24. $4a - 9b - 6a + 3b$ $-2a - 6b$
25. $5a + 7 - 4 + 2a - 6a + 3$ $a + 6$
26. $9x + 12 - 8 - 7x + 5x + 10$ $7x + 14$
27. $x + y - z - 3x + 4z - 7y$ $-2x - 6y + 3z$
28. $a + b + c - 5a - 4b + 8c$ $-4a - 3b + 9c$
29. $3a^2b + 4b^2 - 9a^2b - 6b^2$ $-6a^2b - 2b^2$
30. $5x^2y^2 + 4x^3 - 8x^2y^2 - 12x^3$ $-3x^2y^2 - 8x^3$
31. $8x^2 - 3xy + 12y^2 + x^2 - y^2 + 5xy + 4y^2$ $9x^2 + 2xy + 15y^2$
32. $a^2 - 2ab + b^2 - 9a^2 + 5ab - 4b^2 + a^2$ $-7a^2 + 3ab - 3b^2$
33. $3y^2 - 2yz - 2z^2 + 5y^2 + 2z^2 - 3yz - 4y^2 + 5yz - z^2$ $4y^2 - z^2$
34. $x^4 - 5x^2 + 2x - 4 + 2x^3 + 3x + 5 - 4x^4 + x^3 - 7x$ $-3x^4 + 3x^3 - 5x^2 - 2x + 1$

▮▮▮▮▮ Arrange in descending order. (*See Example 11.*)

35. $x - 3x^2 + 1 + x^3$ $x^3 - 3x^2 + x + 1$
36. $x^2 - 8x^4 + 9 - x^3$ $-8x^4 - x^3 + x^2 + 9$
37. $a - a^3 + 5a^5 - 9 + 6a^2$ $5a^5 - a^3 + 6a^2 + a - 9$
38. $y^2 - 9y^4 + 18 - y + 7y^5$ $7y^5 - 9y^4 + y^2 - y + 18$

Arrange in ascending order. (*See Example 12.*)

39. $2y^3 - y + y^4 - 7 + 3y^2$ $-7 - y + 3y^2 + 2y^3 + y^4$
40. $5y^4 - 4y^3 + 8y - 11 - 2y^2$ $-11 + 8y - 2y^2 - 4y^3 + 5y^4$
41. $x^2 - x + 5x^5 - 9x^3 + 18x^4$ $-x + x^2 - 9x^3 + 5x^5 + 18x^4$
42. $-6x^3 + 9x - 42 - 3x^2 + 5x^4$ $-42 + 9x - 3x^2 - 6x^3 + 5x^4$

Arrange in descending powers of *y*. (*See Example 13.*)

43. $x^2y^2 + x^3y - xy^3 + 1$ $-xy^3 + x^2y^2 + x^3y + 1$
44. $x^3y - x^2y^2 + xy^3 + 6$ $xy^3 - x^2y^2 + x^3y + 6$

Arrange in ascending powers of *x*. (*See Example 14.*)

45. $-9x^3y + 3xy^3 + x^2y^2 + 2x^4$ $3xy^3 + x^2y^2 - 9x^3y + 2x^4$
46. $5x^2y^2 - 9xy + 8x^3y^2 - 5x^4$ $-9xy + 5x^2y^2 + 8x^3y^2 - 5x^4$

▮▮▮▮▮▮ Tell whether each polynomial is a monomial, binomial, trinomial, or none of these. (*See Example 15.*)

47. $y^3 - 8y$ Binomial
48. $-9y^4 - 3y^3 + 5y^2 + 2$ None of these
49. $5x^2 - 9xy + 8$ Trinomial
50. $-11x^2$ Monomial
51. $50x^2$ Monomial
52. $-12x^2 - xy + y^2$ Trinomial
53. $8x^3 - 9x^2y + 15x^3y^2 - 9$ None of these
54. $x^2 - 81$ Binomial

Calculator Exercises

Collect like terms.

55. $0.00976x^2y^2 - 0.08054x^3y + 0.80149x^2y^2 + 0.00943x^3y$ $0.81125x^2y^2 - 0.07111x^3y$
56. $8{,}592{,}429xy^2z - 42.004x^2y^2 + 5{,}976.006x^2y^2 - 4{,}008{,}793xy^2z$ $4{,}583{,}636xy^2z + 5934.002x^2y^2$

6-2 *Calculations with Polynomials*

After finishing Lesson 6-2, you should be able to
  ❙ add polynomials.
  ❙❙ rename the additive inverse of a polynomial without using parentheses.
  ❙❙❙ subtract polynomials.

❙ Addition

The sum of two polynomials is a polynomial. To add polynomials
we can write a plus sign between them and then collect like terms.

Example 1. Add $-5x^3 + 3x - 5$ and $8x^3 + 4x^2 + 7$.

$$(-5x^3 + 3x - 5) + (8x^3 + 4x^2 + 7) = (-5 + 8)x^3 + 4x^2 + 3x + (-5 + 7)$$
$$= 3x^3 + 4x^2 + 3x + 2$$

We still arrange the terms in descending order.

TRY THIS ➡

Add.

1. $3x^3 + 4x^2 - 7x - 2$ and
    $-7x^3 - 2x^2 + 3x + 4$
    $-4x^3 + 2x^2 - 4x + 2$

The use of columns is often helpful. To do this we
write the polynomials one under the other, writing
like terms under one another and leaving spaces for
missing terms. Let us do the addition in Example 1
using columns.

$$\begin{array}{r} -5x^3 \qquad + 3x - 5 \\ \underline{8x^3 + 4x^2 \qquad + 7} \\ 3x^3 + 4x^2 + 3x + 2 \end{array}$$

Example 2. Add $4ax^2 + 4bx - 5$ and $3ax^2 + 5bx + 8$.

$$\begin{array}{r} 4ax^2 + 4bx - 5 \\ \underline{3ax^2 + 5bx + 8} \\ 7ax^2 + 9bx + 3 \end{array}$$

Although the use of columns is helpful for complicated examples,
you should attempt to write only the answer when you can.

Example 3. Add.

$$(13x^3y + 3x^2y - 5y) + (x^3y + 4x^2y - 3xy + 3y) = 14x^3y + 7x^2y - 3xy - 2y$$

TRY THIS ➤

Add.

2. $7y^5 - 5$ and
   $3y^5 - 4y^4 + 10$
3. $5p^2q^4 - 2p^2q^2 - 3q$ and
   $-6pq^2 + 3p^2q + 5$

Answers.   2. $10y^5 - 4y^4 + 5$ 3. $5p^2q^4 - 2p^2q^2 - 6pq^2 + 3p^2q - 3q + 5$

⊪ Additive Inverses

If the sum of two polynomials is 0, they are called *additive inverses* of each other. For example, $(3x - 2) + (-3x + 2) = 0$, so the additive inverse of $(3x - 2)$ is $(-3x + 2)$. In symbols, $-(3x - 2) = -3x + 2$.

THEOREM 6-1
The additive inverse of a polynomial can be found by multiplying each term by -1.

Examples. Rewrite each additive inverse without parentheses.

4. $-(5x^3 + 2) = -1(5x^3) + (-1)2$ *Multiplying each term by -1 (Theorem 6-1)*
$= -5x^3 - 2$

5. $-(9xy^2 - 4x^3y - 8x^4 + 7) = -1(9xy^2) + (-1)(-4x^3y) + (-1)(-8x^4) + (-1)7$
$= -9xy^2 + 4x^3y + 8x^4 - 7$

Renaming an additive inverse amounts to "changing the sign" of every term inside the parentheses.

Example 6. $-(5xy^2 - 7x^3y - 8x + 4) = -5xy^2 + 7x^3y + 8x - 4$

Answers.   4. $-4x^3 + 5x^2 - \frac{1}{4}x + 10$ 5. $-8xy^2 + 4x^3y^2 + 9x + \frac{1}{5}$
6. $9y^5 + 8y^4 - \frac{1}{2}y^3 + y^2 - y + 1$

TRY THIS ➤

Rename each additive inverse without parentheses.

4. $-(4x^3 - 5x^2 + \frac{1}{4}x - 10)$
5. $-(8xy^2 - 4x^3y^2 - 9x - \frac{1}{5})$
6. $-(-9y^5 - 8y^4 + \frac{1}{2}y^3 - y^2 + y - 1)$

⊪ Subtraction

Subtraction of polynomials is defined like subtraction of numbers.

DEFINITION
For polynomials P and Q, the difference $P - Q$ is the polynomial which when added to Q gives P.

We can subtract polynomials the way we subtract numbers.

THEOREM 6-2
For any polynomials P and Q,
$P - Q = P + (-Q)$.
(We can subtract by adding the inverse of the subtrahend.)

Example 7. Subtract.

$(-9x^5 - x^3 + 2x^2 + 4) - (2x^5 - x^4 + 4x^3 - 3x^2)$

$= (-9x^5 - x^3 + 2x^2 + 4) + [-(2x^5 - x^4 + 4x^3 - 3x^2)]$ *Adding the inverse (Theorem 6-2)*

$= (-9x^5 - x^3 + 2x^2 + 4) + (-2x^5 + x^4 - 4x^3 + 3x^2)$ *Multiplying each term by -1 (Theorem 6-1)*

$= -11x^5 + x^4 - 5x^3 + 5x^2 + 4$

You should try to skip some steps by mentally "changing the sign of each term" and adding like terms. Try to write only the answer.

TRY THIS ➡

Answers.   7. $3x^2 + 5$ 8. $14y^3 - 2y + 4$ 9. $p^2 - 6p - 2$

Subtract.

7. $(6x^2 + 4) - (3x^2 - 1)$
8. $(9y^3 - 2y - 4) - (-5y^3 - 8)$
9. $(-3p^2 + 5p - 4) - (-4p^2 + 11p - 2)$

We can also use columns for subtraction. We mentally change signs in the subtrahend and then add.

Example 8. Subtract: $(4x^2y - 6x^3y^2 + x^2y^2 - 5y) - (4x^2y + x^3y^2 + 3x^2y^3 + 6y)$.

$$
\begin{aligned}
& 4x^2y - 6x^3y^2 + x^2y^2 - 5y \\
& 4x^2y + x^3y^2 + 3x^2y^3 + 6y \\
\hline
& - 7x^3y^2 - 3x^2y^3 + x^2y^2 - 11y
\end{aligned}
$$

As with addition, you should avoid the use of columns as much as possible. Try to write only the answer when subtracting.

TRY THIS ➡

Answers.   10. $3y^5 - 3y^4 + 5y^3 - 2y^2 - 3$ 11. $9p^4q - 10p^3q^2 + 4p^2q^3 + 9q^4$ 12. $y^3 - y^2 + \frac{4}{3}y + 0.1$

Subtract.

10. $(2y^5 - y^4 + 3y^3 - y^2 - y - 7) - (-y^5 + 2y^4 - 2y^3 + y^2 - y - 4)$
11. $(4p^4q - 5p^3q^2 + p^2q^3 + 2q^4) - (-5p^4q + 5p^3q^2 - 3p^2q^3 - 7q^4)$
12. $(\frac{3}{2}y^3 - \frac{1}{2}y^2 + 0.3) - (\frac{1}{2}y^3 + \frac{1}{2}y^2 - \frac{4}{3}y + 0.2)$

Exercise Set 6-2

Add. *(See Examples 1–3.)*

1. $3x^2 + 5y^2 + 6$ and $2x^2 - 3y^2 - 1$ $5x^2 + 2y^2 + 5$

2. $9y^2 + 8y - 4$ and $12y^2 - 5y + 8$ $21y^2 + 3y + 4$

3. $2a + 3b - c$ and $4a - 2b + 2c$ $6a + b + c$

4. $5x - 4y + 2z$ and $9x + 12y - 8z$ $14x + 8y - 6z$

5. $a^2 - 3b^2 + 4x^2$ and $-5a^2 + 2b^2 - c^2$ $-4a^2 - b^2 + 3c^2$

6. $x^2 - 5y^2 - 9z^2$ and $-6x^2 + 9y^2 - 2z^2$ $-5x^2 + 4y^2 - 11z^2$

7. $x^2 + 2x - 3xy - 7$ and $-3x^2 - x + 2xy + 6$ $-2x^2 + x - xy - 1$

8. $3a^2 - 2b + ab + 6$ and $-a^2 + 5b - 5ab - 2$ $2a^2 + 3b - 4ab + 4$

9. $7x^2y - 3xy^2 + 4xy$ and
   $-2x^2y - xy^2 + xy$ $5x^2y - 4xy^2 + 5xy$

10. $7ab - 3ac + 5bc$ and
    $13ab - 15ac - 8bc$ $20ab - 18ac - 3bc$

11. $2r^2 + 12r - 11$ and
    $6r^2 - 2r + 4$ and
    $r^2 - r - 2$ $9r^2 + 9r - 9$

12. $5x^2 + 19x - 23$ and
    $-7x^2 - 11x + 12$ and
    $-x^2 - 9x + 8$ $-3x^2 - x - 3$

13. $2x + 3y + z - 7$ and
    $5x - 2y - z + 8$ and
    $-3x + y - 2z - 4$ $4x + 2y - 2z - 3$

14. $12x^2 + 5y^2 - 2z^2 + 19$ and
    $-4x^2 - 8y^2 + 9z^2 - 3$ and
    $15x^2 - 2y^2 - 11z^2 + 8$ $23x^2 - 5y^2 - 4z^2 + 24$

15. $0.02x^3 - 0.4x^2 + x + 0.07$ and
    $0.03x^3 + 0.5x^2 + 0.84x - 0.03$ $0.05x^3 + 0.01x^2 +$ $1.84x + 0.04$

16. $0.04x^6 + 0.04x^3 - 0.23x + 0.04$ and
    $0.05x^6 - 0.05x^3 + 0.4$ $0.09x^6 - 0.01x^3 - 0.23x$ $+ 0.44$

17. $1.23y^4 - 2.25y^3 - 3.4y - 5.2$ and
    $8.23y^4 + 4.75y^3 - 8.4y + 2.1$ $9.46y^4 + 2.5y^3 - 11.8y$ $- 3.1$

18. $9.22x^5 - 4.02x^3 + 8.41x^2 - 4.9$ and
    $-8.34x^5 + 9.46x^3 - 3.27x^2 + 8.2$ $0.88x^5 + 5.44x^3$ $+ 5.14x^2 + 3.3$

19. $\frac{1}{4}x^4 + \frac{1}{3}x^3 + \frac{3}{8}x^2 + 6$ and
    $-\frac{3}{4}x^4 + \frac{1}{8}x^2 - 9$ $-\frac{1}{2}x^4 + \frac{1}{3}x^3 + \frac{1}{2}x^2 - 3$

20. $\frac{1}{3}y^5 - \frac{1}{5}y^3 - \frac{1}{2}y - 8$ and
    $\frac{1}{6}y^5 - \frac{1}{10}y^3 + \frac{1}{4}y - 11$ $\frac{1}{2}y^5 - \frac{3}{10}y^3 + \frac{1}{4}y - 19$

▌▌ Rename each additive inverse without parentheses. (*See Examples 4–6.*)

21. $-(5x^3 - 7x^2 + 3x - 6)$ $-5x^3 + 7x^2 - 3x + 6$

22. $-(8y^4 - 18y^3 + 4y - 9)$ $-8y^4 + 18y^3 - 4y + 9$

23. $-(-4y^4 + 7y^2 - 2y - 1)$ $4y^4 - 7y^2 + 2y + 1$

24. $-(-9x^5 - 2y^4 - 5x + 8)$ $9x^5 + 2y^4 + 5x - 8$

▌▌▌ Subtract. (*See Examples 7 and 8.*)   See answer section

25. $(8x - 4) - (-5x + 2)$

26. $(9y + 3) - (-4y - 2)$

27. $(-3x^2 + 2x + 9) - (x^2 + 5x - 4)$

28. $(-9y^2 + 4y + 8) - (4y^2 + 2y - 3)$

29. $(5a - 2b + c) - (3a + 2b - 2c)$

30. $(8x - 4y + z) - (4x + 6y - 3z)$

31. $(3x^2 - 2x - x^3) - (5x^2 - 8x - x^3)$

32. $(8y^2 - 3y - 4y^3) - (3y^2 - 9y - 7y^3)$

33. $(5a^2 + 4ab - 3b^2) -$
    $(9a^2 - 4ab + 2b^2)$

34. $(9y^2 - 14yz - 8z^2) -$
    $(12y^2 - 8yz + 4z^2)$

35. $(12x^2 - 9x) - (14x^2 + 8x - 5)$

36. $(18a^2 - 2a) - (22a^2 + 9a - 4)$

37. $9y^3 - (3y^3 + 7y^2 - 8y + 2)$

38. $8x^4 - (2x^4 + 8x^2 - 9x + 4)$

39. $(4a - 2b - c + 3d) -$
    $(-2a + 3b + c - d)$

40. $(5x - 2y - z + 4w) -$
    $(-3x + 4y - 5z + 2w)$

41. $(0.04x^3 - 0.03x^2 + 0.02x) -$
    $(0.05x^3 + 0.08x^2 - 5)$

42. $(0.09y^4 - 0.052y^3 + 0.93) -$
    $(0.03y^4 - 0.084y^3 + 0.94y^2)$

43. $\left(\frac{5}{8}x^4 - \frac{1}{4}x^2 - \frac{1}{2}\right) -$
    $\left(-\frac{3}{8}x^4 + \frac{3}{4}x^2 + \frac{1}{2}\right)$

44. $\left(\frac{1}{5}y^5 + 3y^4 - \frac{1}{6}y^3\right) -$
    $\left(-\frac{4}{5}y^5 + 9y^4 - \frac{5}{6}y^3\right)$

Calculator Exercises

Subtract.   45. $414.9944x^3 - 27.01313x - 0.0484$ 46. $-3,570,010y^4 - 36,890,749y^2 - 45,476,981y$

45. $(852.0092x^3 - 9.00834x - 0.0084) - (437.0148x^3 + 18.00479x + 0.04)$

46. $(8,479,768y^4 - 56,009,728y^2 - 19,429,009y) - (12,049,778y^4 - 19,118,979y^2 + 26,047,972y)$

6-3 Multiplication of Polynomials

After finishing Lesson 6-3, you should be able to
  I   multiply monomials.
  II   multiply monomials and binomials.
  III   multiply any two polynomials.

I Multiplying Monomials

To multiply monomials we multiply the coefficients. Then we multiply the variables. This process is based on the commutative and associative laws of multiplication.

Examples.   Multiply and simplify.

1. $(-8x^4y^7)(5x^3y^2) = -8 \cdot 5 \cdot x^4 \cdot x^3 \cdot y^7 \cdot y^2$
$$= -40x^7y^9$$

2. $(3x^2yz^5)(-6x^5y^{10}z^2) = 3 \cdot (-6) \cdot x^2 \cdot x^5 \cdot y \cdot y^{10} \cdot z^5 \cdot z^2$
$$= -18x^7y^{11}z^7$$

You should try to do this mentally, writing only the answer.

TRY THIS ■■■■■▶

Multiply and simplify.

1. $9y^2$ and $-2y$
2. $4x^3y$ and $6x^5y^2$
3. $-5xy^7z^4$ and $18x^3y^3z^8$

Answers.   1. $-18y^3$ 2. $24x^8y^3$ 3. $-90x^4y^9z^{12}$

II Multiplying Monomials and Binomials

The distributive laws are the basis for multiplying polynomials other than monomials.

Example 3.   Multiply: $2x$ and $3x - 5$.

$2x \cdot (3x - 5) = 2x \cdot (3x) - 2x \cdot (5)$ *Using a distributive law*
$\qquad\qquad = 6x^2 - 10x$ *Multiplying the monomials*

TRY THIS ■■■■■▶

Multiply.

4. $-3y$ and $2y + 6$
5. $2xy$ and $4y^2 - 5$

4. $-6y^2 - 18y$ 5. $8xy^3 - 10xy$

Example 4.   Multiply: $3y^2 + 4$ and $y - 2$.

$$(3y^2 + 4)(y - 2) = (3y^2 + 4)(y) - (3y^2 + 4)(2)$$ *Using a distributive law*
$$\qquad\qquad\qquad\quad ⓐ \qquad\qquad\qquad ⓑ$$

Let us consider the two parts ⓐ and ⓑ separately.

ⓐ $(3y^2 + 4)(y) = (3y^2)(y) + 4 \cdot y$ *Using a distributive law*
$\qquad\qquad\quad = 3y^3 + 4y$ *Multiplying the monomials*

ⓑ $(3y^2 + 4)(2) = (3y^2) \cdot 2 + 4 \cdot 2$ *Using a distributive law*

  $= 6y^2 + 8$ *Multiplying the monomials*

We replace the parts ⓐ and ⓑ in the original expression with their answers, and combine like terms if they exist.

$$(3y^2 + 4)(y - 2) = (3y^3 + 4y) - (6y^2 + 8)$$
$$= 3y^3 - 6y^2 + 4y - 8$$

TRY THIS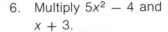

Answers.   6. $5x^3 + 15x^2 - 4x - 12$ 7. $6y^2 - y - 12$

6. Multiply $5x^2 - 4$ and $x + 3$.
7. Multiply $2y + 3$ and $3y - 4$.

ⅢⅢ Multiplying Any Two Polynomials

Example 5. Multiply $p + 2$ and $p^4 - 2p^3 + 3$.

By the distributive laws we have:

$$(p + 2)(p^4 - 2p^3 + 3) = (p + 2)(p^4) - (p + 2)(2p^3) + (p + 2)(3)$$
$$= p \cdot (p^4) + 2(p^4) - p \cdot (2p^3) - 2(2p^3) + p \cdot (3) + 2(3)$$
$$= p^5 + 2p^4 - 2p^4 - 4p^3 + 3p + 6$$
$$= p^5 - 4p^3 + 3p + 6$$

In the last step we collected like terms.

TRY THIS

Answers.   8. $p^4 + p^3 - 12p^2 - 5p + 15$ 9. $2x^4 - 8x^3 + 4x^2 - 21x + 20$

Multiply.

8. $p - 3$ and $p^3 + 4p^2 - 5$
9. $2x^3 + 4x - 5$ and $x - 4$

Now we can see how to multiply any two polynomials.

To multiply two polynomials, multiply each term of one by every term of the other. Then add the results.

We can use columns for long multiplications. We multiply each term at the top by every term at the bottom, keeping like terms in columns. Then we add.

Example 6. Multiply $5x^3 + x - 4$ and $-2x^2 + 3x + 6$.

$$
\begin{array}{l}
5x^3 + x - 4 \\
\underline{-2x^2 + 3x + 6} \\
-10x^5 - 2x^3 + 8x^2 \qquad \textit{Multiplying by } -2x^2 \\
15x^4 + 3x^2 - 12x \qquad \textit{Multiplying by } 3x \\
30x^3 + 6x - 24 \qquad \textit{Multiplying by } 6 \\
\overline{-10x^5 + 15x^4 + 28x^3 + 11x^2 - 6x - 24} \qquad \textit{Adding}
\end{array}
$$

10. Multiply $-4x^3 - 2x + 1$ and $-2x^2 - 3x + 6$.

$8x^5 + 12x^4 - 20x^3 + 4x^2 - 15x + 6$

TRY THIS

Exercise Set 6-3

▌Multiply. (*See Examples 1 and 2.*)

1. $(2y^2)(5y)$ $10y^3$
2. $(3x^2)(2x)$ $6x^3$
3. $(-3y^2)(4xy)$ $-12xy^3$
4. $(-8x^2)(5xy)$ $-40x^3y$
5. $(5x)(-4x^2y)$ $-20x^3y$
6. $(2y)(-9y^2z)$ $-18y^3z$
7. $(-3ab^2)(2a^2b)$ $-6a^3b^3$
8. $(-5xy^3)(7x^2y)$ $-35x^3y^4$
9. $(2x^3y^2)(-5x^2y^4)$ $-10x^5y^6$
10. $(7a^2bc^4)(-8ab^3c^2)$ $-56a^3b^4c^6$

▌▌Multiply. (*See Examples 3 and 4.*)

11. $3x(5x - 2)$ $15x^2 - 6x$
12. $9y(4y - 7)$ $36y^2 - 63y$
13. $-4t(2t - 9)$ $-8t^2 + 36t$
14. $-7y(8y - 6)$ $-56y^2 + 42y$
15. $-2x(3 - x - x^2)$ $-6x + 2x^2 + 2x^3$
16. $-9y(4 - y - y^3)$ $-36y + 9y^2 + 9y^4$
17. $3ab(a + b - 2)$ $3a^2b + 3ab^2 - 6ab$
18. $2xy(2x - 3y + 7xy)$ $4x^2y - 6xy^2 + 14x^2y^2$
19. $a^2(1 - a + 2a^2 - 5a^3)$ $a^2 - a^3 + 2a^4 - 5a^5$
20. $y^3(2 - y + 3y^2 + 8y^3)$ $2y^3 - y^4 + 3y^5 + 8y^6$
21. $(x + 3)(x + 4)$ $x^2 + 7x + 12$
22. $(y + 2)(y + 5)$ $y^2 + 7y + 10$
23. $(x - 2)(x - 5)$ $x^2 - 7x + 10$
24. $(y - 4)(y - 9)$ $y^2 - 13y + 36$
25. $(2x + 3)(x + 4)$ $2x^2 + 11x + 12$
26. $(4y + 5)(y + 3)$ $4y^2 + 17y + 15$
27. $(2x + 5)(3x - 4)$ $6x^2 + 7x - 20$
28. $(3t + 7)(2t - 5)$ $6t^2 - t - 35$
29. $(s + 3t)(s - 3t)$ $s^2 - 9t^2$
30. $(2y + 4)(2y - 4)$ $4y^2 - 16$
31. $(x - y)(x - y)$ $x^2 - 2xy + y^2$
32. $(a + 2b)(a + 2b)$ $a^2 + 4ab + 4b^2$
33. $(y + 8x)(2y - 7x)$ $2y^2 + 9xy - 56x^2$
34. $(a + 9b)(3a - 4b)$ $3a^2 + 23ab - 36b^2$
35. $(x^2 + y)(x^2 - 2y)$ $x^4 - x^2y - 2y^2$
36. $(y^2 + z)(y^2 - 3z)$ $y^4 - 2y^2z - 3z^2$
37. $(a^2 - 2b^2)(a^2 - 3b^2)$ $a^4 - 5a^2b^2 + 6b^4$
38. $(x^2 - 5y^2)(x^2 - 4y^2)$ $x^4 - 9x^2y^2 + 20y^4$

▌▌▌Multiply. (*See Examples 5 and 6.*) See answer section

39. $(x - 4)(x^2 + 4x + 16)$
40. $(y - 2)(y^2 + 5y + 10)$
41. $(y + 3)(y^2 - 3y + 9)$
42. $(x + 2)(x^2 - 4x + 16)$
43. $(x^2 - 2x + 1)(x^2 + x + 2)$
44. $(y^2 - 3y - 7)(y^2 + 4y - 8)$
45. $(3x^3 - x + 9)(-2x^2 + 4x - 3)$
46. $(2x^3 - 3x + 1)(-4x^2 + x - 5)$
47. $(x + y)(x^2 - xy + y^2)$
48. $(a - b)(a^2 + ab + b^2)$
49. $(3a^2 - 1)(a^2 + 4a - 5)$
50. $(5x^2 - 2)(x^2 + 8x - 7)$
51. $(2m^3 - 3)(m^2 + 5m - 7)$
52. $(5t^3 - 5)(t^2 - 4t + 8)$
53. $(4x + 7y)(2x^2 + 3xy + 4y^2)$
54. $(8p + 9q)(5p^2 + 8pq + 7q^2)$

Challenge Exercises 55. $20a^4b^2 - 34a^3b^2 + 43a^2b^3 + 12a^2b^2 - 32ab^3 + 21b^4$ 56. $2x^4 - x^2y^2 - 4x^3y - 2y^4$ $+ 3xy^3$ 57. $3x^5 + 17x^4 + 7x^3 - 19x^2 + 90x - 38$ 58. $2y^6 + 10y^5 - 9y^4 + 7y^3 - 61y^2$ $+ 83y - 42$ 59. $x^4 - 2x^2p^2 + p^4$ 60. $y^8 - 4a^2y^4 - 4a^3y^2 - a^4$

Multiply.

55. $(4a^2b - 2ab + 3b^2)(5a^2b - 6ab + 7b^2)$
56. $(2x^2 + y^2 - 2xy)(x^2 - 2y^2 - xy)$
57. $(3x^3 + 5x^2 - 7x + 19)(x^2 + 4x - 2)$
58. $(2y^4 + 3y^2 - 8y + 7)(y^2 + 5y - 6)$
59. $(x - p)(x + p)(x^2 - p^2)$
60. $(y^2 + a)(y^2 + a)(y^4 - 2ay^2 - a^2)$

6-4 Special Products of Polynomials

After finishing Lesson 6-4, you should be able to
- **I** multiply two binomials using the FOIL rule.
- **II** square binomials.

I Products of Two Binomials

We know that to multiply two polynomials, we multiply each term of one polynomial by every term of the other. To multiply two *binomials,* we multiply the FIRST terms. Then we multiply the OUTSIDE terms, then the INSIDE terms, and finally the LAST terms. If there are like terms we collect them. We can abbreviate the rule like this: F O I L.

Examples. Multiply.

$$\qquad\qquad \overset{\text{F}}{} \quad \overset{\text{O}}{} \quad \overset{\text{I}}{} \quad \overset{\text{L}}{}$$

1. $(x + 5)(x - 8) = x^2 - 8x + 5x - 40$
$$= x^2 - 3x - 40$$

$$\qquad\qquad \overset{\text{F}}{} \quad \overset{\text{O}}{} \quad \overset{\text{I}}{} \quad \overset{\text{L}}{}$$

2. $(p - 3q)(2p - 5q) = 2p^2 - 5pq - 6pq + 15q^2$
$$= 2p^2 - 11pq + 15q^2$$

3. $(3xy + 2x)(x^2 + 2xy^2) = 3x^3y + 6x^2y^3 + 2x^3 + 4x^2y^2$

Answers. 1. $y^2 + 6y - 40$ 2. $2p^2 + 7pq - 15q^2$ 3. $x^3y^3 + x^2y^3 + 2x^2y^2 + 2xy^2$

TRY THIS ⟹

> Multiply.
>
> 1. $(y - 4)(y + 10)$
> 2. $(p + 5q)(2p - 3q)$
> 3. $(x^2y + 2x)(xy^2 + y^2)$

II Squares of Binomials

If we apply the FOIL rule to products like $(a + b)^2$ and $(a - b)^2$ we obtain:

$$
\begin{aligned}
(a + b)^2 &= (a + b)(a + b) & (a - b)^2 &= (a - b)(a - b) \\
&= a^2 + ab + ab + b^2 & &= a^2 - ab - ab + b^2 \\
&= a^2 + 2ab + b^2 & &= a^2 - 2ab + b^2
\end{aligned}
$$

To square a binomial we square the first term. Then we take twice the product of the two terms. Next we square the second term. Then we add.

Examples. Multiply.

4. $(y - 5)^2 = y^2 - 2(5)(y) + 5^2$
$$= y^2 - 10y + 25$$

5. $(2x + 9)^2 = (2x)^2 + 2(2x)(9) + 9^2$
$$= 4x^2 + 36x + 81$$

Whenever possible try to find such products mentally. Try to write only the answer.

TRY THIS ━━━━━━━━━━━━━━▶

Answers.   4. $x^2 - 16x + 64$ 5. $9x^2 + 42x + 49$

Multiply.

4. $(x - 8)^2$
5. $(3x + 7)^2$

Examples.   Multiply.

6. $(2x + 3y)^2 = (2x)^2 + 2(2x)(3y) + (3y)^2$
            $= 4x^2 + 12xy + 9y^2$

7. $(3x^2 - 5xy^2)^2 = (3x^2)^2 - 2(3x^2)(5xy^2) + (5xy^2)^2$
               $= 9x^4 - 30x^3y^2 + 25x^2y^4$

TRY THIS ━━━━━━━━━━━━━━▶

Answers.   6. $16x^2 + 40xy + 25y^2$ 7. $4y^4 - 24x^2y^3 + 36x^4y^2$

Multiply.

6. $(4x + 5y)^2$
7. $(2y^2 - 6x^2y)^2$

Exercise Set 6-4

▮ Multiply. *(See Examples 1–3.)*

1. $(a + 2)(a + 3)$ $a^2 + 5a + 6$
2. $(x + 5)(x + 8)$ $x^2 + 13x + 40$
3. $(y + 3)(y - 2)$ $y^2 + y - 6$
4. $(x + 8)(x - 3)$ $x^2 + 5x - 24$
5. $(y - 4)(y + 7)$ $y^2 + 3y - 28$
6. $(x - 6)(x + 9)$ $x^2 + 3x - 54$
7. $(b - 7)(b - 5)$ $b^2 - 12b + 35$
8. $(y - 3)(y - 7)$ $y^2 - 10y + 21$
9. $(2x + 9)(x + 2)$ $2x^2 + 13x + 18$
10. $(3y + 7)(y + 3)$ $3y^2 + 13y + 21$
11. $(4a + 3)(a - 1)$ $4a^2 - a - 3$
12. $(5x + 2)(x - 3)$ $5x^2 - 13x - 6$
13. $(3y - 2)(y - 3)$ $3y^2 - 11y + 6$
14. $(4x - 7)(x - 4)$ $4x^2 - 23x + 28$
15. $(3b + 8)(2b - 5)$ $6b^2 + b - 40$
16. $(7x + 2)(3x - 6)$ $21x^2 - 36x - 12$
17. $(2x - 5)(3x - 7)$ $6x^2 - 29x + 35$
18. $(4x - 9)(5x - 8)$ $20x^2 - 77x + 72$
19. $(2x + 3y)(4x + 5y)$ $8x^2 + 22xy + 15y^2$
20. $(9a + 7b)(5a + 3b)$ $45a^2 + 62ab + 21b^2$
21. $(a^2 + b)(a^2 - 2b)$ $a^4 - a^2b - 2b^2$
22. $(x^2 + y)(x^2 - 5y)$ $x^4 - 4x^2y - 5y^2$
23. $(2m^2 - n^2)(m^2 + 3n^2)$ $2m^4 + 5m^2n^2 - 3n^4$
24. $(8x^2 - y^2)(x^2 + 7y^2)$ $8x^4 + 55x^2y^2 - 7y^4$
25. $(2x^2 + 3y^2)(4x^2 - 5y^2)$ $8x^4 + 2x^2y^2 - 15y^4$
26. $(4y^2 + 7z^2)(5y^2 - 9z^2)$ $20y^4 - y^2z^2 - 63z^4$
27. $(7m^2 - 8n^2)(3m^2 - 5n^2)$ $21m^4 - 59m^2n^2 + 40n^4$
28. $(9a^2 - 8b^2)(4a^2 - 7b^2)$ $36a^4 - 95a^2b^2 + 56b$

▮▮ Multiply. *(See Examples 4–7.)*

29. $(x + 3)^2$ $x^2 + 6x + 9$
30. $(y + 7)^2$ $y^2 + 14y + 49$
31. $(y - 5)^2$ $y^2 - 10y + 25$
32. $(x - 6)^2$ $x^2 - 12x + 36$
33. $(2s + 3t)^2$ $4s^2 + 12st + 9t^2$
34. $(5x + 7y)^2$ $25x^2 + 70xy + 49y^2$
35. $(5x - 9y)^2$ $25x^2 - 90xy + 81y^2$
36. $(7y - 4z)^2$ $49y^2 - 56yz + 16z^2$
37. $(3a^2 + 2)^2$ $9a^4 + 12a^2 + 4$
38. $(5x^2 + 6)^2$ $25x^4 + 60x^2 + 36$
39. $(7x^2 - 2)^2$ $49x^4 - 28x^2 + 4$
40. $(6y^2 - 5)^2$ $36y^4 - 60y^2 + 25$
41. $(2x - 3y^2)^2$ $4x^2 - 12xy^2 + 9y^4$
42. $(3s^2 - 4t^2)^2$ $9s^4 - 24s^2t^2 + 16t^4$
43. $(a^2b^2 + ab^2)^2$ $a^4b^4 + 2a^3b^4 + a^2b^4$
44. $(x^2y + xy^2)^2$ $x^4y^2 + 2x^3y^3 + x^2y^4$

6-5 More Special Products

After finishing Lesson 6-5, you should be able to
- **▮** multiply the sum and difference of the same two expressions.
- **▮▮** find special products such as those above and those found in Lesson 6-4, when they are mixed together.

▮Products of Sums and Differences

If we apply the FOIL rule to a product like $(a + b)(a - b)$, we obtain:

$$(a + b)(a - b) = a^2 - ab + ab - b^2$$
$$= a^2 - b^2$$

The product of a sum and difference is the difference of two squares. To find such a product we square the first expression and square the second expression. Then write a minus sign between the squares.

Examples. Multiply.

1. $(y + 5)(y - 5) = y^2 - 5^2$
$$= y^2 - 25$$

2. $(3x - 2)(3x + 2) = (3x)^2 - 2^2$
$$= 9x^2 - 4$$

Whenever possible you should avoid writing a middle step as shown in the above examples. Try to write only the answer.

TRY THIS ➡

Examples. Multiply.

3. $(2xy^2 + 3x)(2xy^2 - 3x) = (2xy^2)^2 - (3x)^2$
$$= 4x^2y^4 - 9x^2$$

Multiply.

1. $(x + 8)(x - 8)$
2. $(4y + 7)(4y - 7)$
   1. $x^2 - 64$ 2. $16y^2 - 49$

4. $(5y + 4 - 3x)(5y + 4 + 3x) = (5y + 4)^2 - (3x)^2$
$$= 25y^2 + 40y + 16 - 9x^2$$

5. $(3xy^2 + 4y)(-3xy^2 + 4y) = (4y + 3xy^2)(4y - 3xy^2)$
$$= (4y)^2 - (3xy^2)^2$$
$$= 16y^2 - 9x^2y^4$$

Answers.   3. $9x^4y^2 - 4y^2$ 4. $4x^2 + 12x + 9 - 25y^2$ 5. $25t^2$
$- 4x^6y^4$

▮▮ Multiplications

When multiplying first see what kind of multiplication you have and then use the best method. Following are the methods we have used so far.

① $(A + B)(A + B) = (A + B)^2 = A^2 + 2 \cdot A \cdot B + B^2$
② $(A - B)(A - B) = (A - B)^2 = A^2 - 2 \cdot A \cdot B + B^2$
③ $(A - B)(A + B) = A^2 - B^2$
④   F O I L
⑤   The product of a monomial and any polynomial. Multiply each term of the polynomial by the monomial.

Examples.   Multiply.

6. $(x + 4)(x - 4) = x^2 - 16$ *Using* ③
7. $(x + 8)(x - 2) = x^2 + 6x - 16$ *Using* ④
8. $(x - 6)(x - 6) = x^2 - 12x + 36$ *Using* ②
9. $5x^3(3x^2y^2 + 2xy - 8) = 15x^5y^2 + 10x^4y - 40x^3$ *Using* ⑤
10. $(2x + 7y)(2x + 7y) = 4x^2 + 28xy + 49y^2$ *Using* ①

Answers.   6. $x^2 - 16x + 64$ 7. $4x^2 + 12x + 9$ 8. $4x^2 - 1$
9. $-15x^2y^5 + 10xy^4 - 45y^2$ 10. $p^2 - 3pq - 28q^2$

Exercise Set 6-5

▮ Multiply. (*See Examples 1–5.*)

1. $(c + 2)(c - 2)$ $c^2 - 4$
2. $(x - 3)(x + 3)$ $x^2 - 9$
3. $(x + y)(x - y)$ $x^2 - y^2$
4. $(a + b)(a - b)$ $a^2 - b^2$
5. $(2a + 1)(2a - 1)$ $4a^2 - 1$
6. $(4y + 3)(4y - 3)$ $16y^2 - 9$
7. $(3 - 2x)(3 + 2x)$ $9 - 4x^2$
8. $(5 - 7y)(5 + 7y)$ $25 - 49y^2$
9. $(3m - 2n)(3m + 2n)$ $9m^2 - 4n^2$
10. $(3x - 4y)(3x + 4y)$ $9x^2 - 16y^2$
11. $(x^2 - 9)(x^2 + 9)$ $x^4 - 81$
12. $(3a^2 + 2)(3a^2 - 2)$ $9a^4 - 4$

13. $(5a^2 + 2b)(5a^2 - 2b)$ $25a^4 - 4b^2$

14. $(6y^2 + 7z)(6y^2 - 7z)$ $36y^4 - 49z^2$

15. $(3c^2 - 2d^2)(3c^2 + 2d^2)$ $9c^4 - 4d^4$

16. $(5x^2 - 4y^2)(5x^2 + 4y^2)$ $25x^4 - 16y^4$

■ Multiply. (*See Examples 6–10.*)

17. $(y + 3)(y + 5)$ $y^2 + 8y + 15$

18. $(2x + 3)(3x + 4)$ $6x^2 + 17x + 12$

19. $(2x - 7)(2x + 7)$ $4x^2 - 49$

20. $(5y - 9z)(5y + 9z)$ $25y^2 - 81z^2$

21. $(4x + 2y)^2$ $16x^2 + 16xy + 4y^2$

22. $(5x + 3y)^2$ $25x^2 + 30xy + 9y^2$

23. $(9x - 5y)^2$ $81x^2 - 90xy + 25y^2$

24. $(8t - 4w)^2$ $64t^2 - 64tw + 16w^2$

25. $4x^3(5x^2y^2 + 4xy - 9)$ $20x^5y^2 + 16x^4y - 36x^3$

26. $3y^4(8x^2y^3 + 5xy^2 - 7)$ $24x^2y^7 + 15xy^6 - 21y^4$

27. $(5x + 3)(5x + 3)$ $25x^2 + 30x + 9$

28. $(9y - 4)(9y - 4)$ $81y^2 - 72y + 16$

29. $(2x + 4y)(5x - 7y)$ $10x^2 + 6xy - 28y^2$

30. $(5p - 7q)(4p + 9q)$ $20p^2 + 17pq - 63q^2$

31. $(8y - z)(9y - 7z)$ $72y^2 - 65yz + 7z^2$

32. $(10x - y)(5x + 8y)$ $50x^2 + 75xy - 8y^2$

33. $(7x^2 + 3)(4x^2 - 5)$ $28x^4 - 23x^2 - 15$

34. $(9y^3 - 2)(8y^3 - 7)$ $72y^6 - 79y^3 + 14$

35. $(8x + 9y)^2$ $64x^2 + 144xy + 81y^2$

36. $(9z - 4w)^2$ $81z^2 - 72zw + 16w^2$

37. $(\frac{1}{5}x - \frac{2}{3}y)(\frac{1}{5}x + \frac{2}{3}y)$ $\frac{1}{25}x^2 - \frac{4}{9}y^2$

38. $(\frac{1}{8}a - \frac{3}{4}b)(\frac{1}{8}a + \frac{3}{4}b)$ $\frac{1}{64}a^2 - \frac{9}{16}b^2$

39. $-5y^4(8y^5 - 3y^4 - 9y^3 + y^2 - 8y + 3)$ $-40y^9 + 15y^8 + 45y^7 - 5y^6 + 40y^5 - 15y^4$

40. $-8x^3(9x^6 + 8x^4 - 7x^3 - 3x^2 - 8x - 12)$ $-72x^9 - 64x^7 + 56x^6 + 24x^5 + 64x^4 + 96x^3$

41. $(\frac{1}{3}x - 1)(\frac{1}{3}x + 2)$ $\frac{1}{9}x^2 + \frac{1}{3}x - 2$

42. $(\frac{1}{2}y - 4)(\frac{1}{2}y + 1)$ $\frac{1}{4}y^2 - \frac{3}{2}y - 4$

Challenge Exercises

43. $x^4 - 1$ 44. $y^4 - 16$ 45. $a^4 - b^4$ 46. $16x^4 - y^4$ 47. $a^2 + 2ab + b^2 - 1$
48. $m^2 + 2mn + n^2 - 4$ 49. $4x^2 + 12xy + 9y^2 - 16$ 50. $9a^2 - 12ab + 4b^2 - c^2$

Multiply.

43. $(x + 1)(x - 1)(x^2 + 1)$

44. $(y - 2)(y + 2)(y^2 + 4)$

45. $(a + b)(a - b)(a^2 + b^2)$

46. $(2x - y)(2x + y)(4x^2 + y^2)$

47. $(a + b + 1)(a + b - 1)$

48. $(m + n + 2)(m + n - 2)$

49. $(2x + 3y + 4)(2x + 3y - 4)$

50. $(3a - 2b + c)(3a - 2b - c)$

MATHEMATICAL NOTE: Theorems

One way to disprove a theorem is by counterexample. This involves finding one example that contradicts the theorem. For instance, the statement "All prime numbers are odd" can be disproved by the counterexample 2. 2 is a prime number, and 2 is not odd. So the statement is disproved by counterexample.

Research mathematicians work at proving or disproving theorems. Their proofs may take many years of careful reasoning.

6-6 *The Compound Interest Formula*

After finishing Lesson 6-6, you should be able to
▪ solve certain problems using the compound interest formula.

▪ An important and frequently used formula is the compound interest formula. We first consider simple interest.

Example 1. An investment is made at 8%. It grows to $783 at the end of one year. How much was originally invested?

Rewording and translating we have:

Invested amount	plus	8%	of	Invested amount	is	$783	*Rewording*
↓	↓	↓	↓	↓	↓	↓	
x	$+$	8%	$\cdot$	x	$=$	783	*Translating*

Now we solve the equation.

$$x + 8\%x = 783$$
$$x + 0.08x = 783$$
$$(1 + 0.08)x = 783$$
$$1.08x = 783$$
$$x = \frac{783}{1.08}$$
$$= 725$$

The number 725 checks in the problem situation, so the answer is $725.

TRY THIS

1. An investment is made at 6%. It grows to $848 at the end of one year. How much was originally invested? **$800**

Now we consider compound interest.

THEOREM 6-3
If an amount P is invested at an interest rate of r compounded annually, in t years it will grow to an amount A given by

$$A = P(1 + r)^t.$$

Example 2. Suppose $1000 is invested at 8%, compounded annually. What amount will be in the account at the end of two years?

We use the formula of Theorem 6-3, $A = P(1 + r)^t$. We get

$A = 1000(1 + 0.08)^2$
$= 1000(1.08)^2$
$= 1166.4$

The answer is $1166.40.

TRY THIS

2. Suppose $500 is invested at 6%, compounded annually. What amount will be in the account at the end of two years? **$561.80**

Interest may be compounded more often than once a year. There is a formula that applies.

THEOREM 6-4

If an amount P is invested at an interest rate r, compounded n times per year, in t years it will grow to an amount A given by

$$A = P\left(1 + \frac{r}{n}\right)^{nt}.$$

When problems involving compound interest are translated to mathematical language, the above formula is almost always used.

Example 3. Suppose $1000 is invested at 8%, compounded quarterly. How much will be in the account at the end of two years?

In this case $n = 4$ and $t = 2$. We substitute into the formula.

$$A = P\left(1 + \frac{r}{n}\right)^{nt}$$
$$= 1000\left(1 + \frac{0.08}{4}\right)^{4 \cdot 2}$$
$$= 1000(1.02)^8$$
$$= 1171.66$$

The answer is $1171.66.

TRY THIS

3. Suppose $1000 is invested at 8% compounded semiannually. How much will be in the account at the end of two years? **$1169.86**

Exercise Set 6-6

▌Solve. (*See Examples 1 and 2.*)

1. An investment is made at 9%, compounded annually. It grows to $708.50 at the end of one year. How much was originally invested? $650

2. An investment is made at 7%, compounded annually. It grows to $856 at the end of one year. How much was originally invested? $800

3. An investment is made at 8%, compounded annually. It grows to $648 at the end of one year. How much was originally invested? $600

4. An investment is made at 4%, compounded annually. It grows to $572 at the end of one year. How much was originally invested? $550

5. Suppose $1000 is invested at 4%, compounded annually. What amount will be in the account at the end of two years? $1081.60

6. Suppose $1000 is invested at 6%, compounded annually. What amount will be in the account at the end of two years? $1123.60

7. Suppose $800 is invested at 8%, compounded annually. What amount will be in the account at the end of two years? $933.12

8. Suppose $750 is invested at 5%, compounded annually. What amount will be in the account at the end of two years? $826.88

Solve. (*See Example 3.*)

9. Suppose $1000 is invested at 7%, compounded semiannually. How much will be in the account at the end of one year? $1071.23

10. Suppose $4000 is invested at 9%, compounded semiannually. How much will be in the account at the end of one year? $4368.10

11. Suppose $2000 is invested at 8%, compounded semiannually. How much will be in the account at the end of two years? $2339.72

12. Suppose $3000 is invested at 6%, compounded semiannually. How much will be in the account at the end of two years? $3376.53

Calculator Exercises

13. Suppose $1000 is invested at 6%, compounded monthly. How much will be in the account at the end of two years? $1126.49

14. Suppose $500 is invested at 4%, compounded monthly. How much will be in the account at the end of two years? $541.43

COMPUTER ACTIVITY

Compound Interest

PROBLEM: Let the original amount be $100, and let it be compounded monthly at 1% interest. Compare this with $100 compounded monthly at $1\frac{1}{8}$% interest for the same number of months.

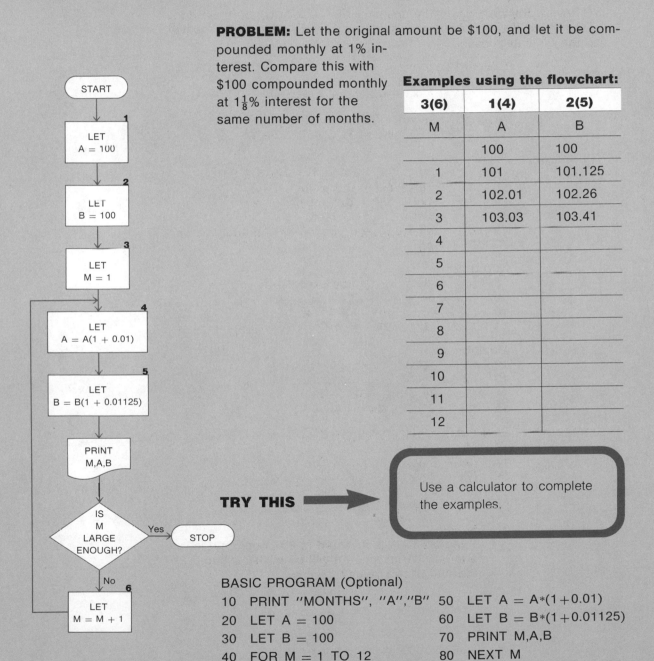

Examples using the flowchart:

3(6)	1(4)	2(5)
M	A	B
	100	100
1	101	101.125
2	102.01	102.26
3	103.03	103.41
4		
5		
6		
7		
8		
9		
10		
11		
12		

TRY THIS

Use a calculator to complete the examples.

BASIC PROGRAM (Optional)

```
10   PRINT "MONTHS", "A","B"    50   LET A = A*(1+0.01)
20   LET A = 100                60   LET B = B*(1+0.01125)
30   LET B = 100                70   PRINT M,A,B
40   FOR M = 1 TO 12            80   NEXT M
```

CHAPTER 6 REVIEW

Review the material in the chapter. Then see how you have done by trying these review exercises. If you miss an exercise, restudy the indicated lesson.

6-1   Collect like terms.
1. $9x - 5y - 3x + y - 7x + 4y$ $-x$
2. $8a^3 + 3a^2 - 2a + 5a + 6a^3 - a^2$ $14a^3 + 2a^2 + 3a$

6-1   Arrange in ascending powers of y.
3. $-12x^3y^2 + 5xy^3 + 14xy - 8 + 9x^4y^4$ $-8 + 14xy - 12x^3y^2 + 5xy^3 + 9x^4y^4$

6-2   Add.
4. $5x^2 - 8x^3 + 3x - 2$ and $4x^3 + 5x^2 + 9 - x$ $-4x^3 + 10x^2 + 2x + 7$
5. $5a^4 + 7a^3 + 6a^2 - 7$ and $3a^4 - 5a^2 + 2 - a^3$ $8a^4 + 6a^3 + a^2 - 5$
6. $8y^2 - 4xy - 5x^2 + 8x^3$ and $7x^3 + 2x^2 - 8xy + 6y^2$ $14y^2 - 12xy - 3x^2 + 15x^3$
7. $p^3 + 5q^2 + 2pq$ and $3pq^3 - p^3 - 6$ and $4pq^2 + 5p^3 - pq + 6$ $5p^3 + 5q^2 + pq + 3pq^3 + 4pq^2$

6-2   Subtract.
8. $(8y^2 + 3y + 6) - (-5y^2 + 4y - 3)$ $13y^2 - y + 9$
9. $(8p - 5q + 7r) - (2p + 5p - 4r)$ $6p - 10q + 11r$
10. $(15a - 5c + 4b) - (8b + 4c + 5a)$ $10a - 4b - 9c$
11. $(8x^2 - 3xy - 7y^2) - (4x^2 - 6xy - 8y^2)$ $4x^2 + 3xy + y^2$

6-3   Multiply.
12. $(-8x^2y)(4xy^2)$ $-32x^3y^3$
13. $4a(5a + 6b)$ $20a^2 + 24ab$
14. $(3x - 2y + 5z)(-3x + 4z)$ $-9x^2 + 6xy - 3xz - 8yz + 20z^2$
15. $(5y^3 + 3y - 6)(6y^3 - 4y + 7)$ $30y^6 - 2y^4 - y^3 - 12y^2 + 45y - 42$

6-4, 6-5   Find these special products.
16. $(4x - 7)(2x + 3)$ $8x^2 - 2x - 21$
17. $(2x - 3)(2x + 3)$ $4x^2 - 9$
18. $(7x - 5y)^2$ $49x^2 - 70xy + 25y^2$
19. $(3x + 4y)^2$ $9x^2 + 24xy + 16y^2$
20. $(7a - 3b)(4a - 6b)$ $28a^2 - 54ab + 18b^2$

6-6   21.   Solve.
           Suppose \$500 is invested at 8%, compounded annually. What amount will be in the account at the end of two years?   \$583.20

CHAPTER 6 TEST

Collect like terms.
1. $6a - 3b - 4a + b - 5a + 7b$ $\quad -3a + 5b$
2. $3x^3 + 2x^2 - 2x + 5x + 4x^3 - x^2$ $\quad 7x^3 + x^2 + 3x$

Arrange in descending powers of x.
3. $18x^2y^3 + 5x^4y^4 - 13xy + 15x^3 + 9$ $\quad 5x^4y^4 + 15x^3 + 18x^2y^3 - 13xy + 9$

Add.
4. $3x^2 - 4x^3 + 2x - 1$ and $5x^3 + 4x^2 + 3 - x$ $\quad x^3 + 7x^2 + x + 2$
5. $4y^4 + 3y^3 + 5y^2 - 6$ and $2y^4 - 2y^2 + 3 - y^3$ $\quad 6y^4 + 2y^3 + 3y^2 - 3$
6. $4y^2 - 3xy - 4x^2 + 7x^3$ and $5x^3 + 3x^2 - 2xy + 5y^2$ $\quad 9y^2 - 5xy - x^2 + 12x^3$
7. $a^3 + 2a^2 + ab$ and $ab^3 - a^3 - 1$ and $2ab^2 + 3a^3 - ab + 1$ $\quad 3a^3 + 2a^2 + ab^3 + 2ab^2$

Subtract.
8. $(7x^2 + 2x + 4) - (-2x^2 + 2x - 2)$ $\quad 9x^2 + 6$
9. $(9a - 4b + 6c) - (3a + 2b - 5c)$ $\quad 6a - 6b + 11c$
10. $(12c - 4b + 6a) - (7a + 2c + 4b)$ $\quad -a - 8b + 10c$
11. $(5r^2 - 2rs - 6s^2) - (3r^2 - 4rs - 7s^2)$ $\quad 2r^2 + 2rs + s^2$

Multiply.
12. $(-4x^2y)(3xy^2)$ $\quad -12x^3y^3$
13. $3b(3a + 4b)$ $\quad 9ab + 12b^2$
14. $(2x - 3y + 4z)(-4x + 3z)$ $\quad -8x^2 + 12xy - 10xz + 9yz + 12z^2$
15. $(3x^3 + 2x - 4)(5x^2 - 2x + 4)$ $\quad 15x^5 - 6x^4 + 22x^3 - 24x^2 + 16x - 16$

Find these special products.
16. $(3x - 5)(3x + 5)$ $\quad 9x^2 - 25$
17. $(8x + 4y)(2x - 3y)$ $\quad 16x^2 - 16xy - 12y^2$
18. $(9x - 4y)^2$ $\quad 81x^2 - 72xy + 16y^2$
19. $(5x + 2y)^2$ $\quad 25x^2 + 20xy + 4y^2$
20. $(9x - 5y)(2x - 7y)$ $\quad 18x^2 - 73xy + 35y^2$

21. Solve.
    Suppose $800 is invested at 6%, compounded annually. What amount will be in the account at the end of two years? $\quad$ $898.88

Ready for Polynomials and Factoring?

1-5   1.   Evaluate $xy - xz$ when $x = -2$, $y = 4$, $z = 3$.   ₋₂ -2

1-5   2.   Factor: $5x + 5y$.   5(x + y)

1-7   3.   Simplify: $(3a)^2$.   9a²

1-8   Multiply and simplify.

     4. $a^4 \cdot a^7$ a¹¹

     5. $7^{-2} \cdot 7^{-3}$ 7⁻⁵

     6. $(8x^{-3}y^4)(3x^{-9}y^{-2})$ 24x⁻¹²y²

1-8   Simplify.

     7. $(2^{-3})^4$ 2⁻¹²

     8. $(x^{-2})^{-4}$ x⁸

2-2   Solve.

     9. $(x - 3)(x + 5) = 0$ 3, −5

     10. $3x(2x + 10) = 0$ 0, −5

6-1   11.   Is $2x - 4$ a monomial, binomial, or trinomial?   Binomial

     Multiply and simplify.

6-3   12. $(2x^2yz^4)(-8x^7y^4z)$ −16x⁹y⁵z⁵

6-3   13. $3x(4x - 7)$ 12x² − 21x

6-3   14. $(4y^2 + 2)(y - 3)$ 4y³ − 12y² + 2y − 6

6-4   15. $(a + 6)(2a - 3)$ 2a² + 9a − 18

6-4   16. $(2xy + 3x)(x^2 + 4xy^2)$ 3x³ + 2x³y + 8x²y³ + 12x²y²

6-4   17. $(2x - 3)^2$ 4x² − 12x + 9

6-4   18. $(3x^2y + 5y^2)^2$ 9x⁴y² + 30x²y³ + 25y⁴

6-5   19. $(4x + 3)(4x - 3)$ 16x² − 9

6-5   20. $(2xy + 4y^2)(-2xy + 4y^2)$ 16y⁴ − 4x²y²

6-5   21. $(x + 7)(x - 1)$ x² + 6x − 7

6-5   22. $4x^4(2x^2y^2 + 8xy - 2)$ 8x⁶y² + 32x⁵y − 8x⁴

6-5   23. $(3x + 4y)(3x + 4y)$ 9x² + 24xy + 16y²

Chapter 7
Polynomials and Factoring

*If a flower bed has an area of 108 m² and the
length is 3 m longer than the width, we can find
its dimensions by solving an equation.*

7-1 Factoring

After finishing Lesson 7-1, you should be able to
- **I** factor polynomials where the terms have a common factor.
- **II** factor polynomials by grouping.
- **III** factor polynomials which are differences of squares.

I Terms with Common Factors

Factoring is the reverse of multiplication. When factoring polynomials first look for common factors.

Example 1. Factor out a common factor.

$$4y^2 - 8 = 4 \cdot y^2 - 4 \cdot 2$$
$$= 4(y^2 - 2)$$

In some cases there is more than one common factor. Then we usually use the one with the largest coefficient and the largest exponent. You should try to write the answer directly.

Examples. Factor out a common factor.

2. $5x^4 - 20x^3 = 5x^3(x - 4)$

3. $15y^5 + 12y^4 - 27y^3 - 3y^2 = 3y^2(5y^3 + 4y^2 - 9y - 1)$

TRY THIS ➡

Answers. 1. $3x(x - 2)$ 2. $4x^3(x^2 - 2)$ 3. $p(1 + rt)$
4. $3y^2(3y^2 - 5y + 1)$

Factor out a common factor.

1. $3x^2 - 6x$
2. $4x^5 - 8x^3$
3. $P + Prt$
4. $9y^4 - 15y^3 + 3y^2$

Examples. Factor out a common factor.

4. $12x^2y - 20x^3y = 4x^2y(3 - 5x)$

5. $10p^6q^2 - 4p^5q^3 + 2p^4q^4 = 2p^4q^2(5p^2 - 2pq + q^2)$

TRY THIS ➡

Answers. 5. $4p^2r(5p + 3)$ 6. $3x^2y(2 - 7xy + y^2)$

Factor out a common factor.

5. $20p^3r + 12p^2r$
6. $6x^2y - 21x^3y^2 + 3x^2y^3$

ⅠⅠ Factoring by Grouping

Sometimes a common factor is itself a binomial, or sometimes pairs of terms have a common factor which can be removed.

Example 6.   Factor.

$$y^2 + 3y + 4y + 12 = y(y + 3) + 4(y + 3)$$
$$= (y + 4)(y + 3)$$

Note that we factored two parts of the expression, $y^2 + 3y$ and $4y + 12$. Then we removed the common binomial factor, $y + 3$.

Examples.   Factor.

7. $4x^2 - 3x + 20x - 15 = 4x^2 + 20x - 3x - 15$
$$= 4x(x + 5) - 3(x + 5)$$
$$= (4x - 3)(x + 5)$$

8. $ax^2 + ay - bx^2 - by = ax^2 + ay + (-bx^2 - by)$
$$= a(x^2 + y) - b(x^2 + y) \quad \text{Factoring out a and } -b$$
$$= (a - b)(x^2 + y)$$

Not all expressions with four terms can be factored by grouping.

TRY THIS ➡

Answers.   7. $(x + 4)(x + 5)$ 8. $(y + 2)(5y + 2)$ 9. $(p - q)(x + y)$

Factor.

7. $x^2 + 5x + 4x + 20$
8. $5y^2 + 2y + 10y + 4$
9. $px + py - qx - qy$

ⅠⅠⅠ Difference of Squares

To factor a difference of two squares we can use the following equation.

$$A^2 - B^2 = (A + B)(A - B)$$

Examples.   Factor.

9. $x^2 - 9 = x^2 - 3^2$
$$= (x + 3)(x - 3)$$

10. $25y^6 - 49x^2 = (5y^3 + 7x)(5y^3 - 7x)$

Factor.

10. $y^2 - 4$
11. $49x^4 - 25y^{10}$
12. $36y^4 - 16y^6$

TRY THIS ➡

Answers.   10. $(y + 2)(y - 2)$ 11. $(7x^2 + 5y^5)(7x^2 - 5y^2)$ 12. $4y^4(3 + 2y)(3 - 2y)$

Exercise Set 7-1

▮ Factor. (*See Examples 1–5.*)

1. $y^2 - 5y$ $y(y - 5)$
2. $x^2 + 9x$ $x(x + 9)$
3. $4a^2 + 2a$ $2a(2a + 1)$
4. $6y^2 + 3y$ $3y(2y + 1)$
5. $y^3 + 9y^2$ $y^2(y + 9)$
6. $x^3 + 8x^2$ $x^2(x + 8)$
7. $3y^2 - 3y - 9$ $3(y^2 - y - 3)$
8. $5x^2 - 5x + 15$ $5(x^2 - x + 3)$
9. $6x^2 - 3x^4$ $3x^2(2 - x^2)$
10. $8y^2 + 4y^4$ $4y^2(2 + y^2)$
11. $4ab - 6ac + 12ad$ $2a(2b - 3c + 6d)$
12. $8xy + 10xz - 14xw$ $2x(4y + 5z - 7w)$
13. $4x^2y - 12xy^2$ $4xy(x - 3y)$
14. $5x^2y^3 + 15x^3y^2$ $5x^2y^2(y + 3x)$
15. $x^6 + x^5 - x^3 + x^2$ $x^2(x^4 + x^3 - x + 1)$
16. $y^4 - y^3 + y^2 + y$ $y(y^3 - y^2 + y + 1)$
17. $24x^3 - 36x^2 + 72x$ $12x(2x^2 - 3x + 6)$
18. $16x^6 - 32x^3 - 48x^2$ $16x^2(x^4 - 2x - 3)$
19. $10a^4 + 15a^2 - 25a - 30$ $5(2a^4 + 3a^2 - 5a - 6)$
20. $12t^5 - 20t^4 + 8t^2 - 16$ $4(3t^5 - 5t^4 + 2t^2 -$
21. $\frac{4}{7}x^6 - \frac{6}{7}x^4 + \frac{1}{7}x^2 - \frac{3}{7}x$ $\frac{1}{7}x(4x^5 - 6x^3 + x - 3)$
22. $\frac{5}{4}y^7 - \frac{3}{4}y^5 + \frac{7}{4}y^3 - \frac{1}{4}y$ $\frac{1}{4}y(5y^6 - 3y^4 + 7y^2 -$

▮▮ Factor. (*See Examples 6–8.*)

23. $a(b - 2) + c(b - 2)$ $(a + c)(b - 2)$
24. $a(x^2 - 3) - 2(x^2 - 3)$ $(a - 2)(x^2 - 3)$
25. $(x - 2)(x + 5) + (x - 2)(x + 8)$ $(x - 2)(2x + 13)$
26. $(m - 4)(m + 3) + (m - 4)(m - 3)$ $2m(m - 4)$
27. $a^2(x - y) + a^2(x - y)$ $2a^2(x - y)$
28. $3x^2(x - 6) + 3x^2(x - 6)$ $6x^2(x - 6)$
29. $ac + ad + bc + bd$ $(a + b)(c + d)$
30. $xy + xz + wy + wz$ $(x + w)(y + z)$
31. $b^3 - b^2 + 2b - 2$ $(b^2 + 2)(b - 1)$
32. $y^3 - y^2 + 3y - 3$ $(y^2 + 3)(y - 1)$
33. $y^2 - 8y - y + 8$ $(y - 1)(y - 8)$
34. $t^2 + 6t - 2t - 12$ $(t - 2)(t + 6)$
35. $2y^4 + 6y^2 + 5y^2 + 15$ $(2y^2 + 5)(y^2 + 3)$
36. $8x^4 - 12x^2 - 12x^2 + 18$ $2(2x^2 - 3)^2$
37. $2xy - x^2y - 6 + 3x$ $(xy - 3)(2 - x)$
38. $4ab - a^2b - 20 + 5a$ $(ab - 5)(4 - a)$

▮▮▮ Factor. Remember to look first for a common factor. (*See Examples 9 and 10.*)

39. $x^2 - 16$ $(x + 4)(x - 4)$
40. $y^2 - 9$ $(y + 3)(y - 3)$
41. $9x^2 - 25$ $(3x + 5)(3x - 5)$
42. $4a^2 - 49$ $(2a + 7)(2a - 7)$
43. $4x^2 - 25$ $(2x + 5)(2x - 5)$
44. $100y^2 - 81$ $(10y + 9)(10y - 9)$
45. $6x^2 - 6y^2$ $6(x + y)(x - y)$
46. $8x^2 - 8y^2$ $8(x + y)(x - y)$
47. $3x^8 - 3y^8$ $3(x^4 + y^4)(x^2 + y^2)(x + y)(x - y)$
48. $5x^4 - 5y^4$ $5(x^2 + y^2)(x + y)(x - y)$
49. $4xy^4 - 4xz^4$ $4x(y^2 + z^2)(y + z)(y - z)$
50. $9a^4 - a^2b^2$ $a^2(3a + b)(3a - b)$
51. $\frac{1}{25} - x^2$ $(\frac{1}{5} + x)(\frac{1}{5} - x)$
52. $\frac{1}{16} - y^2$ $(\frac{1}{4} + y)(\frac{1}{4} - y)$
53. $0.25 - y^2$ $(0.5 + y)(0.5 - y)$
54. $0.16 - x^2$ $(0.4 + x)(0.4 - x)$
55. $0.04x^2 - 0.09y^2$ $(0.2x + 0.3y)(0.2x - 0.3y)$
56. $0.01x^2 - 0.04y^2$ $(0.1x + 0.2y)(0.1x - 0.2y)$

Challenge Exercises

57. $x(x - 6)$ 58. $(y + 2)(y - 6)$ 59. $(2y + 9)(2y - 1)$ 60. $9x(x + 6)$ 61. $(a^8 + 1)$ $(a^4 + 1)(a^2 + 1)(a + 1)(a - 1)$ 62. $(y^{16} + 1)(y^8 + 1)(y^4 + 1)(y^2 + 1)(y + 1)(y - 1)$

Factor.

57. $(x - 3)^2 - 9$
58. $(y - 2)^2 - 16$
59. $(2y + 4)^2 - 25$
60. $(3x + 9)^2 - 81$
61. $a^{16} - 1$
62. $y^{32} - 1$

7-2 Factoring Trinomials

After finishing Lesson 7-2, you should be able to
∎ factor polynomials which are the squares of binomials.
∎∎ factor trinomials of the type $x^2 + ax + b$.

∎ Factoring Squares of Binomials

Some trinomials are squares of binomials. For example,

$$x^2 + 6x + 9 = (x + 3)^2$$

Trinomials like this are sometimes called *trinomial squares*. We must first be able to recognize when a trinomial is a square of a binomial.

a) Two of the terms must be squares (A^2 and B^2).
b) There must be no minus sign before A^2 or B^2.
c) If we multiply A and B (the square roots of these expressions) and double the result, we get the remaining term, $2 \cdot A \cdot B$, or its addltive inverse, $-2 \cdot A \cdot B$.

Example 1. Is $x^2 + 10x + 25$ the square of a binomial?

a) x^2 and 25 are squares.
b) There is no minus sign before x^2 or 25.
c) If we multiply the square roots, x and 5, and double we get the remaining term: $2 \cdot 5 \cdot x$ or $10x$.

Thus $x^2 + 10x + 25$ is the square of a binomial.

Example 2. Is $x^2 + 8x + 13$ the square of a binomial?

The answer is no, since 13 is not a square.

TRY THIS ━━━━▶

To factor squares of binomials we use the following equations.

$$A^2 + 2 \cdot A \cdot B + B^2 = (A + B)^2$$
$$A^2 - 2 \cdot A \cdot B + B^2 = (A - B)^2$$

Which of the following are trinomial squares?

1. $x^2 + 6x + 9$ Yes
2. $x^2 - 8x + 16$ Yes
3. $x^2 + 6x + 11$ No
4. $4x^2 - 20x + 25$ Yes
5. $16x^2 - 20x + 25$ No
6. $5x^2 + 14x + 16$ No
7. $x^2 + 8x - 16$ No
8. $x^2 - 8x - 16$ No

Examples. Factor.

3. $x^2 - 10x + 25 = (x - 5)^2$

4. $16y^2 + 49 + 56y = 16y^2 + 56y + 49$
$$= (4y + 7)^2$$

5. $-20xy + 4y^2 + 25x^2 = 4y^2 - 20xy + 25x^2$
$$= (2y - 5x)^2$$

TRY THIS ➡

Answers. 9. $(x + 7)^2$ 10. $(3y - 5)^2$ 11. $(9y + 4x)^2$

Factor.

9. $x^2 + 14x + 49$
10. $9y^2 + 25 - 30y$
11. $72xy + 16x^2 + 81y^2$

Examples. Factor.

6. $25x^4 + 70x^2y^3 + 49y^6 = (5x^2 + 7y^3)^2$

7. $-4y^2 - 144y^8 + 48y^5 = -4y^2(1 - 12y^3 + 36y^6)$
$$= -4y^2(1 - 6y^3)^2$$

Removing a common factor first

TRY THIS ➡

Answers.   12. $(4x^2 - 5y^3)^2$ 13. $-2(2a - 3b)^2$ 14. $-3y^2(2x^2 - 5y^3)^2$

Factor.

12. $16x^4 - 40x^2y^3 + 25y^6$
13. $24ab - 8a^2 - 18b^2$
14. $-12x^4y^2 + 60x^2y^5 - 75y^8$

▮▮ Factoring Trinomials of the Type $x^2 + ax + b$

Consider this product.

$$\begin{array}{cccc} \text{F} & \text{O} & \text{I} & \text{L} \end{array}$$
$$(x + 3)(x + 5) = x^2 + 5x + 3x + 15$$
$$= x^2 + 8x + 15$$

Note that the coefficient 8 is the sum of 3 and 5, and the 15 is the product of 3 and 5. In general, $(x + a)(x + b) = x^2 + (a + b)x + ab$. To factor we can use this equation in reverse.

$$x^2 + (a + b)x + ab = (x + a)(x + b)$$

Example 8. Factor $x^2 - 3x - 10$.

We look for pairs of integers whose product is -10 and whose sum is -3.

Pairs of Factors	Sum of Factors
$-2, \quad 5$	3
$2, -5$	-3
$10, -1$	9
$-10, \quad 1$	-9

Thus the desired integers are 2 and -5. Then

$$x^2 - 3x - 10 = (x + 2)(x - 5)$$

We can check by multiplying.

TRY THIS ▬▬▬▶

Answers. 15. $(x + 7)(x - 2)$ 16. $(x - 7)(x - 3)$ 17. $(y - 2)(y + 1)$

Factor. Check by multiplying.

15. $x^2 + 5x - 14$
16. $x^2 + 21 - 10x$
17. $y^2 - y - 2$

Exercise Set 7-2

▌Factor. Remember to look first for a common factor. (*See Examples 3–7.*)

1. $y^2 - 6y + 9$ $(y - 3)^2$
2. $x^2 - 8x + 16$ $(x - 4)^2$
3. $x^2 + 14x + 49$ $(x + 7)^2$
4. $x^2 + 16x + 64$ $(x + 8)^2$
5. $x^2 + 1 + 2x$ $(x + 1)^2$
6. $x^2 + 1 - 2x$ $(x - 1)^2$
7. $a^2 + 4a + 4$ $(a + 2)^2$
8. $a^2 - 4a + 4$ $(a - 2)^2$
9. $y^2 + 36 - 12y$ $(y - 6)^2$
10. $y^2 + 36 + 12y$ $(y + 6)^2$
11. $-18y^2 + y^3 + 81y$ $y(y - 9)^2$
12. $24a^2 + a^3 + 144a$ $a(a + 12)^2$
13. $12a^2 + 36a + 27$ $3(2a + 3)^2$
14. $20y^2 + 100y + 125$ $5(2y + 5)^2$
15. $2x^2 - 40x + 200$ $2(x - 10)^2$
16. $32x^2 + 48x + 18$ $2(4x + 3)^2$
17. $1 - 8d + 16d^2$ $(1 - 4d)^2$
18. $1 + 10b + 25b^2$ $(1 + 5b)^2$
19. $64 + 25y^2 - 80y$ $(5y - 8)^2$
20. $81 + 16x^2 + 72x$ $(4x + 9)^2$
21. $x^4y^4 - 8x^2y^2 + 16$ $(xy + 2)^2(xy - 2)^2$
22. $a^4y^4 - 18a^2y^2 + 81$ $(ay + 3)^2(ay - 3)^2$
23. $-24ab + 16a^2 + 9b^2$ $(4a - 3b)^2$
24. $12rs + 4r^2 + 9s^2$ $(2r + 3s)^2$
25. $9y^8 + 12y^4 + 4$ $(3y^4 + 2)^2$
26. $16x^{10} - 8x^5 + 1$ $(4x^5 - 1)^2$
27. $\frac{1}{36}x^8 + \frac{4}{18}x^4 + \frac{4}{9}$ $(\frac{1}{6}x^4 + \frac{2}{3})^2$
28. $\frac{1}{25}y^{10} - \frac{6}{20}y^5 + \frac{9}{16}$ $(\frac{1}{5}y^5 - \frac{3}{4})^2$
29. $0.25x^2 + 0.30x + .09$ $(0.5x + 0.3)^2$
30. $0.04x^2 - 0.28x + 0.49$ $(0.2x - 0.7)^2$

▌▌Factor. (*See Example 8.*)

31. $x^2 + 9x + 20$ $(x + 5)(x + 4)$
32. $y^2 + 8y + 15$ $(x + 5)(x + 3)$
33. $y^2 - 8y + 16$ $(y - 4)^2$
34. $a^2 - 10a + 25$ $(a - 5)^2$
35. $x^2 - 27 - 6x$ $(x - 9)(x + 3)$
36. $t^2 - 15 - 2t$ $(t - 5)(t + 3)$
37. $m^2 - 3m - 28$ $(m - 7)(m + 4)$
38. $x^2 - 2x - 8$ $(x - 4)(x + 2)$
39. $14x + x^2 + 45$ $(x + 9)(x + 5)$
40. $12y + y^2 + 32$ $(y + 8)(y + 4)$
41. $y^2 + 2y - 63$ $(y + 9)(y - 7)$
42. $x^2 + 3x - 40$ $(x + 8)(x - 5)$
43. $t^2 - 11t + 28$ $(t - 7)(t - 4)$
44. $y^2 - 14y + 45$ $(y - 5)(y - 9)$
45. $3x + x^2 - 10$ $(x + 5)(x - 2)$
46. $x + x^2 - 6$ $(x + 3)(x - 2)$
47. $x^2 + 5x + 6$ $(x + 2)(x + 3)$
48. $y^2 + 8y + 7$ $(y + 7)(y + 1)$
49. $32 + 4y - y^2$ $(8 - y)(4 + y)$
50. $56 + x - x^2$ $(8 - x)(7 + x)$
51. $15 + t^2 + 8t$ $(t + 5)(t + 3)$
52. $27 + y^2 + 12y$ $(y + 9)(y + 3)$
53. $x^4 + 11x^2 - 80$ $(x^2 + 16)(x^2 - 5)$
54. $y^4 + 5y^2 - 84$ $(y^2 + 12)(y^2 - 7)$
55. $x^2 - \frac{4}{25} + \frac{3}{5}x$ $(x + \frac{4}{5})(x - \frac{1}{5})$
56. $y^2 - \frac{8}{49} + \frac{2}{7}y$ $(y + \frac{8}{7})(y - \frac{2}{7})$
57. $y^2 + 0.4y - 0.05$ $(y - 0.1)(y + 0.5)$
58. $t^2 + 0.6t - 0.27$ $(t + 0.9)(t - 0.3)$

7-3 *Trinomials of the Type* $ax^2 + bx + c$

After finishing Lesson 7-3, you should be able to
▌ factor trinomials of the type $ax^2 + bx + c$.

▌Consider a multiplication.

$$\begin{array}{cccc} & \text{F} & \text{O} & \text{I} & \text{L} \\ (2x + 3)(5x + 4) = & 10x^2 & + 8x & + 15x & + 12 \\ & 10x^2 & + & 23x & + & 12 \\ & \uparrow & & \uparrow & & \uparrow \end{array}$$

F	O + I	L
$2 \cdot 5$	$2 \cdot 4 + 3 \cdot 5$	$3 \cdot 4$

To factor $ax^2 + bx + c$ we look for two binomials

$$(\underline{}x + \underline{})(\underline{}x + \underline{})$$

where products of numbers in the blanks are as follows.

1. The numbers in the *first* blanks have product a.
2. The *outside* product and the *inside* product add up to b.
3. The numbers in the *last* blanks have product c.

Example 1. Factor $5x^2 - 9x - 2$.

We first look for a common factor. There is none other than 1.
We look for numbers whose product is 5. These are 1, 5 and $-1, -5$.

We have these possibilities.

$$(x +)(5x +) \quad \text{or} \quad (-x +)(-5x +)$$

Now we look for numbers whose product is -2. These are 1, -2 and $-1, 2$.

Then we have these as some of the possibilities for factorization.

a) $(x + 1)(5x - 2)$
b) $(x - 2)(5x + 1)$
c) $(-x + 1)(-5x - 2)$
d) $(-x + 2)(-5x - 1)$

Then we multiply each.
We must get $5x^2 - 9x - 2$.

a) $5x^2 + 3x - 2$
b) $5x^2 - 9x - 2$
c) $5x^2 - 3x - 2$
d) $5x^2 - 9x - 2$

We see that b) and d) are both factorizations. We prefer to have the first coefficients positive when that is possible. Thus the factorization we prefer is $(x - 2)(5x + 1)$.

TRY THIS

Factor.

1. $3x^2 + 5x + 2$
2. $4x^2 - 3 + 4x$

Example 2. Factor $12x^2 + 34x + 14$.

Answers. 1. $(3x + 2)(x + 1)$ 2. $(2x + 3)(2x - 1)$

We first look for a common factor. The number 2 is a common factor, so we factor it out. $2(6x^2 + 17x + 7)$. Now we consider $6x^2 + 17x + 7$. We look for numbers whose product is 6. These are 6, 1 and 2, 3. (From Example 1 we found that we needed to consider only positive factors of the first term.) We then have these possibilities.

$(6x + \ )(x + \ )$ and $(2x + \ )(3x + \ )$

Next we look for pairs of numbers whose product is 7. They are

$7, 1 \qquad -7, -1$ (*Both positive or both negative*)

By multiplying, we find that the answer is $2(2x + 1)(3x + 7)$.

TRY THIS

Factor.

3. $24y^2 - 46y + 10$
4. $16x^2 - 12 + 16x$

Example 3. Factor $x^2y^2 + 5xy + 4$.

Answers. 3. $2(4y - 1)(3y - 5)$ 4. $4(2x - 1)(2x + 3)$

In this case, we can treat xy as if it were a single variable.

$$x^2y^2 + 5xy + 4 = (xy)^2 + (4 + 1)xy + 4 \cdot 1$$
$$= (xy + 4)(xy + 1)$$

TRY THIS

Factor.

5. $p^2q^2 + 7pq + 12$
6. $2x^4y^6 - 3x^2y^3 - 20$

Answers. 5. $(pq + 4)(pq + 3)$ 6. $(2x^2y^3 + 5)(x^2y^3 - 4)$

Another way to factor $ax^2 + bx + c$ is as follows:

a) First look for a common factor.
b) Multiply the first and last coefficients, a and c.
c) Try to factor the product ac so that the sum of the factors is b.
d) Write the middle term, bx, as a sum.
e) Factor by grouping.

Example 4. Factor $2x^2 - 3x - 35$.

a) First look for a common factor. There is none (other than 1).

b) Multiply the first and last coefficients, 2 and -35.

$$2(-35) = -70$$

c)   Try to factor -70 so that the sum of the factors is -3.

Some Pairs of Factors	Sums of Factors
$-2,\quad 35$	33
$2,\ -35$	-33
$-14,\quad 5$	-9
$7,\ -10$	-3

The desired factors are 7 and -10.

d)   Write $-3x$ as a sum using the results of c).

$$-3x = -10x + 7x$$

e)   Factor by grouping.

$$
\begin{aligned}
2x^2 - 3x - 35 &= 2x^2 - 10x + 7x - 35 \\
&= (2x^2 - 10x) + (7x - 35) \\
&= 2x(x - 5) + 7(x - 5) \\
&= (2x + 7)(x - 5)
\end{aligned}
$$

TRY THIS ⟹

Answers.   7. $(3x + 8)(x - 7)$ 8. $(4x + 1)(x + 9)$

Factor.

7. $3x^2 - 13x - 56$
8. $4x^2 + 37x + 9$

Exercise Set 7-3

▌Factor. Remember to look first for a common factor. (*See Examples 1–4.*)

1. $3b^2 + 8b + 4$ $(3b + 2)(b + 2)$
2. $9x^2 + 15x + 4$ $(3x + 1)(3x + 4)$
3. $6y^2 - y - 2$ $(3y - 2)(2y + 1)$
4. $3a^2 - a - 4$ $(3a - 4)(a + 1)$
5. $-7a + 6a^2 - 10$ $(6a + 5)(a - 2)$
6. $-35z + 12z^2 - 3$ $(12z + 1)(z - 3)$
7. $9a^2 + 6a - 8$ $(3a + 4)(3a - 2)$
8. $4t^2 + 4t - 15$ $(2t + 5)(2t - 3)$
9. $3x^2 - 16x - 12$ $(3x + 2)(x - 6)$
10. $6x^2 - 5x - 25$ $(3x + 5)(2x - 5)$
11. $6x^2 - 15 - x$ $(3x - 5)(2x + 3)$
12. $10y^2 - 12 - 7y$ $(5y + 4)(2y - 3)$
13. $3a^2 - 10a + 8$ $(3a - 4)(a - 2)$
14. $12a^2 - 7a + 1$ $(4a - 1)(3a - 1)$
15. $35y^2 + 34y + 8$ $(5y + 2)(7y + 4)$
16. $9a^2 + 18a + 8$ $(3a + 2)(3a + 4)$
17. $2t + 5t^2 - 3$ $(5t - 3)(t + 1)$
18. $4x + 15x^2 - 3$ $(5x + 3)(3x - 1)$
19. $8x^2 - 16 - 28x$ $4(2x + 1)(x - 4)$
20. $18x^2 - 24 - 6x$ $6(3x - 4)(x + 1)$
21. $3x^3 - 5x^2 - 2x$ $x(3x + 1)(x - 2)$
22. $18y^3 - 3y^2 - 10y$ $y(6y - 5)(3y + 2)$
23. $24x^2 - 2 - 47x$ $(24x + 1)(x - 2)$
24. $15y^2 - 10 - 19y$ $(5y + 2)(3y - 5)$
25. $21x^2 + 37x + 12$ $(7x + 3)(3x + 4)$
26. $10y^2 + 23y + 12$ $(5y + 4)(2y + 3)$
27. $17x + 40x^2 - 12$ $(5x + 4)(8x - 3)$
28. $2y + 24y^2 - 15$ $(6y + 5)(4y - 3)$
29. $12a^2 - 17a + 6$ $(4a - 3)(3a - 2)$
30. $20a^2 - 23a + 6$ $(4a - 3)(5a - 2)$
31. $2x^2 + xy - 6y^2$ $(2x - 3y)(x + 2y)$
32. $2m^2 + mn - 10n^2$ $(2m + 5n)(m - 2n)$
33. $-6xy + 8x^2 - 9y^2$ $(2x - 3y)(4x + 3y)$
34. $-7ts + 2t^2 - 4s^2$ $(2t + s)(t - 4s)$
35. $7a^2b^2 + 6 + 13ab$ $(7ab + 6)(ab + 1)$
36. $3m^2n^2 + 6 + 11mn$ $(3mn + 2)(mn + 3)$
37. $9x^2y^2 - 4 + 5xy$ $(9xy - 4)(xy + 1)$
38. $10a^2b^2 - 1 - 9ab$ $(10ab + 1)(ab - 1)$

7-4 Completing the Square

After finishing Lesson 7-4, you should be able to
▮ factor polynomials by completing the square.

▮ A difference of two squares can have more than two terms.

Example 1. Factor.

$$x^2 + 6x + 9 - 25 = (x^2 + 6x + 9) - 25$$
$$= (x + 3)^2 - 5^2$$

This is now a difference of two squares, one of which is a square of a binomial. When we factor, we get

$$(x + 3 + 5)(x + 3 - 5), \text{ or } (x + 8)(x - 2).$$

TRY THIS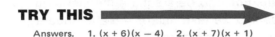

Answers.　1. $(x + 6)(x - 4)$　2. $(x + 7)(x + 1)$

Factor.

1. $x^2 + 2x + 1 - 25$
2. $y^2 + 8y + 16 - 9$

Example 2. Factor.

$$x^2 + 10x + 25 - y^2 + 2y - 1 = (x^2 + 10x + 25) - (y^2 - 2y + 1)$$
$$= (x + 5)^2 - (y - 1)^2$$

This is now a difference of two squares. Factoring, we get

$$[(x + 5) - (y - 1)][(x + 5) + (y - 1)],$$
or $(x + 5 - y + 1)(x + 5 + y - 1)$,
or $(x - y + 6)(x + y + 4)$.

TRY THIS

Answers.　3. $(x + 14)(x - 6)$　4. $(x + y - 6)(x - y - 10)$

Factor.

3. $x^2 + 8x + 16 - 100$
4. $x^2 - 16x + 64 - y^2 - 4y - 4$

We can use this method to factor $x^2 + 10x + 21$. This trinomial is not a square. For it to be a square, the last term would have to be 25. If we add 0, naming it $25 - 25$, we have:

$$x^2 + 10x + 21 = x^2 + 10x + (25 - 25) + 21$$
$$= (x^2 + 10x + 25) + (-25 + 21)$$
$$= (x + 5)^2 - 4$$

This is now a difference of two squares. Factoring, we get

$$(x + 5 - 2)(x + 5 + 2) \text{ or } (x + 3)(x - 7).$$

We added $25 - 25$ to make our trinomial a square.

To use this method we need to determine what the third term would have to be for it to be a square.

Example 3. What must be added to $x^2 - 8x$ to make a trinomial square?

To find the third term we take half of the coefficient of x, and then square it. Half of -8 is -4, and $(-4)^2 = 16$. Thus we must add 16, and $x^2 - 8x + 16$ is a square.

TRY THIS ➡

What must be added to make a trinomial square?

5. $x^2 - 12x$ 6. $x^2 + 6x$
7. $x^2 - 14x$ 8. $x^2 + 22x$
Answers.   5. 36   6. 9   7. 49   8. 121

Example 4. Factor $x^2 - 8x - 9$.

This trinomial is not a square. For it to be a square the last term would have to be 16. To see this we take half of -8 and square it. To get the last term to be 16 we add zero to the trinomial, naming it $16 - 16$.

$$
\begin{aligned}
x^2 - 8x - 9 &= x^2 - 8x + (16 - 16) - 9 \quad \textit{Adding zero} \\
&= (x^2 - 8x + 16) + (-16 - 9) \\
&= (x^2 - 8x + 16) - 25 \\
&= (x - 4)^2 - 5^2 \\
&= (x - 4 + 5)(x - 4 - 5), \text{ or } (x + 1)(x - 9)
\end{aligned}
$$

Example 5. Factor $y^2 + 55 + 16y$.

We first write the polynomial in descending order: $y^2 + 16y + 55$. It is not a square. For it to be a square the last term would have to be 64. To see this we take half of 16 and square it. To get the last term to be 64 we add zero to the trinomial, naming it $64 - 64$.

$$
\begin{aligned}
y^2 + 16y + 55 &= y^2 + 16y + (64 - 64) + 55 \quad \textit{Adding zero} \\
&= (y^2 + 16y + 64) + (-64 + 55) \\
&= (y^2 + 16y + 64) - 9 \\
&= (y + 8)^2 - 3^2 \\
&= (y + 8 + 3)(y + 8 - 3), \text{ or } (y + 11)(y + 5)
\end{aligned}
$$

This procedure is called *completing the square.* Learn to do it even though you could factor another way! We shall use it again later.

TRY THIS ━━━━━➤

Answers.   9. $(x + 6)(x + 2)$ 10. $(y + 4)(y - 8)$

Example 6.   Factor $x^2 - 5x + 4$.

This trinomial is not a square. For it to be a square, the last term would have to be $\frac{25}{4}$. To see this, we take half of -5 and square it. To get the last term to be $\frac{25}{4}$ we add zero to the trinomial, naming it $\frac{25}{4} - \frac{25}{4}$.

$$
\begin{aligned}
x^2 - 5x + 4 &= x^2 - 5x + \left(\tfrac{25}{4} - \tfrac{25}{4}\right) + 4 \qquad \textit{Adding zero}\\
&= \left(x^2 - 5x + \tfrac{25}{4}\right) + \left(-\tfrac{25}{4} + \tfrac{16}{4}\right)\\
&= \left(x^2 - 5x + \tfrac{25}{4}\right) - \tfrac{9}{4}\\
&= \left(x - \tfrac{5}{2}\right)^2 - \left(\tfrac{3}{2}\right)^2\\
&= \left(x - \tfrac{5}{2} + \tfrac{3}{2}\right)\left(x - \tfrac{5}{2} - \tfrac{3}{2}\right), \text{ or } (x - 1)(x - 4)
\end{aligned}
$$

TRY THIS ━━━━━➤

Factor by completing the square.

9. $x^2 + 8x + 12$

10. $-4y - 32 + y^2$

Factor by completing the square. $(x + \frac{3}{2})(x - \frac{1}{2})$

11. $x^2 + x - \frac{3}{4}$

Exercise Set 7-4

▌Factor by completing the square. Show your work. (*See Examples 4–6.*)

1. $c^2 + 8c + 12$ $(c + 6)(c + 2)$
2. $x^2 + 10x + 16$ $(x + 8)(x + 2)$
3. $t^2 - 10t + 21$ $(t - 3)(t - 7)$
4. $a^2 - 8a + 12$ $(a - 2)(a - 6)$
5. $-2y + y^2 - 24$ $(y + 4)(y - 6)$
6. $-10a + a^2 - 24$ $(a + 2)(a - 12)$
7. $x^2 - 14x + 40$ $(x - 4)(x - 10)$
8. $y^2 - 6y + 8$ $(y - 2)(y - 4)$
9. $r^2 + 12r - 28$ $(r + 14)(r - 2)$
10. $y^2 + 16y - 17$ $(y + 17)(y - 1)$
11. $m^2 - 15 + 2m$ $(m + 5)(m - 3)$
12. $r^2 - 15 + 14r$ $(r + 15)(r - 1)$
13. $p^2 + 8p + 15$ $(p + 5)(p + 3)$
14. $a^2 + 8a + 12$ $(a + 6)(a + 2)$
15. $t^2 + 12t + 11$ $(t + 11)(t + 1)$
16. $m^2 + 14m + 13$ $(m + 13)(m + 1)$
17. $3x^2 + 39 - 42x$ $3(x - 1)(x - 13)$
18. $2x^2 + 144 - 36x$ $2(x - 6)(x - 12)$
19. $5a^2 - 40a - 420$ $5(a + 6)(a - 14)$
20. $8x^2 - 64x - 72$ $8(x + 1)(x - 9)$
21. $x^2 + 7x + 6$ $(x + 6)(x + 1)$
22. $x^2 + 5x - 6$ $(x + 6)(x - 1)$
23. $x^2 - 3x + \frac{5}{4}$ $(x - \frac{1}{2})(x - \frac{5}{2})$
24. $x^2 - 5x + \frac{9}{4}$ $(x - \frac{1}{2})(x - \frac{9}{2})$

Calculator Exercises   25. $(x + 5.766)(x - 1.284)$ 26. $(x - 0.56)(x - 0.22)$ 27. $5.72(x + 18.6)(x - 12.4)$
28. $0.24(x + 3.11)(x + 2.83)$

Factor by completing the square.

25. $x^2 + 4.482x - 7.403544$
26. $x^2 - 0.78x + 0.1232$
27. $5.72x^2 + 35.464x - 1319.2608$
28. $0.24x^2 + 1.4256x + 2.112312$

7-5 Sums or Differences of Two Cubes

After finishing Lesson 7-5, you should be able to
▮ factor polynomials that are sums or differences of two cubes.

▮Consider the following.

$$(a + b)(a^2 - ab + b^2) = a(a^2 - ab + b^2) + b(a^2 - ab + b^2)$$
$$= a^3 - a^2b + ab^2 + a^2b - ab^2 + b^3$$
$$= a^3 + b^3$$

$$(a - b)(a^2 + ab + b^2) = a(a^2 + ab + b^2) - b(a^2 + ab + b^2)$$
$$= a^3 + a^2b + ab^2 - a^2b - ab^2 - b^3$$
$$= a^3 - b^3$$

To factor sums or differences of two cubes we use the following equations.

$$a^3 + b^3 = (a + b)(a^2 - ab + b^2)$$
$$a^3 - b^3 = (a - b)(a^2 + ab + b^2)$$

Example 1. Factor $x^3 - 27$.

In one set of parentheses we write the cube root of the first term, the sign of the second term, and then the cube root of the second term.

$$x^3 - 27 = (x - 3)(\qquad\qquad)$$

To get the next factor we think of $x - 3$ and do the following.

1. Square the first term: x^2.
2. Take the product of the first and second terms, $-3x$, and change the sign: $3x$.
3. Square the second term: $(-3)^2 = 9$.

$$= (x - 3)(x^2 + 3x + 9)$$

Note: We cannot factor $x^2 + 3x + 9$. It is not the square of a binomial.

TRY THIS

Answers. 1. $(x - 2)(x^2 + 2x + 4)$ 2. $(y - 3)(y^2 + 3y + 9)$

Factor.

1. $x^3 - 8$
2. $y^3 - 27$

Example 2. Factor $125x^3 + y^3$.

$125x^3 + y^3 = (5x + y)($)   *Writing the sum of the cube roots*

Now we think of $5x + y$ and get the next factor.

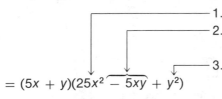

1. Square the first term: $25x^2$.
2. Take the product of the first and second terms, $5xy$, and change the sign: $-5xy$.
3. Square the last term: y^2.

$= (5x + y)(25x^2 - 5xy + y^2)$

TRY THIS ➡️

Factor.

3. $27x^3 + y^3$
4. $8y^3 + z^3$

Answers. 3. $(3x + y)(9x^2 - 3xy + y^2)$ 4. $(2y + z)(4y^2 - 2yz + z^2)$

Example 3. Factor.

$64y^6 - 125x^6 = (4y^2 - 5x^2)[(4y^2)^2 + (4y^2)(5x^2) + (5x^2)^2]$
$\qquad\qquad = (4y^2 - 5x^2)(16y^4 \mid 20y^2x^2 + 25x^4)$

TRY THIS ➡️

Factor.

5. $8x^6 + 27y^6$

Answer. 5. $(2x^2 + 3y^2)(4x^4 - 6x^2y^2 + 9y^4)$

Exercise Set 7-5

▌Factor. Remember to look first for a common factor. (*See Examples 1–3.*)

1. $x^3 + 8$ $(x + 2)(x^2 - 2x + 4)$
2. $c^3 + 27$ $(c + 3)(c^2 - 3c + 9)$
3. $y^3 - 64$ $(y - 4)(y^2 + 4y + 16)$
4. $z^3 - 1$ $(z - 1)(z^2 + z + 1)$
5. $w^3 + 1$ $(w + 1)(w^2 - w + 1)$
6. $x^3 + 125$ $(x + 5)(x^2 - 5x + 25)$
7. $8a^3 + 1$ $(2a + 1)(4a^2 - 2a + 1)$
8. $27x^3 + 1$ $(3x + 1)(9x^2 - 3x + 1)$
9. $y^3 - 8$ $(y - 2)(y^2 + 2y + 4)$
10. $p^3 - 27$ $(p - 3)(p^2 + 3p + 9)$
11. $8 - 27b^3$ $(2 - 3b)(4 + 6b + 9b^2)$
12. $64 - 125x^3$ $(4 - 5x)(16 + 20x + 25x^2)$
13. $64y^3 + 1$ $(4y + 1)(16y^2 - 4y + 1)$
14. $125x^3 + 1$ $(5x + 1)(25x^2 - 5x + 1)$
15. $8x^3 + 27$ $(2x + 3)(4x^2 - 6x + 9)$
16. $27y^3 + 64$ $(3y + 4)(9y^2 - 12y + 16)$
17. $a^3 - b^3$ $(a - b)(a^2 + ab + b^2)$
18. $x^3 - y^3$ $(x - y)(x^2 + xy + y^2)$
19. $a^3 + \frac{1}{8}$ $(a + \frac{1}{2})(a^2 - \frac{1}{2}a + \frac{1}{4})$
20. $b^3 + \frac{1}{27}$ $(b + \frac{1}{3})(b^2 - \frac{1}{3}b + \frac{1}{9})$
21. $8x^3 - 27y^3$ $(2x - 3y)(4x^2 + 6xy + 9y^2)$
22. $64c^3 - 125d^3$ $(4c - 5d)(16c^2 + 20cd + 25d^2)$
23. $rs^3 + 64r$ $r(s + 4)(s^2 - 4s + 16)$
24. $ab^3 + 125a$ $a(b + 5)(b^2 - 5b + 25)$
25. $5x^3 - 40z^3$ $5(x - 2z)(x^2 + 2xz + 4z^2)$
26. $2y^3 - 54z^3$ $2(y - 3z)(y^2 + 3yz + 9z^2)$
27. $x^3 + 0.001$ $(x + 0.1)(x^2 - 0.1x + 0.01)$
28. $y^3 + 0.125$ $(y + 0.5)(y^2 - 0.5y + 0.25)$
29. $64x^6 - 8t^6$ $8(2x^2 - t^2)(4x^4 + 2x^2t^2 + t^4)$
30. $125c^6 - 8d^6$ $(5c^2 - 2d^2)(25c^4 + 10c^2d^2 + 4d^4)$

7-6 Factoring: A General Strategy

After finishing Lesson 7-6, you should be able to
▮ factor polynomials using any of the methods you have learned.

▮ Here is a general strategy for factoring.
  A. Always look first for a common factor.
  B. Then proceed by considering the number of terms.
     Two terms: Try factoring as a difference of two squares, or a sum or difference of two cubes.
     Three terms: (1) Is it a square of a binomial? If so, you know how to factor.
                     (2) Is it a square of a binomial? If not, use trial and error.
     More than three terms: (1) Try grouping.
                              (2) Try differences of squares again.
  C. *Always factor completely*. By this we mean whenever you obtain a factor that can still be factored, you should factor it.

Example 1. Factor $10a^2x - 40b^2x$.

A. We look first for a common factor.

$$10x(a^2 - 4b^2)$$

B. The factor $a^2 - 4b^2$ has only two terms. It is a difference of squares. We factor it.

$$10x(a + 2b)(a - 2b)$$

C. Have we factored completely? Yes, because no factor can be factored further.

Example 2. Factor $x^6 - y^6$.

A. We look for a common factor. There isn't one.

B. There are only two terms. It is a difference of squares: $(x^3)^2 - (y^3)^2$. We factor it.

$$(x^3 + y^3)(x^3 - y^3)$$

One factor is a sum of two cubes, and the other factor is a difference of two cubes. We factor them.

$$(x + y)(x^2 - xy + y^2)(x - y)(x^2 + xy + y^2)$$

C. We have factored completely because no factor can be factored further.

TRY THIS ➡

Answers. 1. $2(1 + 4x^2)(1 + 2x)(1 - 2x)$ 2. $7(a + 1)(a^2 - a + 1)(a - 1)$
$(a^2 + a + 1)$ 3. $(3 + x)(4 + x)$ 4. $(c - d + t + 4)(c - d - t - 4)$

> Factor completely.
>
> 1. $2 - 32x^4$
> 2. $7a^6 - 7$
> 3. $3x + 12 + 4x + x^2$
> 4. $c^2 - 2cd + d^2 - t^2 - 8t - 16$

Exercise Set 7-6

▌Factor completely. Remember to look first for a common factor. (*See Examples 1 and 2.*)

1. $x^2 - 144$ $(x + 12)(x - 12)$
2. $y^2 - 81$ $(y + 9)(y - 9)$
3. $2x^2 + 11x + 12$ $(2x + 3)(x + 4)$
4. $8a^2 + 18a - 5$ $(4x - 1)(2x + 5)$
5. $3x^4 - 12$ $3(x^2 + 2)(x^2 - 2)$
6. $2xy^2 - 50x$ $2x(y + 5)(y - 5)$
7. $a^2 + 25 + 10a$ $(a + 5)^2$
8. $p^2 + 64 + 16p$ $(p + 8)^2$
9. $2x^2 - 10x - 132$ $2(x - 11)(x + 6)$
10. $3y^2 - 15y - 252$ $3(y - 12)(y + 7)$
11. $9x^2 - 25y^2$ $(3x + 5y)(3x - 5y)$
12. $16a^2 - 81b^2$ $(4a + 9b)(4a - 9b)$
13. $4c^2 - 4cd + d^2$ $(2c - d)^2$
14. $70b^2 - 3ab - a^2$ $(10b + a)(7b - a)$
15. $-7x^2 + 2x^3 + 4x - 14$ $(x^2 + 2)(2x - 7)$
16. $9m^2 + 3m^3 + 8m + 24$ $(3m^2 + 8)(m + 3)$
17. $4x^2 - 27x + 45$ $(4x - 15)(x - 3)$
18. $3y^2 + 15y - 42$ $3(y + 7)(y - 2)$
19. $8m^3 + m^6 - 20$ $(m^3 + 10)(m^3 - 2)$
20. $-37x^2 + x^4 + 36$ $(x + 6)(x - 6)(x + 1)(x - 1)$
21. $ac + cd - ab - bd$ $(c - b)(a + d)$
22. $xw - yw + xz - yz$ $(w + z)(x - y)$
23. $m^6 - 1$ $(m + 1)(m^2 - m + 1)(m - 1)(m^2 + m + 1)$
24. $64t^6 - 1$ $(2t + 1)(4t^2 - 2t + 1)(2t - 1)(4t^2 + 2t + 1)$
25. $x^2 + 6x - y^2 + 9$ $(x + y + 3)(x - y + 3)$
26. $t^2 + 10t - p^2 + 25$ $(t + p + 5)(t - p + 5)$
27. $36y^2 - 35 + 12y$ $(6y - 5)(6y + 7)$
28. $2b - 28a^2b + 10ab$ $-2b(7a + 1)(2a - 1)$
29. $a^8 - b^8$ $(a^4 + b^4)(a^2 + b^2)(a + b)(a - b)$
30. $2x^4 - 32$ $2(x^2 + 4)(x + 2)(x - 2)$
31. $8p^3 + 27q^3$ $(2p + 3q)(4p^2 - 6pq + 9q^2)$
32. $125x^3 + 64y^3$ $(5x + 4y)(25x^2 - 20xy + 16y^2)$
33. $64p^3 - 1$ $(4p - 1)(16p^2 + 4p + 1)$
34. $8y^3 - 125$ $(2y - 5)(4y^2 + 10y + 25)$
35. $a^3b - 16ab^3$ $ab(a + 4b)(a - 4b)$
36. $x^3y - 25xy^3$ $xy(x + 5y)(x - 5y)$
37. $-23xy + 20x^2y^2 + 6$ $(4xy - 3)(5xy - 2)$
38. $42ab + 27a^2b^2 + 8$ $(3ab + 4)(9ab + 2)$
39. $2x^3 + 6x^2 - 8x - 24$ $2(x + 2)(x - 2)(x + 3)$
40. $3x^3 + 6x^2 - 27x - 54$ $3(x + 3)(x - 3)(x + 2)$

SCIENCE NOTE: Cosmology

How are stars formed? How large is the universe? What are the properties of space? These are questions from cosmology, a branch of astronomy that is concerned with the physical structure of the universe. (The word *cosmos* means "universe.") Many great mathematicians have contributed work to cosmology.

7-7 Solving Equations by Factoring

After finishing Lesson 7-7, you should be able to
▌ solve equations by factoring and using the principle of zero products.

▌ To solve equations by factoring we will restate an important theorem from Chapter 2.

THEOREM 2-3   (The Principle of Zero Products)
A product is 0 if and only if at least one of the factors is 0.

Notice that Theorem 2-3 says that if a factor is 0, then the product will be 0; and also that if a product is 0, then one of the factors must be 0.

   To use this principle in solving equations, we make sure that there is 0 on one side of the equation and then factor the other side.

Remark (if and only if).   When we use these words in a sentence, what does the sentence mean? It means two things. "*A* if and only if *B*" means "If *A* then *B*, and also if *B* then *A*." In other terms, it means "If *A* then *B*, and the converse." Let us consider Theorem 2-3 in this light. It says that if a product is 0 then one of the factors must be 0 *and also* if one of the factors is 0, then the product is 0.

   What does this mean, in a logical sense, for solving equations? Suppose we have an equation $A \cdot B = 0$. Theorem 2-3 says that if either of the factors is 0 it will be true. It also says that if it is true, then at least one of the factors must be 0. Thus we get solutions by setting the factors equal to 0, and we get *all* of the solutions that way. Thus the statements $A \cdot B = 0$ and $A = 0$ or $B = 0$ are equivalent statements and have the same solutions. This is why, logically, we do not need to check possible solutions of equations found by using the principle of zero products.

Example 1.   Solve $x^2 - 3x - 28 = 0$.

We first factor the polynomial. Then we use the principle of zero products.

$$x^2 - 3x - 28 = 0$$
$$(x - 7)(x + 4) = 0 \qquad \textit{Factoring}$$

The expressions $x^2 - 3x - 28$ and $(x - 7)(x + 4)$ name the same number for any replacement. Hence the equations have the same solutions.

$$x - 7 = 0 \quad \text{or} \quad x + 4 = 0 \quad \text{\textit{Using the principle of zero products}}$$
$$x = 7 \quad \text{or} \quad x = -4$$

Check: For 7: $x^2 - 3x - 28 = 0$ For -4: $x^2 - 3x - 28 = 0$

$7^2 - 3(7) - 28$	0
$49 - 21 - 28$	
0	

$(-4)^2 - 3(-4) - 28$	0
$16 + 12 - 28$	
0	

The solutions are 7 and -4.

When we use the principle of zero products, a check is not necessary except to detect errors.

TRY THIS

Solve.   4, 2

1. $x^2 + 8 = 6x$

Example 2.   Solve $7y + 3y^2 = -2$.

$$3y^2 + 7y + 2 = 0 \quad \text{\textit{Adding 2 to get 0 on one side and arranging in descending order}}$$

$$(3y + 1)(y + 2) = 0 \quad \text{\textit{Factoring}}$$

$$3y + 1 = 0 \quad \text{or} \quad y + 2 = 0 \quad \text{\textit{Using the principle of zero products}}$$
$$3y = -1 \quad \text{or} \quad y = -2$$
$$y = -\tfrac{1}{3} \quad \text{or} \quad y = -2$$

The solutions are $-\tfrac{1}{3}$ and -2.

TRY THIS

Solve. $\tfrac{1}{2}$, -3

2. $5y + 2y^2 = 3$

Example 3.   Solve $5b^2 - 10b = 0$.

$$5b(b - 2) = 0 \quad \text{\textit{Factoring}}$$

$$5b = 0 \quad \text{or} \quad b - 2 = 0 \quad \text{\textit{Using the principle of zero products}}$$
$$b = 0 \quad \text{or} \quad b = 2$$

The solutions are 0 and 2.

TRY THIS

Solve.   0, 2

3. $8b^2 - 16b = 0$

Example 4. Solve $x^2 - 6x + 9 = 0$.
$$(x - 3)(x - 3) = 0 \quad \text{\textit{Factoring}}$$

$$x - 3 = 0 \quad \text{or} \quad x - 3 = 0 \quad \text{\textit{Using the principle of zero products}}$$
$$x = 3 \quad \text{or} \quad x = 3$$

There is only one solution, 3.

TRY THIS

Answers. 4. −5   5. $-\frac{3}{2}, \frac{3}{2}$

Solve.

4. $25 + x^2 = -10x$

5. $4x^2 - 9 = 0$

Exercise Set 7-7

▌Solve. (*See Examples 1–4.*)

1. $x^2 + 3x - 28 = 0$ −7, 4
2. $y^2 - 4y - 45 = 0$ 9, −5
3. $y^2 - 8y + 16 = 0$ 4
4. $r^2 - 2r + 1 = 0$ 1
5. $x^2 - 12x + 36 = 0$ 6
6. $y^2 + 16y + 64 = 0$ −8
7. $9x + x^2 + 20 = 0$ −5, −4
8. $8y + y^2 + 15 = 0$ −5, −3
9. $x^2 + 8x = 0$ 0, −8
10. $t^2 + 9t = 0$ 0, −9
11. $x^2 - 9 = 0$ −3, 3
12. $p^2 - 16 = 0$ −4, 4
13. $z^2 = 36$ −6, 6
14. $y^2 = 81$ −9, 9
15. $x^2 + 14x + 45 = 0$ −5, −9
16. $y^2 + 12y + 32 = 0$ −8, −4
17. $y^2 + 2y = 63$ −9, 7
18. $a^2 + 3a = 40$ −8, 5
19. $p^2 - 11p = -28$ 7, 4
20. $x^2 - 14x = -45$ 9, 5
21. $32 + 4x - x^2 = 0$ 8, −4
22. $27 + 12t + t^2 = 0$ −9, −3
23. $3b^2 + 8b + 4 = 0$ $-\frac{2}{3}, -2$
24. $9y^2 + 15y + 4 = 0$ $-\frac{4}{3}, -\frac{1}{3}$
25. $8y^2 - 10y + 3 = 0$ $\frac{3}{4}, \frac{1}{2}$
26. $4x^2 + 11x + 6 = 0$ $-\frac{3}{4}, -2$
27. $6z - z^2 = 0$ 0, 6
28. $8y - y^2 = 0$ 0, 8
29. $12z^2 + z = 6$ $-\frac{3}{4}, \frac{2}{3}$
30. $6x^2 - 7x = 10$ $-\frac{5}{6}, 2$
31. $5x^2 - 20 = 0$ −2, 2
32. $6y^2 - 54 = 0$ −3, 3
33. $2x^2 - 15x = -7$ $\frac{1}{2}, 7$
34. $x^2 - 9x = -8$ 8, 1
35. $21r^2 + r - 10 = 0$ $-\frac{5}{7}, \frac{2}{3}$
36. $12a^2 - 5a - 28 = 0$ $\frac{7}{4}, -\frac{4}{3}$
37. $15y^2 = 3y$ 0, $\frac{1}{5}$
38. $18x^2 = 9x$ 0, $\frac{1}{2}$
39. $100x^2 = 81$ $-\frac{9}{10}, \frac{9}{10}$
40. $49y^2 = 36$ $-\frac{6}{7}, \frac{6}{7}$

Challenge Exercises

Solve.

41. $x^2 - \frac{1}{25} = 0$ $-\frac{1}{5}, \frac{1}{5}$
42. $y^2 - \frac{1}{64} = 0$ $-\frac{1}{8}, \frac{1}{8}$
43. $x(x + 8) = 16(x - 1)$ 4
44. $m(m + 9) = 4(2m + 5)$ −5, 4
45. $(a - 5)^2 = 36$ −1, 11
46. $(x - 6)^2 = 81$ −3 15

7-8 Solving Problems

After finishing Lesson 7-8, you should be able to
▮ solve problems by translating to equations and solving the equations.

▮ To solve some problems we can first translate the problem situation to an equation and then solve the equation. Then we check to see if the solution(s) satisfies the conditions of the problem.

Example 1. The square of a number minus the number is 20. Find the number.

$$\underbrace{\text{The square of a number}}_{} \quad \text{minus} \quad \underbrace{\text{the number}}_{} \quad \text{is} \quad 20$$

$$\begin{array}{ccccc} \downarrow & \downarrow & \downarrow & \downarrow\downarrow & \\ x^2 & - & x & = 20 & \textit{Translating} \end{array}$$

We solve the equation.

$$\begin{aligned} x^2 - x &= 20 \\ x^2 - x - 20 &= 0 && \textit{Adding } -20 \\ (x - 5)(x + 4) &= 0 && \textit{Factoring} \end{aligned}$$

$$x - 5 = 0 \quad \text{or} \quad x + 4 = 0 \qquad \textit{Using the principle of zero products}$$
$$x = 5 \quad \text{or} \qquad x = -4$$

The numbers 5 and -4 both check. They are the answers to the problem.

TRY THIS ⟹

1. The square of a number minus twice the number is 48. Find the number. 8, −6

It is sometimes helpful to reword a problem before translating.

Example 2. The width of a rectangle is 2 m less than the length. The area is 15 m². Find the dimensions.

$$\underbrace{\text{The length}}_{} \quad \text{times} \quad \underbrace{\text{the length minus 2}}_{} \quad \text{is} \quad 15. \qquad \textit{Rewording}$$

$$\begin{array}{cccc} \downarrow & \downarrow & \downarrow & \downarrow\downarrow \\ \ell & \cdot & (\ell - 2) & = 15 \qquad \textit{Translating} \end{array}$$

We solve the equation.

$$\ell \cdot (\ell - 2) = 15$$
$$\ell^2 - 2\ell = 15 \quad \textit{Multiplying}$$
$$\ell^2 - 2\ell - 15 = 0 \quad \textit{Adding } -15$$
$$(\ell - 5)(\ell + 3) = 0 \quad \textit{Factoring}$$

$$\ell - 5 = 0 \quad \text{or} \quad \ell + 3 = 0 \quad \textit{Using the principle of zero products}$$
$$\ell = 5 \quad \text{or} \quad \ell = -3$$

The solutions of the equation are 5 and -3. Now we check in the problem. The length of a rectangle cannot be negative. Thus the length is 5 m. Since the width is 2 m less than the length, the width is 3 m.

TRY THIS ━━━▶

> 2.   The width of a rectangle is 5 cm less than the length. The area is 24 cm². Find the dimensions.
>
> Length is 8 cm; width is 3 cm

Exercise Set 7-8

▌Solve these problems. (*See Examples 1 and 2.*)

1.   Four times the square of a number is 21 more than eight times the number. What is the number? $\frac{7}{2}, -\frac{3}{2}$

2.   Four times the square of a number is 45 more than eight times the number. What is the number? $\frac{9}{2}, -\frac{5}{2}$

3.   The square of a number plus the number is 132. What is the number? $-12, 11$

4.   The square of a number plus the number is 156. What is the number? $-13, 12$

5.   The length of the top of a table is 5 cm more than the width. Find the length and width if the area is 84 cm².   Length is 12 cm; width is 5 cm

6.   The length of the top of a work bench is 4 cm greater than the width. The area is 96 cm². Find the length and the width. Length is 12 cm; width is

7.   Sam Sylow is planning a garden 25 m longer than it is wide. The garden will have an area of 7500 m². What will its dimensions be?   Length is 100 m; width is 75 m

8.   A flower bed is to be 3 m longer than it is wide. The flower bed will have an area of 108 m². What will its dimensions be?   Length is 12 m; width is 9 m

9.   The sum of the squares of two consecutive odd positive integers is 202. Find the integers.   9 and 11

10.   The sum of the squares of two consecutive odd positive integers is 394. Find the integers.   13 and 15

11.   If the sides of a square are lengthened by 4 cm the area becomes 49 cm². Find the length of a side of the original square.   3 cm

12.   If the sides of a square are lengthened by 6 m the area becomes 144 m². Find the length of a side of the original square.   6 m

13. The base of a triangle is 9 cm greater than the height. The area is 56 cm². Find the height and base. Height is 7 cm; base is 16 cm

14. The base of a triangle is 5 cm less than the height. The area is 18 cm². Find the height and base. Height is 9 cm; base is 4 cm

15. The perimeter of a square is 4 more than its area. Find the length of a side. 2

16. The area of a square is 12 more than its perimeter. Find the length of a side. 6

17. Three consecutive even integers are such that the square of the first plus the square of the third is 136. Find the three integers. −10, −8, and −6; 6, 8, 10

18. Three consecutive even integers are such that the square of the third is 76 more than the square of the second. Find the three integers. 16, 18, and 20

19. Find three consecutive integers such that the product of the first and third minus the second is one more than 10 times the third. 11, 12, and 13; −2, −1, and 0

20. Find three consecutive integers such that four times the square of the third less three times the square of the first minus 41 is twice the square of the second. 9, 10, and 11; 3, 4, and 5

Challenge Exercises

21. A rectangular piece of tin is twice as long as it is wide. Squares 2 cm on a side are cut out of each corner and the ends are turned up to make a box whose volume is 480 cm². What are the dimensions of the piece of tin?

Length is 28 cm; width is 14 cm

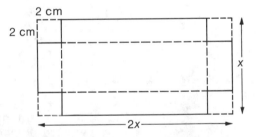

Use Quiz 13 after lesson 7—8.

CONSUMER NOTE: Bait and Switch

The "bait and switch" technique is a way to fool buyers. The bait is an item offered at an incredibly low price. When a person comes in, the salesperson tries to switch to something that costs much more. For instance, an ad may offer cheap repair service. But when a customer requests the service, the salesperson finds reasons to provide different repairs. The salesperson charges a much higher price for these repairs.

The bait-and-switch technique can be used to sell many things. Examples are carpets, television repairs, and home repairs.

CHAPTER 7 REVIEW

Review the material in the chapter. Then see how you have done by trying these review exercises. If you miss an exercise, restudy the indicated lesson.

Factor completely.

7-1 1. $4x + 4$ $4(x + 1)$
7-1 2. $8y - 16$ $8(y - 2)$
7-1 3. $9y^2 - 64$ $(3y + 8)(3y - 8)$
7-1 4. $3a^2 - 75$ $3(a + 5)(a - 5)$
7-2 5. $x^2 - 14x + 49$ $(x - 7)^2$
7-2 6. $4x^2 + 25 + 20x$ $(2x + 5)^2$
7-2 7. $-5x + 6 + x^2$ $(x - 3)(x - 2)$
7-3 8. $2y^2 - 3y - 2$ $(2y + 1)(y - 2)$
7-3 9. $8b^2 + 9 - 18b$ $(4b - 3)(2b - 3)$
7-5 10. $a^3 + 8b^3$ $(a + 2b)(a^2 - 2ab + 4b^2)$
7-5 11. $27b^3 - 64c^3$ $(3b - 4c)(9b^2 + 12bc + 16c^2)$

7-4 12. Factor $x^2 + 21 - 10x$ by completing the square. Show your work. $(x - 3)(x - 7)$

7-7 Solve.
13. $x^2 + 4 = -5x$ $-4, -1$
14. $x^2 - 8x = 0$ $0, 8$

7-8 Solve.
15. The square of a number plus 7 times the number is -12. Find the number. $-4, -3$
16. The length of a rectangle is 3 cm more than the width and the area is 54 cm². Find its dimensions.

Length is 9 cm; width is 6 cm

CHAPTER 7 TEST

Factor completely.
1. $5y + 5$ $5(y + 1)$
2. $9t - 27$ $9(t - 3)$
3. $16x^2 - 81$ $(4x + 9)(4x - 9)$
4. $5b^2 - 180$ $5(b + 6)(b - 6)$
5. $x^2 + 81 - 18x$ $(x - 9)^2$
6. $9x^2 + 24x + 16$ $(3x + 4)^2$
7. $-2x - 15 + x^2$ $(x - 5)(x + 3)$
8. $6x^2 + 11x - 10$ $(3x - 2)(2x + 5)$
9. $-41y + 15y^2 + 28$ $(3y - 4)(5y - 7)$
10. $x^3 + 27y^3$ $(x + 3y)(x^2 - 3xy + 9y^2)$
11. $64p^3 - 125q^3$ $(4p - 5q)(16p^2 + 20pq + 25q^2)$

12. Factor $-16x - 36 + x^2$ by completing the square. Show your work. $(x + 2)(x - 18)$

Solve.
13. $x^2 - 21 = 4x$ $7, -3$
14. $y^2 - 9y = 0$ $0, 9$

Solve.
15. The square of a number plus 9 times the number is -8. Find the number. $-1, -8$
16. The length of a rectangle is 5 cm more than the width and the area is 84 cm². Find its dimensions.   Length is 12 cm; width is 7 cm

Chemical engineers develop new methods of making chemical or petroleum products. Engineers' development work is aided by chemical technicians.

Steel workers in a rolling mill operate machines that turn steel ingots into sheets. The ingots are heated and then squeezed between giant rollers in the mill.

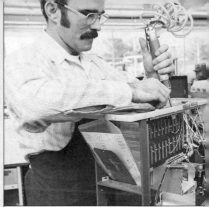

Electronics assemblers put together parts of electronic products. Assemblers may use hand tools, or they may operate machines that make delicate assemblies.

Welders apply heat to materials—usually metals—so they melt and join together. Welding work is needed in many kinds of manufacturing and construction.

CAREERS IN MANUFACTURING AND CONSTRUCTION

Manufacturing is a source of goods. Some are durable. Others, such as food products, paper, clothing, and chemicals, are nondurable. They are used up before long.

Construction also is a source of goods. These include buildings, bridges, dams, and roads.

In the mid-1970s, manufacturing was the leading area of work in the United States. This is shown by the bar graph below. Contract construction, which includes construction of most large buildings, was far behind. Two other goods-producing areas, agriculture and mining, ranked below construction.

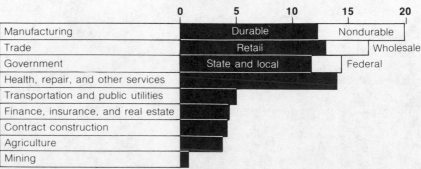

United States Labor Force in 1974

...at cutters prepare meat for sale ...a market. Cutters may also pre- ...re fish and poultry for sale. They ...oduce portions that are ready for ...oking.

Roofers apply weatherproofing material to a rooftop. The material may consist of strips of felt and coats of asphalt or tar, or it may be metal, tile, or slate.

Garment workers do one of the many steps needed to make women's, men's, or children's clothing. The steps include designing, cutting, sewing, and pressing.

Electricians assemble and install the electrical systems in buildings. Electricians may also use testing devices to check that the systems are functioning properly.

Percent change

−40 −30 −20 −10 0 10 20 30 40 50

| Health, repair, and other services |
| Government |
| Finance, insurance, and real estate |
| Contract construction |
| Trade |
| Mining |
| Manufacturing |
| Transportation and public utilities |
| Agriculture |

Projected Changes in United States Labor Force, 1974–1985

Projected changes in these areas are shown above. Construction is likely to grow fastest. Mining and manufacturing are likely to grow less quickly. Agriculture—including unpaid members of farm families—is likely to shrink.

Despite the lower growth rate in manufacturing, it will remain a much larger area than construction. Similarly, agriculture will remain larger than mining, though both areas will be relatively small. They are part of "Other" in the circle graph.

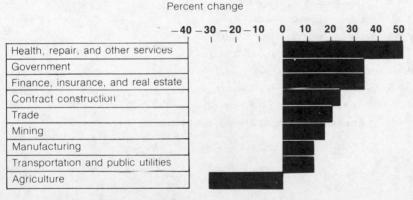

Services

Trade

Government

Various Services

Transportation, communication, and public utilities

Other

Construction

Manufacturing

Goods

Projected United States Labor Force in the mid-1980s

Ready for Relations, Functions, and Transformations?

3-1   1. Draw and label the first and second axes. Then plot these points:

  a) $(3, 2)$ See answer section
  b) $(-2, 4)$
  c) $(-4, -1)$
  d) $(2, 0)$

Graph the following equations.

3-1   2. $y - 3x = 2$ Line through $(0, 2)$ and $(-2, -4)$

3-1   3. $2y = 3x + 2$ Line through $(0, 1)$ and $(-2, -2)$

3-1   4. $\frac{1}{2}x = 4y - 3$ Line through $(2, 1)$ and $(-6, 0)$

3-2   5. $2y + 4 = 3x$ Line through $(1, 2)$ and $(0, -2)$

3-2   6. $y = -1$ Horizontal line through $(0, -1)$

5-4   7. $y > x$ All points above line through $(0, 0)$ and $(4, 4)$

5-4   8. $3x - 6y < 9$ All points above line through $(3, 0)$ and $(-1, -2)$

5-4   9. $x - 2y \geq 5$ All points below, and including, line through $(5, 0)$ and $(1, -2)$

Chapter 8
Relations, Functions, Transformations

The cost of operating a car is a function of speed.

8-1 Relations

After finishing Lesson 8-1, you should be able to
- **I**   find the set of ordered pairs determined by a given relation.
- **II**   list the domain and range of a given relation.
- **III**   graph relations.

I Relations and Ordered Pairs

For certain relations it is easy to determine a set of ordered pairs. We use braces to indicate that we are considering a set.

Example 1. Consider the set $\{2, 3, 5\}$ and the relation $<$ (is less than). This yields the following ordered pairs, in which the first member is less than the second:

(2, 3), (2, 5), (3, 5).

For certain sets of ordered pairs it is easy to determine a relation.

Example 2. Consider the set $\{2, 3, 5\}$ and the following set of ordered pairs:

$\{(2, 2), (3, 3), (5, 5)\}$.

In each ordered pair the first member is the same as the second. This set of ordered pairs determines the relation $=$ (is equal to).

TRY THIS

1. Consider the set $\{4, 5, 6\}$. Find the set of ordered pairs determined by the relation $>$ (is greater than).

Since relations and ordered pairs are so closely associated, we shall actually *define* a relation to *be* a set of ordered pairs. To do this, we will use the idea of a Cartesian product.

II Cartesian Products

DEFINITION

The *Cartesian product* of two sets A and B is the set of *all* ordered pairs having the first member from set A and the second member from set B. The Cartesian product of two sets A and B is symbolized $A \times B$.

Example 3. Consider sets A and B, where $A = \{1, 2, 3\}$ and $B = \{a, b\}$.

The Cartesian product, $A \times B$, is as follows.

$(1, a)$ $(2, a)$ $(3, a)$
$(1, b)$ $(2, b)$ $(3, b)$

TRY THIS ➡️

> 2. Consider sets A and B, where $A = \{a, b, c\}$ and $B = \{1, 2\}$. List all the ordered pairs in $A \times B$.
>
> {(a, 1), (a, 2), (b, 1), (b, 2), (c, 1), (c, 2)}

The sets A and B may be the same.

Example 4. Consider the set $\{2, 3, 4, 5\}$. The Cartesian product of this set by itself is as follows.

5	$(2, 5)$	$(3, 5)$	$(4, 5)$	$(5, 5)$
4	$(2, 4)$	$(3, 4)$	$(4, 4)$	$(5, 4)$
3	$(2, 3)$	$(3, 3)$	$(4, 3)$	$(5, 3)$
2	$(2, 2)$	$(3, 2)$	$(4, 2)$	$(5, 2)$
	2	3	4	5

The headings at the bottom and at the left are only for reference. The Cartesian product consists only of the ordered pairs.

> 3. Consider the set $\{x, y, z\}$. List all the ordered pairs in the Cartesian product of the set by itself.

TRY THIS ➡️

Answer. 3. {(x, x), (x, y), (x, z), (y, x), (y, y), (y, z), (z, x), (z, y), (z, z)}

In a Cartesian product we can pick out ordered pairs that make up a common relation, such as $=$ or $<$ in the next examples.

Example 5. This is the relation $=$ (all ordered pairs in which the first member is the same as the second).

$(2, 5)$ $(3, 5)$ $(4, 5)$ $(5, 5)$
$(2, 4)$ $(3, 4)$ $(4, 4)$ $(5, 4)$
$(2, 3)$ $(3, 3)$ $(4, 3)$ $(5, 3)$
$(2, 2)$ $(3, 2)$ $(4, 2)$ $(5, 2)$

Example 6. This is the relation $<$ (all ordered pairs in which the first member is less than the second).

$(2, 5)$ $(3, 5)$ $(4, 5)$ $(5, 5)$
$(2, 4)$ $(3, 4)$ $(4, 4)$ $(5, 4)$
$(2, 3)$ $(3, 3)$ $(4, 3)$ $(5, 3)$
$(2, 2)$ $(3, 2)$ $(4, 2)$ $(5, 2)$

TRY THIS ▐▬▬▶

> 4. Consider the Cartesian product shown in Example 6. List the ordered pairs in the relation > (all ordered pairs in which the first member is greater than the second).
>
> {(3, 2), (4, 3), (4, 2), (5, 4), (5, 3), (5, 2)}

There are also many relations that do not have common names and relations with which we are not already familiar. Any time we select a set of ordered pairs from a Cartesian product, we have selected some relation. This is true even if we make the selection at random.

DEFINITION

A *relation* from a set A to a set B is any set of ordered pairs in $A \times B$. The set of all first members in a relation is its *domain*. The set of all second numbers in a relation is its *range*.

Example 7. List the domain and range of the relation {(2, 3), (4, 3), (5, 2), (5, 5)}.

The domain is {2, 4, 5}.
The range is {2, 3, 5}.

TRY THIS ▐▬▬▶

> 5. List the domain and range of the relation {(a, 1), (b, 2), (c, 1), (d, 2)}.
>
> Domain: {a, b, c, d}; range: {1, 2}

▥ Relations in Real Numbers

Relations are sets of ordered pairs. Since we know how to graph ordered pairs, we can graph relations.

We shall be most interested in relations from R, the set of real numbers, to itself. To graph such relations, we picture $R \times R$ and then indicate which ordered pairs are in the relation. This is a familiar process. We draw an x-axis and a y-axis. Then each point of the plane corresponds to an ordered pair of real numbers.

This is called a Cartesian coordinate system.

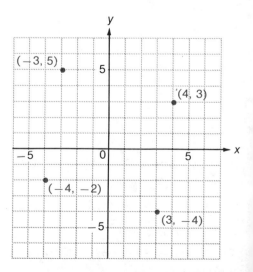

Example 8. Graph the relation {(0, −2), (1, −1), (2, 0), (3, 1)} in $R \times R$.

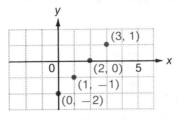

TRY THIS ➡

Graph these relations in $R \times R$.

6. {(−3, 0), (−2, 1), (−1, 2), (0, 3), (1, 4)}.
7. {(1, 1), (1, 2), (1, 3), (2, 1), (2, 2), (3, 1)}.
See answer section

Exercise Set 8-1

▌ For Exercises 1-6, consider the set {−1, 0, 1, 2}. (*See Example 1.*)   See answer section

1. Find the set of ordered pairs determined by the relation < (is less than).

2. Find the set of ordered pairs determined by the relation > (is greater than).

3. Find the set of ordered pairs determined by the relation ≤ (is less than or equal to).

4. Find the set of ordered pairs determined by the relation ≥ (is greater than or equal to).

5. Find the set of ordered pairs determined by the relation =.

6. Find the set of ordered pairs determined by the relation ≠.

▌▌ List all ordered pairs in the following Cartesian products. (*See Examples 3 and 4.*)

7. $A \times B$, where $A = \{0, 2, 4, 5\}$ and $B = \{a, b, c\}$.   See answer section

8. $A \times B$, where $A = \{1, 3, 5, 9\}$ and $B = \{d, e, f\}$.

9. $B \times C$, where $B = \{x, y, z\}$ and $C = \{1, 2\}$.

10. $B \times C$, where $B = \{5, 7, 10\}$ and $C = \{a, z\}$.

11. $D \times D$ where $D = \{−1, 0, 1, 2\}$

12. $E \times E$ where $E = \{−1, 1, 3, 5\}$

List the domain and range for each of the following relations. (*See Example 7.*)

13. {(5, 2), (6, 4), (8, 6)} Domain: {5, 6, 8}; range: {2, 4, 6}

14. {(7, 1), (8, 2), (9, 5)} Domain: {7, 8, 9}; range: {1, 2, 5}

15. {(6, 0), (7, 5), (8, 5)} Domain: {6, 7, 8}; range: {0, 5}

16. {(8, 2), (10, 1), (6, 3)} Domain: {8, 10, 6}; range: {2, 1, 3}

17. {(8, 1), (8, 1), (5, 1)} Domain: {8, 5}; range: {1}

18. {(6, 2), (2, 0), (−3, 0)} Domain: {6, 2, −3}; range: {2, 0}

19. {(5, 6)} Domain: {5}; range: {6}

20. {(7, −4)} Domain: {7}; range: {−4}

▌▌▌ Graph these relations in $R \times R$. (*See Example 8.*)   See answer section

21. {(3, 0), (4, 2), (5, 4), (6, 6)}

22. {(1, 1), (2, 3), (3, 5), (4, 7)}

23. {(3, −4), (3, −3), (3, −2), (3, −1), (3, 0)}

24. {(−2, 1), (−2, 2), (−2, 3), (−2, 4), (−2, 5)}

25. {(4, 3), (4, 2), (3, 2), (3, 3) (5, 2), (5, 3)}

26. {(2, −2), (3, −2), (2, −3), (3, −3), (2, −4), (3, −4)}

27. {(−1, 1), (−2, 1), (−2, 2), (−3, 1), (−3, 2), (−3, 3)}

28. {(−1, −1), (−1, −2), (−1, −3), (−2, −2), (−2, −3), (−3, −3)}

8-2 *Relations and Sentences*

After finishing Lesson 8-2, you should be able to
▮ graph relations which are the solution sets of sentences in two variables.

▮ The set of all replacements which make a sentence true is called
its *solution set*. Some relations are solution sets of sentences in
two variables.

Example 1. Graph the relation which is the solution set of the
sentence $y = 3x - 1$.

Some ordered pairs in this relation are $(-1, -4)$, $(0, -1)$ and $(2, 5)$.
The graph of this relation is also called the *graph of the equation*.

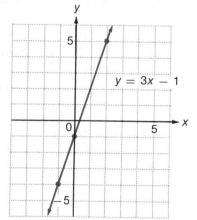

TRY THIS ➡

> 1. Graph the relation which is
>   the solution set of the sen-
>   tence $y = 2x + 1$.
>   **See answer section**

Example 2. Graph the relation which is the solution
set of the sentence $y \geq x^2 - 5$.

First graph $y = x^2 - 5$.

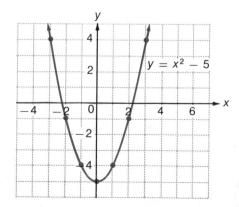

Use (0, 0) as a test point.

$$\frac{y \geq x^2 - 5}{0 \mid 0^2 - 5}$$
$$-5$$

Since (0, 0) makes $y > x^2 - 5$ true we shade in the region containing it.

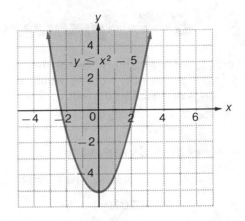

TRY THIS ➡

2. Graph the relation which is the solution set of the sentence $y \geq x^2 - 1$.

    See answer section

Exercise Set 8-2

▌Graph the relations which are the solution sets of the following sentences. (*See Examples 1 and 2.*)

1. $y = 4x + 1$ See answer section
3. $y \geq x^2 + 2$
5. $x = y^2 + 2$
7. $8x - 3y = 24$
9. $3x + 12 = 4y$
11. $y = -2$
13. $x = 3$
15. $y = \dfrac{1}{x}$

2. $y = 2x - 1$
4. $y \geq x^2 - 2$
6. $x = y^2 - 2$
8. $5x - 10y = 50$
10. $4x - 20 = 5y$
12. $y = 6$
14. $x = -7$
16. $y = \dfrac{1}{-x}$

Calculator Exercises
See answer section

Graph.
17. $y = 3.21x^2 - 5.01x + 2.168$
18. $y = -1.055x^2 + 3.001x + 1.444$

Challenge Exercises
See answer section

Graph.
19. $y = |x + 1|$ 20. $y = |x - 1|$ 21. $y = |x^3|$ 22. $y = \sqrt{x}$

8-3 Symmetry

After finishing Lesson 8-3, you should be able to
- ▌ identify figures which are symmetric with respect to a line.
- ▌▌ test the equation of a relation for symmetry with respect to the *x*-axis or *y*-axis.

▌ Line Symmetry

Points *P* and P_1 are symmetric with respect to line ℓ.

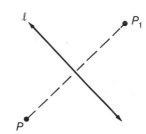

DEFINITION

Two points *P* and P_1 are said to be *symmetric* with respect to a line ℓ when the points are the same distance from ℓ, measured along a perpendicular to ℓ. Line ℓ is known as a line or *axis* of symmetry and P_1 is said to be the image of *P*.

We say, too, that the two points above are *reflections* of each other across the line. The line is known as a *line of reflection*.

DEFINITION

A figure, or set of points, is symmetric with respect to a line when the image of each point in the set is also in the set.

Example 1. The figure at the right is symmetric with respect to line ℓ. Imagine picking this figure up and flipping it over.

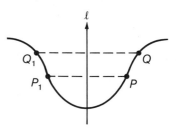

Points *P* and P_1 would be interchanged. Points *Q* and Q_1 would be interchanged. These are pairs of symmetric points. The entire figure would look exactly like it did before flipping.

Example 2. Which of the following figures are symmetric with respect to the given line?

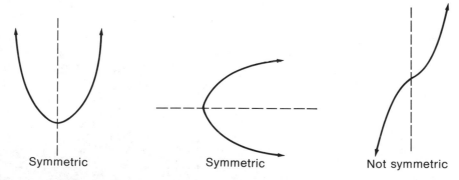

Symmetric   Symmetric   Not symmetric

TRY THIS ➡

1. Which of the following figures are symmetric with respect to the given line?

a and b

a)   b)   c)

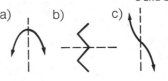

▪▪ Symmetry with Respect to the Axes

There are special and interesting kinds of symmetry in which the x-axis or the y-axis is a line of symmetry.

THEOREM 8-1

Two points are symmetric with respect to the x-axis if and only if their y-coordinates are additive inverses and they have the same x-coordinate. Two points are symmetric with respect to the y-axis if and only if their x-coordinates are additive inverses and they have the same y-coordinate.

Example 3. Plot the point (2, −5) and the point symmetric to it with respect to the x-axis.

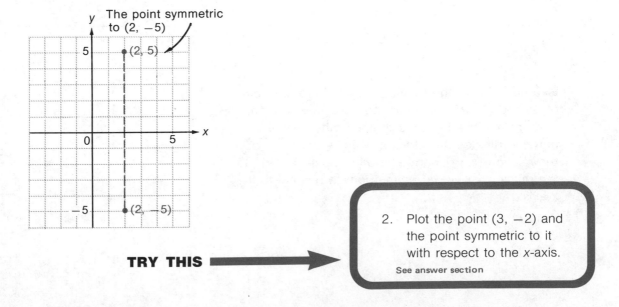

TRY THIS ➡

2. Plot the point (3, −2) and the point symmetric to it with respect to the x-axis.

See answer section

Example 4. Plot the point (3, 5) and the point symmetric to it with respect to the *y*-axis.

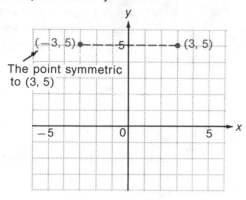

TRY THIS ➡

3. Plot the point (4, −2) and the point symmetric to it with respect to the *y*-axis.

    See answer section

Example 5. In the relation $y = x^2$ there are points (2, 4) and (−2, 4). The first coordinates, 2 and −2, are additive inverses of each other, while the second coordinates are the same. For every point of the relation (x, y), there is another point $(-x, y)$. So the relation $y = x^2$ is symmetric with respect to the *y*-axis.

Example 6. In the relation $x = y^2$ there are points (4, 2) and (4, −2). The second coordinates, 2 and −2, are additive inverses of each other, while the first coordinates are the same. For every point of the relation (x, y), there is another point $(x, -y)$. So the relation $x = y^2$ is symmetric with respect to the *x*-axis.

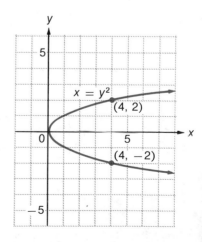

THEOREM 8-2

When a relation is defined by an equation,
1.   its graph is symmetric with respect to the y-axis if and only if replacing x by $-x$ produces an equivalent equation.
2.   its graph is symmetric with respect to the x-axis if and only if replacing y by $-y$ produces an equivalent equation.

We thus have a means of testing a relation for symmetry with respect to the x- and y-axes when it is defined by an equation.

Example 7. Test $y = x^2 + 2$ for symmetry with respect to the axes.

We replace x by $-x$, and obtain $y = (-x)^2 + 2$, which is equivalent to $y = x^2 + 2$. Therefore the graph is symmetric with respect to the y-axis.

We replace y by $-y$ and obtain $-y = x^2 + 2$, which is not equivalent to $y = x^2 + 2$. Therefore the graph is not symmetric with respect to the x-axis.

Example 8. Test $x^2 + y^4 + 5 = 0$ for symmetry with respect to the axes.

We replace x by $-x$, and obtain $(-x)^2 + y^4 + 5 = 0$, which is equivalent to the original equation. Therefore the graph is symmetric with respect to the y-axis.

We replace y by $-y$ and obtain $x^2 + (-y)^4 + 5 = 0$, which is equivalent to the original equation. Therefore the graph is symmetric with respect to the x-axis.

> Test for symmetry with respect to the x-axis and y-axis.
>
> 4. $y = x^2 + 3$
> 5. $x^2 + y^2 = 25$

TRY THIS ➡

Answers.   4. Symmetric with respect to y-axis
5. Symmetric with respect to both axes

Exercise Set 8-3

∎ Which of the following figures are symmetric with respect to the given line? (*See Examples 1 and 2.*)

1. 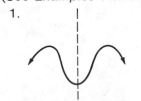   Yes

2. 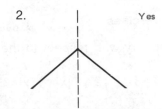   Yes

3. 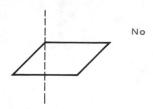 No

4. 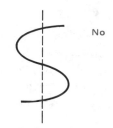 No

5. 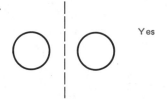 Yes

6. 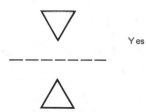 Yes

■■ Use graph paper for Exercises 7–10. (*See Examples 3 and 4.*)   See answer section

7. Plot $(3, -7)$ and the point symmetric to it with respect to the *x*-axis. List the coordinates of that point.

8. Plot $(-5, 2)$ and the point symmetric to it with respect to the *x*-axis. List the coordinates of that point.

9. Plot $(-4, 3)$ and the point symmetric to it with respect to the *y*-axis. List the coordinates of that point.

10. Plot $(1, -6)$ and the point symmetric to it with respect to the *y*-axis. List the coordinates of that point.

Test for symmetry with respect to the *x*-axis and the *y*-axis. (*See Examples 7 and 8.*)

11. $3y = x^2 + 4$ y-axis
12. $5y = 2x^2 - 3$ y-axis
13. $2x^4 + 3 = y^2$ Both axes
14. $3y^2 = 2x^4 - 5$ Both axes
15. $2x - 5 = 3y$ Neither axis
16. $5y = 4x + 5$ Neither axis
17. $y^3 = 2x^2$ y-axis
18. $3y^3 = 4x^2$ y-axis
19. $2y^2 = 5x^2 + 12$ Both axes
20. $3x^2 - 2y^2 = 7$ Both axes
21. $3y^3 = 4x^3 + 2$ Neither axis
22. $x^3 - 4y^3 = 12$ Neither axis

Challenge Exercises   23. y-axis   24. Both axes   25. y-axis   26. y-axis   27. Both axes   28. Both axes

Test for symmetry with respect to the *x*-axis and the *y*-axis.

23. $y = |x|$
24. $|x| = |y|$
25. $y = |x| + 1$
26. $y = |x| - 3$
27. $|x| + |y| = 3$
28. $|x| - |y| = 5$

8-4 Point Symmetry and Inverses

After finishing Lesson 8-4, you should be able to
  I   identify figures which are symmetric with respect to a point.
  II test the equation of a relation for symmetry with respect to the origin.
  III write equations of inverses of relations.
  IIII test the equation of a relation for symmetry with respect to the line $y = x$.

I Point Symmetry

We now define symmetry with respect to a point.

DEFINITION
Two points P and P_1 are symmetric with respect to a point Q when they are the same distance from Q, and all three points are on a line. P_1 is said to be the image of P.

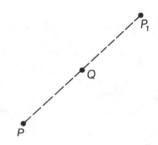

DEFINITION
A figure or *set* of points is symmetric with respect to a point when the image of each point in the set is also in the set.

Example 1. The figure at the right is symmetric with respect to point O. Imagine sticking a pin in this figure at O and then rotating the figure 180°. Points P and P_1 would be interchanged. Points Q and Q_1 would be interchanged. These are pairs of symmetric points. The entire figure would look exactly as it did before rotating. This means that the image of each point of the figure is also on the figure.

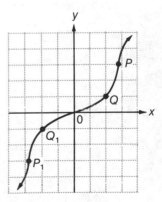

Example 2. Which of the following figures are symmetric with respect to the given point?

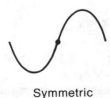

| Symmetric | Symmetric | Not symmetric |

TRY THIS

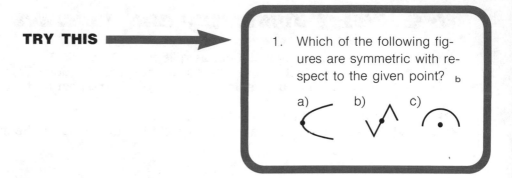

1. Which of the following figures are symmetric with respect to the given point? ь

   a)   b)   c)

■ Symmetry with Respect to the Origin

A special kind of symmetry with respect to a point is symmetry with respect to the origin.

THEOREM 8-3
Two points are symmetric with respect to the origin if and only if both their x and y coordinates are additive inverses of each other.

Example 3. Plot the point (3, 5) and the point symmetric to it with respect to the origin.

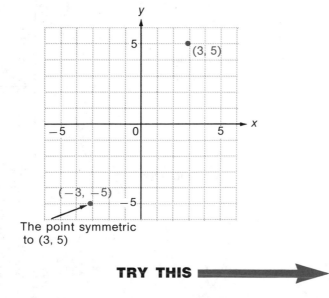

The point symmetric to (3, 5)

TRY THIS

2. Plot the point (4, −2) and the point symmetric to it with respect to the origin.

   See answer section

THEOREM 8-4

A graph of a relation defined by an equation is symmetric with respect to the origin if and only if replacing x by $-x$ and replacing y by $-y$ produces an equivalent equation.

This gives us a means for testing a relation for symmetry with respect to the origin, when it is defined by an equation.

Example 4. Test $x^2 = y^2 + 2$ for symmetry with respect to the origin.

We replace x by $-x$ and y by $-y$, and obtain $(-x)^2 = (-y)^2 + 2$, which is equivalent to $x^2 = y^2 + 2$, the original equation. Therefore the graph is symmetric with respect to the origin.

TRY THIS

> Test each equation for symmetry with respect to the origin.
>
> 3. $y^2 + x^2 = 16$ Yes
> 4. $y = x^3$ Yes
> 5. $y = x^2$ No

ⅠⅠⅠ Inverses of Relations

DEFINITION

If, in a relation, we interchange first and second members in each ordered pair, then we obtain a relation called the *inverse* of the original relation.

Example 5. Find the inverse of the relation $\{(2, 1), (3, 1), (4, 2)\}$.

The inverse is $\{(1, 2), (1, 3), (2, 4)\}$.

TRY THIS

> 6. Find the inverse of the relation $\{(0, 1), (-2, 5), (5, -2)\}$. $\{(1, 0), (5, -2), (-2, 5)\}$

THEOREM 8-5

Interchanging x and y in the equation of a relation produces an equation of the inverse relation.

Example 6. Find an equation of the inverse of $y = x^2 - 5$.

We interchange x and y, and obtain $x = y^2 - 5$. This is an equation of the inverse relation.

TRY THIS

> 7. Find an equation of the inverse of $y = x^2 + 4$. $x = y^2 + 4$

ꞮꞮꞮꞮInverses and Symmetry

Interchanging first and second coordinates in each ordered pair of a relation has the effect of interchanging the *x*-axis and the *y*-axis.

Interchanging the *x*-axis and the *y*-axis has the effect of reflecting across the diagonal line whose equation is *y* = *x*, as shown below. Thus the graphs of a relation and its inverse are always reflections of each other across the line *y* = *x*.

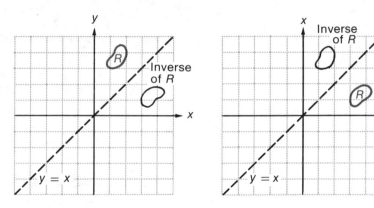

Example 7. Here are some graphs of relations and their inverses.

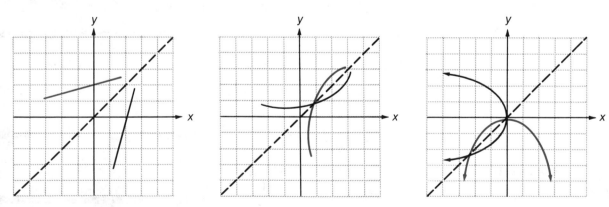

It can happen that a relation is its own inverse: that is, when *x* and *y* are interchanged, or the relation is reflected across the line *y* = *x*, there is no change. Such a relation is symmetric with respect to the line *y* = *x*.

Example 8. Test the relation $3x + 3y = 5$ for symmetry with respect to the line $y = x$.

We interchange x and y in the equation, obtaining $3y + 3x = 5$. This is equivalent to the original equation, so the graph is symmetric with respect to the line $y = x$.

TRY THIS ➡

Test the relations defined by these equations for symmetry with respect to the line $y = x$.

8. $4x + 4y = 6$ Yes
9. $y = 2x^2$ No

Exercise Set 8-4

❚ Which of the following figures are symmetric with respect to the given points? (*See Examples 1 and 2.*)

1.

Yes

2.

Yes

3.

No

4.

No

5.

Yes

6.

Yes

❚❚ Use graph paper for Exercises 7–10. (*See Example 3.*)   See answer section

7. Plot the point $(2, -4)$ and the point symmetric to it with respect to the origin.

8. Plot the point $(4, 3)$ and the point symmetric to it with respect to the origin.

9. Plot the point $(-3, 6)$ and the point symmetric to it with respect to the origin.

10. Plot the point $(-4, -3)$ and the point symmetric to it with respect to the origin.

Test for symmetry with respect to the origin. (*See Example 4.*)

11. $3x^2 - 2y^2 = 3$ Yes

12. $5y^2 = -7x^2 + 4$ Yes

13. $3x + 3y = 0$ Yes

14. $7x = -7y$ Yes

15. $5x - 5y = 0$ Yes

16. $3x = 3y$ Yes

17. $3x = \dfrac{5}{y}$ Yes

18. $3y = \dfrac{7}{x}$ Yes

19. $3x^2 + 4x = 2y$ No

20. $5y = 7x^2 - 2x$ No

21. $y = |2x|$ No

22. $3x = |y|$ No

▌▌▌ Find the inverse of each of the following relations. (*See Example 5.*)   {(−2, −1), (0, 0), (1, 3)}

23. $\{(0, 1), (5, 6), (-2, -4)\}$ {(1, 0), (6, 5), (−4, −2)}

24. $\{(-1, -2), (0, 0), (3, 1)\}$

25. $\{(-1, -1), (-3, -4)\}$ {(−1, −1), (−4, −3)}

26. $\{(5, -5), (6, -6)\}$ {(−5, 5), (−6, 6)}

Write an equation of the inverse relation of the following. (*See Example 6.*)

27. $y = 4x - 5$ x = 4y − 5

28. $y = 3x + 5$ x = 3y + 5

29. $y = 3x^2 + 2$ x = 3y² + 2

30. $y = 5x^2 - 4$ x = 5y² − 4

31. $x^2 - 3y^2 = 3$ y² − 3x² = 3

32. $2x^2 + 5y^2 = 4$ 2y² + 5x² = 4

33. $xy = 7$ y · x = 7

34. $xy = -5$ y · x = −5

▌▌▌▌ Test for symmetry with respect to the line $y = x$. (*See Example 8.*)

35. $3x + 2y = 4$ No

36. $5x - 2y = 7$ No

37. $xy = 10$ Yes

38. $xy = 12$ Yes

39. $4x + 4y = 3$ Yes

40. $5x + 5y = -1$ Yes

41. $3x = \dfrac{4}{y}$ Yes

42. $4y = \dfrac{5}{x}$ Yes

43. $4x^2 + 4y^2 = 3$ Yes

44. $3x^2 + 3y^2 = 5$ Yes

45. $y = |2x|$ No

46. $3x = |2y|$ No

Challenge Exercises

See answer section

47. Graph $y = x^2 + 1$. Then by reflection across the line $y = x$, graph its inverse.

48. Graph $y = x^2 - 3$. Then by reflection across the line $y = x$, graph its inverse.

49. Graph $y = |x|$. Then by reflection across the line $y = x$, graph its inverse.

50. Graph $x = |y|$. Then by reflection across the line $y = x$, graph its inverse.

8-5 Functions

After finishing Lesson 8-5, you should be able to
- **I**   recognize the graph of a function.
- **II**   find function values.
- **III** find outputs for function machines.

I Recognizing Graphs of Functions

A function is a special kind of relation.

DEFINITION

A function is a relation in which no two ordered pairs have the same first coordinate and different second coordinates.

In a function, given one member of the domain, there is one and only one member of the range that goes with it. Thus each member of the domain *determines* a member of the range, but only one member. It is easy to recognize the graph of a function. We can think of vertical lines. If a vertical line could cross the graph in more than one place there would be more than one member of the range for some member of the domain. The graph would not be a graph of a function.

Example 1. Which of the following are graphs of functions?

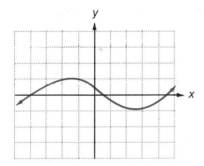 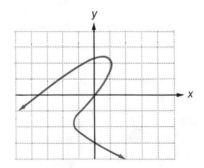 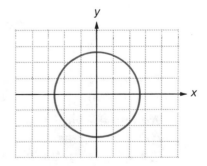

A function
No vertical line can
cross the graph
more than once.

Not a function
Vertical lines can
cross the graph
more than once.

Not a function
Vertical lines can
cross the graph
more than once.

Which of the following are graphs of functions?

TRY THIS

1.   2.   3.

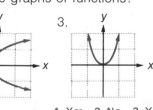

1. Yes   2. No   3. Yes

◼ Function Notation

Functions are often named by letters, such as *f* or *g*. Suppose the function *f* is described by the equation $y = x^3 + 3$. (A function is not an equation, but the solutions of the equation yield a correspondence which is a function.) The symbol $f(x)$, read "*f* of *x*," denotes "the number which corresponds to *x*," or "the *value* of *f* at *x*."

We often write $f(x) = x^2 + 3$ instead of $y = x^2 + 3$. This gives us a recipe for finding the value $f(x)$ in the range which corresponds to a number *x* in the domain.
Note: "$f(x)$" does *not* mean "*f* times *x*."

Example 2.   Consider the function *g* defined as

$$g = \{(1, 4), (2, 3), (3, 2), (4, 4)\}.$$

Here $g(1) = 4$, $g(2) = 3$, $g(3) = 2$, and $g(4) = 4$.

TRY THIS

4.   Consider the function *h* defined as follows.
$h = \{(5, 0), (8, -3), (2, 2),$
$(-3, -4), (-1, 6)\}$. Find
a) $h(5)$, b) $h(2)$, and
c) $h(-3)$.   a) 0   b) 2   c) −4

Example 3.   Given a function *f* described by $f(x) = x^2 + 3$, find
a) $f(-5)$, b) $f(\frac{1}{2})$, c) $f(a)$, and d) $f(a - 1)$.

We find the values by substitution. (It may help to think of $f(x) = x^2 + 3$ as $f(\ ) = (\ )^2 + 3$. Then what goes in the blank on the left goes in the blank on the right.)

a) $f(-5) = (-5)^2 + 3$
$\quad = 28$

b) $f(\frac{1}{2}) = (\frac{1}{2})^2 + 3$
$\quad = 3\frac{1}{4}$

c) $f(a) = (a)^2 + 3$
$\quad = a^2 + 3$

d) $f(a - 1) = (a - 1)^2 + 3$
$\quad = a^2 - 2a + 1 + 3$
$\quad = a^2 - 2a + 4$

Example 4. The function described by $A(r) = \pi r^2$ gives the area of a circle with radius r. Find a) $A(3)$, b) $A(\frac{2}{5})$, and c) $A(1)$.

a) $A(3) = \pi(3)^2$
$\quad = 9\pi$

b) $A(\frac{2}{5}) = \pi(\frac{2}{5})^2$
$\quad = \dfrac{4\pi}{25}$

c) $A(1) = \pi(1)^2$
$\quad = \pi$

TRY THIS

Answers. 5. a) 2 b) −10 c) −4 d) $-\dfrac{13}{4}$ e) $3a - 4$ f) $3a - 7$
g) $3a - 1$ 6. a) 4 b) 9 c) $\dfrac{1}{16}$ d) $x^2 + 2x + 1$

5. Given a function f described by $f(x) = 3x - 4$, find a) $f(2)$, b) $f(-2)$, c) $f(0)$, d) $f(\frac{1}{4})$, e) $f(a)$. f) $f(a - 1)$, and g) $f(a + 1)$.
6. The function $A(s) = s^2$ is related to the area of a square with side s. Find a) $A(2)$, b) $A(3)$, c) $A(\frac{1}{4})$, and d) $A(x + 1)$.

ꟷ Mappings and Function Machines

Functions can be thought of as mappings. A function f *maps* the set of first coordinates (the domain) to the set of second coordinates (the range).

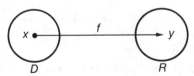

As in this diagram, each x in the domain corresponds to (or is mapped to) just one y in the range. That y is the second coordinate of the ordered pair (x, y).

Example 5. Consider the function f for which $f(x) = 2x + 3$.
Since $f(0)$ is 3, this function maps 0 to 3 and gives the ordered pair $(0, 3)$.
Since $f(3)$ is 9, this function maps 3 to 9 and gives the ordered pair $(3, 9)$.

Sometimes it is helpful to think of functions or mappings in terms of function machines. Inputs are entered into the machine. The machine then gives the proper output.

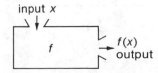

Example 6. This function machine is for the function *f* which maps each input *x* to the output $\frac{1}{x}$. Find a) $f(2)$, b) $f(3)$, and c) $f(-2)$.

a) $f(2) = \frac{1}{2}$

input *x*

$$f(x) = \frac{1}{x} \rightarrow \frac{1}{x} \text{ output}$$

b) $f(3) = \frac{1}{3}$

c) $f(-2) = \frac{1}{-2}$

$$= -\frac{1}{2}$$

Note that *f* is not defined for $x = 0$.

Find the indicated outputs for the function machines described below.

7. Find a) $g(0)$, input *x*
    b) $g(-3)$,
    c) $g(7)$, and $g(x) = x - 4 \rightarrow \frac{x - 4}{\text{output}}$
    d) $g(\frac{1}{2})$.

8. Find a) $h(1)$, input *x*
    b) $h(3)$,
    c) $h(-4)$, $h(x) = x^2 - x \rightarrow \frac{x^2 - x}{\text{output}}$
    and d) $h(5)$.

9. Find a) $f(2)$, input *x*
    b) $f(-4)$,
    c) $f(-3)$, $f(x) = \frac{1}{-x} \rightarrow \frac{1}{-x} \text{ output}$
    and d) $f(\frac{1}{3})$.

TRY THIS ➡

Answers. 7. a) −4 b) −7 c) 3 d) $-\frac{7}{2}$
8. a) 0 b) 6 c) 20 d) 20 9. a) $-\frac{1}{2}$ b) $\frac{1}{4}$
c) $\frac{1}{3}$ d) −3

Exercise Set 8-5

▌Which of the following are graphs of functions? (*See Example 1.*)

1.

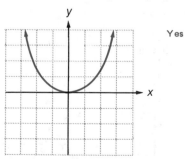

Yes

2.

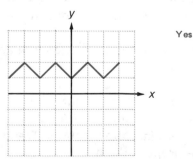

Yes

3.

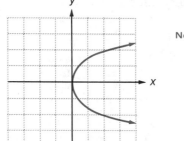

No

4.

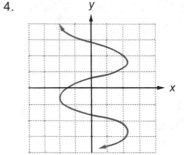

No

5.

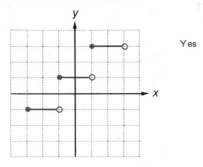

Yes

6.

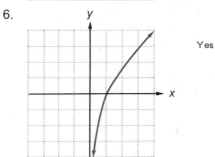

Yes

■■ For each of the functions described below find the indicated function values. (*See Examples 3 and 4.*)

7. $g(x) = x + 1$. Find:
   a) $g(0)$ 1
   b) $g(-4)$ -3
   c) $g(-7)$ -6
   d) $g(8)$ 9

8. $h(x) = x - 4$. Find:
   a) $h(4)$ 0
   b) $h(8)$ 4
   c) $h(-3)$ -7
   d) $h(-4)$ -8

9. $f(x) = 5x^2 + 4x$. Find:
   a) $f(0)$ 0
   b) $f(-1)$ 1
   c) $f(3)$ 57
   d) $f(t)$ $5t^2 + 4t$

10. $g(x) = 3x^2 - 2x$. Find:
    a) $g(0)$ 0
    b) $g(-1)$ 5
    c) $g(3)$ 21
    d) $g(t)$ $3t^2 - 2t$

11. $f(x) = 3x^2 + 2x - 1$. Find:
    a) $f(2)$ 15
    b) $f(3)$ 32
    c) $f(-3)$ 20
    d) $f(1)$ 4

12. $h(x) = 4x^2 - x + 2$. Find:
    a) $h(3)$ 35
    b) $h(0)$ 2
    c) $h(-1)$ 7
    d) $h(-2)$ 20

13. $f(x) = 2|x| + 3x$. Find:
    a) $f(1)$ 5
    b) $f(-2)$ -2
    c) $f(-4)$ -4
    d) $f(2y)$ $4|y| + 6y$

14. $g(x) = 3|x| - 2x$. Find:
    a) $g(1)$ 1
    b) $g(-2)$ 10
    c) $g(-4)$ 20
    d) $g(3y)$ $9|y| - 6y$

▪▪▪ Find the indicated outputs for the function machines described below. (*See Example 6.*)

15. input x

$$g(x) = x + 9 \rightarrow \begin{array}{c} x + 9 \\ \text{output} \end{array}$$

Find a) $g(8)$, b) $g(-3)$, and
c) $g(5)$. a) 17 b) 6 c) 14

16. input x

$$f(x) = x - 4 \rightarrow \begin{array}{c} x - 4 \\ \text{output} \end{array}$$

Find a) $f(-1)$, b) $f(13)$, and
c) $f(-6)$. a) −5 b) 9 c) −10

17. input x

$$\begin{array}{c} h(x) = \\ x^2 + 2x \end{array} \rightarrow \begin{array}{c} x^2 + 2x \\ \text{output} \end{array}$$

Find a) $h(1)$, b) $h(-1)$, and
c) $h(4)$. a) 3 b) −1 c) 24

18. input x

$$\begin{array}{c} g(x) = \\ x^2 - 3x \end{array} \rightarrow \begin{array}{c} x^2 - 3x \\ \text{output} \end{array}$$

Find a) $g(2)$, b) $g(-3)$, and
c) $g(0)$. a) −2 b) 18 c) 0

19. input x

$$f(x) = 2 \cdot |x| \rightarrow \begin{array}{c} 2 \cdot |x| \\ \text{output} \end{array}$$

Find a) $f(4)$, b) $f(-4)$, and
c) $f(6)$. a) 8 b) 8 c) 12

20. input x

$$\begin{array}{c} g(x) = \\ -3 \cdot |x| \end{array} \rightarrow \begin{array}{c} -3 \cdot |x| \\ \text{output} \end{array}$$

Find a) $g(-2)$, b) $g(0)$, and
c) $g(-7)$. a) −6 b) 0 c) −21

Calculator Exercises

For each of the functions described below find the indicated function values.

21. $f(x) = 0.003x + 0.21$
   a) $f(0.01)$ 0.21003
   b) $f(0.03)$ 0.21009
   c) $f(0.08)$ 0.21024
   d) $f(0.09)$ 0.21027

22. $g(x) = 0.0004x - 0.221$
   a) $g(0.02)$ −0.220992
   b) $g(0.003)$ −0.2209988
   c) $g(0.001)$ −0.2209996
   d) $g(0.002)$ −0.2209992

Challenge Exercises

23. The *greatest integer* function $y = [x]$ is defined as follows: $[x]$ is the greatest integer that is less than or equal to x. For example, $[4.5] = 4$, $[-1] = -1$, $[-3.8] = -4$. Graph the greatest integer function for values of x from -5 to 5. See answer section

---

8-6 Inverses of Functions

After finishing Lesson 8-6, you should be able to
▮ find equations for inverses of functions.

▮ All functions have inverses, but the inverse is not necessarily a function. If the inverse of a function f is also a function we denote it by f^{-1} (read "f inverse"). Recall that we obtain the inverse of a relation by interchanging the coordinates of each ordered pair. Thus the domain of a function f is the range of f^{-1} and the range of f is the domain of f^{-1}.

Let us consider inverses of functions in terms of function machines. Suppose that the function f programmed into the machine has an inverse that is also a function. Suppose then that the function machine has a reverse switch. When the switch is thrown the machine is programmed to do the inverse mapping f^{-1}. Inputs then enter at the opposite end and the entire process is reversed.

output $f^{-1}(x)$

f^{-1} ← input x

When a function is defined by an equation, we can sometimes find an equation for its inverse by thinking of interchanging x and y.

Example 1. Given $f(x) = x + 1$, find an equation for $f^{-1}(x)$.

a) Let us think of this as $y = x + 1$.
b) To find the inverse we interchange x and y: $x = y + 1$.
c) Now we solve for y: $y = x - 1$.
d) Thus $f^{-1}(x) = x - 1$.

In Example 1 f maps any x onto $x + 1$ (this function adds 1 to each number of the domain). Its inverse, f^{-1}, maps any number x onto $x - 1$ (this inverse function subtracts 1 from each member of its domain). Thus the function and its inverse do opposite things.

TRY THIS ➡

Answers. 1. $g^{-1}(x) = x - 2$ 2. $g^{-1}(x) = \frac{1}{3}(x - 2)$

1. Given $g(x) = x + 2$, find an equation for $g^{-1}(x)$.
2. Let $g(x) = 3x + 2$. Find a formula for $g^{-1}(x)$.

Example 2. Let $S(x) = \sqrt{x}$. Find an equation for $S^{-1}(x)$.

a) Let us think of this as $y = \sqrt{x}$. Note that the domain and range both consist of nonnegative numbers only.
b) To find the inverse we interchange x and y. $x = \sqrt{y}$.
c) Now we solve for y, squaring both sides: $y = x^2$.
d) Thus $S^{-1}(x) = x^2$, with the understanding that x cannot be negative.

In Example 2, S maps any x onto $\sqrt{x}$ (this function takes the square root of any input). Its inverse, S^{-1}, maps any number x onto x^2 (this function squares each input); thus the function and its inverse do opposite things.

TRY THIS

3. Let $f(x) = \sqrt{x + 1}$. Find an equation for $f^{-1}(x)$. $f^{-1}(x) = x^2 - 1$

Suppose the inverse of a function f is also a function. Let us suppose that we do the mapping f and then do the inverse mapping f^{-1}. We will be back where we started. In other words, if we find $f(x)$ for some x and then find f^{-1} for this number, we will be back at x. In function notation the statement looks like this:

$f^{-1}(f(x)) = x$.

This is read "f inverse of f of x equals x." It means, working from the inside out, to take x, then find $f(x)$, and then find f^{-1} for that number. When we do, we will be back where we started, at x. For similar reasons, the following is also true:

$f(f^{-1}(x)) = x$.

For the statements above to be true, x must of course be in the domain of the function being considered. We summarize these ideas by stating the following theorem.

THEOREM 8-6
For any function f whose inverse is a function: $f^{-1}(f(a)) = a$ for any a in the domain of f. Also $f(f^{-1}(a)) = a$ for any a in the domain of f^{-1}.

Example 3. For the function f of Example 1, find $f^{-1}(f(283))$. Find also $f(f^{-1}(-12,045))$.

We note that every real number is in the domain of both f and f^{-1}. Thus, using Theorem 8-6, we may immediately write the answers, without calculating.

$f^{-1}(f(283)) = 283,$

$f(f^{-1}(-12,045)) = -12,045.$

TRY THIS ➡

> 4. For the function f of Example 1, find $f^{-1}(f(579))$ and $f(f^{-1}(-83,479))$.
>
> $f^{-1}(f(579)) = 579;\ f(f^{-1}(-83,479)) = -83,479$

Exercise Set 8-6

▮In each of the following, find equations for $f^{-1}(x)$. (*See Examples 1 and 2.*)

1. $f(x) = x - 1$ $f^{-1}(x) = x + 1$
2. $f(x) = x - 2$ $f^{-1}(x) = x + 2$
3. $f(x) = x + 4$ $f^{-1}(x) = x - 4$
4. $f(x) = x + 3$ $f^{-1}(x) = x - 3$
5. $t(x) = x + 8$ $f^{-1}(x) = x - 8$
6. $f(x) = x + 7$ $f^{-1}(x) = x - 7$
7. $f(x) = 2x + 5$ $f^{-1}(x) = \frac{x - 5}{2}$
8. $f(x) = 3x + 2$ $f^{-1}(x) = \frac{x - 2}{3}$
9. $f(x) = 3x - 1$ $f^{-1}(x) = \frac{x + 1}{3}$
10. $f(x) = 4x - 3$ $f^{-1}(x) = \frac{x + 3}{4}$
11. $f(x) = 0.5x + 2$ $f^{-1}(x) = 2(x - 2)$
12. $f(x) = 0.7x + 4$ $f^{-1}(x) = \frac{10(x - 4)}{7}$
13. $f(x) = \sqrt{x - 1}$ $f^{-1}(x) = x^2 + 1$
14. $f(x) = \sqrt{x - 2}$ $f^{-1}(x) = x^2 + 2$
15. $f(x) = \sqrt{x + 2}$ $f^{-1}(x) = x^2 - 2$
16. $f(x) = \sqrt{x + 3}$ $f^{-1}(x) = x^2 - 3$

(*See Example 3.*)

17. $f(x) = 35x - 173.$ Find $f^{-1}(f(3)).$ Find $f(f^{-1}(-125)).$ $3; -125$

18. $g(x) = \dfrac{-173x + 15}{3}.$ Find $g^{-1}(g(5)).$ Find $g(g^{-1}(-12)).$ $5; -12$

19. $f(x) = x^3 + 2.$ Find $f^{-1}(f(12,053)).$ Find $f(f^{-1}(-17,243)).$ $12,053; -17,243$

20. $g(x) = x^3 - 486.$ Find $g^{-1}(g(489)).$ Find $g(g^{-1}(-17,422)).$ $489; -17,422$

Challenge Exercises

Functions can be combined in a way called *composition* of functions. The composition of two functions f and g is written $f \circ g$, where $f \circ g(x) = f(g(x))$. For example, given that $f(x) = x^2$ and $g(x) = x + 1$,

$$
\begin{aligned}
f \circ g(x) &= f(g(x)) & g \circ f(x) &= g(f(x)) \\
&= f(x + 1) & &= g(x^2) \\
&= (x + 1)^2 & &= x^2 + 1 \\
&= x^2 + 2x + 1
\end{aligned}
$$

Find $f \circ g(x)$ and $g \circ f(x)$.

21. $f(x) = 2x, g(x) = x^2 + 1$ $2x^2 + 2; 4x^2 + 1$
22. $f(x) = x^2, g(x) = x + 3$ $x^2 + 6x + 9; x^2 + 3$
23. $f(x) = 2x + 3, g(x) = x - 4$ $2x - 5; 2x - 1$
24. $f(x) = 3x^2 + 2, g(x) = 2x - 1$ $12x^2 - 12x + 5; 6x^2 + 3$
25. $f(x) = 4x^2 - 1, g(x) = \dfrac{2}{x}$ $\dfrac{16}{x^2} - 1; \dfrac{2}{4x^2 - 1}$
26. $f(x) = x^2 - 1, g(x) = x^2 - 1$ $x^4 - 2x^2; x^4 - 2x^2$

8-7 Transformations

After finishing Lesson 8-7, you should be able to
▪ sketch graphs which are vertical translations of given graphs.
▪▪ sketch graphs which are horizontal translations of given graphs.

An alteration of a relation is called a *transformation*. If such an alteration consists merely of moving the graph without changing its shape and without rotating it, the transformation is called a *translation*.

▪ Vertical Translations

Compare the graphs of the relations $y = x^2$ and $y = 1 + x^2$.

The graphs have the same shape except that $y = 1 + x^2$ is moved up a distance of 1 unit. Consider any equation $y = f(x)$ and adding a constant a to produce $y = a + f(x)$. This changes each function value by the same amount a, but produces no change in the shape of the graph. If a is positive the graph is translated upward. If a is negative the graph is translated downward.

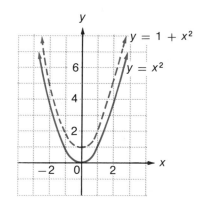

Note that $y = 1 + x^2$ is equivalent to $y - 1 = x^2$. Thus the transformation above amounts to replacing y by $y - 1$ in the original equation.

THEOREM 8-7

In an equation of a relation, replacing y by $y - a$, where a is a constant, translates the graph vertically a distance of $|a|$. If a is positive the translation is in the positive direction (upward). If a is negative the translation is downward.

If in an equation we replace y by $y + 3$, this is the same as replacing it by $y - (-3)$. In this case the constant a is -3 and the translation is downward. If we replace y by $y - 5$, the constant a is 5 and the translation is upward.

Example 1. Sketch the graph of $y = |x|$. Then sketch the graph of $y = -2 + |x|$ by translating it.

The graph of $y = |x|$ is shown below on the left. Note that $y = -2 + |x|$ is equivalent to $y + 2 = |x|$ or $y - (-2) = |x|$. This shows the new equation can be obtained by replacing y by $y - (-2)$, so by Theorem 8-7 the translation is downward, two units.

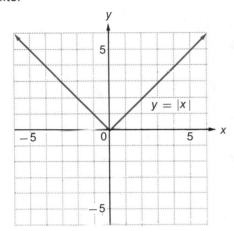
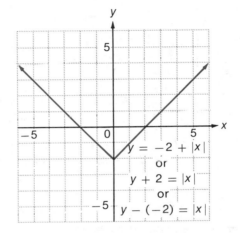

TRY THIS ➡️

Consider the graph of $y = |x|$ as shown in Example 1. Sketch the graph of each of the following by translating.

1. $y = -1 + |x|$
2. $y = 4 + |x|$

See answer section

∎ Horizontal Translations

Translations can also be horizontal. If we replace x by $x - b$ everywhere it occurs in an equation, we translate a distance of $|b|$ horizontally.

THEOREM 8-8
In an equation of a relation, replacing x by $x - b$, where b is a constant, translates the graph horizontally a distance of $|b|$. If b is positive the translation is in the positive direction (to the right). If b is negative, the translation is to the left.

Example 2. Sketch the graph of $y = |x|$. Then sketch the graph of $y = |x + 2|$ by translating it.

Here we note that x is replaced by $x + 2$, or $x - (-2)$. Thus $b = -2$, and by Theorem 8-8 the translated graph will be moved two units in the negative direction (to the left).

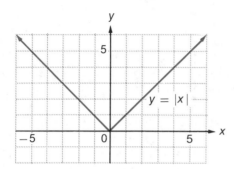 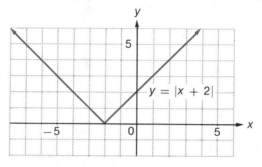

TRY THIS ➡

Relations other than functions can be translated. Theorems 8-7 and 8-8 hold for any relations. A relation may be translated both horizontally and vertically.

Example 3. A circle centered at the origin with radius of length 1 has an equation $x^2 + y^2 = 1$. If we replace x by $x - 1$ and y by $y + 2$, we translate the circle so that the center is at the point $(1, -2)$.

> Consider the graph of $y = |x|$ as shown in Example 2. Sketch the graph of each of the following by translating it.
>
> 3. $y = |x + 3|$
> 4. $y = |x - 1|$
>
> **See answer section**

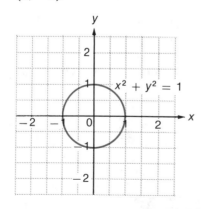 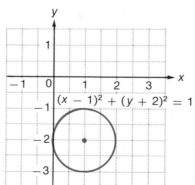

> 5. Consider the circle centered at the origin as shown in Example 3. If we replace x by $x - 2$ and y by $y + 3$, what are the coordinates of the center of the translated circle? **(2, −3)**

TRY THIS ➡

Exercise Set 8-7   See answer section

▌ Here is a graph of $y = |x|$. Sketch graphs of the following by translating this one. (*See Example 1*.)

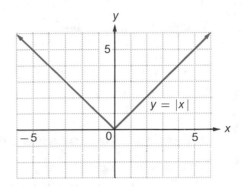

1. $y = 2 + |x|$	2. $y = 3 + |x|$
3. $y = -2 + |x|$	4. $y = -3 + |x|$
5. $y = 5 + |x|$	6. $y = 6 + |x|$
7. $y = -4 + |x|$	8. $y = -5 + |x|$
9. $y = \frac{1}{2} + |x|$	10. $y = \frac{3}{4} + |x|$

▌▌ Consider the graph of $y = |x|$ as shown. Sketch graphs of the following by translating this one. (*See Example 2*.)

11. $y = |x - 3|$	12. $y = |x - 2|$
13. $y = |x + 2|$	14. $y = |x + 4|$
15. $y = |x - 4|$	16. $y = |x - 5|$
17. $y = |x + 5|$	18. $y = |x + 6|$ See answer section
19. $y = |x - \frac{1}{2}|$	20. $y = |x + \frac{3}{4}|$

Challenge Exercises

21. Consider a circle with center at (2, 4). What are the coordinates of the center of the translated circle if we replace x with $x - 3$ and y with $y + 5$ in the equation of the circle?   (5, −1)

COMPUTER NOTE: Mark I

Mark I was the first successful computer. It could add, subtract, multiply, and divide automatically. And it could store and retrieve numbers. Its construction was begun at Harvard University in 1939 and completed in 1944.

    Mark I was both mechanical and electronic. It had some 750,000 parts, including 800 kilometers of wire. It weighed more than 30 tons. It could add or subtract two 23-digit numbers in about three-tenths of a second. Multiplying or dividing such numbers took from four to ten seconds.

    The designer of Mark I was Howard Aiken. He later designed faster, all-electronic computers.

8-8 *Stretching and Shrinking*

After finishing Lesson 8-8, you should be able to
▌   sketch graphs which are vertical stretchings or shrinkings of given graphs.
▌▌ sketch graphs which are horizontal stretchings or shrinkings of given graphs.

▌ Vertical Stretchings and Shrinkings

Compare the graphs of $y = f(x)$, $y = 2f(x)$, and $y = \frac{1}{2}f(x)$.

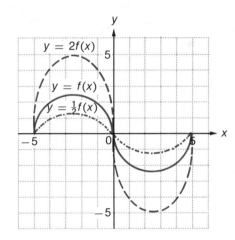

The graph of $y = 2f(x)$ looks like that of $y = f(x)$ but is stretched in a vertical direction. The graph of $y = \frac{1}{2}f(x)$ is flattened or shrunk in a vertical direction.

Consider any equation such as $y = f(x)$. Multiplying on the right by the constant 2 will double every function value, thus stretching the graph both ways away from the horizontal axis. A similar thing is true for any constant greater than 1. Multiplying on the right by $\frac{1}{2}$ will halve every function value, thus shrinking the graph both ways toward the horizontal axis. A similar thing is true for any constant between 0 and 1.

Multiplying $f(x)$ by a constant a is the same as dividing y by a. In an equation of any relation, dividing y by 2 will stretch the graph in the y-direction. Dividing y by $\frac{1}{2}$ will shrink the graph in the y-direction.

Now compare the graphs of $y = f(x)$, $y = -2f(x)$, and $y = -\frac{1}{2}f(x)$.

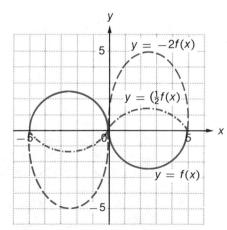

When we multiply by a negative constant, the graph is reflected across the x-axis as well as being stretched or shrunk. Note that if we multiply by -1, this has the effect of replacing y by $-y$ and we obtain a reflection without stretching or shrinking.

THEOREM 8-9

In an equation of a relation, dividing y by a constant does the following to the graph.
1. If $|c| > 1$, the graph is stretched vertically.
2. If $|c| < 1$, the graph is shrunk vertically.
3. If c is negative, the graph is also reflected across the x-axis.

Example 1. Here is a graph of $y = f(x)$. Sketch a graph of $y = 2f(x)$.

$y = 2f(x)$ is equivalent to $\dfrac{y}{2} = f(x)$. By Theorem 8-9 the graph is stretched vertically. Every function value is doubled.

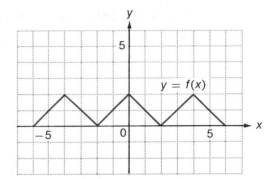

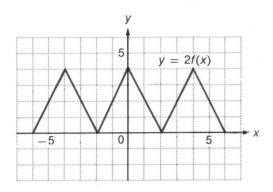

TRY THIS

Consider the graph of $y = f(x)$ as shown in Example 1.

1. Sketch a graph of $y = 3f(x)$.
2. Sketch a graph of $y - \frac{1}{2}f(x)$.

See answer section

Example 2. Here is a graph of $y = g(x)$. Sketch a graph of $y = -\frac{1}{2}g(x)$.

$y = -\frac{1}{2}g(x)$ is equivalent to $\dfrac{y}{-\frac{1}{2}} = g(x)$. By theorem 8-9, the graph is shrunk in the y-direction and also reflected across the x-axis. We halve each function value and change its sign.

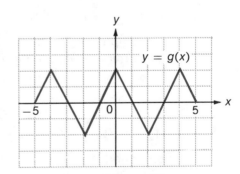

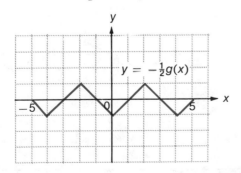

TRY THIS

3. Consider the graph of $y = f(x)$ as shown in Example 1. Sketch a graph of $y = -\frac{1}{2}f(x)$.

See answer section

◾ Horizontal Stretchings and Shrinkings

If we divide y by a constant, a graph is stretched or shrunk vertically. If we divide x by a constant, a graph will be stretched or
shrunk horizontally.

THEOREM 8-10

In an equation of a relation, dividing x wherever it occurs by a
constant d does the following to the graph.
1. If $|d| > 1$, the graph is stretched horizontally.
2. If $|d| < 1$, the graph is shrunk horizontally.
3. If d is negative, the graph is also reflected across the y-axis.

Note that if $d = -1$, this has the effect of replacing x by $-x$ and
we obtain a reflection without stretching or shrinking.

Example 3. Here is a graph of $y = f(x)$.
Sketch a graph of each of the following.
a) $y = f(2x)$
b) $y = f(\frac{1}{2}x)$
c) $y = f(-\frac{1}{2}x)$

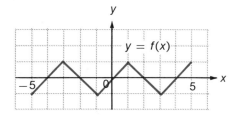

a) $f(2x) = f\left(\dfrac{x}{\frac{1}{2}}\right)$. By Theorem 8-10

the graph will be shrunk. Each
x-coordinate will be halved.

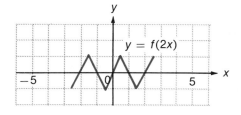

b) $f(\frac{1}{2}x) = f\left(\dfrac{x}{2}\right)$. The graph will be

stretched. Each x-coordinate will
be doubled.

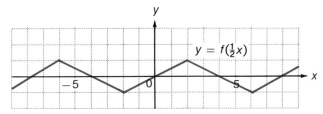

c) $f(-\frac{1}{2}x) = f\left(\dfrac{x}{-2}\right)$. The graph

will be stretched and reflected.

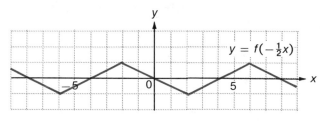

TRY THIS ➡️

Here is a graph of $y = f(x)$.

4. Sketch a graph of $y = f(2x)$.
5. Sketch a graph of $y = f(\frac{1}{2}x)$.
6. Sketch a graph of $y = f(-\frac{1}{2}x)$.

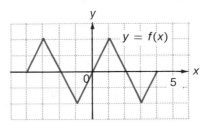

See answer section

Exercise Set 8-8

❚ Here is a graph of $y = |x|$. Sketch graphs by transforming this one. (*See Examples 1 and 2.*)

1. $y = 4|x|$
2. $y = 3|x|$
3. $y = 5|x|$
4. $y = 6|x|$
5. $y = \frac{1}{4}|x|$
6. $y = \frac{1}{3}|x|$
7. $y = -3|x|$
8. $y = -4|x|$
9. $y = -\frac{1}{4}|x|$
10. $y = -\frac{1}{3}|x|$

See answer section

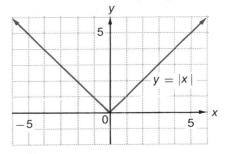

Here is a graph of $y = f(x)$. Sketch graphs by transforming this one. (*See Examples 1 and 2.*)

11. $y = 3f(x)$
12. $y = 2f(x)$
13. $y = -2f(x)$
14. $y = -3f(x)$
15. $y = 4f(x)$
16. $y = 5f(x)$
17. $y = \frac{1}{2}f(x)$
18. $y = \frac{1}{3}f(x)$
19. $y = -\frac{1}{2}f(x)$
20. $y = -\frac{1}{3}f(x)$

See answer section

❚❚ Consider the graph of $y = |x|$ above. Sketch graphs by transforming this one. (*See Example 3.*)

21. $y = |2x|$
22. $y = |3x|$
23. $y = |\frac{1}{2}x|$
24. $y = |\frac{1}{3}x|$

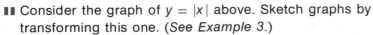

See answer section

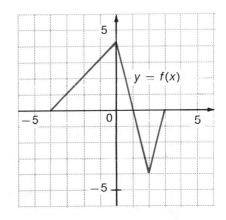

Consider the graph of $y = f(x)$ above. Sketch graphs by transforming this one. (*See Example 3.*)

25. $y = f(3x)$
26. $y = f(2x)$
27. $y = f(\frac{1}{2}x)$
28. $y = f(\frac{1}{3}x)$
29. $y = f(-2x)$
30. $y = f(-3x)$
31. $y = f(-\frac{1}{2}x)$
32. $y = f(-\frac{1}{3}x)$

See answer section

8-9 Some Special Classes of Functions

After finishing Lesson 8-9, you should be able to
▌ find function values for linear functions.
▌▌ show that certain functions are either even or odd.

▌ Linear Functions

DEFINITION
A linear function is any function f described by $f(x) = mx + b$ where m and b are constants.

Example 1. A linear function f is described by $f(x) = 3x - 2$. Find $f(-2)$, $f(1)$, $f(0)$, and graph f.

$f(-2) = 3(-2) - 2 = -8$
$f(1) = 3(1) - 2 = 1$
$f(0) = 3(0) - 2 = -2$

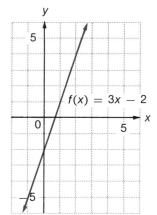

x	-2	1	0
$f(x)$	-8	1	-2

$f(x) = 3x - 2$

TRY THIS ➧

> 1. A linear function f is described by $f(x) = -2x - 3$. Find $f(3)$, $f(0)$, and $f(-3)$. Use graph paper and graph f.
> $-9; -3; 3$
> See answer section

▌▌ Even and Odd Functions

If the graph of a function is symmetric with respect to the y-axis, it is an *even* function. Recall that a function will be symmetric to the y-axis if in its equation we can replace x by $-x$ and obtain an equivalent equation. Thus if we have a function given by $y = f(x)$, then $y = f(-x)$ will give the same function if the function is even.

DEFINITION
A function is an even function when $f(x) = f(-x)$ for all x in the domain of f.

Example 2. Show that $f(x) = x^2 + 1$ is an even function.

$$f(-x) = (-x)^2 + 1 = x^2 + 1 = f(x)$$

Since $f(-x) = f(x)$ for all x in the domain, f is an even function. Note that the graph is symmetric with respect to the y-axis.

Example 3. Show that $f(x) = x^2 + 3x^4$ is an even function.

$$f(-x) = (-x)^2 + 3(-x)^4 = x^2 + 3x^4 = f(x)$$

Since $f(-x) = f(x)$ for all x in the domain, the function is even.

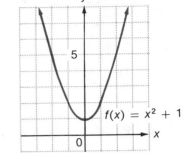

$f(x) = x^2 + 1$

TRY THIS 

2. Show that $f(x) = x^4 + 2x^6$ is an even function.

$f(-x) = (-x)^4 + 2(-x)^6 = x^4 + 2x^6 = f(x)$

If the graph of a function is symmetric with respect to the origin, it is an *odd* function. Recall that a function will be symmetric with respect to the origin if in its equation we can replace x by $-x$ and y by $-y$ and obtain an equivalent equation. Thus if we have a function given by $y = f(x)$, then $-y = f(-x)$ will be equivalent if f is an odd function.

DEFINITION

A function is an odd function when $f(-x) = -f(x)$ for all x in the domain of f.

Example 4. Show that $f(x) = x^3$ is an odd function.

a) $f(-x) = (-x)^3 = -(x)^3$
b) $-f(x) = -x^3$
Since $f(x) = -f(x)$ for all x in the domain, f is odd. Note that the graph is symmetric with respect to the origin.

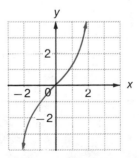

Example 5. Show that $f(x) = x^3 + 5x$ is an odd function.

a) $f(-x) = (-x)^3 + 5(-x) = -x^3 - 5x$
b) $-f(x) = -(x^3 + 5x) = -x^3 - 5x$
Since $f(-x) = -f(x)$ for all x in the domain, f is odd.

3. Show that
$$f(x) = x^5 - 3x^3$$
is an odd function.

TRY THIS 

Answer. 3. $f(-x) = (-x)^5 - 3(-x)^3 = -x^5 + 3x^3$; $-f(x) = -(x^5 - 3x^3) = -x^5 + 3x^3$ Since $f(-x) = -f(x)$ for all x in the domain, f is odd.

Exercise Set 8-9

▎ For each of the linear functions described below find the indicated function values. Then graph the function. (*See Example 1.*)   See answer section

1. $f(x) = x - 3$; find $f(-5)$, $f(-3)$, and $f(2)$.   −8; −6; −1

2. $f(x) = x + 5$; find $f(-4)$, $f(-6)$, and $f(7)$.   1; −1; 12

3. $g(x) = 2x - 3$; find $g(2)$, $g(0)$, and $g(-4)$.   1; −3; −11

4. $g(x) = 3x + 4$; find $g(-3)$, $g(6)$, and $g(4)$.   −5; 22; 16

5. $h(x) = -3x + 2$; find $h(-1)$, $h(2)$, and $h(-3)$.   5; −4; 11

6. $h(x) = -5x + 1$; find $h(0)$, $h(-2)$, and $h(6)$.   1; 11; −29

7. $f(x) = \frac{1}{2}x + 1$; find $f(6)$, $f(2)$, and $f(-8)$.   4; 2; −3

8. $f(x) = \frac{1}{3}x + 2$; find $f(3)$, $f(9)$, and $f(-6)$.   3; 5; 0

▎▎ Show that the following functions are even. (*See Examples 2 and 3.*)

9. $f(x) = 2x^4 + 4x^2$

10. $f(x) = 5x^2 + 3x^4$

11. $f(x) = |2x|$ See answer section

12. $f(x) = |3x|$

13. $f(x) = 3x^4 - 4x^6$

14. $f(x) = 5x^8 - 3x^2$

Show that the following functions are odd. (*See Examples 4 and 5.*)

15. $g(x) = 4x^3 - x$ See answer section

16. $f(x) = -3x^3 + 2x$

17. $h(x) = 2x + 5x^3$

18. $h(x) = 4x^3 - 5x$

19. $f(x) = 4x$

20. $f(x) = -4x$

21. $f(x) = x^5 + x^3 + x$

22. $f(x) = -3x^5 - 2x^3 - x$

23. Which of the following functions are even? odd? neither even nor odd?

24. Which of the following functions are even? odd? neither even nor odd?

a)
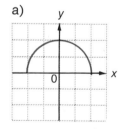

b)
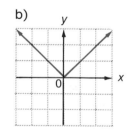

a)
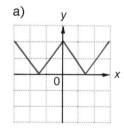

b)
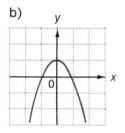

a) Even   b) Even   c) Odd   d) Neither

a) Even   b) Even   c) Odd   d) Neither

c)
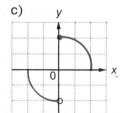

d)
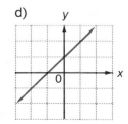

c)
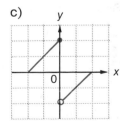

d)
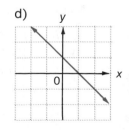

Use Quiz 15 after lesson 8–9.

COMPUTER ACTIVITY

Composition of Functions

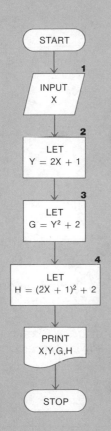

PROBLEM: Let $F(X) = 2X + 1$
and $G(X) = X^2 + 2$.
Compute $H(X) = G(F(X))$. (Hint: $H(X) = G(F(X)) = G(2X + 1) = (2X + 1)^2 + 2$.)

Examples using the flowchart:

1	2	3	4	
X	Y = F(X)	G = G(Y)	H = H(X)	Does G = H?
1	3	11	11	Yes
1.25	3.5	14.25	14.25	Yes
−5	−9	83	83	Yes

TRY THIS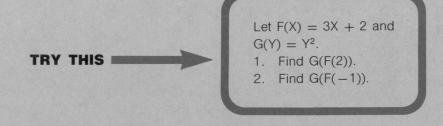

Let $F(X) = 3X + 2$ and $G(Y) = Y^2$.
1. Find $G(F(2))$.
2. Find $G(F(-1))$.

BASIC PROGRAM (Optional)
```
10  INPUT X
20  LET Y = 2*X+ 1
30  LET G = Y↑2 + 2
40  LET H =(2*X + 1)↑2 + 2
50  PRINT X,Y,G,H
```

CHAPTER 8 REVIEW

Review the material in the chapter. Then see how you have done by trying these review exercises. If you miss an exercise, restudy the indicated lesson.

8-1   1.   Domain: $\{-6, -1, 0, 1, 2\}$; range: $\{-4, \sqrt{3}, 2, 4, 5\}$
          List the domain and range of the relation $\{(1, 2), (-1, 4), (0, 5), (2, -4), (-6, \sqrt{3})\}$.

8-2   2.   Graph the relation which is the solution set of $y \geq x^2 + 1$.   See answer section

8-3   Test for symmetry with respect to the *x*-axis and the *y*-axis.
         3. $y = 7$ y-axis
         4. $y^2 = x^2 + 3$ Both
         5. $x^2 + y^2 = 4$ Both
         6. $x = 3$ x-axis
         7. $x^3 = y^3 - y$ Neither
         8. $x^2 = y + 3$ y-axis

8-4   Test for symmetry with respect to the origin.
         9. $x + y = 3$ No
       10. $y = x^3$ Yes
       11. $x = 2$ No

8-4   12.   Write an equation of the inverse relation of $y = 3x^2 + 2x - 1$.
                         $x = 3y^2 + 2y - 1$

8-5   Which of the following are graphs of functions?
       13.

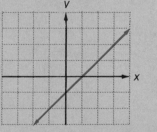

Yes

       14.

Yes

15.

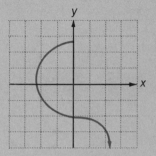

No

8-5   16. $f(x) = 3\sqrt{x} + 2$. Find
          a) $f(2)$ 6
          b) $f(0)$ $3\sqrt{2}$
          c) $f(-2)$ 0

8-6   17. $g(x) = \dfrac{\sqrt{x}}{2} + 2$. Find an equation for $g^{-1}(x)$. $g^{-1}(x) = 4x^2 - 16x + 16$

Here is a graph of $g(x)$. Sketch graphs of the following equations.

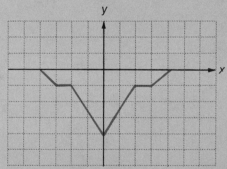

See answer section

8-7   18. $y = g(x) + 2$
8-7   19. $y = g(x - 1)$
8-8   20. $y = \frac{1}{2}g(x)$
8-9   21.   Show that $f(x) = -2x^2 - 2$ is an even function. $f(-x) = -2(-x)^2 - 2 = -2x^2 - 2 = f(x)$
8-9   22.   Show that $f(x) = x^5 + x$ is an odd function.
            $f(-x) = (-x)^5 + (-x) = -x^5 - x$;
            $-f(x) = -(x^5 + x) = -x^5 - x$

CHAPTER 8 TEST

1. List the domain and range of the rela-
   tion $\{(-1, 0), (\sqrt{3}, 5), (8, -4), (7, 0), (-6, -2)\}$.

   Domain: $\{-6, -1, \sqrt{3}, 7, 8\}$; range: $\{-4, -2, 0, 5\}$

2. Graph the relation which is the solution
   set of $y \geq x^2 + 3$ See answer section

Test for symmetry with respect to the x-axis
and the y-axis.

3. $y = 4$ y-axis
4. $y^2 = x^2 + 8$ Both
5. $x^2 + y^2 = 9$ Both
6. $x = 5$ x-axis
7. $x^5 = y^5 - y$ Neither
8. $x^2 - y = 4$ y-axis

Test for symmetry with respect to the origin.

9. $x + y = 7$ No
10. $y = 2x^3$ Yes
11. $x = 4$ No

12. Write an equation of the inverse rela-
    tion of $y = 2x^2 - 3x + 1$. $x = 2y^2 - 3y + 1$

Which of the following are graphs of
functions?

13.

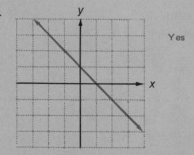

Yes

14.

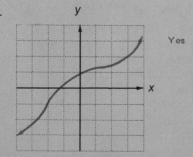

Yes

15.

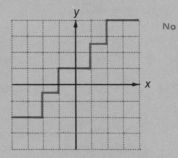

No

16. $g(x) = 4\sqrt{x - 3}$. Find
    a) $g(8)$ $4\sqrt{5}$
    b) $g(3)$ 0
    c) $g(12)$ 12

17. $f(x) = \dfrac{\sqrt{x}}{3} + 1$. Find an equation for
    $f^{-1}(x)$. $f^{-1}(x) = 9x^2 - 18x + 9$

Here is a graph of $y = f(x)$. Sketch graphs
of the following equations.

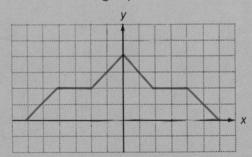

18. $y = \frac{1}{2}f(x)$ See answer section
19. $y = f(x) - 2$
20. $y = f(x - 1)$
21. Show that $f(x) = -3x^4 - 2$ is an even
    function. $f(-x) = -3(-x)^4 - 2 = -3x^4 - 2 = f(x)$
22. Show that $g(x) = x^7 + x$ is an odd
    function. $g(-x) = (-x)^7 + (-x) = -x^7 - x;$
    $-g(x) = -(x^7 + x) = -x^7 - x$

Use Cumulative Test 2 after Cumulative Review below.

CUMULATIVE REVIEW FOR CHAPTERS 5–8

5-1   1.   Graph on a number line: $y \geq -5$. All points right of, and including, -5

5-1   2.   Solve using the addition principle: $x + 12 < -3$. $x < -15$

5-2   3.   Graph: $-6 < x \leq -1$. All points between -6 and -1, including -1

5-2   4.   Graph: $x \leq 3$ or $x \geq 6$. All points left of, and including, 3 and right of,

5-2   5.   Solve using the multiplication principle: $-4w \leq 28$.   and including 6

5-2   6.   Solve: $-3 + 7x < 2x + 9$. $x < \frac{12}{5}$ $w \geq -7$

5-3   7.   Solve: $|4 - y| < 10$. $-6 < y < 14$

5-4   8.   Graph: $-3x + y > 1$.   All points above line through (0, 1) and (-2, -5)

5-5   9.   Graph this system: $y > x - 1$ All points above line through (0, -1) and (2, 1
                                   $2x + y < 5$ and also below line through (0, 5) and (2, 1)

5-5   10.   Graph. If a polygon is formed, find the vertices.

$y \leq -x - 1$ All points inside, and including triangle with vertices
$y \leq 3$ (-3, 2), (1, -2), (-5, -2)
$y - 2x \leq 8$
$y \geq -2$

5-6   11.   Find the maximum and minimum values, and where
they occur.   Maximum R = 6 at (4, 2); minimum R = -51 at (6, -9)

$R = 5y - x$ subject to: $11x + 2y \leq 48$
                            $6x + 8y \geq -36$
                            $5x - 6y \geq 8$

6-1   12.   Collect like terms: $5m + 2 - 3n + 6m - n + 8$. $11m - 4n + 10$

6-1   13.   Arrange in descending powers of t:
$6s^3t - 2s^2t^2 + 5st^3$. $5st^3 - 2s^2t^2 + 6s^3t$

6-2   14.   Add: $3ab^2 - a^2b + 6a^3$ and
$-4a^2b + 5b^3 + 2ab^2$. $6a^3 - 5a^2b + 5ab^2 + 5b^3$

6-2   15.   Subtract: $(-2y + 6y^2 - 3) - (-y^3 + 4y - 5y^2)$.
                                  $y^3 + 11y^2 - 6y - 3$

6-3   Multiply.

16. $(3m^2n)(-2mn^2)$ 17. $(x - 3y)(2x^3)$

18. $(y^2 - y + 3)(2y + 5)$ 16. $-6m^3n^3$ 17. $2x^4 - 6x^3y$ 18. $2y^3 + 3y^2 + y + 15$

6-4, 6-5   Find these special products.

19. $(5 - 3x)(-2 + 7x)$ 20. $(3x + 2y)^2$

21. $(5x - 2)(-5x - 2)$
                19. $-10 + 29x - 21x^2$ 20. $9x^2 + 12xy + 4y^2$ 21. $-25x^2 + 4$

6-6   Solve.

22.   An investment is made at 8%, compounded annually. It grows to $1053 at the end of one year. How
much was originally invested? $975

23.   Suppose $2500 is invested at 11%, compounded
semiannually. How much will be in the account at
the end of two years? $3097.06

Factor completely.

7-1   24. $9y - 12y^2$ 25. $7m^4 - 112m^2$

7-2   26. $12m + 36 + m^2$ 27. $x^2 - 15 - 2x$

7-3   28. $6 + 20y^2 - 23y$

24. $3y(3-4y)$ 25. $7m^2(m-4)(m+4)$ 26. $(m+6)^2$ 27. $(x-5)(x+3)$ 28. $(3-4y)(2-5y)$

7-4   29. Factor $x^2 - 20 - 8x$ by completing the square.
            Show your work. $(x - 10)(x + 2)$

7-5   30. Factor: $16a^3 + 2b^3$. $2(2a+b)(4a^2-2ab+b^2)$

7-5   31. Factor: $64 - 27n^3$. $(4-3n)(16+12n+9n^2)$

7-7   32. Solve: $3 - 5x = 2x^2$. $\frac{1}{2}, -3$

7-8   33. Solve: If the sides of a square are lengthened by
            8 cm the area becomes 100 cm². Find the length of
            the side of the original square.   2 cm

8-1   34. List the domain and range of the relation   Domain: {3, 1, −4, 0, 7};
            $\{(3, -6), (1, -1), (-4, -2), (0, 0), (7, -1)\}$ range: {−6, −1, −2, 0}

8-2   35. Graph the relation which is the solution set of
            $3x - y = 7$.   Line through (0, −7) and (1, −4)

8-3   36. Test for symmetry with respect to the x-axis and the
            y-axis: $x^2 - y^3 = 8$. Not symmetric with respect to x-axis; symmetric with respect to y-axis

8-4   37. Test for symmetry with respect
Symmetric with respect to origin   to the origin: $x + y = 0$.

8-4   38. Write an equation of the inverse
            relation of $3x - y = 2$.   3y − x = 2

8-5   39. Is the graph at the right that of
            a function?   No

8-5   40. $p(x) = x - 4x^2$. Find $p(-1)$ and
            $p(10)$.   −5; −390

8-6   41. $h(x) = 3x - 5$. Find an equation
            for $h^{-1}(x)$. $h^{-1}(x) = \frac{1}{3}x + \frac{5}{3}$

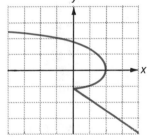

The graph of $y = f(x)$ is shown at
the right. Sketch graphs of the
following.

8-7   42. $y = f(x) - 5$

8-7   43. $y = f(x + 1)$

8-8   44. $y = 2f(x)$

8-9   45. Show that $f(x) = 2x^5 - x^3$
            is an odd function.

8-9   46. Show that $f(x) = -x^2 - 3$
            is an even function.

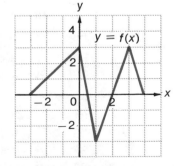

42. Graph consists of segments from (−3, −5) to (0, −2) to (1, −8) to (3, −2) to (4, −5)   43. Graph consists of segments
from (−4, 0) to (−1, 3) to (0, −3) to (2, 3) to (3, 0)   44. Graph consists of segments from (−3, 0) to (0, 6) to (1, −6) to
(3, 6) to (4, 0)   45. $f(-x) = 2(-x)^5 - (-x)^3 = -2x^5 + x^3$; $-f(x) = -(2x^5 - x^3) = -2x^5 + x^3$; $f(-x) = -f(x)$ 46. $f(-x)$
$= -(-x)^2 - 3 = -x^2 - 3$; $f(-x) = f(x)$

Ready for Fractional Expressions and Equations?

1-2 1. Add: $\frac{2}{7} + (-\frac{7}{9})$. $-\frac{31}{63}$

1-3 2. Subtract: $-\frac{5}{3} - (-\frac{3}{5})$. $-\frac{16}{15}$

1-4 3. Multiply: $7 \cdot (-\frac{2}{3})$. $-\frac{14}{3}$

1-4 Find the reciprocal of each.

     4. $\frac{3}{4}$ 5. 6   6. $-\frac{5}{4}$ 4. $\frac{4}{3}$ 5. $\frac{1}{6}$ 6. $-\frac{4}{5}$

1-4 Divide.

     7. $\frac{2}{3} \div \frac{3}{4}$ 8. $-\frac{7}{8} \div \frac{1}{2}$ 9. $\frac{3}{4} \div (-\frac{1}{4})$ 7. $\frac{8}{9}$ 8. $-\frac{7}{4}$ 9. -3

1-5 10. Evaluate $xy - xz$ when $x = 3$, $y = -2$, $z = 4$. -18

1-5 Factor.

     11. $4x + 4y$ 12. $3y + 6$ 13. $cx - cr + cw$

                 11. $4(x + y)$ 12. $3(y + 2)$ 13. $c(x - r + w)$

1-8 Multiply and simplify.

     14. $x^2 \cdot x^5$ 15. $3^4 \cdot 3^{-1}$ 16. $(7x^3y^{-2})(2x^{-2}y^4)$

1-8 Divide.

                         14. x^7 15. 3^3 16. $14xy^2$

     17. $\dfrac{5^9}{5^{-2}}$ 18. $\dfrac{4^{-3}}{4^{-5}}$ 19. $\dfrac{y^{-2}}{y^6}$ 20. $\dfrac{10x^5y^2}{2xy^4}$

                17. 5^{11} 18. 4^2 19. y^{-8} 20. $5x^4y^{-2}$

1-8 Simplify.

     21. $(4^3)^5$ 22. $(y^{-2})^3$ 23. $(2x^2y^{-4}z^3)^4$

                21. 4^{15} 22. y^{-6} 23. $16x^8y^{-16}z^{12}$

2-2 24. Solve: $8 - 3(a - 1) = 2 + 4(3 - a)$ 3

2-4 25. Solve $E = mc^2$, for m. $m = \frac{E}{c^2}$

6-2 26. Add: $(5ax^2 + 4bx - 7)$ and $(3ax^2 - 5bx + 2)$. $8ax^2 - bx - 5$

6-2 27. Subtract: $(-3x^4 + x^3 - 2x^2 + 1) - (2x^4 + 3x^2 - 4)$. $-5x^4 + x^3 - 5x^2 + 5$

6-3 28. Multiply: $(a + 3)(a^4 - 3a^2 + 2)$ $a^5 + 3a^4 - 3a^3 - 9a^2 + 2a + 6$

7-1 Factor out a common factor.

     29. $12y^4 - 15y^3 + 3y^2$ 30. $8x^2y - 28x^3y^2 + 4x^2y^3$

                        29. $3y^2(4y^2 - 5y + 1)$ 30. $4x^2y(2 - 7xy + y^2)$

     Factor.

7-1 31. $x^2 - 25$ 32. $16y^8 - 36x^4$

7-2 33. $x^2 - 14x + 49$ 34. $4y^2 - 16xy + 16x^2$

7-2 35. $3y^2 - 24y^3 + 48y^4$ 36. $x^2 - 6x + 8$

7-3 37. $6x^2 + 39x + 45$ 38. $x^4y^4 + 7x^2y^2 + 6$

31. $(x + 5)(x - 5)$ 32. $4(2y^4 + 3x^2)(2y^4 - 3x^2)$ 33. $(x - 7)^2$ 34. $4(y - 2x)^2$ 35. $3y^2(1 - 4y)^2$
36. $(x - 4)(x - 2)$ 37. $3(x + 5)(2x + 3)$ 38. $(x^2y^2 + 6)(x^2y^2 + 1)$

Chapter 9
Fractional Expressions and Equations

How much garbage is produced in a city in one year?

9-1 Multiplying and Dividing

After finishing Lesson 9-1, you should be able to

❚ multiply fractional expressions.

❚❚ multiply a fractional expression by 1, using an expression for 1 like $\frac{A}{A}$.

❚❚❚ simplify fractional expressions by factoring numerator and denominator and removing factors of 1.

❚❚❚❚ multiply fractional expressions and simplify.

❚❚❚❚❚ divide fractional expressions and simplify.

These are *fractional expressions*.

$$\frac{7}{8}, \qquad \frac{8}{y + 5}, \qquad \frac{x^2 + 7xy - 4}{x^3 - y^3}$$

Fractional expressions show quotients of polynomials.

$$\frac{7}{8} \text{ means } 7 \div 8 \text{ and } \frac{8}{y + 5} \text{ means } 8 \div (y + 5).$$

Certain substitutions are not sensible in fractional expressions. Since division by 0 is not defined, any number that makes a denominator 0 is not a sensible replacement. In $\frac{8}{y + 5}$, -5 is not a sensible replacement.

❚ Multiplying

To multiply two fractional expressions, multiply numerators and multiply denominators.

Example 1. Multiply.

$$\frac{x + 3}{y - 4} \cdot \frac{x^3}{y + 5} = \frac{(x + 3)x^3}{(y - 4)(y + 5)} \qquad \text{\textit{Multiplying numerators and multiplying denominators}}$$

$$= \frac{x^4 + 3x^3}{y^2 + y - 20} \qquad \text{\textit{Simplifying}}$$

TRY THIS ➡

Multiply.

1. $\dfrac{x - 2}{5} \cdot \dfrac{x + 2}{x + 4}$

2. $\dfrac{x + y}{x + 3} \cdot \dfrac{x + y}{x - 3}$

Answers. 1. $\dfrac{x^2 - 4}{5x + 20}$ 2. $\dfrac{x^2 + 2xy + y^2}{x^2 - 9}$

ıı **Multiplying by 1**

Any number multiplied by 1 is that same number. Any fractional expression with the same numerator and denominator names the number 1.

$$\frac{y + 5}{y + 5}, \frac{4x^2 - 5}{4x^2 - 5}, \frac{-1}{-1}$$ *All name the number 1 for all sensible replacements*

We can multiply by 1 to get equivalent expressions. For example, let us multiply $\dfrac{x + y}{5}$ by 1.

$$\frac{x + y}{5} \cdot \frac{x - y}{x - y} = \frac{(x + y)(x - y)}{5(x - y)}$$
$$= \frac{x^2 - y^2}{5x - 5y}$$

We know now that $\dfrac{x + y}{5}$ and $\dfrac{x^2 - y^2}{5x - 5y}$ are equivalent. This means that they will name the same number for all replacements, except those that make a denominator zero.

Examples. Multiply.

2. $\dfrac{x^2 + 3}{x - 1} \cdot \dfrac{x + 1}{x + 1} = \dfrac{(x^2 + 3)(x + 1)}{(x - 1)(x + 1)}$
$$= \frac{x^3 + x^2 + 3x + 3}{x^2 - 1}$$

3. $\dfrac{-1}{-1} \cdot \dfrac{x - 4}{x - y} = \dfrac{-1 \cdot (x - 4)}{-1 \cdot (x - y)}$
$$= \frac{(-1)x - (-1)4}{(-1)x - (-1)y}$$
$$= \frac{-x + 4}{-x + y}$$
$$= \frac{4 - x}{y - x}$$

TRY THIS

Multiply.

3. $\dfrac{3x + 2y}{5x + 4y} \cdot \dfrac{x}{x}$

4. $\dfrac{2x^2 - y}{3x + 4} \cdot \dfrac{3x + 2}{3x + 2}$

5. $\dfrac{-1}{-1} \cdot \dfrac{2a - 5}{a - b}$

Answers. 3. $\dfrac{3x^2 + 2xy}{5x^2 + 4xy}$ 4. $\dfrac{6x^3 + 4x^2 - 3xy - 2y}{9x^2 + 18x + 8}$ 5. $\dfrac{5 - 2a}{b - a}$

ⅢSimplifying Fractional Expressions

Fractional expressions can be simplified by reversing the previous procedure. That is, we factor numerator and denominator and try to "remove" a factor of 1.

Example 4. Simplify.

$$\frac{4a + 8}{2} = \frac{2 \cdot 2a + 2 \cdot 4}{2 \cdot 1} = \frac{2(2a + 4)}{2 \cdot 1} = \frac{2}{2} \cdot \frac{2a + 4}{1} = 2a + 4$$

TRY THIS

Answers. 6. 7x 7. 2a + 3

Example 5. Simplify.

$$\frac{9x^2 + 6xy - 3y^2}{12x^2 - 12y^2} = \frac{3(x + y)(3x - y)}{12(x + y)(x - y)} \quad \textit{Factoring}$$

$$= \frac{3(x + y)}{3(x + y)} \cdot \frac{3x - y}{4(x - y)}$$

$$= \frac{3x - y}{4(x - y)} \quad \textit{"Removing" a factor of 1}$$

TRY THIS

Canceling is a shortcut for part of the procedure in Examples 4 and 5. The use of canceling saves a step in simplifying. Canceling gives rise to a great many errors. It should be done cautiously, if at all. *Note:* If you can't factor, you can't cancel!

Simplify.

6. $\frac{7x^2}{x}$

7. $\frac{6a + 9}{3}$

Simplify.

8. $\frac{6x^2 + 4x}{2x^2 + 4x}$

9. $\frac{y^2 + 3y + 2}{y^2 - 1}$

Answers. 8. $\frac{3x + 2}{x + 2}$ 9. $\frac{y + 2}{y - 1}$

ⅢⅠMultiplying and Simplifying

After multiplying you should usually simplify, if possible.

Example 6. Multiply and simplify.

$$\frac{x + 2}{x - 2} \cdot \frac{x^2 - 4}{x^2 + x - 2} = \frac{(x + 2)(x^2 - 4)}{(x - 2)(x^2 + x - 2)} \quad \textit{Multiplying numerators and also denominators}$$

$$= \frac{(x + 2)(x - 2)(x + 2)}{(x - 2)(x + 2)(x - 1)} \quad \textit{Factoring numerators and denominators}$$

$$= \frac{(x + 2)(x - 2)}{(x + 2)(x - 2)} \cdot \frac{x + 2}{x - 1}$$

$$= \frac{x + 2}{x - 1} \quad \textit{Simplifying}$$

Example 7. Multiply and simplify.

$$\frac{a^3 - b^3}{a^2 - b^2} \cdot \frac{a^2 + 2ab + b^2}{a^2 + ab + b^2} = \frac{(a^3 - b^3)(a^2 + 2ab + b^2)}{(a^2 - b^2)(a^2 + ab + b^2)}$$

$$= \frac{(a - b)(a^2 + ab + b^2)(a + b)(a + b)}{(a - b)(a + b)(a^2 + ab + b^2)}$$

$$= \frac{(a - b)(a^2 + ab + b^2)(a + b)}{(a - b)(a^2 + ab + b^2)(a + b)} \cdot \frac{a + b}{1}$$

$$= a + b$$

Answers. 10. $\frac{3(x - y)}{x + y}$ 11. $a - b$

TRY THIS ➡

Multiply and simplify.

10. $\dfrac{(x - y)^2}{x + y} \cdot \dfrac{3x + 3y}{x^2 - y^2}$

11. $\dfrac{a^3 + b^3}{a^2 - b^2} \cdot \dfrac{a^2 - 2ab + b^2}{a^2 - ab + b^2}$

ⅼⅼⅼⅼⅼ Dividing and Simplifying

Two expressions are reciprocals of each other If their product is 1.
To find the reciprocal of a fractional expression we interchange numerator and denominator.

Examples.

8. The reciprocal of $\dfrac{x + 2y}{3x^2y + 7}$ is $\dfrac{3x^2y + 7}{x + 2y}$.

9. The reciprocal of $y - 8$ is $\dfrac{1}{y - 8}$.

TRY THIS ➡

Find the reciprocal.

12. $\dfrac{x + 3}{x - 5}$ $\dfrac{x - 5}{x + 3}$

13. $x + 7$ $\dfrac{1}{x + 7}$

14. $\dfrac{1}{y^3 - 9}$ $y^3 - 9$

We can divide fractional expressions by multiplying by the reciprocal of the divisor.

We usually simplify answers if possible.

Example 10. Divide and simplify.

$$\frac{a^2 - 1}{a + 1} \div \frac{a^2 - 2a + 1}{a + 1} = \frac{a^2 - 1}{a + 1} \cdot \frac{a + 1}{a^2 - 2a + 1} \quad \text{\textit{Multiplying by the reciprocal}}$$

$$= \frac{(a + 1)(a - 1)}{a + 1} \cdot \frac{a + 1}{(a - 1)(a - 1)} \quad \text{\textit{Factoring numerator and denominator}}$$

$$= \frac{(a + 1)(a - 1)}{(a + 1)(a - 1)} \cdot \frac{a + 1}{a - 1}$$

$$= \frac{a + 1}{a - 1} \quad \text{\textit{Simplifying}}$$

TRY THIS

Answers. 15. $\dfrac{x+5}{x-5}$ 16. $\dfrac{2ab(a+b)}{a-b}$

Divide and simplify.

15. $\dfrac{x^2 + 7x + 10}{y} \div \dfrac{x^2 - 3x - 10}{y}$

16. $\dfrac{a^2 - b^2}{ab} \div \dfrac{a^2 - 2ab + b^2}{2a^2b^2}$

Exercise Set 9-1

▌Multiply. (*See Example 1.*)

1. $\dfrac{y+3}{4} \cdot \dfrac{y-2}{y+4}$ $\dfrac{y^2 + y - 6}{4y + 16}$

2. $\dfrac{x+7}{5} \cdot \dfrac{x-3}{x+6}$ $\dfrac{x^2 + 4x - 21}{5x + 30}$

3. $\dfrac{z-1}{z+1} \cdot \dfrac{z+2}{z-3}$ $\dfrac{z^2 + z - 2}{z^2 - 2z - 3}$

4. $\dfrac{x-4}{x+3} \cdot \dfrac{x+6}{x-2}$ $\dfrac{x^2 + 2x - 24}{x^2 + x - 6}$

5. $\dfrac{x-y}{2x+y} \cdot \dfrac{x+y}{2x-y}$ $\dfrac{x^2 - y^2}{4x^2 - y^2}$

6. $\dfrac{2y+3}{y-5} \cdot \dfrac{2y-5}{y+6}$ $\dfrac{4y^2 - 4y - 15}{y^2 + y - 30}$

7. $\dfrac{x-2}{x+1} \cdot \dfrac{x^2 + 2x + 4}{x^2 - x + 1}$ $\dfrac{x^3 - 8}{x^3 + 1}$

8. $\dfrac{x-y}{x+y} \cdot \dfrac{x^2 + xy + y^2}{x^2 - xy + y^2}$ $\dfrac{x^3 - y^3}{x^3 + y^3}$

▌▌Multiply. (*See Examples 2 and 3.*)

9. $\dfrac{3x}{3x} \cdot \dfrac{x+1}{x+3}$ $\dfrac{3x^2 + 3x}{3x^2 + 9x}$

10. $\dfrac{y}{y} \cdot \dfrac{4y-3}{2y+5}$ $\dfrac{4y^2 - 3y}{2y^2 + 5y}$

11. $\dfrac{4-y^2}{6-y} \cdot \dfrac{-1}{-1}$ $\dfrac{y^2 - 4}{y - 6}$

12. $\dfrac{8-x^3}{4-x} \cdot \dfrac{-1}{-1}$ $\dfrac{x^3 - 8}{x - 4}$

13. $\dfrac{t-3}{t+2} \cdot \dfrac{t-3}{t-3}$ $\dfrac{t^2 - 6t + 9}{t^2 - t - 6}$

14. $\dfrac{p-4}{p+5} \cdot \dfrac{p+5}{p+5}$ $\dfrac{p^2 + p - 20}{p^2 + 10p + 25}$

15. $\dfrac{4x-3}{x+5} \cdot \dfrac{x^2-1}{x^2-1}$ $\dfrac{4x^3 - 3x^2 - 4x + 3}{x^3 + 5x^2 - x - 5}$

16. $\dfrac{5y-1}{3y+4} \cdot \dfrac{y^2+3}{y^2+3}$ $\dfrac{5y^3 - y^2 + 15y - 3}{3y^3 + 4y^2 + 9y + 12}$

▌▌▌Simplify. (*See Examples 4 and 5.*)

17. $\dfrac{9y^2}{15y}$ $\dfrac{3y}{5}$

18. $\dfrac{6x^3}{18x^2}$ $\dfrac{x}{3}$

19. $\dfrac{2a-6}{2}$ $a-3$

20. $\dfrac{3a-6}{3}$ $a-2$

21. $\dfrac{4y-12}{4y+12}$ $\dfrac{y-3}{y+3}$

22. $\dfrac{8x+16}{8x-16}$ $\dfrac{x+2}{x-2}$

23. $\dfrac{t^2-16}{t^2-8t+16}$ $\dfrac{t+4}{t-4}$

24. $\dfrac{p^2-25}{p^2+10p+25}$ $\dfrac{p-5}{p+5}$

25. $\dfrac{x^2+7x-8}{4x^2-8x+4}$ $\dfrac{x+8}{4(x-1)}$

26. $\dfrac{y^2+4y-12}{3y^2-12y+12}$ $\dfrac{y+6}{3(y-2)}$

27. $\dfrac{x^4 - 4x^2}{x^3 + 2x^2}$ $x - 2$

28. $\dfrac{r^4 - 9r^2}{r^3 - 3r^2}$ $r + 3$

29. $\dfrac{a^3 - b^3}{a^2 - b^2}$ $\dfrac{a^2 + ab + b^2}{a + b}$

30. $\dfrac{x^3 + y^3}{x^2 - y^2}$ $\dfrac{x^2 - xy + y^2}{x - y}$

▮▮▮▮ Multiply and simplify. (*See Examples 6 and 7.*)

31. $\dfrac{x^2 - 16}{x^2} \cdot \dfrac{x^2 - 4x}{x^2 - x - 12}$ $\dfrac{(x + 4)(x - 4)}{x(x + 3)}$

32. $\dfrac{y^2 + 10y + 25}{y^2 - 9} \cdot \dfrac{y + 3}{y + 5}$ $\dfrac{y + 5}{y - 3}$

33. $\dfrac{y^2 - 16}{2y + 6} \cdot \dfrac{y + 3}{y - 4}$ $\dfrac{y + 4}{2}$

34. $\dfrac{m^2 - n^2}{4m + 4n} \cdot \dfrac{m + n}{m - n}$ $\dfrac{m + n}{4}$

35. $\dfrac{x^2 - 2x - 35}{2x^3 - 3x^2} \cdot \dfrac{4x^3 - 9x}{7x - 49}$ $\dfrac{(x + 5)(2x + 3)}{7x}$

36. $\dfrac{y^2 - 10y + 9}{y^2 - 1} \cdot \dfrac{y + 4}{y^2 - 5y - 36}$ $\dfrac{1}{y + 1}$

37. $\dfrac{c^3 + 8}{c^2 - 4} \cdot \dfrac{c^2 - 4c + 4}{c^2 - 2c + 4}$ $c - 2$

38. $\dfrac{x^3 - 27}{x^2 - 9} \cdot \dfrac{x^2 - 6x + 9}{x^2 + 3x + 9}$ $\dfrac{(x - 3)^2}{x + 3}$

39. $\dfrac{x^2 - y^2}{x^3 - y^3} \cdot \dfrac{x^2 + xy + y^2}{x^2 + 2xy + y^2}$ $\dfrac{1}{x + y}$

40. $\dfrac{64x^3 + 27y^3}{16x^2 - 9y^2} \cdot \dfrac{16x^2 - 24xy + 9y^2}{4x^2 - 12xy + 9y^2}$
   $\dfrac{(16x^2 - 12xy + 9y^2)(4x - 3y)}{(2x - 3y)^2}$

▮▮▮▮ Divide and simplify. (*See Example 10.*)

41. $\dfrac{3y + 15}{y} \div \dfrac{y + 5}{y}$ 3

42. $\dfrac{6x + 12}{x} \div \dfrac{x + 2}{x^3}$ $6x^2$

43. $\dfrac{y^2 - 9}{y} \div \dfrac{y + 3}{y + 2}$ $\dfrac{(y - 3)(y + 2)}{y}$

44. $\dfrac{x^2 - 4}{x} \div \dfrac{x - 2}{x + 4}$ $\dfrac{(x + 2)(x + 4)}{x}$

45. $\dfrac{4a^2 - 1}{a^2 - 4} \div \dfrac{2a - 1}{a - 2}$ $\dfrac{2a + 1}{a + 2}$

46. $\dfrac{25x^2 - 4}{x^2 - 9} \div \dfrac{5x - 2}{x + 3}$ $\dfrac{5x + 2}{x - 3}$

47. $\dfrac{x^2 - 16}{x^2 - 10x + 25} \div \dfrac{3x - 12}{x^2 - 3x - 10}$ $\dfrac{(x + 4)(x + 2)}{3(x - 5)}$

48. $\dfrac{y^2 - 36}{y^2 - 8y + 16} \div \dfrac{3y - 18}{y^2 - y + 12}$ $\dfrac{(y + 6)(y + 3)}{3(y - 4)}$

49. $\dfrac{y^3 + 3y}{y^2 - 9} \div \dfrac{y^2 + 5y - 14}{y^2 + 4y - 21}$ $\dfrac{y(y^2 + 3)}{(y + 3)(y - 2)}$

50. $\dfrac{a^3 + 4a}{a^2 - 16} \div \dfrac{a^2 + 8a + 15}{a^2 + a - 20}$ $\dfrac{a(a^2 + 4)}{(a + 4)(a + 3)}$

51. $\dfrac{x^3 - 64}{x^3 + 64} \div \dfrac{x^2 - 16}{x^2 - 4x + 16}$ $\dfrac{x^2 + 4x + 16}{(x + 4)^2}$

52. $\dfrac{8y^3 + 27}{64y^3 - 1} \div \dfrac{4y^2 - 9}{16y^2 + 4y + 1}$ $\dfrac{4y^2 - 6y + 9}{(4y - 1)(2y - 3)}$

Calculator Exercises

Multiply or divide.

53. $\dfrac{834x}{y - 427.2} \cdot \dfrac{26.3x}{y + 427.2}$ $\dfrac{21,934.2x^2}{y^2 - 182,499.84}$

54. $\dfrac{0.0049t}{t + 0.007} \cdot \dfrac{27,000t}{t - 0.007}$ $\dfrac{132.3t^2}{t^2 - 0.000049}$

55. $\dfrac{527}{x + 93.87} \div \dfrac{x - 93.87}{468}$ $\dfrac{246,636}{x^2 - 8811.5769}$

56. $\dfrac{y + 924.6}{0.003} \div \dfrac{0.421}{y - 924.6}$ $\dfrac{y^2 - 854,885.16}{0.001263}$

9-2 *Least Common Multiple*

After finishing Lesson 9-2, you should be able to
▮ find least common multiples of algebraic expressions.

▮ To add fractional expressions we first find a common denomina-
tor. Consider $\frac{5}{42} + \frac{7}{12}$. We look for a common multiple of 42 and
12. Usually we try to get the smallest such number, or the *least
common multiple* (LCM). To find the LCM we factor.

$$42 = 2 \cdot 3 \cdot 7$$
$$12 = 2 \cdot 2 \cdot 3$$

The LCM is the number that has 2 as a factor twice, 3 as a factor once, and 7 as a factor once. The LCM is $2 \cdot 2 \cdot 3 \cdot 7$, or 84.

To obtain the LCM we use each factor the greatest number of
times it occurs in any one factorization.

Example 1. Find the LCM of 18 and 24.

$$18 = 3 \cdot 3 \cdot 2$$
$$24 = 2 \cdot 2 \cdot 2 \cdot 3$$

The LCM is $3 \cdot 3 \cdot 2 \cdot 2 \cdot 2$, or 72.

TRY THIS

Find the LCM by factoring.

1. 18, 30 **90**
2. 28, 36 **252**
3. 12, 18, 24 **72**

To find the LCM of two or more algebraic expressions we factor
them. Then we use each factor the greatest number of times it
occurs in any one expression.

Example 2. Find the LCM of $12xy^2$, $15x^3y$.

$$12xy^2 = 2 \cdot 2 \cdot 3 \cdot x \cdot y \cdot y$$
$$15x^3y = 3 \cdot 5 \cdot x \cdot x \cdot x \cdot y$$

The LCM is $2 \cdot 2 \cdot 3 \cdot 5 \cdot x \cdot x \cdot x \cdot y \cdot y$, or $60x^3y^2$.

TRY THIS

Find the LCM.

4. $18a^2b^2$, $15a^3b$
   90a³b²

Example 3. Find the LCM of $y^2 + 5y + 4$, $y^2 + 2y + 1$.

$$y^2 + 5y + 4 = (y + 4)(y + 1)$$
$$y^2 + 2y + 1 = (y + 1)(y + 1)$$

The LCM is $(y + 4)(y + 1)(y + 1)$.

Example 4. Find the LCM of $x^2 + 8$, $x + 2$, and 7.

These expressions are not factorable, so their LCM is their product, $7(x^2 + 8)(x + 2)$.

Example 5. Find the LCM of $x^2 - y^2$, $x^3 + y^3$, $x^2 + 2xy + y^2$.

$$x^2 - y^2 = (x - y)(x + y)$$
$$x^3 + y^3 = (x + y)(x^2 - xy + y^2)$$
$$x^2 + 2xy + y^2 = (x + y)(x + y)$$

The LCM is $(x - y)(x + y)(x + y)(x^2 - xy + y^2)$.

If an LCM is multiplied by -1 we still consider the answer to be an LCM. For example, the LCM of 7 and -7 is either 7 or -7. The LCM of $x - 3$ and $3 - x$ is either $x - 3$ or $3 - x$.

Example 6. Find the LCM of $x^2 - y^2$ and $3y - 3x$.

$$x^2 - y^2 = (x + y)(x - y)$$
$$3y - 3x = 3(y - x)$$

The LCM is $3(x + y)(x - y)$, or $3(x + y)(y - x)$.

TRY THIS

Answers. 5. $(x + 1)(x + 1)(x + 4)$ 6. $5(x - 3)(x^2 + 10)$
7. $2(a + b)(a - b)$ or $2(a + b)(b - a)$ 8. $(y + 4)(y + 4)(y + 3)$

Find the LCM.

5. $x^2 + 2x + 1$, $x^2 + 5x + 4$
6. $x^2 + 10$, $x - 3$, 5
7. $a^2 - b^2$, $2b - 2a$
8. $y^2 + 7y + 12$,
    $y^2 + 8y + 16$, $y + 4$

Exercise Set 9-2

▌Find the LCM. (*See Examples 1–6.*)

1. 14, 20   See answer section
3. 24, 36, 42
5. $8x^2$, $12x^3$
7. $12x^2y$, $4xy$
9. $15ab^2$, $3ab$, $10a^3b$
11. $a + b$, $a - b$
13. $3(y - 2)$, $6(2 - y)$
15. $y^2 - 9$, $3y + 9$
17. $5y - 15$, $y^2 - 6y + 9$
19. $(a + 1)$, $(a - 1)^2$, $a^2 - 1$
21. $x^2 - 4$, $2 - x$
23. $x^2 + 10x + 25$, $x^2 + 2x - 15$
25. $2r^2 - 5r - 12$, $3r^2 - 13r + 4$
27. $2x^2 - 5x - 3$, $2x^2 - x - 1$,
    $x^2 - 6x + 9$

2. 18, 26
4. 24, 42, 60
6. $4y^2$, $24y^3$
8. $18r^2s$, $12rs^3$
10. $6x^2y^2$, $9x^3y$, $15y^3$
12. $x - 4$, $x + 4$
14. $5(y - 1)$, $10(1 - y)$
16. $a^2 - b^2$, $ab + b^2$
18. $4x - 16$, $x^2 - 8x + 16$
20. $(x - 2)$, $(x + 2)^2$, $x^2 - 4$
22. $y^2 - 9$, $3 - y$
24. $y^2 + 8x + 16$, $y^2 - 3y - 28$
26. $3x^2 - 4x - 4$, $4x^2 - 5x - 6$
28. $3x^2 + 4x - 4$, $2x^2 + 7x + 6$,
    $x^2 - 4x + 4$

9-3 *Addition and Subtraction*

After finishing Lesson 9-3, you should be able to

■ add and subtract fractional expressions having the same denominator.

■■ add and subtract fractional expressions whose denominators are additive inverses of each other.

■■■ add and subtract fractional expressions having different denominators.

■■■■ simplify combined additions and subtractions of fractional expressions.

■ Addition and Subtraction, Same Denominator

When denominators are the same, we add or subtract the numerators and keep the same denominator.

Example 1. Add.

$$\frac{3 + x}{x} + \frac{4}{x} = \frac{7 + x}{x}$$

Example 1 shows that $\frac{3 + x}{x} + \frac{4}{x}$ and $\frac{7 + x}{x}$ are equivalent expressions.

They name the same number for all replacements except 0.

Example 2. Add.

$$\frac{4x^2 - 5xy}{x^2 - y^2} + \frac{2xy - y^2}{x^2 - y^2} = \frac{4x^2 - 3xy - y^2}{x^2 - y^2}$$

$$= \frac{(4x + y)(x - y)}{(x + y)(x - y)}$$

$$= \frac{x - y}{x - y} \cdot \frac{4x + y}{x + y}$$

$$= \frac{4x + y}{x + y}$$

TRY THIS

Example 3. Subtract.

$$\frac{4x + 5}{x + 3} - \frac{x - 2}{x + 3} = \frac{4x + 5 - (x - 2)}{x + 3}$$

$$= \frac{4x + 5 - x + 2}{x + 3}$$

$$= \frac{3x + 7}{x + 3}$$

Add.

1. $\dfrac{5 + y}{y} + \dfrac{7}{y}$

2. $\dfrac{2x^2 + 5x - 9}{x - 5} +$ $\dfrac{x^2 - 19x + 4}{x - 5}$

Answers. 1. $\dfrac{12 + y}{y}$

2. $3x + 1$

In Example 3, note the use of parentheses. This is important, to make sure you subtract the entire numerator and not just part of it.

TRY THIS ➡

Answers. 3. $\dfrac{a-b}{b+2}$ 4. $\dfrac{y+12}{x^2+y^2}$

> Subtract.
>
> 3. $\dfrac{a}{b+2} - \dfrac{b}{b+2}$
>
> 4. $\dfrac{4y+7}{x^2+y^2} - \dfrac{3y-5}{x^2+y^2}$

∎ Addition and Subtraction When Denominators are Additive Inverses

When one denominator is the additive inverse of the other, we first multiply one expression by $\dfrac{-1}{-1}$. This will give us a common denominator.

Example 4. Add.

$$\frac{a}{2a} + \frac{a^3}{-2a} = \frac{a}{2a} + \frac{-1}{-1} \cdot \frac{a^3}{-2a} \qquad \textit{Multiplying by } \frac{-1}{-1}$$

$$= \frac{a}{2a} + \frac{-a^3}{2a}$$

$$= \frac{a - a^3}{2a}$$

$$= \frac{a(1 - a^2)}{2a}$$

$$= \frac{a}{a} \cdot \frac{1 - a^2}{2}$$

$$= \frac{1 - a^2}{2}$$

Answers. 5. $\dfrac{1-b^2}{3}$ 6. $\dfrac{2x^2+11}{x-5}$

TRY THIS ➡

> Add.
>
> 5. $\dfrac{b}{3b} + \dfrac{b^3}{-3b}$
>
> 6. $\dfrac{3x^2+4}{x-5} + \dfrac{x^2-7}{5-x}$

Example 5. Subtract.

$$\frac{5x}{x-2y} - \frac{3y-7}{2y-x} = \frac{5x}{x-2y} - \frac{-1}{-1} \cdot \frac{3y-7}{2y-x}$$

$$= \frac{5x}{x-2y} - \frac{7-3y}{x-2y}$$

$$= \frac{5x - (7-3y)}{x-2y} \qquad \textit{Subtracting numera-}$$
$$\textit{tors (remember the}$$
$$\textit{parentheses)}$$

$$= \frac{5x - 7 + 3y}{x-2y}$$

> Subtract.
>
> 7. $\dfrac{3}{4y} - \dfrac{7x}{-4y}$
>
> 8. $\dfrac{4x^2}{x-y} - \dfrac{7x^2}{y-x}$

TRY THIS ➡

Answers. 7. $\dfrac{3+7x}{4y}$ 8. $\dfrac{11x^2}{x-y}$

ꜰꜰꜰ Addition and Subtraction, Different Denominators

When denominators are different, but not additive inverses of each other, we first find a common denominator, using the LCM, and then add or subtract numerators.

Example 6. Add.

$$\frac{2a}{5} + \frac{3b}{2a}$$

First find the LCM of the denominators.

$$\begin{matrix} 5 \\ 2a \end{matrix}$$ The LCM is $5 \cdot 2a$ or $10a$.

Now we multiply by 1 to get the LCM in each expression. Then we add and simplify.

$$\frac{2a}{5} \cdot \frac{2a}{2a} + \frac{3b}{2a} \cdot \frac{5}{5} = \frac{4a^2}{10a} + \frac{15b}{10a} = \frac{4a^2 + 15b}{10a}$$

TRY THIS ━━━▶

Add. $\frac{9x^2 + 28y}{21x}$

9. $\frac{3x}{7} + \frac{4y}{3x}$

Example 7. Add.

$$\frac{1}{2x} + \frac{5x}{x^2 - 1} + \frac{3}{x + 1}$$

We first find the LCM of the denominators.

$$\left.\begin{matrix} 2x = 2x \\ x^2 - 1 = (x - 1)(x + 1) \\ x + 1 = x + 1 \end{matrix}\right\} \text{The LCM is } 2x(x - 1)(x + 1).$$

Now we multiply by 1 to get the LCM in each expression. Then we add and simplify. We leave the denominator factored to ease possible simplifying at the end.

$$\frac{1}{2x} \cdot \frac{(x - 1)(x + 1)}{(x - 1)(x + 1)} + \frac{5x}{(x - 1)(x + 1)} \cdot \frac{2x}{2x} + \frac{3}{x + 1} \cdot \frac{2x(x - 1)}{2x(x - 1)}$$

$$= \frac{(x - 1)(x + 1)}{2x(x - 1)(x + 1)} + \frac{10x^2}{2x(x - 1)(x + 1)} + \frac{6x(x - 1)}{2x(x - 1)(x + 1)}$$

$$= \frac{x^2 - 1}{2x(x - 1)(x + 1)} + \frac{10x^2}{2x(x - 1)(x + 1)} + \frac{6x^2 - 6x}{2x(x - 1)(x + 1)}$$

$$= \frac{17x^2 - 6x - 1}{2x(x - 1)(x + 1)}$$

Here no simplifying can be done. We have left the denominator factored. In some cases denominators are best left this way. In other cases it is best to multiply them out.

TRY THIS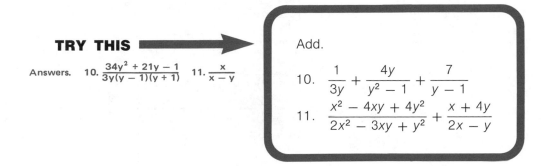

Answers. 10. $\dfrac{34y^2 + 21y - 1}{3y(y - 1)(y + 1)}$ 11. $\dfrac{x}{x - y}$

Add.

10. $\dfrac{1}{3y} + \dfrac{4y}{y^2 - 1} + \dfrac{7}{y - 1}$

11. $\dfrac{x^2 - 4xy + 4y^2}{2x^2 - 3xy + y^2} + \dfrac{x + 4y}{2x - y}$

Example 8. Subtract.

$$\frac{2y + 1}{y^2 - 7y + 6} - \frac{y + 3}{y^2 - 5y - 6} = \frac{2y + 1}{(y - 6)(y - 1)} - \frac{y + 3}{(y - 6)(y + 1)} \qquad \begin{array}{l} \textit{The LCM is} \\ (y - 6)(y - 1)(y + 1) \end{array}$$

$$= \frac{2y + 1}{(y - 6)(y - 1)} \cdot \frac{y + 1}{y + 1} - \frac{y + 3}{(y - 6)(y + 1)} \cdot \frac{y - 1}{y - 1}$$

$$= \frac{(2y + 1)(y + 1) - (y + 3)(y - 1)}{(y - 6)(y - 1)(y + 1)}$$

$$= \frac{2y^2 + 3y + 1 - (y^2 + 2y - 3)}{(y - 6)(y - 1)(y + 1)}$$

$$= \frac{2y^2 + 3y + 1 - y^2 - 2y + 3}{(y - 6)(y - 1)(y + 1)}$$

$$= \frac{y^2 + y + 4}{(y - 6)(y - 1)(y + 1)}$$

TRY THIS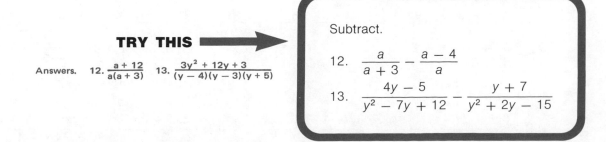

Answers. 12. $\dfrac{a + 12}{a(a + 3)}$ 13. $\dfrac{3y^2 + 12y + 3}{(y - 4)(y - 3)(y + 5)}$

Subtract.

12. $\dfrac{a}{a + 3} - \dfrac{a - 4}{a}$

13. $\dfrac{4y - 5}{y^2 - 7y + 12} - \dfrac{y + 7}{y^2 + 2y - 15}$

▪▪▪▪ Simplifying Combined Additions and Subtractions

Example 9. Simplify.

$$\frac{2x}{x^2 - 4} + \frac{5}{2 - x} - \frac{1}{2 + x} = \frac{2x}{(x - 2)(x + 2)} + \frac{5}{2 - x} - \frac{1}{2 + x}$$

$$= \frac{2x}{(x - 2)(x + 2)} + \frac{-1}{-1} \cdot \frac{5}{(2 - x)} - \frac{1}{x + 2}$$

$$= \frac{2x}{(x - 2)(x + 2)} + \frac{-5}{x - 2} - \frac{1}{x + 2} \qquad \text{The LCM is } (x - 2)(x + 2)$$

$$= \frac{2x}{(x - 2)(x + 2)} + \frac{-5}{x - 2} \cdot \frac{x + 2}{x + 2} - \frac{1}{x + 2} \cdot \frac{x - 2}{x - 2}$$

$$= \frac{2x - 5(x + 2) - (x - 2)}{(x - 2)(x + 2)}$$

$$= \frac{2x - 5x - 10 - x + 2}{(x - 2)(x + 2)}$$

$$= \frac{-4x - 8}{(x - 2)(x + 2)}$$

$$= \frac{-4(x + 2)}{(x - 2)(x + 2)}$$

$$= \frac{-4}{x - 2} \cdot \frac{x + 2}{x + 2}$$

$$= \frac{-4}{x - 2}$$

We leave the denominator factored to ease possible simplifying at the end.

TRY THIS ▮▮▮▶

Simplify. $\dfrac{6x^2 - 2x - 3}{x^2(x + 1)}$

14. $\dfrac{1}{x} - \dfrac{3}{x^2} + \dfrac{5}{x + 1}$

Exercise Set 9-3

▪ Add or subtract. Simplify if possible. (*See Examples 1–3.*)

1. $\dfrac{3 - a}{a} + \dfrac{5 + 2a}{a}$ $\quad \frac{a + 8}{a}$

2. $\dfrac{5 - 2x}{x} + \dfrac{4 + 4x}{x}$ $\quad \frac{2x + 9}{x}$

3. $\dfrac{a - 3b}{a + b} + \dfrac{a + 5b}{a + b}$ $\quad 2$

4. $\dfrac{x - 5y}{x + y} + \dfrac{x + 7y}{x + y}$ $\quad 2$

5. $\dfrac{5x^2 - 4x + 7}{x^3} + \dfrac{4x^2 + 9x + 3}{x^3}$ $\quad \frac{9x^2 + 5x + 10}{x^3}$

6. $\dfrac{7t^2 - 3t + 2}{t^4} + \dfrac{8t^2 + 5t - 9}{t^4}$ $\quad \frac{15t^2 + 2t - 7}{t^4}$

7. $\dfrac{4y + 3}{y - 2} - \dfrac{y - 2}{y - 2}$ $\quad \frac{3y + 5}{y - 2}$

8. $\dfrac{3t + 2}{t - 4} - \dfrac{t - 4}{t - 4}$ $\quad \frac{2t + 6}{t - 4}$

9. $\dfrac{10xy}{xy^2} - \dfrac{6xy}{xy^2}$ $\quad \frac{4}{y}$

10. $\dfrac{12ab}{ab^2} - \dfrac{5ab}{ab^2}$ $\quad \frac{7}{b}$

11. $\dfrac{6y^2 - 3y + 1}{2y + 1} - \dfrac{4y^2 - 3y - 1}{2y + 1}$ $\quad \frac{2y^2 + 2}{2y + 1}$

12. $\dfrac{5x^2 + 2x - 3}{3x - 1} - \dfrac{4x^2 - 2x + 5}{3x - 1}$ $\quad \frac{x^2 + 4x - 7}{3x - 1}$

▌▌ Add or subtract. Simplify when possible. (*See Examples 4 and 5.*)

13. $\dfrac{a^2}{a-b}+\dfrac{b^2}{b-a}$ **a + b**

14. $\dfrac{r^2}{r-s}+\dfrac{s^2}{s-r}$ **r + s**

15. $\dfrac{x+2}{3x-4}+\dfrac{2x-3}{4-3x}+\dfrac{5(3x-1)}{3x-4}$ **$\frac{14x}{3x-4}$**

16. $\dfrac{4(y-1)}{2y-5}+\dfrac{5(2y+3)}{5-2y}+\dfrac{y-4}{2y-5}$ **$\frac{-5y-23}{2y-5}$**

17. $\dfrac{3}{x}-\dfrac{8}{-x}$ **$\frac{11}{x}$**

18. $\dfrac{2}{a}-\dfrac{5}{-a}$ **$\frac{7}{a}$**

19. $\dfrac{2x-10}{x^2-25}-\dfrac{5-x}{25-x^2}$ **$\frac{1}{x+5}$**

20. $\dfrac{y-9}{y^2-16}-\dfrac{7-y}{16-y^2}$ **$\frac{-2}{y^2-16}$**

▌▌▌ Add or subtract. Simplify when possible. Leave denominators factored. (*See Examples 6–8.*)

21. $\dfrac{y-2}{y+4}+\dfrac{y+3}{y-5}$ **$\frac{2y^2+22}{(y+4)(y-5)}$**

22. $\dfrac{x-2}{x+3}+\dfrac{x+2}{x-4}$ **$\frac{2x^2-x+14}{(x+3)(x-4)}$**

23. $\dfrac{4xy}{x^2-y^2}+\dfrac{x-y}{x+y}$ **$\frac{x+y}{x-y}$**

24. $\dfrac{5ab}{a^2-b^2}+\dfrac{a+b}{a-b}$ **$\frac{a^2+7ab+b^2}{(a+b)(a-b)}$**

25. $\dfrac{9x+2}{3x^2-2x-8}+\dfrac{7}{3x^2+x-4}$ **$\frac{3x-4}{(x-2)(x-1)}$**

26. $\dfrac{3y+2}{2y^2-y-10}+\dfrac{8}{2y^2-7y+5}$ **$\frac{3y^2+7y+14}{(2y-5)(y+2)(y-1)}$**

27. $\dfrac{4}{x+1}+\dfrac{x+2}{x^2-1}+\dfrac{3}{x-1}$ **$\frac{8x+1}{(x+1)(x-1)}$**

28. $\dfrac{-2}{y+2}+\dfrac{5}{y-2}+\dfrac{y+3}{y^2-4}$ **$\frac{4y+17}{(y+2)(y-2)}$**

29. $\dfrac{1}{x^2+y^2}+\dfrac{1}{x^2-y^2}+\dfrac{2x^2}{y^4-x^4}$ **0**

30. $\dfrac{2}{a^2-b^2}+\dfrac{2}{a^2+b^2}+\dfrac{4a^2}{a^4-b^4}$ **$\frac{8a^2}{(a^2+b^2)(a^2-b^2)}$**

31. $\dfrac{x-1}{3x+15}-\dfrac{x+3}{5x+25}$ **$\frac{2x-14}{15(x+5)}$**

32. $\dfrac{y-2}{4y+8}-\dfrac{y+6}{5y+10}$ **$\frac{y-34}{20(y+2)}$**

33. $\dfrac{5ab}{a^2-b^2}-\dfrac{a-b}{a+b}$ **$\frac{-a^2+7ab-b^2}{(a+b)(a-b)}$**

34. $\dfrac{6xy}{x^2-y^2}-\dfrac{x+y}{x-y}$ **$\frac{-x^2+4xy-y^2}{(x+y)(x-y)}$**

35. $\dfrac{3y}{y^2-7y+10}-\dfrac{2y}{y^2-8y+15}$ **$\frac{y}{(y-2)(y-3)}$**

36. $\dfrac{5x}{x^2-6x+8}+\dfrac{3x}{x^2-x-12}$ **$\frac{2x^2+21x}{(x-4)(x-2)(x+3)}$**

37. $\dfrac{3x-1}{x^2+2x-3}-\dfrac{x+4}{x^2-9}$ **$\frac{2x^2-13x+7}{(x+3)(x-1)(x-3)}$**

38. $\dfrac{3p-2}{p^2+2p-24}-\dfrac{p-3}{p^2-16}$ **$\frac{2p^2+7p+10}{(p+6)(p-4)(p+4)}$**

▌▌▌▌ Simplify. (*See Example 9.*)

39. $\dfrac{1}{x+1}-\dfrac{x}{x-2}+\dfrac{x^2+2}{x^2-x-2}$ **0**

40. $\dfrac{2}{y+3}-\dfrac{y}{y-1}+\dfrac{y^2+2}{y^2+2y-3}$ **$\frac{-y}{(y+3)(y-1)}$**

41. $\dfrac{x-1}{x-2}-\dfrac{x+1}{x+2}+\dfrac{x-6}{x^2-4}$ **$\frac{3}{x+2}$**

42. $\dfrac{y-3}{y-4}-\dfrac{y+2}{y+4}+\dfrac{y-7}{y^2-16}$ **$\frac{4y-11}{(y-4)(y+4)}$**

43. $\dfrac{4x}{x^2-1}+\dfrac{3x}{1-x}-\dfrac{4}{x-1}$ **$\frac{-3x^2-3x-4}{(x+1)(x-1)}$**

44. $\dfrac{5y}{1-2y}-\dfrac{2y}{2y+1}+\dfrac{3}{4y^2-1}$ **$\frac{-14y^2-3y+3}{(2y+1)(2y-1)}$**

9-4 Complex Fractional Expressions

After finishing Lesson 9-4, you should be able to
∎ simplify complex fractional expressions.

∎ **DEFINITION**

A *complex fractional expression* is one which has a fractional expression in its numerator or its denominator, or both.

These are complex fractional expressions.

$$\frac{x}{x - \dfrac{1}{3}}, \quad \frac{2x - \dfrac{4x}{3y}}{\dfrac{5x^2 + 2x}{6y^2}}, \quad \frac{\dfrac{1}{a} + \dfrac{1}{b}}{\dfrac{1}{a} - \dfrac{1}{b}}$$

To simplify complex fractional expressions we first add or subtract or both to get a single fractional expression in both numerator and denominator. Then we divide and simplify.

Example 1. Simplify.

$$\frac{1 + \dfrac{1}{x}}{1 - \dfrac{1}{x^2}} = \frac{\dfrac{x}{x} + \dfrac{1}{x}}{\dfrac{x^2}{x^2} - \dfrac{1}{x^2}} \qquad \textit{Finding LCM and multiplying by 1}$$

$$= \frac{\dfrac{x + 1}{x}}{\dfrac{x^2 - 1}{x^2}} \qquad \textit{Adding in the numerator and denominator}$$

$$= \frac{x + 1}{x} \cdot \frac{x^2}{x^2 - 1} \qquad \begin{array}{l}\textit{Multiplying by the reciprocal}\\ \textit{of the denominator}\end{array}$$

$$= \frac{(x + 1) \cdot x^2}{x(x^2 - 1)}$$

$$= \frac{(x + 1) \cdot x \cdot x}{x(x + 1)(x - 1)}$$

$$= \frac{x}{x - 1} \qquad \textit{Simplifying}$$

Example 1 shows that the expressions $\dfrac{1 + \dfrac{1}{x}}{1 - \dfrac{1}{x^2}}$ and $\dfrac{x}{x - 1}$ are equivalent.

They name the same number for all replacements except 0, 1, and −1.

TRY THIS ━━━━━━━━━━━➤

Answers. 1. $\dfrac{7(2y + 1)}{2(7y - 1)}$ 2. $\dfrac{x}{x + 1}$

Simplify.

1. $\dfrac{y + \frac{1}{2}}{y - \frac{1}{7}}$

2. $\dfrac{1 - \dfrac{1}{x}}{1 - \dfrac{1}{x^2}}$

Example 2. Simplify.

$$\frac{\dfrac{1}{a} + \dfrac{1}{b}}{\dfrac{1}{a^3} + \dfrac{1}{b^3}} = \frac{\dfrac{1}{a} \cdot \dfrac{b}{b} + \dfrac{1}{b} \cdot \dfrac{a}{a}}{\dfrac{1}{a^3} \cdot \dfrac{b^3}{b^3} + \dfrac{1}{b^3} \cdot \dfrac{a^3}{a^3}}$$

$$= \frac{\dfrac{b}{ab} + \dfrac{a}{ab}}{\dfrac{b^3}{a^3b^3} + \dfrac{a^3}{a^3b^3}} \quad \textit{Adding in the numerator and denominator}$$

$$= \frac{\dfrac{b + a}{ab}}{\dfrac{b^3 + a^3}{a^3b^3}}$$

$$= \frac{b + a}{ab} \cdot \frac{a^3b^3}{b^3 + a^3} \quad \textit{Multiplying by the reciprocal of the denominator}$$

$$= \frac{(b + a)a^3b^3}{ab(b^3 + a^3)} \quad \textit{Simplifying}$$

$$= \frac{(b + a) \cdot ab \cdot a^2b^2}{ab(b + a)(b^2 - ab + a^2)}$$

$$= \frac{(b + a)ab}{(b + a)ab} \cdot \frac{a^2b^2}{b^2 - ab + a^2}$$

$$= \frac{a^2b^2}{b^2 - ab + a^2}$$

Simplify.

3. $\dfrac{\dfrac{1}{a} - \dfrac{1}{b}}{\dfrac{1}{a^3} - \dfrac{1}{b^3}}$

4. $\dfrac{\dfrac{1}{a} + \dfrac{1}{b}}{\dfrac{1}{a} - \dfrac{1}{b}}$

5. $\dfrac{\dfrac{1}{a} - \dfrac{1}{a + h}}{h}$

TRY THIS ━━━━━━━━━━━➤

Answers. 3. $\dfrac{a^2b^2}{b^2 + ab + a^2}$ 4. $\dfrac{b + a}{b - a}$ 5. $\dfrac{1}{a(a + h)}$

Exercise Set 9-4

▌Simplify. (*See Examples 1 and 2.*)

1. $\dfrac{\dfrac{1}{x} + 4}{\dfrac{1}{x} - 3}$ $\dfrac{1 + 4x}{1 - 3x}$

2. $\dfrac{\dfrac{1}{y} + 7}{\dfrac{1}{y} - 5}$ $\dfrac{1 + 7y}{1 - 5y}$

3. $\dfrac{x - \dfrac{1}{x}}{x + \dfrac{1}{x}}$ $\dfrac{x^2 - 1}{x^2 + 1}$

4. $\dfrac{y + \dfrac{1}{y}}{y - \dfrac{1}{y}}$ $\dfrac{y^2 + 1}{y^2 - 1}$

5. $\dfrac{\dfrac{3}{x} + \dfrac{4}{y}}{\dfrac{4}{x} - \dfrac{3}{y}}$ $\dfrac{3y + 4x}{4y - 3x}$

6. $\dfrac{\dfrac{2}{y} + \dfrac{5}{z}}{\dfrac{1}{y} - \dfrac{4}{z}}$ $\dfrac{2z + 5y}{z - 4y}$

7. $\dfrac{\dfrac{x^2 - y^2}{xy}}{\dfrac{x - y}{y}}$ $\dfrac{x + y}{x}$

8. $\dfrac{\dfrac{a^2 - b^2}{ab}}{\dfrac{a - b}{b}}$ $\dfrac{a + b}{a}$

9. $\dfrac{a - \dfrac{3a}{b}}{b - \dfrac{b}{a}}$ $\dfrac{a^2(b - 3)}{b^2(a - 1)}$

10. $\dfrac{1 - \dfrac{2}{3x}}{x - \dfrac{4}{9x}}$ $\dfrac{3}{3x + 2}$

11. $\dfrac{\dfrac{1}{a} + \dfrac{1}{b}}{\dfrac{a^2 - b^2}{ab}}$ $\dfrac{1}{a - b}$

12. $\dfrac{\dfrac{1}{x} + \dfrac{1}{y}}{\dfrac{x^2 - y^2}{xy}}$ $\dfrac{1}{x - y}$

13. $\dfrac{\dfrac{1}{x^3} - x}{\dfrac{1}{x^2} - 1}$ $\dfrac{1 + x^2}{x}$

14. $\dfrac{\dfrac{1}{y^3} + y}{\dfrac{1}{y^2} + 1}$ $\dfrac{1 + y^4}{y(1 + y^2)}$

15. $\dfrac{\dfrac{y^2 - y - 6}{y^2 - 5y - 14}}{\dfrac{y^2 + 6y + 5}{y^2 - 6y - 7}}$ $\dfrac{y - 3}{y + 5}$

16. $\dfrac{\dfrac{x^2 - x - 12}{x^2 - 2x - 15}}{\dfrac{x^2 + 8x + 12}{x^2 - 5x - 14}}$ $\dfrac{(x - 4)(x - 7)}{(x - 5)(x + 6)}$

17. $\dfrac{\dfrac{x}{1 - x} + \dfrac{1 + x}{x}}{\dfrac{1 - x}{x} + \dfrac{x}{1 + x}}$ $\dfrac{1 + x}{1 - x}$

18. $\dfrac{\dfrac{y}{x - y} + \dfrac{x + y}{y}}{\dfrac{x - y}{x} + \dfrac{y}{x + y}}$ $\dfrac{x^3(x + y)}{yx^3 - 2xy^3 + y^4}$

19. $\dfrac{\dfrac{3}{a} + \dfrac{3}{b} - \dfrac{6}{ab}}{\dfrac{4}{a} + \dfrac{4}{b} - \dfrac{8}{ab}}$ $\dfrac{3}{4}$

20. $\dfrac{\dfrac{5}{x} - \dfrac{5}{y} + \dfrac{10}{xy}}{\dfrac{6}{x} - \dfrac{6}{y} + \dfrac{12}{xy}}$ $\dfrac{5}{6}$

21. $\dfrac{\dfrac{4}{x - 5} + \dfrac{2}{x + 2}}{\dfrac{2x}{x^2 - 3x - 10} + \dfrac{3}{x - 5}}$ $\dfrac{6x - 2}{5x + 6}$

22. $\dfrac{\dfrac{4a}{2a^2 - a - 1} - \dfrac{4}{a - 1}}{\dfrac{1}{a - 1} + \dfrac{6}{2a + 1}}$ $\dfrac{-4a - 4}{8a - 5}$

9-5 Division of Polynomials

After finishing Lesson 9-5, you should be able to
▌ divide a polynomial by a monomial and check the result.
▌▌ divide a polynomial by a divisor which is not a monomial and, if there is a remainder, express the result two ways.

▌Divisor a Monomial

Remember that fractional expressions indicate division. Division by a monomial can be done by first writing a fractional expression.

Example 1. Divide $12x^3 + 8x^2 + x + 4$ by $4x$.

$\dfrac{12x^3 + 8x^2 + x + 4}{4x}$ *Writing a fractional expression*

$= \dfrac{12x^3}{4x} + \dfrac{8x^2}{4x} + \dfrac{x}{4x} + \dfrac{4}{4x}$ *Doing the reverse of adding*

$= 3x^2 + 2x + \dfrac{1}{4} + \dfrac{1}{4x}$ *Simplifying*

TRY THIS ➡

Divide. $\dfrac{x^2}{2} + 8x + 3$

1. $\dfrac{x^3 + 16x^2 + 6x}{2x}$

Example 2. Divide: $(8x^4 - 3x^3 + 5x^2) \div x^2$.

$\dfrac{8x^4 - 3x^3 + 5x^2}{x^2} = \dfrac{8x^4}{x^2} - \dfrac{3x^3}{x^2} + \dfrac{5x^2}{x^2}$

$= 8x^2 - 3x + 5$

You should try to write only the answer.

To divide a polynomial by a monomial we can divide each term by the monomial.

TRY THIS ➡

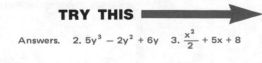

Answers.   2. $5y^3 - 2y^2 + 6y$ 3. $\dfrac{x^2}{2} + 5x + 8$

Divide.

2. $(15y^5 - 6y^4 + 18y^3) \div 3y^2$
3. $(x^4 + 10x^3 + 16x^2) \div 2x^2$

꞉꞉ Divisor Not a Monomial

We use a procedure very much like long division in arithmetic when the divisor is not a monomial.

Example 3. Divide $x^2 + 5x + 6$ by $x + 3$.

$$
\begin{array}{r}
x \\
x + 3 \overline{\smash{)}x^2 + 5x + 6} \\
\underline{x^2 + 3x} \\
2x
\end{array}
$$

⟵ *Divide first term by first term:* $\dfrac{x^2}{x} = x$

⟵ *Multiply x by divisor*

⟵ *Subtract*

We now "bring down" the next term of the dividend, 6.

$$
\begin{array}{r}
x + 2 \\
x + 3 \overline{\smash{)}x^2 + 5x + 6} \\
\underline{x^2 + 3x} \\
2x + 6 \\
\underline{2x + 6} \\
0
\end{array}
$$

⟵ *Divide first term by first term:* $\dfrac{2x}{x} = 2$

⟵ *Multiply 2 by divisor*

⟵ *Subtract*

Answer: Quotient $x + 2$, remainder 0.

To check, we multiply quotient by divisor and add the remainder, if any, to see if we get the dividend.

$(x + 3)(x + 2) = x^2 + 5x + 6$. This answer checks.

TRY THIS ➡

> Divide and check. $x + 5$
>
> 4. $x - 2 \overline{\smash{)}x^2 + 3x - 10}$

Example 4. Divide: $(125y^3 - 8) \div (5y - 2)$.

$$
\begin{array}{r}
25y^2 + 10y + 4 \\
5y - 2 \overline{\smash{)}125y^3 \qquad\quad - 8} \\
\underline{125y^3 - 50y^2} \\
50y^2 \\
\underline{50y^2 - 20y} \\
20y - 8 \\
\underline{20y - 8} \\
0
\end{array}
$$

 ⟵ *Leave space for missing terms*

TRY THIS ➡

> Divide and check.
>
> 5. $(y^4 + y^2 - 20) \div (y + 2)$
> $y^3 - 2y^2 + 5y - 10$

Example 5. Divide: $(x^4 - 9x^2 - 5) \div (x - 2)$.

$$
\begin{array}{r}
x^3 + 2x^2 - 5x - 10 \\
x - 2 \overline{) x^4 \qquad - 9x^2 \qquad\quad - 5} \\
\underline{x^4 - 2x^3} \\
2x^3 - 9x^2 \\
\underline{2x^3 - 4x^2} \\
-5x^2 \\
\underline{-5x^2 + 10x} \\
-10x - 5 \\
\underline{-10x + 20} \\
-25
\end{array}
$$

The answer is $x^3 + 2x^2 - 5x - 10$, R -25, or

$$x^3 + 2x^2 - 5x - 10 + \frac{-25}{x - 2}.$$

TRY THIS

Answers.   6. $y^2 - 8y - 24$, R -66 7. $x + 9$, R $x + 4$

> Divide and check.
>
> 6. $(y^3 - 11y^2 + 6) \div (y - 3)$
> 7. $(x^3 + 9x^2 - 5) \div (x^2 - 1)$

Exercise Set 9-5

▌ Divide. (*See Examples 1 and 2.*)

1. $\dfrac{30x^8 - 15x^6 + 40x^4}{5x^4}$ $6x^4 - 3x^2 + 8$

2. $\dfrac{24y^6 + 18y^5 - 36y^2}{6y^2}$ $4y^4 + 3y^3 - 6$

3. $\dfrac{-14a^3 + 28a^2 - 21a}{7a}$ $-2a^2 + 4a - 3$

4. $\dfrac{-32x^4 - 24x^3 - 12x^2}{4x}$ $-8x^3 - 6x^2 - 3x$

5. $(9y^4 - 18y^3 + 27y^2) \div 9y$ $y^3 - 2y^2 + 3y$

6. $(24a^3 + 28a^2 - 20a) \div 2a$ $12a^2 + 14a - 10$

7. $(36x^6 - 18x^4 - 12x^2) \div -6x$ $-6x^5 + 3x^3 + 2x$

8. $(18y^7 - 27y^4 - 3y^2) \div -3y^2$ $-6y^5 + 9y^2 + 1$

9. $(a^2b - a^3b^3 - a^5b^2) \div a^2b$ $1 - ab^2 - a^3b$

10. $(x^3y^2 - x^3y^3 - x^4y^2) \div x^2y^2$ $x - xy - x^2$

11. $(6p^2q^2 - 9p^2q + 12pq^2) \div -3pq$ $-2pq + 3p - 4q$

12. $(16y^4z^2 - 8y^6z^4 + 12y^8z^3) \div 4y^4z$
     $4z - 2y^2z^3 + 3y^4z^2$

▌▌ Divide and, if directed, check. (*See Examples 3–5.*)

13. $(x^2 + 10x + 21) \div (x + 3)$ $x + 7$

14. $(y^2 - 8y + 16) \div (y - 4)$ $y - 4$

15. $(a^2 - 8a - 16) \div (a + 4)$ $a - 12$, R 32

16. $(y^2 - 10y - 25) \div (y - 5)$ $y - 5$, R -50

17. $(x^2 + 7x + 14) \div (x + 5)$ $x + 2$, R 4

18. $(t^2 - 7t - 9) \div (t - 3)$ $t - 4$, R -21

19. $(y^2 - 25) \div (y + 5)$ $y - 5$

20. $(a^2 - 81) \div (a - 9)$ $a + 9$

21. $(y^3 - 4y^2 + 3y - 6) \div (y - 2)$ $y^2 - 2y - 1$, R -8

22. $(x^3 - 5x^2 + 4x - 7) \div (x - 3)$ $x^2 - 2x - 2$, R -13

23. $(a^3 - a + 12) \div (a - 4)$ $a^2 + 4a + 15$, R 72

24. $(x^3 - x + 6) \div (x + 2)$ $x^2 - 2x + 3$

25. $(8x^3 + 27) \div (2x + 3)$ $4x^2 - 6x + 9$

26. $(64y^3 - 8) \div (4y - 2)$ $16y^2 + 8y + 4$

27. $(x^4 - x^2 - 42) \div (x^2 - 7)$ $x^2 + 6$

28. $(y^4 - y^2 - 54) \div (y^2 - 3)$ $y^2 + 2$, R -48

29. $(x^4 - x^2 - x + 2) \div (x - 1)$ $x^3 + x^2 - 1$, R 1

30. $(y^4 - y^2 - y + 3) \div (y + 1)$ $y^3 - y^2 - 1$, R 4

Use Quiz 16 after lesson 9–5.

9-6 Solving Fractional Equations

After finishing Lesson 9-6, you should be able to
▌ solve fractional equations.

▌ A fractional equation is an equation which contains one or more fractional expressions. These are fractional equations.

$$\frac{2}{3} + \frac{5}{6} = \frac{1}{x}, \qquad \frac{x-1}{x-5} = \frac{4}{x-5}$$

To solve a fractional equation we multiply on both sides by the LCM of all the denominators. This is called *clearing of fractions*.

Example 1. Solve: $\dfrac{2}{3} - \dfrac{5}{6} = \dfrac{1}{x}$.

The LCM of all denominators is $6x$, or $2 \cdot 3 \cdot x$. We multiply on both sides by this.

$$(2 \cdot 3 \cdot x) \cdot \left(\frac{2}{3} - \frac{5}{6}\right) = (2 \cdot 3 \cdot x) \cdot \frac{1}{x} \qquad \textit{Multiplying by LCM}$$

$$2 \cdot 3 \cdot x \cdot \frac{2}{3} - 2 \cdot 3 \cdot x \cdot \frac{5}{6} = 2 \cdot 3 \cdot x \cdot \frac{1}{x} \qquad \begin{array}{l}\textit{Multiplying to remove}\\ \textit{parentheses}\end{array}$$

$$\frac{2 \cdot 3 \cdot x \cdot 2}{3} - \frac{2 \cdot 3 \cdot x \cdot 5}{6} = \frac{2 \cdot 3 \cdot x}{x}$$

$$4x - 5x = 6 \qquad \textit{Simplifying}$$

$$-x = 6$$

$$-1 \cdot x = 6$$

$$x = -6$$

Check: $\dfrac{2}{3} - \dfrac{5}{6} = \dfrac{1}{x}$

$$\begin{array}{c|c} \dfrac{2}{3} - \dfrac{5}{6} & \dfrac{1}{-6} \\[2mm] \dfrac{4}{6} - \dfrac{5}{6} & -\dfrac{1}{6} \\[2mm] -\dfrac{1}{6} & \end{array}$$

Note that when we *clear of fractions* all the denominators disappear. Thus we have an equation without fractional expressions, which we know how to solve.

TRY THIS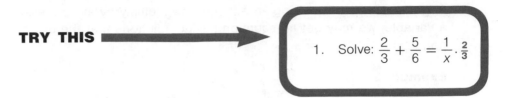

1. Solve: $\dfrac{2}{3} + \dfrac{5}{6} = \dfrac{1}{x} \cdot \dfrac{2}{3}$

When clearing of fractions, always be sure to multiply *all* terms in the equation by the LCM.

When we multiply by an expression with a variable, we may not get equivalent equations. Thus we must *always* check possible solutions in the original equation.

Example 2. Solve: $\dfrac{x-1}{x-5} = \dfrac{4}{x-5}$.

The LCM of the denominators is $x - 5$. We multiply by $x - 5$.

$$(x-5) \cdot \frac{x-1}{x-5} = (x-5) \cdot \frac{4}{x-5}$$
$$x - 1 = 4$$
$$x = 5$$

Check:
$$\frac{x-1}{x-5} = \frac{4}{x-5}$$

$$
\begin{array}{c|c}
\dfrac{5-1}{5-5} & \dfrac{4}{5-5} \\[2ex]
\dfrac{4}{0} & \dfrac{4}{0}
\end{array}
$$

5 is not a solution of the original equation because it results in division by 0. In fact, the equation has no solution.

2. Solve: $\dfrac{x-7}{x-9} = \dfrac{2}{x-9}$.

No solution

TRY THIS

Remark. Example 2 above again illustrates the fact that when we prove a theorem we cannot make any statements about the converse of the theorem. In Example 2 we proved "If $\dfrac{x-1}{x-5} = \dfrac{4}{x-5}$, then $x = 5$." The converse of this theorem is "If $x = 5$, then $\dfrac{x-1}{x-5} = \dfrac{4}{x-5}$."

The converse is not true. The check shows this.

In general, when in solving an equation we multiply by an expression containing a variable, we may get an equation having solutions that the original one does not.

Example 3. Solve: $\dfrac{x^2}{x-2} = \dfrac{4}{x-2}$.

The LCM of all the denominators is $x - 2$. We multiply by $x - 2$ to clear of fractions.

$$(x - 2) \cdot \frac{x^2}{x - 2} = (x - 2) \cdot \frac{4}{x - 2}$$
$$x^2 = 4$$
$$x^2 - 4 = 0$$
$$(x + 2)(x - 2) = 0$$

$x = -2$ or $x = 2$ *Using the principle of zero products*

The number -2 checks, but 2 does not (it results in division by 0). The solution is -2.

TRY THIS

3.   Solve: $\dfrac{x^2}{x+3} = \dfrac{9}{x+3}$.   **3**

Exercise Set 9-6

▌Solve. (*See Examples 1–3.*)

1. $\dfrac{2}{5} + \dfrac{7}{8} = \dfrac{y}{20}$ $\dfrac{51}{2}$

2. $\dfrac{4}{5} + \dfrac{1}{3} = \dfrac{t}{9}$ $\dfrac{51}{5}$

3. $\dfrac{1}{3} - \dfrac{5}{6} = \dfrac{1}{x}$ -2

4. $\dfrac{5}{8} - \dfrac{2}{5} = \dfrac{1}{y}$ $\dfrac{40}{9}$

5. $\dfrac{x}{3} - \dfrac{x}{4} = 12$ **144**

6. $\dfrac{y}{5} - \dfrac{y}{3} = 15$ $\dfrac{225}{-2}$

7. $y + \dfrac{5}{y} = -6$ **−5, −1**

8. $x + \dfrac{4}{x} = -5$ **−4, −1**

9. $\dfrac{4}{z} + \dfrac{2}{z} = 3$ **2**

10. $\dfrac{4}{3y} - \dfrac{3}{y} = \dfrac{10}{3}$ $-\dfrac{1}{2}$

11. $\dfrac{x-3}{x+2} = \dfrac{1}{5}$ $\dfrac{17}{4}$

12. $\dfrac{y-5}{y+1} = \dfrac{3}{5}$ **14**

13. $\dfrac{3}{y+1} = \dfrac{2}{y-3}$ **11**

14. $\dfrac{4}{x-1} = \dfrac{3}{x+2}$ **−11**

15. $\dfrac{y-1}{y-3} = \dfrac{2}{y-3}$ **No solution**

16. $\dfrac{x-2}{x-4} = \dfrac{2}{x-4}$ **No solution**

17. $\dfrac{x+1}{x} = \dfrac{3}{2}$ 2

18. $\dfrac{y+2}{y} = \dfrac{5}{3}$ 3

19. $\dfrac{2}{x} - \dfrac{3}{x} + \dfrac{4}{x} = 5$ $\frac{3}{5}$

20. $\dfrac{4}{y} - \dfrac{6}{y} + \dfrac{8}{y} = 8$ $\frac{3}{4}$

21. $\dfrac{1}{2} - \dfrac{4}{9x} = \dfrac{4}{9} - \dfrac{1}{6x}$ 5

22. $-\dfrac{1}{3} - \dfrac{5}{4y} = \dfrac{3}{4} - \dfrac{1}{6y}$ −1

23. $\dfrac{60}{x} - \dfrac{60}{x-5} = \dfrac{2}{x}$ −145

24. $\dfrac{50}{y} - \dfrac{50}{y-2} = \dfrac{4}{y}$ −23

25. $\dfrac{7}{5x-2} = \dfrac{5}{4x}$ $-\frac{10}{3}$

26. $\dfrac{5}{y+4} = \dfrac{3}{y-2}$ 11

27. $\dfrac{x}{x-2} + \dfrac{x}{x^2-4} = \dfrac{x+3}{x+2}$ −3

28. $\dfrac{3}{y-2} + \dfrac{2y}{4-y^2} = \dfrac{5}{y+2}$ 4

29. $\dfrac{a}{2a-6} - \dfrac{3}{a^2-6a+9} = \dfrac{a-2}{3a-9}$ −6, 5

30. $\dfrac{2}{x+4} + \dfrac{2x-1}{x^2+2x-8} = \dfrac{1}{x-2}$ 3

BIOGRAPHICAL NOTE: Diophantus

The early Greek mathematicians focused their studies on geometry. Diophantus, a Greek who lived hundreds of years after Euclid and Archimedes, focused on algebra. He introduced new symbols into mathematical writing. He also studied equations in several variables that have only positive integers as solutions. Today, these are called Diophantine equations.

Little is known about the life of Diophantus. However, one famous problem about him may give some accurate information: His boyhood lasted $\frac{1}{6}$ of his life. His beard grew after $\frac{1}{12}$ more. After $\frac{1}{7}$ more of his life he married. His son was born 5 years later. The son lived to $\frac{1}{2}$ Diophantus's age. Diophantus died 4 years after his son died. What was his age at his death? In modern terms,

$x = \frac{1}{6}x + \frac{1}{12}x + \frac{1}{7}x + 5 + \frac{1}{2}x + 4$. So $x = 84$.

Diophantus is known to have lived and worked in Alexandria, Egypt. The date of his death is about A.D. 320.

9-7 Formulas

After finishing Lesson 9-7, you should be able to
∎ solve a formula for a given letter.

∎ As mentioned earlier the skill of solving formulas for a letter is important in applications of mathematics to many fields, such as science, engineering, and technology.

Example 1. Solve $\dfrac{PV}{T} = k$ for T.

We multiply by the LCM, which is T:

$$T \cdot \frac{PV}{T} = T \cdot k$$

$$\frac{T}{T} \cdot PV = Tk$$

$$PV = Tk$$

$$\frac{PV}{k} = T$$

TRY THIS ➡️

1. Solve $\dfrac{E}{R} = I$, for R.

$$R = \frac{E}{I}$$

Example 2. Solve $\dfrac{1}{R} = \dfrac{1}{r_1} + \dfrac{1}{r_2}$, for r_1.

We multiply by the LCM, which is Rr_1r_2.

$$Rr_1r_2 \cdot \frac{1}{R} = Rr_1r_2 \cdot \left(\frac{1}{r_1} + \frac{1}{r_2}\right)$$

$$Rr_1r_2 \cdot \frac{1}{R} = Rr_1r_2 \cdot \frac{1}{r_1} + Rr_1r_2 \cdot \frac{1}{r_2} \qquad \textit{Using a distributive law}$$

$$\frac{R}{R} \cdot r_1r_2 = \frac{r_1}{r_1} \cdot Rr_2 + \frac{r_2}{r_2} \cdot Rr_1$$

$$r_1r_2 = Rr_2 + Rr_1 \qquad \textit{Simplifying}$$

We might be tempted at this point to multiply by $\dfrac{1}{r_2}$ to get r_1 alone on the left, BUT note that there is an r_1 on the right. We must get all the terms involving r_1 on the *same side* of the equation.

$$r_1r_2 - Rr_1 = Rr_2 \qquad \textit{Adding } -Rr_1$$
$$r_1(r_2 - R) = Rr_2$$
$$r_1 = \frac{Rr_2}{r_2 - R}$$

TRY THIS ➡️

2. Solve $\dfrac{1}{R} = \dfrac{1}{r_1} + \dfrac{1}{r_2}$, for R. $\quad R = \frac{r_1 r_2}{r_1 + r_2}$

Exercise Set 9-7

▌Solve each formula for the given letter. (*See Examples 1 and 2.*)

1. $\dfrac{W_1}{W_2} = \dfrac{d_1}{d_2}$; d_1 $\qquad d_1 = \frac{d_2 W_1}{W_2}$

2. $\dfrac{W_1}{W_2} = \dfrac{d_1}{d_2}$; W_2 $\qquad W_2 = \frac{d_2 W_1}{d_1}$

3. $S = \dfrac{(v_1 + v_2)t}{2}$; t $\qquad t = \frac{2S}{v_1 + v_2}$

4. $S = \dfrac{(v_1 + v_2)t}{2}$; v_1 $\qquad v_1 = \frac{2S - v_2 t}{t}$

5. $\dfrac{1}{R} = \dfrac{1}{R_1} + \dfrac{1}{R_2}$; R_1 $\qquad R_1 = \frac{RR_2}{R_2 - R}$

6. $\dfrac{1}{R} = \dfrac{1}{R_1} + \dfrac{1}{R_2}$; R $\qquad R = \frac{R_1 R_2}{R_2 + R_1}$

7. $R = \dfrac{gs}{g + s}$; s $\qquad s = \frac{Rg}{g - R}$

8. $R = \dfrac{gs}{g + s}$; g $\qquad g = \frac{Rs}{s - R}$

9. $I = \dfrac{2V}{R + 2r}$; r $\qquad r = \frac{2V - IR}{2I}$

10. $I = \dfrac{2V}{R + 2r}$; R $\qquad R = \frac{2V - 2Ir}{I}$

11. $\dfrac{1}{p} + \dfrac{1}{q} = \dfrac{1}{f}$; f $\qquad f = \frac{pq}{q + p}$

12. $\dfrac{1}{p} + \dfrac{1}{q} = \dfrac{1}{f}$; p $\qquad p = \frac{fq}{q - f}$

13. $I = \dfrac{nE}{R + nr}$; r $\qquad r = \frac{nE - IR}{In}$

14. $I = \dfrac{nE}{R + nr}$; n $\qquad n = \frac{Ir}{E - Ir}$

15. $S = \dfrac{H}{m(t_1 - t_2)}$; H $\qquad H = m(t_1 - t_2)S$

16. $\dfrac{H}{m(t_1 - t_2)}$; t_1 $\qquad t_1 = \frac{H + Smt_2}{Sm}$

17. $\dfrac{E}{e} = \dfrac{R + r}{r}$; e $\qquad e = \frac{Er}{R + r}$

18. $\dfrac{E}{e} = \dfrac{R + r}{r}$; r $\qquad r = \frac{eR}{E - e}$

19. $S = \dfrac{a - ar^n}{1 - r}$; a $\qquad a = \frac{S - Sr}{1 - r^n}$

20. $S = \dfrac{a}{1 - r}$; r $\qquad r = \frac{S - a}{S}$

MATHEMATICAL NOTE: & = +

One of the first mathematical symbols a student learns is $+$.
It appears in simple addition. It appears also in polynomials.
Where did the symbol come from? It may have developed
from the ampersand, &. When an ampersand is written very
quickly, it resembles a plus sign. Writers of mathematics
may have used $+$ as a quick and easy substitute for &.

9-8 Solving Problems

After finishing Lesson 9-8, you should be able to
■ solve problems using fractional equations.

■ Sometimes fractional equations can help in solving problems.

Example 1. The reciprocal of 2 more than a number is three times the reciprocal of the number. Find the number.

Letting *x* represent the number, we translate.

Reciprocal of 2 more than a number is three times the reciprocal of the number

$$\frac{1}{x + 2} = 3 \cdot \frac{1}{x}$$

The LCM is $x(x + 2)$.

$$\frac{x(x + 2)}{x + 2} = \frac{3x(x + 2)}{x}$$
$$x = 3(x + 2)$$
$$x = 3x + 6$$
$$x = -3$$

Check: Go to the original problem. The number to be checked is −3. Two more than this is −1. The reciprocal of −1 is −1. The reciprocal of the number itself is $\frac{1}{-3}$ and three times this is −1.
So, −3 is the solution.

TRY THIS ➡

> 1. The reciprocal of 2 less than a certain number is twice the reciprocal of the number itself. What is the number?   **4**

Recall the definition of speed, $r = \frac{d}{t}$, and the other two formulas easily obtained from this one, $d = rt$ and $t = \frac{d}{r}$.

Example 2. An airplane flies 1062 km with the wind in the same time that it takes to fly 738 km against the wind. The speed of the plane in still air is 200 km/h. Find the speed of the wind.

We first make a drawing.
We let r represent the speed
of the wind and summarize the
facts in a chart.

1062 km t_1 hours

200 + r (The wind increases the speed.)

t_2 hours   738 km

200 − r (The wind decreases the speed.)

	r	d	t
With wind	200 + r	$d_1 = 1062$	t_1
Against wind	200 − r	$d_2 = 738$	t_2

The times are the same, so $t_1 = t_2$. From $t = \dfrac{d}{r}$ we have

$$t_1 = \frac{1062}{200 + r} \text{ and } t_2 = \frac{738}{200 - r}.$$

Since $t_1 = t_2$ it follows that

$$\frac{1062}{200 + r} = \frac{738}{200 - r}$$

Solving for r, we get 36. This checks. Thus the
speed of the wind is 36 km/h.

TRY THIS

2. A boat travels 246 km
    downstream in the same
    amount of time that it takes
    to travel 180 km upstream.
    The speed of the current in
    the stream is 5.5 km/h.
    Find the speed of the boat
    in still water.   **35.5 km/h**

Suppose a person can do a job in 5 hours. Then in 1 hour $\frac{1}{5}$ of
the job is done and in 3 hours $\frac{3}{5}$ of it can be done.

If a job can be done in t hours (or days), then $\dfrac{1}{t}$ of it can be

done in 1 hour (or day).

Example 3. Lon Moore can mow a lawn in 4 hours. Penny
Push can mow the same lawn in 5 hours. How long would it take
both of them, working together, to mow the lawn?

Lon can mow the lawn in 4 hours. Thus he can mow $\frac{1}{4}$ of it in 1
hour. Penny can mow the lawn in 5 hours. Thus she can mow $\frac{1}{5}$
of it in 1 hour. Thus they can mow $\frac{1}{4} + \frac{1}{5}$ of it in 1 hour. Let t
represent the amount of time it takes them to mow the lawn if

they work together. Then they mow $\dfrac{1}{t}$ of the lawn in 1 hour. Thus

$$\frac{1}{4} + \frac{1}{5} = \frac{1}{t}.$$

Solving for t, we get $t = 2\frac{2}{9}$ hours. This checks. Thus it takes Lon and Penny $2\frac{2}{9}$ hours to mow the lawn working together.

TRY THIS

3. Fred Huntinpeck does a certain typing job in 6 hours. Fran Ikfingers can do the same job in 4 hours. How long would it take both persons, working together, to do the same amount of typing? $2\frac{2}{5}$ **hours**

Example 4. At a factory, smokestack A pollutes the air twice as fast as smokestack B. When the stacks operate together they yield a certain amount of pollution in 15 hours. Find the amount of time it would take each to yield the same amount of pollution if it operated alone.

Let x represent the amount of time it takes smokestack A to yield the pollution. Then $2x$ represents the amount of time it takes smokestack B to yield the pollution. Then

$\dfrac{1}{x}$ is the amount of pollution yielded in 1 hour by A.

$\dfrac{1}{2x}$ is the amount of pollution yielded in 1 hour by B.

In 1 hour both stacks yield $\dfrac{1}{x} + \dfrac{1}{2x}$ of the pollution. They also

yield $\dfrac{1}{15}$ of it. We have the equation

$$\frac{1}{x} + \frac{1}{2x} = \frac{1}{15}.$$

Solving for x, we get $x = 22\frac{1}{2}$ hours, and $2x = 45$ hours. This checks. Thus stack B takes 45 hours to yield the pollution and stack A takes $22\frac{1}{2}$ hours.

TRY THIS

4. Two pipes carry water to the same tank. Pipe A, working alone, can fill the tank three times as fast as pipe B. Working together the pipes can fill the tank in 24 hours. Find the time each would take to fill the tank alone.
   Pipe A 32 hours, Pipe B 96 hours

Exercise Set 9-8

▎Solve. (*See Examples 1–4.*)

1. The reciprocal of 5 plus the reciprocal of 7 is the reciprocal of what number? $\frac{35}{12}$

2. The reciprocal of 3 plus the reciprocal of 6 is the reciprocal of what number? 2

3. The sum of a number and 6 times its reciprocal is −5. Find the number. −3, −2

4. The sum of a number and 21 times its reciprocal is −10. Find the number. −7, −3

5. In a fractional numeral the numerator is 3 more than the denominator. If 2 is added to both numerator and denominator, the result is $\frac{3}{2}$. Find the original fractional numeral. $\frac{7}{4}$

6. In a fractional numeral the denominator is 8 more than the numerator. If 5 is added to both numerator and denominator, the result is $\frac{1}{2}$. Find the original fractional numeral. $\frac{3}{11}$

7. The speed of a stream is 3 km/h. A boat travels 4 km upstream in the same time it takes to travel 10 km downstream. What is the speed of the boat in still water? 7 km/h

8. The speed of a stream is 4 km/h. A boat travels 6 km upstream in the same time it takes to travel 12 km downstream. What is the speed of the boat in still water? 12 km/h

9. The speed of Train A is 12 km/h slower than the speed of Train B. Train A travels 230 km in the same time it takes Train B to travel 290 km. Find the speed of each train. Train A 46 km/h, Train B 58 km/h

10. The speed of a passenger train is 14 km/h faster than the speed of a freight train. The passenger train travels 400 km in the same time it takes the freight train to travel 330 km. Find the speed of each train. Passenger 80 km/h, Freight 66 km/h

11. George Skiff has a boat that can move at a speed of 15 km/h in still water. He rides 140 km downstream in a river in the same time it takes to ride 35 km upstream. What is the speed of the river? 9 km/h

12. A paddleboat can move at a speed of 2 km/h in still water. The boat is paddled 4 km downstream in a river in the same time it takes to go 1 km upstream. What is the speed of the river? $1\frac{1}{5}$ km/h

13. Ollie Carr has just enough money to rent a canoe for $1\frac{1}{2}$ hours. How far out on a lake can he paddle and return on time if he paddles out at 2 km/h and back at 4 km/h? 2 km

14. Polly Paddle has just enough money to rent a canoe for $2\frac{1}{2}$ hours. How far out on the lake can she paddle and return on time if she paddles out at 3 km/h and back at 2 km/h? 3 km

15. Sam Strong, an experienced shipping clerk, can fill a certain order in 5 hours. Willy Weak, a new clerk, needs 9 hours to do the same job. Working together, how long would it take them to fill the order? $3\frac{3}{14}$ hours

16. Paul Putty can paint a room in 4 hours. Sally Spackle can paint the same room in 3 hours. Working together, how long would it take them to paint the room? $1\frac{5}{7}$ hours

17. Harry Hammer can frame in a room in 5 hours. Sue Saul can do the same job in 4 hours. Working together, how long will it take them to frame in a room? $2\frac{2}{9}$ hours

18. Sally Stilson can complete a plumbing job in 6 hours. Wally Wrench can do the same job in 4 hours. Working together, how long will it take them to complete the job? $2\frac{2}{5}$ hours

19. A swimming pool can be filled in 12 hours if water enters through a pipe alone, or in 30 hours if water enters through a hose alone. If water is entering through the pipe and the hose, how long will it take to fill the pool? $8\frac{4}{7}$ hours

20. A tank can be filled in 18 hours by pipe A alone and in 22 hours by pipe B alone. How long would it take to fill the tank if both pipes were working? $9\frac{9}{10}$ hours

21. One car goes 25 km/h faster than another. While one goes 300 km the other goes 450 km. Find their speeds.

22. One car goes 30 km/h faster than another. While one goes 450 km the other goes 600 km. Find their speeds. 90 km/h and 120 km/h

23. Bull Dozer can clear a lot in 5.5 hours. His partner can do the same job in 7.5 hours. How long would it take them to clear the lot working together? $3\frac{3}{14}$ hours   50 km/h and 75 km/h

24. One of Ty Psetter's printing presses can print an order of booklets in 4.5 hours. Another press can do the same job in 5.5 hours. How long would it take if both presses are used? 2.475 hours

SCIENCE NOTE: Weight and Mass

Weight is a measure of the pull of gravity on an object. A golf ball, for example, has a certain weight on earth. It has a different weight on the moon. The force of gravity is less there, so the golf ball weighs less.

Mass is the amount of matter in an object. It is not changed by changes in gravity. The golf ball's mass is the same on earth as it is on the moon.

Grams and kilograms are really measures of mass. Technically, a weight should not be stated in grams. The correct unit for stating weight is the newton. It is named for the great English mathematician and physicist, Sir Isaac Newton. It is a unit of force. On the surface of the earth, the force of gravity is roughly the same in all places. Differences in weight on earth are equivalent to differences in mass. So weights are commonly stated in terms of grams and kilograms.

9-9 *Variation*

After finishing Lesson 9-9, you should be able to
- **I** find an equation of variation given a description of direct variation.
- **II** solve problems involving direct variation.
- **III** find an equation of variation given a description of inverse variation.
- **IIII** solve problems involving inverse variation.

I Direct Variation

A plumber earns $9 per hour. In 1 hour, $9 is earned. In 2 hours, $18 is earned. In 3 hours, $27 is earned, and so on. This gives rise to a set of ordered pairs of numbers, all having the same ratio:

(1, 9), (2, 18), (3, 27), (4, 36), and so on.

The ratio of earnings to time is always $\frac{9}{1}$, or 9.

Whenever a situation gives rise to pairs of numbers in which the ratio is constant, we say that there is *direct variation*. Here the earnings vary directly as the time.

$$\frac{e}{t} = 9 \text{ (a constant), or } e = 9t$$

DEFINITION
Whenever a situation gives rise to a relation among variables $y = kx$, where k is a constant, we say that there is *direct* variation, or that y *varies directly as* x. The number k is called the *variation constant*.

Example 1. Find an equation of variation where y varies directly as x, and $y = 32$ when $x = 2$.

First substitute to find k.

$$y = kx$$
$$32 = k \cdot 2$$
$$\frac{32}{2} = k, \text{ or } k = 16$$

Then the equation of variation is $y = 16x$.

Answers. 1. $y = \frac{2}{5}x$ 2. $y = 0.7x$

Find an equation of variation where y varies directly as x, and

1. $y = 8$ when $x = 20$
2. $y = 5.6$ when $x = 8$

TRY THIS ➡

ıı Direct Variation Problems

Example 2. The number of centimeters W of water which is produced from melting snow varies directly as the number of centimeters S of snow. Meteorologists have found that 150 cm of snow will melt to 16.8 cm of water. 200 cm of snow will melt to how many centimeters of water?

a) First find an equation of variation.

$$W = kS$$
$$16.8 = k \cdot 150$$
$$\frac{16.8}{150} = k$$
$$0.112 = k$$

The equation of variation is $W = 0.112S$.

b) Use the equation to find how many centimeters of water will result from 200 cm of snow.

$$W = 0.112S$$
$$W = 0.112(200)$$
$$W = 22.4$$

200 cm of snow will melt to 22.4 cm of water.

TRY THIS

3. *Ecology Problem.* The amount of garbage G produced in the United States varies directly as the number of people N who produce the garbage. It is known that 50 tons of garbage is produced by 200 people in 1 year. The population of San Francisco is about 700,000. About how much garbage is produced by people in San Francisco in 1 year? **175,000 tons**

ııı Inverse Variation

A bus is traveling a distance of 20 km. At a speed of 20 km/h, it will take 1 hour. At 40 km/h, it will take $\frac{1}{2}$ hour. At 60 km/h it will take $\frac{1}{3}$ hour, and so on. This gives rise to a set of pairs of numbers, all having the same product:

$(20, 1)$, $(40, \frac{1}{2})$, $(60, \frac{1}{3})$, $(80, \frac{1}{4})$, and so on.

Note that as the first number gets larger the second number gets smaller. Whenever a situation gives rise to pairs of numbers whose product is constant, we say that there is *inverse variation*. Here the *time varies inversely as the speed*.

$$rt = 20 \text{ (a constant) or } t = \frac{20}{r}$$

DEFINITION

Whenever a situation gives rise to a relation among variables $y = \dfrac{k}{x}$, where k is a constant, we say that there is *inverse variation,* or that y *varies inversely as* x. The number k is called the *variation constant.*

Example 3. Find an equation of variation where y varies inversely as x, and $y = 32$ when $x = 0.2$.

First substitute to find k.

$$y = \frac{k}{x}$$

$$32 = \frac{k}{0.2}$$

$$(0.2)32 = k$$

$$6.4 = k$$

The equation of variation is $y = \dfrac{6.4}{x}$.

TRY THIS

4. Find an equation of variation where y varies inversely as x, and $y = 0.012$ when $x = 50$.    $y = \frac{0.6}{x}$

⁍⁍⁍⁍ Inverse Variation Problems

Example 4. The time t required to do a certain job varies inversely as the number P of people who work on the job (assuming each does the same amount of work). It takes 4 hours for 12 people to erect some football bleachers. How long would it take 3 people to do the same job?

a) First, find an equation of variation.

$$t = \frac{k}{P}$$

$$4 = \frac{k}{12} \qquad \textit{Substituting}$$

$$12 \cdot 4 = k$$

$$48 = k$$

The equation of variation is $t = \dfrac{48}{P}$.

b) Use the equation to find the time it would take 3 people to do the same job.

$$t = \frac{48}{P}$$

$$t = \frac{48}{3} \qquad \textit{Substituting 3 for P}$$

$$= 16$$

It would take 16 hours.

TRY THIS

5. The time t required to drive a fixed distance varies inversely as the speed r. It takes 5 hours at 60 km/h to drive a fixed distance. How long would it take to drive the fixed distance at 40 km/h? $7\frac{1}{2}$ **hours**

Exercise Set 9-9

▌ Find an equation of variation where y varies directly as x and the following are true. (*See Example 1.*)

1. $y = 24$ when $x = 3$ y = 8x
2. $y = 5$ when $x = 12$ $y = \frac{5}{12}x$
3. $y = -6$ when $x = 1$ y = −6x
4. $y = 2$ when $x = 5$ $y = \frac{2}{5}x$
5. $y = 15$ when $x = 3$ y = 5x
6. $y = 1$ when $x = -2$ $y = -\frac{1}{2}x$
7. $y = 30$ when $x = 8$ $y = \frac{15}{4}x$
8. $y = -1$ when $x = 1$ y = −x
9. $y = 0.8$ when $x = 0.5$ $y = \frac{8}{5}x$
10. $y = 0.6$ when $x = 0.4$ $y = \frac{3}{2}x$

▌▌ Solve. (*See Example 2.*)

11. The electric current I, in amperes, in a circuit varies directly as the voltage V. When 12 volts are applied, the current is 4 amperes. What is the current when 18 volts are applied?   6 amperes

12. Hooke's law states that the distance d a spring is stretched by a hanging object varies directly as the weight w of the object. If the distance is 40 cm when the weight is 3 kg, what is the distance when the weight is 5 kg? $66\frac{2}{3}$ kg

13. The number N of plastic straws produced by a machine varies directly as the amount of time t the machine is operating. If the machine produces 20,000 straws in 8 hours, how many straws can it produce in 50 hours?   125,000

14. The number N of aluminum cans used each year varies directly as the number of people using the cans. If 250 people use 60,000 cans in one year, how many cans are used each year in Dallas, population 850,000?   204,000,000

15. The amount of pollution A entering the atmosphere varies directly as the number of people N living in an area. If 60,000 people result in 42,600 tons of pollutants entering the atmosphere, how many tons enter the atmosphere in a city with a population of 750,000?   532,500 tons

16. The weight M of an object on the moon varies directly as its weight E on earth. A person who weighs 95 kg on earth weighs 15.2 kg on the moon. How much would a 105 kg person weigh on the moon?   16.8 kg

Use Quiz 17 after lesson 9—9.

17. The weight M of an object on Mars varies directly as its weight E on earth. A person who weighs 95 kilograms on earth weighs 38 kg on Mars. How much would a 100 kg person weigh on Mars?   **40 kg**

18. The number of kilograms of water W in a human body varies directly as the total weight. A person weighing 96 kg contains 64 kg of water. How many kilograms of water are in a person weighing 75 kg?   **50 kg**

■■■ Find an equation of variation where y varies inversely as x, and the following are true. (*See Example 3.*)

19. $y = 6$ when $x = 10$ $y = \frac{60}{x}$
20. $y = 16$ when $x = 4$ $y = \frac{64}{x}$
21. $y = 4$ when $x = 3$ $y = \frac{12}{x}$
22. $y = 4$ when $x = 9$ $y = \frac{36}{x}$
23. $y = 12$ when $x = 3$ $y = \frac{36}{x}$
24. $y = 9$ when $x = 5$ $y = \frac{45}{x}$
25. $y = 27$ when $x = \frac{1}{3}$ $y = \frac{9}{x}$
26. $y = 81$ when $x = \frac{1}{9}$ $y = \frac{9}{x}$
27. $y = 0.4$ when $x = 0.8$ $y = \frac{0.32}{x}$
28. $y = 1.5$ when $x = 0.3$ $y = \frac{0.45}{x}$

■■■■ Solve. (*See Example 4.*)

29. The current I in an electrical conductor varies inversely as the resistance R of the conductor. If the current is $\frac{1}{2}$ ampere when the resistance is 240 ohms, what is the current when the resistance is 540 ohms? $\frac{2}{9}$ ampere

30. The time t required to empty a tank varies inversely as the rate r of pumping. If a pump can empty a tank in 45 minutes at the rate of 600 kl per minute, how long will it take the pump to empty the same tank at the rate of 1000 kl per minute?   **27 minutes**

31. The volume V of a gas varies inversely as the pressure P upon it. The volume of a gas is 200 cm³ under a pressure of 32 kg/cm². What will be its volume under a pressure of 40 kg/cm²?   **160 cm³**

32. The time T required to do a job varies inversely as the number of people P working. It takes 5 hours for 7 bricklayers to complete a certain job. How long would it take 10 bricklayers to complete the job?   **3.5 hours**

33. The time t required to drive a fixed distance varies inversely as the speed r. It takes 5 hours at 80 km/h to drive a fixed distance; how long would it take to drive the fixed distance at 60 km/h? $6\frac{2}{3}$ hours

34. The wavelength W of a radio wave varies inversely as its frequency F. A wave with a frequency of 1200 kilocycles per second has a length of 300 meters. What is the length of a wave with a frequency of 800 kilocycles per second?   **450 m**

35. The weight W that a horizontal beam can support varies inversely as the length L of the beam? Suppose an 8-meter beam can support 1200 kilograms. How many kilograms can a 14-meter beam support? $685\frac{5}{7}$ kg

36. The length L of rectangles of fixed area varies inversely as the width W. Suppose the length is 64 m when the width is 3 m. Find the length when the width is 12 m. What is the fixed area?   **16 m, 192 m²**

CHAPTER 9 REVIEW

Review the material in the chapter. Then see how you have done by trying these review exercises. If you miss an exercise, restudy the indicated lesson.

9-1   1.   Simplify: $\dfrac{3x^2 - 4x - 4}{4x^2 - 3x - 10}$. $\frac{3x + 2}{4x + 5}$

9-1   2.   Multiply and simplify: $\dfrac{x^2 - 64}{8x} \cdot \dfrac{4x}{x + 8} \cdot \dfrac{x - 8}{2}$

9-1   3.   Divide and simplify: $\dfrac{6y^4}{y^2 - 9} \div \dfrac{3y^2}{2y^2 + 7y + 3}$ $\frac{2y^2 (2y + 1)}{y - 3}$

9-3   Add.

     4. $\dfrac{a + 9}{a + 3} + \dfrac{12 - 5a}{a + 3}$ $\frac{21 - 4a}{a + 3}$

     5. $\dfrac{y + 2}{y - 3} + \dfrac{y}{3 - y}$ $\frac{2}{y - 3}$

     6. $\dfrac{5}{4x - 2} + \dfrac{x + 3}{4x^2 - 4x + 1}$ $\frac{12x + 1}{2(2x - 1)^2}$

9-3   Subtract.

     7. $\dfrac{8y}{y - 4} - \dfrac{12y}{y - 4}$ $\frac{-4y}{y - 4}$

     8. $\dfrac{a + 5}{a - 7} - \dfrac{a}{7 - a}$ $\frac{2a + 5}{a - 7}$

     9. $\dfrac{7}{x^2 - 81} - \dfrac{x - 4}{3x^2 - 25x - 18}$ $\frac{-x^2 + 16x + 50}{(x + 9)(x - 9)(3x + 2)}$

9-4   10.   Simplify: $\dfrac{\dfrac{1}{2x} - 3}{\dfrac{1}{x} - 4}$. $\frac{1 - 6x}{2(1 - 4x)}$

9-5   11.   Divide: $2x - 3 \overline{) 4x^4 - 5x^2 + 2x - 10}$. $2x^3 + 3x^2 + 2x + 4$, R 2

9-6   12.   Solve: $\dfrac{15}{y} - \dfrac{15}{y - 2} = -2$.   5, −3

9-7   13.   Solve for P: $T = Rn + \dfrac{mn}{P}$. $P = \frac{mn}{T - Rn}$

9-8   14.   In a fractional numeral, the numerator is 16 more than the denominator. If the numerator is decreased by 3, the result is equal to $\frac{4}{3}$. Find the original fractional numeral. $\frac{55}{39}$

9-9   15.   The number N of parts a punch press can produce varies directly as the time it operates. It can produce 1200 parts in 2 hours. How many can it produce in 5 hours?   3000

9-9   16.   The time T required to do a certain job varies inversely as the number of people P working. It takes 16 hours for 2 people to repaint a gymnasium. How long would it take 6 people to do the job? $5\frac{1}{3}$ hours

Use Midterm Test after Chapter 9.

CHAPTER 9 TEST

1. Simplify: $\dfrac{5x^2 + 38x + 21}{3x^2 + 22x + 7}$. $\frac{5x+3}{3x+1}$

2. Multiply and simplify: $\dfrac{y^2 - 100}{9y} \cdot \dfrac{3y}{y + 10}$. $\frac{y-10}{3}$

3. Divide and simplify: $\dfrac{8t^5}{t^2 - 25} \div \dfrac{4t^2}{7t^2 - 34t - 5}$. $\frac{2t^3(7t+1)}{t+5}$

Add.

4. $\dfrac{x + 3}{x + 8} + \dfrac{14 - 5x}{x + 8}$ $\frac{17-4x}{x+8}$

5. $\dfrac{t + 9}{t - 5} + \dfrac{2t}{5 - t}$ $\frac{9-t}{t-5}$

6. $\dfrac{4}{5x - 15} + \dfrac{x + 8}{4x^2 - 11x - 3}$ $\frac{21x+44}{5(x-3)(4x+1)}$

Subtract.

7. $\dfrac{9x}{x - 5} - \dfrac{15x}{x - 5}$ $\frac{-6x}{x-5}$

8. $\dfrac{p + 7}{3 - p} - \dfrac{p}{p - 3}$ $\frac{2p+7}{3-p}$

9. $\dfrac{8}{y^2 - 64} - \dfrac{y - 5}{2y^2 - 15y - 8}$ $\frac{-y^2+13y+48}{(x+8)(x-8)(2y+1)}$

10. Simplify: $\dfrac{\dfrac{1}{3a} - 4}{\dfrac{1}{2a} - 1}$. $\frac{2(1-12a)}{3(1-2a)}$

11. Divide: $a + 3\overline{)2a^3 - 13a + 15}$. $2a^2 - 6a + 5$

12. Solve: $\dfrac{15}{x} - \dfrac{15}{x + 2} = 2$. $-5, 3$

13. Solve for T: $\dfrac{E}{e} = \dfrac{T + r}{r}$. $T = \frac{Er}{e} - r$

14. One car travels 90 km in the same time a car going 10 km/h slower travels 60 km. Find the speed of each. 30 km/h and 20 km/h

15. The amount of garbage G produced in the United States varies directly as the number of people N who produce the garbage. It is known that 50 tons of garbage is produced by 200 people in 1 year. The population of Minneapolis is 434,400. How much garbage is produced by Minneapolis in 1 year? 108,600 tons

16. The cost C, per person, of renting a beach cottage varies inversely as the number of people N who rent the cottage. It costs $12 per person for 4 people to rent the cottage for a day. How much does it cost per person for 6 people to rent the cottage? $8

Ready for Exponents, Powers, and Roots?

1-2 Simplify.
  1. $|-8|$
  2. $|0|$
  3. $|\sqrt{3}|$ 1. 8   2. 0   3. $\sqrt{3}$

2-2 Solve.
  4. $(x + 5)(x - 7) = 0$ −5, 7
  5. $3x(3x + 5) = 0$ $0, -\frac{5}{3}$

1-8 Multiply and simplify.
  6. $y^7 \cdot y^3$ y^{10}
  7. $8^3 \cdot 8^{-2}$ 8
  8. $(3x^2y^{-4})(4x^3y^2)$ $12x^5y^{-2}$

1-8 Divide.
  9. $\dfrac{4^8}{4^2}$
  10. $\dfrac{7^8}{7^{-2}}$
  11. $\dfrac{5^{-3}}{5^3}$
  12. $\dfrac{3^{-4}}{3^{-6}}$
  13. $\dfrac{y^4}{y^6}$
  14. $\dfrac{32x^3y^{10}}{4x^4y^4}$

9. 4^6 10. 7^{10} 11. 5^{-6} 12. 3^2 13. y^{-2} 14. $8x^{-1}y^6$

1-8 Simplify.
  15. $(4^2)^4$ 4^8
  16. $(a^{-3})^{-4}$ a^{12}
  17. $(4xy^{-3})^3$ $64x^3y^{-9}$
  18. $(10x^3y^{-2}z^{-4})^2$ $100x^6y^{-4}z^{-8}$

2-2 Solve.
  19. $4x - 1 = 15$ 4
  20. $2(8 - 3x) = 3 - 5(x - 1)$ 8

7-2 Factor.
  21. $x^2 - 12x + 36$ $(x - 6)^2$
  22. $9y^2 - 12y + 4$ $(3y - 2)^2$
  23. $4y^2 + 28xy + 49x^2$ $(2y + 7x)^2$
  24. $16x^4 - 40x^2y^4 + 25y^8$ $(4x^2 - 5y^4)^2$
  25. $-27x^2 + 36x - 12$ $-3(3x - 2)^2$
  26. $x^2 - 6x - 16$ $(x - 8)(x + 2)$
  27. $x^2 - 13x + 36$ $(x - 4)(x - 9)$

Chapter 10
Exponents, Powers, and Roots

How long should the letters of a road message be to be the most recognizable?

10-1 Scientific Notation

After finishing Lesson 10-1, you should be able to
- **I** simplify expressions involving integer exponents.
- **II** convert from decimal notation to scientific notation and from scientific notation to decimal notation.
- **III** multiply and divide using scientific notation.

I Integer Exponents

Recall some of the definitions and properties of integer exponents.

$$a^1 = a$$

$$a^0 = 1, a \neq 0$$

$$a^{-n} = \frac{1}{a^n}, a \neq 0$$

$$a^m a^n = a^{m+n} \quad \textit{(Theorem 1-4)}$$

$$\frac{a^m}{a^n} = a^{m-n} \quad \textit{(Theorem 1-5)}$$

$$(a^m)^n = a^{mn} \quad \textit{(Theorem 1-6)}$$

Examples. Simplify.

1. $(4xy)^1 = 4xy$

2. $(-8x^3y^7)^0 = 1$ assuming neither x nor y is 0

3. $5x^{-3}y^{-4} = 5 \cdot \frac{1}{x^3} \cdot \frac{1}{y^4} = \frac{5}{x^3y^4}$

4. $(-8x^5y^7)(4x^3y^{-2}) = -32x^8y^5$ *Using Theorem 1-4*

5. $\frac{42x^8y^3}{21x^4y^8} = 2x^4y^{-5}$ *Using Theorem 1-5*

6. $(5x^{-2}y^4)^3 = 5^3x^{-6}y^{12} = 125x^{-6}y^{12}$ *Using Theorem 1-6*

TRY THIS ➡

Simplify.

1. $(-9ab^2)^1$
2. $(-9x^2y)^0$
3. $-2a^{-5}b^{-6}$
4. $(x^2 + y^2)^{-3}$
5. $30a^4 \cdot 6a^{-9}$
6. $(-5a^2b^{-3})(4a^{-3}b^6)$
7. $\frac{-24x^{-3}y^5}{6x^5y^7}$
8. $\frac{10a^3b^2c^5}{15a^5b^7c^2}$
9. $(y^{-4})^6$
10. $(8a^2b^{-4})^3$

Answers. 1. $-9ab^2$ 2. 1   3. $-\frac{2}{a^5b^6}$ 4. $\frac{1}{(x^2 + y^2)^3}$ 5. $180a^{-5}$ 6. $-20a^{-1}b^3$
7. $-4x^{-8}y^{-2}$ 8. $\frac{2}{3}a^{-2}b^{-5}c^3$ 9. y^{-24} 10. $512a^6b^{-12}$

Note the following.

$$\left(\frac{x}{y}\right)^3 = \frac{x}{y} \cdot \frac{x}{y} \cdot \frac{x}{y} = \frac{x \cdot x \cdot x}{y \cdot y \cdot y} = \frac{x^3}{y^3}$$

This illustrates the following new theorem.

THEOREM 10-1

For any real numbers a and b, $b \neq 0$, and any integer n,

$$\left(\frac{a}{b}\right)^n = \frac{a^n}{b^n}$$

Example 7. Simplify.

$$\left(\frac{4x^2}{y}\right)^3 = \frac{(4x^2)^3}{y^3} = \frac{4^3 x^6}{y^3} = \frac{64x^6}{y^3}$$

TRY THIS

Answers. 11. $\frac{a^4}{b^4}$ 12. $\frac{x^8 y^{-12}}{81a^4}$

Simplify.

11. $\left(\dfrac{a}{b}\right)^4$

12. $\left(\dfrac{x^2 y^{-3}}{3a}\right)^4$

▪ Scientific Notation

Scientific notation is useful when calculations involve large or small numbers.

DEFINITION

Scientific notation for a number consists of exponential notation for a power of 10 and, if needed, a decimal numeral for a number between 1 and 10, and a multiplication sign.

We can convert to scientific notation by multiplying by 1, choosing an appropriate symbol $\dfrac{10^k}{10^k}$ for 1.

Example 8. Light travels about 9,460,000,000,000 kilometers in one year. Write scientific notation for the number.

We want to move the decimal point 12 places, between the 9 and the 4, so we multiply by $\dfrac{10^{12}}{10^{12}}$.

$$9{,}460{,}000{,}000{,}000 = 9{,}460{,}000{,}000{,}000 \times \frac{10^{12}}{10^{12}}$$

Using 10^{12} to "move the decimal point" between 9 and 4

$$= \frac{9{,}460{,}000{,}000{,}000}{10^{12}} \times 10^{12}$$

$$= 9.46 \times 10^{12}$$

With practice such conversions can be performed mentally and you should try to do this as much as possible.

TRY THIS

Answers. 13. 4.6×10^{11} 14. 1.5×10^8

13. Convert 460,000,000,000 to scientific notation.

14. The distance from the earth to the sun is about 150,000,000 km. Write scientific notation for this number.

Example 9. Write scientific notation for 0.0000000000156.

We want to move the decimal point 11 places, between the 1 and the 5, so we multiply by $\frac{10^{11}}{10^{11}}$.

$$0.0000000000156 = 0.0000000000156 \times \frac{10^{11}}{10^{11}} \qquad \text{Multiplying by 1}$$
$$= (0.0000000000156 \times 10^{11}) \times 10^{-11}$$
$$= 1.56 \times 10^{-11}$$

You should try to make such conversions mentally as much as possible.

TRY THIS

> 15. Convert 0.00000001235 to scientific notation. **1.235 × 10⁻⁸**
> 16. The mass of a hydrogen atom is 0.00000000000000000000000017 grams. Write scientific notation for this number. **1.7 × 10⁻²⁴**

Examples. Convert to decimal notation.

10. $7.893 \times 10^5 = 789{,}300$ *Moving the decimal point 5 places to the right*

11. $4.7 \times 10^{-8} = 0.000000047$ *Moving the decimal point 8 places to the left*

TRY THIS

> Convert to decimal notation.
> 17. 7.893×10^{11} **789,300,000,000**
> 18. 5.67×10^{-5} **0.0000567**

Ⅲ Multiplying and Dividing

Multiplying and dividing in scientific notation is easy because we can use the properties of exponents.

Example 12. Multiply: $(3.1 \times 10^5)(4.5 \times 10^{-3})$.

We apply the commutative and associative laws to get

$$(3.1 \times 4.5)(10^5 \times 10^{-3}) = 13.95 \times 10^2.$$

To find scientific notation for the result, we convert 13.95 to scientific notation and then simplify.

$$13.95 \times 10^2 = (1.395 \times 10^1) \times 10^2$$
$$= 1.395 \times 10^3$$

TRY THIS ━━━▶

> Multiply and write scientific notation for the answer.
>
> 19. $(9.1 \times 10^{-17})(8.2 \times 10^3)$
> 20. $(1.12 \times 10^{-8})(5 \times 10^{-7})$

Example 13. Divide: $\dfrac{6.4 \times 10^{-7}}{8.0 \times 10^6}$.

$$\frac{6.4 \times 10^{-7}}{8.0 \times 10^6} = \frac{6.4}{8.0} \times \frac{10^{-7}}{10^6} \qquad \textit{Factoring}$$

$$= 0.8 \times 10^{-13} \qquad \textit{Doing the divisions separately}$$

$$= (8.0 \times 10^{-1}) \times 10^{-13} \qquad \textit{Converting answer to scientific notation}$$

$$= 8.0 \times 10^{-14}$$

TRY THIS ━━━▶

> Divide and write scientific notation for the answer.
>
> 21. $\dfrac{4.2 \times 10^5}{2.1 \times 10^2}$ 2×10^3
>
> 22. $\dfrac{1.1 \times 10^{-4}}{2.0 \times 10^{-7}}$ 5.5×10^2

Exercise Set 10-1

Simplify. (*See Examples 1–7.*)

1. $(-4m^2n^3)^0$ 1
2. $(-9x^3y^5)^0$ 1
3. $(x^2 + y)^1$ $x^2 + y$
4. $(y^3 + z)^1$ $y^3 + z$
5. $3a^{-1}b^{-2}$ $\dfrac{3}{ab^2}$
6. $6x^{-2}y^{-3}$ $\dfrac{6}{x^2y^3}$
7. $\dfrac{r^{-1}s^{-2}}{t^{-3}}$ $\dfrac{t^3}{rs^2}$
8. $\dfrac{x^{-4}y^{-3}}{z^{-2}}$ $\dfrac{z^2}{x^4y^3}$
9. $(x^3 + y^3)^{-2}$ $\dfrac{1}{(x^3 + y^3)^2}$
10. $(a^5 - b^4)^{-3}$ $\dfrac{1}{(a^5 - b^4)^3}$
11. $(-2a^2b^3)(6a^{-4}b^{-1})$ $-12a^{-2}b^2$
12. $(-5c^3d^{-5})(7d^4c^{-1})$ $-35c^2d^{-1}$
13. $\dfrac{a^2b^{-3}}{a^4b^{-2}}$ $a^{-2}b^{-1}$
14. $\dfrac{x^3y^{-5}}{x^5y^{-7}}$ $x^{-2}y^2$
15. $\dfrac{-6^5y^4z^{-5}}{2^{-2}y^{-2}z^3}$ $-31{,}104y^6z^{-8}$
16. $\dfrac{9^{-2}x^{-4}y}{3^{-3}x^{-3}y^2}$ $\dfrac{x^{-1}y^{-1}}{3}$
17. $(-2m^{-2}n^3)^3$ $-8m^{-6}n^9$
18. $(-3x^{-3}y^5)^2$ $9x^{-6}y^{10}$
19. $(2x^{-4}y^{-2})^{-3}$ $\dfrac{x^{12}y^6}{8}$
20. $(4a^{-4}b^{-5})^{-3}$ $\dfrac{a^{12}b^{15}}{64}$
21. $\left(\dfrac{3a^{-2}b}{c^2}\right)^3$ $\dfrac{27a^{-6}b^3}{c^6}$
22. $\left(\dfrac{2x^2y^{-2}}{3a^2}\right)^3$ $\dfrac{8x^6y^{-6}}{27a^6}$

∎∎ Convert to scientific notation. (*See Examples 8 and 9.*)

23. 47,000,000,000 4.7×10^{10}
24. 2,600,000,000,000 2.6×10^{12}
25. 863,000,000,000,000,000 8.63×10^{17}
26. 957,000,000,000,000,000 9.57×10^{17}
27. 0.000000016 1.6×10^{-8}
28. 0.000000263 2.63×10^{-7}
29. 0.00000000007 7×10^{-11}
30. 0.00000000009 9×10^{-11}

Convert to decimal notation. (*See Examples 10 and 11.*)

31. 4×10^{-4} 0.0004
32. 5×10^{-5} 0.00005
33. 6.73×10^{8} 673,000,000
34. 9.24×10^{7} 92,400,000
35. 8.923×10^{-10} 0.0000000008923
36. 7.034×10^{-2} 0.07034

Write scientific notation for the number in each of the following. (*See Examples 8 and 9.*)

37. The mass of an electron is 0.00000000000000000000000000911 g. 9.11×10^{-28}
38. The population of the United States is about 215,000,000. 2.15×10^{8}
39. An electron carries a charge of 0.00000000048 electrostatic units. 4.8×10^{-10}
40. A helium atom has a diameter of 0.000000022 cm. 2.2×10^{-8}

∎∎∎ Multiply and write scientific notation for the answer. (*See Example 12.*)

41. $(2.3 \times 10^{6})(4.2 \times 10^{-11})$ 9.66×10^{-5}
42. $(6.5 \times 10^{3})(5.2 \times 10^{-8})$ 3.38×10^{-4}
43. $(2.34 \times 10^{-8})(5.7 \times 10^{-4})$ 1.3338×10^{-11}
44. $(3.26 \times 10^{-6})(8.2 \times 10^{-6})$ 2.6732×10^{-11}

Divide and write scientific notation for the answer. (*See Example 13.*)

45. $\dfrac{8.5 \times 10^{8}}{3.4 \times 10^{5}}$ 2.5×10^{3}
46. $\dfrac{5.1 \times 10^{6}}{3.4 \times 10^{3}}$ 1.5×10^{3}
47. $\dfrac{4.0 \times 10^{-6}}{8.0 \times 10^{-3}}$ 5×10^{-4}
48. $\dfrac{7.5 \times 10^{-9}}{2.5 \times 10^{-4}}$ 3×10^{-5}

COMPUTER NOTE: Monitoring

After heavy rains, people monitor the level of water in a river. Graphs can be drawn and analyzed. By keeping track of the level, people can tell whether flooding is likely.

Computers aid in such monitoring. They help monitor air pollution in some places by keeping track of the many different pollutants. If the pollutant level becomes too high, they give warning.

Computers also monitor the conditions of some hospital patients. These computers keep track of heart beat, respiration rate, and other life processes. They sound an alarm if any condition becomes critical.

10-2 *Radical Expressions*

After finishing Lesson 10-2, you should be able to
I find principal square roots and their additive inverses.
II simplify radical expressions with perfect square radicands.
III find principal *k*th roots of expressions.
IIII simplify expressions of the form $\sqrt[k]{a^k}$.

I Square Roots

DEFINITION
The number c is a square root of a if $c^2 = a$.

For example,

> 5 is a square root of 25 because $(5)^2 = 5 \cdot 5 = 25$.
> -5 is a square root of 25 because $(-5)^2 = (-5)(-5) = 25$.

This illustrates the following theorem.

THEOREM 10-2
Every positive real number has two real number square roots.
The number 0 has just one square root, 0 itself.

Negative real numbers do not have real number square roots.
For example, -4 does not have a real number square root because there is no real number b such that $b^2 = -4$.

Example 1. Find the two square roots of 64.

The square roots are 8 and -8, because $8^2 = 64$ and $(-8)^2 = 64$.

TRY THIS ▬▬▬▶

Find the
square roots
of each
number.

1. 9 **3, −3**
2. 36 **6, −6**
3. 121 **11, −11**

DEFINITION
The *principal square root* of a nonnegative number is its nonnegative
square root. The symbol $\sqrt{a}$ represents the principal square root of a.

Examples. Simplify.

2. $\sqrt{25} = 5$ *Remember, $\sqrt{}$ means to take the principal
(nonnegative) square root*

3. $\sqrt{\dfrac{25}{64}} = \dfrac{5}{8}$

4. $\sqrt{0.0049} = 0.07$

TRY THIS ▬▬▬▶

Simplify.

4. $\sqrt{1}$ **1**
5. $\sqrt{36}$ **6**
6. $\sqrt{\dfrac{81}{100}}$ **$\dfrac{9}{10}$**
7. $\sqrt{0.0064}$
              0.08

To name the negative square root of a we write $-\sqrt{a}$.

Example 5. Find $-\sqrt{64}$.

$$-\sqrt{64} = -8 \qquad \sqrt{64} = 8, \text{ so } -\sqrt{64} = -8$$

TRY THIS ▬▬▬▬▶

Find the following.

8. $-\sqrt{16}$ −4
9. $-\sqrt{49}$ −7
10. $-\sqrt{196}$ −14

DEFINITION

The symbol $\sqrt{}$ is called a *radical*. An expression written with a radical is called a *radical expression*. The expression written under the radical is called the *radicand*.

These are radical expressions.

$$\sqrt{5}, \qquad \sqrt{a}, \qquad -\sqrt{5x}, \qquad \frac{\sqrt{y^2 + 7}}{\sqrt{x}}$$

Example 6. Identify the radicand in $\sqrt{x^2 - 9}$.

The radicand is $x^2 - 9$.

TRY THIS ▬▬▬▬▶

Identify the radicand in each expression.

11. $\sqrt{28 + x}$ 28 + x
12. $\sqrt{\dfrac{y}{y + 3}}$ $\frac{y}{y+3}$

⊪ Simplifying $\sqrt{a^2}$.

In the expression $\sqrt{a^2}$, the radicand is a perfect square.

Suppose $a = 5$. Then we have $\sqrt{5^2}$, which is $\sqrt{25}$, or 5.
Suppose $a = -5$. Then we have $\sqrt{(-5)^2}$, which is $\sqrt{25}$, or 5.
Suppose $a = 0$. Then we have $\sqrt{0^2}$, which is $\sqrt{0}$, or 0.

The symbol $\sqrt{a^2}$ does not represent a negative number. It represents the principal square root of a^2. Note that if a represents a positive number or 0, then $\sqrt{a^2}$ represents a. If a is negative, then $\sqrt{a^2}$ represents the additive inverse of a. In all cases the radical expression represents the absolute value of a.

THEOREM 10-3

For any real number a, $\sqrt{a^2} = |a|$. The principal (nonnegative) square root of a^2 is the absolute value of a.

Examples. Simplify.

7. $\sqrt{(-16)^2} = |-16|$, or 16
8. $\sqrt{(3b)^2} = |3b|$, or $3|b|$
9. $\sqrt{(x - 1)^2} = |x - 1|$

10. $\sqrt{x^2 + 8x + 16} = \sqrt{(x + 4)^2}$
$= |x + 4|$

TRY THIS ➡

Answers. **13.** |y| **14. 24** **15.** 5|y| **16.** |x + 7| **17.** |x − 3|

Simplify.

13. $\sqrt{y^2}$
14. $\sqrt{(-24)^2}$
15. $\sqrt{25y^2}$
16. $\sqrt{(x + 7)^2}$
17. $\sqrt{x^2 - 6x + 9}$

ⅢPrincipal *k*th Roots

DEFINITION
The number c is the cube root of a if $c^3 = a$.

For example,

2 is the cube root of 8 because $2^3 = 2 \cdot 2 \cdot 2 = 8$.
-4 is the cube root of -64 because $(-4)^3 = (-4)(-4)(-4) = -64$.

We used the word "the" with cube roots because of the following theorem.

THEOREM 10-4
Every real number has exactly one cube root in the system of real numbers.

The symbol $\sqrt[3]{a}$ represents the cube root of a.

Examples. Simplify.

11. $\sqrt[3]{8} = 2$

12. $\sqrt[3]{-27} = -3$

13. $\sqrt[3]{-\dfrac{216}{125}} = -\dfrac{6}{5}$

TRY THIS ➡

Simplify.

18. $\sqrt[3]{0}$ ₀
19. $\sqrt[3]{-8}$ −2
20. $\sqrt[3]{216}$ 6
21. $\sqrt[3]{-\dfrac{343}{64}}$ −$\frac{7}{4}$

A fourth root of a number a is a number whose fourth power is a. Numbers can also have fifth roots, sixth roots, and so on.

DEFINITION
A number c is a kth root of a if $c^k = a$. The symbol $\sqrt[k]{a}$ represents the principal (nonnegative) kth root if one exists. If no such root exists, but there is a negative kth root, then $\sqrt[k]{a}$ represents that number. The number k is called the *index* and must be a natural number greater than 1. If k is 2, it is usually not written.

Examples. Simplify.

14. $\sqrt[5]{32} = 2$

15. $\sqrt[4]{81} = 3$

16. $\sqrt[5]{-243} = -3$

17. $\sqrt[4]{-26}$ does not represent a real number.

Note that $\sqrt[4]{81}$ is 3 although -3 is also a fourth root of 81. To represent the negative root we use $-\sqrt[4]{81}$, or -3.

TRY THIS

Simplify.

22. $\sqrt[4]{16}$ **2**
23. $\sqrt[5]{-32}$ **-2**
24. $\sqrt[3]{-125}$ **-5**
25. $\sqrt[3]{-1}$ **-1**

▥ Simplifying $\sqrt[k]{a^k}$

Recall that $\sqrt{a^2} = |a|$. Consider the problem of simplifying $\sqrt[3]{a^3}$.

$$\sqrt[3]{2^3} = \sqrt[3]{8} = 2, \qquad \sqrt[3]{(-4)^3} = \sqrt[3]{-64} = -4$$

Since any real number has only one real number cube root, for any real number a, $\sqrt[3]{a^3} = a$. We do not use absolute value when simplifying cube roots. In general,

THEOREM 10-5

For any real number a,

a) $\sqrt[k]{a^k} = |a|$, (*k* even) We must use absolute value when *k* is even unless *a* is nonnegative.

b) $\sqrt[k]{a^k} = a$, (*k* odd) We do not use absolute value when *k* is odd.

Examples. Simplify.

18. $\sqrt[5]{x^5} = x$

19. $\sqrt[8]{(-9)^8} = |-9|$, or 9

20. $\sqrt[4]{(y + 7)^4} = |y + 7|$

21. $\sqrt[3]{(4xy)^3} = 4xy$

TRY THIS

Simplify.

26. $\sqrt[6]{a^6}$
27. $\sqrt[5]{(y + 7)^5}$
28. $\sqrt[4]{(-5)^4}$
29. $\sqrt[244]{(5xy)^{244}}$

Answers. 26. |a| 27. y + 7 28. 5 29. 5|xy|

Exercise Set 10-2

▌Find the square roots of each number. (*See Example 1.*)

1. 16   4, −4
2. 225   15, −15
3. 144   12, −12
4. 9   3, −3
5. 400   20, −20
6. 81   9, −9

Find the following. (*See Examples 2–5.*)

7. $-\sqrt{\dfrac{49}{36}}$ $-\dfrac{7}{6}$

8. $-\sqrt{\dfrac{361}{9}}$ $-\dfrac{19}{3}$

9. $\sqrt{289}$ 17

10. $\sqrt{441}$ 21

11. $-\sqrt{\dfrac{16}{81}}$ $-\dfrac{4}{9}$

12. $-\sqrt{\dfrac{81}{144}}$ $-\dfrac{9}{12}$

13. $\sqrt{0.09}$ 0.3

14. $\sqrt{0.36}$ 0.6

15. $-\sqrt{0.0049}$ −0.07

16. $\sqrt{0.0144}$ 0.12

Identify the radicand in each expression. (*See Example 6.*)

17. $5\sqrt{p^2 + 4}$ $p^2 + 4$

18. $-7\sqrt{y^2 - 8}$ $y^2 - 8$

19. $x^2 y^2 \sqrt{\dfrac{x}{y + 4}}$ $\dfrac{x}{y + 4}$

20. $a^2 b^3 \sqrt{\dfrac{a}{a^2 - b}}$ $\dfrac{a}{a^2 - b}$

▌▌Simplify. (*See Examples 7–10.*)

21. $\sqrt{16x^2}$ 4|x|
22. $\sqrt{25t^2}$ 5|t|
23. $\sqrt{(-7c)^2}$ 7|c|
24. $\sqrt{(-6b)^2}$ 6|b|
25. $\sqrt{(a + 1)^2}$ |a + 1|
26. $\sqrt{(5 - b)^2}$ |5 − b|
27. $\sqrt{x^2 - 4x + 4}$ |x − 2|
28. $\sqrt{y^2 + 16y + 64}$ |y + 8|
29. $\sqrt{4x^2 + 28x + 49}$ |2x + 7|
30. $\sqrt{9x^2 - 30x + 25}$ |3x − 5|

▌▌▌Simplify. (*See Examples 11–17.*)

31. $\sqrt[3]{8}$ 2
32. $\sqrt[3]{64}$ 4
33. $\sqrt[3]{-27}$ −3
34. $\sqrt[3]{-125}$ −5
35. $\sqrt[3]{-216}$ −6
36. $\sqrt[3]{-1000}$ −10
37. $\sqrt[3]{0.343}$ 0.7
38. $\sqrt[3]{0.000008}$ 0.02
39. $\sqrt[4]{625}$ 5
40. $\sqrt[4]{256}$ 4
41. $\sqrt[5]{-1}$ −1
42. $\sqrt[5]{-32}$ −2
43. $\sqrt[5]{-\dfrac{32}{243}}$ $-\dfrac{2}{3}$
44. $\sqrt[5]{-\dfrac{1}{32}}$ $-\dfrac{1}{2}$

▌▌▌▌Simplify. (*See Examples 18–21.*)

45. $\sqrt[6]{x^6}$ |x|
46. $\sqrt[8]{y^8}$ |y|
47. $\sqrt[4]{(5a)^4}$ 5|a|
48. $\sqrt[4]{(7b)^4}$ 7|b|
49. $\sqrt[10]{(-6)^{10}}$ 6
50. $\sqrt[12]{(-10)^{12}}$ 10
51. $\sqrt[414]{(a + b)^{414}}$ |a + b|
52. $\sqrt[1976]{(2a + b)^{1976}}$ |2a + b|

10-3 Multiplying and Simplifying

After finishing Lesson 10-3, you should be able to
  I multiply with radical notation.
  II simplify radical expressions.
  III multiply and simplify radical expressions.
  IIII simplify and approximate expressions using a square root table.

I Multiplying

Notice that $\sqrt{4}\,\sqrt{25} = 2 \cdot 5 = 10$.
Also $\sqrt{4 \cdot 25} = \sqrt{100} = 10$.
Likewise, $\sqrt[3]{27}\,\sqrt[3]{8} = 3 \cdot 2 = 6$ and $\sqrt[3]{27 \cdot 8} = \sqrt[3]{216} = 6$.

These examples suggest the following theorem.

THEOREM 10-6
For any nonnegative real numbers a and b, and any index n,
$\sqrt[n]{a} \cdot \sqrt[n]{b} = \sqrt[n]{ab}$.

Examples.   Multiply.

1. $\sqrt{x+2}\,\sqrt{x-2} = \sqrt{(x+2)(x-2)} = \sqrt{x^2 - 4}$

2. $\sqrt[3]{4}\,\sqrt[3]{5} = \sqrt[3]{4 \cdot 5} = \sqrt[3]{20}$

3. $\sqrt[4]{\dfrac{y}{5}}\,\sqrt[4]{\dfrac{7}{x}} = \sqrt[4]{\dfrac{y}{5} \cdot \dfrac{7}{x}} = \sqrt[4]{\dfrac{7y}{5x}}$

TRY THIS ➡️

Answers. 1. $\sqrt{133}$ 2. $\sqrt{x^2 - 4y^2}$ 3. $\sqrt[4]{2821}$ 4. $\sqrt[3]{8x^5 + 40x}$

Multiply.

1. $\sqrt{19}\,\sqrt{7}$
2. $\sqrt{x+2y}\,\sqrt{x-2y}$
3. $\sqrt[4]{403}\,\sqrt[4]{7}$
4. $\sqrt[3]{8x}\,\sqrt[3]{x^4 + 5}$

II Simplifying

From Theorem 10-6 we have $\sqrt[n]{ab} = \sqrt[n]{a} \cdot \sqrt[n]{b}$. This shows a way to simplify radical expressions. Consider $\sqrt{20}$. The number 20 has the factor 4, which is a perfect square. Therefore

$$\begin{aligned}
\sqrt{20} &= \sqrt{4 \cdot 5} \\
&= \sqrt{4} \cdot \sqrt{5} \\
&= 2\sqrt{5}
\end{aligned}$$

To simplify radical expressions containing just one radical sign, we usually look for factors of the radicand which are perfect powers. so that we can simplify by "removing" them.

In many situations, expressions never represent negative numbers. In such situations, absolute value notation is not necessary.

Examples. Simplify.

4. $\sqrt{5x^2} = \sqrt{x^2 \cdot 5}$
$= \sqrt{x^2} \cdot \sqrt{5}$
$= |x| \cdot \sqrt{5}$
$= x\sqrt{5}$ if we know that $x \geq 0$

5. $\sqrt{2x^2 - 4x + 2} = \sqrt{2(x-1)^2}$
$= \sqrt{(x-1)^2} \cdot \sqrt{2}$
$= |x-1| \cdot \sqrt{2}$
$= (x-1)\sqrt{2}$ if we know that $(x-1) \geq 0$

6. $\sqrt{216x^5y^3} = \sqrt{36 \cdot 6 \cdot x^4 \cdot x \cdot y^2 \cdot y}$
$= \sqrt{36 \cdot x^4 \cdot y^2 \cdot 6 \cdot x \cdot y}$
$= 6 \cdot |x^2| \cdot |y| \cdot \sqrt{6xy}$
$= 6x^2 \cdot |y| \cdot \sqrt{6xy}$

Since x^2 is never negative we need not write $|x^2|$. Then if we know that $y \geq 0$, we have $6x^2y\sqrt{6xy}$.

TRY THIS

Simplify. Assume that all expressions represent nonnegative numbers. Hence, no absolute value signs will be needed.

5. $\sqrt{300}$ **10$\sqrt{3}$**
6. $\sqrt{36y^2}$ **6y**
7. $\sqrt{3x^2 + 12x + 12}$ **(x + 2)$\sqrt{3}$**
8. $\sqrt{12ab^3c^2}$ **2bc$\sqrt{3ab}$**

Example 7. Simplify.

$\sqrt[3]{32} = \sqrt[3]{8 \cdot 4}$
$= \sqrt[3]{8} \cdot \sqrt[3]{4}$
$= 2\sqrt[3]{4}$

Answers.   9. $2\sqrt[3]{2}$ 10. $3xy^2$ 11. $(a+b)\sqrt[3]{a+b}$

TRY THIS

Simplify.

9. $\sqrt[3]{16}$
10. $\sqrt[4]{81x^4y^8}$
11. $\sqrt[3]{(a+b)^4}$

ꞁꞁꞁ Multiplying and Simplifying

Sometimes after we multiply we can then simplify.

Examples. Multiply and simplify. Assume that all expressions represent nonnegative numbers.

8. $3\sqrt[3]{25} \cdot 2\sqrt[3]{5} = 6 \cdot \sqrt[3]{25 \cdot 5}$
$$= 6 \cdot \sqrt[3]{125}$$
$$= 6 \cdot 5, \text{ or } 30$$

9. $\sqrt[3]{18y^3}\sqrt[3]{4x^2} = \sqrt[3]{18y^3 \cdot 4x^2} = \sqrt[3]{72y^3x^2}$
$$= \sqrt[3]{8y^3 \cdot 9x^2}$$
$$= \sqrt[3]{8y^3}\sqrt[3]{9x^2}$$
$$= 2y\sqrt[3]{9x^2}$$

TRY THIS

Answers.   12. $3\sqrt{2}$ 13. $6y\sqrt{7}$ 14. $3x\sqrt[3]{4y}$ 15. $7\sqrt{3ab}$
16. $2(y+5)\sqrt[3]{(y+5)^2}$

Multiply and simplify.

12. $\sqrt{3}\sqrt{6}$
13. $\sqrt{18y}\sqrt{14y}$
14. $\sqrt[3]{3x^2y}\sqrt[3]{36x}$
15. $\sqrt{7a}\sqrt{21b}$
16. $\sqrt[3]{2(y+5)}\sqrt[3]{4(y+5)^4}$

ꞁꞁꞁꞁ Approximating Square Roots

Table 1 in the back of the book contains approximate square roots for the natural numbers 1 through 100. If a radicand is not listed in the table we can factor the radical expression, find exact or approximate square roots of the factors, and then find the product of these square roots.

Example 10. Simplify and approximate to the nearest tenth.

$$\sqrt{275} = \sqrt{25 \cdot 11}$$
$$= \sqrt{25} \cdot \sqrt{11}$$
$$\approx 5 \times 3.317$$
$$\approx 16.6 \quad \approx \text{ means approximately equal}$$

TRY THIS

Simplify and approximate to the nearest tenth.

17. $\sqrt{160}$ **12.6**
18. $\sqrt{341}$ **18.5**
(*Hint:* $341 = 11 \cdot 31$)

Example 11. Simplify and approximate to the nearest tenth.

$$\frac{20 - \sqrt{44}}{4} = \frac{20 - \sqrt{4 \cdot 11}}{4}$$

$$= \frac{20 - 2\sqrt{11}}{4}$$

$$= \frac{10 - \sqrt{11}}{2}$$

$$\approx \frac{10 - 3.317}{2} \quad \textit{Using Table 1}$$

$$\approx \frac{6.683}{2}$$

$$\approx 3.342$$

$$\approx 3.3$$

TRY THIS

Simplify and approximate to the nearest tenth.

19. $\dfrac{20 + \sqrt{44}}{4}$ 6.7

20. $\dfrac{12 - \sqrt{45}}{6}$ 0.9

Exercise Set 10-3

▌Assume that all expressions represent nonnegative numbers. Multiply. (*See Examples 1–3.*)

1. $\sqrt{3}\sqrt{2}$ $\sqrt{6}$
2. $\sqrt{5}\sqrt{7}$ $\sqrt{35}$
3. $\sqrt[3]{2}\sqrt[3]{5}$ $\sqrt[3]{10}$
4. $\sqrt[3]{7}\sqrt[3]{2}$ $\sqrt[3]{14}$
5. $\sqrt[4]{8}\sqrt[4]{9}$ $\sqrt[4]{72}$
6. $\sqrt[4]{6}\sqrt[4]{3}$ $\sqrt[4]{18}$
7. $\sqrt{3a}\sqrt{10b}$ $\sqrt{30ab}$
8. $\sqrt{2x}\sqrt{13y}$ $\sqrt{26xy}$
9. $\sqrt[5]{9t^2}\sqrt[5]{2t}$ $\sqrt[5]{18t^3}$
10. $\sqrt[5]{8y^3}\sqrt[5]{10y}$ $\sqrt[5]{80y^4}$
11. $\sqrt{x-a}\sqrt{x+a}$ $\sqrt{x^2-a^2}$
12. $\sqrt{y-b}\sqrt{y+b}$ $\sqrt{y^2-b^2}$
13. $\sqrt[3]{0.3x}\sqrt[3]{0.2x}$ $\sqrt[3]{0.06x^2}$
14. $\sqrt[3]{0.7y}\sqrt[3]{0.3y}$ $\sqrt[3]{0.21y^2}$
15. $\sqrt[4]{x-1}\sqrt[4]{x^2+x+1}$ $\sqrt[4]{x^3-1}$
16. $\sqrt[4]{y+1}\sqrt[4]{y^2-y+1}$ $\sqrt[4]{y^3+1}$
17. $\sqrt[5]{x-2}\sqrt[5]{(x-2)^2}$ $\sqrt[5]{(x-2)^3}$
18. $\sqrt[5]{y-4}\sqrt[5]{(y-4)^3}$ $\sqrt[5]{(y-4)^4}$
19. $\sqrt{\dfrac{6}{x}}\sqrt{\dfrac{y}{5}}$ $\sqrt{\dfrac{6y}{5x}}$
20. $\sqrt{\dfrac{7}{t}}\sqrt{\dfrac{s}{11}}$ $\sqrt{\dfrac{7s}{11t}}$

▌▌Simplify. (*See Examples 4–7.*)

21. $\sqrt{8}$ $2\sqrt{2}$
22. $\sqrt{18}$ $3\sqrt{2}$
23. $\sqrt{24}$ $2\sqrt{6}$
24. $\sqrt{20}$ $2\sqrt{5}$
25. $\sqrt{40}$ $2\sqrt{10}$
26. $\sqrt{90}$ $3\sqrt{10}$
27. $\sqrt{180x^4}$ $6x^2\sqrt{5}$
28. $\sqrt{175y^6}$ $25y^3\sqrt{7}$
29. $\sqrt[3]{54x^8}$ $3x^2\sqrt[3]{2x^2}$
30. $\sqrt[3]{40y^3}$ $2y\sqrt[3]{5}$
31. $\sqrt[3]{80x^8}$ $2x^2\sqrt[3]{10x^2}$
32. $\sqrt[3]{108m^5}$ $3m\sqrt[3]{4m^2}$
33. $\sqrt[4]{32}$ $2\sqrt[4]{2}$
34. $\sqrt[4]{80}$ $2\sqrt[4]{5}$

35. $\sqrt[4]{162c^4d^6}$ $3cd\sqrt[4]{2d^2}$
36. $\sqrt[4]{243x^8y^{10}}$ $3x^2y^2\sqrt[4]{3y^2}$
37. $\sqrt[3]{(x+y)^4}$ $(x+y)\sqrt[3]{x+y}$
38. $\sqrt[3]{(p-q)^5}$ $(p-q)\sqrt[3]{(p-q)^2}$
39. $\sqrt{2x^2+12x+18}$ $(x+3)\sqrt{2}$
40. $\sqrt{3x^2-24x+48}$ $(x-4)\sqrt{3}$

■■■ Multiply and simplify. (*See Examples 8 and 9.*)

41. $\sqrt{3}\,\sqrt{6}$ $3\sqrt{2}$
42. $\sqrt{5}\,\sqrt{10}$ $5\sqrt{2}$
43. $\sqrt{15}\,\sqrt{6}$ $3\sqrt{10}$
44. $\sqrt{2}\,\sqrt{32}$ 8
45. $\sqrt{6}\,\sqrt{8}$ $4\sqrt{3}$
46. $\sqrt{18}\,\sqrt{14}$ $6\sqrt{7}$
47. $\sqrt[3]{3}\,\sqrt[3]{18}$ $3\sqrt[3]{2}$
48. $\sqrt[3]{2}\,\sqrt[3]{20}$ $2\sqrt[3]{5}$
49. $\sqrt{45}\,\sqrt{60}$ $30\sqrt{3}$
50. $\sqrt{24}\,\sqrt{75}$ $30\sqrt{2}$
51. $\sqrt{5b^3}\,\sqrt{10c^4}$ $5bc^2\sqrt{2b}$
52. $\sqrt{2x^3y}\,\sqrt{12xy}$ $2x^2y\sqrt{6}$
53. $\sqrt[3]{y^4}\,\sqrt[3]{16y^5}$ $2y^3\sqrt[3]{2}$
54. $\sqrt[3]{5^2t^4}\,\sqrt[3]{5^4t^6}$ $25t^3\sqrt[3]{t}$
55. $\sqrt[3]{(b-3)^4}\,\sqrt[3]{(b+3)^2}$ $(b+3)^2$
56. $\sqrt[3]{(x+y)^3}\,\sqrt[3]{(x+y)^5}$ $(x+y)^2\sqrt[3]{(x+y)^2}$
57. $\sqrt{12a^3b}\,\sqrt{8a^4b^2}$ $4a^3b\sqrt{6ab}$
58. $\sqrt{18x^2y^3}\,\sqrt{6xy^4}$ $6xy^3\sqrt{3xy}$
59. $\sqrt[3]{3c^2d^5}\,\sqrt[3]{16c^2d^2}$ $2cd^2\sqrt[3]{6cd}$
60. $\sqrt[3]{5a^3b^7}\,\sqrt[3]{32a^2b^4}$ $2ab^3\sqrt[3]{20a^2b^2}$

■■■■ Simplify and approximate to the nearest tenth. (*See Examples 10 and 11.*)

61. $\sqrt{180}$ 13.4
62. $\sqrt{124}$ 11.1
63. $\sqrt{195}$ 14.0
64. $\sqrt{115}$ 10.7
65. $\dfrac{10+\sqrt{20}}{4}$ 3.6
66. $\dfrac{10-\sqrt{20}}{4}$ 1.4
67. $\dfrac{8-\sqrt{124}}{10}$ -0.3
68. $\dfrac{-8-\sqrt{124}}{10}$ -1.9

Calculator Exercises

Wind Chill Temperature. In cold weather we feel colder if there is wind than if there is not. *Wind chill temperature* is the temperature at which, without wind, we would feel as cold as in an actual situation with wind. Here is a formula for finding wind chill temperature.

$$T_w = 33 - \frac{(10.45 + 10\sqrt{v} - v)(33 - T)}{22}$$

where T is the actual temperature given in degrees Celsius and v is the wind speed in m/s. Find the wind chill temperature when

69. $T = 7°C$, $v = 8$ m/s $-3.3°C$
70. $T = 0°C$, $v = 12$ m/s $-16.6°C$
71. $T = -5°C$, $v = 14$ m/s $-25.5°C$
72. $T = -23°C$, $v = 15$ m/s $-54.0°C$

10-4 *Simplifying and Dividing*

After finishing Lesson 10-4, you should be able to
  I   simplify radical expressions where the radicand is a quotient.
 II   divide and simplify radical expressions.
III   find roots of powers.

I Simplifying

Notice that $\sqrt[3]{\dfrac{27}{8}} = \dfrac{3}{2}$ and $\dfrac{\sqrt[3]{27}}{\sqrt[3]{8}} = \dfrac{3}{2}$. These examples suggest the following.

THEOREM 10-7

For any nonnegative number a, any positive number b, and any index n, $\sqrt[n]{\dfrac{a}{b}} = \dfrac{\sqrt[n]{a}}{\sqrt[n]{b}}$.

Examples. Simplify.

1. $\sqrt[3]{\dfrac{27}{125}} = \dfrac{\sqrt[3]{27}}{\sqrt[3]{125}} = \dfrac{3}{5}$

2. $\sqrt{\dfrac{25}{y^2}} = \dfrac{\sqrt{25}}{\sqrt{y^2}} = \dfrac{5}{y}$

3. $\sqrt{\dfrac{16x^3}{y^4}} = \dfrac{\sqrt{16x^3}}{\sqrt{y^4}} = \dfrac{\sqrt{16x^2 \cdot x}}{\sqrt{y^4}} = \dfrac{4x\sqrt{x}}{y^2}$

4. $\sqrt[3]{\dfrac{27y^5}{343x^3}} = \dfrac{\sqrt[3]{27y^5}}{\sqrt[3]{343x^3}} = \dfrac{\sqrt[3]{27y^3 \cdot y^2}}{\sqrt[3]{343x^3}} = \dfrac{\sqrt[3]{27y^3} \cdot \sqrt[3]{y^2}}{\sqrt[3]{343x^3}} = \dfrac{3y\sqrt[3]{y^2}}{7x}$

TRY THIS ➡️

Answers. 1. $\dfrac{5}{6}$ 2. $\dfrac{10}{3}$ 3. $\dfrac{x}{10}$ 4. $\dfrac{2a\sqrt{a}}{b^2}$ 5. $\dfrac{3x\sqrt[3]{2x^2}}{5}$

> Simplify.
>
> 1. $\sqrt{\dfrac{25}{36}}$
>
> 2. $\sqrt[3]{\dfrac{1000}{27}}$
>
> 3. $\sqrt{\dfrac{x^2}{100}}$
>
> 4. $\sqrt{\dfrac{4a^3}{b^4}}$
>
> 5. $\sqrt[3]{\dfrac{54x^5}{125}}$

II Dividing

From Theorem 10-7, we have

$$\dfrac{\sqrt[n]{a}}{\sqrt[n]{b}} = \sqrt[n]{\dfrac{a}{b}}.$$

This shows a way to divide radical expressions.

Example 5. Divide and simplify.

$$\frac{\sqrt{72xy}}{2\sqrt{2}} = \frac{1}{2}\frac{\sqrt{72xy}}{\sqrt{2}} = \frac{1}{2}\sqrt{\frac{72xy}{2}} = \frac{1}{2}\sqrt{36xy} = \frac{1}{2}\sqrt{36}\sqrt{xy} = \frac{1}{2}\cdot 6\sqrt{xy} = 3\sqrt{xy}$$

TRY THIS

Answers. 6. 5   7. $56\sqrt{xy}$ 8. $5a$

Divide and simplify.

6. $\dfrac{\sqrt{75}}{\sqrt{3}}$

7. $\dfrac{14\sqrt{128xy}}{2\sqrt{2}}$

8. $\dfrac{\sqrt{50a^3}}{\sqrt{2a}}$

Examples. Divide and simplify.

6. $\dfrac{5\sqrt[3]{32}}{\sqrt[3]{2}} = 5\sqrt[3]{\dfrac{32}{2}} = 5\sqrt[3]{16} = 5\sqrt[3]{8\cdot 2} = 5\sqrt[3]{8}\sqrt[3]{2} = 5\cdot 2\sqrt[3]{2} = 10\sqrt[3]{2}$

7. $\dfrac{\sqrt[4]{32a^5b^3}}{\sqrt[4]{2b^{-1}}} = \sqrt[4]{\dfrac{32a^5b^3}{2b^{-1}}} = \sqrt[4]{16a^5b^4} = \sqrt[4]{16a^4b^4\cdot a} = \sqrt[4]{16a^4b^4}\sqrt[4]{a} = 2ab\sqrt[4]{a}$

TRY THIS

Divide and simplify.

9. $\dfrac{4\sqrt[3]{250}}{7\sqrt[3]{2}}$ $\dfrac{20}{7}$

10. $\dfrac{\sqrt[3]{8a^3b}}{\sqrt[3]{27b^{-2}}}$ $\dfrac{2ab}{3}$

ꁤ Roots of Powers

Another property of radicals is as follows.

THEOREM 10-8

For any nonnegative number a, any index n, and any natural number m, $(\sqrt[n]{a})^m = \sqrt[n]{a^m}$.

Examples. Simplify.

8. $(\sqrt{5x})^3 = \sqrt{(5x)^3} = \sqrt{(5x)^2\cdot 5x} = \sqrt{(5x)^2}\sqrt{5x} = 5x\sqrt{5x}$

9. $(\sqrt[3]{25})^2 = \sqrt[3]{(25)^2} = \sqrt[3]{(5\cdot 5\cdot 5)\cdot 5} = 5\sqrt[3]{5}$

TRY THIS

Simplify.

11. $(\sqrt[3]{9})^2$

12. $(\sqrt{6y})^3$

Answers.   11. $3\sqrt[3]{3}$ 12. $6y\sqrt{6y}$

Exercise Set 10-4

■ Simplify. (*See Examples 1–4.*)

1. $\sqrt{\dfrac{25}{36}}$ $\dfrac{5}{6}$

2. $\sqrt{\dfrac{100}{81}}$ $\dfrac{10}{9}$

3. $\sqrt[3]{\dfrac{64}{27}}$ $\dfrac{4}{3}$

4. $\sqrt[3]{\dfrac{343}{512}}$ $\dfrac{7}{8}$

5. $\sqrt{\dfrac{49}{y^2}}$ $\dfrac{7}{y}$

6. $\sqrt{\dfrac{121}{x^2}}$ $\dfrac{11}{x}$

7. $\sqrt{\dfrac{25y^3}{x^4}}$ $\dfrac{5y\sqrt{y}}{x^2}$

8. $\sqrt{\dfrac{36a^5}{b^6}}$ $\dfrac{6a^2\sqrt{a}}{b^3}$

9. $\sqrt[3]{\dfrac{8x^5}{27y^3}}$ $\dfrac{2x\sqrt[3]{x^2}}{3y}$

10. $\sqrt[3]{\dfrac{64x^7}{216y^6}}$ $\dfrac{4x^2\sqrt[3]{x}}{6y^2}$

■■ Divide and simplify. (*See Examples 5–7.*)

11. $\dfrac{\sqrt{21a}}{\sqrt{3a}}$ $\sqrt{7}$

12. $\dfrac{\sqrt{28y}}{\sqrt{4y}}$ $\sqrt{7}$

13. $\dfrac{\sqrt[3]{54}}{\sqrt[3]{2}}$ 3

14. $\dfrac{\sqrt[3]{40}}{\sqrt[3]{5}}$ 2

15. $\dfrac{\sqrt{40xy^3}}{\sqrt{8x}}$ $y\sqrt{5y}$

16. $\dfrac{\sqrt{56ab^3}}{\sqrt{7a}}$ $2b\sqrt{2b}$

17. $\dfrac{\sqrt[3]{96a^4b^2}}{\sqrt[3]{12a^2b}}$ $2\sqrt[3]{a^2b}$

18. $\dfrac{\sqrt[3]{189x^5y^7}}{\sqrt[3]{7x^2y^2}}$ $3xy\sqrt[3]{y^2}$

19. $\dfrac{\sqrt{72xy}}{2\sqrt{2}}$ $3\sqrt{xy}$

20. $\dfrac{\sqrt{75ab}}{3\sqrt{3}}$ $\dfrac{5\sqrt{ab}}{3}$

21. $\dfrac{\sqrt{x^3-y^3}}{\sqrt{x-y}}$ $\sqrt{x^2+xy+y^2}$

22. $\dfrac{\sqrt{r^3+s^3}}{\sqrt{r+s}}$ $\sqrt{r^2-rs+s^2}$

■■■ Simplify. (*See Examples 8 and 9.*)

23. $(\sqrt{6a})^3$ $6a\sqrt{6a}$

24. $(\sqrt{7y})^3$ $7y\sqrt{7y}$

25. $(\sqrt[3]{16b^2})^2$ $4b\sqrt[3]{4b}$

26. $(\sqrt[3]{25r^2})^2$ $5r\sqrt[3]{5r}$

27. $(\sqrt{18a^2b})^3$ $54a^3b\sqrt{2b}$

28. $(\sqrt{12x^2y})^3$ $24x^3y\sqrt{3y}$

29. $(\sqrt[3]{12c^2d})^2$ $2c\sqrt[3]{18cd^2}$

30. $(\sqrt[3]{9x^2y})^2$ $3x\sqrt[3]{3xy^2}$

10-5 *Addition and Subtraction*

After finishing Lesson 10-5, you should be able to
▮ add or subtract with radical notation.

▮ Any two real numbers can be added. For instance, the sum of 7 and $\sqrt{3}$ can be expressed as

$$7 + \sqrt{3}.$$

We cannot simplify this name for the sum. However, when we have *like radicals* or radicals having the same index and radicand we can use the distributive laws to simplify.

Examples. Simplify.

1. $6\sqrt{7} + 4\sqrt{7} = (6 + 4)\sqrt{7}$ *Using the distributive law (factoring out $\sqrt{7}$)*
$$= 10\sqrt{7}$$

2. $6\sqrt[5]{4x} + 4\sqrt[5]{4x} - \sqrt[3]{4x} = (6 + 4)\sqrt[5]{4x} - \sqrt[3]{4x}$
$$= 10\sqrt[5]{4x} - \sqrt[3]{4x}$$

TRY THIS ➡

Answers.   1. $13\sqrt{2}$ 2. $10\sqrt[4]{5x} - \sqrt{7}$

> Simplify.
> 1. $5\sqrt{2} + 8\sqrt{2}$
> 2. $7\sqrt[4]{5x} + 3\sqrt[4]{5x} - \sqrt{7}$

Sometimes we need to simplify in order to have like radicals.

Example 3. Simplify.

$$5\sqrt[3]{16y^4} + 7\sqrt[3]{2y} = 5\sqrt[3]{8y^3} \cdot \sqrt[3]{2y} + 7\sqrt[3]{2y} \quad \text{\textit{Using Theorem 10-6}}$$
$$= 5 \cdot 2y \cdot \sqrt[3]{2y} + 7\sqrt[3]{2y} \quad \text{\textit{Simplifying }} \sqrt[3]{8y^3}$$
$$= 10y\sqrt[3]{2y} + 7\sqrt[3]{2y}$$
$$= (10y + 7)\sqrt[3]{2y} \quad \text{\textit{Factoring out }} \sqrt[3]{2y}$$

TRY THIS ➡

Answers.   3. $19\sqrt{5}$ 4. $(3y + 4)\sqrt[3]{y^2} + 2y^2$

> Simplify.
> 3. $7\sqrt{45} - 2\sqrt{5}$
> 4. $3\sqrt[3]{y^5} + 4\sqrt[3]{y^2} + \sqrt[3]{8y^6}$

Example 4. Simplify.

$$\sqrt{9x + 9} - \sqrt{4x + 4} = \sqrt{9(x + 1)} - \sqrt{4(x + 1)} \quad \text{\textit{Factoring radicands}}$$
$$= \sqrt{9}\sqrt{x + 1} - \sqrt{4}\sqrt{x + 1}$$
$$= 3\sqrt{x + 1} - 2\sqrt{x + 1}$$
$$= \sqrt{x + 1}$$

TRY THIS ⟶

> Simplify. $\qquad 2\sqrt{x - 1}$
>
> 5. $\sqrt{25x - 25} - \sqrt{9x - 9}$

Exercise Set 10-5

▌Simplify. (*See Examples 1–4.*)

1. $6\sqrt{3} + 2\sqrt{3}$ $8\sqrt{3}$
2. $8\sqrt{5} + 9\sqrt{5}$ $17\sqrt{5}$
3. $9\sqrt[3]{5} - 6\sqrt[3]{5}$ $3\sqrt[3]{5}$
4. $14\sqrt[5]{2} - 6\sqrt[5]{2}$ $8\sqrt[5]{2}$
5. $4\sqrt[3]{y} + 9\sqrt[3]{y}$ $13\sqrt[3]{y}$
6. $6\sqrt[4]{t} - 3\sqrt[4]{t}$ $3\sqrt[4]{t}$
7. $8\sqrt{2} - 6\sqrt{2} + 5\sqrt{2}$ $7\sqrt{2}$
8. $2\sqrt{6} + 8\sqrt{6} - 3\sqrt{6}$ $7\sqrt{6}$
9. $4\sqrt[3]{5} - \sqrt{3} + 2\sqrt[3]{5} + \sqrt{3}$ $6\sqrt[3]{5}$
10. $5\sqrt{7} - 8\sqrt[4]{11} + \sqrt{7} + 9\sqrt[4]{11}$ $6\sqrt{7} + \sqrt[4]{11}$
11. $6\sqrt{8} + 11\sqrt{2}$ $23\sqrt{2}$
12. $2\sqrt{12} + 5\sqrt{3}$ $9\sqrt{3}$
13. $8\sqrt{27} - 3\sqrt{3}$ $21\sqrt{3}$
14. $9\sqrt{50} - 4\sqrt{2}$ $41\sqrt{2}$
15. $8\sqrt{45} + 7\sqrt{20}$ $38\sqrt{5}$
16. $9\sqrt{12} + 16\sqrt{27}$ $66\sqrt{3}$
17. $18\sqrt{72} + 2\sqrt{98}$ $122\sqrt{2}$
18. $12\sqrt{45} - 8\sqrt{80}$ $4\sqrt{5}$
19. $3\sqrt[3]{16} + \sqrt[3]{54}$ $9\sqrt[3]{2}$
20. $\sqrt[3]{27} - 5\sqrt[3]{8}$ -7
21. $5\sqrt[3]{32} - 2\sqrt[3]{108}$ $4\sqrt[3]{4}$
22. $9\sqrt[3]{40} - 7\sqrt[3]{135}$ $-3\sqrt[3]{5}$
23. $2\sqrt{128} - \sqrt{18} + 4\sqrt{32}$ $29\sqrt{2}$
24. $5\sqrt{50} - 2\sqrt{18} + 9\sqrt{32}$ $55\sqrt{2}$
25. $\sqrt{5a} + 2\sqrt{45a^3}$ $(1 + 6a)\sqrt{5a}$
26. $4\sqrt{3x^3} - \sqrt{12x}$ $(4x - 2)\sqrt{3x}$
27. $\sqrt[3]{24x} - \sqrt[3]{3x^4}$ $(2 - x)\sqrt[3]{3x}$
28. $\sqrt[3]{54x} - \sqrt[3]{2x^4}$ $(3 - x)\sqrt[3]{2x}$
29. $2\sqrt[3]{125a^4} - 5\sqrt[3]{8a}$ $10(a - 1)\sqrt[3]{a}$
30. $9\sqrt[3]{16x^5y} - 2\sqrt[3]{128x^2y}$ $2(9x - 4)\sqrt[3]{2x^2y}$
31. $\sqrt{8y - 8} + \sqrt{2y - 2}$ $3\sqrt{2y - 2}$
32. $\sqrt{12t + 12} + \sqrt{3t + 3}$ $3\sqrt{3t + 3}$
33. $\sqrt{x^3 - x^2} + \sqrt{9x - 9}$ $(x + 3)\sqrt{x - 1}$
34. $\sqrt{4x - 4} - \sqrt{x^3 - x^2}$ $(2 - x)\sqrt{x - 1}$

HISTORICAL NOTE: The Euclid of Algebra

Euclid is famous for his basic work in geometry. Around 300 B.C. he put geometry into a logical framework. George Peacock, a British mathematician, tried to do the same for algebra. Around 1850 he gave statements of the commutative, associative and distributive laws. These laws underlie algebraic proofs. For that reason, he is sometimes called the Euclid of algebra.

10-6 More Multiplication

After finishing Lesson 10-6, you should be able to
▮ multiply expressions involving radicals, where some of the expressions may contain more than one term.

▮ To multiply expressions involving radicals where some of the expressions contain more than one term we use many of the procedures for multiplying polynomials.

Example 1. Multiply.

$$\sqrt[3]{y}(\sqrt[3]{y^2} + \sqrt[3]{2}) = \sqrt[3]{y} \cdot \sqrt[3]{y^2} + \sqrt[3]{y} \cdot \sqrt[3]{2} \quad \text{Using the distributive law}$$
$$= \sqrt[3]{y^3} + \sqrt[3]{2y} \quad \text{Using Theorem 10-6}$$
$$= y + \sqrt[3]{2y} \quad \text{Simplifying}$$

TRY THIS ➡

Answers. 1. $5\sqrt{6} + 3\sqrt{14}$ 2. $a\sqrt[3]{3} - \sqrt[3]{2a^2}$

Multiply.

1. $\sqrt{2}(5\sqrt{3} + 3\sqrt{7})$
2. $\sqrt[3]{a^2}(\sqrt[3]{3a} - \sqrt[3]{2})$

Example 2. Multiply.

$$(4\sqrt{3} + \sqrt{2})(\sqrt{3} - 5\sqrt{2}) = \overset{F}{4(\sqrt{3})^2} - \overset{O}{20\sqrt{3} \cdot \sqrt{2}} + \overset{I}{\sqrt{2} \cdot \sqrt{3}} - \overset{L}{5(\sqrt{2})^2}$$
$$= 4 \cdot 3 - 20\sqrt{6} + \sqrt{6} - 5 \cdot 2 \quad \text{Simplifying}$$
$$= 12 - 20\sqrt{6} + \sqrt{6} - 10$$
$$= 2 - 19\sqrt{6}$$

TRY THIS ➡

Answers. 3. $-4 - 9\sqrt{6}$ 4. $-18 + 2\sqrt{6}$

Multiply.

3. $(\sqrt{3} - 5\sqrt{2})(2\sqrt{3} + \sqrt{2})$
4. $(\sqrt{2} + 2\sqrt{3})(3\sqrt{2} - 4\sqrt{3})$

Example 3. Multiply.

$$(\sqrt{5} + \sqrt{7})(\sqrt{5} - \sqrt{7}) = (\sqrt{5})^2 - (\sqrt{7})^2$$
$$= 5 - 7$$
$$= -2$$

TRY THIS ➡

Multiply.   −3

5. $(\sqrt{2} + \sqrt{5})(\sqrt{2} - \sqrt{5})$

Example 4. Multiply.

$$(\sqrt{3} + x)^2 = (\sqrt{3})^2 + 2x\sqrt{3} + x^2$$
$$= 3 + 2x\sqrt{3} + x^2$$

Answers. 6. $29 - 12\sqrt{5}$ 7. $58 + 12\sqrt{6}$

TRY THIS ➡

Multiply.

6. $(2\sqrt{5} - 3)^2$
7. $(3\sqrt{6} + 2)^2$

Exercise Set 10-6

▌Multiply. (*See Examples 1–4.*)

1. $\sqrt{6}(2 - 3\sqrt{6})$ $2\sqrt{6} - 18$
2. $\sqrt{3}(4 + \sqrt{3})$ $4\sqrt{3} + 3$
3. $\sqrt{2}(\sqrt{3} - \sqrt{5})$ $\sqrt{6} - \sqrt{10}$
4. $\sqrt{5}(\sqrt{5} - \sqrt{2})$ $5 - \sqrt{10}$
5. $\sqrt{3}(2\sqrt{5} - 3\sqrt{4})$ $2\sqrt{15} - 6\sqrt{3}$
6. $\sqrt{2}(3\sqrt{10} - 2\sqrt{2})$ $6\sqrt{5} - 4$
7. $\sqrt[3]{2}(\sqrt[3]{4} - 2\sqrt[3]{32})$ -6
8. $\sqrt[3]{3}(\sqrt[3]{9} - 4\sqrt[3]{21})$ $3 - 4\sqrt[3]{63}$
9. $\sqrt[3]{a}(\sqrt[3]{2a^2} + \sqrt[3]{16a^2})$ $3a\sqrt[3]{2}$
10. $\sqrt[3]{x}(\sqrt[3]{3x^2} - \sqrt[3]{81x^2})$ $-2x\sqrt[3]{3}$
11. $(\sqrt{3} - \sqrt{2})(\sqrt{3} + \sqrt{2})$ 1
12. $(\sqrt{5} + \sqrt{6})(\sqrt{5} - \sqrt{6})$ -1
13. $(\sqrt{8} + 2\sqrt{5})(\sqrt{8} - 2\sqrt{5})$ -12
14. $(\sqrt{18} + 3\sqrt{7})(\sqrt{18} - 3\sqrt{7})$ -45
15. $(\sqrt{a} + \sqrt{b})(\sqrt{a} - \sqrt{b})$ $a - b$
16. $(\sqrt{x} - \sqrt{y})(\sqrt{x} + \sqrt{y})$ $x - y$
17. $(3 - \sqrt{5})(2 + \sqrt{5})$ $1 + \sqrt{5}$
18. $(2 + \sqrt{6})(4 - \sqrt{6})$ $2 + 2\sqrt{6}$
19. $(\sqrt{3} + 1)(2\sqrt{3} + 1)$ $7 + 3\sqrt{3}$
20. $(4\sqrt{3} + 5)(\sqrt{3} - 2)$ $2 - 3\sqrt{3}$
21. $(2\sqrt{7} - 4\sqrt{2})(3\sqrt{7} + 6\sqrt{2})$ -6
22. $(4\sqrt{5} + 3\sqrt{3})(3\sqrt{5} - 4\sqrt{3})$ $24 - 7\sqrt{15}$
23. $(\sqrt{a} + \sqrt{2})(\sqrt{a} + \sqrt{3})$ $a + \sqrt{3a} + \sqrt{2a} + \sqrt{6}$
24. $(2 - \sqrt{x})(1 - \sqrt{x})$ $2 - 3\sqrt{x} + x$
25. $(2\sqrt[3]{3} + \sqrt[3]{2})(\sqrt[3]{3} - 2\sqrt[3]{2})$ $2\sqrt[3]{9} - 3\sqrt[3]{6} - 2\sqrt[3]{4}$
26. $(3\sqrt[4]{7} + \sqrt[4]{6})(2\sqrt[4]{9} - 3\sqrt[4]{6})$
27. $(2 + \sqrt{3})^2$ $7 + 4\sqrt{3}$
28. $(\sqrt{5} + 1)^2$ $6 + 2\sqrt{5}$ $6\sqrt[4]{63} - 9\sqrt[4]{42} + 2\sqrt[4]{54} - 3\sqrt[4]{36}$
29. $(3\sqrt{2} - \sqrt{3})^2$ $21 - 6\sqrt{6}$
30. $(5\sqrt{3} + 3\sqrt{5})^2$ $120 + 30\sqrt{15}$

Challenge Exercises

Multiply.

31. $(\sqrt{x + 3} - 3)(\sqrt{x + 3} + 3)$ $x - 6$
32. $(\sqrt{x + h} - \sqrt{x})(\sqrt{x + h} + \sqrt{x})$ h

COMPUTER NOTE: Maps by Computer

Computers can provide information in many ways. They can print lists of numbers. They can make drawings of molecules, new car designs, and other objects. Special output units can even produce maps showing rainfall, average temperature, and many other kinds of information.

10-7 Rationalizing Denominators or Numerators

After finishing Lesson 10-7, you should be able to
▮ rationalize the denominator of a radical expression.
▮▮ rationalize the numerator of a radical expression.
▮▮▮ rationalize denominators or numerators having two terms.

▮ Rationalizing Denominators

To simplify expressions like $\sqrt{\dfrac{1}{2}}$ we multiply by 1, choosing an

appropriate symbol $\dfrac{n}{n}$.

Example 1. Simplify $\sqrt{\dfrac{1}{2}}$.

We multiply by 1, choosing $\dfrac{2}{2}$ for 1. This makes the denominator
a perfect square.

$$\sqrt{\frac{1}{2}} = \sqrt{\frac{1}{2} \cdot \frac{2}{2}} \qquad \textit{Multiplying by 1}$$

$$= \sqrt{\frac{2}{2 \cdot 2}}$$

$$= \frac{\sqrt{2}}{2} \qquad \textit{Using Theorem 10-6}$$

Notice that there is no radical in the denominator. We have a rational number in the denominator. Thus we say we have *rationalized the denominator*. Radical expressions are usually considered simpler when the denominator is free of radicals.

Example 2. Rationalize the denominator.

$$\sqrt[3]{\frac{7}{9}} = \sqrt[3]{\frac{7}{3 \cdot 3} \cdot \frac{3}{3}} \qquad \textit{Multiplying by } \frac{3}{3} \textit{ to make the denominator}$$
$$\textit{a perfect cube}$$

$$= \sqrt[3]{\frac{21}{3 \cdot 3 \cdot 3}}$$

$$= \frac{\sqrt[3]{21}}{3}$$

TRY THIS ➡

> Rationalize the denominator.
>
> 1. $\sqrt{\dfrac{2}{3}}$ $\quad \dfrac{\sqrt{6}}{3}$
>
> 2. $\sqrt{\dfrac{10}{7}}$ $\quad \dfrac{\sqrt{70}}{7}$
>
> 3. $\sqrt[3]{\dfrac{3}{6}}$ $\quad \dfrac{\sqrt[3]{4}}{2}$

We can use another method for rationalizing denominators.

Example 3. Rationalize the denominator.

$$\sqrt{\frac{2a}{5b}} = \frac{\sqrt{2a}}{\sqrt{5b}}$$

$$= \frac{\sqrt{2a}}{\sqrt{5b}} \cdot \frac{\sqrt{5b}}{\sqrt{5b}} \qquad \textit{Multiplying by 1}$$

$$= \frac{\sqrt{10ab}}{\sqrt{25b^2}} \qquad \textit{The denominator is a perfect square.}$$

$$= \frac{\sqrt{10ab}}{5|b|} \qquad \textit{Simplifying}$$

TRY THIS ➡

Rationalize the denominator.

4. $\sqrt{\dfrac{4a}{3b}}$ $\dfrac{2\sqrt{3ab}}{3|b|}$

5. $\dfrac{\sqrt{4x^5}}{\sqrt{3y^3}}$ $\dfrac{2x^2\sqrt{3xy}}{3y^2}$

Example 4. Rationalize the denominator.

$$\frac{\sqrt[3]{a}}{\sqrt[3]{9x}} = \frac{\sqrt[3]{a}}{\sqrt[3]{9x}} \cdot \frac{\sqrt[3]{3x^2}}{\sqrt[3]{3x^2}} \qquad \textit{Multiplying by 1}$$

$$= \frac{\sqrt[3]{3ax^2}}{\sqrt[3]{27x^3}} \qquad \textit{The denominator is a perfect cube.}$$

$$= \frac{\sqrt[3]{3ax^2}}{3x}$$

TRY THIS ➡

Rationalize the denominator.

6. $\dfrac{\sqrt[3]{7}}{\sqrt[3]{2}}$ $\dfrac{\sqrt[3]{28}}{2}$

7. $\sqrt[3]{\dfrac{3x^5}{2y}}$ $\dfrac{x\sqrt[3]{12x^2y^2}}{2y}$

◗◗ Rationalizing Numerators

Sometimes it is necessary to rationalize the numerator. We use the same procedure.

Examples. Rationalize the numerator.

5. $\dfrac{\sqrt{7}}{\sqrt{5}} = \dfrac{\sqrt{7}}{\sqrt{5}} \cdot \dfrac{\sqrt{7}}{\sqrt{7}} \qquad \textit{Multiplying by 1}$

$$= \frac{\sqrt{49}}{\sqrt{35}} \qquad \textit{The numerator is a perfect square.}$$

$$= \frac{7}{\sqrt{35}}$$

6. $\dfrac{\sqrt[3]{5}}{\sqrt[3]{3}} = \dfrac{\sqrt[3]{5}}{\sqrt[3]{3}} \cdot \dfrac{\sqrt[3]{5^2}}{\sqrt[3]{5^2}}$ *Multiplying by 1*

$\qquad\quad = \dfrac{\sqrt[3]{5^3}}{\sqrt[3]{75}}$

$\qquad\quad = \dfrac{5}{\sqrt[3]{75}}$

Rationalize the numerator.

8. $\dfrac{\sqrt{11}}{\sqrt{6}}$ $\dfrac{11}{\sqrt{66}}$

9. $\dfrac{\sqrt[3]{7}}{\sqrt[3]{4}}$ $\dfrac{7}{\sqrt[2]{196}}$

TRY THIS ➡

Why do we consider these procedures? Suppose we wanted to approximate $\dfrac{\sqrt{3}}{\sqrt{2}}$. We could do it by looking up the approximations for $\sqrt{3}$ and $\sqrt{2}$ in Table 1 and then do the division $\dfrac{1.732}{1.414}$. But this is a rather complicated division. Having rationalized the numerator we could look up $\sqrt{6}$ in the table and do the division $\dfrac{3}{2.449}$. This is an easier computation. But, if we rationalized the denominator the division would have been $\dfrac{2.449}{2}$, which is the easiest of the three. Here is a reason for rationalizing denominators: to ease computations when approximating. In calculus courses it is important to be able to rationalize the numerator. Thus we consider both procedures here.

ⅢⅠ Rationalizing When There are Two Terms

When the denominator to be rationalized has two terms, choose a symbol for 1 as illustrated below.

Example 7. Rationalize the denominator.

$\dfrac{4 + \sqrt{2}}{\sqrt{5} - \sqrt{2}} = \dfrac{4 + \sqrt{2}}{\sqrt{5} - \sqrt{2}} \cdot \dfrac{\sqrt{5} + \sqrt{2}}{\sqrt{5} + \sqrt{2}}$ *Multiplying by 1*

$\qquad\qquad\quad = \dfrac{(4 + \sqrt{2})(\sqrt{5} + \sqrt{2})}{(\sqrt{5} - \sqrt{2})(\sqrt{5} + \sqrt{2})}$

$\qquad\qquad\quad = \dfrac{4\sqrt{5} + 4\sqrt{2} + \sqrt{2}\,\sqrt{5} + (\sqrt{2})^2}{(\sqrt{5})^2 - (\sqrt{2})^2}$

$$= \frac{4\sqrt{5} + 4\sqrt{2} + \sqrt{10} + 2}{5 - 2}$$

$$= \frac{4\sqrt{5} + 4\sqrt{2} + \sqrt{10} + 2}{3}$$

Note that the denominator in this example was $\sqrt{5} - \sqrt{2}$. We choose a symbol for 1 which had $\sqrt{5} + \sqrt{2}$ in the numerator and denominator. If the denominator had been $\sqrt{5} + \sqrt{2}$ we would have chosen $\dfrac{\sqrt{5} - \sqrt{2}}{\sqrt{5} - \sqrt{2}}$ for 1.

Examples. What symbol for 1 would you use to rationalize the denominator?

	Expression	**Symbol for 1**
8.	$\dfrac{3}{2 + \sqrt{7}}$	$\dfrac{2 - \sqrt{7}}{2 - \sqrt{7}}$
9.	$\dfrac{4 + \sqrt{3}}{\sqrt{3} - \sqrt{11}}$	$\dfrac{\sqrt{3} + \sqrt{11}}{\sqrt{3} + \sqrt{11}}$

TRY THIS ➡

What symbol for 1 would you use to rationalize the denominator?

10. $\dfrac{\sqrt{5} + 1}{\sqrt{3} - 1}$ $\dfrac{\sqrt{3} + 1}{\sqrt{3} + 1}$

11. $\dfrac{1}{\sqrt{2} + \sqrt{3}}$ $\dfrac{\sqrt{2} - \sqrt{3}}{\sqrt{2} - \sqrt{3}}$

Example 10. Rationalize the denominator.

$$\frac{4}{\sqrt{3} + 1} = \frac{4}{\sqrt{3} + 1} \cdot \frac{\sqrt{3} - 1}{\sqrt{3} - 1}$$

$$= \frac{4(\sqrt{3} - 1)}{(\sqrt{3} + 1)(\sqrt{3} - 1)}$$

$$= \frac{4(\sqrt{3} - 1)}{(\sqrt{3})^2 - 1^2}$$

$$= \frac{4(\sqrt{3} - 1)}{3 - 1}$$

$$= \frac{4(\sqrt{3} - 1)}{2}$$

$$= 2(\sqrt{3} - 1)$$

TRY THIS ➡

Rationalize the denominator.

12. $\dfrac{5}{1 - \sqrt{2}}$ $-5(1 + \sqrt{2})$

We can also rationalize numerators.

Example 11. Rationalize the numerator.

$$\frac{4 + \sqrt{2}}{\sqrt{5} - \sqrt{2}} = \frac{4 + \sqrt{2}}{\sqrt{5} - \sqrt{2}} \cdot \frac{4 - \sqrt{2}}{4 - \sqrt{2}}$$

$$= \frac{16 - (\sqrt{2})^2}{4\sqrt{5} + \sqrt{5}\sqrt{2} - 4\sqrt{2} + (\sqrt{2})^2}$$

$$= \frac{16 - 2}{4(\sqrt{5} - \sqrt{2}) + \sqrt{5}\sqrt{2} + 2}$$

$$= \frac{14}{4(\sqrt{5} - \sqrt{2}) + \sqrt{10} + 2}$$

TRY THIS ➡

Rationalize the numerator.

13. $\dfrac{3 + \sqrt{5}}{\sqrt{2} - \sqrt{6}}$

$\dfrac{4}{3\sqrt{2} - \sqrt{10} - 3\sqrt{6} + \sqrt{30}}$

Exercise Set 10-7

▌ Rationalize the denominator. (*See Examples 1–4.*)

1. $\sqrt{\dfrac{6}{5}}$ $\frac{\sqrt{30}}{5}$

2. $\sqrt{\dfrac{11}{6}}$ $\frac{\sqrt{66}}{6}$

3. $\sqrt{\dfrac{10}{7}}$ $\frac{\sqrt{70}}{7}$

4. $\sqrt{\dfrac{22}{3}}$ $\frac{\sqrt{66}}{3}$

5. $\dfrac{6\sqrt{5}}{5\sqrt{3}}$ $\frac{2\sqrt{15}}{5}$

6. $\dfrac{2\sqrt{3}}{5\sqrt{2}}$ $\frac{\sqrt{6}}{5}$

7. $\sqrt[3]{\dfrac{16}{9}}$ $\frac{2\sqrt[3]{6}}{6}$

8. $\sqrt[3]{\dfrac{3}{9}}$ $\frac{\sqrt[3]{9}}{3}$

9. $\dfrac{\sqrt[3]{3a}}{\sqrt[3]{5c}}$ $\frac{\sqrt[3]{75ac^2}}{5c}$

10. $\dfrac{\sqrt[3]{7x}}{\sqrt[3]{3y}}$ $\frac{\sqrt[3]{63xy^2}}{3y}$

11. $\dfrac{\sqrt[3]{2y^4}}{\sqrt[3]{6x^4}}$ $\frac{y\sqrt[3]{9yx^2}}{3x^2}$

12. $\dfrac{\sqrt[3]{3a^4}}{\sqrt[3]{7b^2}}$ $\frac{a\sqrt[3]{147ab}}{7b}$

13. $\dfrac{1}{\sqrt[3]{xy}}$ $\frac{\sqrt[3]{x^2y^2}}{xy}$

14. $\dfrac{1}{\sqrt[3]{ab}}$ $\frac{\sqrt[3]{a^2b^2}}{ab}$

▌▌ Rationalize the numerator. (*See Examples 5 and 6.*)

15. $\dfrac{\sqrt{7}}{\sqrt{3}}$ $\frac{7}{\sqrt{21}}$

16. $\dfrac{\sqrt{6}}{\sqrt{5}}$ $\frac{6}{\sqrt{30}}$

17. $\sqrt{\dfrac{14}{21}}$ $\frac{2}{\sqrt{6}}$

18. $\sqrt{\dfrac{12}{15}}$ $\frac{2}{\sqrt{5}}$

19. $\dfrac{4\sqrt{13}}{3\sqrt{7}}$ $\frac{52}{3\sqrt{91}}$

20. $\dfrac{5\sqrt{21}}{2\sqrt{6}}$ $\frac{35}{2\sqrt{14}}$

21. $\dfrac{\sqrt[3]{7}}{\sqrt[3]{2}}$ $\dfrac{7}{\sqrt[3]{98}}$

22. $\dfrac{\sqrt[3]{5}}{\sqrt[3]{4}}$ $\dfrac{5}{\sqrt[3]{100}}$

23. $\sqrt{\dfrac{7x}{3y}}$ $\dfrac{7|x|}{\sqrt{21xy}}$

24. $\sqrt{\dfrac{6a}{2b}}$ $\dfrac{3|a|}{\sqrt{3ab}}$

25. $\dfrac{\sqrt[3]{5y^4}}{\sqrt[3]{6x^5}}$ $\dfrac{5y^2}{x\sqrt[3]{150x^2y^2}}$

26. $\dfrac{\sqrt[3]{3a^5}}{\sqrt[3]{7b^2}}$ $\dfrac{3a^2}{\sqrt[3]{63ab^2}}$

27. $\dfrac{\sqrt{ab}}{3}$ $\dfrac{|ab|}{3\sqrt{ab}}$

28. $\dfrac{\sqrt{xy}}{5}$ $\dfrac{|xy|}{5\sqrt{xy}}$

III Rationalize the denominator. (*See Examples 7–10.*)

29. $\dfrac{5}{8-\sqrt{6}}$ $\dfrac{5(8+\sqrt{6})}{58}$

30. $\dfrac{7}{9+\sqrt{10}}$ $\dfrac{7(9-\sqrt{10})}{71}$

31. $\dfrac{-4\sqrt{7}}{\sqrt{5}-\sqrt{3}}$ $-2\sqrt{7}(\sqrt{5}+\sqrt{3})$

32. $\dfrac{-3\sqrt{2}}{\sqrt{3}-\sqrt{5}}$ $\dfrac{3\sqrt{2}(\sqrt{3}+\sqrt{5})}{2}$

33. $\dfrac{\sqrt{5}-2\sqrt{6}}{\sqrt{3}-4\sqrt{5}}$ $-\dfrac{\sqrt{15}+20-6\sqrt{2}-8\sqrt{30}}{77}$

34. $\dfrac{\sqrt{6}-3\sqrt{5}}{\sqrt{3}-2\sqrt{7}}$ $-\dfrac{3\sqrt{2}+2\sqrt{42}-3\sqrt{15}-6\sqrt{35}}{25}$

35. $\dfrac{\sqrt{x}-\sqrt{y}}{\sqrt{x}+\sqrt{y}}$ $\dfrac{|x|-2\sqrt{xy}+|y|}{|x|-|y|}$

36. $\dfrac{\sqrt{a}+\sqrt{b}}{\sqrt{a}-\sqrt{b}}$ $\dfrac{|a|+2\sqrt{ab}+|b|}{|a|-|b|}$

37. $\dfrac{5\sqrt{3}-3\sqrt{2}}{3\sqrt{2}-2\sqrt{3}}$ $\dfrac{3\sqrt{6}+4}{2}$

38. $\dfrac{7\sqrt{2}+4\sqrt{3}}{4\sqrt{3}-3\sqrt{2}}$ $\dfrac{4\sqrt{6}+9}{3}$

Rationalize the numerator. (*See Example 11.*)

39. $\dfrac{\sqrt{3}+5}{8}$ $\dfrac{-11}{4(\sqrt{3}-5)}$

40. $\dfrac{3-\sqrt{2}}{5}$ $\dfrac{7}{5(3+\sqrt{2})}$

41. $\dfrac{\sqrt{3}-5}{\sqrt{2}+5}$ $\dfrac{-22}{\sqrt{6}+5\sqrt{2}+5\sqrt{3}+25}$

42. $\dfrac{\sqrt{6}-3}{\sqrt{3}+7}$ $\dfrac{-3}{3\sqrt{2}+3\sqrt{3}+7\sqrt{6}+21}$

43. $\dfrac{\sqrt{5}-\sqrt{2}}{\sqrt{2}+\sqrt{3}}$ $\dfrac{3}{\sqrt{10}+2+\sqrt{15}+\sqrt{6}}$

44. $\dfrac{\sqrt{7}-\sqrt{3}}{\sqrt{5}+\sqrt{2}}$ $\dfrac{4}{\sqrt{35}+\sqrt{15}+\sqrt{14}+\sqrt{6}}$

45. $\dfrac{4\sqrt{6}-5\sqrt{3}}{2\sqrt{3}+7\sqrt{6}}$ $\dfrac{21}{129\sqrt{2}+198}$

46. $\dfrac{8\sqrt{2}+5\sqrt{3}}{5\sqrt{3}-7\sqrt{2}}$ $\dfrac{53}{75\sqrt{6}-187}$

Challenge Exercises 47. $\dfrac{x}{\sqrt{x}(\sqrt{x+1}-1)}$ 48. $\dfrac{1}{\sqrt{a+h}+\sqrt{a}}$

Rationalize the numerator. Assume all expressions represent nonnegative numbers.

47. $\dfrac{\sqrt{x+1}+1}{\sqrt{x}}$

48. $\dfrac{\sqrt{a+h}-\sqrt{a}}{h}$

10-8 Rational Numbers as Exponents

After finishing Lesson 10-8, you should be able to
 I write expressions with and without fractional exponents.
 II write expressions without negative rational exponents.
 III use fractional exponents to simplify radical expressions.

I Fractional Exponents

Expressions like $a^{\frac{1}{2}}$, $5^{-\frac{1}{4}}$, and $(2y)^{\frac{4}{5}}$ have not yet been defined. We shall define such expressions in such a way that the usual properties of exponents hold.

Consider $a^{\frac{1}{2}} \cdot a^{\frac{1}{2}}$. If we still want to multiply by adding exponents it must follow that $a^{\frac{1}{2}} \cdot a^{\frac{1}{2}} = a^{\frac{1}{2}+\frac{1}{2}}$, or a^1. Thus we should define $a^{\frac{1}{2}}$ to be a square root of a, $\sqrt{a}$ or $-\sqrt{a}$. Similarly, $a^{\frac{1}{3}} \cdot a^{\frac{1}{3}} \cdot a^{\frac{1}{3}} = a^{\frac{1}{3}+\frac{1}{3}+\frac{1}{3}}$, or a^1, so $a^{\frac{1}{3}}$ should be defined to mean $\sqrt[3]{a}$.

DEFINITION
For any nonnegative number a, and any index n, $a^{\frac{1}{n}}$ means $\sqrt[n]{a}$ (the principal nth root of a).

Examples. Rewrite without fractional exponents.

1. $x^{\frac{1}{2}} = \sqrt{x}$

2. $27^{\frac{1}{3}} = \sqrt[3]{27}$, or 3

3. $(abc)^{\frac{1}{5}} = \sqrt[5]{abc}$

TRY THIS ➡

> Rewrite without fractional exponents.
>
> 1. $y^{\frac{1}{4}}$ $\sqrt[4]{y}$
> 2. $(3a)^{\frac{1}{2}}$ $\sqrt{3a}$
> 3. $16^{\frac{1}{4}}$ $\sqrt[4]{16}$ or 2
> 4. $(125)^{\frac{1}{3}}$ $\sqrt[3]{125}$ or 5
> 5. $(a^3b^2c)^{\frac{1}{5}}$ $\sqrt[5]{a^3b^2c}$

Examples. Rewrite with fractional exponents.

4. $\sqrt[5]{7xy} = (7xy)^{\frac{1}{5}}$

5. $\sqrt[7]{\dfrac{x^3y}{9}} = \left(\dfrac{x^3y}{9}\right)^{\frac{1}{7}}$

TRY THIS ➡

> Rewrite with fractional exponents.
>
> 6. $\sqrt[3]{19}$ $19^{1/3}$
> 7. $\sqrt{abc}$ $(abc)^{1/2}$
> 8. $\sqrt[5]{\dfrac{x^2y}{16}}$ $(\dfrac{x^2y}{16})^{1/5}$

How should we define $a^{\frac{2}{3}}$? If the usual properties of exponents are to hold, we have $a^{\frac{2}{3}} = (a^{\frac{1}{3}})^2$, or $(\sqrt[3]{a})^2$, or $\sqrt[3]{a^2}$. We make the definition accordingly.

DEFINITION

For any natural numbers m and n, and any nonnegative number a, $a^{\frac{m}{n}}$ means $\sqrt[n]{a^m}$.

Thus $a^{\frac{m}{n}}$ represents the principal nth root of a^m. Since, by Theorem 10-8, we know that $\sqrt[n]{a^m} = (\sqrt[n]{a})^m$ it follows that $a^{\frac{m}{n}}$ also represents $(\sqrt[n]{a})^m$.

Examples. Rewrite without fractional exponents.

6. $(27)^{\frac{2}{3}} = (\sqrt[3]{27})^2$
$\quad\quad\quad = (3)^2$
$\quad\quad\quad = 9$

7. $4^{\frac{3}{2}} = (\sqrt[2]{4})^3$
$\quad\quad = 2^3$
$\quad\quad = 8$

TRY THIS →

> Rewrite without fractional exponents.
>
> 9. $x^{\frac{3}{2}}$ $x\sqrt{x}$
> 10. $8^{\frac{2}{3}}$ **4**
> 11. $4^{\frac{5}{2}}$ **32**

Examples. Rewrite with fractional exponents.

8. $(\sqrt[4]{7xy})^5 = (7xy)^{\frac{5}{4}}$

9. $\sqrt[3]{8^4} = 8^{\frac{4}{3}}$

TRY THIS →

> Rewrite with fractional exponents.
>
> 12. $(\sqrt[3]{7abc})^4$ $(7abc)^{4/3}$
> 13. $\sqrt[5]{6^7}$ $6^{7/5}$

∎ Negative Rational Exponents

We now define negative rational number exponents.

DEFINITION

For any rational number $\frac{m}{n}$ and any positive real number a, $a^{-\frac{m}{n}}$ means $\frac{1}{a^{\frac{m}{n}}}$.

Examples. Rewrite with positive exponents.

10. $4^{-\frac{1}{2}} = \dfrac{1}{4^{\frac{1}{2}}}$

11. $(5xy)^{-\frac{4}{5}} = \dfrac{1}{(5xy)^{\frac{4}{5}}}$

TRY THIS

> Rewrite with positive exponents.
>
> 14. $5^{-\frac{1}{4}}$ $\frac{1}{5^{1/4}}$
> 15. $(3xy)^{-\frac{7}{8}}$ $\frac{1}{(3xy)^{7/8}}$

ꟼꟼ Simplifying Radical Expressions

Some simplifying can be done more easily when we use fractional exponents. Note that we have defined fractional exponents *only* for nonnegative radicands. Thus we need not use absolute value notation for an expression like $x^{\frac{2}{2}}$, which means $\sqrt{x^2}$, or x, since x is assumed to be nonnegative.

Examples. Write an exponential expression. Then simplify if possible. Write radical notation for the answer, if appropriate.

12. $\sqrt[6]{x^3} = x^{\frac{3}{6}}$
$\qquad = x^{\frac{1}{2}}$
$\qquad = \sqrt{x}$

13. $\sqrt[6]{4} = 4^{\frac{1}{6}}$
$\qquad = (2^2)^{\frac{1}{6}}$
$\qquad = 2^{\frac{2}{6}}$
$\qquad = 2^{\frac{1}{3}}$
$\qquad = \sqrt[3]{2}$

TRY THIS ➡

> Write an exponential expression. Then simplify, if possible. Write radical notation for the answer, if appropriate.
>
> 16. $\sqrt[4]{a^2}$ $\quad \sqrt{a}$
> 17. $\sqrt[4]{x^4}$ $\quad x$
> 18. $\sqrt[6]{8}$ $\quad \sqrt{2}$

Example 14. Write an exponential expression. Then simplify, if possible. Assume variables stand for nonnegative numbers. Write radical notation for the answer, if appropriate.

$\sqrt[8]{a^2b^4} = (a^2b^4)^{\frac{1}{8}}$
$\qquad = a^{\frac{2}{8}} \cdot b^{\frac{4}{8}}$
$\qquad = a^{\frac{1}{4}} \cdot b^{\frac{2}{4}}$
$\qquad = (ab^2)^{\frac{1}{4}}$
$\qquad = \sqrt[4]{ab^2}$

TRY THIS ➡

> Write an exponential expression. Then simplify, if possible. Assume variables stand for nonnegative numbers. Write radical notation for the answer, if appropriate.
>
> 19. $\sqrt[5]{a^5b^{10}}$ $\quad ab^2$
> 20. $\sqrt[4]{x^4y^{12}}$ $\quad xy^3$

We can use properties of fractional exponents to write a single radical expression for a product or quotient.

Examples. Write a single radical expression.

15. $\sqrt[3]{5} \cdot \sqrt{2} = 5^{\frac{1}{3}} \cdot 2^{\frac{1}{2}}$
$\qquad = 5^{\frac{2}{6}} 2^{\frac{3}{6}}$
$\qquad = (5^2 \cdot 2^3)^{\frac{1}{6}}$
$\qquad = \sqrt[6]{5^2 \cdot 2^3}$
$\qquad = \sqrt[6]{200}$

16.
$$\sqrt{x-2} \cdot \sqrt[4]{3y} = (x-2)^{\frac{1}{2}}(3y)^{\frac{1}{4}}$$
$$= (x-2)^{\frac{2}{4}}(3y)^{\frac{1}{4}}$$
$$= [(x-2)^2(3y)]^{\frac{1}{4}}$$
$$= \sqrt[4]{(x^2-4x+4) \cdot 3y}$$
$$= \sqrt[4]{3x^2y - 12xy + 12y}$$

17.
$$\frac{\sqrt[4]{(x+y)^3}}{\sqrt{x+y}} = \frac{(x+y)^{\frac{3}{4}}}{(x+y)^{\frac{1}{2}}}$$
$$= (x+y)^{\frac{3}{4}-\frac{1}{2}}$$
$$= (x+y)^{\frac{1}{4}}$$
$$= \sqrt[4]{x+y}$$

TRY THIS ➡

> Write a single radical expression.
>
> 21. $\sqrt[4]{7} \cdot \sqrt{3}$ $\sqrt[4]{63}$
>
> 22. $\dfrac{\sqrt[4]{(x+2)^3} \cdot \sqrt[5]{(x+2)}}{\sqrt[20]{(x+2)^9} \ \sqrt{x+2}}$

Example 18. Write a single radical expression.

$$a^{\frac{1}{2}}b^{-\frac{1}{2}}c^{\frac{5}{6}} = a^{\frac{3}{6}}b^{-\frac{3}{6}}c^{\frac{5}{6}} = (a^3b^{-3}c^5)^{\frac{1}{6}} = \sqrt[6]{a^3b^{-3}c^5}$$

TRY THIS ➡

> Write a single radical expression.
>
> 23. $\dfrac{x^{\frac{2}{3}}y^{\frac{1}{2}}z^{\frac{5}{6}}}{\sqrt[6]{x^4y^3z^5}}$ 24. $\dfrac{a^{\frac{1}{2}}b^{\frac{3}{8}}}{a^{\frac{1}{4}}b^{\frac{1}{8}}}$ $\sqrt[4]{ab}$

Exercise Set 10-8

❚ Rewrite without fractional exponents. (*See Examples 1–3, 6, and 7.*)

1. $x^{\frac{1}{4}}$ $\sqrt[4]{x}$

2. $y^{\frac{1}{5}}$ $\sqrt[5]{y}$

3. $(8)^{\frac{1}{3}}$ 2

4. $(16)^{\frac{1}{2}}$ 4

5. $(a^2b^2)^{\frac{1}{5}}$ $\sqrt[5]{a^2b^2}$

6. $(x^3y^3)^{\frac{1}{4}}$ $\sqrt[4]{x^3y^3}$

7. $a^{\frac{2}{3}}$ $\sqrt[3]{a^2}$

8. $b^{\frac{3}{2}}$ $b\sqrt{b}$

9. $16^{\frac{3}{4}}$ 8

10. $4^{\frac{7}{2}}$ 128

Rewrite with fractional exponents. (*See Examples 4, 5, 8, and 9.*)

11. $\sqrt[3]{20}$ $20^{1/3}$

12. $\sqrt[3]{19}$ $19^{1/3}$

13. $\sqrt{17}$ $17^{1/2}$

14. $\sqrt{6}$ $6^{1/2}$

15. $\sqrt[4]{cd}$ $(cd)^{1/4}$

16. $\sqrt[5]{xy}$ $(xy)^{1/5}$

17. $\sqrt[5]{xy^2z}$ $(xy^2z)^{1/5}$

18. $\sqrt[7]{x^3y^2z^2}$ $(x^3y^2z^2)^{1/7}$

19. $(\sqrt{3mn})^3$ $(3mn)^{3/2}$

20. $(\sqrt[3]{7xy})^4$ $(7xy)^{4/3}$

21. $(\sqrt[7]{8x^2y})^5$ $(8x^2y)^{5/7}$

22. $(\sqrt[6]{2a^5b})^7$ $(2a^5b)^{7/6}$

❚❚ Rewrite with positive exponents. (*Examples 10 and 11.*)

23. $x^{-\frac{1}{3}}$ $\dfrac{1}{x^{1/3}}$

24. $y^{-\frac{1}{4}}$ $\dfrac{1}{y^{1/4}}$

25. $(2rs)^{-\frac{3}{4}}$ $\dfrac{1}{(2rs)^{3/4}}$

26. $(5xy)^{-\frac{5}{6}}$ $\dfrac{1}{(5xy)^{5/6}}$

27. $(\frac{1}{10})^{-\frac{2}{3}}$ $10^{2/3}$

28. $(\frac{1}{8})^{-\frac{3}{4}}$ $8^{3/4}$

29. $\dfrac{1}{x^{-\frac{2}{3}}}$ $x^{2/3}$

30. $\dfrac{1}{x^{-\frac{5}{6}}}$ $x^{5/6}$

▮▮▮ Write an exponential expression. Then simplify if possible. Assume variables stand for nonnegative numbers. Write radical notation for the answer, if appropriate. (*See Examples 12–14.*)

31. $\sqrt[6]{a^4}$ $\sqrt[3]{a^2}$

32. $\sqrt[6]{y^2}$ $\sqrt[3]{y}$

33. $\sqrt[3]{8y^6}$ $2y^2$

34. $\sqrt{x^4y^6}$ x^2y^3

35. $\sqrt[5]{32c^{10}d^{15}}$ $2c^2d^3$

36. $\sqrt[4]{16x^{12}y^{16}}$ $2x^3y^4$

37. $\sqrt[6]{\dfrac{m^{12}n^{24}}{64}}$ $\dfrac{m^2n^4}{2}$

38. $\sqrt[5]{\dfrac{x^{15}y^{20}}{32}}$ $\dfrac{x^3y^4}{2}$

39. $\sqrt[8]{r^4s^2}$ $\sqrt[4]{r^2s}$

40. $\sqrt[3]{27a^3b^9}$ $3ab^3$

41. $\sqrt[12]{64t^6s^6}$ $\sqrt{2ts}$

42. $\sqrt[4]{81x^8y^8}$ $3x^2y^2$

Write a single radical expression. (*See Examples 15–18.*)

43. $\sqrt{x}\,\sqrt[3]{x-2}$ $\sqrt[6]{x^5-4x^4+4x^3}$

44. $\sqrt[4]{3x}\,\sqrt{y+4}$ $\sqrt[4]{3xy^2+24xy+48x}$

45. $\dfrac{\sqrt[3]{(a+b)^2}}{\sqrt{(a+b)}}$ $\sqrt[6]{a+b}$

46. $\dfrac{\sqrt[3]{(x+y)^2}}{\sqrt[4]{(x+y)^3}}$ $\sqrt[12]{(x+y)^{-1}}$

47. $a^{\frac{2}{3}}\cdot b^{\frac{3}{4}}$ $\sqrt[12]{a^8b^9}$

48. $x^{\frac{1}{3}}\cdot y^{\frac{1}{4}}\cdot z^{\frac{1}{6}}$ $\sqrt[12]{x^4y^3z^2}$

49. $\dfrac{s^{\frac{7}{12}}\cdot t^{\frac{5}{6}}}{s^{\frac{1}{3}}\cdot t^{-\frac{1}{6}}}$ $\sqrt[4]{st^4}$

50. $\dfrac{x^{\frac{8}{15}}\cdot y^{\frac{4}{5}}}{x^{\frac{1}{3}}\cdot y^{-\frac{1}{5}}}$ $\sqrt[5]{xy^5}$

Challenge Exercises

51. *Road Pavement Messages.* In a psychological study it was determined that the proper length *L* of the letters of a word printed on pavement is given by

$$L = \frac{(0.00252)d^{2.27}}{h},$$

where *d* is the distance of a car from the lettering and *h* is the height of the eye above the surface of the road. All units are in meters. This formula says that if a person is *h* meters above the surface of the road and is to be able to recognize a message *d* meters away, that message will be the most recognizable if the length of the letters is *L*. Find *L*, given the values of *d* and *h*.

a) $h = 1$ m, $d = 60$ m   27.4 m

b) $h = 2.4$ m, $d = 80$ m   21.9 m

c) $h = 0.9906$ m, $d = 75$ m   45.9 m

d) $h = 1.1$ m, $d = 100$ m   79.4 m

e) Find a road pavement message near the school. See if it conforms to this formula. (*Hint:* Don't do your measurements in the middle of a road.)

10-9 *Solving Radical Equations*

After finishing Lesson 10-9, you should be able to
▮ solve radical equations with one radical term.
▮▮ solve radical equations with two radical terms.

▮ The Principle of Powers

These are radical equations.

$$\sqrt{2x} + 1 = 5, \qquad \sqrt[3]{x} + \sqrt[3]{4x - 2} = 7$$

A radical equation is an equation in which variables occur in one or more radicands. To solve such equations we need a new principle for equations. Suppose the equation $a = b$ is true. When we square both sides we still get a true equation, $a^2 = b^2$. This can be generalized.

THEOREM 10-9 (The Principle of Powers)
For any natural number n, if an equation $a = b$ is true, then the equation $a^n = b^n$ is true.

Remark. The converse of Theorem 10-9 is not true. For example, $(3)^2 = (-3)^2$ is true, but $3 = -3$ is not true.

Example 1. Solve: $\sqrt{x} - 3 = 4$.
$$\sqrt{x} = 7 \qquad \textit{Adding 3}$$
$$x = 7^2, \text{ or } 49 \qquad \textit{Principle of powers}$$

Check:
$$\begin{array}{c|c} \sqrt{x} - 3 = 4 \\ \hline \sqrt{49} - 3 & 4 \\ 7 - 3 & \\ 4 & \end{array}$$

The solution is 49.

Since the converse of Theorem 10-9 is not true, the principle of powers does *not* always give equivalent equations.

Example 2. Solve: $\sqrt{x} = -3$.

We might observe at the outset that this equation has no solution because the principal square root of a number is never negative. Let us continue as above, for comparison.

$x = (-3)^2$, or 9   *Principle of powers*

Check: $\dfrac{\sqrt{x} = -3}{\begin{array}{c|c} \sqrt{9} & -3 \\ 3 & \end{array}}$

The number 9 does not check. Hence the equation has no solution.

In solving radical equations, possible solutions found using the principle of powers *must* be checked!

TRY THIS ➤

Answers.   1. 100   2. No solution

Solve.
1. $\sqrt{x} - 7 = 3$
2. $\sqrt{x} = -2$

Example 3. Solve: $x - 5 = \sqrt{x + 7}$.

$x - 5 = \sqrt{x + 7}$ *The radical is already isolated*

$(x - 5)^2 = (\sqrt{x + 7})^2$ *Principle of powers: squaring both sides*

$x^2 - 10x + 25 = x + 7$

$x^2 - 11x + 18 = 0$

$(x - 9)(x - 2) = 0$ *Factoring*

$x = 9$ or $x = 2$ *Using the principle of zero products*

The possible solutions are 9 and 2. Let us check.

For 9: $\dfrac{x - 5 = \sqrt{x + 7}}{\begin{array}{c|c} 9 - 5 & \sqrt{9 + 7} \\ 4 & 4 \end{array}}$ For 2: $\dfrac{x - 5 = \sqrt{x + 7}}{\begin{array}{c|c} 2 - 5 & \sqrt{2 + 7} \\ -3 & 3 \end{array}}$

Since 9 checks but 2 does not, the solution is 9.

TRY THIS ➤

3. Solve: $x - 1 = \sqrt{x + 5}$. 4

◼ Equations With Two Radical Terms

A general strategy for solving equations with two radical terms is as follows:

1. Isolate one of the radical terms.
2. Use Theorem 10-9, the principle of powers.
3. If a radical remains, perform steps 1 and 2 again.
4. Check possible solutions.

Example 4. Solve: $\sqrt{2x - 5} = 1 + \sqrt{x - 3}$.

$(\sqrt{2x - 5})^2 = (1 + \sqrt{x - 3})^2$ *One radical is already isolated; we square both sides*

$2x - 5 = 1 + 2\sqrt{x - 3} + (x - 3)$

$x - 3 = 2\sqrt{x - 3}$ *Isolating the remaining radical*

$(x - 3)^2 = (2\sqrt{x - 3})^2$ *Squaring both sides*

$x^2 - 6x + 9 = 4(x - 3)$

$x^2 - 6x + 9 = 4x - 12$

$x^2 - 10x + 21 = 0$

$(x - 7)(x - 3) = 0$ *Factoring*

$x = 7$ or $x = 3$ *Using the principle of zero products*

The numbers 7 and 3 check and are the solutions.

TRY THIS

4. Solve: $\sqrt{3x + 1} = 1 + \sqrt{x + 4}$.   5

Exercise Set 10-9

◼ Solve. (*See Examples 1–3.*)

1. $\sqrt{2x - 3} = 1$ 2
2. $\sqrt{x + 3} = 6$ 33
3. $\sqrt{y + 1} - 5 = 8$ 168
4. $\sqrt{x - 2} - 7 = -4$ 11
5. $\sqrt[3]{x + 5} = 2$ 3
6. $\sqrt[3]{x - 2} = 3$ 29
7. $\sqrt[4]{y - 3} = 2$ 19
8. $\sqrt[4]{x + 3} = 3$ 78
9. $\sqrt{3y + 1} = 9$ $\frac{80}{3}$
10. $\sqrt{2y + 1} = 13$ 84
11. $3\sqrt{x} = 6$ 4
12. $8\sqrt{y} = 2$ $\frac{1}{16}$
13. $\sqrt[3]{x} = -3$ −27
14. $\sqrt[3]{y} = -4$ −64
15. $\sqrt{y + 3} - 20 = 0$ 397
16. $\sqrt{x + 4} - 11 = 0$ 117
17. $\sqrt{x + 2} = -4$ No solution
18. $\sqrt{y - 3} = -2$ No solution
19. $8 = \dfrac{1}{\sqrt{x}}$ $\frac{1}{64}$
20. $3 = \dfrac{1}{\sqrt{y}}$ $\frac{1}{9}$
21. $\sqrt[3]{6x + 9} + 8 = 5$ −6
22. $\sqrt[3]{3y + 6} + 2 = 3$ $-\frac{5}{3}$

■■ Solve. *(See Example 4.)* Use Quiz 19 after lesson 10—9.

23. $\sqrt{3y + 1} = \sqrt{2y + 6}$ 5

24. $\sqrt{5x - 3} = \sqrt{2x + 3}$ 2

25. $2\sqrt{1 - x} = \sqrt{5}$ $-\frac{1}{4}$

26. $2\sqrt{2y - 3} = \sqrt{4y}$ 3

27. $2\sqrt{t - 1} = \sqrt{3t - 1}$ 3

28. $\sqrt{y + 10} = 3\sqrt{2y + 3}$ −1

29. $\sqrt{y - 5} + \sqrt{y} = 5$ 9

30. $\sqrt{x - 9} + \sqrt{x} = 1$ No solution

31. $3 + \sqrt{z - 6} = \sqrt{z + 9}$ 7

32. $\sqrt{4x - 3} = 2 + \sqrt{2x - 5}$ 7, 3

33. $\sqrt{20 - x} + 8 = \sqrt{9 - x} + 11$ $\frac{80}{9}$

34. $4 + \sqrt{10 - x} = 6 + \sqrt{4 - x}$ $\frac{15}{4}$

35. $\sqrt{x + 2} + \sqrt{3x + 4} = 2$ −1

36. $\sqrt{6x + 7} - \sqrt{3x + 3} = 1$ $1\frac{1}{3}$

37. $\sqrt{4y + 1} - \sqrt{y - 2} = 3$ 6, 2

38. $\sqrt{y + 15} - \sqrt{2y + 7} = 1$ 1

39. $\sqrt{2m - 3} = \sqrt{m + 7} - 2$ 2

40. $\sqrt{3x - 5} + \sqrt{2x + 3} + 1 = 0$ No solution

Challenge Exercises

Solve.

41. 2   42. No solution   43. $-\frac{8}{9}$ 44. 105   45. 8   46. 161,051

41. $\sqrt{x + 2} - \sqrt{x - 2} = \sqrt{2x}$

42. $\sqrt{\sqrt{x + 25} - \sqrt{x}} = 5$

43. $\dfrac{x + \sqrt{x + 1}}{x - \sqrt{x + 1}} = \dfrac{5}{11}$

44. $(x - 5)^{\frac{1}{5}} - 3 = 7$

45. $x^{\frac{1}{3}} + 5 = 7$

46. $x^{\frac{1}{5}} - 7 = 4$

CONSUMER NOTE: Calculating Discounts

Many stores offer discount prices. A discount-store price tag may say, "Original price: $23.80. Our price: $19.04." The difference between these prices is the discount. It is $4.76. To find the rate of discount, divide the difference by the original price. $4.76 \div 23.80 = 0.20$, or 20%. So the discount rate is 20%.

A store may advertise the discount rate. "This week, all tagged items are 12% off." To calculate the discount, multiply the original price by the rate. If an item cost $34.75 originally, a 12% discount is 34.75×0.12. That is 4.17, so the discount is $4.17. The discount subtracted from the original price gives the sale price: $30.58.

Remember, an item you do not really want is no bargain at any discount. Thomas Jefferson said it this way: "Never buy what you do not want, because it is cheap."

COMPUTER ACTIVITY

Finding a Square Root Using the Newton-Raphson Iteration

PROBLEM: Approximate R, the square root of N.

Examples using the flowchart:

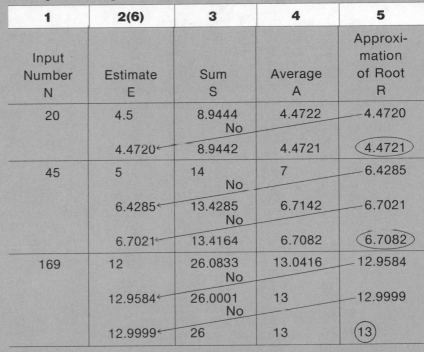

1	2(6)	3	4	5
Input Number N	Estimate E	Sum S	Average A	Approximation of Root R
20	4.5	8.9444 No	4.4722	4.4720
	4.4720	8.9442	4.4721	4.4721
45	5	14 No	7	6.4285
	6.4285	13.4285 No	6.7142	6.7021
	6.7021	13.4164	6.7082	6.7082
169	12	26.0833 No	13.0416	12.9584
	12.9584	26.0001 No	13	12.9999
	12.9999	26	13	13

The flowchart (left side):

START

1 INPUT THE NUMBER N

2 INPUT THE ESTIMATE E

3 LET S = (N ÷ E) + E

4 LET A = S ÷ 2

5 LET R = N ÷ A

LET I = I + 1

6 LET E = R

PRINT E,S,A,R

IS R ACCURATE ENOUGH? — No → (back to 6) / Yes ↓

PRINT N,R,I

STOP

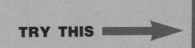 **TRY THIS**

Find the square roots of these input numbers.
1. 225   2. 175

BASIC PROGRAM (Optional)

```
10  INPUT N
20  INPUT E
30  LET S = N/E + E
40  LET A = S/2
50  LET R = N/A
60  PRINT "E ="E, "S ="S,
       "A ="A, "R ="R
70  LET I = I + 1
80  IF ABS(A−R) < 0.0001
       THEN 110
90  LET E = R
100 GO TO 30
110 PRINT "NUMBER ="N,
       "ROOT ="R,
       "ITERATIONS ="I
120 END
```

CHAPTER 10 REVIEW

Review the material in the chapter. Then see how you have done by trying these review exercises. If you miss an exercise, restudy the indicated lesson.

10-1 Convert to scientific notation.
1. $80,200,000,000$ 8.02×10^{10}
2. 0.000000074 7.4×10^{-8}

10-1 Convert to decimal notation.
3. 7.6×10^{14} $760,000,000,000,000$
4. 2.02×10^{-12} 0.00000000000202

10-2 Simplify.
5. $\sqrt{36}$ 6
6. $-\sqrt{81}$ -9
7. $\sqrt{16x^2}$ $4|x|$
8. $\sqrt{x^2 - 2x + 1}$ $|x - 1|$
9. $\sqrt[3]{\dfrac{8}{27}}$ $\dfrac{2}{3}$
10. $\sqrt[3]{0.008}$ 0.2
11. $\sqrt[4]{(2x)^4}$ $2|x|$

10-3 Multiply.
12. $\sqrt{5}\,\sqrt{7}$ $\sqrt{35}$
13. $\sqrt[3]{2a}\,\sqrt[3]{3b}$ $\sqrt[3]{6ab}$
14. $\sqrt[4]{8}\,\sqrt[4]{9}$ $\sqrt[4]{72}$

10-3 Simplify.   15. $4\sqrt{3}$ 16. $2xy\sqrt[3]{3y}$
15. $\sqrt{48}$ 16. $\sqrt[3]{24x^3y^4}$

10-3 Multiply and simplify.
17. $\sqrt{18}\,\sqrt{12}$ $6\sqrt{6}$
18. $\sqrt[3]{a^2b}\,\sqrt[3]{a^4b^6}$ $a^2b^2\sqrt[3]{b}$

10-4 Simplify.
19. $\sqrt{\dfrac{25}{49}}$ 20. $\sqrt[3]{\dfrac{x^3}{27}}$ 19. $\dfrac{5}{7}$ 20. $\dfrac{x}{3}$

10-4 Divide and simplify.
21. $\dfrac{\sqrt{48}}{\sqrt{16}}$ $\sqrt{3}$
22. $\dfrac{\sqrt{6b^2}}{\sqrt{3b}}$ $\sqrt{2b}$
23. $\dfrac{\sqrt[3]{32}}{\sqrt[3]{2}}$ $2\sqrt[3]{2}$

10-4 Simplify.   24. $4\sqrt[3]{4}$ 25. $3x\sqrt{3x}$
24. $(\sqrt[3]{16})^2$ 25. $(\sqrt{3x})^3$

10-5 Simplify.
26. $\sqrt{32} + \sqrt{50}$ $9\sqrt{2}$
27. $\sqrt[3]{24} - \sqrt[3]{81}$ $-\sqrt[3]{3}$

10-6 Multiply.
28. $(7 - 4\sqrt{3})(7 + 4\sqrt{3})$ 1
29. $(2\sqrt{5} + 3\sqrt{2})(\sqrt{5} + \sqrt{2})$ $16 + 5\sqrt{1}$

10-7 Rationalize the denominator.
30. $\dfrac{\sqrt{8}}{\sqrt{3}}$ 31. $\dfrac{6}{3 - \sqrt{17}}$ 30. $\dfrac{2\sqrt{6}}{3}$ 31. $9 + 3\sqrt{7}$

10-7 Rationalize the numerator.
32. $\dfrac{3}{4\sqrt{3}}$
32. $\dfrac{\sqrt{3}}{4}$ 33. $\dfrac{\sqrt{2} + 5}{7 - \sqrt{3}}$
33. $\dfrac{-23}{7\sqrt{2} - 35 - \sqrt{6} + 5\sqrt{3}}$

10-8 Rewrite without fractional exponents.
34. $16^{\frac{3}{4}}$ 35. $(xy^2)^{\frac{1}{3}}$ 34. 8 35. $\sqrt[3]{xy^2}$

10-8 Rewrite with fractional exponents.   36. $9^{1/4}$ or $3^{1/2}$ 37. $(8x^2y^3)^{1/7}$
36. $\sqrt[4]{9}$ 37. $\sqrt[7]{8x^2y^3}$

10-8 Write an exponential expression. Then simplify if possible. Assume variables stand for nonnegative numbers. Write radical notation for the answer, if appropriate.
38. $\sqrt{a^6b^4}$ a^3b^2
39. $\sqrt[3]{\dfrac{27}{a^6}}$ $\dfrac{3}{a^2}$
40. $\sqrt[6]{8x^9y^{12}}$ $xy^2\sqrt{2x}$

10-9 Solve.
41. $\sqrt{5 - 3x} = 6$ $-\dfrac{31}{3}$
42. $\sqrt{7 - 4x} - \sqrt{3 - 2x} = 1$ $-\dfrac{1}{2}, \dfrac{3}{2}$

CHAPTER 10 TEST

Convert to scientific notation.
1. 90,400,000,000 9.04×10^{10}
2. 0.00000752 7.52×10^{-6}

Convert to decimal notation.
3. 8.5×10^{12} $8,500,000,000,000$
4. 3.05×10^{-11} 0.0000000000305

Simplify.
5. $\sqrt{81}$ 9
6. $-\sqrt{121}$ -11
7. $\sqrt{36y^2}$ $6|y|$
8. $\sqrt{x^2 + 4x + 4}$ $|x + 2|$
9. $\sqrt[3]{\dfrac{27}{125}}$ $\dfrac{3}{5}$
10. $\sqrt[3]{-0.027}$ -0.3
11. $\sqrt[6]{(3y)^6}$ $3|y|$

Multiply.
12. $\sqrt{6}\sqrt{5}$ $\sqrt{30}$
13. $\sqrt[3]{3x}\sqrt[3]{4y}$ $\sqrt[3]{12xy}$
14. $\sqrt[4]{7}\sqrt[4]{6}$ $\sqrt[4]{42}$

Simplify.   15. $4\sqrt{6}$ 16. $3ab\sqrt[3]{2b^2}$
15. $\sqrt{96}$
16. $\sqrt[3]{54a^3b^5}$

Multiply and simplify.
17. $\sqrt{20}\sqrt{18}$ $6\sqrt{10}$
18. $\sqrt[3]{x^2y^4}\sqrt[3]{x^5y^2}$ $x^2y^2\sqrt[3]{x}$

Simplify.
19. $\sqrt{\dfrac{36}{100}}$ 20. $\sqrt[3]{\dfrac{y^3}{125}}$ 19. $\dfrac{3}{5}$ 20. $\dfrac{y}{5}$

Divide and simplify.
21. $\dfrac{\sqrt{54}}{\sqrt{18}}$ $\sqrt{3}$
22. $\dfrac{\sqrt{8x^2}}{\sqrt{2x}}$ $2\sqrt{x}$
23. $\dfrac{\sqrt[3]{750}}{\sqrt[3]{3}}$ $5\sqrt[3]{2}$

Simplify.
24. $(\sqrt[3]{18})^2$ 25. $(\sqrt{4y})^3$ 24. $3\sqrt[3]{12}$ 25. $4y\sqrt{4y}$

Simplify.
26. $\sqrt{27} + \sqrt{108}$ $9\sqrt{3}$
27. $\sqrt[3]{40} - \sqrt[3]{135}$ $-\sqrt[3]{5}$

Multiply.
28. $(8 + 5\sqrt{6})(8 - 5\sqrt{6})$ -86
29. $(2\sqrt{7} - 3\sqrt{5})(\sqrt{7} - \sqrt{5})$ $29 - 5\sqrt{35}$

Rationalize the denominator.
30. $\dfrac{\sqrt{5}}{\sqrt{7}}$ 31. $\dfrac{\sqrt{3} + 7}{8 - \sqrt{5}}$ 30. $\dfrac{\sqrt{35}}{7}$
31. $\dfrac{8\sqrt{3} + \sqrt{15} + 56 + 7\sqrt{5}}{59}$

Rationalize the numerator.
32. $\dfrac{\sqrt{6}}{5}$ 33. $\dfrac{\sqrt{5} - \sqrt{2}}{8}$ 32. $\dfrac{6}{5\sqrt{6}}$
33. $\dfrac{3}{8\sqrt{5} + 8\sqrt{2}}$

Rewrite without fractional exponents.
34. $8^{\frac{2}{3}}$ 35. $(pq^3)^{\frac{1}{4}}$ 34. 4 35. $\sqrt[4]{pq^3}$

Rewrite with fractional exponents.
36. $\sqrt[5]{7}$ 37. $\sqrt[6]{9a^2b^4}$ 36. $7^{1/5}$ 37. $(9a^2b^4)^{1/6}$

Write an exponential expression. Then simplify if possible. Assume variables stand for nonnegative numbers. Write radical notation for the answer, if appropriate.
38. $\sqrt{a^8b^4}$ a^4b^2
39. $\sqrt[3]{\dfrac{n^{24}}{a^8}}$ $\dfrac{n^8\sqrt[3]{a}}{a^3}$
40. $\sqrt[4]{81x^8y^8}$ $3x^2y^2$

Solve.
41. $x - 5 = \sqrt{x + 7}$ 9
42. $\sqrt{2x - 5} = 1 + \sqrt{x - 3}$ 7

Clothing buyers for department stores visit manufacturers' showrooms. Buyers inspect clothing and choose styles that are likely to sell well in their stores.

Salesworkers for building materials wholesalers offer many different materials to builders. Salesworkers stress the convenience and reliability of their services.

Restaurant managers are responsible for purchasing food from wholesalers and selling meals to customers. In small restaurants, managers may also work as cooks.

Produce clerks in a food store maintain displays of fruits and vegetables. Clerks prepare these foods for sale and arrange displays so they will look attractive.

CAREERS IN TRADE

Trade careers involve the sale of goods. People who work in trade include salespersons, shipping clerks, receiving clerks, stock clerks, cashiers, and store managers.

The most visible trade workers are in retail trade. They work in stores and restaurants in every town and city. The following pictograph shows relative numbers of retail trade workers in various kinds of trade.

General merchandise	🧍🧍🧍
Food stores	🧍🧍
Apparel and accessories	🧍
Furniture and home furnishings	🧍
Eating and drinking places	🧍🧍🧍🧍
Other retail trade	🧍🧍🧍🧍

Retail Trade Workers

Many people work in retail trade. Each complete figure above represents more than a million workers.

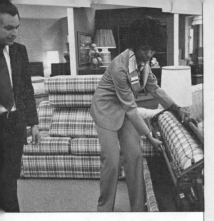

niture salesworkers in a depart-
nt store or furniture store guide
tomer choices. Salesworkers
e information about furniture
dels and materials.

Salesworkers for wholesalers of scientific instruments call on schools
and research firms. Salesworkers
use catalogs or samples to give
product information.

Service station owners sell gasoline,
oil, tires, batteries, fan belts, wind-
shield wiper blades, and so on.
Owners may also provide repair and
maintenance service.

Clerks in catalog stores
take customer orders.
Generally, clerks use catalog order numbers.
When merchandise comes
in, clerks notify customers
of its arrival.

Workers in wholesale trade are not so visible. They help to sell
goods, generally in large quantities, to retail stores. They work in
offices and warehouses. The following pictograph shows relative
numbers of wholesale and retail trade workers.

Retail and Wholesale Trade Workers

In this pictograph, each figure represents roughly 5 million
workers.

According to projections made by analysts
in the United States Bureau of Labor Statistics, the number of trade careers will grow
steadily in the 1980s. Trade careers are not
likely to grow as quickly as careers in government or various services. But they probably will grow more quickly than careers in
manufacturing. By the mid-1980s, trade and
manufacturing will be about equal in numbers of workers. This near equality is repre-
sented in the circle graph.

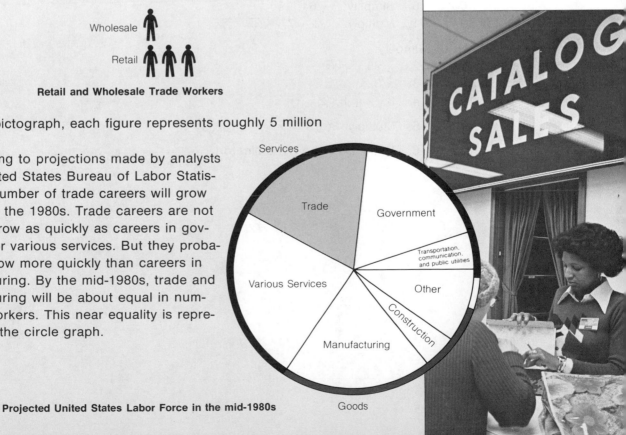

Services

Trade

Government

Transportation,
communication,
and public utilities

Other

Various Services

Construction

Manufacturing

Goods

Projected United States Labor Force in the mid-1980s

Ready for Complex Numbers?

1-5   1.   Collect like terms: $3x - 2y + 4x - 8y$. $7x - 10y$

1-7   2.   Rewrite without exponents: i^2. $i \cdot i$

2-2   Solve.

       3. $9x + 7 - 2x = -12 - 4x + 5$ $-\frac{14}{11}$

       4. $(x - 5)(x + 3) = 0$ $-3, 5$

       Multiply.

6-3   5. $2 - 3y$ and $1 + 4y$ $2 + 5y - 12y^2$

6-4   6. $(3x + 8)^2$ $9x^2 + 48x + 64$

6-5   7. $(2x - 3)(2x + 3)$ $4x^2 - 9$

7-1   8.   Factor: $x^2 - 1$. $(x - 1)(x + 1)$

9-1   9.   Find the reciprocal: $x - 3$. $\frac{1}{x - 3}$

10-2   10.   Simplify: $\sqrt{64}$. 8

10-3   11.   Multiply: $\sqrt{2}\,\sqrt{7}$. $\sqrt{14}$

       Simplify.

10-3   12. $\sqrt{98}$ $7\sqrt{2}$

10-3   13. $\sqrt{3x^2}$ $x\sqrt{3}$

10-5   14. $3\sqrt{2} + 8\sqrt{2}$ $11\sqrt{2}$

10-6   15.   Multiply: $(\sqrt{5} + x)^2$. $5 + 2x\sqrt{5} + x^2$

10-7   16.   Rationalize the denominator: $\dfrac{3}{2 - \sqrt{5}}$. $-6 - 3\sqrt{5}$

Chapter 11
Complex Numbers

Complex numbers are used in the design of electrical equipment.

11-1 Imaginary and Complex Numbers

After finishing Lesson 11-1, you should be able to
I name numbers such as $\sqrt{-7}$ in the form bi.
II multiply imaginary numbers.
III add and subtract complex numbers.

I Imaginary Numbers

In the set of real numbers, negative numbers do not have square roots. An equation like

$$x^2 = -1$$

has no solution. A new kind of number, called *imaginary,* was invented so that negative numbers would have square roots and certain equations would have solutions. These numbers were devised, starting with an imaginary unit, named *i*, with the agreement that

$$i^2 = -1, \text{ or } i = \sqrt{-1}.$$

We assume that *i* acts like a real number in other respects. Square roots of all negative numbers can then be expressed as a product of *i* and a real number.

Examples. Express these numbers in terms of *i*.

1. $\sqrt{-5} = \sqrt{-1 \cdot 5}$
$\qquad = \sqrt{-1}\,\sqrt{5}$
$\qquad = i\sqrt{5} \text{ or } \sqrt{5}i$

2. $-\sqrt{-7} = -\sqrt{-1 \cdot 7}$
$\qquad = -\sqrt{-1}\,\sqrt{7}$
$\qquad = -i\sqrt{7} \text{ or } -\sqrt{7}i$

3. $\sqrt{-99} = \sqrt{-1 \cdot 99}$
$\qquad = \sqrt{-1}\,\sqrt{99}$
$\qquad = i\sqrt{9}\,\sqrt{11}$
$\qquad = 3i\sqrt{11} \text{ or } 3\sqrt{11}i$

TRY THIS ➡

Express these numbers in terms of *i*.

1. $\sqrt{-7}$ $i\sqrt{7}$
2. $-\sqrt{-36}$ $-bi$
3. $\sqrt{-160}$ $4i\sqrt{10}$

DEFINITION

The *imaginary* numbers consist of all numbers bi, where b is a real number and i is the imaginary unit, with the property that $i^2 = -1$.

▮▮ Products

To multiply imaginary numbers or an imaginary number by a real number, it is important first to express the imaginary numbers in terms of i.

Examples.   Multiply.

4. $47i \cdot 2 = 94i$

5. $\sqrt{-5} \cdot 2i = \sqrt{5}i \cdot 2i$
$$= 2\sqrt{5}i^2$$
$$= -2\sqrt{5}$$

6. $-\sqrt{-3} \cdot \sqrt{-7} = -i\sqrt{3} \cdot i\sqrt{7}$
$$= -i^2\sqrt{21}$$
$$= -(-1)\sqrt{21}$$
$$= \sqrt{21}$$

TRY THIS ▬▬▬▬▶

Answers.   4. -18 5. $-3\sqrt{3}$ 6. $-3\sqrt{2}$

Multiply.

4. $6i \cdot 3i$
5. $\sqrt{-3} \cdot 3i$
6. $\sqrt{-3} \cdot \sqrt{-6}$

▮▮▮ Complex Numbers

To construct a complete number system, we shall define sums of real and imaginary numbers. We call these *complex numbers*.

DEFINITION

The *complex* numbers consist of all sums $a + bi$, where a and b are real numbers and i is the imaginary unit. a is called the real part and bi is called the imaginary part.

Every real number a is a complex number because $a = a + 0 \cdot i$. Thus the complex numbers are an extension of the real number system. All imaginary numbers bi are also complex because $bi = 0 + bi$.

We assume that i acts like a real number, obeying the commutative, associative, and distributive laws. Thus to add or subtract complex numbers we can treat i as we would treat a variable. We combine like terms.

Examples. Add.

7. $7i + 9i = (7 + 9)i$
$= 16i$

8. $(-5 + 6i) + (2 - 11i) = -5 + 6i + 2 - 11i$
$= -3 - 5i$

TRY THIS ➡

Add.

7. $3i + 4i$
8. $(2 + 3i) + (2 + 4i)$
9. $(-7 + 4i) + (5 - 9i)$
10. $(-2 + 3i) + (2 - 3i)$

Answers. 7. 7i   8. 4 + 7i   9. −2 − 5i   10. 0

Examples. Subtract.

9. $7i - 9i = (7 - 9)i$
$= -2i$

10. $(2 + 3i) - (4 + 2i) = 2 + 3i - 4 - 2i$
$= -2 + i$

11. $(-6 + 5i) - (-6 + 5i) = -6 + 5i + 6 - 5i$
$= 0$

TRY THIS ➡

Subtract.

11. $3i - 4i$
12. $(2 - 3i) - (5 - 8i)$
13. $(-4 + 10i) - (-2 + 3i)$
14. $(9 - 7i) - (15 + 2i)$

Answers. 11. −i   12. −3 + 5i   13. −2 + 7i   14. −6 − 9i

Remark. The set of complex numbers is closed under addition. To see this, consider any two complex numbers $a + bi$ and $c + di$. We add them. $(a + bi) + (c + di) = (a + c) + (b + d)i$. The answer is again a complex number.

Addition is commutative and associative. There is an additive identity, the number 0 (or $0 + 0i$). Every complex number has an additive inverse (the inverse of $a + bi$ is $-a - bi$). Thus under addition the complex numbers form a *commutative group*.

Exercise Set 11-1

▮Express these numbers in terms of i. *(See Examples 1–3.)*

1. $\sqrt{-2}$ $i\sqrt{2}$
2. $\sqrt{-3}$ $i\sqrt{3}$
3. $\sqrt{-36}$ $6i$
4. $\sqrt{-25}$ $5i$
5. $-\sqrt{-9}$ $-3i$
6. $-\sqrt{-16}$ $-4i$
7. $\sqrt{-128}$ $8i\sqrt{2}$
8. $\sqrt{-12}$ $2i\sqrt{3}$
9. $\sqrt{-\dfrac{9}{16}}$ $\frac{3}{4}i$
10. $\sqrt{-\dfrac{25}{4}}$ $\frac{5}{2}i$
11. $-\sqrt{-80}$ $-4i\sqrt{5}$
12. $-\sqrt{-75}$ $-5i\sqrt{3}$

▌▌ Multiply. (*See Examples 4–6.*)

13. $23i \cdot 4$ 92i
14. $-12i \cdot (-3)$ 36i
15. $\sqrt{-3} \cdot 4i$ $-4\sqrt{3}$
16. $\sqrt{-5} \cdot 6i$ $-6\sqrt{5}$
17. $\sqrt{-2} \sqrt{-3}$ $-\sqrt{6}$
18. $\sqrt{-5} \sqrt{-3}$ $-\sqrt{15}$
19. $-\sqrt{-2} \sqrt{-18}$ 6
20. $-\sqrt{-3} \sqrt{-15}$ $3\sqrt{5}$
21. $\sqrt{-3} \sqrt{-15}$ $-3\sqrt{5}$
22. $\sqrt{-10} \sqrt{-2}$ $-2\sqrt{5}$
23. $-\sqrt{-10}(-\sqrt{-10})$ -10
24. $-\sqrt{-7}(-\sqrt{-7})$ -7

▌▌▌ Add. (*See Examples 7 and 8.*)

25. $5i + 4i$ 9i
26. $-7i + 10i$ 3i
27. $4i + (-10i)$ $-6i$
28. $-2i + (-3i)$ $-5i$
29. $3i + (8 - 5i)$ $8 - 2i$
30. $-2i + (-3 + 8i)$ $-3 + 6i$
31. $(3 + 2i) + (5 - i)$ $8 + i$
32. $(-2 + 3i) + (7 + 8i)$ $5 + 11i$
33. $(4 - 3i) + (5 - 2i)$ $9 - 5i$
34. $(-2 - 5i) + (1 - 3i)$ $-1 - 8i$

Subtract. (*See Examples 9–11.*)

35. $5i - 4i$ i
36. $-7i - 10i$ $-17i$
37. $6i - (-8i)$ 14i
38. $-3i - (-4i)$ i
39. $2i - (4 - 3i)$ $-4 + 5i$
40. $3i - (5 - 2i)$ $-5 + 5i$
41. $(3 - i) - (5 + 2i)$ $-2 - 3i$
42. $(-2 + 8i) - (7 + 3i)$ $-9 + 5i$
43. $(4 - 2i) - (5 - 3i)$ $-1 + i$
44. $(-2 - 3i) - (1 - 5i)$ $-3 + 2i$
45. $(9 + 5i) - (-2 - i)$ $11 + 6i$
46. $(6 - 3i) - (2 + 4i)$ $4 - 7i$

Calculator Exercises

Simplify.

47. $(56.4325 + 789.5097i) + (-456.892 + 809.0568i)$ $-400.4595 + 1598.5665i$
48. $(76.5773 - 567.9076i) - (907.238 - 7890.67i)$ $-830.6607 + 7322.7624i$

Challenge Exercises   49. i   50. 1   51. -1 52. $-i$ 53. $-i$ 54. $-2i$ 55. 0

Powers of i. These four powers of *i* are the keys to finding higher powers of *i*:

$$i^1 = i, \qquad i^2 = -1, \qquad i^3 = -i, \qquad i^4 = 1.$$

For example, $i^{31} = i^{28} \cdot i^3 = (i^4)^7 \cdot i^3 = 1^7 \cdot (-i) = 1 \cdot (-i) = -i$.

Simplify.

49. i^{13}
50. i^{20}
51. i^{18}
52. i^{27}
53. i^{99}
54. $i^{71} - i^{49}$
55. $i^{68} - i^{72} + i^{76} - i^{80}$

11-2 More About Complex Numbers

After finishing Lesson 11-2, you should be able to
▮ solve equations like $3x + yi = 5x + 1 + 2i$ for x and y.
▮▮ multiply complex numbers.
▮▮▮ find conjugates of complex numbers and multiply a complex number by its conjugate.
▮▮▮▮ divide complex numbers.
▮▮▮▮▮ find the reciprocal of a complex number and name in the form $a + bi$.

▮ Equality for Complex Numbers

Equality for complex numbers is the same as for real numbers. A sentence $a + bi = c + di$ says that $a + bi$ and $c + di$ are two names of the same number. For this to be true, a and c must be the same and b and d must be the same. Thus $a + bi = c + di$ when $a = b$ and $c = d$.

Example 1. Suppose that $3x + yi = 5x + 1 + 2i$. Find x and y.

We equate the real parts.

$$3x = 5x + 1$$
$$x = -\tfrac{1}{2} \quad \textit{Solving}$$

We equate the imaginary parts.

$$yi = 2i$$
$$y = 2 \quad \textit{Solving}$$

TRY THIS ➡

Solve.   x = −1, y = 2
1. Suppose $3x + 1 + (y + 2)i$
   $= 2x + 2yi$. Find x and y.

▮▮ Multiplication

We multiply complex numbers as we would multiply monomials or binomials, treating the imaginary parts as like terms. Of course, we remember that $i^2 = -1$.

Examples. Multiply.

2. $3i \cdot 4i = (3 \cdot 4)i^2$
$\qquad = 12(-1)$
$\qquad = -12$

3. $(7i)^2 = 7^2i^2$
$\qquad = 49(-1)$
$\qquad = -49$

4. $(4 + 3i) \cdot (7 + 2i) = 28 + 8i + 21i + 6i^2$
$\qquad\qquad\qquad = 28 + (8i + 21i) + 6(-1) \qquad$ (*Since* $i^2 = -1$)
$\qquad\qquad\qquad = 28 + 29i - 6$
$\qquad\qquad\qquad = 22 + 29i$

5. $(2 - 3i)^2 = 4 - 12i + 9i^2$
$\qquad\qquad = 4 - 12i - 9$
$\qquad\qquad = -5 - 12i$

Answers. 2. −30   3. −100   4. 25 + 45i   5. 3 − 28i   6. −24 − 70i

TRY THIS

> Multiply.
>
> 2. $5i \cdot 6i$
> 3. $(10i)^2$
> 4. $(7 + 2i)(5 + 5i)$
> 5. $(-2 - 3i)(6 + 5i)$
> 6. $(5 - 7i)^2$

III Conjugates

DEFINITION

The *conjugate* of a complex number $a + bi$ is $a - bi$ and the conjugate of $a - bi$ is $a + bi$.

Examples.

6. The conjugate of $3 + 4i$ is $3 - 4i$.
7. The conjugate of $-4 - 7i$ is $-4 + 7i$.
8. The conjugate of $5i$ is $-5i$.
9. The conjugate of 6 is 6.

TRY THIS

> Find the conjugate of each number.
>
> 7. $6 + 3i$ 6 − 3i
> 8. $-9 - 5i$ −9 + 5i
> 9. $-7i$ 7i
> 10. -8 −8

The special product $(A + B)(A - B) = A^2 - B^2$ applies to multiplying a number by its conjugate.

Examples. Multiply.

10. $(5 + 7i)(5 - 7i) = 5^2 - (7i)^2$
$\qquad\qquad\qquad\quad = 25 - (49i^2)$
$\qquad\qquad\qquad\quad = 25 + 49$
$\qquad\qquad\qquad\quad = 74$

11. $(a + bi)(a - bi) = a^2 - (bi)^2$
$\qquad\qquad\qquad\quad = a^2 - b^2i^2$
$\qquad\qquad\qquad\quad = a^2 + b^2$

THEOREM 11-1

The product of a nonzero complex number $a + bi$ and its conjugate $a - bi$ is the positive real number $a^2 + b^2$.

Answers.   11. 53   12. 10   13. p² + q²

TRY THIS

> Multiply.
>
> 11. $(7 - 2i)(7 + 2i)$
> 12. $(-3 + i)(-3 - i)$
> 13. $(p - qi)(p + qi)$

ⅢⅢ Division

To divide complex numbers we can multiply by 1. In choosing the notation for 1, we use the conjugate of the divisor.

Examples. Divide.

12. $\dfrac{-5 + 9i}{1 - i} = \dfrac{-5 + 9i}{1 - i} \cdot \dfrac{1 + i}{1 + i}$

$= \dfrac{-14 + 4i}{1 - i^2}$

$= \dfrac{-14 + 4i}{2}$

$= -7 + 2i$

13. $\dfrac{2 - 3i}{3 + 5i} = \dfrac{2 - 3i}{3 + 5i} \cdot \dfrac{3 - 5i}{3 - 5i}$

$= \dfrac{-9 - 19i}{9 - 25i^2}$

$= \dfrac{-9 - 19i}{34}$

$= \dfrac{-9}{34} - \dfrac{19}{34}i$

TRY THIS ➡

Answers.   14. 2i   15. $\dfrac{10}{17} - \dfrac{11}{17}i$

Divide.

14. $\dfrac{6 + 2i}{1 - 3i}$

15. $\dfrac{2 + 3i}{-1 + 4i}$

ⅢⅢ Reciprocals

The reciprocal of a number $a + bi$ is of course that number by which we multiply $a + bi$ to get 1. By definition of division this is $\dfrac{1}{a + bi}$. To express it in the form $a + bi$ we can do this division.

Example 14. Find the reciprocal of $2 - 3i$ and express it in the form $a + bi$.

a) The reciprocal of $2 - 3i$ is $\dfrac{1}{2 - 3i}$.

b) We can express it in the form $a + bi$ as follows.

$\dfrac{1}{2 - 3i} = \dfrac{1}{2 - 3i} \cdot \dfrac{2 + 3i}{2 + 3i}$

$= \dfrac{2 + 3i}{2^2 - 3^2 i^2}$

$$= \frac{2 + 3i}{4 + 9}$$

$$= \frac{2}{13} + \frac{3}{13}i$$

TRY THIS ➡

> 16. Find the reciprocal of $3 + 4i$ and express it in the form $a + bi$. $\frac{3}{25} - \frac{4}{25}i$

Remark. Multiplication of complex numbers is commutative and associative. There is an identity, the number 1, or $1 + 0i$. Every complex number except 0 has a reciprocal. Thus the set of nonzero complex numbers form a *commutative group*.

Multiplication is distributive over addition, tying the two operations together. Earlier we showed that addition of complex numbers is associative and commutative, 0 is the identity, and every complex number has an additive inverse. So the complex numbers form a *field*.

Exercise Set 11-2

▌Solve for x and y. (*See Example 1.*)

1. $4x + 7i = -6 + yi$ $x = -\frac{3}{2}, y = 7$
2. $8 + 8yi = 4x - 2i$ $x = 2, y = -\frac{1}{4}$
3. $-5x - yi = 10 + 8i$ $x = -2, y = -8$
4. $-3y - 4xi = 2 + 2i$ $x = -\frac{1}{2}, y = -\frac{2}{3}$
5. $3x + 4y - 7i = 18 + (x - 3y)i$ $x = 2, y = 3$
6. $-4 + (x + y)i = 2x - 5y + 5i$ $x = 3, y = 2$

▌▌Multiply. (*See Examples 2–5.*)

7. $7i \cdot 9i$ -63
8. $3i \cdot i$ -3
9. $(9i)^2$ -81
10. $(13i)^2$ -169
11. $(-3i)^2$ -9
12. $(-5i)^2$ -25
13. $(3 + 2i)(1 + i)$ $1 + 5i$
14. $(4 + 3i)(2 + i)$ $5 + 10i$
15. $(2 + 3i)(6 - 2i)$ $18 + 14i$
16. $(5 + 6i)(2 - i)$ $16 + 7i$
17. $(6 - 5i)(3 + 4i)$ $38 + 9i$
18. $(5 - 6i)(4 + 8i)$ $68 + 16i$
19. $(7 - 2i)(2 - 6i)$ $2 - 46i$
20. $(-4 + 5i)(3 - 4i)$ $8 + 31i$
21. $(5 - 2i)^2$ $21 - 20i$
22. $(3 - 5i)^2$ $-16 - 30i$
23. $(1 + 3i)^2$ $-8 + 6i$
24. $(-2 + 2i)^2$ $-8i$

▌▌▌Find the conjugate of each number. (*See Examples 6–9.*)

25. $-4 + 8i$ $-4 - 8i$
26. $-8 + 5i$ $-8 - 5i$
27. $6 - 5i$ $6 + 5i$
28. $7 - i$ $7 + i$
29. $\sqrt{2} - \frac{1}{2}i$ $\sqrt{2} + \frac{1}{2}i$
30. $\sqrt{3} + 0.4i$ $\sqrt{3} - 0.4i$
31. $r - ti$ $r + ti$
32. $-m + ni$ $-m - ni$

Multiply. (*See Examples 10 and 11.*)

33. $(3 + 4i)(3 - 4i)$ $\quad$ 25

34. $(2 - i)(2 + i)$ $\quad$ 5

35. $(1 - i)(1 + i)$ $\quad$ 2

36. $(6 + 3i)(6 - 3i)$ $\quad$ 45

37. $(\frac{1}{2} + i)(\frac{1}{2} - i)$ $\quad$ $\frac{5}{4}$

38. $(1 + \frac{1}{3}i)(1 - \frac{1}{3}i)$ $\quad$ $\frac{10}{9}$

39. $(\sqrt{3} - i)(\sqrt{3} + i)$ $\quad$ 4

40. $(3 - \sqrt{2}i)(3 + \sqrt{2}i)$ $\quad$ 11

IIII Divide. (*See Examples 12 and 13.*)

41. $\dfrac{1 + i}{1 - i}$ $\quad$ i

42. $\dfrac{2 - i}{2 + i}$ $\quad$ $\frac{3}{5} - \frac{4}{5}i$

43. $\dfrac{3 + 2i}{2 + i}$ $\quad$ $\frac{8}{5} + \frac{1}{5}i$

44. $\dfrac{4 + 5i}{5 - i}$ $\quad$ $\frac{15}{26} + \frac{29}{26}i$

45. $\dfrac{5 - 2i}{2 + 5i}$ $\quad$ $-i$

46. $\dfrac{3 - 2i}{4 + 3i}$ $\quad$ $\frac{6}{25} - \frac{17}{25}i$

47. $\dfrac{8 - 3i}{-2 + 7i}$ $\quad$ $-\frac{37}{53} - \frac{50}{53}i$

48. $\dfrac{5 - 10i}{-3 + 4i}$ $\quad$ $-\frac{11}{5} + \frac{2}{5}i$

49. $\dfrac{\sqrt{2} + i}{\sqrt{2} - i}$ $\quad$ $\frac{1}{3} + \frac{2}{3}\sqrt{2}i$

50. $\dfrac{\sqrt{3} - i}{\sqrt{3} + i}$ $\quad$ $\frac{1}{2} - \frac{1}{2}\sqrt{3}i$

51. $\dfrac{3 + 2i}{i}$ $\quad$ $2 - 3i$

52. $\dfrac{2 + 3i}{i}$ $\quad$ $3 - 2i$

53. $\dfrac{i}{2 + i}$ $\quad$ $\frac{1}{5} + \frac{2}{5}i$

54. $\dfrac{i}{1 - i}$ $\quad$ $-\frac{1}{2} + \frac{1}{2}i$

IIIII Find the reciprocal of each number and express it in the form $a + bi$. (*See Example 14.*)

55. i $\quad$ $-i$

56. $-i$ $\quad$ i

57. $2 - 4i$ $\quad$ $\frac{1}{10} + \frac{2}{5}i$

58. $-3 - 5i$ $\quad$ $-\frac{3}{34} + \frac{5}{34}i$

59. $-4 + 7i$ $\quad$ $-\frac{4}{65} - \frac{7}{65}i$

60. $-2 + 6i$ $\quad$ $-\frac{1}{20} - \frac{3}{20}i$

Calculator Exercises

Simplify. $\quad$ 61. $1834.9099 - 490.34708i$ $\quad$ 62. 5192.9629

61. $(43.21 - 5.674i)^2$ $\qquad$ 62. $(45.23 - 56.1i)(45.23 + 56.1i)$

Challenge Exercises $\quad$ 63. i $\quad$ 64. -1 $\quad$ 65. $-$i $\quad$ 66. 1 $\quad$ 67. $-\frac{1}{2} - \frac{1}{2}i$ $\quad$ 68. $-\frac{1}{2} + \frac{1}{2}i$ $\quad$ 69. $\dfrac{2a^2 - 2b^2}{4a^2 + b^2} + \dfrac{5ab}{4a^2 + b^2}i$

Simplify to the form $a + bi$. $\quad$ 70. $\dfrac{3x^2 - 2y^2}{x^2 + y^2} + \dfrac{5xy}{x^2 + y^2}i$ $\quad$ 71. $\dfrac{a}{a^2 + b^2} - \dfrac{b}{a^2 + b^2}i$ $\quad$ 72. $\dfrac{ac + bd}{a^2 + b^2} + \dfrac{ad - bc}{a^2 + b^2}i$

63. i^{-3} $\qquad$ 64. i^2 $\qquad$ 65. i^{-9} $\qquad$ 66. i^{-8}

67. $\dfrac{1 - i}{(1 + i)^2}$ $\qquad$ 68. $\dfrac{1 + i}{(1 - i)^2}$ $\qquad$ 69. $\dfrac{a + 2bi}{2a - bi}$ $\qquad$ 70. $\dfrac{3x + 2yi}{x - yi}$

71. Let $z = a + bi$. Find a general expression for $\dfrac{1}{z}$.

72. Let $z = a + bi$ and $w = c + di$. Find a general expression for $\dfrac{w}{z}$.

11-3 Solutions of Equations

After finishing Lesson 11-3, you should be able to
I determine whether a complex number is a solution of an equation.
II find an equation having given complex numbers as solutions.
III solve first-degree equations having complex numbers as solutions.
IIII verify that a given complex number is a square root of another complex number, then find the other square root.

I Complex Numbers as Solutions of Equations

Example 1. Determine whether $1 + \sqrt{7}i$ is a solution of $x^2 - 2x + 8 = 0$.

$$
\begin{array}{c|c}
x^2 - 2x + 8 = 0 & \\
\hline
(1 + \sqrt{7}i)^2 - 2(1 + \sqrt{7}i) + 8 & 0 \\
1 + 2(\sqrt{7}i) + (\sqrt{7}i)^2 - 2 - 2\sqrt{7}i + 8 & \\
1 + 2\sqrt{7}i - 7 - 2 - 2\sqrt{7}i + 8 & \\
0 &
\end{array}
$$

$1 + \sqrt{7}i$ is a solution.

TRY THIS ➡

> 1. Determine whether $3i$ and $-3i$ are solutions of $x^2 + 9 = 0$.
> 2. Determine whether $1 + i$ is a solution of $x^2 - 2x + 2 = 0$.
> 3. Determine whether $1 - i$ is a solution of $x^2 + 2x + 1 = 0$.
>
> See answer section

II Writing Equations with Given Solutions

The principle of zero products for real numbers states that a product is 0 if and only if at least one of the factors is 0. This principle also holds for complex numbers. Since the principle holds for complex numbers we can write equations having given solutions.

Example 2. Find an equation having -1, i, and $1 + i$ as solutions.

The factors we use will be $x - (-1)$, $x - i$, and $x - (1 + i)$. Next we set the product of these factors equal to 0.

$$[x - (-1)](x - i)[x - (1 + i)] = 0$$

Now we multiply and simplify.

$$(x^2 + x - ix - i)(x - 1 - i) = 0$$
$$x^3 - 2ix^2 - ix - 2x - 1 + i = 0$$

TRY THIS ➡️

Find an equation having the
given numbers as solutions.

4. $i, 1 + i$ $x^2 - 2ix - x + i - 1 = 0$
5. $2, i, -i$ $x^3 - 2x^2 + x - 2 = 0$

ⅢSolving Equations

First-degree equations in complex numbers are solved
very much like first-degree equations in real numbers.

Example 3. Solve $3ix + 4 - 5i = (1 + i)x + 2i$.

$$3ix + 4 - 5i - (1 + i)x = 2i \qquad \textit{Adding } -(1 + i)x$$
$$3ix - (1 + i)x = -4 + 7i \qquad \textit{Adding } -(4 - 5i)$$
$$(-1 + 2i)x = -4 + 7i \qquad \textit{Simplifying}$$
$$x = \frac{-4 + 7i}{-1 + 2i} \qquad \textit{Dividing}$$
$$x = \frac{-4 + 7i}{-1 + 2i} \cdot \frac{-1 - 2i}{-1 - 2i}$$
$$x = \frac{18 + i}{5}$$
$$x = \frac{18}{5} + \frac{1}{5}i$$

TRY THIS ➡️

Solve.   2 + 5i
6. $3 - 4i + 2ix = 3i - (1 - i)x$

Linear equations always have solutions. Complex numbers were
invented so that certain other equations would have solutions.
Suppose we ask what kinds of equations do have solutions. The
answer depends upon a very important theorem.

THEOREM 11-2 (The Fundamental Theorem of Algebra)
Every polynomial with complex coefficients and of degree n
(where $n > 1$) can be factored into n linear factors.

The factors of a polynomial are not always easy to find, but they
exist.

Example 4. Show that $(x + i)(x - i)$ is a factorization of $x^2 + 1$.

We multiply.

$$(x + i)(x - i) = x^2 + ix - ix - i^2$$
$$= x^2 + 1$$

TRY THIS ➡️

7.   Show that $(x + 2i)(x - 2i)$
is a factorization of $x^2 + 4$.
$(x + 2i)(x - 2i) = x^2 + 2ix - 2ix - 4i^2 = x^2 + 4$

We can now answer the question about solutions of equations.

THEOREM 11-3

Every polynomial equation of degree n ($n \geq 1$) with complex co-efficients has at least one solution and at most n solutions in the system of complex numbers.

A Proof of Theorem 11-3

Let us consider a polynomial equation of degree n.

$$P(x) = 0.$$

The polynomial $P(x)$ is either of degree 1, in which case there is a so-lution, or by the fundamental theorem of algebra, it can be factored into n linear factors. We then have

$$(x - a_1)(x - a_2) \ldots (x - a_n) = 0.$$

By the principle of zero products, we get

$$x = a_1 \text{ or } x = a_2 \text{ or } x = a_3 \text{ or } \ldots \text{ or } x = a_n.$$

Thus the equation has solutions $a_1, a_2, \ldots, a_n$. Some of these may be the same. So there is at least one solution, and there are not more than n solutions.

IIII Square Roots of Complex Numbers

The fundamental theorem of algebra can be used to show that all complex numbers have square roots.

THEOREM 11-4

Every nonzero complex number has two square roots. They are additive inverses of each other. Zero has just one square root.

Example 5. Show that $1 + i$ is a square root of $2i$. Then find the other square root.

We square $(1 + i)$ to show that we get $2i$.

$$(1 + 1)^2 = 1 + 2i + i^2$$
$$= 1 + 2i - 1$$
$$= 2i$$

By Theorem 11-4, the other square root of $2i$ is the additive in-verse of $1 + i$, so it is $-1 - i$.

TRY THIS

8. Show that $(-1 + i)$ is a square root of $-2i$. Then find the other square root.

Answer. 8. $(-1 + i)^2 = 1 - 2i + i^2 = 1 - 2i - 1 = -2i,\ 1 - i$

Exercise Set 11-3

▮ Determine whether the given numbers are solutions of the equation. (*See Example 1.*)

1. $2i,\ -2i;\ x^2 + 4 = 0$ Yes, yes
2. $4i,\ -4i;\ x^2 + 16 = 0$ Yes, yes
3. $\sqrt{2}i,\ -\sqrt{3}i;\ x^2 + 3 = 0$ No, yes
4. $\sqrt{3}i,\ -\sqrt{2}i;\ x^2 + 2 = 0$ No, yes
5. $-1 + i,\ -1 - i;\ z^2 + 2z + 2 = 0$ Yes, yes
6. $2 - i,\ 2 + i;\ z^2 - 4z + 5 = 0$ Yes, yes

▮▮ Find an equation having the specified numbers as solutions. (*See Example 2.*)

7. $5i,\ -5i$ $x^2 + 25$
8. $7i,\ -7i$ $x^2 + 49$
9. $1 + i,\ 1 - i$ $x^2 - 2x + 2$
10. $2 + i,\ 2 - i$ $x^2 - 4x + 4$
11. $2 + 3i,\ 2 - 3i$ $x^2 - 4x + 13$
12. $4 + 3i,\ 4 - 3i$ $x^2 - 8x + 25$
13. $3,\ i$ $x^2 - ix - 3x + 3i$
14. $5,\ i$ $x^2 - ix - 5x + 5i$
15. $1,\ 3i,\ -3i$ $x^3 - x^2 + 9x - 9$
16. $1,\ 2i,\ -2i$ $x^3 - x^2 + 4x - 4$
17. $2,\ 1 + i,\ i$ $x^3 - 2ix^2 - 3x^2 + 5ix + x - 2i + 2$
18. $3,\ 1 - i,\ i$ $x^3 - 4x^2 + ix + 4x - 3i - 3$
19. $i,\ 2i,\ -i$ $x^3 - 2ix^2 + x - 2i$
20. $i,\ -2i,\ -i$ $x^3 + 2ix^2 + x + 2i$

▮▮▮ Solve. (*See Example 3.*)

21. $(3 + i)x + i = 5i$ $\frac{2}{5} + \frac{6}{5}i$
22. $(2 + i)x - i = 5 + i$ $\frac{12}{5} - \frac{1}{5}i$
23. $2ix + 5 - 4i = (2 + 3i)x - 2i$ $\frac{8}{5} - \frac{9}{5}i$
24. $5ix + 3 + 2i = (3 - 2i)x + 3i$ $\frac{8}{29} + \frac{9}{29}i$
25. $(1 + 2i)x + 3 - 2i = 4 - 5i + 3ix$ $2 - i$
26. $(1 - 2i)x + 2 - 3i = 5 - 4i + 2x$
27. $(5 + i)x + 1 - 3i =$ $(2 - 3i)x + 2 - i$ $\frac{11}{25} + \frac{2}{25}i$
28. $(5 - i)x + 2 - 3i =$ $(3 - 2i)x + 3 - i$ $-\frac{1}{5} + \frac{7}{5}i$ $\frac{4}{5} + \frac{3}{5}i$

(*See Example 4.*)

29. Show that $(2x + i)(2x - i)$ is a factorization of $4x^2 + 1$.

   $(2x + i)(2x - i) = 4x^2 - 2ix + 2ix - i^2$
   $= 4x^2 + 1$

30. Show that $(2x + 2i)(2x - 2i)$ is a factorization of $4x^2 + 4$.

   $(2x + 2i)(2x - 2i) = 4x^2 - 4ix + 4ix - 4i^2 = 4x^2 + 4$

▮▮▮▮ (*See Example 5.*)

31. Show that $(2 + i)$ is a square root of $3 + 4i$. Then find the other square root. $(2 + i)^2 = 4 + 4i + i^2 = 3 + 4i,\ -2 - i$

32. Show that $(2 - i)$ is a square root of $3 - 4i$. Then find the other square root. $(2 - i)^2 = 4 - 4i + i^2 = 3 - 4i,\ -2 + i$

11-4 Graphical Representation

After finishing Lesson 11-4, you should be able to
▌ graph complex numbers in the plane.
▌▌ find absolute values of complex numbers.

▌ Graphical Representation

The real numbers are graphed on a line. We graph $a + bi$ in the same way we graph ordered pairs of real numbers (a, b). In place of an *x*-axis we have a *real* axis, and in place of a *y*-axis we have an imaginary axis.

Example 1. Graph

A: $3 + 2i$
B: $-4 + 5i$
C: $-5 - 4i$
D: i

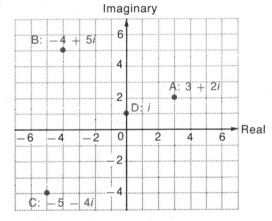

Horizontal distance corresponds to the real part of a number. Vertical distance corresponds to the imaginary part.

TRY THIS

See answer section

1. Graph
   A: $5 - 3i$
   B: $-3 + 4i$
   C: $-5 - 2i$
   D: $-5i$

Absolute Value

From the graph at the right we see that the length of the line drawn from the origin to $a + bi$ is $\sqrt{a^2 + b^2}$. Note that this quantity is a real number. It is called the *absolute value* of $a + bi$ and is denoted $|a + bi|$.

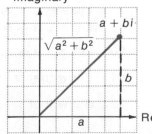

DEFINITION

The *absolute value* of a complex number $a + bi$ is denoted $|a + bi|$ and is defined to be $\sqrt{a^2 + b^2}$.

Example 2. Find $|-3 + 4i|$.

$$\begin{aligned} |-3 + 4i| &= \sqrt{(-3)^2 + 4^2} \\ &= \sqrt{9 + 16} \\ &= \sqrt{25} \\ &= 5 \end{aligned}$$

TRY THIS ➡️

Find the following absolute values.

2. $|4 - 3i|$ 5
3. $|-12 - 5i|$ 13
4. $|1 + i|$ $\sqrt{2}$

Exercise Set 11-4

▌Graph. (*See Example 1.*)   See answer section

1. $3 + 2i, 2 - 5i, -4 - 2i$
3. $-4 + 2i, -3 - 4i, 2 - 3i$
5. $-2 - 5i, 5 + 3i, -3 - 4i$

2. $3 - 4i, -5 + 3i, -2 - 3i$
4. $-5 + 4i, 3 - 2i, -5 + 5i$
6. $2 + 2i, -3 - 3i, 2 - 3i$

▌▌Find the following absolute values. (*See Example 2.*)

7. $|-4 - 3i|$ 5
9. $|8 + 15i|$ 17
11. $|1 - 3i|$ $\sqrt{10}$
13. $|3i|$ 3
15. $|c - di|$ $\sqrt{c^2 + d^2}$

8. $|-3 - 4i|$ 5
10. $|7 - 24i|$ 25
12. $|-2 + i|$ $\sqrt{5}$
14. $|-2i|$ 2
16. $|-c + di|$ $\sqrt{c^2 + d^2}$

Challenge Exercises   See answer section

17. Show that for any complex number z, $|z| = |-z|$. (*Hint:* Let $z = a + bi$.)
18. Show that for any complex number z, $|z| = |$the conjugate of $z|$. (*Hint:* Let $z = a + bi$.)
19. Let $z = a + bi$ and $w = c + di$. Find a general formula for $z \cdot w$.
20. Let $z = a + bi$ and $w = c + di$. Find a general formula for $\dfrac{z}{w}$.
21. Show that $|z \cdot w| = |z| \cdot |w|$.
22. Show that $\left| \dfrac{z}{w} \right| = \dfrac{|z|}{|w|}$.

11-5 Conjugates of Polynomials

After finishing Lesson 11-5, you should be able to
■ find a polynomial in $\bar{z}$ that is the conjugate of a polynomial in z.

We can name a complex number $a + bi$ as z. For the conjugate of z, we write $\bar{z}$, or $\overline{a + bi}$. By definition of conjugates, $\overline{a + bi} = a - bi$ and $\overline{a - bi} = a + bi$. We have already noted (Theorem 11-1) that the product of a number and its conjugate is a real number. We restate that theorem and consider some others.

THEOREM 11-5
For any complex number z, $z \cdot \bar{z}$ is a real number.

The sum of a number and its conjugate is also always real.

THEOREM 11-6
For any complex number, z, $z + \bar{z}$ is a real number.

A Proof of Theorem 11-5
We have said that for any complex number z, $z \cdot \bar{z}$ is a real number.
Let us prove this.
    Let $z = a + bi$. Then $(a - bi)$ is $\bar{z}$, and

$$z \cdot \bar{z} = (a + bi)(a - bi),$$
$$= a^2 - b^2 i^2,$$
$$= a^2 + b^2.$$

Since a and b are real numbers, so is $a^2 + b^2$. Thus $z \cdot \bar{z}$ is a real number.

Taking the conjugate of a sum gives the same result as adding the conjugates.

THEOREM 11-7
For any complex numbers z and w, $\overline{z + w} = \bar{z} + \bar{w}$.

Example 1. Compare $\overline{(2 + 4i) + (5 + i)}$ and $\overline{(2 + 4i)} + \overline{(5 + i)}$

$$\overline{(2 + 4i) + (5 + i)} = \overline{7 + 5i} \quad \textit{Adding the complex numbers}$$
$$= 7 - 5i \quad \textit{Taking the conjugate}$$

$$\overline{(2 + 4i)} + \overline{(5 + i)} = (2 - 4i) + (5 - i) \quad \textit{Taking conjugates}$$
$$= 7 - 5i \quad \textit{Adding}$$

TRY THIS ➡

1. Compare $\overline{(3 + 2i) + (4 - 5i)}$ with $\overline{(3 + 2i)} + \overline{(4 - 5i)}$.

Answer.   1. $\overline{(3 + 2i) + (4 - 5i)} = \overline{(7 - 3i)} = 7 + 3i$,

$\overline{(3 + 2i)} + \overline{(4 - 5i)} = (3 - 2i) + (4 + 5i) = 7 + 3i$

A Proof of Theorem 11-7

We have said that for any complex numbers z and w, $\overline{z + w} = \overline{z} + \overline{w}$. Let us prove this.

Let $z = a + bi$ and $w = c + di$. Then

$$\overline{z + w} = \overline{(a + bi) + (c + di)},$$
$$= \overline{(a + c) + (b + d)i}, \quad \textit{Adding}$$
$$= (a + c) - (b + d)i. \quad \textit{Taking the conjugate}$$

Now,

$$\overline{z} + \overline{w} = \overline{(a + bi)} + \overline{(c + di)},$$
$$= (a - bi) + (c - di), \quad \textit{Taking the conjugates}$$
$$= (a + c) - (b + d)i. \quad \textit{Adding}$$

This is the same result as before. Thus $\overline{z + w} = \overline{z} + \overline{w}$.

Let us next consider the conjugate of a product. The conjugate of a product is the product of the conjugates.

THEOREM 11-8

For any complex numbers z and w, $\overline{z \cdot w} = \overline{z} \cdot \overline{w}$.

Example 2. Compare $\overline{(3 + 2i)(4 - 5i)}$ and $\overline{(3 + 2i)} \cdot \overline{(4 - 5i)}$.

$$\overline{(3 + 2i)(4 - 5i)} = \overline{22 - 7i} \quad \textit{Multiplying}$$
$$= 22 + 7i \quad \textit{Taking the conjugate}$$
$$\overline{(3 + 2i)} \cdot \overline{(4 - 5i)} = (3 - 2i)(4 + 5i) \quad \textit{Taking conjugates}$$
$$= 22 + 7i \quad \textit{Multiplying}$$

TRY THIS ➡

2. Compare $\overline{(2 + 5i)(1 + 3i)}$ and $\overline{(2 + 5i)} \cdot \overline{(1 + 3i)}$.

Answer.   2. $\overline{(2 + 5i)(1 + 3i)} = \overline{(-13 + 11i)} = -13 - 11i$,

$\overline{(2 + 5i)} \cdot \overline{(1 + 3i)} = (2 - 5i)(1 - 3i) = -13 - 11i$

Let us now consider conjugates of powers, using the preceding result. The conjugate of a power is the power of the conjugate.

THEOREM 11-9

For any complex number z, $\overline{z^n} = \overline{z}^n$, where n is a natural number.

Example 3. Show that for any complex number z, $\overline{z^2} = \overline{z}^2$

$$\overline{z^2} = \overline{z \cdot z} \qquad \text{\textit{By definition of exponents}}$$
$$= \overline{z} \cdot \overline{z} \qquad \text{\textit{Using Theorem 11-8}}$$
$$= \overline{z}^2 \qquad \text{\textit{By definition of exponents}}$$

TRY THIS ➡

> 3. Show that for any complex number z, $\overline{z^3} = \overline{z}^3$.
> $$\overline{z^3} = \overline{z \cdot z \cdot z} = \overline{z} \cdot \overline{z} \cdot \overline{z} = \overline{z}^3$$

The conjugate of a real number $a + 0i$ is $a - 0i$, and both are equal to a. Thus a real number is its own conjugate.

THEOREM 11-10

If z is a real number, then $\overline{z} = z$.

▮Conjugates of Polynomials

Given a polynomial in z, where z is a variable for a complex number, we can find its conjugate in terms of $\overline{z}$.

Example 4. Find a polynomial in $\overline{z}$ that is the conjugate of $3z^2 + 2z - 1$.

We write the expression for the conjugate and then use the properties of conjugates.

$$\overline{3z^2 + 2z - 1} = \overline{3z^2} + \overline{2z} + \overline{1} \qquad \text{\textit{Using Theorem 11-7}}$$
$$= \overline{3} \cdot \overline{z^2} + \overline{2} \cdot \overline{z} - \overline{1} \qquad \text{\textit{Using Theorem 11-8}}$$
$$= 3\overline{z^2} + 2\overline{z} - 1 \qquad \text{\textit{Using Theorem 11-10}}$$
$$= 3\overline{z}^2 + 2\overline{z} - 1 \qquad \text{\textit{Using Theorem 11-9}}$$

TRY THIS ➡

> Find a polynomial in $\overline{z}$ that is the conjugate of the following.
>
> 4. $5z^3 + 4z^2 - 2z + 1$
> 5. $7z^5 - 3z^3 + 8z^2 + z$

Answers.  4. $5\overline{z}^3 + 4\overline{z}^2 - 2\overline{z} + 1$ 5. $7\overline{z}^5 - 3\overline{z}^3 + 8\overline{z}^2 + \overline{z}$

Exercise Set 11-5

Use Quiz 20 after lesson 11—5.

■ Find a polynomial in $\bar{z}$ that is the conjugate. (*See Example 4.*)

1. $z^2 - 3z + 5$ $\bar{z}^2 - 3\bar{z} + 5$
2. $z^2 + 4z - 1$ $\bar{z}^2 + 4\bar{z} - 1$
3. $3z^5 - 4z^2 + 3z - 5$ $3\bar{z}^5 - 4\bar{z}^2 + 3\bar{z} - 5$
4. $5z^4 - 2z^3 + 5z - 3$ $5\bar{z}^4 - 2\bar{z}^3 + 5\bar{z} - 3$
5. $7z^4 + 5z^3 - 12z$ $7\bar{z}^4 + 5\bar{z}^3 - 12\bar{z}$
6. $4z^7 - 3z^5 + 4z$ $4\bar{z}^7 - 3\bar{z}^5 + 4\bar{z}$
7. $5z^{10} - 7z^8 + 13z^2 - 4$ $5\bar{z}^{10} - 7\bar{z}^8 + 13\bar{z}^2 - 4$
8. $8z^{12} - 8z^7 + 12z^5 - 8$ $8\bar{z}^{12} - 8\bar{z}^7 + 12\bar{z}^5 - 8$
9. $7z^{100} - 15z^{89} + z^2$ $7\bar{z}^{100} - 15\bar{z}^{89} + \bar{z}^2$
10. $17z^{45} + 70z^3 - 14z + 2$

$17\bar{z}^{45} + 70\bar{z}^3 - 14\bar{z} + 2$

Challenge Exercises

11. Prove Theorem 11-6.
12. Prove Theorem 11-8.

11. Let $z = a + bi$. Then $(a - bi)$ is $\bar{z}$, and $z + \bar{z} = (a + bi) + (a - bi) = 2a$. Since a is a real number, so is $2a$. Thus $z + \bar{z}$ is a real number. 12. Let $z = a + bi$ and $w = c + di$. Then $\overline{z \cdot w} = \overline{(a + bi)(c + di)} = \overline{(ac - bd) + (bc + ad)i} = (ac - bd) - (bc + ad)i$. Now $\bar{z} \cdot \bar{w} = \overline{(a + bi)} \cdot \overline{(c + di)} = (a - bi)(c - di) = (ac - bd) - (bc + ad)i$. Thus $\overline{z \cdot w} = \bar{z} \cdot \bar{w}$.

MATHEMATICAL NOTE: The Rule of False Position

Suppose you know that a number plus a seventh of the number is nineteen. How can you find the number?

One way is to write a linear equation, $x + \frac{1}{7}x = 19$, and solve it for x. Another way is to use the rule of false position.

To use the rule of false position, choose any value for x. Then try it in the equation. Suppose $x = 7$. Then $x + \frac{1}{7}x = 8$, not 19. But you can use your false answer to find the true answer. The ratio of the true value of x is to 7 as 19 is to 8. That is, $\frac{x}{7} = \frac{19}{8}$. The answer then is $\frac{17 \cdot 19}{8}$, or $16\frac{5}{8}$.

This rule was known to mathematicians in both ancient Egypt and ancient China. It appears in texts from the Middle Ages through the 1800s.

COMPUTER ACTIVITY

Finding the Quotient of Two Complex Numbers

PROBLEM: Find the quotient $(A + BI) \div (C + DI)$.

Examples using the flowchart:

	1			2	3	4
A	B	C	D	E $(C^2 + D^2)$	X	Y
2	3	4	−1	17	0.29411	0.82352
3	−1	−1	2	5	−1	−1

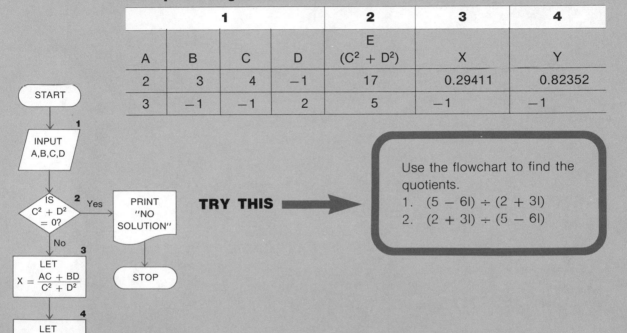

TRY THIS ➡

Use the flowchart to find the quotients.
1. $(5 − 6I) \div (2 + 3I)$
2. $(2 + 3I) \div (5 − 6I)$

BASIC PROGRAM (Optional)
```
10   INPUT A,B,C,D
20   LET E = C↑2 + D↑2
30   IF E = 0 THEN 90
40   LET X = ((A*C) + (B*D))/E
50   LET Y = ((B*C) − (A*D))/E
60   PRINT "E ="E, "X ="X,
        "Y ="Y
70   PRINT "QUOTIENT ="X;" + "Y;"I"
80   GO TO 100
90   PRINT "NO SOLUTION"
100  STOP
```

CHAPTER 11 REVIEW

Review the material in the chapter. Then see how you have done by trying these review exercises. If you miss an exercise, restudy the indicated lesson.

11-1   1. Add: $(6 + 2i) + (-4 - 3i)$. $2 - i$
11-1   2. Subtract: $(3 - 5i) - (2 - i)$. $1 - 4i$
11-2   3. Solve for x and y: $4x + 2i = 8 - (2 + y)i$. $x = 2, y = -4$

11-2   Multiply.
      4. $(7i)^2$ -49
      5. $(2 - 2i)(3 + 4i)$ $14 + 2i$
      6. $(5 + 3i)^2$ $16 + 30i$

11-2   7. Find the conjugate of $-8 - 9i$. $-8 + 9i$
11-2   8. Multiply: $(2 - 3i)(2 + 3i)$. 13
11-2   9. Divide: $\dfrac{2 - 3i}{1 - 3i}$. $\dfrac{11}{10} + \dfrac{3}{10}i$
11-2   10. Find the reciprocal of $4 + i$, and express it in the $\dfrac{4}{17} - \dfrac{1}{17}i$
           form $a + bi$.
11-3   11. Find an equation having the solutions $1 - 2i$,
           $1 + 2i$. $x^2 - 2x + 5$
11-3   12. Solve: $2ix - 5 + 3i = (2 - i)x + i$. $-\dfrac{16}{13} - \dfrac{11}{13}i$
11-4   13. Graph $-3 - 2i$ and $4 + 5i$.   See answer section
11-4   14. Find $|4 - 8i|$. $4\sqrt{5}$
11-5   15. Find a polynomial in $\overline{z}$ that is the conjugate of
           $3z^2 + z - 7$. $3\overline{z}^2 + \overline{z} - 7$

CHAPTER 11 TEST

1. Add: $(3 + 2i) + (2 - 3i)$. $5 - i$
2. Subtract: $(9 - 4i) - (3 + 2i)$. $6 - 6i$
3. Solve for x and y: $3x + i = -4 + yi$. $x = -\frac{4}{3}, y = 1$

Multiply.

4. $8i \cdot 3i$. -24
5. $(1 - 2i)(2 - i)$. $-5i$
6. $(1 - 2i)^2$. $-3 - 4i$

7. Find the conjugate of $-2 + i$. $-2 - i$
8. Multiply: $(2 + 5i)(2 - 5i)$. 29

9. Divide: $\dfrac{4 + 3i}{2 - 1}$. $1 + 2i$

10. Find the reciprocal of $5 - 2i$ and express it in the form $\frac{5}{29} + \frac{2}{29}i$
    $a + bi$.

11. Find an equation having the solutions $2 - i, 2 + i$. $x^2 - 4x + 5$
12. Solve: $-5ix + 8i - 4 = (7 + i)x + 10i$. $-\frac{8}{17} + \frac{2}{17}i$
13. Graph $3 - i$ and $4 + 6i$.   See answer section
14. Find $|4 + 2i|$. $2\sqrt{5}$
15. Find a polynomial in $\overline{z}$ that is the conjugate of $2z^6 - 4z^3 +$
    $z + 1$. $2\overline{z}^6 - 4\overline{z}^3 + \overline{z} + 1$

Use Cumulative Test 3 after Cumulative Review below.

CUMULATIVE REVIEW FOR CHAPTERS 9–11

9-1   1. Simplify: $\dfrac{2x^2 + 5x - 3}{2x^2 - 11x + 5}$. $\frac{x+3}{x-5}$

9-1   2. Multiply and simplify: $\dfrac{x^2 + x - 12}{5x - 5} \cdot \dfrac{x - 1}{x - 3}$. $\frac{x+4}{5}$

9-1   3. Divide and simplify: $\dfrac{4x^3}{2x^2 + 11x - 21} \div \dfrac{12x}{x^2 + 8x + 7}$.

$\frac{x^2(x+1)}{3(2x-3)}$ or $\frac{x^3 + x^2}{6x - 9}$

9-3   Add.

4. $\dfrac{2x + 1}{5 - x} + \dfrac{x - 6}{-x + 5}$ 5. $\dfrac{5x - 1}{x^2 - x} + \dfrac{-x}{x - x^2}$

6. $\dfrac{7x + 5}{x + 3} + \dfrac{x^2 - 3}{x^2 + 2x - 3}$

4. $\frac{3x-5}{5-x}$ 5. $\frac{6x-1}{x^2-x}$ 6. $\frac{2(4x^2-x-4)}{x^2+2x-3}$

9-3   Subtract.

7. $\dfrac{y^2}{y + 9} - \dfrac{-4y^2}{y + 9}$ 8. $\dfrac{3m^2 + 1}{8 - m} - \dfrac{2m^2}{-8 + m}$

9. $\dfrac{7x + 3}{3x^2 - 4x - 4} - \dfrac{x - 1}{3x + 2}$

7. $\frac{5y^2}{y+9}$ 8. $\frac{5m^2+1}{8-m}$ 9. $\frac{-x^2+10x+1}{3x^2-4x-4}$

9-4   10. Simplify: $\dfrac{x - \dfrac{3}{x}}{\dfrac{1}{x^2} + 4}$. $\frac{x^3 - 3x}{1 + 4x^2}$

9-5   11. Divide: $(a^4 - 3a^3 + 7a - 8) \div (a^2 - 5)$. $a^2 - 3a + 5$, R $-8a + 17$

9-6   12. Solve: $\dfrac{5}{4y} = \dfrac{7}{5y - 2}$. $y = -\frac{10}{3}$

9-7   13. Solve for v_s: $F_L = F_s\left(\dfrac{v + v_L}{v - v_s}\right)$. $v_s = \frac{F_L v - F_s v - F_s v_L}{F_L}$

9-8   14. Solve: The speed of a river is 8 km/h. A boat could only travel 8 km upstream in the same time it would take to travel 40 km downstream. What is the speed of the boat in still water?   12 km/h

9-9   15. In physics, the amount of power (measured in watts) it takes to do a fixed amount of work (measured in joules) varies inversely with the time it takes to do the work. If an 18 kilowatt motor can raise an elevator 6 stories in 16 seconds, how much power would a motor need to do the job in 25 seconds?   11.52 kilowatts

10-1   16.   Convert to scientific notation: 0.0000825. 8.25×10^{-5}

10-1   17.   Convert to decimal notation: 2.003×10^4.   20,030

10-2   18.   Simplify: $\sqrt[3]{125x^6}$. $5x^2$

10-3   19.   Multiply: $\sqrt{11}\ \sqrt{5}$. $\sqrt{55}$

10-3   20.   Simplify: $\sqrt{92}$. $2\sqrt{23}$

10-3   21.   Multiply and simplify: $\sqrt{20y^3}\ \sqrt{32y}$. $8y^2\sqrt{10}$

10-4   22.   Simplify: $\sqrt[3]{\frac{125}{8}}$. $\frac{5}{2}$

10-4   23.   Divide and simplify: $\dfrac{\sqrt{14m^3}}{\sqrt{2m}}$. $m\sqrt{7}$

10-4   24.   Simplify: $(\sqrt[3]{9y})^2$. $3\sqrt[3]{3y^2}$

10-5   25.   Simplify: $\sqrt{27} + \sqrt{147}$. $10\sqrt{3}$

10-7   26.   Rationalize the denominator: $\sqrt{\dfrac{3y^2}{2x}}$. $\frac{y\sqrt{6x}}{2x}$

10-7   27.   Rationalize the numerator: $\sqrt[3]{\dfrac{4}{9x}}$. $\frac{2}{\sqrt[3]{18x}}$

10-7   28.   Rationalize the denominator: $\dfrac{\sqrt{2x}}{\sqrt{5} + \sqrt{x}}$. $\frac{\sqrt{10x}\ -\ x\sqrt{2}}{5\ -\ x}$

        29.   Rewrite without fractional exponents: $(m^5n^5)^{\frac{1}{3}}$. $mn\sqrt[3]{m^2n^2}$

10-8   30.   Rewrite with fractional exponents: $\sqrt[3]{x^7}$. $x^{7/3}$

10-8   31.   Use exponential notation to write the expression $\sqrt[6]{m^3n^2}$. Then simplify if possible. Assume variables stand for nonnegative numbers. Write radical notation for the answer, if appropriate. $\sqrt{m}\sqrt[3]{n}$

10-9   32.   Solve: $\sqrt{2x + 3} = 4$. $x = \frac{13}{2}$

10-9   33.   Solve: $2\sqrt{10 - 3x} = 1 + \sqrt{51 - 14x}$.   No real roots

11-1   34.   Add: $(-5 - 2i) + (4 + 3i)$. $-1 + i$

11-1   35.   Subtract: $(7 - 2i) - (3 - 4i)$. $4 + 2i$

11-2   36.   Solve for x and y: $-5y + 15i = 30 - 3xi$. $x = -5,\ y = -6$

11-2   37.   Multiply: $(3 + 5i)(2 - 6i)$. $36 - 8i$

11-2   38.   Find the conjugate of $-3 + 7i$. $-3 - 7i$

11-2   39.   Multiply: $(-4 + 2i)(-4 - 2i)$.   20

11-2   40.   Divide: $\dfrac{3 + 2i}{1 - 3i}$. $\frac{-3 + 11i}{10}$

11-2   41.   Find the reciprocal of $-2 + 3i$ and express it in the form $a + bi$. $-\frac{2}{13} - \frac{3}{13}i$

11-3   42.   Find an equation having the solutions $2 - 3i$, $2 + 3i$. $x^2 - 4x + 13 = 0$

11-3   43.   Solve: $(3 - 2i)x - 5ix - 2i = 3 - 3i$. $\frac{8 + 9i}{29}$

11-4   44.   Graph: $2 - 3i$ and $-8 + 6i$.   See answer section

11-4   45.   Find: $|-3 + 2i|$. $\sqrt{13}$

11-5   46.   Find a polynomial in $\bar{z}$ that is the conjugate of $7z^2 + z$. $7\bar{z}^2 + \bar{z}$

Ready for Quadratic Equations?

Solve.

2-2   1. $(x - 5)(x + 3) = 0$ 5, −3

7-7   2. $x^2 - 5x - 14 = 0$ 7, −2

7-7   3. $4x^2 - 8x = 0$ 0, 2

7-7   4. $x^2 + 10x + 25 = 0$ −5

7-7   5. $x^2 - 9 = 0$ 3, −3

7-8   6.   The length of a rectangle is 5m more than the width. The area is 24m². Find the dimensions.   Length is 8 m; width is 3 m

Simplify.

10-2   7. $\sqrt{49}$ 7

10-3   8. $\sqrt{88}$ $2\sqrt{22}$

10-3   9.   Simplify and approximate to the nearest tenth: $\dfrac{14 - \sqrt{88}}{10}$ 0.5

10-7   10.   Rationalize the denominator: $\sqrt{\dfrac{2}{5}}$ $\frac{\sqrt{10}}{5}$

11-1   Express in terms of i.

11. $\sqrt{-7}$ $\sqrt{7}i$

12. $\sqrt{-20}$ $2\sqrt{5}i$

11-2   13.   Find the conjugate of $-2 + 3i$.   −2, − 3i

11-3   14.   Determine whether $1 + i$ is a solution of $x^2 + 2x + 1 = 0$.   No

Chapter 12
Quadratic Equations

How long would it take an object dropped from
the top of the arch to reach the ground?

12-1 Introduction to Quadratic Equations

After finishing Lesson 12-1, you should be able to
▪ solve equations of the type $ax^2 = k$, where $k \neq 0$.

▪ Equations of second degree are called *quadratic*.

DEFINITION

An equation of the type $ax^2 + bx + c = 0$, where a, b and c are constants and $a \neq 0$, is called the *standard form of a quadratic equation*.

We first consider solving equations in which $b = 0$, that is equations $ax^2 + c = 0$, or $ax^2 = -c$. In other words, equations in which we have ax^2 equal to some constant.

Example 1. Solve: $3x^2 = 6$.
$$x^2 = 2 \qquad \text{\textit{Multiplying by }} \tfrac{1}{3}$$

By Theorem 11-4, every complex number has two square roots that are additive inverses of each other. We take the two square roots.

$$\sqrt{x^2} = \sqrt{2} \qquad \sqrt{x^2} = -\sqrt{2}$$

We have

$$x = \sqrt{2} \text{ or } x = -\sqrt{2}.$$

Abbreviating, we have $x = \pm\sqrt{2}$.

TRY THIS ➡

Sometimes we rationalize denominators to simplify answers.

Solve.

1. $5x^2 = 15$ $\pm\sqrt{3}$
2. $7x^2 = 0$ 0

Example 2. Solve: $-5x^2 + 2 = 0$.
$$-5x^2 = -2 \qquad \text{\textit{Adding }} -2$$
$$x^2 = \frac{2}{5} \qquad \text{\textit{Multiplying by }} -\frac{1}{5}$$

$$x = \sqrt{\frac{2}{5}} \quad \text{ or } \quad x = -\sqrt{\frac{2}{5}} \qquad \text{\textit{Taking square roots}}$$

$$x = \sqrt{\frac{2}{5}\cdot\frac{5}{5}} \quad \text{ or } \quad x = -\sqrt{\frac{2}{5}\cdot\frac{5}{5}} \qquad \text{\textit{Rationalizing the denominators}}$$

$$x = \frac{\sqrt{10}}{5} \quad \text{ or } \quad x = -\frac{\sqrt{10}}{5}$$

The solutions are $\dfrac{\sqrt{10}}{5}$ and $-\dfrac{\sqrt{10}}{5}$.

TRY THIS ➡

> Solve. $\pm\dfrac{2\sqrt{6}}{3}$
>
> 3. $-3x^2 + 8 = 0$

Example 3. Solve: $4x^2 + 9 = 0$.

$$4x^2 = -9 \qquad \text{Adding } -9$$
$$x^2 = -\tfrac{9}{4} \qquad \text{Multiplying by } \tfrac{1}{4}$$

$$x = \sqrt{-\tfrac{9}{4}} \quad \text{or} \quad x = -\sqrt{-\tfrac{9}{4}} \qquad \text{Taking square roots (Theorem 11-4)}$$
$$x = \tfrac{3}{2}i \qquad \text{or} \quad x = -\tfrac{3}{2}i$$

TRY THIS ➡

> Solve. $\pm\dfrac{i\sqrt{2}}{2}$
>
> 4. $2x^2 + 1 = 0$

Exercise Set 12-1

▌Solve. (*See Examples 1–3.*)

1. $4x^2 = 20$ $\pm\sqrt{5}$
2. $3x^2 = 21$ $\pm\sqrt{7}$
3. $10x^2 = 0$ 0
4. $9x^2 = 0$ 0
5. $2x^2 - 3 = 0$ $\pm\dfrac{\sqrt{6}}{2}$
6. $3x^2 - 7 = 0$ $\pm\dfrac{\sqrt{21}}{3}$
7. $-3x^2 + 5 = 0$ $\pm\dfrac{\sqrt{15}}{3}$
8. $-2x^2 + 1 = 0$ $\pm\dfrac{\sqrt{2}}{2}$
9. $4x^2 - 1 = 0$ $\pm\dfrac{1}{2}$
10. $9x^2 - 1 = 0$ $\pm\dfrac{1}{3}$
11. $25x^2 + 4 = 0$ $\pm\dfrac{2}{5}i$
12. $9x^2 + 16 = 0$ $\pm\dfrac{4}{3}i$
13. $3x^2 + 1 = 0$ $\pm\dfrac{i\sqrt{3}}{3}$
14. $5x^2 + 1 = 0$ $\pm\dfrac{i\sqrt{5}}{5}$
15. $x^2 + 5 = 0$ $\pm i\sqrt{5}$
16. $x^2 + 6 = 0$ $\pm i\sqrt{6}$
17. $2x^2 + 14 = 0$ $\pm i\sqrt{7}$
18. $3x^2 + 15 = 0$ $\pm i\sqrt{5}$
19. $\tfrac{4}{9}x^2 - 1 = 0$ $\pm\dfrac{3}{2}$
20. $\tfrac{16}{25}x^2 - 1 = 0$ $\pm\dfrac{5}{4}$

Calculator Exercises

Solve.

21. $16.3x^2 = 798.7$ ± 7
22. $14.24x^2 = 512.64$ ± 6
23. $25.55x^2 - 1635.2 = 0$ ± 8
24. $24.48x^2 - 1982.88 = 0$ ± 9

Challenge Exercises

Solve for x.

25. $ax^2 - b = 0$
26. $ax^2 + b = 0$ 25. $\pm\dfrac{\sqrt{ab}}{a}$ 26. $\pm\dfrac{\sqrt{-ab}}{a}$

12-2 Solving by Factoring

After finishing Lesson 12-2, you should be able to
 - ▮ solve quadratic equations of the type $ax^2 + bx = 0$, $a \neq 0$, $b \neq 0$, by factoring.
 - ▮▮ solve certain quadratic equations of the type $ax^2 + bx + c = 0$, $a \neq 0$, $b \neq 0$, $c \neq 0$, by factoring.

▮ Equations of the Type $ax^2 + bx = 0$

When c is 0 ($a \neq 0$, $b \neq 0$), we can factor and use the principle of zero products.

Example 1. Solve: $3x^2 + 5x = 0$.
$$x(3x + 5) = 0 \qquad \textit{Factoring}$$

$x = 0$ or $3x + 5 = 0$ *Principle of zero products*
$x = 0$ or $3x = -5$
$x = 0$ or $x = -\frac{5}{3}$

The solutions are 0 and $-\frac{5}{3}$.

A quadratic equation of this type will always have 0 as one solution and a nonzero number as the other solution.

TRY THIS ▬▬▶

> Solve. $0, \frac{3}{4}$
>
> 1. $4x^2 - 3x = 0$

▮▮ Equations of the Type $ax^2 + bx + c = 0$

By the fundamental theorem of algebra, every quadratic polynomial $ax^2 + bx + c$ with complex coefficients can be factored into two linear factors. However, the factors may not be easy to find. Factoring offers a good method of solving if the factoring is easy.

Example 2. Solve $3x^2 + x - 2 = 0$.
$$(3x - 2)(x + 1) = 0 \qquad \textit{Factoring}$$

$3x - 2 = 0$ or $x + 1 = 0$
$3x = 2$ or $x = -1$
$x = \frac{2}{3}$ or $x = -1$

The solutions are $\frac{2}{3}$ and -1.

TRY THIS ▬▬▶

> Solve. $\frac{3}{5}, 1$
>
> 2. $5x^2 - 8x + 3 = 0$

Example 3. A rectangular garden is 60 m by 80 m. Part of the garden is torn up to install a strip of lawn of uniform width around the garden. The new area of the garden is $\frac{1}{6}$ of the old area. How wide is the strip of lawn?

First make a drawing.

Let x represent the width of the strip of lawn. Then,

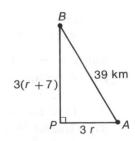

Area of old garden $= 60 \cdot 80$ *Multiplying length and width*
Area of new garden $= (60 - 2x)(80 - 2x)$

Since the new garden is $\frac{1}{6}$ of the old we have

$$(60 - 2x)(80 - 2x) = \tfrac{1}{6} \cdot 60 \cdot 80$$
$$4800 - 160x - 120x + 4x^2 = 800$$
$$4x^2 - 280x + 4000 = 0 \quad \textit{Writing the standard form}$$
$$x^2 - 70x + 1000 = 0$$
$$(x - 20)(x - 50) = 0$$

$$x = 20 \quad \text{or} \quad x = 50$$

Checking in the original problem we see that 50 is not a solution because when $x = 50$, $60 - 2x = -40$, and the width of the garden cannot be negative. The number 20 checks. Thus the width of the strip of lawn is 20 cm.

TRY THIS

3. An open box is to be made from a 10 cm by 20 cm rectangular piece of cardboard by cutting a square from each corner. The area of the bottom of the box is 96 cm². What is the length of the sides of the squares which are cut from the corners?   **2 cm**

Example 4. Bicycles A and B leave the same point P at the same time at right angles. B travels 7 km/h faster than A. After 3 hours they are 39 km apart. Find the speed of each.

We first make a drawing, letting r be the speed of A and $r + 7$ be the speed of B. Since they both travel 3 hr, their distances from P are $3r$ and $3(r + 7)$, respectively. To translate we use the Pythagorean Theorem.

$$[3(r + 7)]^2 + [3r]^2 = 39^2$$
$$9(r + 7)^2 + 9r^2 = 1521$$
$$(r + 7)^2 + r^2 = 169 \quad \textit{Multiplying by } \tfrac{1}{9}$$
$$r^2 + 14r + 49 + r^2 = 169$$
$$2r^2 + 14r + 49 = 169$$

We write the equation in standard form.

$$2r^2 + 14r - 120 = 0$$
$$r^2 + 7r - 60 = 0 \qquad \textit{Multiplying by } \tfrac{1}{2}$$
$$(r + 12)(r - 5) = 0$$

$$r + 12 = 0 \qquad \text{or} \quad r - 5 = 0$$
$$r = -12 \quad \text{or} \qquad r = 5$$

The solutions of the equation are -12 and 5. Since speed cannot be negative in this problem, -12 is not a solution. The number 5 checks, so the speed of A is 5 km/h and the speed of B is 12 km/h.

TRY THIS ▆▶

4. Joggers A and B leave the same point P at right angles. A jogs 1 km/h faster than B. After 2 hours they are 10 km apart. Find the speed of each.
A: 4 km/h; B: 3 km/h

Exercise Set 12-2

▎Solve. (*See Example 1.*)

1. $x^2 - 5x = 0$ 0, 5
2. $x^2 - 6x = 0$ 0, 6
3. $5x^2 + 10x = 0$ 0, -2
4. $3x^2 + 12x = 0$ 0, -4
5. $3x^2 - 2x = 0$ $0, \frac{2}{3}$
6. $7x^2 - 3x = 0$ $0, \frac{3}{7}$
7. $14x^2 + 9x = 0$ $0, -\frac{9}{14}$
8. $19x^2 + 8x = 0$ $0, -\frac{8}{19}$
9. $11x^2 - 55x = 0$ 0, 5
10. $13x^2 + 65x = 0$ 0, -5

▌▌Solve. (*See Example 2.*)

11. $x^2 - 6x + 5 = 0$ 5, 1
12. $x^2 - 7x + 6 = 0$ 6, 1
13. $x^2 - 4x - 5 = 0$ 5, -1
14. $x^2 - 6x - 7 = 0$ 7, -1
15. $x^2 + 8x + 15 = 0$ -5, -3
16. $x^2 + 9x + 14 = 0$ -7, -2
17. $6x^2 - x - 2 = 0$ $\frac{2}{3}, -\frac{1}{2}$
18. $2x^2 + 13x + 15 = 0$ $-\frac{3}{2}, -5$
19. $9t^2 + 15t + 4 = 0$ $-\frac{4}{3}, -\frac{1}{3}$
20. $3y^2 + 10y - 8 = 0$ $\frac{2}{3}, -4$
21. $6x^2 + 4x = 10$ $-\frac{5}{3}, 1$
22. $3x^2 + 7x = 20$ $\frac{5}{3}, -4$
23. $2x(4x - 5) = 3$ $-\frac{1}{4}, \frac{3}{2}$
24. $t(2t + 9) = -7$ $-\frac{7}{2}, -1$
25. $(p - 3)(p - 4) = 42$ 10, -3
26. $16(t - 1) = t(t + 8)$ 4
27. $4x(x - 2) - 5x(x - 1) = 2$ -2, -1
28. $14(x - 4) - (x + 2) = (x + 2)(x - 4)$
    10, 5

Solve. (*See Examples 3 and 4.*)

29. A picture frame measures 14 cm by 20 cm. 160 cm² of picture shows. Find the width of the frame.   2 cm
30. A picture frame measures 12 cm by 20 cm. 84 cm² of picture shows. Find the width of the frame.   3 cm
31. The width of a rectangle is 4 m less than the length. The area is 12 m². Find the length and width. Length is 6 m; width is 2 m
32. The width of a rectangle is 5 m less than the length. The area is 24 m². Find the length and width.
    Length is 8 m; width is 3 m

33. The length of a rectangle is twice the width. The area is 288 m². Find the length and width.   Length is 24 m; width is 12 m

34. The length of a rectangle is twice the width. The area is 338 km². Find the length and width. Length is 26 m; width is 13 m

35. The hypotenuse of a right triangle is 5 m long. One leg is 1 m less than the other. Find the lengths of the legs.   4 m and 3 m

36. The hypotenuse of a right triangle is 13 m long. One leg is 7 m longer than the other. Find the lengths of the legs.   12 m and 5 m

37. The hypotenuse of a right triangle is 26 m long. The length of one leg is 14 m longer than the other. Find the lengths of the legs.   24 m and 10 m

38. The hypotenuse of a right triangle is 25 km long. The length of one leg is 17 km less than the other. Find the lengths of the legs.   24 km and 7 km

39. Trains *A* and *B* leave the same city at the same time at right angles. Train *B* travels 5 km/h faster than Train *A*. After 2 hr they are 50 km apart. Find the speed of each train.   A: 15 km/h; B: 20 km/h

40. Boats *A* and *B* leave the same point at the same time at right angles. *B* travels 7 km/h slower than *A*. After 4 hr they are 68 km apart. Find the speed of each boat. A: 15 km/h; B: 8 km/h

---

Challenge Exercises

Solve.

41. $(3x^2 - 7x - 20)(2x - 5) = 0$ $-\frac{5}{3}, 4, \frac{6}{2}$

42. $(12x^2 - 5x - 2)(8x + 11) = 0$ $-\frac{1}{4}, \frac{2}{3}, -\frac{11}{8}$

43. The sum of the squares of two consecutive positive integers is 61. What are the integers?   5 and 6

44. Find three consecutive integers such that the square of the first plus the product of the other two is 46.   4, 5, and 6

45. During the first part of a trip a man travels 80 km at a certain speed. He travels 35 km on the second part of the trip at a speed which is 5 km/h slower. The total time for the trip is 3 hours. How fast did he travel on each part of the trip?   First part: 40 km/h; second part: 35 km/h

46. A woman travels 280 km at a certain speed. If she had increased her speed 5 km/h, she could have made the trip in 1 hour less time. Find her actual speed.   35 km/h

47. Airplane *A* travels 2800 km at a certain speed. Airplane *B* travels 2000 km at a speed which is 50 km/h faster than Plane *A* in 3 hours less time. Find the speed of each plane.   A: 350 km/h; B: 400 km/h

48. Two pipes are connected to the same tank. When working together they can fill the tank in 2 hours. The pipes are of different size. The larger one, working alone, can fill the tank in 3 hours less time than the smaller one. How long would the smaller one take, working alone, to fill the tank?   6 hours

12-3 The Quadratic Formula

After finishing Lesson 12-3, you should be able to
▮ solve quadratic equations using the quadratic formula.
▮▮ find approximate solutions using a square root table.

▮ Solving Equations Using the Quadratic Formula

Here is a formula for finding the solutions of any quadratic equation.

THEOREM 12-1

The solutions of any quadratic equation (with complex coefficients) $ax^2 + bx + c = 0$ are given by $x = \dfrac{-b \pm \sqrt{b^2 - 4ac}}{2a}$.

The equation $x = \dfrac{-b \pm \sqrt{b^2 - 4ac}}{2a}$ is called the *quadratic formula*.

Example 1. Solve: $5x^2 - 8x = 3$.

First find standard form and determine a, b, and c.

$$5x^2 - 8x - 3 = 0$$
$$a = 5, \; b = -8, \; c = -3$$

Then use the quadratic formula.

$$x = \frac{-b \pm \sqrt{b^2 - 4ac}}{2a}$$
$$x = \frac{-(-8) \pm \sqrt{(-8)^2 - 4 \cdot 5 \cdot (-3)}}{2 \cdot 5}$$
$$x = \frac{8 \pm \sqrt{64 + 60}}{10}$$
$$x = \frac{8 \pm \sqrt{124}}{10}$$
$$x = \frac{8 \pm \sqrt{4 \cdot 31}}{10}$$
$$x = \frac{8 \pm 2\sqrt{31}}{10}$$
$$= \frac{4 \pm \sqrt{31}}{5}$$

The solutions are $\dfrac{4 + \sqrt{31}}{5}$ and $\dfrac{4 - \sqrt{31}}{5}$.

TRY THIS ➡

We can get complex solutions.

Example 2. Solve: $x^2 + x + 1 = 0$.

$a = 1$, $b = 1$, $c = 1$

$$x = \frac{-b \pm \sqrt{b^2 - 4ac}}{2a}$$

$$x = \frac{-1 \pm \sqrt{1^2 - 4 \cdot 1 \cdot 1}}{2 \cdot 1}$$

$$x = \frac{-1 \pm \sqrt{1 - 4}}{2}$$

$$x = \frac{-1 \pm \sqrt{-3}}{2}$$

$$= \frac{-1 \pm i\sqrt{3}}{2}$$

The solutions are $\dfrac{-1 + i\sqrt{3}}{2}$ and $\dfrac{-1 - i\sqrt{3}}{2}$.

Solve using the quadratic formula.

1. $3x^2 + 2x = 7$ $\quad \dfrac{-1 \pm \sqrt{22}}{3}$

Solve. $\dfrac{1 \pm i\sqrt{7}}{2}$

2. $x^2 - x + 2 = 0$

TRY THIS ➡

A Proof of Theorem 12-1

Let us consider any quadratic equation $ax^2 + bx + c = 0$. The coefficients can be any complex numbers except that $a \neq 0$. We multiply on both sides by $4a$, to obtain $4a^2x^2 + 4abx + 4ac = 0$. Now we add $b^2 - b^2$ on the left and rearrange. This gives us

$$4a^2x^2 + 4abx + b^2 - (b^2 - 4ac) = 0$$
or $\qquad 4a^2x^2 + 4abx + b^2 = b^2 - 4ac$
or $\qquad (2ax + b)^2 = b^2 - 4ac.$

By Theorem 11-4, every complex number has two square roots that are additive inverses of each other. We take the two square roots.

$$2ax + b = \sqrt{b^2 - 4ac} \text{ or } 2ax + b = -\sqrt{b^2 - 4ac}$$

Solving for x, we get

$$x = \frac{-b + \sqrt{b^2 - 4ac}}{2a} \text{ or } x = \frac{-b - \sqrt{b^2 - 4ac}}{2a}.$$

Example 3. Solve: $2 + \dfrac{7}{x} = \dfrac{4}{x^2}$

First find standard form.

$$2x^2 + 7x = 4 \qquad \text{\textit{Multiplying by} } x^2\text{, \textit{the LCM of the denominators}}$$
$$2x^2 + 7x - 4 = 0 \qquad \text{\textit{Adding }} -4$$

$a = 2,\ b = 7,\ c = -4$

$$x = \frac{-7 \pm \sqrt{7^2 - 4 \cdot 2 \cdot (-4)}}{2 \cdot 2}$$

$$x = \frac{-7 \pm \sqrt{49 + 32}}{4}$$

$$x = \frac{-7 \pm \sqrt{81}}{4} = \frac{-7 \pm 9}{4}$$

$$x = \frac{-7 + 9}{4} = \frac{1}{2} \text{ or } x = \frac{-7 - 9}{4} = -4$$

The solutions are $\dfrac{1}{2}$ and -4.

The solutions of a quadratic equation can *always* be found using the quadratic formula. They are not always easy to find by factoring. A general strategy for solving quadratic equations is

    a) Try factoring.
    b) If factoring seems difficult, use the quadratic formula; it *always works!*

TRY THIS ━━━━▶

Solve. $2, -\dfrac{1}{3}$

3. $3 - \dfrac{5}{x} = \dfrac{2}{x^2}$

▪ Approximating Solutions

A square root table can be used to approximate solutions.

Example 4. Approximate the solutions of the equation in Example 1.

From Table 1 in the back of the book, $\sqrt{31} \approx 5.568$.

$$\frac{4 + \sqrt{31}}{5} \approx \frac{4 + 5.568}{5}$$

$$\approx \frac{9.568}{5}$$

$$\approx 1.9 \text{ (Rounded to the nearest tenth)}$$

$$\frac{4 - \sqrt{31}}{5} \approx \frac{4 - 5.568}{5}$$

$$\approx \frac{-1.568}{5}$$

$$\approx -0.3 \text{ (Rounded to the nearest tenth)}$$

TRY THIS

4. Approximate the solutions to margin exercise 1. **1.2, −1.9** Round to the nearest tenth.

Exercise Set 12-3

▮Solve. (*See Examples 1–3.*)

1. $x^2 + 6x + 4 = 0$ $-3 \pm \sqrt{5}$
2. $x^2 - 6x - 4 = 0$ $3 \pm \sqrt{13}$
3. $x^2 + 4x - 5 = 0$ $1, -5$
4. $x^2 - 2x - 15 = 0$ $5, -3$
5. $y^2 + 7y = 30$ $3, -10$
6. $y^2 - 7y = 30$ $10, -3$
7. $2t^2 - 3t - 2 = 0$ $2, -\frac{1}{2}$
8. $5m^2 + 3m - 2 = 0$ $\frac{2}{5}, -1$
9. $3p^2 = -8p - 5$ $-1, -\frac{5}{3}$
10. $3u^2 = 18u - 6$ $3 \pm \sqrt{7}$
11. $x^2 - x + 1 = 0$ $\frac{1 \pm i\sqrt{3}}{2}$
12. $x^2 + x + 2 = 0$ $\frac{-1 \pm i\sqrt{7}}{2}$
13. $1 + \frac{2}{x} + \frac{5}{x^2} = 0$ $-1 \pm 2i$
14. $1 + \frac{5}{x^2} = \frac{2}{x}$ $1 \pm 2i$
15. $x^2 - 2x + 5 = 0$ $1 \pm 2i$
16. $x^2 - 4x + 5 = 0$ $2 \pm i$
17. $x^2 + 13 = 4x$ $2 \pm 3i$
18. $x^2 + 13 = 6x$ $3 \pm 2i$
19. $z^2 + 5 = 0$ $\pm i\sqrt{5}$
20. $t^2 + 3 = 0$ $\pm i\sqrt{3}$
21. $r^2 + 3r = 8$ $\frac{-3 \pm \sqrt{41}}{2}$
22. $h^2 + 4 = 6h$ $3 \pm \sqrt{5}$
23. $2x^2 = 5$ $\pm\frac{\sqrt{10}}{2}$
24. $3x^2 = 2$ $\pm\frac{\sqrt{6}}{3}$
25. $3x + x(x - 2) = 0$ $0, -1$
26. $4x + x(x - 3) = 0$ $0, -1$
27. $5x^2 + 2x + 1 = 0$ $\frac{-1 \pm 2i}{5}$
28. $3x^2 + x + 2 = 0$ $\frac{-1 \pm 23i}{6}$
29. $(2t - 3)^2 + 17t = 15$ $\frac{3}{4}, -2$
30. $2y^2 - (y + 2)(y - 3) = 12$ $2, -3$
31. $(x - 2)^2 + (x + 1)^2 = 0$ $\frac{1 \pm 3i}{2}$
32. $(x + 3)^2 + (x - 1)^2 = 0$ $-1 \pm 2i$
33. $x + \frac{1}{x} = \frac{13}{6}$ $\frac{3}{2}, \frac{2}{3}$
34. $\frac{3}{x} + \frac{x}{3} = \frac{5}{2}$ $6, \frac{3}{2}$

▮▮ Use the square root table, Table 1, in the back of the book to approximate solutions to the nearest tenth. (*See Example 4.*)

35. $x^2 + 4x - 7 = 0$ $1.3, -5.3$
36. $x^2 + 6x + 4 = 0$ $-0.8, -5.2$
37. $x^2 - 6x + 4 = 0$ $5.2, 0.8$
38. $x^2 - 4x + 1 = 0$ $3.7, 0.3$
39. $2x^2 - 3x - 7 = 0$ $2.8, -1.3$
40. $3x^2 - 3x - 2 = 0$ $1.5, -0.5$
41. $3x^2 + 8x + 2 = 0$ $-0.3, -2.4$
42. $5x^2 + 7x + 1 = 0$ $0.1, -1.5$

Calculator Exercises

Solve.

43. $t^2 + 0.2t - 0.3 = 0$ 0.4567764, −0.6567764

44. $p^2 + 0.3p - 0.2 = 0$ 0.321699, −0.621699

45. $x^2 - 0.75x - 0.5 = 0$ 1.1753905, −0.4253905

46. $z^2 + 0.84z - 0.4 = 0$ 1.179201, −0.3392101

47. $5.33x^2 - 8.23x - 3.24 = 0$ 1.869284, −0.3251939

48. $0.034x^2 + 7.01x - 0.0356 = 0$
0.0053926, −206.18185

Challenge Exercises

Solve.

49. $x^2 + x - \sqrt{2} = 0$ $\quad \frac{-1 \pm \sqrt{1 + 4\sqrt{2}}}{2}$

50. $x^2 - x - \sqrt{3} = 0$ $\quad \frac{1 \pm \sqrt{1 + 4\sqrt{3}}}{2}$

51. $x^2 + \sqrt{5}x - \sqrt{3} = 0$ $\quad \frac{-\sqrt{5} \pm \sqrt{5 + 4\sqrt{3}}}{2}$

52. $\sqrt{2}x^2 + 5x + \sqrt{2} = 0$ $\quad \frac{-5\sqrt{2} \pm \sqrt{34}}{4}$

53. $x^2 + 3x + i = 0$ $\quad \frac{-3 \pm \sqrt{9 - 4i}}{2}$

54. $ix^2 - 2x + 1 = 0$ $\quad \frac{1 \pm \sqrt{1 - i}}{i}$

55. The hypotenuse of a right triangle is 6 cm long. One leg is 1 cm less than the other. Find the lengths of the legs. Round to the nearest tenth. 4.7 cm and 3.7 cm

56. The hypotenuse of a right triangle is 8 m long. One leg is 2 m longer than the other. Find the lengths of the legs. Round to the nearest tenth. 4.6 m and 6.6 m

57. A boat travels 2 km upstream and 2 km downstream. The total time for both parts of the trip is 1 hour. The speed of the stream is 2 km/h. What is the speed of the boat in still water? Round to the nearest tenth. 4.8 km/h

58. Person *A* can do a certain job in 3 hours less time than Person *B*. Together they can do the same job in 6 hours. How long would each take to do the job alone? Give an approximate answer. Round to the nearest tenth. A: 10.7 h; B: 13.7 h

59. Solve $3x^2 + xy + 4y^2 - 9 = 0$ for x terms of y. $\quad x = \frac{-y \pm \sqrt{-47y^2 + 108}}{6}$

60. Derive the quadratic formula by completing the square. Assume $a > 0$ in the standard form. See answer section

61. One solution of $kx^2 + 3x - k = 0$ is -2. Find the other. $\quad \frac{1}{2}$

62. Prove that the solutions of $ax^2 + bx + c = 0$ are See answer section
    a) the reciprocals of the solutions of $cx^2 - bx + a = 0$.
    b) the additive inverses of the solutions of $ax^2 - bx + c = 0$.

63. Prove that if $ac \neq 0$, then the following could be used as a formula for solving quadratic equations.

$$x = \frac{2c}{-b \pm \sqrt{b^2 - 4ac}}$$

$$x = \frac{2c}{-b \pm \sqrt{b^2 - 4ac}} = \frac{2c}{-b \pm \sqrt{b^2 - 4ac}} \cdot \frac{-b \mp \sqrt{b^2 - 4ac}}{-b \mp \sqrt{b^2 - 4ac}} = \frac{-2bc \mp 2c\sqrt{b^2 - 4ac}}{b^2 - (b^2 - 4ac)}$$

$$= \frac{-2bc \mp 2c\sqrt{b^2 - 4ac}}{4ac} = \frac{-b \pm \sqrt{b^2 - 4ac}}{2a}$$

12-4 The Discriminant

After finishing Lesson 12-4, you should be able to
▌ determine the nature of the solutions of a quadratic equation with real coefficients, without solving it.

▌ We now consider quadratic equations with real number coefficients. The expression

$$b^2 - 4ac$$

in the quadratic formula is called the *discriminant*. From this number we can determine the nature of the solutions.

THEOREM 12-2

An equation $ax^2 + bx + c = 0$, with $a \neq 0$ and all coefficients real numbers, has
a) Exactly one real number solution if $b^2 - 4ac = 0$.
b) Two real number solutions if $b^2 - 4ac > 0$.
c) Two complex, but not real, number solutions that are conjugates of each other if $b^2 - 4ac < 0$.

Example 1. Determine the nature of the solutions of
$9x^2 - 12x + 4 = 0$.

$a = 9$, $b = -12$, and $c = 4$.
We compute the discriminant.

$$\begin{aligned} b^2 - 4ac &= (-12)^2 - 4 \cdot 9 \cdot 4 \\ &= 144 - 144 \\ &= 0 \end{aligned}$$

By Theorem 12-2, there is just one solution and it is a real number.

Example 2. Determine the nature of the solutions of
$x^2 + 5x + 8 = 0$.

$a = 1$, $b = 5$, and $c = 8$.
We compute the discriminant.

$$\begin{aligned} b^2 - 4ac &= 5^2 - 4 \cdot 1 \cdot 8 \\ &= 25 - 32 \\ &= -7 \end{aligned}$$

Since the discriminant is negative, there are two nonreal solutions that are complex conjugates of each other.

Example 3.   Determine the nature of the solutions of
$x^2 + 5x + 6 = 0$.

$a = 1$, $b = 5$, and $c = 6$.

$$b^2 - 4ac = 5^2 - 4 \cdot 1 \cdot 6$$
$$= 1$$

Since the discriminant is positive, there are two
solutions and they are real numbers.

TRY THIS ➡

Determine the nature of the solutions of each equation.

1. $x^2 + 5x - 3 = 0$ Two real
2. $9x^2 - 6x + 1 = 0$ One real
3. $3x^2 - 2x + 1 = 0$ Two nonreal

Exercise Set 12-4

▮ Determine the nature of the solutions of each equation. (*See Examples 1–3.*)

1. $x^2 - 6x + 9 = 0$ One real
2. $x^2 + 10x + 25 = 0$ One real
3. $x^2 + 7 = 0$ Two nonreal
4. $x^2 + 2 = 0$ Two nonreal
5. $x^2 - 2 = 0$ Two real
6. $x^2 - 5 = 0$ Two real
7. $4x^2 - 12x + 9 = 0$ One real
8. $4x^2 + 8x - 5 = 0$ Two real
9. $x^2 - 2x + 4 = 0$ Two nonreal
10. $x^2 + 3x + 4 = 0$ Two nonreal
11. $9t^2 - 3t = 0$ Two real
12. $4m^2 + 7m = 0$ Two real
13. $y^2 = \frac{1}{2}y + \frac{3}{5}$ Two real
14. $y^2 + \frac{9}{4} = 4y$ Two real
15. $4x^2 - 4\sqrt{3}x + 3 = 0$ One real
16. $6y^2 - 2\sqrt{3}y - 1 = 0$ Two real

Challenge Exercises   See answer section

In each of the following find k so that: a) there are two real number
solutions, b) there is one real number solution, and c) there are two
solutions which are complex conjugates.

17. $x^2 + 3x + k = 0$
18. $x^2 + x + k = 0$
19. $kx^2 - 4x + 1 = 0$
20. $x^2 - x + 3x + k = 0$
21. $x^2 + x = 1 - k$
22. $3x^2 + 4x = k - 5$

Suppose in a quadratic equation $ax^2 + bx + c = 0$, a, b, and c are integers.

23.   Prove that the quadratic equation has two rational number solutions if
the discriminant is positive and a perfect square.
24.   Use the result of Exercise 23 to determine if each equation has rational solutions.
a) $6x^2 + 5x + 1 = 0$ b) $x^2 + 4x - 2 = 0$
25.   Prove that every polynomial equation with rational coefficients is
equivalent to one with integer coefficients.
26.   Prove Theorem 12-2. (*Hint:* Use the quadratic formula.)

12-5 *Solutions and Coefficients*

After finishing Lesson 12-5, you should be able to
- **I** find, without solving, the sum and product of the solutions of a quadratic equation.
- **II** find a quadratic equation for which the sum and product of the solutions are given.
- **III** find an equation having specified numbers as solutions.

I Sum and Product of Solutions

THEOREM 12-3

For the equation $ax^2 + bx + c = 0$,

the *sum* of the solutions is $-\dfrac{b}{a}$,

the *product* of the solutions is $\dfrac{c}{a}$.

Note that if we express $ax^2 + bx + c = 0$ in the equivalent form, $x^2 + \dfrac{b}{a}x + \dfrac{c}{a} = 0$, then the sum of the solutions is the additive inverse of the x coefficient and their product is the constant term.

Example 1. Without solving, find the sum and product of the solutions of $2x^2 = 6x + 5$.

Let x_1 and x_2 represent the solutions.

Since $2x^2 - 6x - 5 = 0$, we have $a = 2$, $b = -6$, and $c = -5$

Then, $x_1 + x_2 = -\dfrac{b}{a}$

$$= -\left(\frac{-6}{2}\right)$$

$$= 3,$$

$$x_1 \cdot x_2 = \frac{c}{a}$$

$$= \frac{-5}{2}.$$

TRY THIS ➡

Find, without solving, the sum and product of the solutions.

1. $3x^2 + 4 = 12x$
2. $x^2 + \sqrt{2}x - 4 = 0$

Answers. 1. Sum = 4; product = $\frac{4}{3}$ 2. Sum = $-\sqrt{2}$; product = -4

ıı Sum and Product Given

Example 2. Find a quadratic equation for which the *sum* of the solutions is $-\frac{4}{5}$ and the *product* of the solutions is $\frac{2}{3}$

$$x^2 - \left(-\frac{b}{a}\right)x + \frac{c}{a} = x^2 - \left(-\frac{4}{5}\right)x + \frac{2}{3} = x^2 + \frac{4}{5}x + \frac{2}{3} = 0$$

Thus we have $x^2 + \frac{4}{5}x + \frac{2}{3} = 0$, or $15x^2 + 12x + 10 = 0$.

TRY THIS

> 3. Find a quadratic equation for which the sum of the solutions is 3 and the product is $-\frac{1}{4}$. $4x^2 - 12x - 1 = 0$

ııı Writing Equations from Solutions

We can use the principle of zero products to write a quadratic equation whose solutions are known.

Example 3. Find a quadratic equation whose solutions are 3 and $-\frac{2}{5}$.

$$x = 3 \quad \text{or} \qquad x = -\tfrac{2}{5}$$
$$x - 3 = 0 \quad \text{or} \quad x + \tfrac{2}{5} = 0$$

$$(x - 3)(x + \tfrac{2}{5}) = 0 \qquad \textit{Multiplying}$$
$$x^2 - \tfrac{13}{5}x - \tfrac{6}{5} = 0, \text{ or } 5x^2 - 13x - 6 = 0$$

When radicals are involved, it is sometimes easier to use the properties of the sum and product.

Example 4. Find a quadratic equation whose solutions are $2 + \sqrt{5}$ and $2 - \sqrt{5}$.

$$x_1 + x_2 = (2 + \sqrt{5}) + (2 - \sqrt{5})$$
$$= 4$$

$$x_1 \cdot x_2 = (2 + \sqrt{5}) \cdot (2 - \sqrt{5})$$
$$= 4 - 5 = -1$$

$$x^2 - \left(-\frac{b}{a}\right)x + \frac{c}{a} = x^2 - (4)x + (-1) = 0;$$

or $x^2 - 4x - 1 = 0$

> Find a quadratic equation whose solutions are the following.
>
> 4. $-4, \dfrac{5}{3}$
>
> 5. $-7, 8$
> 6. m, n
> 7. $8, -9$
> 8. $3 + \sqrt{2}, 3 - \sqrt{2}$
> 9. $\dfrac{2 + \sqrt{5}}{2}, \dfrac{2 - \sqrt{5}}{2}$

TRY THIS

Answers. 4. $3x^2 + 7x - 20 = 0$ 5. $x^2 - x - 56 = 0$ 6. $x^2 - (m + n)x + mn = 0$
7. $x^2 + x - 72 = 0$ 8. $x^2 - 6x + 7 = 0$ 9. $4x^2 - 8x - 1 = 0$

Exercise Set 12-5

▮ Without solving, find the sum and product of the solutions. (*See Example 1.*)

1. $x^2 + 7x + 8 = 0$ Sum = −7; product = 8
2. $x^2 − 2x + 10 = 0$ Sum = 2; product = 10
3. $x^2 − x + 1 = 0$ Sum = 1; product = 1
4. $x^2 + x − 1 = 0$ Sum = −1; product = −1
5. $8 − 2x^2 + 4x = 0$ Sum = 2; product = −4
6. $4 + x + 2x^2 = 0$ Sum = −$\frac{1}{2}$; product = 2
7. $m^2 = 25$ Sum = 0; product = −25
8. $t^2 = 49$ Sum = 0; product = −49
9. $(2 + 3x)^2 = 7x$ Sum = −$\frac{5}{9}$; product = $\frac{4}{9}$
10. $2x − 1 = (1 − 5x)^2$ Sum = $\frac{12}{25}$; product = $\frac{2}{25}$
11. $5(t − 3)^2 = 4(t + 3)^2$ Sum = 54; product = 9
12. $3(y + 4)^2 = 2(y + 5)^2$ Sum = −4; product = −2

▮▮ Find a quadratic equation for which the: (*See Example 2.*) See answer section

13. Sum of solutions = 5; product = $\frac{1}{2}$.
14. Sum of solutions = −π; product = $\frac{1}{4}$.
15. Sum of solutions = $\sqrt{3}$; product = 8.
16. Sum of solutions = 5; product = −$\sqrt{2}$.

▮▮▮ Find a quadratic equation whose solutions are the following. (*See Example 3.*)

17. −11, 9 $x^2 + 2x − 99 = 0$
18. −4, 4 $x^2 − 16 = 0$
19. 7, only solution $x^2 − 14x + 49 = 0$
20. −5, only solution $x^2 + 10x + 25 = 0$
21. −$\frac{2}{5}$, $\frac{6}{5}$ $25x^2 − 20x − 12 = 0$
22. −$\frac{1}{4}$, −$\frac{1}{2}$ $8x^2 + 6x + 1 = 0$
23. $\frac{c}{2}$, $\frac{d}{2}$ $4x^2 − 2(c + d)x + cd = 0$
24. $\frac{k}{3}$, $\frac{m}{4}$ $12x^2 − (4k + 3m)x + km = 0$
25. $\sqrt{2}$, $3\sqrt{2}$ $x^2 − 4\sqrt{2}x + 6 = 0$
26. −$\sqrt{3}$, $2\sqrt{3}$ $x^2 − \sqrt{3}x − 6 = 0$
27. π, −2π $x^2 + \pi x − 2\pi^2 = 0$
28. −3π, 4π $x^2 − \pi x − 12\pi^2 = 0$

Use the sum and product properties to write a quadratic equation whose solutions are the following. (*See Example 4.*)

29. 4, 3 $x^2 − 7x + 12 = 0$
30. 5, 6 $x^2 − 11x + 30 = 0$
31. −2, $\frac{5}{4}$ $4x^2 + 3x − 10 = 0$
32. −6, $\frac{1}{4}$ $4x^2 + 23x − 6 = 0$
33. $1 + \sqrt{2}$, $1 − \sqrt{2}$ $x^2 − 2x − 1 = 0$
34. $2 + \sqrt{3}$, $2 − \sqrt{3}$ $x^2 − 4x + 1 = 0$
35. $\frac{2 + \sqrt{3}}{2}$, $\frac{2 − \sqrt{3}}{2}$ $4x^2 − 8x + 1 = 0$
36. $\frac{1 + \sqrt{13}}{2}$, $\frac{1 − \sqrt{13}}{2}$ $x^2 − x − 3 = 0$
37. $\frac{m}{n}$, −$\frac{n}{m}$ $mnx^2 − (m^2 − n^2)x − mn = 0$
38. $\frac{g}{h}$, −$\frac{h}{g}$ $ghx^2 − (g^2 − h^2)x − gh = 0$
39. $2 − 5i$, $2 + 5i$ $x^2 − 4x + 29 = 0$
40. $4 + 3i$, $4 − 3i$ $x^2 − 8x + 25 = 0$

Challenge Exercises   41. a) $\frac{11}{2}$ b) k = 2   42. a) −$\frac{1}{3}$ b) k = −$\frac{3}{5}$ 43. a) 5   b) k = 0   44. −1

For each equation under the given condition, a) find the other solution, and b) find *k*.

41. $kx^2 − 17x + 33 = 0$; one solution is 3
42. $kx^2 − 2x + k = 0$; one solution is −3
43. $x^2 − kx − 25 = 0$; one solution is −5
44. Find *k* if $kx^2 − 4x + (2k − 1) = 0$ and the product of the solutions is 3.
45. Prove Theorem 12-3. (*Hint:* Use the quadratic formula.)   See answer section

12-6 Formulas

After finishing Lesson 12-6, you should be able to
▮ solve a formula for a given letter.

▮ To solve a formula for a given letter, we try to get the letter alone on one side.

Example 1. Solve $T = 2\pi\sqrt{\dfrac{m}{g}}$, for m.

$$\frac{T}{2\pi} = \sqrt{\frac{m}{g}}$$

$$\left(\frac{T}{2\pi}\right)^2 = \left(\sqrt{\frac{m}{g}}\right)^2 \qquad \textit{Squaring both sides}$$

$$\frac{T^2}{4\pi^2} = \frac{m}{g}$$

$$\frac{gT^2}{4\pi^2} = m \qquad \textit{Multiplying by g}$$

In most formulas the letters represent nonnegative numbers, so absolute values are not needed when taking principal square roots.

Example 2. Solve $c^2 = a^2 + b^2$, for c.

$$c = \sqrt{a^2 + b^2} \qquad \textit{Taking square root}$$

Example 3. Solve $h = v_0 t + 16t^2$, for t

$$16t^2 + v_0 t - h = 0 \qquad \textit{Finding standard form}$$

$$a = 16,\ b = v_0,\ c = -h$$

$$t = \frac{-b \pm \sqrt{b^2 - 4ac}}{2a}$$

$$t = \frac{-v_0 \pm \sqrt{v_0^2 - 4 \cdot 16 \cdot (-h)}}{2 \cdot 16} \qquad \textit{Substituting into the quadratic formula}$$

$$t = \frac{-v_0 \pm \sqrt{v_0^2 + 64h}}{32}$$

We choose the plus sign, $\dfrac{-v_0 + \sqrt{v_0^2 + 64h}}{32}$, because the negative square root would give a negative answer.

TRY THIS ➡

Solve for the indicated letter.

1. $A = \sqrt{\dfrac{w_1}{w_2}}$; w_2. $\quad w_2 = \dfrac{w_1}{A^2}$

2. $V = \pi r^2 h$; r. $\quad r = \sqrt{\dfrac{V}{\pi h}}$

3. $Ls^2 - Rs = C$; s. $\quad s = \dfrac{R \pm \sqrt{R^2 + 4LC}}{2L}$

Exercise Set 12-6

▌Solve for the indicated letter. (*See Examples 1–3.*)

1. $P = 4s^2$; s $s = \frac{\sqrt{P}}{2}$

2. $A = \pi r^2$; r $r = \sqrt{\frac{A}{\pi}}$

3. $F = \dfrac{Gm_1 m_2}{r^2}$; r $r = \sqrt{\frac{Gm_1 m_2}{F}}$

4. $K = \dfrac{Qab}{t^2}$; t $t = \sqrt{\frac{Qab}{K}}$

5. $T = 4\pi \sqrt{\dfrac{L}{g}}$; L $L = \frac{gT^2}{16\pi^2}$

6. $\sqrt{\dfrac{E}{m}} = c$; E $E = mc^2$

7. $x^2 + y^2 = r^2$; r $r = \sqrt{x^2 + y^2}$

8. $a^2 + b^2 = h^2$; h $h = \sqrt{a^2 + b^2}$

9. $x^2 + y^2 + z^2 = d^2$; z $z = \sqrt{d^2 - x^2 - y^2}$

10. $a^2 + b^2 + c^2 = t^2$; b $b = \sqrt{t^2 - a^2 - c^2}$

11. $h = v_0 t - 16t^2$; t $t = \frac{v_0 \pm \sqrt{v_0{}^2 - 64h}}{32}$

12. $A = \pi rs + \pi r^2$; r $r = \frac{-\pi s + \sqrt{\pi^2 s^2 + 4\pi A}}{2\pi}$

13. $S = \dfrac{1}{2} gt^2$; t $t = \sqrt{\frac{2S}{g}}$

14. $h = \dfrac{V^2}{2g}$; V $V = \sqrt{2gh}$

15. $A = 2\pi r^2 + 2\pi rh$; r $r = \frac{-\pi h + \sqrt{\pi^2 h^2 + 2\pi A}}{2\pi}$

16. $h = 2v_0 + 10t^2$; t $t = \sqrt{\frac{h - 2v_0}{10}}$

17. $\sqrt{2}t^2 + 3k = \pi t$; t $t = \frac{\pi \pm \sqrt{\pi^2 - 12k\sqrt{2}}}{2\sqrt{2}}$

18. $\sqrt{3}t^2 - 4\pi = 0.2t$; t $t = \frac{0.2 \pm \sqrt{0.04 + 16\pi\sqrt{3}}}{2\sqrt{3}}$

Challenge Exercises

Solve for the indicated letter.

19. $m = \dfrac{m_0}{\sqrt{1 - \dfrac{v^2}{c^2}}}$; v $v = \frac{c\sqrt{m^2 - m_0{}^2}}{m}$

20. $T = \sqrt{\dfrac{a^2 + b^2}{a^2}}$; a $a = \frac{b}{\sqrt{T^2 - 1}}$

HISTORICAL NOTE: How Many Rabbits? How Many Pheasants?

Several ancient Chinese books included problems that can be solved by systems of equations. *Arithmetical Rules in Nine Sections* was a book of 246 problems compiled by Chang Tsang, who died in 152 B.C. One of the problems is: Suppose there are a number of rabbits and pheasants confined in a cage. In all, there are 35 heads and 94 feet. How many rabbits are there? How many pheasants are there?

Chang Tsang based his book on an older text. It includes problems about proportion, square roots, and right triangles. It is the earliest work to mention negative numbers.

12-7 Solving Problems

After finishing Lesson 12-7, you should be able to
- ▮ use quadratic equations to solve certain interest problems.
- ▮▮ use quadratic equations to solve motion problems.

▮ Interest Problems

An amount of money P is invested at interest rate r. In t years it will grow to the amount A given by

$$A = P(1 + r)^t,$$

where interest is compounded annually.

Example 1. $2560 is invested at an interest rate r, and grows to $3240 in 2 years. What is the interest rate?

We substitute 2560 for P, 3240 for A, and 2 for t in the formula

$$A = P(1 + r)^t$$
$$3240 = 2560(1 + r)^2$$
$$\frac{3240}{2560} = (1 + r)^2$$
$$\pm\sqrt{\frac{324}{256}} = 1 + r \qquad \textit{Taking square root}$$
$$\pm\frac{18}{16} = 1 + r$$

$$-1 + \frac{18}{16} = r \quad \text{or} \quad -1 - \frac{18}{16} = r$$
$$\frac{2}{16} = r \quad \text{or} \qquad -\frac{34}{16} = r$$

Since the interest rate cannot be negative,
$$r = \frac{2}{16} = \frac{1}{8} = 0.125 = 12.5\%.$$

TRY THIS

> 1. $2560 is invested at interest rate r, and grows to $2890 in 2 years. What is the interest rate? **6.25%**

▮▮ Motion Problems

When an object is dropped or thrown downward, the distance, in meters, that it falls in t seconds is given by

$$s = 4.9t^2 + v_0 t.$$

In this formula v_0 is the initial velocity.

Example 2.

a) An object is dropped from the top of the Gateway Arch in St. Louis, which is 195 meters high. How long does it take to reach the ground?

Since the object was *dropped* its initial velocity was 0. So we substitute 0 for v_0 and 195 for s and then solve for t:

$$195 = 4.9t^2 + 0 \cdot t$$
$$195 = 4.9t^2$$
$$t^2 \approx 39.8$$
$$t \approx \sqrt{39.8} \qquad \text{\textit{We take the positive square root because t}}$$
$$t \approx 6.31 \qquad \text{\textit{cannot be negative}}$$

Thus it takes about 6.31 seconds to reach the ground.

b) An object is thrown downward from the top of the arch at an initial velocity of 16 meters per second (m/s). How long does it take to reach the ground?

We substitute 195 for s and 16 for v_0 and solve for t:

$$195 = 4.9t^2 + 16t$$
$$0 = 4.9t^2 + 16t - 195$$

By the quadratic formula we obtain

$$t = -8.15 \text{ or } t = 4.88.$$

The negative answer is meaningless in this problem, so the answer is 4.88 seconds.

c) How far will an object fall in 3 seconds if it is thrown downward from the top of the arch at an initial velocity of 16 m/s?

We substitute 16 for v_0 and 3 for t and solve for s.

$$s = 4.9t^2 + v_0t$$
$$= 4.9(3)^2 + 16 \cdot 3$$
$$= 92.1$$

Thus the object falls 92.1 meters in 3 seconds.

TRY THIS ━━━➤

Solve.

2. **a)** An object is dropped from the top of the Statue of Liberty, which is 92 meters high. How long does it take to reach the ground? 4.33 s

 b) An object is thrown downward from the top of the statue at an initial velocity of 40 m/s. How long does it take to reach the ground? 1.87 s

 c) How far will an object fall in 1 second, thrown downward from the top of the statue at an initial velocity of 40 m/s? 44.9 m

Exercise Set 12-7

▍What is the interest rate? (*See Example 1.*)

1. $1000 grows to $1690 in 2 years. _{30%}
2. $1000 grows to $1210 in 2 years. _{10%}
3. $2560 grows to $4000 in 2 years. _{25%}
4. $2560 grows to $3610 in 2 years. _{18.75%}
5. $6400 grows to $8100 in 2 years. _{12.5%}
6. $6250 grows to $7290 in 2 years. _{8%}
7. For $1000 to triple itself in 2 years, what would the interest rate have to be? _{73.2%}
8. For $1000 to double itself in 2 years, what would the interest rate have to be? _{41.4%}

▌▌Solve. For Exercises 9 and 10 use the formula $s = 4.9t^2 + v_0t$. (*See Example 2.*)

9.
a) An object is dropped 75 m from an airplane. How long does it take to reach the ground? _{3.91 s}
b) An object is thrown downward from the plane at an initial velocity of 30 m/s. How long does it take to reach the ground? _{1.91 s}
c) How far will an object fall in 2 seconds, thrown downward at an initial velocity of 30 m/s? _{79.6 m}

10.
a) An object is dropped 500 m from an airplane. How long does it take to reach the ground? _{10.10 s}
b) An object is thrown downward from the plane at an initial velocity of 30 m/s. How long does it take to reach the ground? _{7.49 s}
c) How far will an object fall in 5 seconds, thrown downward at an initial velocity of 30 m/s? _{272.5 m}

Calculator Exercises

Solve.

11. $1000 is invested at interest rate r. In 2 years it grows to $1166.40. What is the interest rate? _{8%}
12. $1000 is invested at interest rate r. In 2 years it grows to $1144.90. What is the interest rate? _{7%}
13. $8000 is invested at interest rate r. In 2 years it grows to $9856.80. What is the interest rate? _{11%}
14. $6000 is invested at interest rate r. In 2 years it grows to $6615. What is the interest rate? _{5%}

Challenge Exercises

Solve.

15. What is the interest rate when $4913 grows to $5832 in 3 years? _{5.9%}
16. What is the interest rate when $9826 grows to $13,704 in 3 years? _{11.7%}

12-8 Equations Quadratic in Form

After finishing Lesson 12-8, you should be able to
■ solve equations which are quadratic in form.

■ Look for a pattern.

a) $x^4 - 9x^2 + 8 = 0$, let $u = x^2$. Then $u^2 - 9u + 8 = 0$
b) $x - 5\sqrt{x} + 4 = 0$, let $u = \sqrt{x}$. Then $u^2 - 5u + 4 = 0$
c) $(x^2 - 1)^2 - (x^2 - 1) - 2 = 0$, let $u = x^2 - 1$. Then $u^2 - u - 2 = 0$

The equations on the left are not quadratic, but after a substitution we get quadratic equations. Such equations are said to be *quadratic in form*.

To solve such equations, we first make a substitution, solve for the new variable, then solve for the original variable.

Example 1. Solve: $x^4 - 9x^2 + 8 = 0$.

Let $u = x^2$. Then we solve the equation found by substituting u for x^2.

$$u^2 - 9u + 8 = 0$$
$$(u - 8)(u - 1) = 0$$

$$u - 8 = 0 \quad \text{or} \quad u - 1 = 0$$
$$u = 8 \quad \text{or} \quad u = 1$$

Now we substitute x^2 for u and solve these equations.

$$x^2 = 8 \qquad \text{or} \quad x^2 = 1$$
$$x = \pm\sqrt{8} \quad \text{or} \quad x = \pm 1$$
$$x - \pm 2\sqrt{2} \quad \text{or} \quad x - \pm 1$$

To check first note that when $x = 2\sqrt{2}$, $x^2 = 8$ and $x^4 = 64$.
Also, when $x = -2\sqrt{2}$, $x^2 = 8$ and $x^4 = 64$. Similarly, when
$x = 1$, $x^2 = 1$ and $x^4 = 1$, and when $x = -1$, $x^2 = 1$ and $x^4 = 1$.
Thus instead of making four checks we can shorten them to two.

Check: for $\pm 2\sqrt{2}$: $x^4 - 9x^2 + 8 = 0$ | for ± 1: $x^4 - 9x^2 + 8 = 0$

$$
\begin{array}{c|c}
(\pm 2\sqrt{2})^4 - 9(\pm 2\sqrt{2})^2 + 8 & 0 \\
64 - 9 \cdot 8 + 8 & \\
0 &
\end{array}
\qquad
\begin{array}{c|c}
(\pm 1)^4 - 9(\pm 1)^2 + 8 & 0 \\
1 - 9 + 8 & \\
0 &
\end{array}
$$

The solutions are $1, -1, 2\sqrt{2}, -2\sqrt{2}$.

TRY THIS ➡️

> Solve.   ±3, ±1
>
> 1. $x^4 - 10x^2 + 9 = 0$

Example 2.   Solve: $x - 3\sqrt{x} - 4 = 0$.

Let $u = \sqrt{x}$. Then we solve the equation found by substituting u for $\sqrt{x}$.

$$u^2 - 3u - 4 = 0$$
$$(u - 4)(u + 1) = 0$$
$$u = 4 \quad \text{or} \quad u = -1$$

Now we substitute $\sqrt{x}$ for u and solve these equations.

$$\sqrt{x} = 4 \quad \text{or} \quad \sqrt{x} = -1$$

Squaring the first equation we get $x = 16$. The second equation has no real solution since principal square roots are never negative.

The number 16 checks and is the solution.

TRY THIS ➡️

> 2.   Solve $x + 3\sqrt{x} - 10 = 0$.
>   Be sure to check.   4

Example 3.   Solve: $(x^2 - 1)^2 - (x^2 - 1) - 2 = 0$.

Let $u = x^2 - 1$. Then we solve the equation found by substituting u for $x^2 - 1$.

$$u^2 - u - 2 = 0$$
$$(u - 2)(u + 1) = 0$$
$$u = 2 \quad \text{or} \quad u = -1$$

Now we substitute $x^2 - 1$ for u and solve these equations.

$$x^2 - 1 = 2 \quad \text{or} \quad x^2 - 1 = -1$$
$$x^2 = 3 \quad \text{or} \quad x^2 = 0$$
$$x = \pm\sqrt{3} \quad \text{or} \quad x = 0$$

The numbers $\sqrt{3}$, $-\sqrt{3}$, and 0 check. They are the solutions.

TRY THIS ➡️

> Solve.
>
> 3. $(x^2 - x)^2 - 14(x^2 - x) + 24 = 0$ 4, 2, −1, −3

Example 4. Solve: $t^{\frac{2}{5}} - t^{\frac{1}{5}} - 2 = 0$.

Let $u = t^{\frac{1}{5}}$. Then solve the equation found by substituting u for $t^{\frac{1}{5}}$.

$$u^2 - u - 2 = 0$$
$$(u - 2)(u + 1) = 0$$

$$u = 2 \quad \text{or} \quad u = -1$$

Now we substitute $t^{\frac{1}{5}}$ for u and solve.

$$t^{\frac{1}{5}} = 2 \quad \text{or} \quad t^{\frac{1}{5}} = -1$$
$$t = 32 \quad \text{or} \quad t = -1 \qquad \textit{Principal of powers; raising to the 5th power}$$

The numbers 32 and -1 check and are the solutions.

TRY THIS

Solve.   **125, –8**

4. $t^{\frac{2}{3}} - 3t^{\frac{1}{3}} - 10 = 0$

Exercise Set 12-8

▮ Solve. (*See Examples 1–4.*)

1. $x - 10\sqrt{x} + 9 = 0$ **81, 1**
2. $2x - 9\sqrt{x} + 4 = 0$ $\frac{1}{4}$, **16**
3. $x^4 - 10x^2 + 25 = 0$ $\pm\sqrt{5}$
4. $x^4 - 3x^2 + 2 = 0$ $\pm\sqrt{2}, \pm1$
5. $t^{\frac{2}{3}} + t^{\frac{1}{3}} - 6 = 0$ **–27, 8**
6. $w^{\frac{2}{3}} - 2w^{\frac{1}{3}} - 8 = 0$ **64, –8**
7. $z^{\frac{1}{2}} - z^{\frac{1}{4}} - 2 = 0$ **16**
8. $m^{\frac{1}{3}} - m^{\frac{1}{6}} - 6 = 0$ **729**
9. $(x^2 - 6x)^2 - 2(x^2 - 6x) - 35 = 0$ **7, –1, 5, 1**
10. $(1 + \sqrt{x})^2 + (1 + \sqrt{x}) - 6 = 0$ **1**
11. $(y^2 - 5y)^2 - 2(y^2 - 5y) - 24 = 0$ **4, 1, 6, –1**
12. $(2t^2 + t)^2 - 4(2t^2 + t) + 3 = 0$ $-\frac{3}{2}, 1, \frac{1}{2}, -1$
13. $w^4 - 4w^2 - 2 = 0$ $\pm\sqrt{2 + \sqrt{6}}, \pm\sqrt{2 - \sqrt{6}}$
14. $t^4 - 5t^2 + 5 = 0$ $\pm\sqrt{\frac{5 + \sqrt{5}}{2}}, \pm\sqrt{\frac{5 - \sqrt{5}}{2}}$
15. $x^{-2} - x^{-1} - 6 = 0$ $\frac{1}{3}, -\frac{1}{2}$
16. $4x^{-2} - x^{-1} - 5 = 0$ $\frac{4}{5}, -1$
17. $2x^{-2} + x^{-1} - 1 = 0$ **2, –1**
18. $m^{-2} + 9m^{-1} - 10 = 0$ $-\frac{1}{10}, 1$

Calculator Exercises

Solve. Check possible solutions by substituting into the original equation.

19. $6.75x - 35\sqrt{x} - 5.36 = 0$ **28.5**
20. $\pi x^4 - \pi^2 x^2 - \sqrt{99.3} = 0$ ±2.0

Challenge Exercises

Solve.   21. $\frac{9 \pm \sqrt{89}}{2}, -1 \pm \sqrt{3}$ 22. $\frac{5 \pm \sqrt{21}}{2}, \frac{3 \pm \sqrt{5}}{2}$ 23. $\frac{100}{99}$ 24. $-\frac{6}{7}$

21. $\left(\frac{x^2 - 2}{x}\right)^2 - 7\left(\frac{x^2 - 2}{x}\right) - 18 = 0$
22. $\left(\frac{x^2 + 1}{x}\right)^2 - 8\left(\frac{x^2 + 1}{x}\right) + 15 = 0$
23. $\frac{x}{x - 1} - 6\sqrt{\frac{x}{x - 1}} - 40 = 0$
24. $5\left(\frac{x + 2}{x - 2}\right)^2 - 3\left(\frac{x + 2}{x - 2}\right) - 2 = 0$

CHAPTER 12 REVIEW

Review the material in the chapter. Then see how you have done by trying these review exercises. If you miss an exercise, restudy the indicated lesson.

Solve.

12-1   1. $4x^2 + 2 = 0$ $\pm i\frac{\sqrt{2}}{2}$

12-2   2. $7x^2 - 6x = 0$ $0, \frac{6}{7}$

12-2   3. $3x^2 + 10x - 8 = 0$ $\frac{2}{3}, -4$

12-3   4. $x^2 + 4x - 7 = 0$ $-2 \pm \sqrt{11}$

12-3   5. $x^2 + x + 4 = 0$ $\frac{-1 \pm i\sqrt{15}}{2}$

12-3   6.   Use the square root table, Table 1, in the back of the book to approximate solutions of $x^2 - 8x + 5 = 0$ to the nearest tenth.   7.3, 0.7

12-4   7.   Determine the nature of the solutions of $4y^2 + 5y + 1 = 0$.   Two real solutions

12-5   8.   Without solving, find the sum and product of the solutions of $5s^2 - 4s + 2 = 0$.   Sum $= \frac{4}{5}$; product $= \frac{2}{5}$

12-5   9.   Find a quadratic equation whose solutions are -3 and $-\frac{1}{2}$. $2x^2 + 7x + 3 = 0$

12-6   10.   Solve $v = \sqrt{2gh}$ for h. $h = \frac{v^2}{2g}$

12-7   11.   \$2000 is invested at interest rate r. In 2 years it grows to \$3920. What is the interest rate?   40%

12-7   12.   From a height of 200 m, an object is thrown downward at an initial velocity of 20 m/s. How long does it take to reach the ground? Round to the nearest hundredth.   4.67 s

12-8   13.   Solve: $y^4 - 2y^2 + 1 = 0$. ± 1

CHAPTER 12 TEST

Solve.

1. $16x^2 = -9$ $\pm\frac{3}{4}i$
2. $5x^2 + 8x = 0$ $0, -\frac{8}{5}$
3. $x^2 - 6x + 7 = 0$ $3 \pm \sqrt{2}$
4. $5x^2 + 13x - 6 = 0$ $\frac{2}{5}, -3$
5. $2x^2 - x - 1 = 0$ $1, -\frac{1}{2}$
6. Use the square root table, Table 1, in the back of the book to approximate solutions of $x^2 + 6x + 7 = 0$ to the nearest tenth. $-1.6, -4.4$
7. Determine the nature of the solutions of $t^2 - 12t + 12 = 0$. Two real solutions
8. Without solving, find the sum and product of the solutions of $6y^2 + 8y - 7 = 0$. Sum $= -\frac{4}{3}$; product $= -\frac{7}{6}$
9. Find a quadratic equation whose solutions are $3 + \sqrt{2}$ and $3 - \sqrt{2}$. $x^2 - 6x + 7 = 0$
10. Solve $A^2 + a^2 = 1$ for A. $A = \sqrt{1 - a^2}$
11. $2000 is invested at interest rate r. In 2 years it grows to $3380. What is the interest rate? 30%
12. An object is dropped from a height of 980 m. How long does it take to reach the ground? 14.14 s
13. Solve: $(x^2 + 1)^2 - 15(x^2 + 1) + 50 = 0$. $\pm 3, \pm 2$

Ready for Quadratic Functions?

3-1   1.   Graph: $2y = \frac{1}{3}x - 1$. Line through (3, 0) and (−3, −1)

3-2   2.   Find the intercepts of $2x - 5y = 10$.   y-intercept: (0, −2); x-intercept: (5, 0)

7-4   Factor by completing the square.

   3. $x^2 - 8x + 12$ (x − 2)(x − 6)
   4. $x^2 - 3x - 4$ (x − 4)(x + 1)

8-3   5.   Which of the figures is symmetric with respect to the given line?   b

   a)   b)

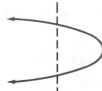

8-5   6.   Which are graphs of functions?   b

   a)   b)

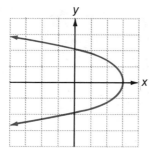

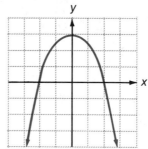

Given this graph of $y = f(x)$,

8-7   7.   Graph $y = f(x) - 2$.
8-7   8.   Graph $y = f(x + 2)$.
8-8   9.   Graph $y = 2f(x)$.
8-8   10.   Graph $y = -\frac{1}{2}f(x)$.

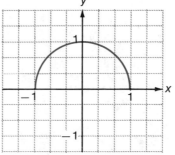

7. Semicircle from (−1, −2) to (0, −1) to (1, −2)   8. Semicircle from (−3, 0) to (−2, 1) to (−1, 0)   9. Curve from
(−1, 0) to (0, 2) to (1, 0)   10. Curve from (−1, 0) to
$(0, -\frac{1}{2})$ to (1, 0)

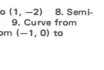

Chapter 13
Quadratic Functions

The price of pizza can be expressed as a quadratic function of diameter.

13-1 Graphs of f(x) = ax²

After finishing Lesson 13-1, you should be able to
- **I** graph a function $f(x) = ax^2$ and determine the vertex and the line of symmetry.
- **II** graph a function $f(x) = a(x - h)^2$ and determine the vertex and the line of symmetry.

I Graphs of f(x) = ax²

A quadratic function can be described using a second degree polynomial with real coefficients.

DEFINITION

A *quadratic function* is a function that can be described as follows: $f(x) = ax^2 + bx + c, a \neq 0$.

Graphs of quadratic functions are called *parabolas*.
  Consider the graph of $f(x) = x^2$ shown among those at the right. This function is even because $f(-x) = f(x)$ for all x. Thus the y-axis is a line of symmetry. The point $(0, 0)$, where the graph crosses the line of symmetry, is called the *vertex* of the parabola.
  Next consider $f(x) = ax^2$, where a is a positive number. By Theorem 8-9, we know the following about its graph.

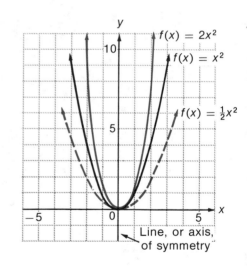

$f(x) = 2x^2$
$f(x) = x^2$
$f(x) = \frac{1}{2}x^2$
Line, or axis, of symmetry

Compared with the graph of $f(x) = x^2$,
  a) if $|a| > 1$ the graph is stretched vertically.
  b) if $|a| < 1$ the graph is shrunk vertically.

TRY THIS ➡️

1. a) Graph $f(x) = 3x^2$.
    b) Does the graph open upward or downward?
    c) What is the line of symmetry?
    d) What is the vertex?

Now consider $f(x) = ax^2$, where a is negative. By Theorem 8-9, we know the following.

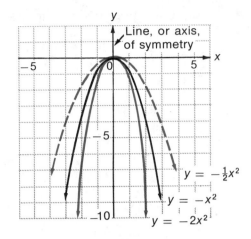

Compared with the graph of $f(x) = x^2$,
a) If $|a| > 1$, the graph is stretched vertically.
b) If $|a| < 1$ the graph is shrunk vertically.
c) Since $a < 0$, the graph is reflected across the x-axis.

TRY THIS

2. a) Graph $f(x) = -\frac{1}{4}x^2$
    b) Does the graph open upward or downward?
    c) What is the line of symmetry?
    d) What is the vertex?

▮▮ Graphs of $f(x) = a(x - h)^2$

In $f(x) = ax^2$, let us replace x by $x - h$. By Theorem 8-8, if h is positive the graph will be translated to the right. If h is negative the translation will be to the left. The line, or axis, of symmetry and the vertex will also be translated the same way. Thus for $f(x) = a(x - h)^2$

the line, or axis, of symmetry is $x = h$, and the vertex is $(h, 0)$.

Example.   a)   Graph $f(x) = 2x^2$.

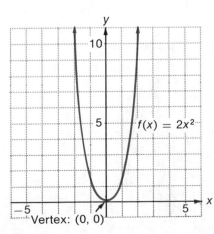

b) Use the graph in a) to graph $f(x) = 2(x + 3)^2$.

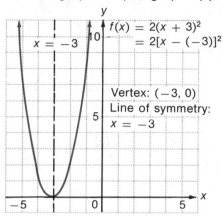

$f(x) = 2(x + 3)^2$
$= 2[x - (-3)]^2$

Vertex: $(-3, 0)$
Line of symmetry:
$x = -3$

$x = -3$

c) Use the graph in a) to graph $f(x) = 2(x - 1)^2$.

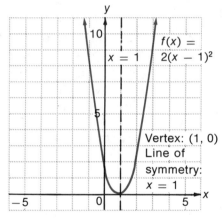

$f(x) = 2(x - 1)^2$

$x = 1$

Vertex: $(1, 0)$
Line of symmetry:
$x = 1$

d) Use the graph in a) to graph $f(x) = -2(x - 1)^2$.

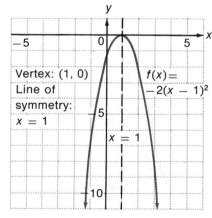

Vertex: $(1, 0)$
Line of symmetry:
$x = 1$

$f(x) = -2(x - 1)^2$

$x = 1$

TRY THIS ➡

3. a) Graph $f(x) = 3x^2$.
    b) Use the graph in a) to graph $f(x) = 3(x - 2)^2$.
    c) What is the vertex?
    d) What is the line of symmetry?
    e) Does the graph open upward or downward?
    f) Is the graph of $f(x) = 3(x - 2)^2$ a horizontal translation to the left or to the right?
4. a) Graph $f(x) = -3x^2$.
    b) Use the graph in a) to graph $f(x) = -3(x + 2)^2 = -3[x - (-2)]^2$.
    c) What is the vertex?
    d) What is the line of symmetry?
    e) Does the graph open upward or downward?
    f) Is the graph of $f(x) = -3(x + 2)^2$ a horizontal translation to the left or to the right?

Exercise Set 13-1

∎∎ For each of the following functions,

  a) graph the function.
  b) find the vertex.
  c) find the line of symmetry.

(See the Example.)

1. $f(x) = x^2$ See answer section
3. $f(x) = -4x^2$
5. $f(x) = (x - 3)^2$
7. $f(x) = 2(x - 3)^2$
9. $f(x) = -2(x + 9)^2$
11. $f(x) = 3(x - 1)^2$
13. $f(x) = -2(x + \frac{1}{2})^2$

2. $f(x) = -x^2 \, (-x^2 = -1 \cdot x^2)$
4. $f(x) = 2x^2$
6. $f(x) = (x - 7)^2$
8. $f(x) = -4(x - 7)^2$
10. $f(x) = 2(x + 7)^2$
12. $f(x) = -4(x - 2)^2$
14. $f(x) = -3(x - \frac{1}{2})^2$

Challenge Exercises

Graph these quadratic inequalities.   See answer section
15. $y \leq x^2$ 16. $y > x^2$ 17. $y > 2x^2$
18. $y \leq 2x^2$ 19. $y < -x^2$ 20. $y \geq -x^2$

13-2 Graphs of f(x) = a(x − h)² + k

After finishing Lesson 13-2, you should be able to
▪ graph a function $f(x) = a(x − h)^2 + k$ and determine the vertex, the line of symmetry, and the maximum value or minimum value.
▪▪ without graphing determine the vertex, the line of symmetry, and the maximum or minimum value of a function $f(x) = a(x − h)^2 + k$.

▪ Graphs of f(x) = a(x − h)² + k

In $f(x) = a(x − h)^2$, let us replace $f(x)$ by $f(x) − k$. This amounts to the same thing as replacing the right side by $a(x − h)^2 + k$. By Theorem 8-7, we know that the graph will be translated upward if k is positive and downward if k is negative.

The vertex will be translated the same way. The line, or axis, of symmetry will not be affected. Thus, for $f(x) = a(x − h)^2 + k$,

the line of symmetry is $x = h$,
the vertex is (h, k).

The maximum or the minimum function value occurs at the vertex.

If a graph opens upward ($a > 0$) there is a minimum function value, k.
If a graph opens downward ($a < 0$) there is a maximum function value k.

Example 1.

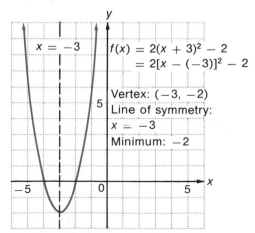

$f(x) = 2(x + 3)^2 − 2$
$\quad\quad = 2[x − (−3)]^2 − 2$

Vertex: $(−3, −2)$
Line of symmetry:
$x = −3$
Minimum: $−2$

Example 2.

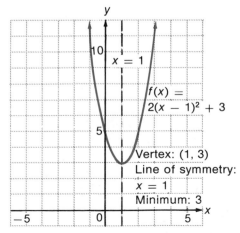

$f(x) = 2(x − 1)^2 + 3$

Vertex: $(1, 3)$
Line of symmetry:
$x = 1$
Minimum: 3

Example 3.

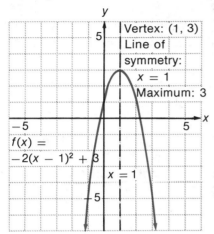

Vertex: (1, 3)
Line of symmetry:
$x = 1$
Maximum: 3

$f(x) = -2(x - 1)^2 + 3$

$x = 1$

TRY THIS ➡

1. a) Graph $f(x) = 3(x - 2)^2 + 4$.
    b) What is the vertex?
    c) What is the line of symmetry?
    d) Is there a minimum? If so, what is it?
    e) Is there a maximum? If so, what is it?
2. a) Graph $f(x) = -3(x + 2)^2 - 1$
            $= -3[x - (-2)]^2 - 1$
    b) What is the vertex?
    c) What is the line of symmetry?
    d) Is there a minimum? If so, what is it?
    e) Is there a maximum? If so, what is it?

Answers.   1. a) See answer section   b) (2, 4) c) x = 2 d) Yes, 4 e) No
2. a) See answer section   b) (−2, 1) c) x = −2 d) No e) Yes, −1

▮▮ Analyzing $f(x) = a(x - h)^2 + k$ Without Graphing

Without actually graphing, we can determine a lot of information about a function

$$f(x) = a(x - h)^2 + k.$$

The following table contains examples.

Function	$f(x) = 3(x - \frac{1}{4})^2 - 2$	$g(x) = -3(x + 5)^2 + 7$ $= -3[x - (-5)]^2 + 7$
a) What is the vertex?	$(\frac{1}{4}, -2)$	$(-5, 7)$
b) What is the line of symmetry?	$x = \frac{1}{4}$	$x = -5$
c) Is there a maximum? What is it?	No, graph extends upward, 3 > 0	Yes, 7, graph extends downward, −3 < 0
d) Is there a minimum? What is it?	Yes, −2, graph extends upward, 3 > 0	No, graph extends downward, −3 < 0

TRY THIS ➡

Answers. 3. a) (5, 40) b) x = 5 c) Yes, 40 d) No 4. a) (5, 0)
b) x = 5 c) No d) Yes, 0 5. a) $(-\frac{3}{4}, -6)$ b) $x = -\frac{3}{4}$ c) Yes, −6
d) No 6. a) (−9, 3) b) x = −9 c) No d) Yes, 3

Without graphing, answer the following questions for each function.

a) What is the vertex?
b) What is the line of symmetry?
c) Is there a minimum? If so, what is it?
d) Is there a maximum? If so, what is it?

3. $f(x) = (x - 5)^2 + 40$
4. $f(x) = -3(x - 5)^2$
5. $f(x) = 2(x + \frac{3}{4})^2 - 6$
6. $f(x) = -\frac{1}{4}(x + 9)^2 + 3$

Exercise Set 13-2

∎ For each of the following,

    a) graph the function.
    b) find the vertex.
    c) find the line of symmetry.
    d) find the maximum value, or the minimum value.

(See Examples 1–3.)   See answer section

1. $f(x) = (x - 3)^2 + 1$
2. $f(x) = (x + 2)^2 - 3$
3. $f(x) = (x + 1)^2 - 2$
4. $f(x) = (x - 1)^2 + 2$
5. $f(x) = 2(x - 1)^2 - 3$
6. $f(x) = 2(x + 1)^2 + 4$
7. $f(x) = -3(x + 4)^2 + 1$
8. $f(x) = -2(x - 5)^2 - 3$

∎∎ Without graphing,

    a) find the vertex.
    b) find the line of symmetry.
    c) find the maximum value, or the minimum value.

(See page 401.)   See answer section

9. $f(x) = 8(x - 9)^2 + 5$
10. $f(x) = 10(x + 5)^2 - 8$
11. $f(x) = 5(x + \frac{1}{4})^2 - 13$
12. $f(x) = 6(x - \frac{1}{4})^2 + 19$
13. $f(x) = -7(x - 10)^2 - 20$
14. $f(x) = -9(x + 12)^2 + 23$
15. $f(x) = \sqrt{2}(x + 4.58)^2 + 65\pi$
16. $f(x) = 4\pi(x - 38.2)^2 - \sqrt{34}$

13-3 Standard Form for Quadratic Functions

After finishing Lesson 13-3, you should be able to
▮ given a function described by $f(x) = ax^2 + bx + c$, complete the square to express it as $f(x) = a(x - h)^2 + k$. Then find the vertex, line of symmetry, and the maximum value or the minimum value.
▮▮ solve maximum and minimum problems involving quadratic functions.

▮ Completing the Square

Consider a quadratic function described by

$$f(x) = ax^2 + bx + c.$$

By completing the square we can describe it

$$f(x) = a(x - h)^2 + k.$$

Example 1. For $f(x) = x^2 - 6x + 4$,
a) find an equation of the type $f(x) = a(x - h)^2 + k$.
b) find the vertex, line of symmetry, and the maximum or minimum value.

a) $f(x) = x^2 - 6x + 4$
$\qquad = (x^2 - 6x) + 4$

We complete the square inside the parentheses. We take half the x coefficient:

$$\tfrac{1}{2} \cdot (-6) = -3$$

We square it:

$$(-3)^2 = 9$$

Then we add $9 - 9$ inside the parentheses.

$f(x) = (x^2 - 6x + 9 - 9) + 4$
$\qquad = (x^2 - 6x + 9) + (-9 + 4)$ *Rearranging terms*
$\qquad = 1 \cdot (x - 3)^2 - 5$

b) The vertex is $(3, -5)$.
The line of symmetry is $x = 3$.
Since the coefficient, 1, is positive, there is a minimum function value. It is -5.

Answers. 1. a) $f(x) = (x - 2)^2 + 3$ b) $(2, 3)$, $x = 2$, Min. $= 3$

TRY THIS ➡

1. For $f(x) = x^2 - 4x + 7$,
   a) find an equation of the type $f(x) = a(x - h)^2 + k$.
   b) find the vertex, line of symmetry, and the maximum or minimum value.

Example 2. For $f(x) = -2x^2 + 10x - 7$,
a) find an equation of the type $f(x) = a(x - h)^2 + k$.
b) find the vertex, line of symmetry, and the maximum or minimum value.

a) We first factor the expression $-2x^2 + 10x$. Then we proceed as before

$$f(x) = -2x^2 + 10x - 7$$

We "remove" -2 from the first two terms. This makes the coefficient of x^2 inside the parentheses a 1.

$$f(x) = -2(x^2 - 5x) - 7$$

We take half of the x-coefficient and square it, to get $\frac{25}{4}$. Then we add $\frac{25}{4} - \frac{25}{4}$ inside the parentheses.

$$\begin{aligned} f(x) &= -2(x^2 - 5x + \tfrac{25}{4} - \tfrac{25}{4}) - 7 \\ &= -2(x^2 - 5x + \tfrac{25}{4}) + 2(\tfrac{25}{4}) - 7 \\ &= -2(x - \tfrac{5}{2})^2 + \tfrac{11}{2} \end{aligned}$$

Multiplying by -2, using the distributive law, and rearranging terms

b) The vertex is $(\frac{5}{2}, \frac{11}{2})$.
The line of symmetry is $x = \frac{5}{2}$.
The coefficient -2 is negative, so there is a maximum. It is $\frac{11}{2}$.

TRY THIS

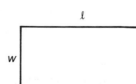

2. For $f(x) = -4x^2 + 12x - 5$,
 a) find an equation of the type $f(x) = a(x - h)^2 + k$.
 b) find the vertex, line of symmetry, and the maximum or minimum value.

Answers. 2. a) $f(x) = -4(x - \frac{3}{2})^2 + 4$ b) $(\frac{3}{2}, 4)$, $x = \frac{3}{2}$, Max. = 4

▪▪ Maximum and Minimum Problems

Some maximum or minimum problems involve quadratic functions. To solve such a problem, we translate by finding the appropriate function. Then we find the maximum or minimum value of that function.

Example 3. What are the dimensions of the largest rectangular pen that can be enclosed with 64 meters of fence?

We make a drawing and label it.
The perimeter must be 64 m,
so we have

$$2w + 2l = 64. \qquad \textbf{(1)}$$

We wish to find the maximum area, so we try to find a quadratic function for the area.

$$A = lw$$

Solving **(1)** for l, we get $l = 32 - w$.
Substituting, we get

$$A = (32 - w)w$$
$$= -w^2 + 32w$$

Completing the square, we get

$$A = -(w - 16)^2 + 256$$

The maximum function value is 256. It occurs when $w = 16$. Thus the dimensions are 16 m by 16 m.

TRY THIS ➡

3. What is the maximum product of two numbers whose sum is 30? 225
4. What are the dimensions of the largest rectangular pen that can be enclosed with 100 meters of fence?
25 m by 25 m

Exercise Set 13-3

▮ For each function,

    a) find an equation of the type $f(x) = a(x - h)^2 + k$.
    b) find the vertex, line of symmetry, and the maximum or minimum value.

(*See Examples 1 and 2.*)   See answer section

1. $f(x) \doteq x^2 - 2x - 3$
2. $f(x) = x^2 + 2x - 5$
3. $f(x) = -x^2 + 4x + 6$
4. $f(x) = -x^2 - 4x + 3$
5. $f(x) = x^2 + 3x - 10$
6. $f(x) = x^2 + 5x + 4$
7. $f(x) = x^2 - 9x$
8. $f(x) = x^2 + x$
9. $f(x) = 3x^2 - 24x + 50$
10. $f(x) = 4x^2 + 8x - 3$
11. $f(x) = \frac{3}{4}x^2 + 9x$
12. $f(x) = \frac{3}{2}x^2 - 3x$
13. $f(x) = -2x^2 + 2x + 1$
14. $f(x) = -2x^2 - 2x + 3$

▮▮ (*See Example 3.*)

15. A rancher is fencing off a rectangular area with a fixed perimeter of 76 m. What dimensions would yield the maximum area? What is the maximum area?   19 m by 19 m; 361 m²

16. A carpenter is building a rectangular room with a fixed perimeter of 68 m. What dimensions would yield the maximum area? What is the maximum area?   17 m by 17 m; 289 m²

17. What is the maximum product of two numbers whose sum is 22? What numbers yield this product?   121; 11 and 11

18. What is the maximum product of two numbers whose sum is 45? What numbers yield this product?
506.25; 22.5 and 22.5

19. What is the minimum product of two numbers whose difference is 4? What are the numbers?   −4; 2 and −2

20. What is the minimum product of two numbers whose difference is 6? What are the numbers?   −9; 3 and −3

21. What is the minimum product of two numbers whose difference is 5? What are the numbers? $-\frac{25}{4}$; $\frac{5}{2}$ and $-\frac{5}{2}$

22. What is the minimum product of two numbers whose difference is 7? What are the numbers? $-\frac{49}{4}$; $\frac{7}{2}$ and $-\frac{7}{2}$

Calculator Exercises   23. Min. ≈ −6.9536605   24. Max. ≈ 7.0141259

Find the maximum or minimum value for each function.

23. $f(x) = 2.31x^2 - 3.135x - 5.89$ 24. $f(x) = -18.8x^2 + 7.92x + 6.18$

Challenge Exercises

25. What is the minimum product of two numbers whose difference is 4.932? What are the numbers?   −6.081156

26. The sum of the base and height of a triangle is 20. Find the dimensions for which the area is a maximum.   Base = 10; height = 10

27. Find the dimensions and area of the largest rectangle which can be inscribed as shown in a right triangle ABC whose sides have lengths 9 cm, 12 cm, and 15 cm.
    Length is 6 cm; width is 4.5 cm; area is 27 cm²

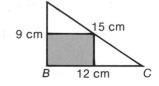

28. Bea Yeld wants to build a rectangular fence near a river. She is going to use 120 m of fencing. What is the largest area she can enclose? Note that she does not fence in the side next to the river.   1800 m²

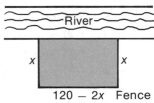

Use Quiz 23 after lesson 13–3.

COMPUTER NOTE: Traffic Flow

Some cities use computers to keep traffic flowing during rush hours. The computers are linked to traffic lights. During rush hours, the computers receive information about the flow of cars. Then the computers adjust the timing of traffic signals to prevent traffic jams.

13-4 x-Intercepts and Graphs

After finishing Lesson 12-4, you should be able to
▮ find the *x*-intercepts of the graph of a quadratic function, if they exist.

▮ The points at which a graph crosses the *x*-axis are
called its *x-intercepts*. These are of course the
points at which $y = 0$.
   To find the *x*-intercepts of a quadratic function
$f(x) = ax^2 + bx + c$ we solve the equation

$$0 = ax^2 + bx + c.$$

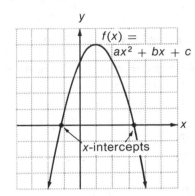

Example. Find the *x*-intercepts of the graph of
$f(x) = x^2 - 2x - 2$.

We solve the equation

$$0 = x^2 - 2x - 2.$$

The equation is difficult to factor, so we use the quadratic
formula and get $x = 1 \pm \sqrt{3}$. Thus the *x*-intercepts are
$(1 - \sqrt{3}, 0)$ and $(1 + \sqrt{3}, 0)$. We sometimes refer to the
x-coordinates of these points as *intercepts*.

TRY THIS

Find the *x*-intercepts.

1. $f(x) = x^2 - 2x - 5$
    $(1 + \sqrt{6}, 0), (1 - \sqrt{6}, 0)$

The discriminant, $b^2 - 4ac$, tells us how many real number solutions the equation $0 = ax^2 + bx + c$ has, so it also indicates
how many intercepts there are. Compare.

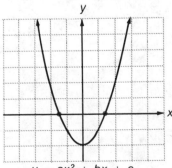

$y = ax^2 + bx + c$
$b^2 - 4ac > 0$
Two real solutions
Two *x*-intercepts

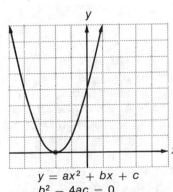

$y = ax^2 + bx + c$
$b^2 - 4ac = 0$
One real solution
One *x*-intercept

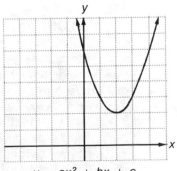

$y = ax^2 + bx + c$
$b^2 - 4ac < 0$
No real solutions
No *x*-intercepts

TRY THIS ➡️

Find the *x*-intercepts, if they exist.

2. $f(x) = x^2 - 2x - 3$ (3, 0), (−1, 0)
3. $f(x) = x^2 + 8x + 16$ (−4, 0)
4. $f(x) = -2x^2 - 4x - 3$ None

Exercise Set 13-4

▌Find the *x*-intercepts. (*See the Example.*)

1. $f(x) = x^2 - 4x + 1$ $(2 + \sqrt{3}, 0), (2 - \sqrt{3}, 0)$
2. $f(x) = x^2 + 6x + 10$ None
3. $f(x) = -x^2 + 2x + 3$ (3, 0), (−1, 0)
4. $f(x) = -x^2 + 3x + 4$ (4, 0), (−1, 0)
5. $f(x) = 2x^2 - 4x + 6$ None
6. $f(x) = 2x^2 + 4x - 1$ $(\frac{-2 + \sqrt{6}}{2}, 0), (\frac{-2 - \sqrt{6}}{2}, 0)$
7. $f(x) = x^2 - x + 2$ None
8. $f(x) = x^2 - x + 1$ None
9. $f(x) = 4x^2 + 12x + 9$ $(-\frac{3}{2}, 0)$
10. $f(x) = 3x^2 - 6x + 1$ $(\frac{3 + \sqrt{6}}{3}, 0), (\frac{3 - \sqrt{6}}{3}, 0)$

Calculator Exercises

Find the *x*-intercepts.

11. $f(x) = 0.05x^2 - 4.735x + 100.23$
12. $f(x) = 1.13x^2 + 2.809x - 7.114$

11. (62.758520, 0), (31.941480, 0)   12. (1.5571557, 0), (−4.042996, 0)

Challenge Exercises

Graph these quadratic inequalities.

13. $y < x^2 - 4x - 1$ See answer section
14. $y \geq x^2 + 3x - 4$
15. $y > 3x^2 + 6x + 2$
16. $y > 2x^2 + 4x - 2$

HISTORICAL NOTE: Parabolas

In ancient Greece, pebbles were used to make calculations. Pebbles also can be used to demonstrate an important curve, the parabola. Simply toss a pebble into the air. The path it describes is a parabola. Wind or air resistance will affect the path a little, so it won't be a perfect parabola. But it will be close. A pop fly in baseball and a punt in football follow parabolic paths.

   The first person to notice that the path of a tossed object is a parabola was Galileo. He discovered this fact in the early 1600s.

13-5 *Applications of Quadratic Functions*

After finishing Lesson 13-5, you should be able to
▮ fit a quadratic function to three data points and solve related problems.
▮▮ solve problems involving quadratic functions.

▮Fitting Quadratic Functions to Data

In many problems, a quadratic function can be used to describe the situation. We can find a quadratic function if we know three inputs and their outputs. Each such ordered pair is called a *data point*.

Example 1. Pizza Unlimited has the following prices for pizzas.

Diameter in cm	Price
20	$3.00
30	$4.25
40	$5.75

Is price a quadratic function of diameter? Probably so, because the price should be proportional to the area, and the area is a quadratic function of the diameter (the area of a circular region is given by $A = \pi r^2$ or $A = \frac{\pi}{4}d^2$).

a) Fit a quadratic equation to the data points (20, 3) (30, 4.25), and (40, 5.75).
b) Use the function to find the price of a 35 cm pizza.

a) We use the three data points to obtain a, b, and c in
$f(x) = ax^2 + bx + c$.

$$3.00 = a \cdot 20^2 + b \cdot 20 + c$$
$$4.25 = a \cdot 30^2 + b \cdot 30 + c$$
$$5.75 = a \cdot 40^2 + b \cdot 40 + c$$

Simplifying, we get the system

$$3.00 = 400a + 20b + c$$
$$4.25 = 900a + 30b + c$$
$$5.75 = 1600a + 40b + c$$

We solve this system obtaining (0.00125, 0.0625, 1.25).
$a = 0.00125$, $b = 0.0625$, and $c = 1.25$. Thus the function
$f(x) = 0.00125x^2 + 0.0625x + 1.25$.

b) To find the price of 35-cm pizza, we find $f(35)$:

$$f(35) = 0.00125(35)^2 + 0.0625(35) + 1.25$$
$$= \$4.97 \quad \textit{Rounded to the nearest cent}$$

It should be noted that this price function always gives results greater than \$1.25 since $f(0) = 1.25$. The \$1.25 is the fixed cost involved in making a pizza.

TRY THIS

Answers. 1. f(x) = x² − 2x + 1 2. a) f(x) = 0.625x² − 50x + 1150 b) 510

1. Find the quadratic function that fits the data points $(1, 0)$, $(-1, 4)$, and $(2, 1)$.
2. The following table shows the accident records in a city. It has values that a quadratic function will fit.

Age of driver	Number of accidents (in a year)
20	400
40	150
60	400

a) Assuming that a quadratic function will describe the situation, find the number of accidents as a function of age.
b) Use the function to calculate the number of accidents a typical 16-year-old is involved in.

ⅠⅠ Solving Problems

A theory from physics shows that when an object such as a bullet or ball is shot or thrown upward with an initial velocity v_0, its height is given, approximately, by a quadratic function.

$$s = -4.9t^2 + v_0t + h,$$

where h is the starting height (in meters), s is the actual height (in meters), and t is the time from projection in seconds.

Example 2. A model rocket is fired upward. At the end of the burn it has an upward velocity of 49 m/s and is 155 m high. Find
a) its maximum height and when it is attained;
b) when it reaches the ground.

a) We will start counting time at the end of the burn. Thus $v_0 = 49$ and $h = 155$. We will graph the appropriate function, and we begin by completing the square.

$$s = -4.9\left(t^2 - \frac{49}{4.9}t\right) + 155$$
$$= -4.9(t^2 - 10t) + 155$$
$$= -4.9(t^2 - 10t + 25 - 25) + 155$$
$$= -4.9(t^2 - 10t + 25) + (-4.9)(-25) + 155$$
$$= -4.9(t - 5)^2 + 277.5$$

The vertex of the graph is the point (5, 277.5). The graph is shown at the right. The maximum height reached is 277.5 m and it is attained 5 seconds after the end of the burn.

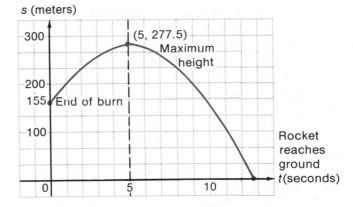

b) To find when the rocket reaches the ground, we set $s = 0$ in our equation and solve for t.

$$-4.9(t - 5)^2 + 277.5 = 0$$
$$(t - 5)^2 = \frac{277.5}{4.9}$$
$$t - 5 = \sqrt{\frac{277.5}{4.9}}$$
$$t - 5 \approx 7.525$$
$$t \approx 12.525.$$

The rocket will reach the ground about 12.525 seconds after the end of the burn.

Answers.   3. a) Max. height = 12.4 m in 0.286 s
b) 1.876 s

TRY THIS ➡

3. A ball is thrown upward from the top of a cliff 12 meters high, at a velocity of 2.8 m/s. Find
a) its maximum height and when it is attained.
b) when it reaches the ground.

Exercise Set 13-5

❚ Find the quadratic function which fits each set of data points. (*See Example 1.*)

1. $(1, 4)$, $(-1, -2)$, $(2, 13)$ $f(x) = 2x^2 + 3x - 1$

2. $(1, 4)$, $(-1, 6)$, $(-2, 16)$ $f(x) = 3x^2 - x + 2$

3. $(1, 5)$, $(2, 9)$, $(3, 7)$ $f(x) = -3x^2 + 13x - 5$

4. $(1, -4)$, $(2, -6)$, $(3, -6)$ $f(x) = x^2 - 5x$

❚❚ (*See Example 2.*)

5. *Predicting earnings.* A business earns $38 in the first week, $66 in the second week, and $86 in the third week. The manager graphs the points $(1, 38)$ $(2, 66)$, and $(3, 86)$ and uses a quadratic function to describe the situation.
   a) Find a quadratic function that fits the data. $f(x) = -4x^2 + 40x + 2$
   b) Using the function, predict the earnings for the fourth week. $98

6. *Predicting earnings.* A business earns $1000 in its first month, $2000 in the second month, and $8000 in the third month. The manager plots the points $(1, 1000)$, $(2, 2000)$, and $(3, 8000)$ and uses a quadratic function to describe the situation.
   a) Find a quadratic function that fits the data. $f(x) = 2500x^2 - 6500x + 5000$
   b) Using the function, predict the earnings for the fourth month. $19,00

7. a) Find a quadratic function that fits the following data. $f(x) = 0.05x^2 - 10.5x + 650$

Travel Speed in km/h	Number of Daytime Accidents (For every 200 million km)
60	200
80	130
100	100

   b) Use your function to calculate the number of daytime accidents which occur at 50 km/h.   250

8. a) Find a quadratic function that fits the following data. $f(x) = \frac{3}{16}x^2 - \frac{135}{4}x + 1750$

Travel Speed in km/h	Number of Nighttime Accidents (for every 200 million km)
60	400
80	250
100	250

   b) Use the function to calculate the number of nighttime accidents which occur at 50 km/h.   531.25

9. A rocket is fired upward from ground level at a velocity of 147 m/s. Find
   a) its maximum height and when it is attained;   Max. height = 1102.5 m in 15 s
   b) when it reaches the ground.   30 s

10. A rocket is fired upward from ground level at a velocity of 245 m/s. Find
    a) its maximum height and when it is attained;   Max. height = 3062.5 m in 25 s
    b) when it reaches the ground.   50 s

Calculator Exercises

Find the quadratic function which fits each set of data points.

11. (20.34, −5.86), (34.67, −6.02), (28.55, −8.46) $f(x) = 0.0499218x^2 - 2.7573651x + 29.571379$

12. (0.789, 245), (0.988, 350), (1.233, 404) $f(x) = -691.96016x^2 + 1757.2031x - 710.6735$

Challenge Exercises

13. *Maximizing revenue.* When a theatre owner charges $3 for admission he averages 100 people attending. For each 10¢ increase in admission price the average number attending decreases by 1. What should he charge to make the most money? $6.50

SCIENCE NOTE: Ice Ages

There have been several ice ages in the history of the earth. The most recent one began about 70,000 years ago. For some reason, the earth's average temperature fell about 3 or 4°C. That caused an increase in the accumulation of snow each year. As more and more snow stayed unmelted each year, glaciers formed. They moved slowly southward from the northern ice cap at the rate of about 1 kilometer each 20 years.

The ice sheets made four major advances in the most recent ice age. They reached as far south as St. Louis, Cleveland, and New York City. About 10,000 years ago, they began their last retreat. They are still retreating.

During each ice age, as more water turned to snow and ice, there was less water for the oceans. The level of the oceans dropped by as much as 90 meters. When the ocean level dropped, more land was exposed. Part of the exposed land connected Asia and Alaska. The first people to reach North America probably walked across this land. The land they crossed is now under the water of the Bering Strait, off Alaska.

13-6 Quadratic Variation

After finishing Lesson 13-6, you should be able to
I given a type of variation, find an equation of variation.
II solve problems involving variation.

I Finding Equations of Variation

We now consider variation when the equations involved are of second degree, or higher. Consider the equation for the area of a circle.

$$A = \pi r^2$$

We say that the area varies directly as the square of the radius. When (r_1, A_1) and (r_2, A_2) are solutions of the equation we have $A_1 = \pi r_1^2$ and $A_2 = \pi r_2^2$. Then

$$\frac{A_1}{A_2} = \frac{\pi r_1^2}{\pi r_2^2} = \frac{r_1^2}{r_2^2}.$$

A proportion like $\dfrac{A_1}{A_2} = \dfrac{r_1^2}{r_2^2}$ can be helpful in solving problems.

DEFINITION

y varies directly as the square of *x* if there is some positive number *k* such that $y = kx^2$.

Example 1. Find an equation of variation where *y* varies directly as the square of *x*, and $y = 12$ when $x = 2$.

We write an equation of variation and find *k*.

$$y = kx^2, \text{ so } 12 = k \cdot 2^2 \text{ and } 3 = k.$$

Thus $y = 3x^2$.

TRY THIS ➡️

1. Find an equation of variation where *y* varies directly as the square of *x* and $y = 175$ when $x = 5$. $y = 7x^2$

From the law of gravity, we know that the weight *W* of an object varies inversely as the square of the distance *d* from the center of the earth.

$$W = \frac{k}{d^2}$$

When (d_1, W_1) and (d_2, W_2) are solutions of the equation we have $W_1 = \dfrac{k}{d_1^2}$ and $W_2 = \dfrac{k}{d_2^2}$. Then

$$\frac{W_1}{W_2} = \frac{\dfrac{k}{d_1^2}}{\dfrac{k}{d_2^2}} = \frac{k}{d_1^2} \cdot \frac{d_2^2}{k} = \frac{d_2^2}{d_1^2}.$$

A proportion like $\dfrac{W_1}{W_2} = \dfrac{d_2^2}{d_1^2}$ can be helpful in solving problems.

DEFINITION

y varies inversely as the square of x if there is some positive number k such that $y = \dfrac{k}{x^2}$.

Example 2. Find an equation of variation where W varies inversely as the square of d, and $W = 3$ when $d = 5$.

$$W = \frac{k}{d^2}, \text{ so } 3 = \frac{k}{5^2} \text{ and } 75 = k.$$

Thus $W = \dfrac{75}{d^2}$.

TRY THIS ➡

2. Find an equation of variation where y varies inversely as the square of x, and $y = \frac{1}{4}$ when $x = 6$. $y = \dfrac{9}{x^2}$

Consider the equation for the area A of a triangle with height h and base b.

$$A = \tfrac{1}{2}bh$$

We say that the area varies *jointly* as the height and the base. From two solutions of the equation we get the proportion

$$\frac{A_1}{A_2} = \frac{b_1 h_1}{b_2 h_2}.$$

DEFINITION

y varies jointly as x and z if there is some positive number k such that $y = kxz$.

Example 3. Find an equation of variation where y varies jointly as x and z, and $y = 42$ when $x = 2$ and $z = 3$.

$$y = kxz, \text{ so } 42 = k \cdot 2 \cdot 3 \text{ and } 7 = k.$$

Thus $y = 7xz$.

TRY THIS ➡

The equation

$$y = k \cdot \frac{xz^3}{w}$$

asserts that y varies jointly as x and the cube of z, and inversely as w.

3. Find an equation of variation where y varies jointly as x and z, and $y = 65$ when $x = 10$ and $z = 13.$ $y = \frac{1}{2}xz$

Example 4. Find an equation of variation where y varies jointly as x and z and inversely as the square of w, and $y = 105$ when $x = 3$, $z = 20$ and $w = 2$.

$$y = k \cdot \frac{xz}{w^2}, \text{ so } 105 = k \cdot \frac{3 \cdot 20}{2^2} \text{ and } k = 7.$$

Thus $y = 7 \cdot \dfrac{xz}{w^2}$.

TRY THIS ➡

4. Find an equation of variation where y varies jointly as x and the square of z and inversely as w, and $y = 80$ when $x = 4$, $z = 10$, and $w = 25$. $y = \frac{5xz^2}{w}$

▪ Solving Problems

Many problem situations can be described with equations of variation.

Example 5. The volume of wood V in a tree varies jointly as the height h and the square of the girth g (girth is distance around). If the volume of a redwood tree is 216 m³ when the height is 30 m and the girth is 1.5 m, what is the height of a tree whose volume is 960 m³ and girth is 2 m?

Method 1: First find k using the first set of data. Then solve for h using the second set of data.

$$V = khg^2$$
$$216 = k \cdot 30 \cdot 1.5^2$$
$$3.2 = k$$

Then

$$960 = 3.2 \cdot h \cdot 2^2$$
$$75 = h$$

Method 2: Let h_1 represent the height of the first tree and h_2 the height of the second tree. Use a proportion to solve for h_2 without first finding the variation constant.

$$\frac{V_1}{V_2} = \frac{h_1 \cdot g_1{}^2}{h_2 \cdot g_2{}^2}$$

$$\frac{216}{960} = \frac{30 \cdot 1.5^2}{h_2 \cdot 2^2}$$

$$h_2 = \frac{960 \cdot 67.5}{4 \cdot 216}$$

$$h_2 = 75 \text{ m}$$

Example 6. The intensity I of a TV signal varies inversely as the square of the distance d from the transmitter. If the intensity is 23 watts per square meter (W/m²) at a distance of 2 km, what is the intensity at a distance of 6 km?

We use the proportion.

$$\frac{I_1}{I_2} = \frac{d_2{}^2}{d_1{}^2}$$

$$\frac{I_2}{23} = \frac{2^2}{6^2}$$

$$I_2 = \frac{4 \cdot 23}{36}$$

$$I_2 = 2.56 \text{ W/m}^2 \qquad \textit{Rounded to the nearest hundredth}$$

TRY THIS

5. The distance s that an object falls when dropped from some point above the ground varies directly as the square of the time t it falls. If the object falls 19.6 m in 2 seconds, how far will the object fall in 10 seconds? **490 m**

6. At a fixed temperature, the resistance R of a wire varies directly as the length l and inversely as the square of its diameter d. If the resistance is 0.1 ohm when the diameter is 1 mm and the length is 50 cm, what is the resistance when the length is 2000 cm and the diameter is 2 mm? **1 ohm**

7. In Example 6, why is the equation not appropriate when the distance is 0 km from a transmitter whose initial signal is 316,000 W/m²? **Division by zero is undefined.**

Exercise Set 13-6

▌Find an equation of variation where: (*See Examples 1–4.*)

1. y varies directly as the square of x, and $y = 0.15$ when $x = 0.1$. **y = 15x²**

2. y varies directly as the square of x, and $y = 6$ when $x = 3$. **y = $\frac{2}{3}$x²**

3. y varies inversely as the square of x, and $y = 0.15$ when $x = 0.1$. **y = $\frac{0.0015}{x^2}$**

4. y varies inversely as the square of x, and $y = 6$ when $x = 3$. **y = $\frac{54}{x^2}$**

5. *y* varies jointly as *x* and *z*, and *y* = 56 when *x* = 7 and *z* = 8. $y = xz$

6. *y* varies directly as *x* and inversely as *z*, and *y* = 4 when *x* = 12 and *z* = 15. $y = \frac{5x}{z}$

7. *y* varies jointly as *x* and the square of *z*, and *y* = 105 when *x* = 14 and *z* = 5. $y = \frac{3}{10}xz^2$

8. *y* varies jointly as *x* and *z* and inversely as *w*, and *y* = $\frac{3}{2}$ when *x* = 2, *z* = 3, and *w* = 4. $y = \frac{xz}{w}$

9. *y* varies jointly as *x* and *z* and inversely as the product of *w* and *p*, and *y* = $\frac{3}{28}$ when *x* = 3, *z* = 10, *w* = 7, and *p* = 8. $y = \frac{1}{5}\frac{xz}{wp}$

10. *y* varies jointly as *x* and *z* and inversely as the square of *w*, and *y* = $\frac{12}{5}$ when *x* = 16, *z* = 3, and *w* = 5. $y = \frac{5}{4}\frac{xz}{w^2}$

■■ Solve. (*See Examples 5 and 6.*)

11. *Stopping Distance of a Car.* The stopping distance *d* of a car after the brakes are applied varies directly as the square of the speed *r*. If a car traveling 60 km/h can stop in 80 m, how many feet will it take the same car to stop when it is traveling 90 km/h?   180 m

12. *Area of a Cube.* The area of a cube varies directly as the square of the length of a side. If a cube has an area 168.54 m² when the length of a side is 5.3 m, what will the area be when the length of a side is 10.2 m?   624.24 m²

13. *Weight of an Astronaut.* The weight *W* of an object varies inversely as the square of the distance *d* from the center of the earth. At sea level (6400 km from the center of the earth) an astronaut weighs 100 kg. Find his weight when 200 km above the surface of the earth and the spacecraft is not in motion.   94.03 kg

14. *Intensity of Light.* The intensity of light *I* from a light bulb varies inversely as the square of the distance *d* from the bulb. Suppose *I* is 90 W/m² when the distance is 5 m. Find the intensity at a distance of 10 m.   22.5 W/m²

15. *Earned Run Average.* A pitcher's earned run average *A* varies directly as the number of earned runs *R* allowed and inversely as the number *I* of innings pitched. In a recent year Tom Seaver had an earned run average of 2.92. He gave up 85 earned runs in 262 innings. How many earned runs would he have given up had he pitched 300 innings? Round to the nearest whole number.   97

16. *Volume of a Gas.* The volume *V* of a given mass of a gas varies directly as the temperature *T* and inversely as the pressure *P*. If *V* = 231 cm³ when *T* = 42° and *P* = 20 kg/cm², what is the volume when *T* = 30° and *P* = 15 kg/cm²?   220 cm³

Calculator Exercises

17. *A sighting problem.* The distance d that one can see to the horizon varies directly as the square root of the height above sea level. If a person 19.5 m above sea level can see 15.46 km, how high above sea level must one be to see 54.32 km?   240.73273 m
18. *Electrical resistance.* At a fixed temperature and chemical composition, the resistance of a wire varies directly as the length l and inversely as the square of the diameter d. If the resistance of a certain kind of wire is 0.112 ohms when the diameter is 0.254 cm and the length is 15.24 m, what is the resistance of a wire whose length is 608.7 m and whose diameter is 0.478 cm?   1.2631298 ohms

Challenge Exercises

19. The area of a circle varies directly as the square of the length of a diameter. What is the variation constant? $k = \dfrac{A}{d^2}$
20. The area of a circle varies directly as the square of its circumference. What is the variation constant? $k = \dfrac{A}{c^2}$
21. *The Gravity Model in Sociology.* It has been determined that the average number of telephone calls in a day N, between two cities, is directly proportional to the populations P_1 and P_2 of the cities and inversely proportional to the square of the distance d between the cities. That is, $N = \dfrac{kP_1 P_2}{d^2}$.

   a) The population of Indianapolis is 744,624 and the population of Cincinnati is 452,524 and the distance between the cities is 174 km. The average number of daily phone calls between the two cities is 11,153. Find the value k and write the equation of variation. $N = \dfrac{0.001 P_1 P_2}{d^2}$
   b) The population of Detroit is 1,511,482 and it is 446 km from Indianapolis. Find the average number of daily phone calls between Detroit and Indianapolis.   5658
   c) The average number of daily phone calls between Indianapolis and New York is 4270 and the population of New York is 7,895,563. Find the distance between Indianapolis and New York.   1173 km
   d) Why is this model not appropriate for adjoining cities such as Minneapolis and St. Paul? Sociologists say that as the communication between two cities increases, the cities tend to merge. Division by zero is undefined.

CHAPTER 13 REVIEW

Review the material in the chapter. Then see how you have done by trying these review exercises. If you miss an exercise, restudy the indicated lesson.

Graph. See answer section

13-1 1. $f(x) = -2x^2$
13-1 2. $f(x) = -2(x + 1)^2$
13-2 3. $f(x) = -2(x + 1)^2 + 3$

13-2 4. For $f(x) = -2(x + 1)^2 + 3$, find the vertex, line of symmetry, and the maximum value or the minimum value. $(-1, 3)$, $x = -1$, Max. = 3

13-3 For each function,
   a) find an equation of the type $f(x) = a(x - h)^2 + k$.
   b) find the vertex, line of symmetry, and the maximum value or minimum value.
   5. $f(x) = x^2 - 8x + 5$ a) $f(x) = (x - 4)^2 - 11$ b) $(4, -11)$, $x = 4$, Min. = -11
   6. $f(x) = \frac{4}{5}x^2 - 16x$ a) $f(x) = \frac{4}{5}(x - 10)^2 - 80$ b) $(2, -80)$, $x = 2$, Min. = -80

13-4 7. Find the x-intercepts of $f(x) = -2x^2 - 4x + 3$, if they exist. $(\frac{-2 + \sqrt{10}}{2}, 0)$, $(\frac{-2 - \sqrt{10}}{2}, 0)$

13-4 8. Find the x-intercepts of $f(x) = -x^2 - 2x + 4$, if they exist. $-1 \pm \sqrt{5}$

13-5 9. Find the quadratic function that fits data points $(1, -3)$, $(-1, 5)$, and $(2, -13)$. $f(x) = -2x^2 - 4x + 3$

13-5 10. A rocket is fired upward from ground level at a velocity of 98 m/s. Find
   a) its maximum height and when it is attained;   Max. height = 490 m in 10 s
   b) when it reaches the ground.   20 s

13-6 11. The area of a sphere varies directly as the square of its radius. If the area is 1257 m² when the radius is 10 m, what is the area when the radius is 3 m?   113.13 m²

CHAPTER 13 TEST

Graph. See answer section
1. $f(x) = 2x^2$
2. $f(x) = 2(x - 5)^2$
3. $f(x) = 2(x - 5)^2 - 4$

4. For $f(x) = 10(x + 3)^2 + 14$, find the vertex, line of symmetry, and the maximum or minimum value. $(-3, 14), x = -3, \text{Min.} = 14$

For each function,
a) find an equation of the type $f(x) = a(x - h)^2 + k$.
b) find the vertex, line of symmetry, and the maximum or minimum value.
5. $f(x) = -x^2 - 6x + 7$ a) $f(x) = -(x + 3)^2 + 16$ b) $(-3, 16), x = -3, \text{Max.} = 16$
6. $f(x) = 2x^2 - 10x - 7$ a) $f(x) = 2(x - \frac{5}{2})^2 - \frac{39}{2}$ b) $(\frac{5}{2}, -\frac{39}{2}), x = \frac{5}{2}, \text{Min.} = -\frac{39}{2}$
7. Find the x-intercepts of $f(x) = 2x^2 - 5x + 8$, if they exist. None
8. Find the x-intercepts of $f(x) = -x^2 - 2x + 2$, if they exist. $-1 \pm \sqrt{3}$
9. Find the quadratic equation which fits the data points $(-1, 6), (1, 4),$ and $(2, 9)$. $f(x) = 2x^2 - x + 3$
10. An appliance store sells 10 TV's the first month, 20 TV's the second month, and 40 TV's the third month. The manager graphs the points $(1, 10), (2, 20),$ and $(3, 40)$, and finds that a quadratic function might fit the data.
    a) Find a quadratic function that fits the data. $f(x) = 5x^2 - 5x + 10$
    b) Using your function, predict the sales for the fourth month. 70
11. The time T which it takes a group of people to do a certain job varies inversely as the product of the number of people and the time t, in hours per day, they work. If 16 people work 5 hours per day they can complete a certain job in 9 days. How many days will it take 15 people working 6 hours per day to complete the same job? 8

Science teachers in public high schools specialize in one area of science. Teachers direct students' laboratory activities and scientific problem solving.

Firefighters reduce the destructiveness of fires in towns or cities. Firefighters work as members of teams to reach fires quickly and to control them.

School librarians organize books and other items, and guide studen in using them. Librarians work wit teachers and supervisors to give i formation.

Construction inspectors visit sites to see that builders have proper permits and meet safety standards. Inspectors may visit a large project many times.

CAREERS IN GOVERNMENT

The words *careers in government* make many people think of work for the Federal government. In fact, most careers in government in the United States exist on state and local levels. Government careers at these levels have grown significantly since 1950, as the line graph shows. Careers at the Federal level have grown relatively little in that time.

Workers (in millions)

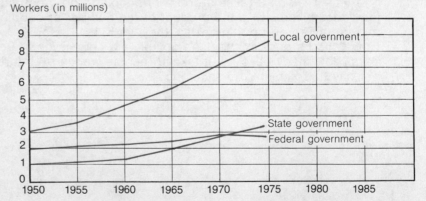

Numbers of Federal, State, and Local Government Workers

ofessors of mathematics at large ate universities do teaching and search. Professors may teach th graduate and undergraduate dents.

Social workers help individuals, families, or larger groups cope with problems such as alcoholism, the illness or death of a parent, or legal disputes.

Members of the United States Foreign Service work to support the diplomatic actions of the nation. Their careers usually call for living in various countries.

Soil conservationists for the Federal government advise farmers and ranchers about soil use. Conservationists may draw maps, write plans, and estimate costs.

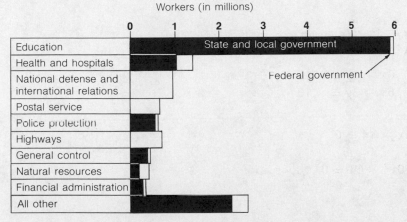

Workers (in millions)

	0	1	2	3	4	5	6
Education							
Health and hospitals							
National defense and international relations							
Postal service							
Police protection							
Highways							
General control							
Natural resources							
Financial administration							
All other							

State and local government

Federal government

Government Employment in the Mid-1970s

About three of every seven government workers are in education. The bar graph above indicates the importance of education in government work. Note that nearly all workers in education are state and local employees, as shown in the graph.

Some people who follow careers in government are pictured here. The projected place of such careers in the total labor force is shown in the circle graph.

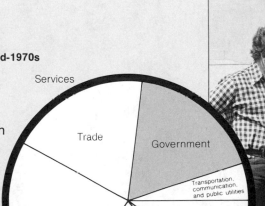

Services

Trade

Government

Various Services

Transportation, communication, and public utilities

Other

Construction

Manufacturing

Goods

Projected United States Labor Force in the mid-1980s

Ready for Equations of Second Degree?

Simplify.

10-2   1. $\sqrt{169}$ 13

10-3   2. $\sqrt{48}$ $4\sqrt{3}$

7-4   Factor by completing the square.

     3. $x^2 - 2x - 15$ $(x-5)(x+3)$

     4. $y^2 - 9y + 14$ $(y-7)(y-2)$

Graph.

3-1   5. $y = 3x - 1$ Line through (2, 5) and (0, −1)

13-1   6. $y = 3x^2$ Parabola through (−1, 3), (0, 0), (1, 3)

4-2   7.   Solve: $6x + 3y = -12$

              $6x - 3y = 18$ $(\frac{1}{2}, -5)$

Solve.

7-7   8. $x^2 - 9x + 14 = 0$ 2, 7

12-1   9. $x^2 = 5$ $\sqrt{5}, -\sqrt{5}$

12-8   10. $x^4 - 20x^2 + 64 = 0$ 2, −2, 4, −4

Chapter 14
Equations of Second Degree

Some comets travel in elliptical paths. A famous comet, Halley's comet, last seen in 1910 will return in 1985.

14-1 The Distance Formula

After finishing Lesson 14-1, you should be able to
∎ use the distance formula to find the distance between any two points in the plane.
∎∎ find the coordinates of the midpoint of a segment, given the endpoints.

∎ The Distance Formula

The following formula is important in many ways.

THEOREM 14-1 (The Distance Formula)
The distance between any two points (x_1, y_1) and (x_2, y_2) is given
by $d = \sqrt{(x_1 - x_2)^2 + (y_1 - y_2)^2}$.

Example 1. Find the distance between the points (8, 7) and (3, −5).

We substitute the coordinates into the distance formula.

$d = \sqrt{(8 - 3)^2 + [7 - (-5)]^2}$
$= \sqrt{5^2 + 12^2}$
$= \sqrt{25 + 144}$
$= \sqrt{169}$
$= 13$

TRY THIS

Find the distance be-
tween the points.

1. $(-5, 3)$ and $(2, -7)$
2. $(3, 3)$ and $(-3, -3)$
   1. $\sqrt{149}$ 2. $6\sqrt{2}$

A Proof of Theorem 14-1

The proof of this theorem involves two cases, one where the points are on either a horizontal or vertical line, and the other where the points are not on a horizontal or vertical line. We prove the latter case as follows.

Consider any two points not on a horizontal or vertical line, (x_1, y_1) and (x_2, y_2). These points are vertices of a right triangle as shown. The other vertex is (x_2, y_1). The legs of the triangle have lengths $|x_1 - x_2|$ and $|y_1 - y_2|$. By the Pythagorean Theorem, $d^2 = |x_1 - x_2|^2 + |y_1 - y_2|^2$. We can do away with the absolute value signs since squares of numbers are never negative. Thus $d^2 = (x_1 - x_2)^2 + (y_1 - y_2)^2$.
Taking the principal square root, we get $d = \sqrt{(x_1 - x_2)^2 + (y_1 - y_2)^2}$.

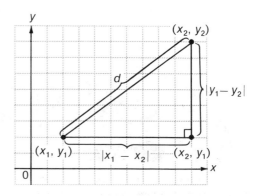

∎ Midpoints of Segments

The distance formula can be used to verify a formula for finding the coordinates of the midpoint of a segment when the coordinates of the endpoints are known.

THEOREM 14-2 (The Midpoint Formula)

If the endpoints of a segment are (x_1, y_1) and (x_2, y_2), then the coordinates of the midpoint are $\left(\dfrac{x_1 + x_2}{2}, \dfrac{y_1 + y_2}{2}\right)$.

The coordinates of the midpoint can be found by averaging those of the endpoints.

Example 2. Find the midpoint of the segment with endpoints $(-3, 5)$ and $(4, -7)$.

Using the midpoint formula, we get

$$\left(\frac{-3 + 4}{2}, \frac{5 + (-7)}{2}\right), \text{ or } (\tfrac{1}{2}, -1).$$

TRY THIS ➡

Find the midpoints of the segments having endpoints as given.

3. $(-2, 1)$ and $(5, -6)$ $(\tfrac{3}{2}, -\tfrac{5}{2})$
4. $(9, -6)$ and $(9, -4)$ $(9, -5)$

Exercise Set 14-1

∎ Find the distance between the points. (*See Example 1.*)

1. $(-3, -2)$ and $(1, 1)$ 5
2. $(5, 9)$ and $(-1, 6)$ $3\sqrt{5}$
3. $(0, -7)$ and $(3, -4)$ $3\sqrt{2}$
4. $(2, 2)$ and $(-2, -2)$ $4\sqrt{2}$
5. $(9, 5)$ and $(6, 1)$ 5
6. $(1, 10)$ and $(7, 2)$ 10
7. $(5, 6)$ and $(5, -2)$ 8
8. $(5, 6)$ and $(0, 6)$ 5
9. $(a, -3)$ and $(2a, 5)$ $\sqrt{a^2 + 64}$
10. $(5, 2k)$ and $(-3, k)$ $\sqrt{64 + k^2}$
11. $(0, 0)$ and (a, b) $\sqrt{a^2 + b^2}$
12. $(\sqrt{2}, \sqrt{3})$ and $(0, 0)$ $\sqrt{5}$
13. $(\sqrt{a}, \sqrt{b})$ and $(-\sqrt{a}, \sqrt{b})$ $2\sqrt{a}$
14. $(c - d, c + d)$ and $(c + d, d - c)$ $2\sqrt{d^2 + c^2}$

∎ Find the midpoints of the segments having the following endpoints. (*See Example 2.*)

15. $(-4, 7)$ and $(3, -9)$ $(-\tfrac{1}{2}, -1)$
16. $(4, 5)$ and $(6, -7)$ $(5, -1)$
17. $(2, -5)$ and $(-9, -10)$ $(-\tfrac{7}{2}, -\tfrac{15}{2})$
18. $(8, -4)$ and $(-3, 9)$ $(\tfrac{5}{2}, \tfrac{5}{2})$
19. $(2, 2)$ and $(6, 6)$ $(4, 4)$
20. $(-2, 0)$ and $(3, 0)$ $(\tfrac{1}{2}, 0)$
21. (a, b) and $(a, -b)$ $(a, 0)$
22. $(-c, d)$ and (c, d) $(0, d)$

Challenge Exercises   See answer section

23. Prove that the distance between pairs of points on either a horizontal line or a vertical line can be found using the distance formula.
24. Prove the midpoint formula, Theorem 14-2.

14-2 Circles

After finishing Lesson 14-2, you should be able to
- **I** given the center and radius of a circle, find an equation for the circle.
- **II** find the center and radius of a circle by putting the equation in the form $(x - h)^2 + (y - k)^2 = r^2$. Then graph the circle.

I Circles

Some equations of second degree have graphs that are circles.

DEFINITION

A *circle* is the set of all points in a plane which are at a fixed distance from a fixed point. The fixed point is the *center*. The fixed distance is the *radius*.

THEOREM 14-3

The equation (in standard form) of the circle centered at the origin with radius r is $x^2 + y^2 = r^2$.

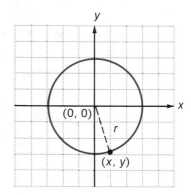

Example 1. What is the radius of the circle with the equation $x^2 + y^2 = 25$?

$$r^2 = 25$$
$$r = 5$$

TRY THIS

What is the radius of each circle?

1. $x^2 + y^2 = 36$ 6
2. $x^2 + y^2 = 100$ 10
3. $x^2 + y^2 = 50$ $5\sqrt{2}$

A Proof of Theorem 14-3

We must prove that a point (x, y) is on the circle centered at the origin with radius r if and only if $x^2 + y^2 = r^2$. To prove a sentence 'P if and only if Q' we must prove 'If P, then Q' and 'If Q, then P'. Thus there are two parts to the proof.

i) Assume (x, y) is on the circle. Then it is a distance r from $(0, 0)$. By the distance formula,

$$r = \sqrt{(x - 0)^2 + (y - 0)^2},$$

or $r^2 = x^2 + y^2.$

We have now shown that if (x, y) is on the circle then $x^2 + y^2 = r^2$.

ii) Now assume $x^2 + y^2 = r^2$ is true for a point (x, y). This can be expressed as

$$(x - 0)^2 + (y - 0)^2 = r^2$$

Taking the principal square root we get

$$\sqrt{(x - 0)^2 + (y - 0)^2} = r.$$

Thus the distance from (x, y) to $(0, 0)$ is r, so (x, y) is on the circle. We have now shown that if $x^2 + y^2 = r^2$, then (x, y) is on the circle.

The two parts of the proof together show that the equation

$$x^2 + y^2 = r^2$$

gives *all* the points of the circle, *and no others*.

By Theorems 8-7 and 8-8, when a circle is translated so its center is (h, k), we can find an equation for it by replacing x by $x - h$ and y by $y - k$.

THEOREM 14-4

The equation (in standard form) of a circle with center (h, k) and radius r is $(x - h)^2 + (y - k)^2 = r^2$.

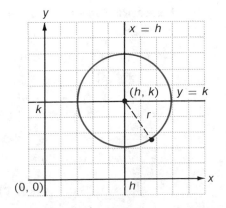

Example 2. Find an equation of a circle with center at $(-1, 3)$ and radius $\sqrt{2}$.

$$[x - (-1)]^2 + (y - 3)^2 = (\sqrt{2})^2$$
$$(x + 1)^2 + (y - 3)^2 = 2$$

TRY THIS ▬▬▬▬▶

Find an equation of a circle with center and radius as given.

4.   Center: $(5, -2)$
     Radius: $\sqrt{3}$
5.   Center: $(-2, -6)$
     Radius: $\sqrt{7}$

ıı Finding the Center and Radius

Example 3.   Find the center and radius of $(x - 2)^2 + (y + 3)^2 = 16$. Then graph the circle.

We may first rewrite the equation as

$$(x - 2)^2 + [y - (-3)]^2 = 4^2.$$

Then the *center* is $(2, -3)$ and the *radius* is 4. The graph is then easy to draw, as shown, using a compass.

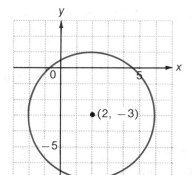

6.   Find the center and radius of
     $(x + 1)^2 + (y - 3)^2 = 4$.
     Then graph the circle.
     See answer section

TRY THIS ▬▬▬▬▶

Completing the square allows us to find the standard form for the equation of a circle.

Example 4.   Find the center and radius of the circle $x^2 + y^2 + 8x - 2y + 15 = 0$.

We complete the square twice to get the standard form.

$$(x^2 + 8x + \quad) + (y^2 - 2y + \quad) = -15$$
$$(x^2 + 8x + 16) + (y^2 - 2y + 1) = -15 + 16 + 1$$
$$(x + 4)^2 + (y - 1)^2 = 2$$
$$[x - (-4)]^2 + (y - 1)^2 = (\sqrt{2})^2$$

The *center* is $(-4, 1)$ and the *radius* is $\sqrt{2}$.

7. Find the center and radius
   of the circle
   $x^2 + y^2 - 14x + 4y - 11 = 0$. $(7, -2), r = 8$

TRY THIS ▬▬▬▬▶

Exercise Set 14-2

▮ Find an equation of a circle with center and radius as given. (*See Example 2.*)

1. Center: (0, 0)
   Radius: 7 $x^2 + y^2 = 49$

2. Center: (0, 0)
   Radius: π $x^2 + y^2 = \pi^2$

3. Center: $(-2, 7)$ $(x + 2)^2 + (y - 7)^2 = 5$
   Radius: $\sqrt{5}$

4. Center: (5, 6) $(x - 5)^2 + (y - 6)^2 = 12$
   Radius: $2\sqrt{3}$

▮▮ Find the center and radius of each circle. Then graph the circle. (*See Example 3.*)   See answer section

5. $(x + 1)^2 + (y + 3)^2 = 4$

6. $(x - 2)^2 + (y + 3)^2 = 1$

Find the center and radius of each circle. (*See Examples 3 and 4.*)

7. $(x - 8)^2 + (y + 3)^2 = 40$ (8, −3), r = $2\sqrt{10}$

8. $(x + 5)^2 + (y - 1)^2 = 75$ (−5, 1), r = $5\sqrt{3}$

9. $x^2 + y^2 = 2$ (0, 0), r = $\sqrt{2}$

10. $x^2 + y^2 = 3$ (0, 0), r = $\sqrt{3}$

11. $(x - 5)^2 + y^2 = \frac{1}{4}$ (5, 0), r = $\frac{1}{2}$

12. $x^2 + (y - 1)^2 = \frac{1}{25}$ (0, 1), r = $\frac{1}{5}$

13. $x^2 + y^2 + 8x - 6y - 15 = 0$ (−4, 3), r = $2\sqrt{10}$

14. $x^2 + y^2 + 6x - 4y - 15 = 0$ (−3, 2), r = $2\sqrt{7}$

15. $x^2 + y^2 - 8x + 2y + 13 = 0$ (4, −1), r = 2

16. $x^2 + y^2 + 6x + 4y + 12 = 0$ (−3, −2), r = 1

17. $x^2 + y^2 - 4x = 0$ (2, 0), r = 2

18. $x^2 + y^2 + 10y - 75 = 0$ (0, −5), r = 10

Calculator Exercises

Find the center and radius of each circle.

19. $x^2 + y^2 + 8.246x - 6.348y - 74.35 = 0$ (−4.123, 3.174), r ≈ 10.070918

20. $x^2 + y^2 + 25.074x + 10.004y + 12.054 = 0$ (−12.537, −5.002), r ≈ 13.043862

Challenge Exercises

21. Use Theorem 14-4 to find an equation of a circle satisfying the given conditions.
    a) Center (0, 0), passing through $(\frac{\sqrt{3}}{2}, \frac{1}{2})$ $x^2 + y^2 = 1$
    b) Center (3, −2), passing through (11, −2) $(x - 3)^2 + (y + 2)^2 = 64$
    c) Center (2, 4) and tangent (touching at one point) to the *x*-axis $(x - 2)^2 + (y - 4)^2 = 16$

22. Find an equation of a circle such that: a) $(x - 1)^2 + (y - 2)^2 = 41$ b) $(x - 3)^2 + y^2 = 25$
    a) The endpoints of a diameter are (5, −3) and (−3, 7)
    b) The endpoints of a diameter are (7, 3) and (−1, −3)

23. Prove that $\angle ABC$ is a right angle. Assume point *B* is on the circle whose radius is *a* and whose center is at the origin. (*Hint:* Use slopes and an equation of the circle.)
    See answer section

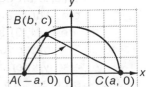

14-3 Ellipses

After finishing Lesson 14-3, you should be able to
■ given an equation of an ellipse, find the center, vertices, and foci. Then graph the ellipse.

■ An ellipse is defined as follows.

DEFINITION

An ellipse is the set of all points P in a plane such that the sum of the distances from P to two fixed points F_1 and F_2 is constant. Each fixed point is called a *focus* (plural: *foci*) of the ellipse.

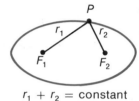

$r_1 + r_2 =$ constant

We first obtain an equation of an ellipse whose center is at the origin and whose foci lie on one of the coordinate axes.

THEOREM 14-5

The equation (in standard form) of the ellipse centered at the origin with foci on the x-axis is $\dfrac{x^2}{a^2} + \dfrac{y^2}{b^2} = 1$.

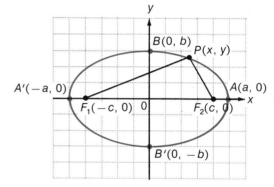

From this equation, we see that the graph is symmetric with respect to both axes and the origin. The longer axis of symmetry $\overline{A'A}$ is called the *major axis*. The shorter axis of symmetry $\overline{B'B}$ is called the *minor axis*. The intersection of these axes is called the *center*. The points A, A', B, and B' are called *vertices*. The constant distance, $F_1P + F_2P$, is $2a$ and $c^2 = a^2 - b^2$.

Example 1. For the ellipse $x^2 + 16y^2 = 16$, find the vertices and the foci. Then graph the ellipse.

a) We multiply by $\frac{1}{16}$ to get 1 on the right.

$$\frac{x^2}{16} + \frac{y^2}{1} = 1, \text{ or } \frac{x^2}{4^2} + \frac{y^2}{1^2} = 1$$

This is an equation of an ellipse centered at the origin. Thus, $a = 4$ and $b = 1$. Then two of the vertices are $(-4, 0)$ and $(4, 0)$. These are also x-intercepts. The other vertices are $(0, 1)$ and $(0, -1)$. These are also y-intercepts. Since $c^2 = a^2 - b^2$, $c^2 = 16 - 1$, so $c = \sqrt{15}$ and the foci are $(-\sqrt{15}, 0)$ and $(\sqrt{15}, 0)$.

b) The graph is at the right.

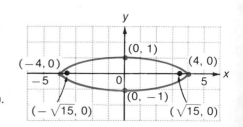

TRY THIS ➡

For this ellipse, find the vertices and foci. Then graph the ellipse.

1. $x^2 + 9y^2 = 9$

See answer section

The foci of an ellipse can be on the *y*-axis.

THEOREM 14-6

The equation (in standard form) of an ellipse centered at the origin, with foci on the *y*-axis is $\dfrac{x^2}{a^2} + \dfrac{y^2}{b^2} = 1$.

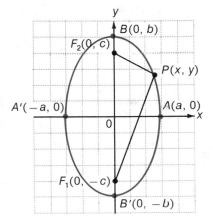

This is the same equation we have in Theorem 14-5. If $a > b$, the foci will be on the *x*-axis. If $b > a$, the foci will be on the *y*-axis.
In this case, the major axis is $\overline{B'B}$, and the minor axis is $\overline{A'A}$. The constant distance, $F_1P + F_2P$, is $2b$ and $c^2 = b^2 - a^2$.

Example 2. For the ellipse $9x^2 + 2y^2 = 18$, find the vertices and foci. Then graph the ellipse.

a) We first multiply by $\dfrac{1}{18}$.

$$\frac{x^2}{2} + \frac{y^2}{9} = 1 \text{ or } \frac{x^2}{(\sqrt{2})^2} + \frac{y^2}{3^2} = 1$$

Thus, $a = \sqrt{2}$ and $b = 3$. Then the vertices are $(-\sqrt{2}, 0)$, $(\sqrt{2}, 0)$, $(0, 3)$, and $(0, -3)$.

b) Since $b > a$ the foci are on the *y*-axis and the major axis lies along the *y*-axis. To find *c* in this case we proceed as follows.

$$\begin{aligned} c^2 &= b^2 - a^2 \\ &= 9 - 2 \\ &= 7 \\ c &= \sqrt{7} \end{aligned}$$

So, the foci are $(0, \sqrt{7})$ and $(0, -\sqrt{7})$.

c) The graph is at the right.

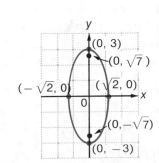

TRY THIS ➡

When an ellipse is translated so that its center is (h, k), then by Theorems 8-7 and 8-8, we can find an equation for it by replacing x by $x - h$ and y by $y - k$.

For each ellipse find the vertices and foci. Then graph the ellipse.

2. $25x^2 + 9y^2 = 225$
3. $4x^2 + 2y^2 = 8$

See answer section

THEOREM 14-7

The equation (in standard form) of an ellipse with center (h, k) is $\dfrac{(x - h)^2}{a^2} + \dfrac{(y - k)^2}{b^2} = 1$.

Example 3.   For the ellipse $16x^2 + 4y^2 + 96x - 8y + 84 = 0$, find the center, vertices, and foci. Then graph the ellipse.

a) We first complete the square to get standard form.

$$16(x^2 + 6x + \quad) + 4(y^2 - 2y + \quad) = -84$$
$$16(x^2 + 6x + 9) + 4(y^2 - 2y + 1) = -84 + 16 \cdot 9 + 4 \cdot 1$$
$$16(x + 3)^2 + 4(y - 1)^2 = 64$$
$$\frac{(x + 3)^2}{2^2} + \frac{(y - 1)^2}{4^2} = 1.$$

The center is $(-3, 1)$, $a = 2$, and $b = 4$.

b) We first find the vertices of the untranslated ellipse $\dfrac{x^2}{2^2} + \dfrac{y^2}{4^2} = 1$.

They are $(2, 0)$, $(-2, 0)$, $(0, 4)$, and $(0, -4)$, and since $c^2 = 16 - 4 = 12$, $c = 2\sqrt{3}$, and its foci are $(0, 2\sqrt{3})$ and $(0, -2\sqrt{3})$.

c) Then the vertices and foci of the translated ellipse are found by translation in the same way in which the center has been translated. The center was translated from $(0, 0)$ to $(-3, 1)$. So we subtract 3 from all x-coordinates and add 1 to all y-coordinates. The vertices are $(2 - 3, 0 + 1)$, $(-2 - 3, 0 + 1)$, $(0 - 3, 4 + 1)$, $(0 - 3, -4 + 1)$, or

$(-1, 1)$, $(-5, 1)$, $(-3, 5)$, $(-3, -3)$.

The foci are $(0 - 3, 2\sqrt{3} + 1)$ and $(0 - 3, -2\sqrt{3} + 1)$ or $(-3, 1 + 2\sqrt{3})$ and $(-3, 1 - 2\sqrt{3})$.

d) The graph is as follows.

For each ellipse find the center, vertices, and the foci. Then graph the ellipse.

4. $25x^2 + 9y^2 + 150x - 36y + 260 = 0$

5. $9x^2 + 25y^2 - 36x + 150y + 260 = 0$

See answer section

TRY THIS

Exercise Set 14-3

■ For each ellipse find the center, vertices, and foci. Then graph the ellipse.
(*See Examples 1–3.*)   See answer section

1. $\dfrac{x^2}{4} + \dfrac{y^2}{1} = 1$

2. $\dfrac{x^2}{1} + \dfrac{y^2}{4} = 1$

3. $\dfrac{(x-1)^2}{4} + \dfrac{(y-2)^2}{1} = 1$

4. $\dfrac{(x-1)^2}{1} + \dfrac{(y-2)^2}{4} = 1$

5. $\dfrac{(x+3)^2}{25} + \dfrac{(y-2)^2}{16} = 1$

6. $\dfrac{(x-2)^2}{25} + \dfrac{(y+3)^2}{16} = 1$

7. $16x^2 + 9y^2 = 144$

8. $9x^2 + 16y^2 = 144$

9. $3(x+2)^2 + 4(y-1)^2 = 192$

10. $4(x-5)^2 + 3(y-5)^2 = 192$

11. $2x^2 + 3y^2 = 6$

12. $5x^2 + 7y^2 = 35$

13. $4x^2 + 9y^2 = 1$

14. $25x^2 + 16y^2 = 1$

15. $4x^2 + 9y^2 - 16x + 18y - 11 = 0$

16. $x^2 + 2y^2 - 10x + 8y + 29 = 0$

17. $4x^2 + y^2 - 8x \quad 2y \mid 1 = 0$

18. $9x^2 + 4y^2 + 54x - 8y + 49 = 0$

Challenge Exercises

19. Find the equation of the ellipse with the following vertices. (*Hint:* Graph the vertices.)
    a) $(2, 0), (-2, 0), (0, 3), (0, -3)$
    b) $(1, 1), (5, 1), (3, 6), (3, -4)$

    a) $\dfrac{x^2}{4} + \dfrac{y^2}{9} = 1$ b) $\dfrac{(x-3)^2}{4} + \dfrac{(y-1)^2}{25} = 1$

20. Find an equation of an ellipse satisfying the given conditions.
    a) Center at $(-2, 3)$ with major axis of length 4 and parallel to the y-axis, minor axis of length 1.
    b) Vertices $(3, 0)$ and $(-3, 0)$ and containing the point $(2, \frac{22}{3})$.

    a) $\dfrac{(x+2)^2}{1/4} + \dfrac{(y-3)^2}{4} = 1$

    b) $\dfrac{x^2}{9} + \dfrac{y^2}{484/5} = 1$

14-4 Hyperbolas

After finishing Lesson 14-4, you should be able to
∎ given an equation of a hyperbola, find the center, vertices, foci, and asymptotes. Then graph the hyperbola.
∎∎ graph equations of hyperbolas of the type $xy = c$, $c \neq 0$.

∎ Equations of Hyperbolas

We define a hyperbola as follows.

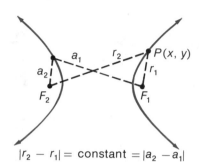

DEFINITION

A *hyperbola* is a set of all points P in a plane such that the absolute value of the difference of the distances from P to two fixed points F_1 and F_2 is constant. The fixed points F_1 and F_2 are called *foci*. The midpoint of the segment F_1F_2 is called the *center*.

We first obtain an equation of a hyperbola whose center is at the origin and whose foci lie on one of the coordinate axes.

THEOREM 14-8

The equation (in standard form) of a hyperbola centered at the origin with foci on the x-axis is $\dfrac{x^2}{a^2} - \dfrac{y^2}{b^2} = 1$.

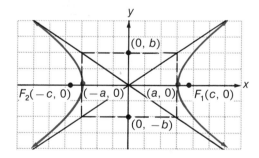

The two parts of the hyperbola are called *branches*. Points $(a, 0)$ and $(-a, 0)$ are called the *vertices,* and the line segment joining them is called the *transverse axis*. The line segment from $(0, b)$ to $(0, -b)$ is called the *conjugate axis*. By looking at the equation, we can see that the hyperbola is symmetric with respect to the origin, and that the x- and y-axes are lines of symmetry.

The lines $y = \left(\dfrac{b}{a}\right)x$ and $y = -\left(\dfrac{b}{a}\right)x$ are called *asymptotes*. They have slopes $\dfrac{b}{a}$ and $-\dfrac{b}{a}$.

The constant distance, $|PF_2 - PF_1|$, is $2a$ and $c^2 = a^2 + b^2$.

Example 1. For the hyperbola $9x^2 - 16y^2 = 144$, find the vertices, foci, and asymptotes. Then graph the hyperbola.

a) We first multiply by $\dfrac{1}{144}$ to find the standard form: $\dfrac{x^2}{16} - \dfrac{y^2}{9} = 1$.

Thus $a = 4$ and $b = 3$. The vertices are $(4, 0)$ and $(-4, 0)$. Since $c^2 = a^2 + b^2$, $c = \sqrt{a^2 + b^2} = \sqrt{4^2 + 3^2} = 5$. Thus the foci are $(5, 0)$ and $(-5, 0)$. The asymptotes are $y = \frac{3}{4}x$ and $y = -\frac{3}{4}x$.

b) To graph the hyperbola it is helpful to first graph the asymptotes. An easy way to do this is to draw the rectangle shown in the figure. The asymptotes are found by extending the diagonals. Then draw the branches of the hyperbola outward from the vertices toward the asymptotes.

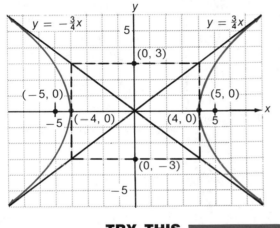

TRY THIS

The foci of a hyperbola can be on the y-axis.

For each hyperbola find the vertices, foci, and asymptotes. Then graph.

1. $4x^2 - 9y^2 = 36$
2. $x^2 - y^2 = 16$

See answer section

THEOREM 14-9

The equation (in standard form) of a hyperbola centered at the origin with foci on the y-axis is $\dfrac{y^2}{b^2} - \dfrac{x^2}{a^2} = 1$.

In this case the slopes of the asymptotes are still $\pm\dfrac{b}{a}$ and it is still true that $c^2 = a^2 + b^2$. There are now y-intercepts and they are $(0, b)$ and $(0, -b)$. The constant distance, $|PF_2 - PF_1|$, is $2b$.

Example 2. For the hyperbola $25y^2 - 16x^2 = 400$, find the vertices, the foci, and the asymptotes. Then graph the hyperbola.

a) We first multiply by $\dfrac{1}{400}$ to find the standard form: $\dfrac{y^2}{16} - \dfrac{x^2}{25} = 1$.

Thus $a = 5$ and $b = 4$. The vertices are $(0, 4)$ and $(0, -4)$. Since $c = \sqrt{4^2 + 5^2} = \sqrt{41}$, the foci are $(0, \sqrt{41})$ and $(0, -\sqrt{41})$. The asymptotes are $y = \frac{4}{5}x$ and $y = -\frac{4}{5}x$.

b) The graph is as follows.

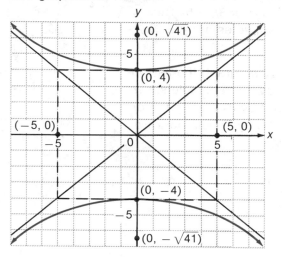

For each hyperbola find the
vertices, foci, and asymptotes.
Then graph the hyperbola.

3. $9y^2 - 25x^2 = 225$
4. $y^2 - x^2 = 25$

See answer section

TRY THIS

If the center of a hyperbola is not at the origin, but at some
point (h, k), then its equation is found by replacing x by $x - h$
and y by $y - k$.

THEOREM 14-10

The equation (in standard form) of a hyperbola with center (h, k) is

$$\frac{(x - h)^2}{a^2} - \frac{(y - k)^2}{b^2} = 1 \text{ if the transverse axis is parallel to the } x\text{-axis, or}$$

$$\frac{(y - k)^2}{b^2} - \frac{(x - h)^2}{a^2} = 1 \text{ if the transverse axis is parallel to the } y\text{-axis.}$$

Example 3. For the hyperbola $4x^2 - y^2 + 24x + 4y + 28 = 0$,
find the center, the vertices, the foci, and the asymptotes. Then
graph the hyperbola.

a) We complete the square to find standard form.

$$4(x^2 + 6x + \quad) - (y^2 - 4y + \quad) = -28$$
$$4(x^2 + 6x + 9) - (y^2 - 4y + 4) = -28 + 4 \cdot 9 + (-1 \cdot 4)$$
$$4(x + 3)^2 - (y - 2)^2 = 4$$
$$\frac{(x + 3)^2}{1} - \frac{(y - 2)^2}{4} = 1$$

The center is $(-3, 2)$.

b) Consider the untranslated hyperbola $\frac{x^2}{1} - \frac{y^2}{4} = 1$. We have

$a = 1$ and $b = 2$. The vertices of this hyperbola are $(1, 0)$ and $(-1, 0)$. Also, $c = \sqrt{1^2 + 2^2} = \sqrt{5}$, so the foci are $(\sqrt{5}, 0)$ and $(-\sqrt{5}, 0)$. The asymptotes are $y = 2x$ and $y = -2x$.

c) The vertices, foci, and asymptotes of the translated hyperbola are found in the same way in which the center has been translated. The vertices are $(1 - 3, 0 + 2)$, $(-1 - 3, 0 + 2)$, or $(-2, 2)$, $(-4, 2)$. The foci are $(-3 + \sqrt{5}, 2)$ and $(-3 - \sqrt{5}, 2)$. The asymptotes are $y - 2 = 2(x + 3)$ and $y - 2 = -2(x + 3)$.

d) The graph is as follows.

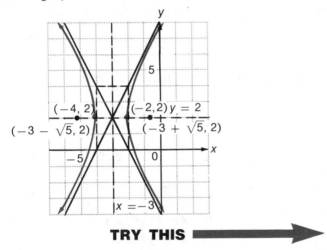

TRY THIS

For each hyperbola, find the center, vertices, foci, and asymptotes. Then graph the hyperbola.

5. $4x^2 - 25y^2 - 8x - 100y - 196 = 0$

6. $\frac{(y - 2)^2}{9} - \frac{(x + 1)^2}{16} = 1$

See answer section

∎ Equations of the Type $xy = c$

Another type of equation whose graph is a hyperbola is the following.

$$xy = c \text{ or } y = \frac{c}{x}, \text{ where } c \neq 0.$$

The coordinate axes are asymptotes.

If c is positive, the branches of the hyperbola lie in the first and third quadrants. If c is negative, the branches lie in the second and fourth quadrants. In either case, the asymptotes are the x-axis and the y-axis.

Example 4.   Graph $xy = 12$.

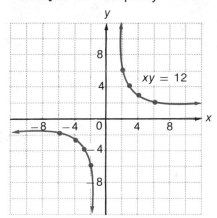

x	1	-1	2	-2	3	-3	4	-4	6	-6	12	-12
y	12	-12	6	-6	4	-4	3	-3	2	-2	1	-1

Graph.

7. $xy = 3$

8. $xy = -1$

See answer section

TRY THIS

Exercise Set 14-4

▌ For each hyperbola find the center, vertices, foci, and asymptotes. Then graph the hyperbola. (*See Examples 1–3.*)   See answer section

1. $\dfrac{x^2}{9} - \dfrac{y^2}{1} = 1$

2. $\dfrac{x^2}{1} - \dfrac{y^2}{9} = 1$

3. $\dfrac{(x - 2)^2}{9} - \dfrac{(y + 5)^2}{1} = 1$

4. $\dfrac{(x - 2)^2}{1} - \dfrac{(y + 5)^2}{9} = 1$

5. $\dfrac{(y + 3)^2}{4} - \dfrac{(x + 1)^2}{16} = 1$

6. $\dfrac{(y + 3)^2}{25} - \dfrac{(x + 1)^2}{16} = 1$

7. $x^2 - 4y^2 = 4$

8. $4x^2 - y^2 = 4$

9. $x^2 - y^2 = 2$

10. $x^2 - y^2 = 3$

11. $x^2 - y^2 - 2x - 4y - 4 = 0$

12. $4x^2 - y^2 + 8x - 4y - 4 = 0$

13. $36x^2 - y^2 - 24x + 6y - 41 = 0$

14. $9x^2 - 4y^2 + 54x + 8y + 41 = 0$

▌▌ Graph. (*See Example 4.*)

15. $xy = 1$

16. $xy = -4$

17. $xy = -8$

18. $xy = 2$

Challenge Exercises

19.   Find an equation of a hyperbola having:

    a)   Vertices at $(1, 0)$ and $(-1, 0)$; and foci at $(2, 0)$ and $(-2, 0)$. $\dfrac{x^2}{1} - \dfrac{y^2}{3} = 1$

    b)   Asymptotes $y = \frac{3}{4}x$ and $y = -\frac{3}{4}x$ and one vertex $(4, 0)$. $\dfrac{x^2}{16} - \dfrac{y^2}{9} = 1$

14-5 The Parabola

After finishing Lesson 14-5, you should be able to
▮ given an equation of a parabola, find the vertex, focus, and the directrix. Then graph the parabola.

▮ We define a parabola as follows.

DEFINITION

A *parabola* is a set of all points P in a plane, equidistant from a fixed line I, called the *directrix*, and a fixed point F, called the *focus*.

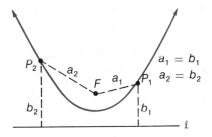

We first obtain an equation of a parabola with focus on the y-axis, directrix parallel to the x-axis, and vertex at the origin.

THEOREM 14-11

The equation (in standard form) of a parabola with focus at $(0, p)$, directrix $y = -p$, vertex $(0, 0)$, and y-axis as the only line of symmetry is $x^2 = 4py$.

If p is negative in an equation $x^2 = 4py$, the graph is a reflection across the x-axis, hence is still a parabola.

Example 1. For the parabola $y = x^2$, find the vertex, the focus, and the directrix. Then graph.

We first write $x^2 = 4py$.

$x^2 = 4(\tfrac{1}{4})y.$

Vertex: $(0, 0)$
Focus: $(0, \tfrac{1}{4})$
Directrix: $y = -\tfrac{1}{4}$

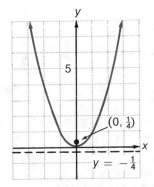

TRY THIS

For each parabola find the vertex, focus, and directrix. Then graph the parabola.

1. $y = 2x^2$
2. $8y = x^2$
3. $y = -x^2$

See answer section

The next two theorems follow from Theorem 14-11 by transformations.

THEOREM 14-12

The equation (in standard form) of a parabola with focus $(p, 0)$, directrix $x = -p$, vertex $(0, 0)$, and x-axis as the line of symmetry is $y^2 = 4px$.

Example 2. For the parabola $y^2 = -12x$, find the vertex, the focus, and the directrix. Then graph the parabola.

We first write $y^2 = 4px$.

$$y^2 = 4(-3)x$$

Vertex: $(0, 0)$
Focus: $(-3, 0)$
Directrix: $x = -(-3) = 3$

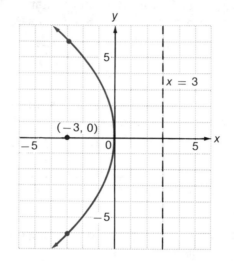

TRY THIS ➡

4. For the parabola $y^2 = -6x$, find the vertex, focus, and directrix. Then graph the parabola.
See answer section

THEOREM 14-13

The equation (in standard form) of a parabola with vertex (h, k), focus $(h, k + p)$, and directrix $y = k - p$, is

$$(x - h)^2 = 4p(y - k).$$

The equation (in standard form) of a parabola with vertex (h, k), focus $(h + p, k)$, and directrix $x = h - p$, is

$$(y - k)^2 = 4p(x - h).$$

Example 3. For the parabola $x^2 + 6x + 4y + 5 = 0$, find the vertex, the focus, and the directrix. Then graph the parabola.

We complete the square.

$$x^2 + 6x \qquad = -4y - 5$$
$$x^2 + 6x + 9 = -4y - 5 + 9$$
$$(x + 3)^2 = -4y + 4$$
$$(x + 3)^2 = 4(-1)(y - 1).$$

Vertex: $(-3, 1)$
Focus: $(-3, 1 + (-1))$, or $(-3, 0)$
Directrix: $y = 2$

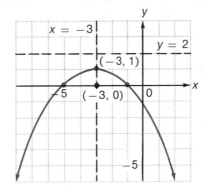

Example 4. For the parabola $y^2 + 6y - 8x - 31 = 0$, find the vertex, the focus, and the directrix. Then graph the parabola.

We complete the square.

$$y^2 + 6y \qquad = 8x + 31$$
$$y^2 + 6y + 9 = 8x + 31 + 9$$
$$(y + 3)^2 = 8x + 40$$
$$\qquad = 8(x + 5)$$
$$\qquad = 4(2)(x + 5)$$

Vertex: $(-5, -3)$
Focus: $(-5 + 2, -3)$, or $(-3, -3)$
Directrix: $x = -5 - 2$
$$x = -7$$

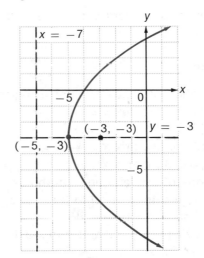

TRY THIS ➡️

For each parabola, find the vertex, the focus, and the directrix, and graph the parabola.

5. $x^2 + 2x - 8y - 3 = 0$
6. $y^2 + 2y + 4x - 7 = 0$

See answer section

Exercise Set 14-5

▌For each parabola find the vertex, focus, and directrix. Then graph the parabola. (*See Examples 1–4.*)   See answer section

1. $x^2 = 8y$
2. $x^2 = 16y$
3. $y^2 = -6x$
4. $y^2 = -2x$
5. $x^2 - 4y = 0$
6. $y^2 + 4x = 0$
7. $y = 4x^2$
8. $y = \frac{1}{2}x^2$
9. $(x + 2)^2 = -6(y - 1)$
10. $(y - 3)^2 = -20(x + 2)$
11. $x^2 + 2x + 2y + 7 = 0$
12. $y^2 + 6y - x + 16 = 0$
13. $x^2 - y - 2 = 0$
14. $x^2 - 4x - 2y = 0$
15. $y = x^2 + 4x + 3$
16. $y = x^2 + 6x + 10$
17. $4y^2 - 4y - 4x + 24 = 0$
18. $4y^2 + 4y - 4x - 16 = 0$

Calculator Exercises

For each parabola find the vertex, focus, and directrix.

19. $x^2 = 8056.25y$
20. $y^2 = -7645.88x$

19. Vertex: (0, 0); focus: (0, 2014.0625); y = −2014.0625
20. Vertex: (0, 0); focus: (−1911.47, 0); x = 1911.47

Challenge Exercises

21. Find an equation of a parabola satisfying the given conditions.
    a) Focus (4, 0), directrix $x = -4$ $y^2 = 16x$
    b) Focus $(0, \frac{1}{4})$, directrix $y = -\frac{1}{4}$ $x^2 = y$
    c) Focus (3, 2), directrix $x = -4$ $(y - 2)^2 = 16(x + 1)$
    d) Focus (−2, 3), directrix $y = -3$ $(x + 2)^2 = 12y$
22. Find equations of the following parabolas.
    a) Line of symmetry parallel to the y-axis, vertex (−1, 2), and passing through (−3, 1). $(x + 1)^2 = -4(y - 2)$
    b) Line of symmetry parallel to the x-axis, vertex (2, 1), and passing through $(4, \frac{1}{3})$. $(y - 1)^2 = \frac{2}{9}(x - 2)$

HISTORICAL NOTE: Uses of the Abacus

The abacus is not just an Oriental device. It was used in ancient Greece and Rome. And it is still used in parts of Russia to add restaurant bills and do other calculations.

14-6 Systems of Equations

After finishing Lesson 14-6, you should be able to
▮ solve systems of one first-degree and one second-degree equation algebraically.
▮▮ solve problems involving systems of one first-degree and one second-degree equation.

▮ Algebraic Solutions

We consider systems of one first-degree and one second-degree equation. Let us consider the case in which the graphs are a circle and a line. The drawing shows the three ways in which the two graphs might intersect.

For L_1 there is no point of intersection, hence no real solution to the system. For L_2 there is one point of intersection, hence one real solution. For L_3 there are two points of intersection, hence two real solutions.

In solving systems where one equation is of first degree and one is of second degree, it is preferable to use the *substitution* method.

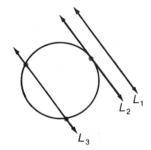

Example 1. Solve this system algebraically: $\quad x^2 + y^2 = 25 \qquad$ **(1)**
$$3x - 4y = 0 \qquad \textbf{(2)}$$

First solve the linear equation **(2)** for x.

$$x = \tfrac{4}{3}y$$

Then substitute $\tfrac{4}{3}y$ for x in equation **(1)** and solve for y.

$$(\tfrac{4}{3}y)^2 + y^2 = 25$$
$$\tfrac{16}{9}y^2 + y^2 = 25$$
$$\tfrac{25}{9}y^2 = 25$$
$$y^2 = 9$$
$$y = \pm 3$$

Now substitute these numbers into the linear equation and solve for x.

$$x = \tfrac{4}{3}(3), \text{ or } 4$$
$$x = \tfrac{4}{3}(-3), \text{ or } -4$$

The pairs $(4, 3)$ and $(-4, -3)$ check, so they are solutions.

Answers.   1. $(4, 3)$, $(-3, -4)$ 2. $(4, 7)$, $(-1, 2)$ 3. $(-4, 4)$, $(2, 1)$

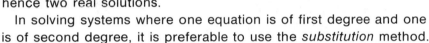

TRY THIS

Solve these systems algebraically.

1. $x^2 + y^2 = 25$
   $y - x = -1$
2. $y = x^2 - 2x - 1$
   $y = x + 3$
3. $y = \dfrac{x^2}{4}$
   $x + 2y = 4$

Example 2.   Solve the system: $y + 3 = 2x$ **(1)**
$$x^2 + 2xy = -1$$ **(2)**

First solve the linear equation **(1)** for y.

$y = 2x - 3$

Then substitute $2x - 3$ for y in equation **(2)** and solve for x.

$x^2 + 2x(2x - 3) = -1$
$5x^2 - 6x + 1 = 0$
$(5x - 1)(x - 1) = 0$ *Factoring*

$5x - 1 = 0$ $x - 1 = 0$ *Using the principle of zero products*
$x = \frac{1}{5}$ or $x = 1$

Now substitute these numbers into the linear equation and solve for y.

$y = 2(\frac{1}{5}) - 3$, or $-\frac{13}{5}$
$y = 2(1) - 3$, or -1.

The pairs $(\frac{1}{5}, -\frac{13}{5})$ and $(1, -1)$ check, so they are
solutions.

TRY THIS

> 4.   Solve: $y + 3x = 1$
> $$x^2 - 2xy = 5$$
> $(-\frac{5}{7}, \frac{22}{7})$, $(1, -2)$

▪ Solving Problems

Example 3.   The perimeter of a rectangular field is 204 m and
the area is 2565 m². Find the dimensions of the field.

We first translate the conditions of the problem to equations,
using w for the width and l for the length.

Perimeter: $2w + 2l = 204$
Area: $lw = 2565$

Now we solve the system

$2w + 2l = 204$
$lw = 2565$

and get the solution (45, 57). Now we check in the
original problem: The perimeter is $2 \cdot 45 + 2 \cdot 57$,
or 204. The area is $45 \cdot 57$, or 2565. The numbers
check, so the answer is $l = 57$ m, $w = 45$ m.

Answers.   5. 11 and 7   6. Length is 12 m; width is 5 m

TRY THIS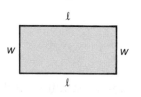

> 5.   The difference of two num-
> bers is 4 and the difference
> of their squares is 72. What
> are the numbers?
>
> 6.   The perimeter of a
> rectangular field is 34 m
> and the length of a diago-
> nal is 13 m. Find the di-
> mensions of the field.

Exercise Set 14-6

▌Solve. (*See Examples 1 and 2.*)

1. $x^2 + y^2 = 25$ (−4, −3), (3, 4)
   $y - x = 1$

2. $x^2 + y^2 = 100$ (−8, −6), (6, 8)
   $y - x = 2$

3. $4x^2 + 9y^2 = 36$ (0, 2), (3, 0)
   $3y + 2x = 6$

4. $9x^2 + 4y^2 = 36$ (2, 0), (0, 3)
   $3x + 2y = 6$

5. $y^2 = x + 3$ (−2, 1)
   $2y = x + 4$

6. $y = x^2$ (2, 4), (1, 1)
   $3x = y + 2$

7. $x^2 + 4y^2 = 25$ (4, $\frac{3}{2}$), (3, 2)
   $x + 2y = 7$

8. $y^2 - x^2 = 16$ (−$\frac{5}{3}$, −$\frac{13}{3}$), (3, 5)
   $2x - y = 1$

9. $x^2 - xy + 3y^2 = 27$
   $x - y = 2$ ($\frac{5 + \sqrt{70}}{3}$, $\frac{-1 + \sqrt{70}}{3}$), ($\frac{5 - \sqrt{70}}{3}$, $\frac{-1 - \sqrt{70}}{3}$)

10. $2y^2 + xy + x^2 = 7$ ($\frac{11}{4}$, −$\frac{9}{8}$), (1, −2)
    $x - 2y = 5$

11. $3x + y = 7$
    $4x^2 + 5y = 56$ ($\frac{15 + \sqrt{561}}{8}$, $\frac{11 - 3\sqrt{561}}{8}$), ($\frac{15 - \sqrt{561}}{8}$, $\frac{11 + 3\sqrt{561}}{8}$)

12. $2y^2 + xy = 5$ (−3, $\frac{5}{2}$), (3, 1)
    $4y + x = 7$

▌▌(*See Example 3.*)

13. The sum of two numbers is 14 and the sum of their squares is 106. What are the numbers?   9 and 5

14. The sum of two numbers is 15 and the difference of their squares is also 15. What are the numbers?   8 and 7

15. A rectangle has perimeter 28 cm and the length of a diagonal is 10 cm. What are its dimensions?   Length is 8 cm; width is 6 cm

16. A rectangle has perimeter 6 m and the length of a diagonal is $\sqrt{5}$ m. What are its dimensions?   Length is 2 m; width is 1 m

17. A rectangle has area 20 m² and perimeter 18 m. Find its dimensions.   Length is 5 m; width is 4 m

18. A rectangle has area 2 cm² and perimeter 6 cm. Find its dimensions.   Length is 2 cm; width is 1 cm

---

Challenge Exercises

19. Given the area A and the perimeter P of a rectangle, show that the length L and the width W are given by the formulas
    $L = \frac{1}{4}(P + \sqrt{P^2 - 16A})$,
    $W = \frac{1}{4}(P - \sqrt{P^2 - 16A})$.   See answer section

20. Show that a hyperbola cannot intersect its asymptotes. That is, solve the system
    $\frac{x^2}{a^2} - \frac{y^2}{b^2} = 1$
    $y = \frac{b}{a}x \left(\text{or, } y = -\frac{b}{a}x\right)$.

    Substitute $\frac{b}{a}x$ for y in $\frac{x^2}{a^2} - \frac{y^2}{b^2} = 1$ and simplify. $\frac{x^2}{a^2} - \frac{(\frac{b}{a}x)^2}{b^2} = 1$, $\frac{x^2}{a^2} - \frac{x^2}{a^2} = 1$, 0 = 1. Substituting $-\frac{b}{a}x$ for y also results in 0 = 1. Since 0 ≠ 1 (no real solutions), there are no points of intersection of a hyperbola and its asymptotes.

21. Find an equation of a circle that passes through the points (2, 4) and (3, 3) and whose center is on the line $3x - y = 3$.   (x − 2)² + (y − 3)² = 1

14-7 Two Second-Degree Equations

After finishing Lesson 14-7, you should be able to
∎ solve systems of second-degree equations algebraically.
∎∎ solve problems involving systems of second-degree equations.

∎ Algebraic Solutions

We now consider systems of two second-degree equations. Let us consider the case in which the graphs are a circle and a hyperbola. The drawing shows the five ways in which the two graphs might intersect.

| 4 real solutions | 3 real solutions | 2 real solutions | 1 real solution | 0 real solutions |

To solve systems of two second-degree equations we can use either the substitution or the addition method.

Example 1. Solve this system:
$$2x^2 + 5y^2 = 22 \qquad \textbf{(1)}$$
$$3x^2 - y^2 = -1 \qquad \textbf{(2)}$$

Here we use the addition method.

$$2x^2 + 5y^2 = 22$$
$$\underline{15x^2 - 5y^2 = -5} \qquad \textit{Multiplying by 5 on both sides of } \textbf{(2)}$$
$$17x^2 = 17 \qquad \textit{Adding}$$
$$x^2 = 1$$
$$x = \pm 1.$$

If $x = 1$, $x^2 = 1$, and if $x = -1$, $x^2 = 1$, so substituting 1 or -1 for x in equation **(2)** we have

$$3 \cdot 1 - y^2 = -1$$
$$y^2 = 4$$
$$y = \pm 2.$$

Thus, if $x = 1$, $y = 2$ or $y = -2$, and if $x = -1$, $y = 2$ or $y = -2$. The possible solutions are $(1, 2)$, $(1, -2)$, $(-1, 2)$, $(-1, -2)$.

Check: Since $(2)^2 = 4$, $(-2)^2 = 4$, $(1)^2 = 1$, and $(-1)^2 = 1$, we can check all four pairs at one time.

$$\begin{array}{c|c}
\multicolumn{2}{c}{2x^2 + 5y^2 = 22} \\
\hline
2(\pm 1)^2 + 5(\pm 2)^2 & 22 \\
2 + 20 & \\
22 &
\end{array} \qquad
\begin{array}{c|c}
\multicolumn{2}{c}{3x^2 - y^2 = -1} \\
\hline
3(\pm 1)^2 - (\pm 2)^2 & -1 \\
3 - 4 & \\
-1 &
\end{array}$$

TRY THIS

Solve.

1. $2y^2 - 3x^2 = 6$
    $5y^2 + 2x^2 = 53$
    (2, 3), (2, −3), (−2, 3), (−2, −3)

Example 2. Solve the system: $x^2 + 4y^2 = 20$ **(1)**
$xy = 4$ **(2)**

Here we use the substitution method. First solve equation **(2)** for y.

$$y = \frac{4}{x}$$

Then substitute $\frac{4}{x}$ for y in equation **(1)** and solve for x.

$$x^2 + 4\left(\frac{4}{x}\right)^2 = 20$$

$$x^2 + \frac{64}{x^2} = 20$$

$$x^4 + 64 = 20x^2 \qquad \textit{Multiplying by } x^2$$

$$x^4 - 20x^2 + 64 = 0$$

$$u^2 - 20u + 64 = 0 \qquad \textit{Letting } u = x^2$$

Then $x = 4$ or $x = -4$ or $x = 2$ or $x = -2$.

Since $y = \frac{4}{x}$, if $x = 4$, $y = 1$; if $x = -4$, $y = -1$; if $x = 2$, $y = 2$;

if $x = -2$, $y = -2$.

The ordered pairs (4, 1), (−4, −1), (2, 2), (−2, −2) check.
They are the solutions.

TRY THIS

Solve.

2. $x^2 + xy + y^2 = 19$
    $xy = 6$
    (3, 2), (−3, −2), (2, 3), (−2, −3)

▮▮ Solving Problems

Example 3.   The area of a rectangle is 300 m² and the length of a diagonal is 25 m. Find the dimensions.

First draw a picture.

We use *l* for the length and *w* for the width and translate to equations.

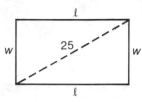

From the Pythagorean theorem: $l^2 + w^2 = 25^2$

Area: $lw = 300$

Now we solve the system

$$l^2 + w^2 = 625$$
$$lw = 300$$

We get (15, 20) and (−15, −20). Now we check in the original problem: $15^2 + 20^2 = 25^2$ and $15 \cdot 20 = 300$, so (15, 20) is a solution of the problem. Lengths of sides cannot be negative so (−15, −20) is not a solution. The answer is *l* = 20 m and *w* = 15 m.

TRY THIS

3.   The area of a rectangle is 2 cm² and the length of a diagonal is $\sqrt{5}$ cm. Find the dimensions of the rectangle.

Length is 2 cm; width is 1 cm

Exercise Set 14-7

▮ Solve. (*See Examples 1 and 2.*)

1. $x^2 + y^2 = 25$ (−5, 0), (4, 3), (4, −3)
     $y^2 = x + 5$

2. $y = x^2$ (0, 0), (1, 1)
     $x = y^2$

3. $x^2 + y^2 = 9$ (3, 0), (−3, 0)
     $x^2 - y^2 = 9$

4. $y^2 - 4x^2 = 4$ (0, 2), (0, −2)
     $4x^2 + y^2 = 4$

5. $x^2 + y^2 = 4$ No real solution
     $16x^2 + 9y^2 = 144$

6. $x^2 + y^2 = 25$ (0, −5), (0, 5)
     $25x^2 + 16y^2 = 400$

7. $x^2 + y^2 = 16$ $(\sqrt{2}, \sqrt{14}), (\sqrt{2}, -\sqrt{14}), (-\sqrt{2}, \sqrt{14}),$
     $y^2 - 2x^2 = 10$ $(-\sqrt{2}, -\sqrt{14})$

8. $x^2 + y^2 = 14$ $(3, \sqrt{5}), (3, -\sqrt{5}), (-3, \sqrt{5}),$
     $x^2 - y^2 = 4$ $(-3, -\sqrt{5})$

9. $x^2 + y^2 = 5$ (1, 2), (−1, −2), (2, 1), (−2, −1)
     $xy = 2$

10. $x^2 + y^2 = 20$ (2, 4), (−2, −4), (4, 2), (−4, −2)
     $xy = 8$

11. $xy - y^2 = 2$ (3, 2), (−3, −2)
     $2xy - 3y^2 = 0$

12. $2xy + 3y^2 = 7$ (2, 1), (−2, −1)
     $3xy - 2y^2 = 4$

■■ (*See Example 3.*)

Use Quiz 26 after lesson 14—7.

13. The product of two numbers is 156. The sum of their squares is 313. Find the numbers.   13 and 12, −13 and −12

14. The product of two numbers is 60. The sum of their squares is 136. Find the numbers.   6 and 10, −6 and −10

15. The area of a rectangle is $\sqrt{3}$ m² and the length of a diagonal is 2 m. Find the dimensions.   Length is $\sqrt{3}$ m; width is 1 m

16. The area of a rectangle is $\sqrt{2}$ m² and the length of a diagonal is $\sqrt{3}$ m. Find the dimensions. Length is $\sqrt{2}$ m; width is 1 m

17. A garden contains two square peanut beds. The sum of their areas is 832 m², and the difference of their areas is 320 m². Find the length of each bed.   24 m and 16 m

18. A certain amount of money saved for 1 year at a certain interest rate yielded $7.50. If the principal had been $25 more and the interest rate 1% less, the interest would have been the same. Find the principal and the rate of interest.
Principal is $125; interest rate is 6%

Calculator Exercises

Solve.

19. $18.456x^2 + 788.723y^2 = 6408$
    $106.535x^2 - 788.723y^2 = 2692$

20. $0.319x^2 + 2688.7y^2 = 56{,}548$
    $0.306x^2 - 2688.7y^2 = 43{,}452$

19. (8.5325987, 2.5339482), (8.5325987, −2.5339482), (−8.5325987, 2.5339482), (−8.5325987, −2.5339482)   20. (400, 1.4312839), (400, −1.4312839), (−400, 1.4312839), (−400, −1.4312839)

Challenge Exercises

21. Find an equation of the circle that passes through the points (4, 6), (−6, 2), and (1, −3). $(x + \frac{5}{13})^2 + (y - \frac{32}{13})^2 = \frac{5365}{169}$

22. Find an equation of the circle that passes through the points (2, 3), (4, 5), and (0, −3). $(x - 10)^2 + (y + 3)^2 = 100$

SCIENCE NOTE: Halley's Comet

In 1985 you will have a chance to see a once-in-a-lifetime event, Halley's comet. It is named for Edmund Halley, an English astronomer. After the comet appeared in 1682, Halley used mathematics to predict that it would return once every 75 years or so. And it did.

Halley's comet follows a path through the solar system. The path is near the sun at one end and near the planet Pluto at the other.

CHAPTER 14 REVIEW

Review the material in the chapter. Then see how you have done by trying these review exercises. If you miss an exercise, restudy the indicated lesson.

14-1 1. Find the distance between $(-3, 4)$ and $(7, 0)$. $2\sqrt{29}$

14-1 2. Find the midpoint of the segment with endpoints $(-3, 4)$ and $(7, 0)$. $(2, 2)$

14-2 3. Find an equation of the circle with center $(-2, 6)$ and radius $\sqrt{13}$. $(x + 2)^2 + (y - 6)^2 = 13$

14-2 4. Find the center and radius of the circle $2x^2 + 2y^2 - 3x - 5y + 3 = 0$.   Center: $(\frac{3}{4}, \frac{5}{4})$, $r = \frac{\sqrt{10}}{4}$

14-3 5. Find the center, vertices, and foci of the ellipse $16x^2 + 25y^2 - 64x + 50y - 311 = 0$. Then graph the ellipse.   See answer section

14-4 6. Find the center, vertices, foci, and asymptotes of the hyperbola $x^2 - 2y^2 + 4x + y - \frac{1}{8} = 0$. Then graph the hyperbola.   See answer section

14-5 7. Find the vertex, focus, and directrix of the parabola $y^2 = -12x$. Then graph the parabola.   See answer section

14-6 8. Solve: $\dfrac{x^2}{16} + \dfrac{y^2}{9} = 1$

$3x + 4y = 12$ $(4, 0), (0, 3)$

14-6 9. The sum of two numbers is 11 and the sum of their squares is 65. Find the numbers.   4 and 7

14-7 10. Solve: $x^2 + y^2 = 16$

$\dfrac{x^2}{16} + \dfrac{y^2}{9} = 1$ $(4, 0), (-4, 0)$

14-7 11. The sides of a triangle are 8, 10, and 14. Find the altitude to the longest side. $\dfrac{16\sqrt{6}}{7}$

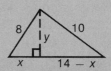

CHAPTER 14 TEST

1. Find the distance between $(-3, 4)$ and $(7, 6)$. $2\sqrt{26}$
2. Find the midpoint of the segment with endpoints $(-3, 4)$ and $(7, 6)$. $(2, 5)$
3. Find an equation of the circle with center $(4, -1)$ and radius 5. $(x - 4)^2 + (y + 1)^2 = 25$
4. Find the center and radius of the circle $x^2 + y^2 - 8x + 12y + 49 = 0$. Center: $(4, -6)$, $r = \sqrt{3}$
5. Find the center, vertices, and foci of the ellipse $9x^2 + 16y^2 + 36x - 32y - 92 = 0$. Then graph the ellipse. See answer section
6. Find the center, vertices, foci, and asymptotes of the hyperbola $8x^2 - 3y^2 = 48$. Then graph the hyperbola. See answer section
7. Find the vertex, focus, and directrix of the parabola $x^2 + 2x + 6y - 11 = 0$. Then graph the parabola. See answer section
8. Solve: $x^2 + y^2 = 74$
    $x - y = 2$ $(-5, -7)$, $(7, 5)$
9. Two squares whose sides differ in length by 9 m have areas which differ by 153 m². Find the length of a side of each. 13 m and 4 m
10. Solve: $3x^2 - 2y^2 = 30$
    $2x^2 + 5y^2 = 77$ $(4, 3)$, $(-4, 3)$, $(4, -3)$, $(-4, -3)$
11. The area of a rectangle is 240 cm² and the length of a diagonal is 26 cm. Find the dimensions of the rectangle. Length is 24 cm; width is 10 cm

Ready for Polynomial Functions?

11-3   1. Determine whether $1 + i$ is a solution of $x^2 - 2x + 1 = 0$.   No

7-2   2. Factor: $x^2 + x - 6$.   (x + 3)(x − 2)

12-5   3. Find a quadratic equation whose solutions are -5 and $\frac{2}{3}$. 3x² + 13x − 10 = 0

12-5   4. Find a quadratic equation whose solutions are $1 - \sqrt{2}$ and $1 + \sqrt{2}$. x² − 2x − 1 = 0

11-3   5. Find an equation having -2, i, and $3i$ as solutions.
            x³ − 4ix² + 2x² − 8ix − 3x − 6

11-3   6. Show that $-1 - i$ is a square root of $2i$. Then find the other square root. (−1 − i)² = 2i; 1 + i

11-2   7. Find the conjugate of $-3 + 8i$. −3 − 8i

11-2   8. Multiply: $(1 - 5i)(1 + 5i)$.   26

Chapter 15
Polynomial Functions

Many things considered in aircraft design, such as lift and drag, are given by polynomial functions.

15-1 Polynomials and Polynomial Functions

After finishing Lesson 15-1, you should be able to
∎ determine whether a number is a root of a polynomial.
∎∎ given a polynomial $P(x)$ and a divisor $d(x)$, find the quotient $Q(x)$ and the remainder $R(x)$. Then express $P(x)$ in the form $P(x) = d(x) \cdot Q(x) + R(x)$.

Recall the definition of a polynomial: A polynomial in x is any expression equivalent to one of this form

$$a_n x^n + a_{n-1} x^{n-1} + a_{n-2} x^{n-2} + \cdots + a_1 x + a_0.$$

We will usually assume the coefficients are complex numbers, but in some cases will consider them to be real numbers, or rational numbers, or integers. The coefficient of the term of highest degree, a_n, is called the *leading coefficient*.

∎ Roots of Polynomials

When a number is substituted for the variable in a polynomial, the result is some unique number. Thus every polynomial defines a function. We often refer to polynomials, therefore, using function notation $P(x)$.

DEFINITION

If a number a makes a polynomial 0, then a is called a *root*, or a *zero*, of the polynomial.

Examples. $P(x) = x^3 + 2x^2 - 5x - 6.$

1. Is 3 a root of $P(x)$?

We substitute 3 into the polynomial:

$$P(3) = 3^3 + 2(3)^2 - 5 \cdot 3 - 6 = 24.$$

Since $P(3) \neq 0$, 3 is not a root.

2. Is -1 a root of $P(x)$?

$$P(-1) = (-1)^3 + 2(-1)^2 - 5(-1) - 6 = 0.$$

Since $P(-1) = 0$, -1 is a root of the polynomial.

TRY THIS ▬▬▶

1. Determine whether the following numbers are roots of the polynomial $P(x) = x^2 - 4x - 21$.
   a) 7   b) 3
   c) -3
2. Determine whether the following numbers are roots of the polynomial $P(x) = x^4 - 16$.
   a) 2   b) -2
   c) -1 d) 0
3. Determine whether the following numbers are roots of the polynomial $P(x) = x^2 + 1$.
   a) 1   b) -1
   c) $1 + i$ d) $-i$

ı ı Dividing Polynomials

When we divide one polynomial by another we obtain a quotient and a remainder. If the remainder is 0, then the divisor is a *factor* of the dividend.

Example 3. Divide, to find whether $x^2 + 9$ is a factor of $x^4 - 81$.

$$
\begin{array}{r}
x^2 - 9 \\
x^2 + 9 \overline{)x^4 - 81} \\
\underline{x^4 + 9x^2 } \\
- 9x^2 - 81 \\
\underline{- 9x^2 - 81} \\
0
\end{array}
$$

Spaces have been left for missing terms in the dividend.

Since the remainder is 0, we know that $x^2 + 9$ is a factor.

Example 4. Divide, to find whether $x^2 + 3x - 1$ is a factor of $x^4 - 81$.

$$
\begin{array}{r}
x^2 - 3x + 10 \\
x^2 + 3x - 1 \overline{)x^4 - 81} \\
\underline{x^4 + 3x^3 - x^2 } \\
- 3x^3 + x^2 \\
\underline{- 3x^3 - 9x^2 + 3x } \\
10x^2 - 3x - 81 \\
\underline{10x^2 + 30x - 10} \\
- 33x - 71
\end{array}
$$

Since the remainder is not 0, we know that $x^2 + 3x - 1$ is not a factor of $x^4 - 81$.

TRY THIS

Answers. 4. a) Yes b) No   5. a) No b) Yes c) No

4. By division, determine whether the following polynomials are factors of the polynomial $x^4 - 16$.
    a) $x - 2$
    b) $x^2 + 3x - 1$

5. By division, determine whether the following polynomials are factors of the polynomial $x^3 + 2x^2 - 5x - 6$.
    a) $x - 3$
    b) $x + 1$
    c) $x^2 + 3x - 1$

When we divide a polynomial $P(x)$ by a divisor $d(x)$ we obtain a polynomial $Q(x)$ for a quotient and a polynomial $R(x)$ for a remainder. The remainder must either be 0 or have degree less than that of $d(x)$. To check we multiply the quotient by the divisor and add the remainder, to see if we get the dividend. Thus these polynomials are related as follows:

$$P(x) = d(x) \cdot Q(x) + R(x).$$

Example 5. If $P(x) = x^4 - 81$ and $d(x) = x^2 + 9$, find $Q(x)$ and $R(x)$. (See Example 3.)

$$x^4 - 81 = (x^2 + 9) \cdot (x^2 - 9) + 0$$
$$P(x) = \quad d(x) \quad \cdot \quad Q(x) \quad + R(x)$$

Example 6. $P(x) = x^4 - 81$ and $d(x) = x^2 + 3x - 1$. Find $Q(x)$ and $R(x)$. (See Example 4.)

$$x^4 - 81 = (x^2 + 3x - 1) \cdot (x^2 - 3x + 10) + (-33x - 71)$$
$$P(x) = \quad d(x) \quad \cdot \quad Q(x) \quad + \quad R(x)$$

TRY THIS

Answer. 6. $x^3 + 2x^2 - 5x - 6 = (x - 3)(x^2 + 5x + 10) + 24$

> 6. Divide $x^3 + 2x^2 - 5x - 6$ by $x - 3$.
> Then express the dividend as $P(x) = d(x) \cdot Q(x) + R(x)$.

Exercise Set 15-1

▮ Determine whether the given numbers are roots of the polynomial $P(x)$. (*See Examples 1 and 2.*)

1. 2, 3, -1;   Yes, no, no
   $P(x) = x^3 + 6x^2 - x - 30$
3. 0, $-$, $1 + i\sqrt{7}$, $1 - i\sqrt{7}$;   Yes, no, yes, yes
   $P(x) = x^3 - 2x^2 + 8x$

2. 2, 3, -1;   No, no, no
   $P(x) = 2x^3 - 3x^2 + x - 1$
4. 0, -2, $1 + i$, $1 - i$;   Yes, no, yes, yes
   $P(x) = x^3 - 2x^2 + 2x$

▮▮ By division, determine whether the polynomials are factors of the polynomial $P(x)$. (*See Examples 3 and 4.*)   See answer section

5. $P(x) = x^3 + 6x^2 - x - 30$
   a) $x - 2$ b) $x - 3$ c) $x + 1$
7. $P(x) = x^4 - 81$
   a) $x - 3$ b) $x + 3$ c) $x + 9$

6. $P(x) = 2x^3 - 3x^2 + x - 1$
   a) $x - 2$ b) $x - 3$ c) $x + 1$
8. $P(x) = x^5 + 32$
   a) $x - 2$ b) $x + 2$ c) $x - 4$

In each of the following, a polynomial $P(x)$ and a divisor $d(x)$ are given. Find the quotient $Q(x)$ and the remainder $R(x)$ when $P(x)$ is divided by $d(x)$ and express $P(x)$ in the form $d(x) \cdot Q(x) + R(x)$. (*See Examples 5 and 6.*)

9. $P(x) = x^3 + 6x^2 - x - 30$,
   $d(x) = x - 2$ $x^3 + 6x^2 - x - 30 = (x - 2)(x^2 + 8x + 15) + 0$
11. $P(x)$ as in Exercise 9,
   $d(x) = x - 3$ $x^3 + 6x^2 - x - 30 = (x - 3)(x^2 + 9x + 26) + 48$
13. $P(x) = x^3 - 8$,
   $d(x) = x + 2$ $x^3 - 8 = (x + 2)(x^2 - 2x + 4) + (-16)$
15. $P(x) = x^4 + 9x^2 + 20$,
   $d(x) = x^2 + 4$ $x^4 + 9x^2 + 20 = (x^2 + 4)(x^2 + 5) + 0$

10. $P(x) = 2x^3 - 3x^2 + x - 1$,
   $d(x) = x - 2$ $2x^3 - 3x^2 + x - 1 = (x - 2)(2x^2 + x + 3) + 5$
12. $P(x)$ as in Exercise 10,
   $d(x) = x - 3$ $2x^3 - 3x^2 + x - 1 = (x - 3)(2x^2 + 3x + 10) + 29$
14. $P(x) = x^3 + 27$,
   $d(x) = x + 1$ $x^3 + 27 = (x + 1)(x^2 - x + 1) + 26$
16. $P(x) = x^4 + x^2 + 2$,
   $d(x) = x^2 + x + 1$ $x^4 + x^2 + 2 = (x^2 + x + 1)(x^2 - x + 1) + 1$

15-2 The Remainder and Factor Theorems

After finishing Lesson 15-2, you should be able to

I use the Remainder Theorem to find the remainder $P(r)$ when a polynomial $P(x)$ is divided by $x - r$.

II determine whether $x - r$ is a factor of a polynomial $P(x)$ by determining whether $P(r) = 0$.

III use the Factor Theorem to find complete factorizations of polynomials.

▮The Remainder Theorem

The next theorem states a remarkable fact about polynomials.

THEOREM 15-1 (The Remainder Theorem)

For a polynomial $P(x)$, the function value $P(r)$ is the remainder when $P(x)$ is divided by $x - r$.

In other words, if we divide a polynomial by $x - r$, the remainder would be the same as if we substituted r in the polynomial and evaluated.

Example 1. If $P(x) = x^3 + 6x^2 - x - 30$, what is the remainder when $P(x)$ is divided by $x + 1$ or $[x - (-1)]$?

$$P(-1) = (-1)^3 + 6(-1)^2 - (-1) - 30$$
$$= -1 + 6 + 1 - 30$$
$$= -24$$

Thus, by the Remainder Theorem, when $P(x)$ is divided by $x + 1$, the remainder is -24.

Example 2. If $P(x)$, in Example 1, is divided by $x - 2$, what is the remainder?

$$P(2) = 2^3 + 6 \cdot 2^2 - 2 - 30$$
$$= 8 + 24 - 2 - 30$$
$$= 0$$

Thus, by the Remainder Theorem, when $P(x)$ is divided by $x - 2$, the remainder is 0. Note that this also tells us that $x - 2$ is a factor of $x^3 + 6x^2 - x - 30$.

TRY THIS ➡️

1. If $P(x) = x^3 - x^2 + 1$ is divided by $x + 1$, what is the remainder?

2. If $P(x) = x^4 - 2x^3 + 5x - 7$ is divided by $x - 2$, what is the remainder?

3. If $P(x) = 2x^{15} + x^{12} + 1$ is divided by $x + 1$, what is the remainder?

‖ Determining Factors

The next theorem follows from the Remainder Theorem.

THEOREM 15-2 (The Factor Theorem)
For a polynomial $P(x)$, if $P(r) = 0$, then $x - r$ is a factor of $P(x)$.

Note that if $P(r)$ is 0, r is a root, or zero, of $P(x)$.

Example 3. Let $P(x) = x^3 + 2x^2 - 5x - 6$. Determine whether $x + 1$ is a factor of $P(x)$.

We think of $x + 1$ as $x - (-1)$. Thus we find $P(-1)$.
   $P(-1) = (-1)^3 + 2(-1)^2 - 5(-1) - 6 = 0$.

Since $P(-1) = 0$, by the Factor Theorem we know that $x + 1$ is a factor of $P(x)$.

A Proof of Theorem 15-2
Consider dividing a polynomial $P(x)$ by $x - r$. From the Remainder Theorem we have

$$P(x) = (x - r) \cdot Q(x) + P(r).$$

Then if $P(r) = 0$, we have

$$P(x) = (x - r) \cdot Q(x),$$

so $x - r$ is a factor of $P(x)$.

TRY THIS

4. Determine whether $x - \frac{1}{2}$ is a factor of $4x^4 + 2x^3 + 8x - 1$. No
5. Determine whether $x + 5$ is a factor of $x^4 + 625$. No

‖‖ Factorizations

The Factor Theorem is helpful in factoring polynomials.

Example 4. Consider the polynomial $P(x)$ in Example 3.

a) Find another factor of $P(x)$.

We divide $P(x)$ by $x + 1$, obtaining for a quotient $x^2 + x - 6$.

b) Find a complete factorization of $P(x)$.

By part **a)** we know that
$P(x) = (x + 1)(x^2 + x - 6)$. The second
factor can be factored further giving the
complete factorization:

$$(x + 1)(x + 3)(x - 2).$$

TRY THIS

6. a) Let
$P(x) = x^3 + 6x^2 - x - 30.$
Determine whether $x - 2$
is a factor of $P(x)$.
   b) Find another factor of $P(x)$.
   c) Find a complete factorization of $P(x)$.

a) Yes b) $x^2 + 8x + 15$ c) $(x - 2)(x + 5)(x + 3)$

Exercise Set 15-2

I What is the remainder when $P(x)$ is divided by the binomial? Use the Remainder Theorem. (*See Examples 1 and 2.*)

1. $P(x) = x^3 - 2x^2 + 5x - 4; x - 2$ 6
2. $P(x) = x^3 - 2x^2 + 5x - 4; x + 2$ −30
3. $P(x) = x^5 - 3x^2 + 2x - 1; x - 1$ −1
4. $P(x) = x^5 - 3x^2 + 2x - 1; x + 1$ −7
5. $P(x) = x^3 - 2x^2 + 5x - 4; x + 1$ −12
6. $P(x) = x^3 - 2x^2 + 5x - 4; x - 1$ 0
7. $P(x) = x^3 + 8; x + 2$ 0
8. $P(x) = x^4 - 65; x - 4$ 191
9. $P(x) = x^2 - 8x + 4; x - 3i$ −5 − 24i
10. $P(x) = x^2 + 8x - 4; x - 2i$ −8 + 16i
11. $P(x) = x^2 + 2x + 2; x - (1 + i)$ 4 + 4i
12. $P(x) = x^2 - 2x + 5; x - (1 + 2i)$ 0

II Determine whether the expressions of the type $x - r$ are factors of the polynomial $P(x)$. Use the Factor Theorem. (*See Example 3.*)

13. $P(x) = x^3 - 3x^2 - 4x - 12; x + 2$ No
14. $P(x) = x^3 - 4x^2 + 3x + 8; x + 1$ Yes
15. $P(x) = 2x^2 + 2x + 1; x - (-\frac{1}{2} - \frac{1}{2}i)$ Yes
16. $P(x) = 9x^2 + 6x + 2; x - (\frac{1}{3} - \frac{1}{3}i)$ No
17. $P(x) = x^5 - 1; x - 1$ Yes
18. $P(x) = x^5 + 1; x + 1$ Yes
19. $P(x) = x^4 + x^3 - 13x^2 - x + 12;$ Yes, yes,
$x - 3, x + 4, x + 1, x - 1, x + 2$ yes, yes, no
20. $P(x) = x^3 - 2x^2 + 1; x - 3,$ No, no, no,
$x - 2, x + 3, x + 2, x - 1$ no, yes

III (*See Example 4.*)

21. a) Let $P(x) = x^3 + 2x^2 - x - 2$. Determine whether $x - 1$ is a factor of $P(x)$.
   b) Find another factor of $P(x)$.
   c) Find a complete factorization of $P(x)$.

a) Yes b) $x^2 + 3x + 2$ c) $(x - 1)(x + 2)(x + 1)$

22. a) Let $P(x) = x^3 + 4x^2 - x - 4$. Determine whether $x + 1$ is a factor of $P(x)$.
   b) Find another factor of $P(x)$.
   c) Find a complete factorization of $P(x)$.

a) Yes b) $x^2 + 3x - 4$ c) $(x + 1)(x + 4)(x - 1)$

Challenge Exercises

23. Find k so that $x - 1$ is a factor of $x^3 - 3x^2 + kx - 1$.   3
24. Use the Factor Theorem to prove that $x + a$ is a factor of $x^{2n} - a^{2n}$,
for any natural number n. $x + a = x - (-a)$. $P(-a) = (-a)^{2n} - a^{2n} = a^{2n} - a^{2n} = 0$. If $P(-a) = 0$, then $x + a$
is a factor of $x^{2n} - a^{2n}$.

15-3 *Synthetic Division*

After finishing Lesson 15-3, you should be able to
 - **I**   use synthetic division to find the quotient and remainder when a polynomial is divided by a binomial $x - r$.
 - **II**   use synthetic division to find function values of a polynomial.
 - **III**   use synthetic division to determine whether a number is a root of a polynomial.

I Synthetic Division

To streamline division, we can arrange the work so that duplicate writing is avoided. Compare the following.

A
$$x - 2 \overline{)\begin{array}{l} 4x^2 + 5x + 11 \\ 4x^3 - 3x^2 + x + 7 \end{array}}$$
$$\begin{array}{r} 4x^3 - 8x^2 \\ \hline 5x^2 + x \\ 5x^2 - 10x \\ \hline 11x + 7 \\ 11x - 22 \\ \hline 29 \end{array}$$
remainder

B
$$1 - 2 \overline{)\begin{array}{l} 4 \quad 5 \quad 11 \\ 4 - 3 + 1 + 7 \end{array}}$$
$$\begin{array}{r} 4 - 8 \\ \hline 5 + 1 \\ 5 - 10 \\ \hline 11 + 7 \\ 11 - 22 \\ \hline 29 \end{array}$$
remainder

In **A** we performed a division. In **B** we performed the same division, but we wrote only the coefficients. If there had been any missing terms, we would have written 0's. Note that the numerals in color are duplicated. There would be no loss of understanding if we did not write them twice. Note also that when we subtract we add an additive inverse. We can accomplish this by using the additive inverse of -2, and then adding instead of subtracting.

C Synthetic Division

$$\underline{2|}\begin{array}{r} 4 - 3 + 1 + 7 \\ + 8 + 10 + 22 \\ \hline 4 + 5 + 11 \ \big| + 29 \end{array}$$

In **C,**

Step 1.   Write down the 2 of the divisor and the coefficients.

$$\underline{2|} \qquad 4 - 3 + 1 + 7$$

Step 2. Bring down the first coefficient (4), then multiply it by the 2 and write the result under the next coefficient (-3).

$$
\begin{array}{r|l}
2 & 4 - 3 + 1 + 7 \\
& \underline{+\ 8 } \\
& 4
\end{array}
$$

Step 3. Add -3 and 8, multiply the sum (5) by the 2, and write the result under the next coefficient (1).

$$
\begin{array}{r|l}
2 & 4 - 3 + \ 1 + 7 \\
& \underline{+\ 8 + 10 } \\
& 4 \quad 5
\end{array}
$$

Step 4. Add 1 and 10, multiply the sum (11) by 2, and write the result under the next coefficient (7). Then add.

$$
\begin{array}{r|l}
2 & 4 - 3 + \ 1 + \ 7 \\
& \underline{ 8 \quad 10 \quad 22} \\
& 4 \quad 5 \quad 11 \quad 29
\end{array}
$$

$$\underbrace{4x^2 + 5x + 11}_{\text{quotient}} \quad \text{remainder}$$

Example 1. Use synthetic division to find the quotient and remainder: $(2x^3 + 7x^2 - 5) \div (x + 3)$.

First note that $x + 3 = x - (-3)$.

$$
\begin{array}{r|l}
-3 & 2 + 7 + 0 \quad -5 \\
& \underline{-6 - 3 \quad +9} \\
& 2 + 1 - 3 \ \big|\ +4
\end{array}
$$

The quotient is $2x^2 + 1x - 3$. The remainder is 4.

TRY THIS ➡

Use synthetic division to find the quotient and remainder.

1. $(x^3 + 6x^2 - x - 30) \div (x - 2)$
2. $(x^3 - 2x^2 + 5x - 4) \div (x + 2)$
3. $(y^3 + 1) \div (y + 1)$
4. $(x^5 - 1) \div (x - 1)$

Answers. 1. Q: $x^2 + 8x + 15$, R: 0   2. Q: $x^2 - 4x + 13$, R: -30
3. Q: $y^2 - y + 1$, R: 0   4. Q: $x^4 + x^3 + x^2 + x + 1$, R: 0

ɪɪ Finding Function Values

We can also use synthetic division to find function values, especially when large powers are involved.

Example 2. $P(x) = 2x^5 - 3x^4 + x^3 - 2x^2 + x - 8$. Find $P(10)$.

Recall that $P(10)$ is the remainder when $P(x)$ is divided by $x - 10$.

10	2	-3	$+1$	-2	$+1$	-8
		20	170	1710	17,080	170,810
	2	17	171	1708	17,081	170,802

Thus $P(10) = 170,802$.

TRY THIS

> 5. Let $P(x) = x^5 - 2x^4 - 7x^3 + x^2 + 20$.
>   Use synthetic division to find
>   a) $P(10)$ **73, 120**
>   b) $P(-8)$. **−37, 292**

ɪɪɪ Roots

We can use synthetic division to determine whether a number is a root of a polynomial.

Example 3. Let $P(x) = x^3 + 8x^2 + 8x - 32$. Determine whether -4 is a root of $P(x)$.

We must decide if $P(-4) = 0$. We find $P(-4)$ as the remainder, using synthetic division.

-4	1	$+8$	$+8$	-32
		-4	-16	$+32$
	1	$+4$	-8	0

Since $P(-4) = 0$, -4 is a root of $P(x)$.

TRY THIS

> 6. Let $P(x) = x^3 + 6x^2 - x - 30$. Using synthetic division, determine whether the given numbers are roots of $P(x)$.
>   a) 2 **Yes**
>   b) 5 **No**
>   c) -3 **Yes**

Exercise Set 15-3

I Use synthetic division to find the quotient and remainder. (*See Example 1.*)

1. $(x^3 - 7x^2 - 13x + 3) \div (x + 2)$
2. $(x^3 - 7x^2 + 13x + 3) \div (x - 2)$
3. $(2x^4 + 7x^3 + x - 12) \div (x - 3)$
4. $(2x^4 - 3x^2 + x - 7) \div (x + 4)$
5. $(x^3 - 2x^2 - 8) \div (x + 2)$
6. $(x^3 - 3x + 10) \div (x - 2)$
7. $(x^3 + 27) \div (x + 3)$
8. $(x^3 - 27) \div (x - 3)$
9. $(x^4 - 1) \div (x - 1)$
10. $(x^5 + 32) \div (x + 2)$
11. $(2x^4 + 3x^2 - 1) \div (x - \frac{1}{2})$
12. $(3x^4 - 2x^2 + 2) \div (x - \frac{1}{4})$
13. $(x^4 - 16) \div (x - 2)$
14. $(x^6 + 1) \div (x + 1)$
15. $(x^3 - 2ix^2 + ix + 5) \div (x - i)$
16. $(x^3 + 3ix^2 - 4ix - 2) \div (x + i)$

See answer section

II Use synthetic division to find the function values. (*See Example 2.*)

17. $P(x) = x^3 - 6x^2 + 11x - 6$;
    find $P(1)$, $P(-2)$, $P(3)$. P(1) = 0, P(-2) = -60, P(3) = 0
18. $P(x) = x^3 + 7x^2 - 12x - 3$;
    find $P(-3)$, $P(-2)$, $P(1)$. P(-3) = 69, P(-2) = 41, P(1) = -7
19. $P(x) = 2x^5 - 3x^4 + 2x^3 - x + 8$;
    find $P(20)$, $P(-3)$. P(20) = 5,935,988, P(-3) = -772
20. $P(x) = x^5 - 10x^4 - 20x^3 - 5x - 100$;
    find $P(-10)$, $P(5)$.
    P(-10) = -180,050, P(5) = -5750

III Using synthetic division, determine whether the numbers are roots of the polynomials. (*See Example 3.*) See answer section

21. $-3, 2; P(x) = 3x^3 + 5x^2 - 6x + 18$
22. $-4, 2; P(x) - 3x^3 + 11x^2 - 2x + 8$
23. $-3, \frac{1}{2}; P(x) = x^3 - \frac{7}{2}x^2 + x - \frac{3}{2}$
24. $-6, \frac{1}{4}; P(x) = x^3 - \frac{7}{2}x^2 - 13x + 3$
25. $i, -i, -2; P(x) = x^3 + 2x^2 + x + 2$
26. $i, -i, 4; P(x) = x^3 - 4x^2 + x - 4$

Calculator Exercises

27. Given that $f(x) = 2.13x^5 - 42.1x^3 + 17.5x^2 + 0.953x - 1.98$, find $f(3.21)$
    a) by synthetic division; −485.15873
    b) by substitution. −485.15882
28. Given that $f(x) = 0.673x^4 - 17.3x^2 + 923x - 1230$, find $f(-16.3)$
    a) by synthetic division; 26636.524
    b) by substitution. 26636.524

COMPUTER NOTE: The Electronic Algebra Student

A computer has been programmed to solve problems in algebra. The computer translates each problem into algebraic terms. Then the computer solves the problem. If it has difficulty, it asks for more information. The program was written to provide knowledge of computer capabilities.

15-4 Theorems About Roots

After finishing Lesson 15-4, you should be able to

I given a polynomial factored into linear factors, find the roots and state the multiplicities.

II find a polynomial with roots of given multiplicities.

III given that a polynomial of certain degree with real coefficients has given numbers as some of its roots, find the other roots.

IIII given that a polynomial of certain degree with rational coefficients has given numbers as some of its roots, find the other roots.

IIIII find a polynomial of lowest degree with rational coefficients which has given numbers as some of its roots.

IIIIII given a polynomial and some of its roots, find the other roots.

I The Fundamental Theorem of Algebra

By the fundamental theorem of algebra (Theorem 11-2), every polynomial of degree n can be factored into n linear factors. For example,

Polynomial	**Roots**
$P_1(x) = x^4 + x^3 - 13x^2 - x + 12$	
$\qquad = (x - 3)(x + 4)(x + 1)(x - 1)$	$3, -4, -1, 1$
$P_2(x) = 3x^4 - 15x^3 + 18x^2 + 12x - 24$	
$\qquad = 3(x - 2)(x - 2)(x - 2)(x + 1)$	
$\qquad = 3(x - 2)^3(x + 1)$	$2, -1$

Note that while the polynomial $P_2(x)$ has 4 linear factors, it has only 2 roots. We say that *2 is a root of multiplicity 3 and −1 is a root of multiplicity 1*.

TRY THIS ➡

Find the roots of each polynomial and state the multiplicity of each.

1. $P(x) = (x - 5)(x - 5)$ $(x + 6)$
2. $P(x) = 4(x + 7)^2(x - 3)$
3. $P(x) = (x + 2)^3(x^2 - 9)$
4. $P(x) = (x^2 - 7x + 12)^2$ (*Hint:* Factor first.)
5. $P(x) = 5x^2 - 5$

ıı Finding Polynomials With *n* Given Roots

Given the roots of a polynomial, we can find the polynomial.

Example 1. Find a polynomial of degree three, having the roots -2, 1, and $3i$.

Such a polynomial has factors $x + 2$, $x - 1$, and $x - 3i$, so we have

$$P(x) = a_n(x + 2)(x - 1)(x - 3i).$$

The number a_n can be any nonzero number. The simplest polynomial will be obtained if we let it be 1. If we then multiply the factors we obtain

$$P(x) = x^3 + (1 - 3i)x^2 + (-2 - 3i)x + 6i.$$

Example 2. Find a polynomial of degree 5 with -1 as a root of multiplicity 3, 4 as a root of multiplicity 1, and 0 as a root of multiplicity 1.

Proceeding as in Example 1, letting $a_n = 1$, we obtain

$$(x + 1)^3(x - 4)(x - 0).$$
$$x^5 - x^4 - 9x^3 - 11x^2 - 4x.$$

TRY THIS

6. Find a polynomial of degree 3 which has -1, 2, and 5 as roots.

7. Find a polynomial of degree 3 which has -1, 2, and $-5i$ as roots.

8. Find a polynomial of degree 5 with -2 as a root of multiplicity 3, and 0 as a root of multiplicity 2.

9. Find a polynomial of degree 4 with 1 as a root of multiplicity 3 and -5 as a root of multiplicity 1.

Answers. 6. $x^3 - 6x^2 + 3x + 10$
7. $x^3 - (1 - 5i)x^2 - (2 + 5i)x - 10i$ 8. $x^5 + 6x^4 + 12x^3 + 8x^2$
9. $x^4 + 2x^3 - 12x^2 + 14x - 5$

ııı Roots of Polynomials With Real Coefficients

Consider the quadratic equation $x^2 - 2x + 2 = 0$, with real coefficients. Its roots are $1 + i$, and $1 - i$. Note that they are complex conjugates. This generalizes to any polynomial with real coefficients.

THEOREM 15-3

If a complex number z is a root of a polynomial $P(x)$ of degree greater than or equal to 1 with real coefficients, then its conjugate $\bar{z}$ is also a root. (Complex roots occur in conjugate pairs.)

It is essential that the coefficients be real numbers. This can be seen by considering Example 1. In that polynomial the root $3i$ occurs but its conjugate does not. This can happen because some of the coefficients of the polynomial are not real.

Example 3. Suppose a polynomial of degree 5 with real coefficients has 8, $-3 + i$, and $7 - 6i$ as some of its roots. Find the other roots.

By Theorem 15-3, the conjugates of $-3 + i$ and $7 - 6i$ must be roots. They are $-3 - i$ and $7 + 6i$. There are no other roots since the degree is 5. (Recall that by Theorem 11-3, every polynomial of degree n with complex coefficients, $n \geq 1$, has at least one complex number root and at most n complex number roots.)

TRY THIS

10. Suppose a polynomial of degree 5 with real coefficients has -4, $6 - 2i$, and $\sqrt{3} - i$ as some of its roots. Find the other roots. $6 + 2i, \sqrt{3} + i$

11. Suppose a polynomial of degree 3 with real coefficients has 10 and $24 + 5i$ as some of its roots. Find the other roots. $24 - 5i$

ⅠⅠⅠⅠ Rational Coefficients

When a polynomial has rational numbers for coefficients, certain irrational roots also occur in pairs, as described in the following theorem.

THEOREM 15-4

Suppose $P(x)$ is a polynomial with rational coefficients and of degree greater than or equal to 1. Then if either of the following is a root, so is the other: $a + c\sqrt{b}$, $a - c\sqrt{b}$.

Example 4. Suppose a polynomial of degree 6 with rational coefficients has $-2 + 5i$, $-i$, and $1 - \sqrt{3}$ as some of its roots. Find the other roots.

By Theorem 15-3, the conjugates of $-2 + 5i$ and $-i$ are roots. They are $-2 - 5i$ and i. By Theorem 15-4, since $1 - \sqrt{3}$ is a root, $1 + \sqrt{3}$ is also a root. There are no other roots since the degree is 6.

TRY THIS

12. Suppose a polynomial of degree 5 with rational coefficients has -4, $7 - 2i$, and $3 + \sqrt{5}$ as roots. Find the other roots.
$7 + 2i, 3 - \sqrt{5}$

||||| Finding Polynomials

Example 5. Find a polynomial of lowest degree with rational coefficients which has $1 - \sqrt{2}$ and $1 + 2i$ as some of its roots.

By Theorem 15-3, $1 - 2i$ is a root. By Theorem 15-4, $1 + \sqrt{2}$ is a root. Thus the polynomial is

$$[x - (1 - \sqrt{2})][x - (1 + \sqrt{2})][x - (1 + 2i)][x - (1 - 2i)],$$

or

$$(x^2 - 2x - 1)(x^2 - 2x + 5),$$

or

$$x^4 - 4x^3 + 8x^2 - 8x - 5.$$

TRY THIS

13. Find a polynomial of lowest degree with rational coefficients which has $2 + \sqrt{3}$ and $1 - i$ as some of its roots.
14. Find a polynomial of lowest degree with real coefficients which has $2i$ and 2 as some of its roots.

Answers.   13. $x^4 - 6x^3 + 11x^2 - 10x + 2$ 14. $x^3 - 2x^2 + 4x - 8$

||||| Finding Roots

Example 6. Let $P(x) = x^4 - 5x^3 + 10x^2 - 20x + 24$. Find the other roots of $P(x)$, given that $2i$ is a root.

Since $2i$ is a root, we know that $-2i$ is also a root. Thus

$$P(x) = (x - 2i)(x + 2i) \cdot Q(x)$$

for some $Q(x)$. Since $(x - 2i)(x + 2i) = x^2 + 4$, we know that

$$P(x) = (x^2 + 4) \cdot Q(x).$$

We find, using division, that $Q(x) = x^2 - 5x + 6$, and since we can factor $x^2 - 5x + 6$, we get

$$P(x) = (x^2 + 4)(x - 2)(x - 3).$$

Thus the other roots are $-2i$, 2, and 3.

TRY THIS

15. Find the other roots of $x^4 + x^3 - x^2 + x - 2$ given that i is a root.
$-i, -2, 1$

Exercise Set 15-4

▌ Find the roots of each polynomial and state the multiplicity of each. (*See page 466.*)

1. $(x + 3)^2(x - 1)$ See answer section
2. $-4(x + 2)(x - \pi)^5$
3. $-8(x - 3)^2(x + 4)^3x^4$
4. $x^3(x - 1)^2(x + 4)$
5. $(x^2 - 5x + 6)^2$
6. $(x^2 - x - 2)^2$

▌▌ Find a polynomial of degree 3 with the given numbers as roots. (*See Example 1.*)

7. $-2, 3, 5$ $x^3 - 6x^2 - x + 30$
8. $3, 2, -1$ $x^3 - 4x^2 + x + 6$
9. $2, i, -i$ $x^3 - 2x^2 + x - 2$
10. $-3, 2i, -2i$ $x^3 + 3x^2 + 4x + 12$
11. $2 + i, 2 - i, 3$ $x^3 - 7x^2 + 17x - 15$
12. $1 + 4i, 1 - 4i, -1$ $x^3 - x^2 + 15x + 17$
13. $\sqrt{2}, -\sqrt{2}, \sqrt{3}$. Are the coefficients rational? $x^3 - \sqrt{3}x^2 - 2x + 2\sqrt{3}$, No
14. $\sqrt{3}, -\sqrt{3}, \sqrt{2}$. Are the coefficients rational? $x^3 - \sqrt{2}x^2 - 3x + 3\sqrt{2}$, No

(*See Example 2.*)

15. Find a polynomial of degree 4 with 0 as a root of multiplicity 2 and 5 as a root of multiplicity 2. $x^4 - 10x^3 + 25x^2$
16. Find a polynomial of degree 4 with 0 as a root of multiplicity 4. x^4
17. Find a polynomial of degree 4 with -2 as a root of multiplicity 1, 3 as a root of multiplicity 2, and -1 as a root of multiplicity 1. $x^4 - 3x^3 - 7x^2 + 15x + 18$
18. Find a polynomial of degree 5 with 4 as a root of multiplicity 3 and -2 as a root of multiplicity 2.
$x^5 - 8x^4 + 4x^3 + 80x^2 - 64x - 256$

▌▌▌ Suppose a polynomial of degree 6 with real coefficients has the given roots. Find the other roots. (*See Example 3.*)

19. $-5, 6, 5 + i, -2i$ $5 - i, 2i$
20. $8, 6, -3 - 2i, 4i$ $-3 + 2i, -4i$

▌▌▌▌ Suppose a polynomial of degree 5 with rational coefficients has the given roots. Find the other roots. (*See Example 4.*)

21. $6, -3 + 4i, 4 - \sqrt{5}$ $-3 - 4i, 4 + \sqrt{5}$
22. $8, 6 - 7i, \frac{1}{2} + \sqrt{11}$ $6 + 7i, \frac{1}{2} - \sqrt{11}$
23. $-2, 3, 4, 1 - i$ $1 + i$
24. $3, 4, -5, 7 + i$ $7 - i$

▌▌▌▌▌ Find a polynomial of lowest degree with rational coefficients that has the given numbers as some of its roots. (*See Example 5.*)

25. $1 + i, 2$ $x^3 - 4x^2 + 6x - 4$
26. $2 - i, -1$ $x^3 - 3x^2 + x + 5$
27. $3i, -2$ $x^3 + 2x^2 + 9x + 18$
28. $-4i, 5$ $x^3 - 5x^2 + 16x - 80$
29. $2 - \sqrt{3}, 1 + i$ $x^4 - 6x^3 + 11x^2 - 10x + 2$
30. $3 + \sqrt{2}, 2 - i$ $x^4 - 10x^3 + 36x^2 - 58x + 35$
31. $\sqrt{5}, -3i$ $x^4 + 4x^2 - 45$
32. $-\sqrt{2}, 4i$ $x^4 + 14x^2 - 32$

▌▌▌▌▌▌ Given that the polynomial has the given root, find the other roots. (*See Example 6.*)

33. $x^4 - 5x^3 + 7x^2 - 5x + 6; -i$ $i, 3, 2$
34. $x^3 - 4x^2 + x - 4; -i$ $i, 4$
35. $x^4 - 16; 2i$ $-2i, 2, -2$
36. $x^4 - 1; i$ $-i, 1, -1$
37. $x^3 - x^2 - 7x + 15; -3$ $2 + i, 2 - i$
38. $x^3 - 6x^2 + 13x - 20; 4$ $1 + 2i, 1 - 2i$
39. $x^3 - 8; 2$ $-1 + i\sqrt{3}, -1 - i\sqrt{3}$
40. $x^3 + 8; -2$ $1 + i\sqrt{3}, 1 - i\sqrt{3}$

15-5 Rational Roots

After finishing Lesson 15-5, you should be able to
▮ given a polynomial with integer coefficients, find the rational roots. Find the other roots, if possible.

▮ Finding the roots of a polynomial is not always easy. However, if a polynomial has integer coefficients, there is a procedure for finding all of the rational roots.

THEOREM 15-5 (Rational Roots Theorem)

Let $P(x) = a_n x^n + a_{n-1} x^{n-1} + \cdots + a_1 x + a_0$, where all the coefficients are integers. Consider a rational number denoted by $\frac{c}{d}$, where c and d have no common factor besides 1 and -1. If $\frac{c}{d}$ is a root of $P(x)$, then c is a factor of a_0 and d is a factor of a_n.

Example 1. Let $P(x) = 3x^4 - 11x^3 + 10x - 4$. Find the rational roots of $P(x)$. If possible, find the other roots.

By the rational roots theorem if $\frac{c}{d}$ is a root of $P(x)$, then c must be a factor of -4 and d must be a factor of 3. Thus the possibilities for c and d are

c: $1, -1, 4, -4, 2, -2$
d: $1, -1, 3, -3$

Then the resulting possibilities for $\frac{c}{d}$ are

$$1, -1, 4, -4, \frac{1}{3}, -\frac{1}{3}, \frac{4}{3}, -\frac{4}{3}, \frac{2}{3}, -\frac{2}{3}, 2, -2.$$

Of these 12 possibilities, we know that at most 4 of them could be roots because $P(x)$ is of degree 4. To find which are roots we can use synthetic division.

We try 1:

1⌋	3	-11	0	10	-4
		3	-8	-8	2
	3	-8	-8	2	-2

$P(1) = -2$, so 1 is not a root.

We try -1:

$$
\begin{array}{r|rrrrr}
-1 & 3 & -11 & 0 & 10 & -4 \\
   &   & -3 & 14 & -14 & 4 \\
\hline
   & 3 & -14 & 14 & -4 & 0
\end{array}
$$

$P(-1) = 0$, so -1 is a root, and

$$P(x) = (x + 1)(3x^3 - 14x^2 + 14x - 4).$$

We now use $3x^3 - 14x^2 + 14x - 4$ and check the other possible roots.

We try $\frac{2}{3}$:

$$
\begin{array}{r|rrrr}
\frac{2}{3} & 3 & -14 & 14 & -4 \\
            &   & 2 & -8 & 4 \\
\hline
            & 3 & -12 & 6 & 0
\end{array}
$$

$P(\frac{2}{3}) = 0$, so $\frac{2}{3}$ is a root. We now know that

$$P(x) = (x + 1)(x - \tfrac{2}{3})(3x^2 - 12x + 6).$$

Since the factor $3x^2 - 12x + 6$ is quadratic, we can use the quadratic formula to find the other roots. They are $2 + \sqrt{2}$ and $2 - \sqrt{2}$. Thus the rational roots are -1 and $\frac{2}{3}$.

1. Let $P(x) = 2x^4 - 7x^3 - 35x^2 + 13x + 3$. If $\frac{c}{d}$ is a rational root of $P(x)$, then:

   a) What are the possibilities for c?

   b) What are the possibilities for d?

   c) What are the possibilities for $\frac{c}{d}$?

   d) Find the rational roots.

   e) If possible, find the other roots.

TRY THIS ▶

Answers.   1. a) $1, -1, 3, -3$ b) $1, -1, 2, -2$ c) $1, -1, \frac{1}{2}, -\frac{1}{2}, 3, -3, \frac{3}{2}, -\frac{3}{2}$
d) $-3, \frac{1}{2}$ e) $3 + \sqrt{10}, 3 - \sqrt{10}$

Example 2.   Let $P(x) = x^3 + 6x^2 + x + 6$. Find the rational roots of $P(x)$. If possible, find the other roots.

By the rational roots theorem if $\frac{c}{d}$ is a root of $P(x)$, then c must be a factor of 6 and d must be a factor of 1. Thus the possibilities for c and d are

   c: $1, -1, 2, -2, 3, -3, 6, -6$
   d: $1, -1$

Then the resulting possibilities for $\frac{c}{d}$ are

   $1, -1, 2, -2, 3, -3, 6, -6.$

These are the same as the possibilities for c. Since the leading coefficient is 1, we need only check the factors of the last coefficient.

There is another aid in eliminating possibilities for rational roots. Note that all coefficients of $P(x)$ are positive. Thus when any positive number is substituted in $P(x)$, we get a positive value, never 0. Therefore no positive number can be a root. Thus the only possibilities for roots are

$$-1, -2, -3, -6.$$

We try -6:

$$
\begin{array}{r|rrrr}
-6 & 1 & 6 & 1 & 6 \\
   &   & -6 & 0 & -6 \\
\hline
   & 1 & 0 & 1 & \,0 \\
\end{array}
$$

$P(-6) = 0$, so -6 is a root. We now know that

$$P(x) = (x + 6)(x^2 + 1).$$

Now $x^2 + 1$ has no real roots, so the only rational root of $P(x)$ is -6. The other roots are i and $-i$.

TRY THIS ➡️

2. Let $P(x) = x^3 + 7x^2 + 4x + 28$.
   If $\dfrac{c}{d}$ is a rational root of $P(x)$, then:
   a) What are the possibilities for c?
   b) What are the possibilities for d?
   c) What are the possibilities for $\dfrac{c}{d}$?
   d) How can you tell without substitution or synthetic division that there are no positive roots?
   e) Find the rational roots of $P(x)$.
   f) Find the other roots if they exist.

Example 3. Find the rational roots of $x^4 + 2x^3 + 2x^2 - 4x - 8$.

Since the leading coefficient is 1, the only possibilities for rational roots are the factors of the last coefficient, -8:

$$1, -1, 2, -2, 4, -4, 8, -8.$$

But, using substitution or synthetic division, we find that none of the possibilities is a root. Thus there are no rational roots.

TRY THIS ➡️

3. Let $P(x) = x^4 + x^2 + 2x + 6$.
   a) How do you know at the outset that this polynomial has no positive roots?
   b) Find the rational roots of $P(x)$.

4. a) Find the rational roots of $x^2 + 3x + 3$.
   b) Can you find the other roots of this polynomial? What are they? Why can you find them?

Answers. 2. a) 1, −1, 2, −2, 4, −4, 7, −7, 14, −14, 28, −28 b) 1, −1 c) 1, −1, 2, −2, 4, −4, 7, −7, 14, −14, 28, −28 d) All coefficients of P(x) are positive. When any positive number is substituted in P(x), we get a positive value, never 0. e) −7 f) 2i, −2i 3. a) All coefficients of P(x) are positive b) None 4. a) None b) $\dfrac{-3 + i\sqrt{3}}{2}$, $\dfrac{-3 - i\sqrt{3}}{2}$, Since $x^2 + 3x + 3$ is quadratic, the quadratic formula can be used.

Exercise Set 15-5

Use Quiz 27 after lesson 15–5.

▌Find the rational roots, if they exist, of each polynomial. If possible, find the other roots. (*See Examples 1–3.*)

1. $x^3 + 3x^2 - 2x - 6$ $-3, \sqrt{2}, -\sqrt{2}$
2. $x^3 - x^2 - 3x + 3$ $1, \sqrt{3}, -\sqrt{3}$
3. $5x^4 - 4x^3 + 19x^2 - 16x - 4$ $1, -\frac{1}{5}, 2i, -2i$
4. $3x^4 - 4x^3 + x^2 + 6x - 2$ $-1, \frac{1}{3}, 1 + i, 1 - i$
5. $x^4 - 3x^3 - 20x^2 - 24x - 8$ $-1, -2, 3 + \sqrt{13},$ $3 - \sqrt{13}$
6. $x^4 + 5x^3 - 27x^2 + 31x - 10$ $1, 2, \frac{-4 + \sqrt{21}}{}$ $-4 - \sqrt{21}$
7. $x^3 + 3x^2 - x - 3$ $1, -1, -3$
8. $x^3 + 5x^2 - x - 5$ $1, -1, -5$
9. $x^3 + 8$ $-2, 1 + i\sqrt{3}, 1 - i\sqrt{3}$
10. $x^3 - 8$ $1, -1 + i\sqrt{3}, -1 - i\sqrt{3}$
11. $4x^3 - 3x^2 + 4x - 3$ $\frac{3}{4}, i, -i$
12. $2x^3 - 3x^2 - x + 1$ $\frac{1}{2}, \frac{1 + \sqrt{5}}{2}, \frac{1 - \sqrt{5}}{2}$
13. $x^5 - 5x^4 + 5x^3 + 15x^2 - 36x + 20$ $1, 2, -2, 2 +$
14. $x^5 - 3x^4 - 3x^3 + 9x^2 - 4x + 12$ $2, -2, 3,$
    $i, 2 - i$ $i, -i$
15. $x^4 + 32$ No rational
16. $x^6 + 8$ No rational
17. $x^3 - x^2 - 4x + 3$ No rational
18. $2x^3 + 3x^2 + 2x + 3$ $-\frac{3}{2}, i, -i$
19. $x^4 + 2x^3 + 2x^2 - 4x - 8$ No rational
20. $x^4 + 6x^3 + 17x^2 + 36x + 66$ No rational

Challenge Exercises

21. a) 2(multiplicity 2), −3(multiplicity 1)   b) $1, -1, \frac{2}{3}, -\frac{1}{2}$ 22. 4 cm

21. Rational Coefficients. The polynomial $P(x) = \frac{1}{12}x^3 - \frac{1}{12}x^2 - \frac{2}{3}x + 1$ does not have all integer coefficients, but all are rational. If we multiply by the LCM of the denominators, 12, we get a polynomial which does have all integer coefficients. Any rational root of $12P(x)$ is a rational root of $P(x)$, and conversely. Find the rational roots of each polynomial.

    a) $\frac{1}{12}x^3 - \frac{1}{12}x^2 - \frac{2}{3}x + 1$ b) $x^4 - \frac{1}{6}x^3 - \frac{4}{3}x^2 + \frac{1}{6}x + \frac{1}{3}$

22. The volume of a cube is 64 cm³. Find the length of a side. (*Hint:* Solve $x^3 - 64 = 0$.)

Graph.   See answer section

23. $P(x) = x^3 + 3x^2 - 2x - 6$
24. $P(x) = x^3 - 3x + 1$
25. $P(x) = x^4 + x^2 + 1$
26. $P(x) = x^4 - 4x^2 + 5$

CONSUMER NOTE: Car Costs

The costs of owning a car begin with the purchase price. They include sales tax, license fees, ownership fees, and insurance costs. They also include interest if the car is bought with borrowed money. Then there are the costs of gas, oil, and maintenance.

COMPUTER ACTIVITY

Approximating Roots of a Polynomial by the Bisection Method

PROBLEM: Find the roots of $F(X) = X^2 - 5X + 4$.

Example using the flowchart:

1		2	3	4
Input				
A(**5**)	B(**6**)	X	F(X)	F(X) = 0?
1	5	$\dfrac{1 + 5}{2} = 3$	$3^2 - 5(3) + 4 = -2$	
3	5	$\dfrac{3 + 5}{2} = ④$	$4^2 - 5(4) + 4 = 0$	Stop

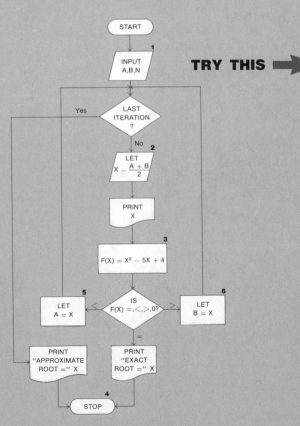

TRY THIS ➡

Find the roots of
$F(X) = X^2 + 3X + 1$. Use A = −1
and B = 0 for the larger root.
Then determine suitable values
for A and B and find a good
approximation for the smaller root.

BASIC PROGRAM (Optional)

```
*10   INPUT A,B,N
 20   DEF FNF(X) = X↑2 − 5*X + 4
 30   FOR I = 1 TO N
 40   LET X = (A + B)/2
 50   PRINT X
 60   IF FNF(X) = 0 THEN 140
 70   IF FNF(X) < 0 THEN 100
 80   LET B = X
 90   GO TO 110
100   LET A = X
110   NEXT I
120   PRINT "APPROXIMATE
         ROOT ="X
130   GO TO 150
140   PRINT "EXACT ROOT ="X
150   STOP
```

* A and B are estimates that are
larger and smaller than the exact
roots. N is the number of iterations.

CHAPTER 15 REVIEW

Review the material in the chapter. Then see how you have done by trying these review exercises. If you miss an exercise, restudy the indicated lesson.

15-1   1.   Determine whether $2 + i$ is a root of $P(x) = x^2 - 4x + 5$.   Yes

15-2   2.   What is the remainder when $-3x^3 + 6x^2 - x + 1$ is divided by $x + 2$?   51

15-2   3.   Determine whether $x + i$ is a factor of $P(x) = x^4 - 1$.   Yes

15-3   4.   Use synthetic division to find the quotient and remainder: $(5x^6 - 6x^4 + 1) \div (x + 1)$.   Q: $5x^5 - 5x^4 - x^3 + x^2 - x + 1$, R: 0

15-3   5.   Use synthetic division to find $P(-4)$: $P(x) = -2x^4 - 8x^3 + 4x^2 - 2x + 1$.   73

15-4   6.   Find a polynomial of degree 4 with roots $-1, 1, i, -i$. $x^4 - 1$

15-4   7.   Find a polynomial of degree 3 with -1 as a root of multiplicity 1 and 1 as a root of multiplicity 2. $x^3 - x^2 - x + 1$

15-4   8.   Suppose a polynomial of degree 5 with rational coefficients has roots $7, -3 + 4i, 2 - \sqrt{5}$. Find the other roots. $-3 - 4i, 2 + \sqrt{5}$

15-4   9.   Find the other roots of $x^4 - x^3 + 2x^2 - 4x - 8$ given that one root is $2i$. $-2i, -1, 2$

15-5   10.   Find the rational roots of $20x^3 - 30x^2 + 12x - 1$, if they exist. If possible, find the other roots. $\frac{1}{2}, \frac{5 + \sqrt{15}}{10}, \frac{5 - \sqrt{15}}{10}$

CHAPTER 15 TEST

1. Determine whether $2i$ is a root of $P(x) = x^2 + 2$.   No
2. What is the remainder when $x^4 + 3x^3 + 3x^2 + 2$ is divided by $x - 2$?   54
3. Determine whether $x + 1$ is a factor of $P(x) = x^3 + 6x^2 + x + 30$.   No
4. Use synthetic division to find the quotient and remainder: $(2x^4 - 6x^3 + 7x^2 - 5x + 1) \div (x + 2)$.   Q: $2x^3 - 10x^2 + 27x - 59$, R: 119
5. Use synthetic division to find $P(3)$: $P(x) = 2x^4 - 3x^3 + x^2 - 3x + 7$.   88
6. Find a polynomial of degree 3 with roots 0, 1, and i. $x^3 - x^2i - x^2 + xi$
7. Find a polynomial of degree 7 with 1 as a root of multiplicity 1, -1 as a root of multiplicity 1, 2 as a root of multiplicity 2, and -3 as a root with multiplicity 3. $x^7 + 5x^6 - 6x^5 - 50x^4 + 5x^3 + 153x^2 - 108$
8. Suppose a polynomial of degree 4 with rational coefficients has roots $-8 - 7i$ and $10 + \sqrt{3}$. Find the other roots. $-8 + 7i$, $10 - \sqrt{3}$
9. Find the other roots of $x^3 - 1$ given that one of the roots is 1. $\frac{-1 + i\sqrt{3}}{2}$, $\frac{-1 - i\sqrt{3}}{2}$
10. Find the rational roots of $x^3 - 7x^2 + 16x - 12$, if they exist. If possible, find the other roots.   2(multiplicity 2), 3(multiplicity 1)

Use Cumulative Test 4 after Cumulative Review below.

CUMULATIVE REVIEW FOR CHAPTERS 12–15

Solve.

12-1   1. $9x^2 - 2 = 0$ $\frac{\sqrt{2}}{3}, -\frac{\sqrt{2}}{3}$

12-2   2. $3x^2 = 4x$ $0, \frac{4}{3}$

12-2   3. $2x^2 - 8x - 42 = 0$ $7, -3$

12-3   4. $x^2 - 3x - 9 = 0$ $\frac{3 \pm \sqrt{45}}{2}$

12-3   5. Use the square root table, Table 1, in the back of the book to approximate solutions of $3x^2 + 7x - 1 = 0$ to the nearest tenth. $0.1, -2.5$

12-4   6. Without solving, determine the nature of the solutions of $4x^2 - 3x + 7 = 0$.   Two nonreal solutions

12-5   7. Without solving, find the sum and product of the solutions of $15x^2 - 7x - 2 = 0$. $\frac{7}{15}, -\frac{2}{15}$

12-5   8. Find a quadratic equation whose solutions are $\frac{1}{2}$ and $-\frac{3}{4}$. $8x^2 + 2x - 3 = 0$

12-6   9. Solve $v = \sqrt{\frac{4}{3}gh}$ for h. $h = \frac{3v^2}{4g}$

12-7   10. $2560 grows to $4000 in 2 years. What is the interest rate?   25%

12-7   11. From a height of 360 m, an object is thrown downward at an initial velocity of 12 m/sec. How long does it take to reach the ground? Round to the nearest tenth.   7.4 s

12-8   12. Solve: $(3 + 2\sqrt{x})^2 + (3 + 2\sqrt{x}) - 20 = 0$. $\frac{1}{4}$

13-1   13. Graph: $f(x) = -\frac{1}{10}x^2$.   Parabola through $(-10, -10)$, $(0, 0)$, $(10, -10)$

13-1   14. Graph: $f(x) = 3(x - 2)^2$.   Parabola through $(1, 3)$, $(2, 0)$, $(3, 3)$

13-2   15. Graph $f(x) = -4(x + 1)^2 - 2$. Then find the vertex, line of symmetry, and maximum or minimum value.   See answer section

13-2   16. Without graphing, find the vertex, line of symmetry, and maximum or minimum value of $f(x) = 6(x - \frac{1}{4})^2 + 19$.   See answer section

13-3   17. Find an equation of the type $f(x) = a(x - h)^2 + k$ for $f(x) = 3x^2 - 24x + 50$. Then find the vertex, line of symmetry, and the maximum or minimum value.   See answer section

13-4   18. Find the x-intercepts of $f(x) = x^2 + 2x - 3$. $(1, 0)$, $(-3, 0)$

13-5   19. Find the quadratic function that fits the data points $(1, 4)$, $(-1, 6)$, $(-2, 16)$. $f(x) = 3x^2 - x + 2$

13-5   20. A rocket is fired upward from ground level at a velocity of 147 m/s. Find a) its maximum height and when it is attained; and b) when it reaches the ground.   a) Max. height = 1102.5 m in 15 s   b) 30 s

13-6   21. The area of a cube varies directly as the square of the length of a side. If a cube has an area 168.54 m² when the length of a side is 5.3 m, what will the area be when the length of a side is 10.2 m?   624.24 m²

14-1   22. Find the distance between the points $(5, 6)$ and $(5, -2)$.   8

14-1   23. Find the midpoints of the segment with endpoints $(4, 5)$ and $(6, -7)$. $(5, -1)$

14-2 24. Find an equation of a circle with center at $(-2, 7)$ and radius $\sqrt{5}$. $(x + 2)^2 + (y - 7)^2 = 5$

14-2 25. Find the center and radius of the circle $(x + 1)^2 + (y + 3)^2 = 4$. Then graph the circle. Circle with center $(-1, -3)$, radius 2

14-3 26. Find the center, vertices, and foci for the ellipse $16x^2 + 9y^2 = 144$. Then graph the ellipse. Center: (0, 0); vertices: $(-3, 0)$, (3, 0), (0, 4),

14-4 27. Find the vertices, foci, and asymptotes for the hyper- $(0, -4)$; foci: $(0, \sqrt{7})$,
bola $\dfrac{(y + 3)^2}{25} - \dfrac{(x + 1)^2}{16} = 1$. Graph the hyperbola. $(0, -\sqrt{7})$ See answer section

14-4 28. Graph: $xy = -4$. See answer section

14-5 29. Find the vertex, focus, and directrix for the parabola $y^2 + 4x = 0$. Then graph the parabola. See answer section

14-6 30. Solve: $\begin{aligned} 9x^2 + 4y^2 &= 36 \\ 3x + 2y &= 6 \end{aligned}$ (2, 0), (0, 3)

14-6 31. A rectangle has perimeter 28 cm, and the length of a diagonal is 10 cm. What are its dimensions? Length is 8 cm; width is 6 cm

14-7 32. Solve: $\begin{aligned} x^2 + y^2 &= 20 \\ xy &= 8 \end{aligned}$ (2, 4), (-2, -4), (4, 2), (-4, -2)

14-7 33. The product of two numbers is 60. The sum of their squares is 136. Find the numbers. 6 and 10, -6 and -10

15-1 34. Is 2 a root of $p(x) = 2x^3 - 3x^2 + x - 1$? No

15-1 35. Divide to find whether $x - 3$ is a factor of $x^4 - 81$. Yes

15-2 36. Use the Remainder Theorem to find the remainder when $p(x) = x^3 - 2x^2 + 5x - 4$ is divided by $x + 2$. -30

15-2 37. Find a complete factorization of $P(x) = x^3 + 2x^2 - 2$. $(x - 1)(x + 2)(x + 1)$

15-3 38. Use synthetic division to find the quotient and remainder: $(x^3 - 27) \div (x - 3)$. Q: $x^2 + 3x + 9$, R 0

15-3 39. Let $P(x) = x^3 + 7x^2 - 12x - 3$. Find $P(-3)$ using synthetic division. 69

15-3 40. Let $P(x) = 3x^3 + 11x^2 - 2x + 8$. Use synthetic division to determine whether -4 is a root of $P(x)$. Yes

15-4 41. Find the roots of the polynomial $P(x) =$ 0(multiplicity 3), $x^3(x - 1)^2(x + 4)$ and state the multiplicity of each. 1(multiplicity 2), -4(multiplicity 1)

15-4 42. Find a polynomial of degree 4 with 0 as a root of multiplicity 2 and 5 as a root of multiplicity 2. $x^4 - 10x^3 + 25x^2$

15-4 43. Suppose a polynomial of degree 5 with rational coefficients has roots 8, $6 - 7i$, $\frac{1}{2} + \sqrt{11}$. Find the other roots. $6 + 7i$, $\frac{1}{2} - \sqrt{11}$

15-4 44. Find a polynomial of lowest degree with rational coefficients which has $3 + \sqrt{2}$ and $2 - i$ as some of its roots. $x^4 - 10x^3 + 36x^2 - 58x + 35$

15-4 45. Let $P(x) = x^3 - 4x^2 + x - 4$. Find the other roots of $P(x)$, given that $-i$ is a root. i, 4

15-5 46. Find the rational roots of $2x^3 - 3x^2 - x + 1$, if they exist. If possible, find the other roots. $\frac{1}{2}$, $\frac{1 + \sqrt{5}}{2}$, $\frac{1 - \sqrt{5}}{2}$

Ready for Exponential and Logarithm Functions?

10-8   1.   Rewrite without fractional exponents: $x^{\frac{4}{5}}$. $\sqrt[5]{x^4}$

1-7   Rename without using an exponent.

      2. 5^1 5

      3. 8^0 1

1-7   4.   Rename without using a negative exponent: 8^{-4}. $\frac{1}{8^4}$

8-4   5.   Find an equation of the inverse of $y = x^3 + 4$. $x = y^3 + 4$

10-9   6.   Solve: $\sqrt{x} = 7$.   49

1-8   7.   Multiply and simplify: $x^{-5} \cdot x^3$. x^{-2}

1-8   8.   Divide and simplify: $\dfrac{x^{-3}}{x^4}$. x^{-7}

1-8   9.   Simplify: $(x^{-3})^4$. x^{-12}

10-1   Convert to scientific notation.

      10.   5240 5.24×10^3

      11.   0.0845 8.45×10^{-2}

10-1   Convert to decimal notation.

      12. 4.335×10^5 433,500

      13. 1.06×10^{-3} 0.00106

2-2   14.   Solve: $3x - 5 = 16$.   7

Chapter 16
Exponential and Logarithm Functions

The loudness of an airplane during takeoff is measured using a logarithmic scale.

16-1 Exponential Functions

After finishing Lesson 16-1, you should be able to
▮ graph exponential functions.

▮In Chapter 10 we gave meaning to expressions with rational exponents such as

$$5^{\frac{1}{4}}, \; 5^{-\frac{3}{4}}, \; 7^{2.34}, \; 5^{1.73}.$$

For example, $5^{1.73}$ or $5^{\frac{173}{100}}$, means to raise 5 to the 173 power and take the 100th root. We shall now give meaning to expressions with irrational exponents such as

$$5^{\sqrt{2}}, \; 7^{\pi}, \; 9^{-\sqrt{5}}, \; 5^{\sqrt{3}}.$$

Let us think about $5^{\sqrt{3}}$. We consider 5^r, where r is rational. The exponent $\sqrt{3}$ is irrational, but we can let r come very close to it. As this happens 5^r gets close to $5^{\sqrt{3}}$.

r	5^r
$1 < \sqrt{3} < 2$	$5^1 < p < 5^2$
$1.7 < \sqrt{3} < 1.8$	$5^{1.7} < p < 5^{1.8}$
$1.73 < \sqrt{3} < 1.74$	$5^{1.73} < p < 5^{1.74}$
$1.732 < \sqrt{3} < 1.733$	$5^{1.732} < p < 5^{1.733}$

As r closes in on $\sqrt{3}$, 5^r closes in on exactly one real number p. We *define* $5^{\sqrt{3}}$ to be the number p.

We can define any irrational exponent in a similar way. Thus any exponential expression a^x now has meaning, whether x is rational or irrational. The usual laws of exponents still hold, but we will not prove that here.

DEFINITION
The function $f(x) = a^x$, where a is a positive constant, is called the *exponential function, base a*.

Example 1. Graph $y = 2^x$.

a) First, we find some solutions (ordered pairs). To do this we choose numbers for x and then find the corresponding y values.

x	0	1	2	-1	-2	-3
y	1	2	4	$\frac{1}{2}$	$\frac{1}{4}$	$\frac{1}{8}$

b)   Next, we plot these points and connect them with a smooth curve.

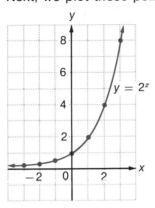

Note that as *x* increases, the function values increase indefinitely. As *x* decreases, the function values decrease toward 0.

TRY THIS

1.   Graph $y = 3^x$.
   a)   Complete this table of solutions.

x	0	1	2	−1	−2	−3
y						

   b)   Plot the points from the table and connect them with a smooth curve.

Example 2.   Graph $y = (\frac{1}{2})^x$.

We could plot points and connect them, but we note that $(\frac{1}{2})^x = (2^{-1})^x = 2^{-x}$. Thus the function we wish to graph is

$$y = 2^{-x}.$$

Compare this with the graph of $y = 2^x$. The graph of $y = 2^{-x}$ is a reflection of it across the *y*-axis because we have replaced *x* by −*x*. Knowing this allows us to graph $y = 2^{-x}$ at once.

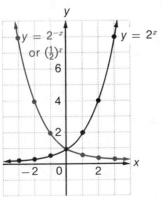

Answers.   1. a) 1, 3, 9, $\frac{1}{3}, \frac{1}{9}, \frac{1}{27}$.
b) See answer section

See answer section

2.   Graph $y = (\frac{1}{3})^x$.

TRY THIS

The preceding examples and exercises illustrate exponential functions of various bases. If $a = 1$ the graph is the horizontal line $y = 1$. For other positive values of a, the graphs are more interesting. We can describe exponential functions as follows.

1. When $a > 1$, the function $f(x) = a^x$ is an increasing function. The greater the value of a, the faster the function increases.
2. When $a < 1$, the function $f(x) = a^x$ is a decreasing function. The greater the value of a, the more slowly the function decreases.

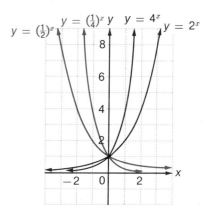

Exercise Set 16-1

▌Graph. Where possible, use transformations. (*See Examples 1 and 2.*)

1. $y = 2^x$
2. $y = 3^x$ See answer section
3. $y = 5^x$
4. $y = 6^x$
5. $y = (\frac{1}{4})^x$
6. $y = (\frac{1}{5})^x$
7. $y = (0.4)^x$
8. $y = (0.3)^x$
9. $y = 2^{x-1}$
10. $y = 3^{x+1}$
11. $y = 5^{x+2}$
12. $y = 6^{x-2}$

Calculator Exercises

Graph.   See answer section

13. $y = (2.34)^x$
14. $y = (0.568)^x$

Challenge Exercises

Graph.   See answer section

15. $y = 3^{|x|}$
16. $y = 2^{|x-1|}$
17. $y = 3^x + 3^{-x}$
18. $y = 2^x + 2^{-x}$

16-2 Logarithmic Functions

After finishing Lesson 16-2, you should be able to
▌ graph logarithmic functions.
▌▌ convert from exponential equations to logarithmic equations.
▌▌▌ convert from logarithmic equations to exponential equations.
▌▌▌▌ solve certain logarithmic equations.
▌▌▌▌▌ find simple logarithms.
▌▌▌▌▌▌ simplify expressions like $a^{\log_a x}$ and $\log_a a^x$.

▌ Logarithmic Functions

The inverse of an exponential function, for $a > 0$ and $a \neq 1$, is called a *logarithmic function,* or *logarithm function.* Thus one way to describe a logarithm function is to interchange variables in $y = a^x$:

$$x = a^y.$$

The most useful and interesting logarithmic functions are those for which $a > 1$. The graph of such a function is a reflection of $y = a^x$ across the line $y = x$. The domain of a logarithm function is the set of all positive real numbers.

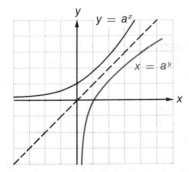

We use the symbol $\log_a x$ to denote the second coordinates of a logarithm function $x = a^y$. Thus a logarithm function can be described as $y = \log_a x$.

DEFINITION
$y = \log_a x$ is defined to mean $x = a^y$, where $x > 0$, $a > 0$, $a \neq 1$.

$\text{Log}_a x$ represents the exponent in the equation $x = a^y$, so the logarithm, base a, of a number x is the power to which a is raised to get x.

Let us graph a logarithmic function.

Example 1. Graph $y = \log_5 x$.

We graph $y = 5^x$ and reflect it across the line $y = x$.

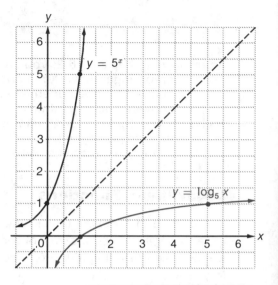

For any base a, $\log_a a = 1$ and $\log_a 1 = 0$.

$\log_a a = 1$ follows from the exponential equation $a^1 = a$. Similarly, $\log_a 1 = 0$ follows from the exponential equation $a^0 = 1$.

‖ Converting from Exponential to Logarithmic Equations

We use the definition above to convert from exponential to logarithmic equations.

Examples. Convert to logarithmic equations.

2. $8 = 2^x \rightarrow x = \log_2 8$

3. $y^{-1} = 4 \rightarrow -1 = \log_y 4$

4. $a^b = c \rightarrow b = \log_a c$

It helps, in such conversions, to remember that a logarithm is an exponent.

ⅠⅠⅠ Converting from Logarithmic to Exponential Equations

We also use the definition to convert from logarithmic to exponential equations.

Examples. Convert to exponential equations.

5. $y = \log_3 5 \rightarrow 3^y = 5$

Again, it helps to remember that a logarithm is an exponent.

6. $-2 = \log_a 7 \rightarrow a^{-2} = 7$

7. $a = \log_b d \rightarrow b^a = d$

TRY THIS ➡️

Answers.   10. $2^5 = 32$ 11. $10^3 = 1000$ 12. $a^7 = Q$ 13. $t^x = M$

> Convert to exponential equations.
>
> 10. $\log_2 32 = 5$
> 11. $\log_{10} 1000 = 3$
> 12. $\log_a Q = 7$
> 13. $\log_t M = x$

ⅠⅠⅠⅠ Solving Logarithmic Equations

Certain equations involving logarithms can be solved by first converting to exponential equations.

Example 8.   Solve $\log_2 x = -3$.

$$2^{-3} = x \qquad \text{\textit{Converting to an exponential equation}}$$
$$x = \tfrac{1}{8}$$

Example 9.   Solve $\log_x 4 = \tfrac{1}{2}$.

$$x^{\frac{1}{2}} = 4 \qquad \text{\textit{Converting to an exponential equation}}$$
$$(x^{\frac{1}{2}})^2 = 4^2 \qquad \text{\textit{Squaring both sides}}$$
$$x = 16$$

This checks, so the solution is 16.

TRY THIS ➡️

Answers.   14. 10,000   15. 3

> Solve.
>
> 14. $\log_{10} x = 4$
> 15. $\log_x 81 = 4$

ⅠⅠⅠⅠⅠ Finding Logarithms

We can find some logarithms by first converting to exponential notation.

Example 10.   Find $\log_{10} 100$.

Let $x = \log_{10} 100$. Then

$$10^x = 100. \qquad \text{\textit{Converting to an exponential equation}}$$

Since we also know that

$$10^2 = 100,$$

we know that $x = 2$, so $\log_{10} 100 = 2$.

Example 11. Find $\log_{27} 3$.

Let $x = \log_{27} 3$. Then

$$27^x = 3.$$

Since we also know that

$$27^{\frac{1}{3}} = 3,$$

we know that $x = \frac{1}{3}$, so $\log_{27} 3 = \frac{1}{3}$.

Example 12. Find $\log_{10} 0.001$.

Let $x = \log_{10} 0.001$. Then

$$10^x = 0.001.$$

Since we also know that

$$10^{-3} = 0.001,$$

it follows that $x = -3$, so $\log_{10} 0.001 = -3$.

TRY THIS ➡️

Answers. 16. 3 17. 4 18. 1 19. −2 20. −2

Find.

16. $\log_{10} 1000$
17. $\log_2 16$
18. $\log_3 3$
19. $\log_{10} 0.01$
20. $\log_5 \frac{1}{25}$

▥ Simplifying Expressions Like $a^{\log_a x}$ and $\log_a a^x$

Exponential and logarithm functions are inverses of each other. Let us also recall an important fact about functions and their inverses. If the domains are suitable, then for any x,

$$f(f^{-1}(x)) = x \qquad \text{and} \qquad f^{-1}(f(x)) = x.$$

When we apply this fact to exponential and logarithm functions, we get the following.

THEOREM 16-1

For any number a, suitable as a logarithm base,
1. $a^{\log_a x} = x$, for any positive number x; and
2. $\log_a a^x = x$, for any number x.

Examples. Simplify.

13. $2^{\log_2 5} = 5$
14. $10^{\log_{10} t} = t$
15. $\log_e e^{-3} = -3$
16. $\log_{10} 10^{5.6} = 5.6$

TRY THIS ➡️

Simplify.

21. $7^{\log_7 \pi}$ π
22. $\log_5 5^{97}$ 97
23. $\log_e e^M$ M
24. $b^{\log_b 42}$ 42

Exercise Set 16-2

▮ Graph. Where possible, use transformations. (*See Example 1.*)   See answer section

1. $y = \log_2 x$
2. $y = \log_3 x$
3. $y = \log_2 (x + 1)$
4. $y = \log_3 (x - 2)$

▮▮ Convert to logarithmic equations. (*See Examples 2–4.*)

5. $10^3 = 1000$ $3 = \log_{10} 1000$
6. $10^2 = 100$ $2 = \log_{10} 100$
7. $5^{-3} = \frac{1}{125}$ $-3 = \log_5 \frac{1}{125}$
8. $4^{-5} = \frac{1}{1024}$ $-5 = \log_4 \frac{1}{1024}$
9. $8^{\frac{1}{3}} = 2$ $\frac{1}{3} = \log_8 2$
10. $16^{\frac{1}{4}} = 2$ $\frac{1}{4} = \log_{16} 2$
11. $10^{0.3010} = 2$ $0.3010 = \log_{10} 2$
12. $10^{0.4771} = 3$ $0.4771 = \log_{10} 3$
13. $a^{-b} = c$ $-b = \log_a c$
14. $P^t = M$ $t = \log_p M$

▮▮▮ Convert to exponential equations. (*See Examples 5–7.*)

15. $t = \log_3 8$ $3^t = 8$
16. $h = \log_7 10$ $7^h = 10$
17. $\log_5 25 = 2$ $5^2 = 25$
18. $\log_6 6 = 1$ $6^1 = 6$
19. $\log_{10} 0.1 = -1$ $10^{-1} = 0.1$
20. $\log_{10} 0.01 = -2$ $10^{-2} = 0.01$
21. $\log_{10} 7 = 0.845$ $10^{0.845} = 7$
22. $\log_{10} 3 = 0.4771$ $10^{0.4771} = 3$
23. $\log_b M = N$ $b^N = M$
24. $\log_k A = c$ $k^c = A$

▮▮▮▮ Solve. (*See Examples 8 and 9.*)

25. $\log_3 x = 2$ 9
26. $\log_4 x = 3$ 64
27. $\log_x 16 = 2$ 4
28. $\log_x 64 = 3$ 4
29. $\log_2 x = -1$ $\frac{1}{2}$
30. $\log_3 x = -2$ $\frac{1}{9}$
31. $\log_8 x = \frac{1}{3}$ 2
32. $\log_{32} x = \frac{1}{5}$ 2

▮▮▮▮▮ Find. (*See Examples 10–12.*)

33. $\log_2 64$ 6
34. $\log_4 64$ 3
35. $\log_{10} 10^2$ 2
36. $\log_3 3^4$ 4
37. $\log_{10} 0.1$ -1
38. $\log_{10} 10,000$ 4
39. $\log_{10} 1$ 0
40. $\log_{10} 10$ 1

▮▮▮▮▮▮ Simplify. (*See Examples 13–16.*)

41. $3^{\log_3 4}$ 4
42. $7^{\log_7 10}$ 10
43. $\log_t t^9$ 9
44. $\log_p p^a$ a
45. $\log_Q Q^{\sqrt{5}}$ $\sqrt{5}$
46. $\log_m m^{\pi}$ π
47. $A^{\log_A 56}$ 56
48. $Q^{\log_Q W}$ W

Challenge Exercises

Graph.   See answer section

49. $y = \log_2 |x|$
50. $y = \log_3 |x|$

16-3 Properties of Logarithmic Functions

After finishing Lesson 16-3, you should be able to
- **I** express the logarithm of a product as a sum of logarithms, and conversely.
- **II** express the logarithm of the nth power of a number, $\log_a (M^n)$, as a product $n \cdot \log_a M$, and conversely.
- **III** express the logarithm of a quotient, $\log_a \dfrac{M}{N}$, as a difference of logarithms, $\log_a M - \log_a N$, and conversely.
- **IIII** convert from logarithms of sums or differences to single logarithms, and convert from single logarithms to logarithms of sums or differences.
- **IIIII** given logarithms of some numbers, find logarithms of other numbers, using properties of logarithms.

I Logarithms of Products

We now establish some basic properties of logarithms.

THEOREM 16-2
For any positive numbers M and N,
$\log_a (M \cdot N) = \log_a M + \log_a N$,
where a is any positive number different from 1.

Theorem 16-2 says that the logarithm of a product is the sum of logarithms.

Example 1. Express $\log_2 (4 \cdot 16)$ as a sum of logarithms.

$\log_2 (4 \cdot 16) = \log_2 4 + \log_2 16$ *By Theorem 16-2*

TRY THIS ➡

Express as a sum of logarithms.

1. $\log_5 (25 \cdot 5)$ $\log_5 25 + \log_5 5$
2. $\log_b PQ$ $\log_b P + \log_b Q$

Express as a single logarithm.

3. $\log_3 7 + \log_3 5$ $\log_3 (7 \cdot 5)$
4. $\log_a C + \log_a A + \log_a B + \log_a I + \log_a N$
   $\log_a C \cdot A \cdot B \cdot I \cdot N$

A Proof of Theorem 16-2
Let $\log_a M = x$ and $\log_a N = y$. Converting to exponential equations, we have $a^x = M$ and $a^y = N$.

Next we multiply, to obtain

$$M \cdot N = a^x \cdot a^y = a^{x+y}.$$

Now, converting back to a logarithmic equation, we get

$\log_a (M \cdot N) = x + y$, or
$\log_a (M \cdot N) = \log_a M + \log_a N$,

which was to be shown.

ıı Logarithms of Powers

THEOREM 16-3

For any positive number M and any number p,

$\log_a M^p = p \cdot \log_a M$,

where a is any positive number different from 1.

Theorem 16-3 says that the logarithm of a power of a number is the exponent times the logarithm of the number.

Examples. Express as a product.

2. $\log_b 9^{-5} = -5 \log_b 9$ *By Theorem 16-3*

3. $\log_a \sqrt[4]{5} = \log_a 5^{\frac{1}{4}}$ *Writing exponential notation*

         $= \frac{1}{4}\log_a 5$ *By Theorem 16-3*

TRY THIS ▶

> Express as a product.
>
> **5.** $\log_7 4^5$ $5 \log_7 4$
> **6.** $\log_a \sqrt{5}$ $\frac{1}{2} \log_a 5$

A Proof of Theorem 16-3

Let $x = \log_a M$. Then, converting to an exponential equation we get $a^x = M$. Raising both sides to the pth power, we get

$$(a^x)^p = M^p, \text{ or}$$
$$a^{xp} = M^p.$$

Converting back to a logarithmic equation,

$$\log_a M^p = \log_a a^{xp} = xp.$$

But $x = \log_a M$, so

$$\log_a M^p = (\log_a M)p = p \cdot \log_a M,$$

which was to be shown.

ııı Logarithms of Quotients

THEOREM 16-4

For any positive numbers M and N,

$\log_a \dfrac{M}{N} = \log_a M - \log_a N$,

where a is any positive number different from 1.

Theorem 16-4 says that the logarithm of a quotient is the difference of the logarithms (the logarithm of the dividend minus the logarithm of the divisor).

Example 4. Express as a difference of logarithms.

$$\log_t \frac{6}{U} = \log_t 6 - \log_t U \qquad \textit{By Theorem 16-4}$$

TRY THIS ➡️

Express as a difference.

7. $\log_b \dfrac{P}{Q}$ $\log_b P - \log_b Q$

8. $\log_c \dfrac{1}{4}$ $-\log_c 4$

A Proof of Theorem 16-4

$\dfrac{M}{N} = M \cdot N^{-1}$, so $\log_a \dfrac{M}{N} = \log_a (M \cdot N^{-1})$.

By Theorem 16-2, $\log_a (M \cdot N^{-1}) = \log_a M + \log_a N^{-1}$
and by Theorem 16-3 $\log_a N^{-1} = -1 \cdot \log_a N$.
So we have

$$\log_a \frac{M}{N} = \log_a M - \log_a N,$$

which was to be shown.

▏▏▏▏ Using the Properties

Example 5. Express in terms of logarithms of x, y, and z.

$$\log_a \sqrt{\frac{xy}{z^3}} = \log_a \left(\frac{xy}{z^3}\right)^{\frac{1}{4}} \qquad \textit{Writing exponential notation}$$

$$= \tfrac{1}{4} \cdot \log_a \frac{xy}{z^3} \qquad \textit{Using Theorem 16-3}$$

$$= \tfrac{1}{4}[\log_a xy - \log_a z^3] \qquad \textit{Using Theorem 16-4}$$

$$= \tfrac{1}{4}[\log_a x + \log_a y - 3 \log_a z] \qquad \textit{Using Theorems 16-2 and 16-3}$$

TRY THIS ➡️

Express in terms of logarithms of x, y, and z.

9. $\log_a \sqrt{\dfrac{z^3}{xy}}$

   $\tfrac{1}{2}[3 \log_a z - \log_a x - \log_a y]$

Example 6. Express as a single logarithm.

$$\tfrac{1}{2}\log_a x - 7\log_a y + \log_a z = \log_a \sqrt{x} - \log_a y^7 + \log_a z \qquad \textit{Using Theorem 16-3}$$

$$= \log_a \frac{\sqrt{x}}{y^7} + \log_a z \qquad \textit{Using Theorem 16-4}$$

$$= \log_a \frac{z\sqrt{x}}{y^7} \qquad \textit{Using Theorem 16-2}$$

TRY THIS ➡

Express as a single logarithm.

10. $5\log_a x - \log_a y + \tfrac{1}{4}\log_a z$ $\log_a \dfrac{x^5 z^{1/4}}{y}$

ⅠⅠⅠⅠⅠ Finding Logarithms

Given certain logarithms, we can find certain others using the properties we have developed.

Examples. Given that $\log_a 2 = 0.301$ and $\log_a 3 = 0.477$, find:

7. $\log_a 6 = \log_a (2 \cdot 3)$
$\qquad = \log_a 2 + \log_a 3 \qquad \textit{Using Theorem 16-2}$
$\qquad = 0.301 + 0.477$
$\qquad = 0.778$

8. $\log_a \sqrt{3} = \log_a 3^{\frac{1}{2}}$
$\qquad = \tfrac{1}{2} \cdot \log_a 3$
$\qquad = \tfrac{1}{2} \cdot (0.477)$
$\qquad = 0.2385$

9. $\log_a \tfrac{2}{3} = \log_a 2 - \log_a 3 \qquad \textit{Using Theorem 16-4}$
$\qquad = 0.301 - 0.477$
$\qquad = -0.176$

10. $\log_a 5$; *No way to find, using these properties.*
($\log_a 5 \neq \log_a 2 + \log_a 3$).

11. $\dfrac{\log_a 2}{\log_a 3} = \dfrac{0.301}{0.477} \approx 0.63$. Note that we could not use any of the properties; we simply divided.

TRY THIS ➡

Given that $\log_a 2 = 0.301$ and $\log_a 3 = 0.477$ find:

11. $\log_a 9$ 0.954
12. $\log_a \sqrt{2}$ 0.1505
13. $\log_a \sqrt[3]{2}$ 0.1003
14. $\log_a \tfrac{3}{2}$ 0.176
15. $\dfrac{\log_a 3}{\log_a 2}$ 1.584

Exercise Set 16-3

▌ Express as a sum of logarithms. (*See Example 1.*)

1. $\log_2(32 \cdot 8)$ $\log_2 32 + \log_2 8$
2. $\log_3(27 \cdot 81)$ $\log_3 27 + \log_3 81$
3. $\log_4(64 \cdot 16)$ $\log_4 64 + \log_4 16$
4. $\log_5(25 \cdot 125)$ $\log_5 25 + \log_5 125$
5. $\log_c Bx$ $\log_c B + \log_c x$
6. $\log_t 5Y$ $\log_t 5 + \log_t Y$

Express as a single logarithm. (*See Example 1.*)

7. $\log_a 6 + \log_a 70$ $\log_a (6 \cdot 70)$
8. $\log_b 65 + \log_b 2$ $\log_b (65 \cdot 2)$
9. $\log_c K + \log_c y$ $\log_c (k \cdot y)$
10. $\log_t H + \log_t M$ $\log_t (H \cdot M)$

▌▌ Express as a product. (*See Examples 2 and 3.*)

11. $\log_a x^3$ $3 \log_a x$
12. $\log_b t^5$ $5 \log_b t$

▌▌▌ Express as a difference of logarithms. (*See Example 4.*)

13. $\log_a \dfrac{67}{5}$ $\log_a 67 - \log_a 5$
14. $\log_t \dfrac{T}{7}$ $\log_t T - \log_t 7$

▌▌▌▌ Express in terms of logarithms of *x*, *y*, and *z*. (*See Example 5.*)

15. $\log_a x^2 y^3 z$ $2 \log_a x + 3 \log_a y + \log_a z$
16. $\log_a 5xy^4 z^3$ $\log_a 5 + \log_a x + 4 \log_a y + 3 \log_a z$
17. $\log_b \dfrac{xy^2}{z^3}$ $\log_b x + 2 \log_b y - 3 \log_b z$
18. $\log_c \sqrt[3]{\dfrac{x^4}{y^3 z^2}}$ $\frac{1}{3}[4 \log_c x - 3 \log_c y - 2 \log_c z]$

Express as a single logarithm and simplify if possible. (*See Example 6.*)

19. $\frac{2}{3}\log_a x - \frac{1}{2}\log_a y$ $\log_a 4$
20. $\frac{1}{2}\log_a x + 3 \log_a y - 2 \log_a x$ $\log_a \frac{\sqrt{x}y^3}{x^2}$
21. $\log_a 2x + 3(\log_a x - \log_a y)$ $\log_a \frac{2x^4}{y^3}$
22. $\log_a x^2 - 2 \log_a \sqrt{x}$ $\log_a x$
23. $\log_a \dfrac{a}{\sqrt{x}} - \log_a \sqrt{ax}$ $\log_a \frac{\sqrt{a}}{x}$
24. $\log_a (x^2 - 4) - \log_a (x - 2)$ $\log_a (x + 2)$

▌▌▌▌▌ Given $\log_{10} 2 = 0.301$, $\log_{10} 3 = 0.477$, and $\log_{10} 10 = 1$, find the following. (*See Examples 7–11.*)

25. $\log_{10} 4$ **0.602**
26. $\log_{10} 5$ (*Hint:* $5 = \frac{10}{2}$) **0.699**
27. $\log_{10} 50$ (*Hint:* $50 = \frac{100}{2}$) **1.699**
28. $\log_{10} 12$ **1.079**
29. $\log_{10} 60$ **1.778**
30. $\log_{10} \frac{1}{3}$ **−0.477**
31. $\log_{10} \sqrt{\frac{2}{3}}$ **−0.088**
32. $\log_{10} \sqrt[5]{12}$ **0.2158**
33. $\log_{10} 90$ **1.954**
34. $\log_{10} \frac{9}{8}$ **0.051**
35. $\log_{10} \frac{1}{4}$ **−0.602**
36. $\log_{10} \frac{9}{10}$ **−0.046**

Challenge Exercises

37. −2   38. −2

37. If $\log_a x = 2$, what is $\log_a \left(\dfrac{1}{x}\right)$?

38. If $\log_a x = 2$, what is $\log_{\frac{1}{a}} x$?

16-4 Common Logarithms

After finishing Lesson 16-4, you should be able to

I use Table 2 to find logarithms and antilogarithms.

II use Table 2 and scientific notation to find logarithms of numbers not in the table.

III reverse the process above to find antilogarithms.

Base ten logarithms are known as *common logarithms*. Table 2 in the back of the book contains common logarithms of numbers from 1 to 10.

▮Logarithms in Computation

Before calculators and computers became so readily available, common logarithms were used extensively to do calculations. In fact, this is why logarithms were developed. Today, computations with logarithms are mainly of historical interest, but logarithm functions are still of substantial importance. The study of logarithms in computation does help one become more familiar with the properties of logarithm functions.

The following is a short table of powers of 10, or logarithms base 10.

$$
\begin{aligned}
1 &= 10^{0.0000}, &&\text{or} &\log_{10} 1 &= 0.0000 \\
2 &\approx 10^{0.3010}, &&\text{or} &\log_{10} 2 &\approx 0.3010 \\
3 &\approx 10^{0.4771}, &&\text{or} &\log_{10} 3 &\approx 0.4771 \\
4 &\approx 10^{0.6021}, &&\text{or} &\log_{10} 4 &\approx 0.6021 \\
5 &\approx 10^{0.6990}, &&\text{or} &\log_{10} 5 &\approx 0.6990 \\
6 &\approx 10^{0.7782}, &&\text{or} &\log_{10} 6 &\approx 0.7782 \\
7 &\approx 10^{0.8451}, &&\text{or} &\log_{10} 7 &\approx 0.8451 \\
8 &\approx 10^{0.9031}, &&\text{or} &\log_{10} 8 &\approx 0.9031 \\
9 &\approx 10^{0.9542}, &&\text{or} &\log_{10} 9 &\approx 0.9542 \\
10 &= 10^{1.0000}, &&\text{or} &\log_{10} 10 &= 1.0000 \\
11 &\approx 10^{1.0414}, &&\text{or} &\log_{10} 11 &\approx 1.0414 \\
12 &\approx 10^{1.0792}, &&\text{or} &\log_{10} 12 &\approx 1.0792 \\
13 &\approx 10^{1.1139}, &&\text{or} &\log_{10} 13 &\approx 1.1139 \\
14 &\approx 10^{1.1461}, &&\text{or} &\log_{10} 14 &\approx 1.1461 \\
15 &\approx 10^{1.1761}, &&\text{or} &\log_{10} 15 &\approx 1.1761 \\
16 &\approx 10^{1.2041}, &&\text{or} &\log_{10} 16 &\approx 1.2041
\end{aligned}
$$

The exponents are approximate, but accurate to four decimal places. To illustrate how logarithms can be used for computation we will use the above table and do some easy calculations.

Example 1. Find 3×4 using the table of exponents.

$$3 \times 4 \approx 10^{0.4771} \times 10^{0.6021}$$
$$\approx 10^{1.0792} \quad \textit{Adding exponents}$$

From the table we see that $10^{1.0792} \approx 12$, so $3 \times 4 \approx 12$.

TRY THIS

Answer. 1. $2 \times 8 \approx 10^{0.3010} \times 10^{0.9031} \approx 10^{1.2041} \approx 16$

1. Find 2×8 using the table.

Note in Example 1 that we can find a product by adding the logarithms of the factors and then finding the number having the result as its logarithm. That is, we found the number $10^{1.0792}$. This number is often referred to as the *antilogarithm* of 1.0792. To state this another way, if

$$f(x) = \log_{10} x,$$

then $\quad f^{-1}(x) = \text{antilog}_{10} x = 10^x.$

In other words, an antilogarithm function is simply an exponential function. It is the inverse of a logarithm function.

Example 2. Find $\frac{14}{2}$ using base 10 logarithms.

$$\log_{10} \frac{14}{2} = \log_{10} 14 - \log_{10} 2 \quad \textit{Using Theorem 16-4}$$
$$\approx 1.1461 - 0.3010 \quad \textit{Finding the logs from the table}$$
$$\log_{10} \frac{14}{2} \approx 0.8451 \quad \textit{Subtracting}$$
$$\frac{14}{2} \approx \text{antilog}_{10} 0.8451 \approx 7 \quad \textit{Using the table in reverse}$$

Example 3. Find $\sqrt[4]{16}$ using base 10 logarithms.

$$\log_{10} \sqrt[4]{16} = \log_{10} 16^{\frac{1}{4}}$$
$$= \frac{1}{4} \cdot \log_{10} 16 \quad \textit{Using Theorem 16-3}$$
$$\approx \frac{1}{4} \cdot 1.2041$$
$$\log_{10} \sqrt[4]{16} \approx 0.3010 \quad \textit{Rounding to four decimal places}$$
$$\sqrt[4]{16} \approx \text{antilog}_{10} 0.3010 \approx 2$$

Example 4. Find 2^3 using base 10 logarithms.

$$\log_{10} 2^3 = 3 \cdot \log_{10} 2 \quad \textit{Using Theorem 16-3}$$
$$\approx 3 \cdot 0.3010 \approx 0.9030$$
$$\log_{10} 2^3 \approx 0.9030$$
$$2^3 \approx \text{antilog}_{10} 0.9030 \approx 8$$

TRY THIS

Answers. 2. $\log_{10}(4 \times 2) = \log_{10} 4 + \log_{10} 2 \approx 0.6021 + 0.3010 \approx 0.9031$; $4 \times 2 \approx \text{antilog}_{10} 0.9031 \approx 8$ 3. $\log_{10} \frac{15}{3} = \log_{10} 15 - \log_{10} 3 \approx 1.1761 - 0.4771 \approx 0.6990$; $\frac{15}{3} \approx \text{antilog}_{10} 0.6990 \approx 5$ 4. $\log_{10} \sqrt[3]{8} = \frac{1}{3} \log_{10} 8 \approx \frac{1}{3}(0.9031) \approx 0.3010$; $\sqrt[3]{8} \approx \text{antilog}_{10} 0.3010 \approx 2$ 5. $\log_{10} 3^2 = 2 \log_{10} 3 \approx 2(0.4771) \approx 0.9542$; $3^2 \approx \text{antilog}_{10} 0.9542 \approx 9$

Using base 10 logarithms and the table, find:

2. 4×2
3. $\frac{15}{3}$
4. $\sqrt[3]{8}$
5. 3^2

ⅠⅠ Using a Logarithm Table

We will often omit the base, 10, when working with common logarithms. That is,

log M will be agreed to mean $\log_{10} M$.

Table 2 contains logarithms of numbers from 1 to 10. Part of that table is as follows.

x	0	1	2	3	4	5	6	7	8	9
5.0	0.6990	0.6998	0.7007	0.7016	0.7024	0.7033	0.7042	0.7050	0.7059	0.7067
5.1	0.7076	0.7084	0.7093	0.7101	0.7110	0.7118	0.7126	0.7135	0.7143	0.7152
5.2	0.7160	0.7168	0.7177	0.7185	0.7193	0.7202	0.7210	0.7218	0.7226	0.7235
5.3	0.7234	0.7251	0.7259	0.7267	0.7275	0.7284	0.7292	0.7300	0.7308	0.7316
5.4	0.7324	0.7332	0.7340	0.7348	0.7356	0.7364	0.7372	0.7380	0.7388	0.7396

To illustrate the use of the table, let us find log 5.24. We locate the row headed **5.2**, then move across to the column headed **4**. We find log 5.24 (the red entry in the table).

We can find antilogarithms by reversing this process. For example, antilog $0.7193 = 10^{0.7193} \approx 5.24$. Similarly, antilog $0.7292 \approx 5.36$.

TRY THIS ➡

Using Table 2 and scientific notation we can find logarithms of numbers that are not between 1 and 10. First recall the following:

$\log_a a^k = k$ for any number k.

Thus

$\log_{10} 10^k = k$ for any number k.

Use Table 2 to find each logarithm.

6. log 3.14   0.4969
7. log 9.99   0.9996
8. log 4.00   0.6021

Use Table 2 to find each antilogarithm.

9.   antilog 0.7589   5.74
10. antilog 0.0000   1
11. antilog 0.5587   3.62

Examples

5. log 52.4 = log(5.24×10^1)   *Writing scientific notation for 52.4*

= log 5.24 + log 10^1 *Using Theorem 16-2*

$\approx$ **0.7193** + 1   *Using log table*

6. log 52,400 = log(5.24×10^4)

= log 5.24 + log 10^4

$\approx$ **0.7193** + 4

7.   log 0.00524 = log(5.24 × 10⁻³)
$$= \log 5.24 + \log 10^{-3}$$
$$\approx \textbf{0.7193} + (-3)$$

TRY THIS ━━━━━━━━━━━━━━━━━━━▶

Answers.   12. 0.4609 + 2   13. 0.4609 + (−4)

Use scientific notation and Table 2 to find each logarithm.

12.   log 289
13.   log 0.000289

In all of the examples above 0.7193 is the fractional part of the logarithm. It is called a *mantissa*. The integer part varies and is known as the *characteristic*. Table 2 contains only mantissas. Characteristics must be supplied. The characteristic is the exponent used in writing scientific notation.

$$\log 5240 \approx 0.7193 + 3$$
  mantissa   *characteristic*

The preceding examples illustrate the importance of using the base 10. It allows great economy in the printing of tables. If we know the logarithms of numbers from 1 to 10 we can find the logarithm of any number. For any base other than 10 this would not be the case.

Example 8.   Find log 0.0538, indicating the characteristic and mantissa.

We first write scientific notation:

$$5.38 \times 10^{-2}.$$

Then we find log 5.38, the mantissa:

$$\log 5.38 \approx 0.7308.$$

The characteristic is the exponent −2.
Now log 0.0538 ≈ 0.7308 + (−2), or −1.2692.

When negative characteristics occur, it is helpful to name the logarithm in such a way that the characteristic and mantissa are preserved. In the preceding example, we have

$$\log 0.0538 \approx -1.2692.$$

This notation displays neither the characteristic nor the mantissa. We can rename the characteristic −2 as 8 − 10 and then add the mantissa to obtain

$$8.7308 - 10.$$

This preserves both mantissa and characteristic.

Example 9. Find log 0.00687.

We write scientific notation (or at least visualize it):

$$0.00687 = 6.87 \times 10^{-3}.$$

The characteristic is -3, or $7 - 10$. The mantissa from the table is 0.8370. Thus log $0.00687 \approx 7.8370 - 10$.

TRY THIS ▶

ᴵᴵᴵ Antilogarithms

To find antilogarithms, we reverse the procedure for finding logarithms.

Example 10. Find antilog 2.6085.

$$\text{antilog } 2.6085 = 10^{2.6085} = 10^{(2+0.6085)}$$
$$= 10^2 \cdot 10^{0.6085}$$

From the table we can find $10^{0.6085}$, or antilog 0.6085. It is 4.06. Hence we have

$$\text{antilog } 2.6085 \approx 10^2 \times 4.06, \text{ or } 406.$$

In this example, we in effect separate the number 2.6085 into an integer and a number between 0 and 1. We use the latter with the table, after which we have scientific notation for our answer.

Example 11. Find antilog 3.7118.

From the table we find antilog $0.7118 \approx 5.15$. Thus

$$\text{antilog } 3.7118 \approx 5.15 \times 10^3 \qquad \text{\textit{Note that 3 is the}}$$
$$\approx 5150. \qquad \qquad \text{\textit{characteristic.}}$$

Example 12. Find antilog $(7.7143 - 10)$.

The characteristic is -3 and the mantissa is 0.7143. From the table we find that antilog $0.7143 \approx 5.18$. Thus

$$\text{antilog } (7.7143 - 10) \approx 5.18 \times 10^{-3}$$
$$\approx 0.00518.$$

TRY THIS ▶

Answers. 21. 64,100   22. 64,100   23. 8560   24. 0.000425   25. 0.0159

Find the following. Use Table 2 and try to write only the answers. Where appropriate, name the answers so that positive mantissas are preserved.

14. log 67,800   4.8312
15. log 892,000   5.9504
16. log 45.9   1.6618
17. log 609,000,000   8.7846
18. log 0.0782   8.8932 − 10
19. log 0.000111   6.0453 − 10
20. log 0.0079   7.8976 − 10

Find the following. Use Table 2. Try to write only the answers.

21. antilog 4.8069
22. $10^{4.8069}$
23. $10^{3.9325}$
24. antilog 6.6284 − 10
25. $10^{8.2014-10}$

Exercise Set 16-4 Use Quiz 28 after lesson 16—4.

▮▮ Use Table 2 to find each of the following. (*See page 497.*)

1. log 2.46 0.3909
2. log 7.65 0.8837
3. log 5.31 0.7251
4. log 8.57 0.9330
5. log 3.72 0.5705
6. log 9.04 0.9562
7. log 1.07 0.0294
8. log 4.60 0.6628
9. antilog 0.8657 7.34
10. antilog 0.3502 2.24
11. antilog 0.6803 4.79
12. antilog 0.1399 1.38
13. antilog 0.7574 5.72
14. antilog 0.9191 8.30
15. $10^{0.5551}$ 3.59
16. $10^{0.8021}$ 6.34
17. $10^{0.5911}$ 3.90
18. $10^{0.9609}$ 9.14
19. $10^{0.3502}$ 2.24
20. $10^{0.8657}$ 7.34

Find these logarithms using Table 2. Try to write only the answers. Where appropriate, name the answers so that positive mantissas are preserved. (*See Examples 8 and 9.*)

21. log 347 2.5403
22. log 8720 3.9405
23. log 52.5 1.7202
24. log 20.6 1.3139
25. log 834 2.9212
26. log 92.4 1.9657
27. log 3870 3.5877
28. log 624,000 5.7952
29. log 0.00134 7.1271 − 10
30. log 0.0702 8.8463 − 10
31. log 0.64 9.8062 − 10
32. log 0.000216 6.3345 − 10
33. log 0.173 9.2380 − 10
34. log 0.00347 7.5403 − 10
35. log 0.0000404 5.6064 − 10
36. log 0.00006 5.7782 − 10

▮▮▮ Find these antilogarithms using Table 2. Try to write only the answers. (*See Examples 10–12.*)

37. antilog 3.3674 2330
38. antilog 4.9222 83,600
39. antilog 1.2553 18
40. antilog 2.6294 426
41. antilog 9.7875 − 10 0.613
42. antilog 8.9881 − 10 0.0973
43. antilog 7.5391 − 10 0.00346
44. antilog 7.7774 − 10 0.00599
45. $10^{1.4014}$ 25.2
46. $10^{2.5391}$ 346
47. $10^{7.9881-10}$ 0.00973
48. $10^{8.5391-10}$ 0.0346
49. $10^{6.7875-10}$ 0.000613
50. $10^{4.6294-10}$ 0.00000426

Challenge Exercises

Find *x*. 51. 6.34 52. 15,500 53. 0.613 54. 0.4265 55. 2.5378 56. 3.7536

51. log *x* = 0.8021
52. log *x* = 4.1903
53. log *x* = 9.7875 − 10
54. $10^x = 2.67$
55. $10^x = 345$
56. $10^x = 5670$

16-5 Calculations With Logarithms

After finishing Lesson 16-5, you should be able to
▮ use logarithms for certain calculations.

▮ The kinds of calculations in which logarithms may be helpful are multiplication, division, taking powers, and taking roots.

Example 1. Find $\dfrac{0.0578 \times 32.7}{8460}$.

We write a *plan* for the use of logarithms, then look up all of the mantissas at one time.

Let

$$N = \frac{0.0578 \times 32.7}{8460}.$$

Then

log N = log 0.0578 + log 32.7 − log 8460.

This gives us the plan.
We use a straight line to indicate addition and a wavy line to indicate subtraction.

Completion of plan:

log 0.0578 $\approx$ 8.7619 − 10
   log 32.7 $\approx$ 1.5145

---

log numerator $\approx$ 10.2764 − 10
   log 8460 $\approx$ 3.9274

$\sim\sim\sim\sim\sim\sim$

log fraction $\approx$ 6.3490 − 10
   fraction $\approx$ 0.0002234   *Taking antilog*

This answer was found from the table. We sometimes need to estimate the fourth digit.

Example 2. Use logarithms to find $(92.8)^3 \times \sqrt[5]{0.986}$.

Let $N = (92.8)^3 \times \sqrt[5]{0.986}$.

Then $\log N = \log (92.8)^3 + \log \sqrt[5]{0.986} = 3 \log 92.8 + \frac{1}{5} \log 0.986$. Note that powers and roots are involved. In such cases it is easier to first find the following logs:

$$\log 92.8 \approx 1.9675$$
$$\log 0.986 \approx 9.9939 - 10$$

Consider $9.9939 - 10$. We are going to multiply this number by $\frac{1}{5}$. Now in order to obtain -10 as a term in the result, we rename this number as follows.

$$\log 0.986 \approx 49.9939 - 50$$

Now we will obtain -10 as a term when we multiply by $\frac{1}{5}$. Thus

$\log (92.8)^3 \approx 5.9025$	$\log 92.8 \approx 1.9675$
$\log \sqrt[5]{0.986} \approx 9.9988 - 10$	$\log 0.986 \approx 49.9939 - 50$

$$\log N \approx 15.9013 - 10$$
$$\approx 5.9013$$
$$N \approx 796{,}700 \quad \textit{Taking antilog; we estimated the fourth digit}$$

TRY THIS

Answers. 1. 0.05340   2. 13.51

Use logarithms to calculate.

1. $\dfrac{78.6 \times 0.00642}{9.45}$

2. $\sqrt[4]{0.325} \times (4.23)^2$

Exercise Set 16-5

▌Use logarithms to calculate. (*See Examples 1 and 2.*)

1. 3.14×60.4 189.6
2. 541×0.0152 8.222
3. $286 \div 1.05$ 272.4
4. $12.8 \div 81.6$ 0.1569
5. $\sqrt{76.9}$ 8.770
6. $\sqrt{678}$ 26.04
7. $\sqrt[3]{56.9}$ 3.846
8. $\sqrt[4]{2600}$ 7.142
9. $(1.36)^{4.2}$ 3.637
10. $(0.727)^{3.6}$ 0.3173
11. $\sqrt[3]{\dfrac{3.24 \times (3.16)^2}{78.4 \times 24.6}}$ 0.2560
12. $\dfrac{70.7 \times (10.6)^2}{18.6 \times \sqrt{276}}$ 25.71

16-6 Interpolation

After finishing Lesson 16-6, you should be able to
▌ use linear interpolation to find logarithms with four-digit precision.
▌▌ use linear interpolation to find antilogarithms with four-digit precision.

▌ Logarithms

In Lesson 16-4 we developed procedures for using Table 2 with three-digit precision. By a procedure called *interpolation* we can find values between those listed in the table, obtaining four-digit precision. Interpolation can be done in various ways, the simplest and most common being *linear* interpolation. What we say applies to a table for any continuous function.

Let us consider how a table of values for any function is made. We select numbers of the domain x_1, x_2, x_3, and so on. Then we compute or somehow determine the corresponding function values (outputs), $f(x_1)$, $f(x_2)$, $f(x_3)$, and so on. Then we tabulate the results. We might also graph the results.

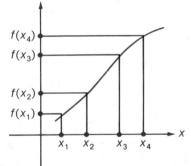

x	x_1	x_2	x_3	x_4	$\cdots$
$f(x)$	$f(x_1)$	$f(x_2)$	$f(x_3)$	$f(x_4)$	$\cdots$

Suppose we want to find an output $f(x)$ for an x not in the table. If x is halfway between x_1 and x_2, then we can take the number halfway between $f(x_1)$ and $f(x_2)$ as an approximation to $f(x)$. If x is one-fifth of the way between x_2 and x_3, we can take the number that is one-fifth of the way between $f(x_2)$ and $f(x_3)$ as an approximation to $f(x)$. What we do is divide the length from x_2 to x_3 in a certain ratio, and then divide the length from $f(x_2)$ to $f(x_3)$ in the same ratio. This is *linear interpolation*.

We can show this geometrically. The length from x_1 to x_2 is divided in a certain ratio by x. The length from $f(x_1)$ to $f(x_2)$ is divided in the same ratio by y. The number y approximates $f(x)$ with the noted error.

Note the slanted line in the figure. The approximation y comes from this line. This explains the use of the term *linear interpolation*. Let us apply linear interpolation to Table 2 of common logarithms.

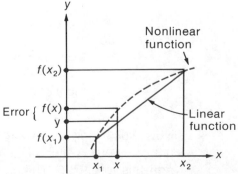

Example 1. Find log 34870.

a) Find the characteristic. Since $34870 = 3.487 \times 10^4$, the characteristic is 4.

b) Find the mantissa. From Table 2 we have:

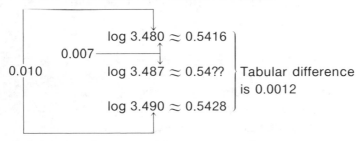

log 3.480 ≈ 0.5416
0.007
0.010   log 3.487 ≈ 0.54??   } Tabular difference
                                      is 0.0012
             log 3.490 ≈ 0.5428

The tabular difference (difference between consecutive values in the table) is 0.0012. Now 3.487 is $\frac{7}{10}$ of the way from 3.480 to 3.490. So we take 0.7 of 0.0012, which is 0.00084, and round it to 0.0008. We add this to 0.5416. The mantissa is 0.5424.

c) Add the characteristic and mantissa:
     log 34870 ≈ 4.5424.

With practice you will take 0.7 of 12, forgetting the zeros, but adding in the same way.

TRY THIS

1. Find log 4562.
   3.6592

Example 2. Find log 0.009543.

a) Find the characteristic. Since $0.009543 = 9.543 \times 10^{-3}$, the characteristic is -3, or $7 - 10$.

b) Find the mantissa. From Table 2 we have:

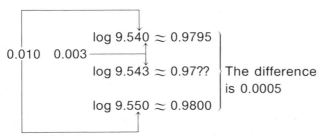

             log 9.540 ≈ 0.9795
0.010   0.003   } The difference
             log 9.543 ≈ 0.97??   is 0.0005
             log 9.550 ≈ 0.9800

Now 9.543 is $\frac{3}{10}$ of the way from 9.540 to 9.550, so we take 0.3 of 0.0005, which is 0.00015, and round it to 0.0002. We add this to 0.9795. The mantissa that results is 0.9797.

c) Add the characteristic and the mantissa:

$$\log 0.009543 \approx 7.9797 - 10.$$

TRY THIS

2. Find log 0.02387.
   8.3779 − 10

■ Antilogarithms

We interpolate when finding antilogarithms, using the table in reverse.

Example 3. Find antilog 4.9164.

a) The characteristic is 4. The mantissa is 0.9164.

b) Find the antilog of the mantissa, 0.9164. From Table 2 we have:

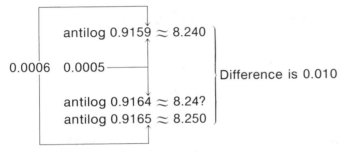

0.0006   0.0005 ─── antilog 0.9159 ≈ 8.240

antilog 0.9164 ≈ 8.24?
antilog 0.9165 ≈ 8.250

Difference is 0.010

The difference between 0.9159 and 0.9165 is 0.0006. Thus
0.9164 is $\frac{0.0005}{0.0006}$, or $\frac{5}{6}$, of the way between 0.9159 and 0.9165.
Then antilog 0.9164 is $\frac{5}{6}$ of the way between 8.240 and 8.250,
so we take $\frac{5}{6}$ (0.010), which is 0.00833..., and round it to
0.008. Thus the antilog of the mantissa is 8.248.

Thus antilog $4.9164 \approx 8.248 \times 10^4 = 82{,}480$.

TRY THIS

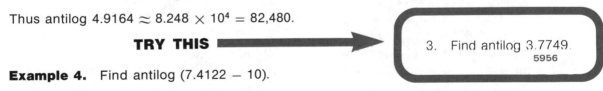

3. Find antilog 3.7749.
   5956

Example 4. Find antilog (7.4122 − 10).

a) The characteristic is −3. The mantissa is 0.4122.

b) Find the antilog of the mantissa, 0.4122. From Table 2 we have:

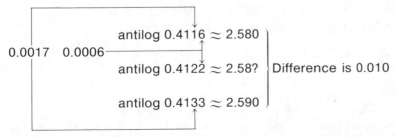

0.0017   0.0006 ─── antilog 0.4116 ≈ 2.580

antilog 0.4122 ≈ 2.58?

antilog 0.4133 ≈ 2.590

Difference is 0.010

The difference between 0.4116 and 0.4133 is 0.0017. Thus 0.4122 is $\frac{0.0006}{0.0017}$, or $\frac{6}{17}$, of the way between 0.4116 and 0.4133. Then antilog 0.4122 is $\frac{6}{17}$ of the way between 2.580 and 2.590, so we take $\frac{6}{17}$ (0.010), which is 0.0035 to four places. We round it to 0.004. Thus the antilog of the mantissa is 2.584.

So antilog $(7.4122 - 10) \approx 2.584 \times 10^{-3} = 0.002584$.

TRY THIS

4. Find antilog $6.4557 - 10$.

0.0002856

Exercise Set 16-6

▮ Find each of the following logarithms using interpolation. (*See Examples 1 and 2.*)

1. log 41.63   1.6194
2. log 472.1   2.6740
3. log 2.944   0.4689
4. log 21.76   1.3377
5. log 650.2   2.8130
6. log 37.37   1.5725
7. log 0.1425   9.1538 − 10
8. log 0.09045   8.9564 − 10
9. log 0.004257   7.6291 − 10
10. log 4518   3.6549
11. log 0.1776   9.2494 − 10
12. log 0.08356   8.9220 − 10
13. log 600.6   2.7786
14. log 800.1   2.9032

▮▮ Find each of the following antilogarithms using interpolation. (*See Examples 3 and 4.*)

15. antilog 1.6350   43.15
16. antilog 2.3512   224.5
17. antilog 0.6478   4.444
18. antilog 1.1624   14.53
19. antilog 0.0342   1.082
20. antilog 4.8453   70,030
21. antilog 9.8564 − 10   0.7185
22. antilog 8.9659 − 10   0.09245
23. antilog 7.4128 − 10   0.002587
24. antilog 9.7278 − 10   0.5343
25. antilog 8.2010 − 10   0.01589
26. antilog 7.8630 − 10   0.007295

Challenge Exercises

27. 773.2   28. 0.8268   29. 9.6786 − 10   30. 9.8445 − 10

Use logarithms and interpolation to do the following calculations. Use four-digit precision. Answers may be checked using a calculator.

27. $\dfrac{35.24 \times (16.77)^3}{12.93 \times \sqrt{276.2}}$

28. $\sqrt[5]{\dfrac{16.79 \times (4.234)^3}{18.81 \times 175.3}}$

Find.

29. log (log 3)

30. log (log 5)

16-7 Exponential and Logarithmic Equations

After finishing Lesson 16-7, you should be able to
∎ solve exponential equations.
∎∎ solve logarithmic equations.

∎ Exponential Equations

Equations with variables in exponents, such as $3^{2x-1} = 4$, are called *exponential equations*. We can often solve such equations by taking the logarithm on both sides and then using Theorem 16-3.

Example 1. Solve $2^{3x-5} = 16$.

Method 1. $\log 2^{3x-5} = \log 16$ *Taking log on both sides*
$(3x - 5)\log 2 = \log 16$ *Using Theorem 16-3*

$$3x - 5 = \frac{\log 16}{\log 2}$$

$$x = \frac{\dfrac{\log 16}{\log 2} + 5}{3} \qquad \text{\textit{Solving for x}}$$

$$x \approx \frac{\dfrac{1.2041}{0.3010} + 5}{3} \qquad \text{\textit{Finding logs}}$$

$$x \approx 3.0001 \qquad \text{\textit{Calculating}}$$

The answer is approximate because the logarithms are approximate.

Method 2. Note that $16 = 2^4$. Then we have

$2^{3x-5} = 2^4$.

Since the base is the same, 2, on both sides, the exponents must be the same. Thus

$3x - 5 = 4$.

We solve this equation to get

$x = 3$.

This answer is exact.

TRY THIS ➡

1. Solve $4^{2x-3} = 64$.
   a) Use a method like Method 1 of Example 1.
   b) Use a method like Method 2 of Example 1. Note that $4^3 = 64$.

   a) 2.9999 b) 3

ıı **Logarithmic Equations**

Equations that contain logarithmic expressions are called *logarithmic equations*. To solve such equations we try to obtain a single logarithmic expression on one side of the equation and then take the antilogarithm on both sides.

Example 2. Solve $\log x + \log (x - 3) = 1$.

$$\log x(x - 3) = 1 \qquad \textit{Using Theorem 16-1 to obtain a single logarithm}$$
$$x(x - 3) = 10^1 \qquad \textit{Taking the antilog on both sides}$$
$$x^2 - 3x - 10 = 0$$
$$(x + 2)(x - 5) = 0 \qquad \textit{Factoring and principle of zero products}$$

$x = -2$ or $x = 5$

Check:
$\log x + \log (x - 3) = 1$		$\log x + \log (x - 3) = 1$	
$\log (-2) + \log (-2 - 3)$	1	$\log 5 + \log (5 - 3)$	1
		$\log 5 + \log 2$	
		$\log 10$	
		1	

The number -2 is not a solution because negative numbers do not have logarithms.

The solution is 5.

TRY THIS

> 2. Solve.
> $\log x + \log (x + 3) = 1$. 2

Exercise Set 16-7

ı Solve. (*See Example 1.*)

1. $2^x = 8$ 3
2. $2^x = 32$ 5
3. $2^x = 10$ 3.3223
4. $2^x = 33$ 5.0449
5. $5^{4x-7} = 125$ $\frac{5}{2}$
6. $4^{3x+5} = 16$ -1
7. $3^{x^2+4x} = \frac{1}{27}$ $-3, -1$
8. $3^{5x} \cdot 9^{x^2} = 27$ $-3, \frac{1}{2}$
9. $4^x = 7$ 1.4036
10. $8^x = 10$ 1.1073
11. $2^x = 3^{x-1}$ 2.7093
12. $3^{x+2} = 5^{x-1}$ 7.4502
13. $(2.8)^x = 41$ 3.6064
14. $(1.7)^x = 20$ 5.6467

ıı Solve. (*See Example 2.*)

15. $\log x + \log(x - 9) = 1$ 10
16. $\log x + \log(x + 9) = 1$ 1
17. $\log x - \log(x + 3) = -1$ $\frac{1}{3}$
18. $\log(x + 9) - \log x = 1$ 1
19. $\log_4 (x + 3) + \log_4 (x - 3) = 2$ 5
20. $\log_5 (x + 4) + \log_5 (x - 4) = 2$ $\sqrt{41}$
21. $\log \sqrt[3]{x} = \sqrt{\log x}$ $1, 10^9$
22. $\log \sqrt[4]{x} = \sqrt{\log x}$ $1, 10^{16}$
23. $\log_5 \sqrt{x^2 + 1} = 1$ $\pm 2\sqrt{6}$
24. $\log \sqrt[3]{x^2} + \log \sqrt[3]{x^4} = \log 2^{-3}$ $\pm \frac{\sqrt{2}}{4}$

16-8 Applications

After finishing Lesson 16-8, you should be able to
▮ solve problems involving exponential and logarithmic functions and equations.

▮ Exponential and logarithmic functions and equations have many applications.

Example 1. (*Compound Interest*) The amount A that principal P will be worth after t years at interest rate r, compounded annually, is given by the formula

$$A = P(1 + r)^t.$$

Suppose \$4000 principal is invested at 6% interest and yields \$5353. How many years was it invested?

Using the formula $A = P(1 + r)^t$, we have

$$5353 = 4000(1 + 0.06)^t, \text{ or } 5353 = 4000(1.06)^t.$$

Solving for t, we have

$$\log 5353 = \log 4000(1.06)^t$$
$$\log 5353 = \log 4000 + t \log 1.06$$
$$\frac{\log 5353 - \log 4000}{\log 1.06} = t$$
$$\frac{3.7286 - 3.6021}{0.0253} \approx t$$
$$5 \approx t.$$

The money was invested for 5 years.

TRY THIS ➡

> 1. Suppose \$5000 principal is invested at 8% interest and yields \$8569. How many years was it invested?   7

Example 2. (*Loudness of Sound*) The sensation of loudness of sound is not proportional to the energy intensity, but rather is a logarithmic function. *Loudness* in bels (after Alexander Graham Bell) of a sound of intensity I is defined to be

$$L = \log \frac{I}{I_0},$$

where I_0 is the minimum intensity detectable by the human ear (such as the tick of a watch at 6 meters under quiet conditions).

When a sound is 10 times as intense as another, its loudness is 1 bel greater. If a sound is 100 times as intense as another, it is louder by 2 bels, and so on. The bel is a large unit, so a subunit one tenth as large (a *decibel*) is usually used. For L in decibels, the formula is as follows:

$$L = 10 \log \frac{I}{I_0}.$$

a) Find the loudness in decibels of the background noise in a radio studio, for which the intensity I is 199 times I_0.

We substitute into the formula and calculate, using Table 2.

$$L = 10 \log \frac{199 \cdot I_0}{I_0}$$
$$= 10 \log 199$$
$$\approx 10(2.2989)$$
$$\approx 23 \text{ decibels}$$

b) Find the loudness of the sound of a heavy truck, for which the intensity is 10^9 times I_0.

$$L = 10 \log \frac{10^9 \cdot I_0}{I_0}$$
$$= 10 \log 10^9$$
$$= 10 \cdot 9$$
$$= 90 \text{ decibels}$$

TRY THIS

2. Find the loudness in decibels of the sound in a library, for which the intensity I is 2510 times I_0. **34 decibels**

3. Find the loudness in decibels of conversational speech, for which the intensity is 10^6 times I_0. **60 decibels**

Example 3. (*Earthquake Magnitude*) The magnitude R (on the Richter scale) of an earthquake of intensity I is defined as follows:

$$R = \log \frac{I}{I_0},$$

where I_0 is a minimum intensity used for comparison.

An earthquake has an intensity $10^{8.6}$ times I_0. What is its magnitude on the Richter scale?

We substitute into the formula:

$$R = \log \frac{10^{8.6} \cdot I_0}{I_0}$$
$$= \log 10^{8.6}$$
$$= 8.6$$

TRY THIS

4. The earthquake in Anchorage, Alaska on March 27, 1964 had an intensity $10^{8.4}$ times I_0. What was its magnitude on the Richter scale?   **8.4**

Example 4.   (*Forgetting*) A group of people take a test and make an average score of S. After a time t they take an equivalent form of the same test. At that time the average score is $S(t)$. According to one theory, $S(t)$ is given by the following function.

$$S(t) = A - B \log (t + 1),$$

where t is in months and the constants A and B are determined by experiment.

Students in a zoology class took an exam. They took equivalent forms of the test at monthly intervals thereafter. The average scores were found to be given by the function

$$S(t) = 78 - 15 \log (t + 1).$$

What was the average score **a)** when they took the test originally? **b)** after 4 months?

We substitute into the equation defining the function.

a) $S(0) = 78 - 15 \log(0 + 1)$
$= 78 - 15 \log 1$
$= 78 - 0$
$= 78$

b) $S(4) = 78 - 15 \log (4 + 1)$
$= 78 - 15 \log 5$
$\approx 78 - 15 \cdot 0.6990$
$\approx 78 - 10.49$
$\approx 67.51.$

TRY THIS

5. Students in an accounting course take an exam and are then retested at monthly intervals. The forgetting function is given by $S(t) = 68 - 14 \log (t + 1)$. What was the average score
a) when they took the exam originally?   **68**
b) after 5 months?   **57.11**

Exercise Set 16-8 Use Quiz 29 after lesson 16—8.

■ (*See Examples 1–4.*)

1. (*Doubling time*) How many years will it take an investment of $1000 to double itself when interest is compounded annually at 6%? 11.9

2. (*Tripling time*) How many years will it take an investment of $1000 to triple itself when interest is compounded annually at 5%? 22.5

3. Find the loudness in decibels of the sound of an automobile having an intensity 3,100,000 times I_0. 65 decibels

4. Find the loudness in decibels of the sound of a dishwasher having an intensity 2,500,000 times I_0. 63 decibels

5. Find the loudness in decibels of the threshold of sound pain, for which the intensity is 10^{14} times I_0. 140 decibels

6. Find the loudness in decibels of a jet aircraft having an intensity 10^{12} times I_0. 120 decibels

7. The Los Angeles earthquake of 1971 had an intensity $10^{6.7}$ times I_0. What was its magnitude on the Richter scale? 6.7

8. The San Francisco earthquake of 1906 had an intensity $10^{8.25}$ times I_0. What was its magnitude on the Richter scale? 8.25

9. An earthquake has a magnitude of 5 on the Richter scale. What is its intensity? 10^5 times I_0

10. An earthquake has a magnitude of 7 on the Richter scale. What is its intensity? 10^7 times I_0

11. Students in an industrial mathematics course take an exam and are then retested at monthly intervals. The forgetting function is given by $S(t) = 82 - 18 \log (t + 1)$.
    a) What was the average score on the original exam? 82
    b) What was the average score after 5 months had elapsed? 67.99

12. Students graduating from a cosmetology curriculum take an exam and are then retested at monthly intervals. The forgetting function is given by $S(t) = 75 - 20 \log (t + 1)$.
    a) What was the average score on the original exam? 75
    b) What was the average score after 6 months had elapsed? 58.10

13. Refer to Exercise 11. How much time will elapse before the average score has decreased to 64? 9 months

14. Refer to Exercise 12. How much time will elapse before the average score has decreased to 61? 4 months

In chemistry, pH is defined as follows:

$$pH = -\log [H^+],$$

where $[H^+]$ is the hydrogen ion concentration in moles per liter. For example, the hydrogen ion concentration in milk is 4×10^{-7} moles per liter, so $pH = -\log (4 \times 10^{-7}) = -[\log 4 + (-7)] \approx 6.4$.

15. For tomatoes, $[H^+]$ is about 6.3×10^{-5}. Find the pH. 4.2

16. For eggs, $[H^+]$ is about 1.6×10^{-8}. Find the pH. 7.8

Challenge Exercises

The average walking speed V of a person in a city of population p, in thousands, is given by

$$V(p) = 0.26 \log p + 0.015,$$

where V is in meters per second.

17. The population of Seattle, Washington is 531,000. What is the average walking speed of a person in Seattle? (Let $p = 531$.)   0.72 m/s

18. The population of New York City is 7,900,000. What is the average walking speed of a person in New York? (Let $p = 7900$.)   1.03 m/s

19. What is the population of your city? What is the average walking speed of a person in your city?   Answers may vary.

20. The population of a small town is 2000. What is the average walking speed of a person in that town?   0.09 m/s

21. Solve $R = \log \dfrac{I}{I_0}$ for I. $I = 10^R \cdot I_0$

22. Solve $A = P(1 + r)^t$ for t. $t = \dfrac{\log A - \log P}{\log (1 + r)}$

BIOGRAPHICAL NOTE: Hypatia

Hypatia was a woman of outstanding abilities in mathematics. Luckily, she was born in circumstances that allowed her abilities to flourish.

She was born about A.D. 370. Her father, Theon, was a professor of mathematics at the University of Alexandria in Egypt. He encouraged her interest in mathematics, astronomy, and other areas of learning. Eventually she became a teacher of mathematics and philosophy at the university. She lectured on the algebra of first- and second-degree equations and on other subjects. Her lectures were very popular. They attracted students from Africa, Asia, and Europe.

Her popularity did not protect Hypatia from the cruelty of power struggles in Alexandria. In 415 she was murdered by extremists there.

CHAPTER 16 REVIEW

Review the material in the chapter. Then see how you have done by trying these review exercises. If you miss an exercise, restudy the indicated lesson.

16-1   1. Graph $y = 5^x$.   See answer section
16-1   2. Graph $y = \log_5 x$.
16-2   3. Convert to a logarithmic equation: $7^{2.3} = x$. $2.3 = \log_7 x$
16-2   4. Convert to an exponential equation: $\log_8 M = t$. $8^t = M$
16-2   5. Solve $\log_x 64 = 3$.   4
16-2   6. Solve $\log_{16} 4 = x$. $\frac{1}{2}$
16-2   7. Simplify $\log_h h^3$.   3
16-3   8. Express as a single logarithm:
            $\frac{1}{2} \log_b a + \frac{3}{2} \log_b c - 4 \log_b d$. $\log_b \frac{\sqrt{a} \cdot c^{3/2}}{d^4}$

16-3   9. Express in terms of logarithms of M and N: $\log \sqrt[3]{\dfrac{M^2}{N}}$. $\frac{1}{3}[2 \log M - \log N]$

16-3   Given that $\log_a 2 = 0.301$, $\log_a 3 = 0.477$, and
        $\log_a 7 = 0.845$, find:
        10. $\log_a 18$ 1.255
        11. $\log_a \frac{7}{2}$ 0.544
        12. $\log_a \frac{1}{4}$ −0.602
        13. $\log_a \sqrt{3}$ 0.2385

16-4   Use Table 2 to find each of the following.
        14. log 26.2   1.4183
        15. log 0.00806   7.9063 − 10
        16. $10^{1.8686}$ 73.9

16-5   17. Use logarithms to calculate $(0.0524)^2 \cdot \sqrt{0.0638}$.   0.0006934

16-6   Use Table 2 to find each of the following.
        18. log 2904   3.4630
        19. antilog 8.4414 − 10   0.02763
        20. Solve $3^{1-x} = 9^{2x}$. $\frac{1}{5}$

16-7   21. Solve $\log (x^2 - 1) - \log (x - 1) = 1$.   9
16-8   22. How many years will it take an investment of $1000 to double itself if interest is compounded annually at 5%?   14.2
16-8   23. What is the loudness in decibels of a sound which is 1000 times I_0?   30 decibels

CHAPTER 16 TEST

1. Graph $y = 3^x$.
2. Graph $y = \log_3 x$.   See answer section
3. Convert to a logarithmic equation: $3^x = 25$. $x = \log_3 25$
4. Convert to an exponential equation: $\log_3 9 = 2$. $3^2 = 9$
5. Solve $\log_x 125 = 3$.   5
6. Solve $\log_{25} 5 = x$. $\frac{1}{2}$
7. Simplify $14^{\log_{14} 7t}$.   7t
8. Express as a single logarithm: $2 \log_a b - 3 \log_a c + \frac{1}{2} \log_a d$. $\log_a \frac{b^2 \sqrt{d}}{c^3}$
9. Express in terms of logarithms of x and y: $\log_a \sqrt[3]{\dfrac{x}{y^2}}$. $\frac{1}{3}[\log_a x - 2 \log_a y]$

Given $\log_a 3 = 0.451$, $\log_a 4 = 0.510$, and $\log_a 5 = 0.565$, find:

10. $\log_a 9$ 0.902
11. $\log_a 20$ 1.075
12. $\log_a \frac{4}{3}$ 0.059
13. $\log_a 2$ 0.255

Use Table 2 to find each of the following.

14. $\log 14.3$ 1.1553
15. $\log 0.00324$ 7.5105 − 10
16. antilog 7.5340 − 10   0.00342

17. Use logarithms to calculate 3^{20}.   3,483,000,000

Use Table 2 to find each of the following.

18. $\log 456.1$ 2.6591
19. $10^{3.6409}$ 4374
20. Solve $2^{x-1} = 32$.   6

21. Solve $\log 4x + \log x = 2$.   5
22. How many years will it take an investment of $1000 to triple itself when interest is compounded annually at 8%?   14.3
23. The forgetting function for a certain test is $S(t) = 80 - 5 \log(t + 1)$. What was the average score after 9 months?   75

Technical writers for telephone companies assist communication within the companies. The writers describe new methods or products so other workers can understand them.

Supervisors in telephone company business offices coordinate the work of company representatives. They help to handle the requests and complaints of customers.

Pilots for large companies fly executives from place to place on business trips. The routes and schedules they follow depend on company needs.

Material handlers for trucking firms work in warehouses. Handlers may work alone or in a group to load and unload goods with handtrucks and other devices.

CAREERS IN TRANSPORTATION, COMMUNICATION, AND PUBLIC UTILITIES

Careers in transportation involve movement of goods or people by various means, including pipelines, trucks, trains, planes, buses, and cabs. Careers in communication involve movement of information. The means are telephone, telegraph, radio, and television systems. Careers in public utilities involve movement of water, electricity, gas, or waste materials by conduits or other means.

Some subdivisions of transportation careers are listed in the table below. It gives percentages of workers in transportation, communication, and public utilities.

	Percentages of workers in mid-1960s	Percentages of workers in mid-1970s
Trucking and warehousing	24%	25%
Railroads	19	12.5
Local and interurban lines	7	6
Airlines	5.5	8
Other transportation	9	7.5
Total transportation	63.5%	59.0%
Communication	21	25
Public utilities	15.5	16

Percentages of Workers in Transportation, Communication, and Public Utilities

rain signal-department workers are
sponsible for train signals and
ntrol systems. Workers may install
ew signal equipment or inspect
nd maintain existing equipment.

Taxicab drivers provide individual
transportation service. Drivers may
respond to calls from radio dis-
patchers or to signals from people
on the street.

Local truck drivers transport goods
from terminals or warehouses to
local stores, factories, or homes.
Drivers may also pick up goods on
the way.

Meter readers for electric
companies go to custom-
ers' homes or businesses.
Readers note how much
electricity has been used
so customers can be
billed correctly.

In the 10 years from the mid-1960s to the mid-1970s, the total of
all these careers grew 18%. To increase its share of the total, a
career area had to grow *more* than 18%. The area of communication careers, for example, grew 41%. It raised its share of the total
from 21% to 25%. Airline careers grew 71% in the 10 years. Local
and interurban lines, which include subways and local buses, did
not grow at all. Only one area shrank. Railroad careers decreased
23%. (Even so, a number of workers were hired by railroads to replace some of those who retired, died, or transferred to other
areas of work.)

A few of the people who work in transportation, communication, and public utilities are pictured here. The projected place
of these careers in the United States labor
force is shown in the circle graph.

Information about many different career
trends is given in *Occupational Outlook
Handbook*. It is compiled by the United
States Bureau of Labor Statistics. The *Handbook* describes more than 250 occupations,
and it gives facts about the labor force. It is
available at many libraries.

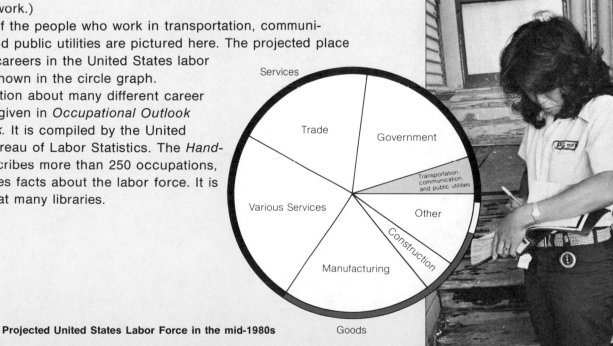

Projected United States Labor Force in the mid-1980s

Ready for Sequences and Series?

8-5   1. Given a function f described by $f(x) = 3x + 2$, find $f(1)$, $f(2)$, and $f(3)$.   **5, 8, 11**

8-5   2. Given a function f described by $f(x) = 3x^2 - 1$, find $f(1)$, $f(2)$, and $f(3)$.   **2, 11, 26**

8-5   3. Given a function f described by $f(x) = 3^x$, find $f(1)$, $f(2)$, and $f(3)$.   **3, 9, 27**

Simplify.

10-2   4. $\sqrt{1}$ **1**

10-2   5. $\sqrt{4}$ **2**

10-3   6. $\sqrt{56}$ **$2\sqrt{14}$**

4-2   7. Solve: $x + 15y = 47$ **(2, 3)**
                   $x + 2y = 8$

1-1   8. Find decimal notation for $\frac{3}{11}$.   **$0.27\overline{27}$**

Chapter 17
Sequences and Series

*The arrangement of the seeds on this sunflower
is given by a certain kind of sequence.*

17-1 Sequences

After finishing Lesson 17-1, you should be able to
▌ given a formula for the general term of a sequence, find the *n*th term.
▌▌ given a sequence, look for a pattern, and try to guess a rule for the general term.

▌ Sequences

DEFINITION
A *sequence* is an ordered set of numbers.

Here is an example of a sequence.

3, 5, 7, 9, . . .

The dots mean that there are more numbers in the sequence. A sequence that does not end is called *infinite*.

Each number is called a *term* of the sequence. The first term is 3, the second term is 5, the third term is 7, and so on. We can think of a sequence as a function *a* whose domain is a set of consecutive natural numbers.

Some sequences have a rule which describes the *n*th term. The above sequence could be described 3, 5, 7, 9, . . . , $2n + 1$, . . . where the *n*th term is $2n + 1$. We also say $a(n) = 2n + 1$.

We can find the terms of the sequence by consecutively substituting the numbers 1, 2, 3, . . . , *n*, and so on. Thus

$$a(1) = 2 \cdot 1 + 1, \text{ or } 3$$
$$a(2) = 2 \cdot 2 + 1, \text{ or } 5$$
$$a(3) = 2 \cdot 3 + 1, \text{ or } 7$$
$$\vdots \qquad \qquad \vdots$$

The *n*th term is also called the *general term*. It is customary to use a_n, instead of $a(n)$ for the general term of a sequence. The letter *k* is often used instead of *n*.

Example 1. Find the first two terms of the sequence whose general term is given by $a_n = \dfrac{(-1)^n}{n + 1}$.

$$a_1 = \frac{(-1)^1}{1 + 1} = \frac{-1}{2} = -\frac{1}{2} \qquad a_2 = \frac{(-1)^2}{2 + 1} = \frac{(-1)^2}{3} = \frac{1}{3}$$

TRY THIS ➡

1. A sequence is given by $a_n = 2n - 1$.
   a) Find the first three terms. 1, 3, 5
   b) Find the 34th term. 67
2. A sequence is given by $a_n = 2^n$. Find the first four terms. 2, 4, 8, 16
3. A sequence is given by $a_n = (-1)^n n^2$. Find the first four terms.
   −1, 4, −9, 16

ıı Finding General Terms

We may know the first few terms of a sequence, but not the general term. In such a case we cannot know for sure what the general term is, but we can make a guess by looking for a pattern.

Examples. For each sequence, make a guess at the general term.

2. $1, 4, 9, 16, 25, \ldots$
These are squares of numbers, so the general term may be n^2.

3. $\sqrt{1}, \sqrt{2}, \sqrt{3}, \sqrt{4}, \ldots$
These are square roots of numbers, so the general term may be $\sqrt{n}$.

4. $-1, 2, -4, 8, -16, \ldots$
These are powers of 2 with alternating signs, so the general term may be $(-1)^n 2^{n-1}$.

TRY THIS

> For each sequence try to find a rule for finding the general term or the nth term.
>
> Answers may vary.
>
> **4.** $2, 4, 6, 8, 10, \ldots$ $2n$
> **5.** $1, 2, 3, 4, 5, 6, \ldots$ n
> **6.** $1, 8, 27, 64, 125, \ldots$ n^3
> **7.** $x, \dfrac{x^2}{2}, \dfrac{x^3}{3}, \dfrac{x^4}{4}, \dfrac{x^5}{5}, \ldots$ $\dfrac{x^n}{n}$
> **8.** $1, 2, 4, 8, 16, 32, \ldots$ 2^{n-1}

Exercise Set 17-1

ı In each of the following the nth term of a sequence is given. In each case find the first four terms, the 10th term, and the 15th term. (*See Example 1.*)

1. $a_n = 3n + 1$ $4, 7, 10, 13; 31; 46$

2. $a_n = 3n - 1$ $2, 5, 8, 11; 29; 44$

3. $a_n = \dfrac{n}{n + 1}$ $\dfrac{1}{2}, \dfrac{2}{3}, \dfrac{3}{4}, \dfrac{4}{5}; \dfrac{10}{11}; \dfrac{15}{16}$

4. $a_n = n^2 + 1$ $2, 5, 10, 17; 101; 226$

5. $a_n = n^2 - 2n + 1$ $0, 1, 4, 9; 81; 196$

6. $a_n = \dfrac{n^2 - 1}{n^2 + 1}$ $0, \dfrac{3}{5}, \dfrac{4}{5}, \dfrac{15}{17}; \dfrac{99}{101}; \dfrac{112}{113}$

7. $a_n = n + \dfrac{1}{n}$ $2, 2\dfrac{1}{2}, 3\dfrac{1}{3}, 4\dfrac{1}{4}; 10\dfrac{1}{10}; 15\dfrac{1}{15}$

8. $a_n = n + \dfrac{(-1)^n}{n}$ $0, 2\dfrac{1}{2}, 2\dfrac{2}{3}, 4\dfrac{1}{4}; 10\dfrac{1}{10}; 14\dfrac{14}{15}$

9. $a_n = \left(-\dfrac{1}{2}\right)^{n-1}$ $1, -\dfrac{1}{2}, \dfrac{1}{4}, -\dfrac{1}{8}; -\dfrac{1}{512}; \dfrac{1}{16{,}384}$

10. $a_n = 2^n$ $2, 4, 8, 16; 1024; 32{,}768$

ıı For each of the following sequences find a rule for finding the general term or nth term. (*See Examples 2–4.*)   Answers may vary.

11. $1, 3, 5, 7, 9, \ldots$ $2n - 1$

12. $3, 9, 27, 81, 243, \ldots$ 3^n

13. $\dfrac{2}{3}, \dfrac{3}{4}, \dfrac{4}{5}, \dfrac{5}{6}, \dfrac{6}{7}, \ldots$ $\dfrac{n+1}{n+2}$

14. $\sqrt{2}, \sqrt{4}, \sqrt{6}, \sqrt{8}, \sqrt{10}, \ldots$ $\sqrt{2n}$

15. $\sqrt{3}, 3, 3\sqrt{3}, 9, 9\sqrt{3}, \ldots$ $3^{n/2}$

16. $1 \cdot 2, 2 \cdot 3, 3 \cdot 4, 4 \cdot 5, \ldots$ $n(n + 1)$

17. $-1, -4, -7, -10, -13, \ldots$ $-(3n - 2)$

18. $\dfrac{1}{10}, \dfrac{2}{100}, \dfrac{3}{1000}, \ldots$ $\dfrac{n}{10^n}$

17-2 Series

After finishing Lesson 17-2, you should be able to
▪ name a series with or without sigma notation.

DEFINITION

A series is the sum of the terms in a sequence.

With any sequence there is an associated *series*. For example, associated with the sequence

$$3, 5, 7, 9, \ldots, 2n + 1$$

is the series

$$3 + 5 + 7 + 9 + \cdots + (2n + 1).$$

This is the sum of the first n terms of the sequence.

TRY THIS

For each sequence find the associated series.

1. 2, 4, 8, 16, 25, 36
2. −2, 4, −6, 8, −10
3. $x, x^2, x^3, x^4, \ldots, x^n$

Answers. 1. 2 + 4 + 8 + 16 + 25 + 36   2. −2 + 4 + (−6) + 8 + (−10)
3. $x + x^2 + x^3 + x^4 + \ldots + x^n$

▪ **Sigma Notation**

The Greek letter Σ (sigma) can be used to simplify notation when a series has a formula for the general term. The series above can be named

$$\sum_{k=1}^{n} (2k + 1).$$

This is read "the sum as k goes from 1 to n, of $(2k + 1)$."

Example 1. Name $\sum_{k=1}^{4} (2^k + k)$ without using sigma notation.

To find the terms we replace k successively by each of the numbers 1 through 4.

For $k = 1$: $2^1 + 1 = 3$
For $k = 2$: $2^2 + 2 = 6$
For $k = 3$: $2^3 + 3 = 11$
For $k = 4$: $2^4 + 4 = 20$

Then $\sum_{k=1}^{4} (2^k + k) = 3 + 6 + 11 + 20$.

We can try to find sigma notation for a series by guessing a rule for the nth term. Answers can vary, of course.

Examples.   Write sigma notation for each series.

2. $1 + 4 + 9 + 16 + 25$; These are sums of squares, so the

general term is k^2. Sigma notation is $\displaystyle\sum_{k=1}^{5} k^2$.

3. $-1 + 3 - 5 + 7$; These are odd integers with alternating
signs. The general term is $(-1)^k(2k - 1)$ or $(-1)^{k+1}(2k + 1)$,
depending upon where k begins. Sigma notation is

$$\sum_{k=1}^{4} (-1)^k(2k - 1) \text{ or } \sum_{k=0}^{3} (-1)^{k+1}(2k + 1).$$

4. $\sqrt{1} + \sqrt{2} + \sqrt{3} + \cdots \sqrt{n}$; The general

term is $\sqrt{k}$. Sigma notation is $\displaystyle\sum_{k=1}^{n} \sqrt{k}$.

> Write sigma notation for each series.
> Answers may vary.
> **4.** $2 + 4 + 6 + 8 + 10$
> **5.** $1 + 8 + 27 + 64 + \cdots + n^3$
> **6.** $x + \dfrac{x^2}{2} + \dfrac{x^3}{3} + \dfrac{x^4}{4} + \dfrac{x^5}{5} + \dfrac{x^6}{6}$
> **7.** $2 + 3 + 4 + 5 + \cdots + n$

TRY THIS

Answers. $4. \displaystyle\sum_{k=1}^{5} 2k$ $5. \displaystyle\sum_{k=1}^{n} k^3$ $6. \displaystyle\sum_{k=1}^{6} \frac{x^k}{k}$ $7. \displaystyle\sum_{k=2}^{n} k$

Exercise Set 17-2

▌Name each series without using Σ. (*See Example 1.*)

1. $\displaystyle\sum_{k=1}^{5} \frac{1}{2k}$ $\frac{1}{2} + \frac{1}{4} + \frac{1}{6} + \frac{1}{8} + \frac{1}{10}$

2. $\displaystyle\sum_{k=1}^{6} \frac{1}{2k + 1}$ $\frac{1}{3} + \frac{1}{5} + \frac{1}{7} + \frac{1}{9} + \frac{1}{11} + \frac{1}{13}$

3. $\displaystyle\sum_{k=0}^{5} 2^k$ $2^0 + 2^1 + 2^2 + 2^3 + 2^4 + 2^5$

4. $\displaystyle\sum_{k=4}^{7} \sqrt{2k - 1}$ $\sqrt{7} + \sqrt{9} + \sqrt{11} + \sqrt{13}$

5. $\displaystyle\sum_{k=7}^{10} \log k$ $\log 7 + \log 8 + \log 9 + \log 10$

6. $\displaystyle\sum_{k=0}^{4} \pi k$ $0 + \pi + 2\pi + 3\pi + 4\pi$

7. $\displaystyle\sum_{k=1}^{5} k^3$ $1^3 + 2^3 + 3^3 + 4^3 + 5^3$

8. $\displaystyle\sum_{k=1}^{4} t^k$ $t + t^2 + t^3 + t^4$

Write sigma notation. (*See Examples 2–4.*)   Answers may vary.

9. $\frac{1}{2} + \frac{2}{3} + \frac{3}{4} + \frac{4}{5} + \frac{5}{6} + \frac{6}{7}$ $\displaystyle\sum_{k=1}^{6} \frac{k}{k+1}$

10. $3 + 6 + 9 + 12 + 15$ $\displaystyle\sum_{k=1}^{5} 3k$

11. $-2 + 4 - 8 + 16 - 32 + 64$ $\displaystyle\sum_{k=1}^{6} (-1)^k 2^k$

12. $\frac{1}{1^2} + \frac{1}{2^2} + \frac{1}{3^2} + \frac{1}{4^2} + \frac{1}{5^2}$ $\displaystyle\sum_{k=1}^{5} \frac{1}{k^2}$

13. $1 + 2 + 4 + 8 + 16 + 32$ $\displaystyle\sum_{k=1}^{6} 2^{k-1}$

14. $\frac{1}{3} + \frac{1}{9} + \frac{1}{27} + \frac{1}{81}$ $\displaystyle\sum_{k=1}^{4} \frac{1}{3^k}$

15. $-1 - 2 - 3 - 4 - 5 - 6 - 7$ $\displaystyle\sum_{k=1}^{7} -k$

16. $1 + \frac{1}{\sqrt{2}} + \frac{1}{\sqrt{3}} + \frac{1}{2}$ $\displaystyle\sum_{k=1}^{4} \frac{1}{\sqrt{k}}$

17. $4 + 5 + 6 + 7 + 8 + \cdots + n$ $\displaystyle\sum_{k=4}^{n} k$

18. $8 + 9 + 10 + \cdots + n$ $\displaystyle\sum_{k=8}^{n} k$

19. $4 - 9 + 16 - 25 + \cdots (-1)^n n^2$ $\displaystyle\sum_{k=2}^{n} (-1)^k k^2$

20. $9 - 16 + 25 + \cdots + (-1)^{n+1} n^2$

$\displaystyle\sum_{k=3}^{n} (-1)^{k+1} k^2$

17-3 Arithmetic Sequences

After finishing Lesson 17-3, you should be able to
- **I** identify the first term and the common difference of an arithmetic sequence.
- **II** given any three of the numbers a_1, a_n, d, or n, associated with an arithmetic sequence, solve for the fourth using $a_n = a_1 + (n - 1)d$.
- **III** given any two terms of an arithmetic sequence and their places in the sequence, find a_1 and d.

I Arithmetic Sequences

Look at the sequence

$$2, 5, 8, 11, 14, \ldots$$

Note that 3 can be added to each term to get the next term.

DEFINITION

A sequence in which a constant d can be added to each term to get the next is called an *arithmetic sequence*. The constant d is called the *common difference*.

The following notation is used with arithmetic sequences.

a_1 is the first term.
a_2 is the second term.
a_n is the nth term.
n is the number of terms from a_1 up to and including a_n.

To find the common difference, subtract any term from the one that follows it.

Examples. The following are arithmetic sequences. Identify the first term and the common difference.

Sequence	First term	Common difference
1. 4, 9, 14, 19, 24, . . .	4	5
2. 34, 27, 20, 13, 6, −1, −8, . . .	34	−7
3. 2, $2\frac{1}{2}$, 3, $3\frac{1}{2}$, 4, $4\frac{1}{2}$, . . .	2	$\frac{1}{2}$

Identify the first term and the common difference of each arithmetic sequence.

1. 2, 3, 4, 5, 6, . . .
2. 1, 4, 7, 10, 13, . . .
3. 19, 14, 9, 4, −1, −6, . . .
4. 10, 20, 30, 40, . . .
5. 5, $5\frac{1}{4}$, $5\frac{1}{2}$, $5\frac{3}{4}$, 6, $6\frac{1}{4}$, . . .
6. 10, $9\frac{1}{2}$, 9, $8\frac{1}{2}$, 8, $7\frac{1}{2}$, . . .

TRY THIS ➡

Answers. 1. $a_1 = 2$, $d = 1$ 2. $a_1 = 1$, $d = 3$ 3. $a_1 = 19$, $d = -5$ 4. $a_1 = 10$, $d = 10$ 5. $a_1 = 5$, $d = \frac{1}{4}$ 6. $a_1 = 10$, $d = -\frac{1}{2}$

‖ The *n*th Term

The first term of an arithmetic sequence is a_1. We add d to get the next term, $a_1 + d$. We add d again to get the next term, $(a_1 + d) + d$, and so on. There is a pattern.

$$a_1$$
$$a_2 = a_1 + d$$
$$a_3 = (a_1 + d) + d = a_1 + 2d$$
$$a_4 = (a_1 + d) + d + d = a_1 + 3d$$
$$\vdots$$
$$a_n = a_1 + (n - 1)d$$

We have a theorem.

THEOREM 17-1

The *n*th term of an arithmetic sequence is given by
$a_n = a_1 + (n - 1)d$.

Example 4. Find the 14th term of the arithmetic sequence
$4, 7, 10, 13, \ldots$.

First note that $a_1 = 4$, $d = 3$, and $n = 14$. Then using the formula of Theorem 17-1 we have

$$a_{14} = 4 + (14 - 1)3$$
$$= 4 + 39$$
$$a_{14} = 43.$$

Example 5. In the sequence of Example 4, which term is 301? That is, what is n if $a_n = 301$?

$$a_n = a_1 + (n - 1)d \qquad \textit{Theorem 17-1}$$
$$301 = 4 + (n - 1)3 \qquad \textit{Substituting}$$
$$301 = 4 + 3n - 3$$
$$300 = 3n$$
$$100 = n$$

Thus the 100th term is 301.

In a similar manner we can find a_1 if we know n, a_n, and d. Also, we can find d if we know a_1, n, and a_n.

TRY THIS ➡

7. Find the 13th term of the sequence $2, 6, 10, 14, \ldots$ **50**
8. In the sequence of Exercise 7, what term is 298? That is, what is n if $a_n = 298$? **75th**
9. Find a_7 when $a_1 = 5$ and $d = 2$. **17**
10. Find a_1 when $d = \frac{1}{2}$, $n = 7$, and $a_n = 16$. **13**

ııı **Constructing Sequences**

Given two terms and their places in a sequence, we can find a_1 and d and then construct the sequence.

Example 6. The 3rd term of an arithmetic sequence is 8 and the 16th term is 47. Find a_1 and d. Construct the sequence.

Using the formula $a_n = a_1 + (n - 1)d$, where $a_3 = 8$, we have

$$8 = a_1 + (3 - 1)d \qquad \text{or} \qquad 8 = a_1 + 2d.$$

Using the same formula where $a_{16} = 47$, we have

$$47 = a_1 + (16 - 1)d \qquad \text{or} \qquad 47 = a_1 + 15d.$$

Now we solve the system of equations.

$$a_1 + 15d = 47$$
$$a_1 + 2d = 8$$

$$\begin{array}{ll} a_1 + 15d = 47 & \\ \underline{-a_1 - \ 2d = -8} & \textit{Multiplying by } -1 \\ \qquad\quad 13d = 39 & \textit{Adding} \\ \qquad\qquad d = 3 & \end{array}$$

$$a_1 + 2 \cdot 3 = 8$$
$$a_1 = 2$$

Thus a_1 is 2, d is 3, and the sequence is 2, 5, 8, 11, 14, . . .

TRY THIS ➡

> 11. The 7th term of an arithmetic sequence is 79 and the 13th term is 151. Find a_1 and d. Construct the sequence.
>
> $a_1 = 7, d = 12; 7, 19, 31, 43, . . .$

Exercise Set 17-3

ı For each of the following arithmetic sequences find the first term and the common difference. (*See Examples 1–3.*)

1. 2, 7, 12, 17, . . . $a_1 = 2, d = 5$

2. 1.06, 1.12, 1.18, 1.24, . . . $a_1 = 1.06, d = 0.06$

3. 7, 3, -1, -5, . . . $a_1 = 7, d = -4$

4. $-9, -6, -3, 0, \ldots$ $a_1 = -9, d = 3$

5. $\frac{3}{2}, \frac{9}{4}, 3, \frac{15}{4}, \ldots$ $a_1 = \frac{3}{2}, d = \frac{3}{4}$

6. $\frac{3}{5}, \frac{1}{10}, -\frac{2}{5}, \ldots$ $a_1 = \frac{3}{5}, d = -\frac{1}{2}$

ıı (*See Example 4.*)

7. Find the 12th term of the arithmetic sequence 2, 6, 10, . . .   46

8. Find the 11th term of the arithmetic sequence 0.07, 0.12, 0.17, . . .   0.57

9. Find the 17th term of the arithmetic sequence 7, 4, 1, . . . -41

10. Find the 14th term of the arithmetic sequence 3, $\frac{7}{3}, \frac{5}{3}, \ldots$ $-\frac{17}{3}$

(*See Example 5.*)

11. In the sequence of Exercise 7, what term is 106?   27th

12. In the sequence of Exercise 8, what term is 1.67?   33rd

13. In the sequence of Exercise 9, what term is -296?   102nd

14. In the sequence of Exercise 10, what term is -27?   46th

15. Find a_{17} when $a_1 = 5$ and $d = 6$.   101

16. Find a_{20} when $a_1 = 14$ and $d = -3$. -43

17. Find a_1 when $d = 4$ and $a_8 = 33$.   5

18. Find d when $a_1 = 8$ and $a_{11} = 26$.   1.8

19. Find n when $a_1 = 5$, $d = -3$, and $a_n = -76$.   28

20. Find n when $a_1 = 25$, $d = -14$, and $a_n = -507$.   39

■■■ (*See Example 6.*)

21. In an arithmetic sequence $a_{17} = -40$ and $a_{28} = -73$. Find a_1 and d. Write the first 5 terms of the sequence.
   8, 5, 2, -1, -4

22. In an arithmetic sequence $a_{17} = \frac{25}{3}$ and $a_{32} = \frac{95}{6}$. Find a_1 and d. Write the first 5 terms of the sequence.
   $\frac{1}{3}$, $\frac{5}{6}$, $\frac{4}{3}$, $\frac{11}{6}$, $\frac{7}{3}$

Challenge Exercises

23. A bomb drops from an airplane. It falls 4.88 m the first second, 14.64 m the second second, and so on, forming an arithmetic sequence. How many meters will the bomb fall during the 20th second?   190.32 m

24. Smalltown, whose population was 18,395 ten years ago, has lost 270 inhabitants each year since then. What is the present population of Smalltown?   15,695

25. Find the first term and the common difference for the arithmetic sequence $3x + 2y$, $4x + y$, $5x$, $6x - y$, . . . $a_1 = 3x + 2y$, $d = x - y$

26. Find the first term and the common difference for the arithmetic sequence where $a_2 = 4p - 3q$ and $a_4 = 10p + q$. $a_1 = p - 5q$, $d = 3p + 2q$

HISTORICAL NOTE: Measuring Things by 360s

The Sumerians—who lived in what is now Iraq—had a unified system of notation and measures more than 4000 years ago. The number 360 was important to the ancient Sumerians. For a while they thought there were 360 days in a year. They divided each day into 360 parts (each equal to four minutes of our time). They applied 360 to other measures, including circles. Today, we divide a circle into 360 degrees because of their influence.

17-4 Arithmetic Series

After finishing Lesson 17-4, you should be able to
∎ given an arithmetic sequence or series determine a_1, a_n, and n, and use the formula $S_n = \frac{n}{2}(a_1 + a_n)$ to find the sum of the first n terms. Or, determine a_1, n, and d, and use the formula $S_n = \frac{n}{2}[2a_1 + (n-1)d]$ to find the sum of the first n terms.

∎ An arithmetic series is a series associated with an arithmetic sequence. Two theorems give useful formulas for finding the sum of the first n terms.

THEOREM 17-2
The sum of the first n terms of an arithmetic series is given by
$S_n = \frac{n}{2}(a_1 + a_n)$.

This formula is useful when we know a_1 and a_n.

THEOREM 17-3
The sum of the first n terms of an arithmetic series is given by
$S_n = \frac{n}{2}[2a_1 + (n-1)d]$.

This formula is useful when we do not know a_n.

Example 1. Find the sum of the first 100 natural numbers.

The sum of the first 100 natural number is $1 + 2 + 3 + \cdots + 100$. This is an arithmetic series.
$a_1 = 1$, $a_n = 100$, and $n = 100$. We use Theorem 17-2.

$$S_n = \frac{n}{2}(a_1 + a_n)$$

Substituting, we get

$$S_{100} = \frac{100}{2}(1 + 100)$$

$$= 50(101), \text{ or } 5050.$$

TRY THIS ⟹

1. Find the sum of the first 200 natural numbers.

    20,100

A Proof of Theorem 17-2

Let us write out the sum of the first n terms of an arithmetic sequence in two different ways.

$$S_n = a_1 + (a_1 + d) + (a_1 + 2d) + \cdots + (a_n - 2d) + (a_n - d) + a_n.$$
$$S_n = a_n + (a_n - d) + (a_n - 2d) + \cdots + (a_1 + 2d) + (a_1 + d) + a_1.$$

We now add, obtaining

$$2S_n = (a_1 + a_n) + (a_1 + a_n) + \cdots + (a_1 + a_n), \; n \text{ summands.}$$

Thus $2S_n = n(a_1 + a_n)$, and $S_n = \dfrac{n}{2}(a_1 + a_n)$.

Example 2. Find the sum of the first 14 terms of the arithmetic series $2 + 5 + 8 + 11 + 14 + 17 + \cdots$

Note that $a_1 = 2$, $d = 3$, and $n = 14$. We use Theorem 17-3.

$$S_n = \frac{n}{2}[2a_1 + (n - 1)d]$$
$$S_{14} = \tfrac{14}{2} \cdot [2 \cdot 2 + (14 - 1)3]$$
$$= 7 \cdot [4 + 13 \cdot 3]$$
$$= 7 \cdot 43$$
$$S_{14} = 301$$

TRY THIS ➡

> 2. Find the sum of the first 15 terms of the arithmetic series
> $$1 + 3 + 5 + 7 + 9 + \ldots$$
> 225

Example 3. Find the sum of the series $\displaystyle\sum_{k=1}^{13} (4k + 5)$.

First find a few terms.

$$9 + 13 + 17 + \cdots$$

We see that this is an arithmetic series with $a_1 = 9$, $d = 4$, and $n = 13$. We use Theorem 17-3.

$$S_n = \frac{n}{2}[2a_1 + (n - 1)d]$$
$$S_{13} = \tfrac{13}{2}[2 \cdot 9 + (13 - 1)4]$$
$$= \tfrac{13}{2}[18 + 12 \cdot 4]$$
$$= \tfrac{13}{2} \cdot 66$$
$$S_{13} = 429.$$

TRY THIS ➡

> 3. Find the sum of the series
> $$\sum_{k=1}^{10} (9k - 4).$$
> 455

Example 4. Money is saved in an arithmetic sequence. $500 is saved one year, $600 the next, $700 the next, and so on, for 10 years. How much is saved?

We have the arithmetic series $500 + 600 + 700 + \cdots$
Thus $a_1 = 500$, $n = 10$, and $d = 100$. We use Theorem 17-3.

$$S_n = \frac{n}{2}[2a_1 + (n-1)d]$$

Substituting, we get

$$S_{10} = \tfrac{10}{2}[2 \cdot 500 + (10-1)100]$$
$$S_{10} = 9500.$$

$9500 is saved.

TRY THIS ➡

4. A cheerleader pyramid has 15 students on the bottom row, 14 on the next row, and so on until there is 1 student on top. How many cheerleaders are in the pyramid? (How would you like being on the bottom?) **120**

Exercise Set 17-4

(See Examples 1 and 2.)

1. Find the sum of the first 20 terms of the series $5 + 8 + 11 + 14 + \cdots$ **670**
2. Find the sum of the first 14 terms of the series $11 + 7 + 3 + \cdots$ **−210**
3. Find the sum of the first 15 terms of the series $5 + \frac{55}{7} + \frac{75}{7} + \frac{95}{7} + \cdots$ **375**
4. Find the sum of the first 16 terms of the series $\frac{3}{4} + \frac{5}{4} + \frac{7}{4} + \cdots$ **72**
5. Find the sum of the even numbers from 2 to 100, inclusive. **2550**
6. Find the sum of the odd numbers from 1 to 99, inclusive. **2500**
7. If an arithmetic series has $a_1 = 2$, $d = 5$, and $n = 20$, find S_n. **990**
8. If an arithmetic series has $a_1 = 7$, $d = -3$, and $n = 32$, find S_n. **−1264**

Find the sum of each series. *(See Example 3.)*

9. $\displaystyle\sum_{k=1}^{12}(6k - 3)$ **432**
10. $\displaystyle\sum_{k=1}^{16}(7k - 76)$ **−264**
11. $\displaystyle\sum_{k=1}^{18}5k$ **855**
12. $\displaystyle\sum_{k=1}^{20}3k$ **630**

(See Example 4.)

13. How many poles will be in a pile of telephone poles if there are 30 in the first layer, 29 in the second, and so on until there is one in the last layer? **465**
14. If 10¢ is saved on October 1, 20¢ on October 2, 30¢ on October 3, and so on, how much is saved during October? (October has 31 days). **$49.60**

Use Quiz 30 after lesson 17–4.

17-5 Geometric Sequences

After finishing Lesson 17-5, you should be able to
▮ find the common ratio of a geometric sequence.
▮▮ given a geometric sequence, determine a_1 and r; and find the nth term using the formula $a_n = a_1 r^{n-1}$.

▮ Geometric Sequences

The following sequence is not arithmetic.

    3, 6, 12, 24, 48, 96, . . .

If we multiply each term by 2 we get the next term.

DEFINITION
A sequence in which a constant r can be multiplied by each term to get the next is called a *geometric sequence*. The constant r is called the *common ratio*.

To find the common ratio, divide any term by the one before it.

Examples.   Each of the following are geometric sequences. Identify the common ratio.

Sequence	Common ratio
1. 3, 6, 12, 24, . . .	2
2. 3, −6, 12, −24, . . .	−2
3. 1, $\frac{1}{2}$, $\frac{1}{4}$, $\frac{1}{8}$, . . .	$\frac{1}{2}$

TRY THIS ▮▬▬▬▶

Identify the common ratio of each geometric sequence.

1. 1, 5, 25, 125, . . .   **5**
2. 3, −9, 27, −81, . . .   **−3**
3. 48, −12, 3, . . .   **$-\frac{1}{4}$**

▮▮ The nth Term

If we let a_1 be the first term and r be the common ratio, then $a_1 r$ is the second term, $a_1 r^2$ is the third term, and so on. Generalizing, we have the following.

THEOREM 17-4
In a geometric sequence, the nth term is given by $a_n = a_1 r^{n-1}$.

Note that the exponent is one less than the number of the term.

Example 4. Find the 6th term of the geometric sequence 4, 20, 100, . . .

Note that $a_1 = 4$, $n = 6$, and $r = \frac{20}{4}$, or 5. We use Theorem 17-4.

$$a_n = a_1 r^{n-1}$$
$$a_6 = 4 \cdot 5^{6-1}$$
$$= 4 \cdot 5^5$$
$$= 4 \cdot 3125, \text{ or } 12{,}500.$$

TRY THIS

4. Find the 8th term of the geometric sequence 2, 4, 8, 16, . . .   256

Example 5. Find the 11th term of the geometric sequence 64, −32, 16, −8, . . .

Note that $a_1 = 64$, $n = 11$, and $r = \frac{-32}{64}$, or $-\frac{1}{2}$. We use Theorem 17-4.

$$a_n = a_1 r^{n-1}$$
$$a_{11} = 64 \cdot \left(-\frac{1}{2}\right)^{11-1}$$
$$= 64 \cdot \left(-\frac{1}{2}\right)^{10}$$
$$= 2^6 \cdot \frac{1}{2^{10}}$$
$$= 2^{-4}, \text{ or } \frac{1}{16}.$$

TRY THIS

5. Find the 6th term of the geometric sequence 3, −15, 75, . . .   −9375

Example 6. A college student borrows $600 at 7% interest compounded annually. The student pays off the loan at the end of 3 years. How much does the student pay?

For any principal P, at 7% interest, the student will owe $P + 0.07P$ at the end of 1 year, or $1.07P$. Then $1.07P$ is the principal for the second year. So at the end of the second year the student owes $1.07(1.07P)$. Then the principal at the beginning of consecutive years is

$$P, 1.07P, 1.07(1.07P), \ldots$$

This is a geometric sequence with $a_1 = 600$, $n = 4$, $r = 1.07$. We use Theorem 17-4.

$$a_n = a_1 r^{n-1}$$
$$a_4 = 600 \cdot (1.07)^{4-1}$$
$$= 600 \cdot (1.07)^3$$
$$= 600 \cdot 1.225043$$
$$\approx 735.03$$

Thus the student pays $735.03.

TRY THIS

6. A college student borrows $400 at 6% interest compounded annually. The loan is paid in full at the end of 3 years. How much has the student paid? **$476.41**

Exercise Set 17-5

▌For each geometric sequence find the common ratio. (*See Examples 1–3.*)

1. 4, 8, 16, 32, . . . 2
2. 2, 1, $\frac{1}{2}$, $\frac{1}{4}$, $\frac{1}{8}$, . . . $\frac{1}{2}$
3. 12, -4, $\frac{4}{3}$, $-\frac{4}{9}$, . . . $-\frac{1}{3}$
4. 5, 15, 45, 135, . . . 3
5. 1, -1, 1, -1, 1, . . . -1
6. -5, -0.5, -0.05, -0.005, . . . 0.1
7. $\frac{1}{x}$, $\frac{1}{x^2}$, $\frac{1}{x^3}$, . . . $\frac{1}{x}$
8. 5, $\frac{5m}{2}$, $\frac{5m^2}{4}$, $\frac{5m^3}{8}$, . . . $\frac{m}{2}$

▌▌(*See Examples 4 and 5.*)

9. Find the 6th term of the geometric sequence 1, 3, 9, . . . 243
10. Find the 10th term of the geometric sequence $\frac{8}{243}$, $\frac{4}{81}$, $\frac{2}{27}$, . . . $\frac{81}{64}$
11. Find the 5th term of the geometric sequence 2, -10, 50, . . . 1250
12. Find the 9th term of the geometric sequence 2, 2$\sqrt{3}$, 6, . . . 162

(*See Example 6.*)

13. A college student borrows $800 at 8% interest compounded annually. The loan is paid in full at the end of 2 years. How much has the student paid? **$933.12**
14. A college student borrows $1000 at 8% interest compounded annually. The loan is paid in full at the end of 4 years. How much has the student paid? **$1360.49**

Calculator Exercises

Find the first four terms of the geometric sequence where:

15. $a_1 = 678.4$ and $r = 0.87$
16. $a_1 = 1.34$ and $r = 1.67$

15. 678.4, 590.208, 513.48096, 446.72843   16. 1.34, 2.2378, 3.737126, 6.2410004

Challenge Exercises

17. A ping-pong ball is dropped from a height of 16 cm and always rebounds $\frac{1}{4}$ of the distance of the previous fall. What distance does it rebound the 6th time? $\frac{1}{256}$ cm
18. The population of a town is P and is growing at the rate of 24% each year. What will its population be in k years? $P(1.24)^k$

17-6 Geometric Series

After finishing Lesson 17-6, you should be able to
∎ find the sum of the first n terms of a geometric series by identifying a_1 and r and using the formula $S_n = \dfrac{a_1 - a_1 r^n}{1 - r}$.

∎ A geometric series is a series associated with a geometric sequence. The next theorem gives a formula for the first n terms of a geometric series.

THEOREM 17-5
The sum of the first n terms of a geometric series is given by

$$S_n = \frac{a_1 - a_1 r^n}{1 - r}$$

Example 1.   Find the sum of the first 6 terms of the geometric series $3 + 6 + 12 + 24 + \cdots$

$a_1 = 3$, $n = 6$, and $r = \frac{6}{3}$, or 2.

$$S_n = \frac{a_1 - a_1 r^n}{1 - r} \qquad \text{\textit{Using Theorem 17-5}}$$

$$S_6 = \frac{3 - 3 \cdot 2^6}{1 - 2}$$

$$= \frac{3 - 192}{-1}, \text{ or } 189.$$

TRY THIS ▆▆▆▆▆➤

1.   Find the sum of the first 6 terms of the geometric series $3 + 15 + 75 + 375 + \cdots$ **11,718**
2.   Find the sum of the first 10 terms of the geometric series $2 - 1 + \frac{1}{2} - \frac{1}{4} + \cdots$ $\frac{341}{256}$

A Proof of Theorem 17-5

Let us describe the sum of a geometric series as follows.

$$S_n = a_1 + a_1 r + a_1 r^2 + \cdots + a_1 r^{n-2} + a_1 r^{n-1}.$$

We multiply on both sides by $-r$. This gives us

$$-rS_n = -a_1 r - a_1 r^2 - \cdots - a_1 r^{n-1} - a_1 r^n.$$

Next, we add the two equations and solve for S_n.

$$S_n - rS_n = a_1 - a_1 r + a_1 r + a_1 r^2 - a_1 r^2 + \cdots - a_1 r^n$$
$$= a_1 - a_1 r^n$$
$$S_n = \frac{a_1 - a_1 r^n}{1 - r}$$

Example 2. Find the sum of the series $\sum_{k=1}^{5} \left(\frac{1}{2}\right)^{k+1}$.

First find a few terms.

$$\left(\tfrac{1}{2}\right)^2 + \left(\tfrac{1}{2}\right)^3 + \left(\tfrac{1}{2}\right)^4 + \cdots$$

We see that this is a geometric series with $a_1 = \frac{1}{4}$, $n = 5$, and $r = \frac{1}{2}$.

$$S_n = \frac{a_1 - a_1 r^n}{1 - r} \qquad \text{Using Theorem 17-5}$$

$$S_5 = \frac{\tfrac{1}{4} - \tfrac{1}{4} \cdot \left(\tfrac{1}{2}\right)^5}{1 - \tfrac{1}{2}}$$

$$= \tfrac{31}{64}.$$

TRY THIS ➡

> 3. Find the sum of the geo-
> metric series
>
> $$\sum_{k=1}^{5} 3^k. \qquad 363$$

Exercise Set 17-6

▌ (*See Example 1.*)

1. Find the sum of the first 7 terms of the geometric series
   $6 + 12 + 24 + \cdots$ 762

2. Find the sum of the first 6 terms of the geometric series
   $16 - 8 + 4 - \cdots$ $10\frac{1}{2}$

3. Find the sum of the first 8 terms of the geometric series
   $5 + 10 + 20 + \cdots$ 1275

4. Find the sum of the first 6 terms of the geometric series
   $24 + 12 + 6 + \cdots$ $47\frac{1}{4}$

5. Find the sum of the first 7 terms of the geometric series $\frac{1}{18} - \frac{1}{6} + \frac{1}{2} - \cdots$ $\frac{547}{18}$

6. Find the sum of the first 5 terms of the geometric series
   $6 + 0.6 + 0.06 + \cdots$ $\frac{33{,}333}{5000}$

7. Find the sum of the first 8 terms of the series $1 + x + x^2 + x^3 + \cdots$ $\frac{1 - x^8}{1 - x}$

8. Find the sum of the first 10 terms of the series $1 + x^2 + x^4 + x^6 + \cdots$ $\frac{1 - x^{20}}{1 - x^2}$

Find the sum of each geometric series. (*See Example 2.*)

9. $\sum_{k=1}^{6} \left(\frac{1}{2}\right)^{k-1}$ $\frac{63}{32}$

10. $\sum_{k=1}^{8} 2^k$ 510

11. $\sum_{k=1}^{7} 4^k$ 21,844

12. $\sum_{k=1}^{5} \left(\frac{1}{3}\right)^{k-1}$ $\frac{121}{81}$

Challenge Exercises

13. Find the sum of $-8 + 4 - 2 + \cdots - \frac{1}{32}$. $-\frac{171}{32}$
14. Find the sum of the first n terms of $1 + x + x^2 + x^3 + \cdots$ $\frac{1 - x^n}{1 - x}$

17-7 Infinite Geometric Series

After finishing Lesson 17-7, you should be able to
■ determine whether an infinite geometric series has a sum.
■■ find the sum of an infinite geometric series when $|r| < 1$.
■■■ convert from repeating decimal notation for a number to fractional notation.

■ Sums of Infinite Geometric Series

By an *infinite* series we mean one that is unending. Let us consider two different infinite geometric series.

$$2 + 4 + 8 + 16 + 32 + 64 + \cdots + 2^n + \cdots$$

As we take n larger and larger, the sum of the first n terms gets large without bound. The next example, however, is different.

$$\frac{1}{2} + \frac{1}{4} + \frac{1}{8} + \frac{1}{16} + \cdots + \frac{1}{2^n} + \cdots$$

Let us look at the sum of the first n terms for some values of n.

$$S_1 = \frac{1}{2}$$

$$S_2 = \frac{1}{2} + \frac{1}{4} = \frac{3}{4}$$

$$S_3 = \frac{1}{2} + \frac{1}{4} + \frac{1}{8} = \frac{7}{8}$$

$$S_4 = \frac{1}{2} + \frac{1}{4} + \frac{1}{8} + \frac{1}{16} = \frac{15}{16}$$

We see a pattern, which we can describe as follows.

$$S_n = \frac{2^n - 1}{2^n}.$$

We can see that as n gets very very large, S_n gets very very close to 1. We say that S_n approaches a *limit* of 1. We *define* the sum of the infinite series to be 1.

DEFINITION
If, in an infinite series, S_n approaches some limit as n becomes very large, that limit is defined to be the *sum* of the series.

TRY THIS ➡

1. Consider the infinite geometric series
$$1 - \tfrac{1}{2} + \tfrac{1}{4} - \tfrac{1}{8} + \cdots$$
$$+ (-1)^{n-1}(\tfrac{1}{2})^{n-1} + \cdots$$
a) Find $S_1, S_2, S_3, S_4,$ and S_5. $1, \frac{1}{2}, \frac{3}{4}, \frac{5}{8}, \frac{11}{16}$
b) What appears to be the sum of the series? $\frac{2}{3}$

Some infinite series have sums and some do not.

THEOREM 17-6
An infinite geometric series has a sum if and only if $|r| < 1$. (The absolute value of the common ratio is less than 1.)

Examples. Determine which series have sums.

1. $1 - \frac{1}{2} + \frac{1}{4} - \frac{1}{8} + \frac{1}{16} + \cdots$
$r = -\frac{1}{2}, |r| < 1$
Series has a sum, by Theorem 17-6.

2. $1 + 5 + 25 + 125 + \cdots$
$r = 5, |r| > 1$
Series does not have a sum.

3. $1 + (-1) + 1 + (-1) + \cdots$
$r = -1, |r| = 1$
Series does not have a sum.

TRY THIS ➡

Decide which geometric series have sums.

2. $4 + 16 + 64 + \cdots$ No
3. $5 - 30 + 180 - \cdots$ No
4. $1 + \frac{1}{3} + \frac{1}{9} + \frac{1}{27} + \cdots$ Yes

‖ Finding Sums

THEOREM 17-7
The sum of an infinite geometric series, with $|r| < 1$, is given by

$$S = \frac{a_1}{1 - r}.$$

Example 4. Find the sum of the infinite geometric series
$5 + \frac{5}{2} + \frac{5}{4} + \frac{5}{8} + \cdots$

Note that $a_1 = 5$ and $r = \frac{1}{2}$. We use Theorem 17-7.

$$S = \frac{a_1}{1 - r}$$

Substituting, we get

$$S = \frac{5}{1 - \frac{1}{2}}$$

$$S = 10$$

TRY THIS ➡

Find the sum of each geometric series.

5. $1 + \frac{1}{3} + \frac{1}{9} + \frac{1}{27} + \cdots$ $\frac{3}{2}$

6. $4 - 1 + \frac{1}{4} - \frac{1}{16} + \cdots$ $\frac{16}{5}$

A Proof of Theorem 17-7

We look at the sum of the first n terms of an infinite geometric series.

$$S_n = \frac{a_1 - a_1 r^n}{1 - r}$$

As n gets very large, we look at r^n, and see that, since $|r| < 1$, r^n gets very small, approaching 0. Thus the numerator approaches a_1. The limit of S_n as n gets very large is therefore $\frac{a_1}{1 - r}$, and we have $S = \frac{a_1}{1 - r}$.

▮ Repeating Decimals

The *repeating decimal* 0.66666666..., represents an infinite geometric series,

$$0.6 + 0.06 + 0.006 + 0.0006 + \cdots$$

Thus $a_1 = 0.6$ and $r = 0.1$. So $|r| < 1$ and we can use Theorem 17-7.

$$S = \frac{a_1}{1 - r}$$
$$S = \frac{0.6}{1 - 0.1}$$
$$= \frac{0.6}{0.9}$$
$$= \frac{2}{3}.$$

Thus $0.666\ldots = \frac{2}{3}$.

We can use a bar to indicate the repeating cycle, as follows: $0.66\overline{6}$.

Example 5. Find fractional notation for $0.27\overline{27}$.

Note that $a_1 = 0.27$ and $r = 0.01$ so

$$S = \frac{a_1}{1 - r} \qquad \textit{Using Theorem 17-7}$$
$$= \frac{0.27}{1 - 0.01}$$
$$= \frac{0.27}{0.99}$$
$$= \frac{3}{11}$$

Thus $0.2\overline{27} = \frac{3}{11}$.

This can be checked by doing the division $3 \div 11$.

TRY THIS ➡

Exercise Set 17-7

> Find fractional notation for each number.
>
> 7. $0.45\overline{45}$ $\frac{5}{11}$
> 8. $5.3\overline{636}$ $\frac{59}{11}$

▌ In each geometric series find r and determine which series have sums. (*See Examples 1–3.*)

1. $5 + 10 + 20 + 40 + \cdots$ 2, No
2. $16 + 8 + 4 + 2 + \cdots$ $\frac{1}{2}$, Yes
3. $6 + 2 + \frac{2}{3} + \frac{3}{9} + \cdots$ $\frac{1}{3}$, Yes
4. $2 - 4 + 8 - 16 + 32 - \cdots$ -2, No
5. $1 + 0.1 + 0.01 + 0.001 + \cdots$ 0.1, Yes
6. $-\frac{5}{3} - \frac{10}{9} - \frac{20}{27} - \frac{40}{81} - \cdots$ $\frac{2}{3}$, Yes
7. $1 - \frac{1}{5} + \frac{1}{25} - \frac{1}{125} + \cdots$ $-\frac{1}{5}$, Yes
8. $6 + \frac{42}{5} + \frac{294}{25} + \cdots$ $\frac{7}{5}$, No

▌▌ Find the sum of each geometric series. (*See Example 4.*)

9. $4 + 2 + 1 + \cdots$ 8
10. $7 + 3 + \frac{9}{7} + \cdots$ $\frac{49}{4}$
11. $25 - 20 + 16 - \cdots$ $\frac{125}{9}$
12. $12 - 9 + \frac{27}{4} - \cdots$ $\frac{48}{7}$
13. $1 + \frac{1}{2} + \frac{1}{4} + \cdots$ 2
14. $\frac{8}{3} + \frac{4}{3} + \frac{2}{3} + \cdots$ $\frac{16}{3}$
15. $16 + 1.6 + 0.16 + \cdots$ $\frac{160}{9}$
16. $4 + 2.4 + 1.44 + \cdots$ 10

▌▌▌ Find fractional notation for each number. (*See Example 5.*)

17. $0.7\overline{77}$ $\frac{7}{9}$
18. $0.3\overline{33}$ $\frac{1}{3}$
19. $0.21\overline{21}$ $\frac{7}{33}$
20. $0.63\overline{63}$ $\frac{7}{11}$
21. $5.15\overline{15}$ $\frac{170}{33}$
22. $4.125\overline{125}$ $\frac{4121}{999}$

Challenge Exercises   Use Quiz 31 after lesson 17–7.

23. The infinite series
$$2 + \frac{1}{2} + \frac{1}{2 \cdot 3} + \frac{1}{2 \cdot 3 \cdot 4} + \frac{1}{2 \cdot 3 \cdot 4 \cdot 5} + \frac{1}{2 \cdot 3 \cdot 4 \cdot 5 \cdot 6} + \cdots \text{ is not}$$
geometric, but does have a sum. Find values of S_1, S_2, S_3, S_4, S_5, and S_6. Make a conjecture about the value of S. $2\frac{3}{4}$

24. How far up and down will a ball travel before stopping if it is dropped from a height of 12 m, and each rebound is $\frac{1}{3}$ of the previous distance? (*Hint:* Use an infinite geometric series.)   24 m

25. The sides of a square are each 16 cm long. A second square is inscribed by joining the midpoints of the sides, successively. In the second square we repeat the process, inscribing a third square. If this process is continued indefinitely, what is the sum of all of the squares? (*Hint:* Use an infinite geometric series.)   512 cm²

COMPUTER ACTIVITY

Generating Terms in the Fibonacci Sequence

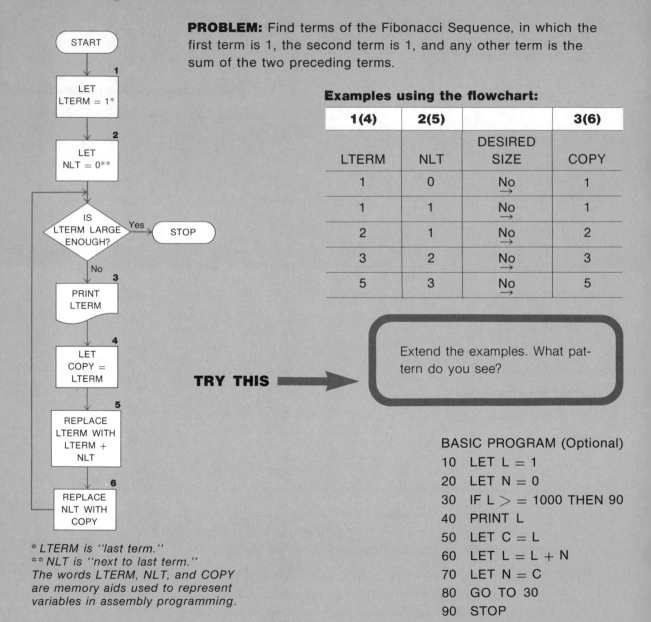

PROBLEM: Find terms of the Fibonacci Sequence, in which the first term is 1, the second term is 1, and any other term is the sum of the two preceding terms.

Examples using the flowchart:

1(4)	2(5)		3(6)
LTERM	NLT	DESIRED SIZE	COPY
1	0	No →	1
1	1	No →	1
2	1	No →	2
3	2	No →	3
5	3	No →	5

TRY THIS ➡️ Extend the examples. What pattern do you see?

* *LTERM is "last term."*
** *NLT is "next to last term."*
The words LTERM, NLT, and COPY are memory aids used to represent variables in assembly programming.

BASIC PROGRAM (Optional)
```
10  LET L = 1
20  LET N = 0
30  IF L > = 1000 THEN 90
40  PRINT L
50  LET C = L
60  LET L = L + N
70  LET N = C
80  GO TO 30
90  STOP
```

CHAPTER 17 REVIEW

Review the material in the chapter. Then see how you have done
by trying these review exercises. If you miss an exercise, restudy
the indicated lesson.

17-1   1.   Find the first four terms of the sequence given by $a_n = \dfrac{n-1}{n+1}$. $0, \frac{1}{3}, \frac{2}{4}, \frac{3}{5}$

17-2   2.   Write sigma notation for this series: $4^2 + 4^3 + 4^4 + 4^5 + 4^6$.   Answers may vary. $\sum\limits_{k=1}^{5} 4^{k+1}$

17-3   3.   In an arithmetic sequence, find d when $a_1 = 5$ and $a_{17} = 53$. $d = 3$

17-4   4.   Find the sum of the first 30 positive integers.   465

17-5   5.   In a geometric sequence, $a_1 = 0.27$ and $r = 0.1$. Find the fifth term.   0.000027

17-5   6.   The present population of a city is 30,000. Its population is
supposed to double every 10 years. If it does, what will its population be at the end of 80 years?   7,680,000

17-6   7.   Find the sum of the first 9 terms of the geometric series
$5 - 10 + 20 - 40 + \cdots$ 855

17-7   8.   Find the sum of the infinite geometric series $8 - 2 + 0.5 - \cdots$ $\frac{32}{5}$

17-7   9.   Find fractional notation for $0.\overline{59}$. $\frac{59}{99}$

CHAPTER 17 TEST

1.   Find the first four terms of the sequence given by $a_n = (-1)^n 3^n$. $-3, 9, -27, 81$

2.   Write sigma notation for this series: $\dfrac{5}{3} + \dfrac{5}{3^2} + \dfrac{5}{3^3} + \dfrac{5}{3^4} + \dfrac{5}{3^5} + \dfrac{5}{3^6}$.   Answers may vary. $\sum\limits_{k=1}^{6} \dfrac{5}{3^k}$

3.   Find the 6th term in the arithmetic sequence $a - b, a, a + b, \ldots$ $a + 4b$

4.   Deposits are made as follows: \$10 for the first week, \$13 the
second week, \$16 the third week, and so on, for 52 deposits.
What is the sum of the deposits?   \$4498

5.   For this geometric sequence find the common ratio: $24, 16, 10\frac{2}{3}, \ldots$ $\frac{2}{3}$

6.   Find the 6th term of the geometric sequence $-2, -4, -8, \ldots$ -64

7.   Find the sum of the first 9 terms of the geometric series
$1 + x^3 + x^6 + x^9 + x^{12} + \cdots$ $\dfrac{1 - x^{27}}{1 - x^3}$ or $1 + x^3 + x^6$

8.   Find the sum of the infinite geometric series $64 - 8 + 1 - 0.125 + \cdots$ $\frac{512}{9}$

9.   Find fractional notation for $0.2\overline{4}$. $\frac{8}{33}$

Ready for Matrices and Determinants?

4-1   1.   Determine whether $(-2, 4)$ is a solution of the system:
$$x + y = -3 \quad \text{No}$$
$$2x - y = -8$$

4-2   Solve.

2. $x + y = 6 \quad$ **(5, 1)**
$x - y = 4$

3. $5x + 3y = 7 \quad$ **(−1, 4)**
$3x - 5y = -23$

4-4   4.   Determine whether $(-1, 2, 1)$ is a solution of the system:
$$x + y + z = 2 \quad \text{No}$$
$$x - y - z = 4$$
$$x - y + z = -5$$

4-4   5.   Solve: $2x - y + 4z = -3 \quad$ **(3, 7, $-\frac{1}{2}$)**
$$x \qquad - 4z = \quad 5$$
$$6x - y + 2z = 10$$

1-5   6.   Evaluate and simplify: $-2(5) - (-3)(-4)$.   **−22**

1-5   7.   Evaluate $x(y + z)$ when $x = -2$, $y = 3$, and $z = 8$.   **−22**

1-5   8.   Evaluate $xy + xz$ when $x = -2$, $y = 3$, and $z = 8$.   **−22**

1-2   9.   Name the additive inverse of -12.   **12**

1-3   10.   Subtract: $-2 - 8$.   **−10**

Chapter 18
Matrices and Determinants

This mathematician is using matrices in her work with computers.

18-1 Systems of Equations in Two Variables

After finishing Lesson 18-1, you should be able to
∎ solve systems of two linear equations in two variables using matrices.

∎ In solving systems of equations, we work with the constants. The variables play no essential role in the process. We can simplify the writing by omitting the variables. For example, the system

$$5x + 3y = 7$$
$$3x - 5y = -23$$

simplifies to

$$\begin{array}{ccc} 5 & 3 & 7 \\ 3 & -5 & -23 \end{array}$$

We have written a rectangular array of numbers called a *matrix* (plural *matrices*). We ordinarily write brackets around matrices. The following are matrices.

$$\begin{bmatrix} 4 & 1 & 3 & 5 \\ 1 & 0 & 1 & 2 \\ 6 & 3 & -2 & 0 \end{bmatrix}, \begin{bmatrix} 6 & 2 & 1 & 4 & 7 \\ 1 & 2 & 1 & 3 & 1 \\ 4 & 0 & -2 & 0 & -3 \end{bmatrix}, \begin{bmatrix} 1 & 2 \\ 145 & 0 \\ -7 & 9 \\ 8 & 1 \\ 0 & 0 \end{bmatrix}$$

The *rows* of a matrix are horizontal, and the *columns* are vertical.

$$\begin{bmatrix} 5 & -2 & 2 \\ 1 & 0 & 1 \\ 0 & 1 & 2 \end{bmatrix} \begin{array}{l} \leftarrow row\ 1 \\ \leftarrow row\ 2 \\ \leftarrow row\ 3 \end{array}$$

column 1 column 2 column 3

Let us now use matrices to solve systems of linear equations.

Example. Solve: $5x + 3y = 7$
$\qquad\qquad 3x - 5y = -23$

We first write a matrix, using only the constants.

$$\begin{bmatrix} 5 & 3 & 7 \\ 3 & -5 & -23 \end{bmatrix}$$

We do about the same calculations as if we wrote the entire equations, but we are going to use a procedure that is a bit new.

The first thing we do is make the first number in the row 1. We multiply the first row by $\frac{1}{5}$.

$$\begin{bmatrix} 1 & \frac{3}{5} & \frac{7}{5} \\ 3 & -5 & -23 \end{bmatrix}$$ *This corresponds to multiplying the first equation by $\frac{1}{5}$.*

Now we multiply the first row by -3 (this gives $-3 \quad -\frac{9}{5} \quad -\frac{21}{5}$) and add it to the second row.

$$\begin{bmatrix} 1 & \frac{3}{5} & \frac{7}{5} \\ 0 & -\frac{34}{5} & -\frac{136}{5} \end{bmatrix}$$ *This corresponds to multiplying the first equation by -3 and adding to the second. (We retain the row in which the first number is 1.)*

Our goal was to get a 1 in the first row, first column, and a 0 in the second row, first column. Next we want to get a 1 in the second row, second column. To do this we multiply by $-\frac{5}{34}$.

$$\begin{bmatrix} 1 & \frac{3}{5} & \frac{7}{5} \\ 0 & 1 & 4 \end{bmatrix}$$ *This corresponds to multiplying the second equation by $-\frac{5}{34}$.*

We now work back up. We want to get a 0 in the first row, second column. We multiply the second row by $-\frac{3}{5}$, (this gives $0 \quad -\frac{3}{5} \quad -\frac{12}{5}$) and add to the first row.

$$\begin{bmatrix} 1 & 0 & -1 \\ 0 & 1 & 4 \end{bmatrix}$$

If we now put the variables back we have

$$x \quad = -1$$
$$y = \quad 4$$

The solution is $(-1, 4)$.

Notice that we reduced the matrix to the form

$$\begin{bmatrix} 1 & 0 & p \\ 0 & 1 & q \end{bmatrix}$$

If the equations are not arranged in the form of the Example, we must first arrange them that way.

TRY THIS ➡

Answers. 1. $(-\frac{63}{29}, -\frac{114}{29})$ 2. $(-2, -5)$

Solve, using matrices.

1. $5x - 2y = -3$
   $2x + 5y = -24$
2. $3y + 11 = 2x$
   $5y + 17 - 4x = 0$

There are some shortcuts when using the matrices. One is to interchange two rows before beginning. For example, in the matrix

$$\begin{bmatrix} 3 & -5 & 17 \\ 1 & 2 & 4 \end{bmatrix}$$

we can interchange the two rows to get a 1 in the first row, first column:

$$\begin{bmatrix} 1 & 2 & 4 \\ 3 & -5 & 17 \end{bmatrix}$$

This corresponds to interchanging equations. Another shortcut consists of multiplying one or more rows by a power of 10 before beginning in order to eliminate decimal points.

In the procedure we are developing, it is important not to use any shortcuts other than these two.

TRY THIS

Answers. 3. (1, 2) 4. (2, −1)

Solve, using matrices.

3. $5x - 2y = 1$
    $x + 3y = 7$
4. $0.2x + 0.3y = 0.1$
    $0.3x - 0.1y = 0.7$

Exercise Set 18-1

▌Solve, using matrices. (*See the Example.*)

1. $4x + 2y = 11$ $(\frac{3}{2}, \frac{5}{2})$
    $3x - y = 2$

2. $3x - 3y = 11$ $(-\frac{1}{3}, -4)$
    $9x - 2y = 5$

3. $5x + 2 = 3y$ $(\frac{1}{2}, \frac{3}{2})$
    $4x + 2y - 5 = 0$

4. $3x + 3y - 7 = 0$ $(-\frac{16}{21}, \frac{65}{21})$
    $2y = 10 + 5x$

5. $3x + y = 7$ $(3, -2)$
    $x + y = 1$

6. $2x + y = 7$ $(\frac{39}{11}, -\frac{1}{11})$
    $x - 5y = 4$

7. $0.3x + 0.2y = -0.9$ $(-3, 0)$
    $0.2x - 0.3y = -0.6$

8. $0.2x - 0.3y = 0.3$ $(\frac{1}{2}, -\frac{2}{3})$
    $0.4x + 0.6y = -0.2$

Challenge Exercises

9. A grocer mixes candy worth $0.80 per kg with nuts worth $0.70 per kg to get a 20-kg mixture worth $0.77 per kg. How many kg of candy and how many kg of nuts were used?   14 kg of candy; 6 kg of nuts

10. One year some money was invested at $5\frac{1}{2}\%$ and another amount invested at $5\frac{3}{4}\%$. The income from the investments was $1355. The income from the $5\frac{1}{2}\%$ investment was $255 less than from the $5\frac{3}{4}\%$ investment. How much as invested at each rate? (Recall the formula $I = Prt$, for simple interest.) $10,000 at $5\frac{1}{2}\%$; $14,000 at $5\frac{3}{4}\%$

18-2 Systems of Equations in Three Variables

After finishing Lesson 18-2, you should be able to
▮ solve systems of three linear equations in three variables using matrices.

▮ **Example.**   Solve: $2x - y + 4z = -3$
$$x \qquad - 4z = 5$$
$$6x - y + 2z = 10$$

We first write a matrix. We write a 0 for the missing term in the second equation.

$$\begin{bmatrix} 2 & -1 & 4 & -3 \\ 1 & 0 & -4 & 5 \\ 6 & -1 & 2 & 10 \end{bmatrix}$$

To make the first number in the first row 1, we interchange the first and second rows.

$$\begin{bmatrix} 1 & 0 & -4 & 5 \\ 2 & -1 & 4 & 3 \\ 6 & -1 & 2 & 10 \end{bmatrix}$$ *This corresponds to interchanging the first and second equations.*

Next, we multiply the first row by -2 and add it to the second row.

$$\begin{bmatrix} 1 & 0 & -4 & 5 \\ 0 & -1 & 12 & -13 \\ 6 & -1 & 2 & 10 \end{bmatrix}$$ *This corresponds to multiplying the first equation by -2 and adding it to the second equation.*

Now we multiply the first row by -6 and add it to the third row.

$$\begin{bmatrix} 1 & 0 & -4 & 5 \\ 0 & -1 & 12 & -13 \\ 0 & -1 & 26 & -20 \end{bmatrix}$$ *This corresponds to multiplying the first equation by -6 and adding it to the third equation.*

Next we multiply row 2 by -1.

$$\begin{bmatrix} 1 & 0 & -4 & 5 \\ 0 & 1 & -12 & 13 \\ 0 & -1 & 26 & -20 \end{bmatrix}$$ *This corresponds to multiplying the second equation by -1 to make the y-coefficient 1.*

Now we add row 2 to row 3.

$$\begin{bmatrix} 1 & 0 & -4 & 5 \\ 0 & 1 & -12 & 13 \\ 0 & 0 & 14 & -7 \end{bmatrix}$$

Then we multiply row 3 by $\frac{1}{14}$.

$$\begin{bmatrix} 1 & 0 & -4 & 5 \\ 0 & 1 & -12 & 13 \\ 0 & 0 & 1 & -\frac{1}{2} \end{bmatrix}$$ *This corresponds to making the z-coefficient 1.*

Now we work back up. We multiply the third row by 12 and add it to the second row.

$$\begin{bmatrix} 1 & 0 & -4 & 5 \\ 0 & 1 & 0 & 7 \\ 0 & 0 & 1 & -\frac{1}{2} \end{bmatrix}$$

We multiply the third row by 4 and add it to the first row.

$$\begin{bmatrix} 1 & 0 & 0 & 3 \\ 0 & 1 & 0 & 7 \\ 0 & 0 & 1 & -\frac{1}{2} \end{bmatrix}$$

If we now put the variables back we have

$$x \quad\quad = 3$$
$$\quad y \quad = 7$$
$$\quad\quad z = -\tfrac{1}{2}.$$

The solution is $(3, 7, -\frac{1}{2})$.

Notice that in this case, we found a matrix of the form

$$\begin{bmatrix} 1 & 0 & 0 & p \\ 0 & 1 & 0 & q \\ 0 & 0 & 1 & r \end{bmatrix}$$

TRY THIS ➡

1. Solve, using matrices.

$$x - 2y + 3z = 4$$
$$2x - y + z = -1$$
$$4x + y + 2z = 4$$
$$(-1, 2, 3)$$

Exercise Set 18-2

▌Solve, using matrices. (*See the Example.*)

1. $x + 2y - 3z = 9$
   $2x - y + 2z = -8$ $\quad(-1, 2, -2)$
   $3x - y - 4z = 3$

2. $x - y + 2z = 0$
   $x - 2y + 3z = -1$ $\quad(0, 2, 1)$
   $2x - 2y + z = -3$

3. $4x - y - 3z = 1$
   $8x + y - z = 5$ $\quad(\frac{3}{2}, -4, 3)$
   $2x + y + 2z = 5$

4. $3x + 2y + 2z = 3$
   $x + 2y - z = 5$ $\quad(2, \frac{1}{2}, -2)$
   $2x - 4y + z = 0$

5. $p + q + r = 1$
   $p + 2q + 3r = 4$ $\quad(1, -3, 3)$
   $p + 3q + 7r = 13$

6. $m + n + t = 9$
   $m - n - t = -15$ $\quad(-3, 5, 7)$
   $m + n - t = -5$

18-3 Determinants and Two Equations

After finishing Lesson 18-3, you should be able to
▮ evaluate determinants of second order.
▮▮ solve systems of two equations in two variables, using Cramer's Rule.

▮ Determinants of Second Order

A matrix with the same number of rows as columns is called a *square* matrix. With every square matrix is associated a number called its *determinant*.

DEFINITION

The determinant of a matrix $\begin{bmatrix} a & c \\ b & d \end{bmatrix}$ is denoted $\begin{vmatrix} a & c \\ b & d \end{vmatrix}$ and is defined as follows: $\begin{vmatrix} a & c \\ b & d \end{vmatrix} = ad - bc$.

The determinant of a 2×2 matrix is said to be of *second order;* the determinant of a 3×3 matrix is said to be of *third order;* and so on.

Examples. Evaluate.

1. $\begin{vmatrix} 2 & 5 \\ 6 & 7 \end{vmatrix} = 2 \cdot 7 - 6 \cdot 5 = -16$ *The arrows indicate the way we multiply.*

2. $\begin{vmatrix} -2 & -4 \\ -3 & 5 \end{vmatrix} = -2 \cdot 5 - (-3)(-4) = -10 - 12 = -22$

TRY THIS

Answers.   1. -5 2. -5 3. $\frac{79}{2}$ 4. -9

> Evaluate.
>
> 1. $\begin{vmatrix} 2 & 3 \\ 7 & 8 \end{vmatrix}$
>
> 2. $\begin{vmatrix} -2 & \frac{1}{2} \\ 6 & 1 \end{vmatrix}$
>
> 3. $\begin{vmatrix} 4 & -2 \\ -\frac{1}{4} & 10 \end{vmatrix}$
>
> 4. $\begin{vmatrix} -3 & -6 \\ -4 & -5 \end{vmatrix}$

▮▮ Solving by Determinants

Determinants can be used to solve equations.

THEOREM 18-1 (Cramer's Rule)

If the system $a_1 x + b_1 y = c_1$
$\qquad\qquad a_2 x + b_2 y = c_2$

has exactly one solution, it is given by

$$x = \frac{\begin{vmatrix} c_1 & b_1 \\ c_2 & b_2 \end{vmatrix}}{\begin{vmatrix} a_1 & b_1 \\ a_2 & b_2 \end{vmatrix}} \quad \text{and} \quad y = \frac{\begin{vmatrix} a_1 & c_1 \\ a_2 & c_2 \end{vmatrix}}{\begin{vmatrix} a_1 & b_1 \\ a_2 & b_2 \end{vmatrix}}$$

Compare the values of x and y in Cramer's Rule. The same determinant

$$\begin{vmatrix} a_1 & b_1 \\ a_2 & b_2 \end{vmatrix}, \text{ which we call } D,$$

occurs as the denominator of both x and y. The determinant

$$\begin{vmatrix} a_1 & c_1 \\ a_2 & c_2 \end{vmatrix}, \text{ which we call } D_y,$$

is the numerator of y and is obtained from the determinant D by replacing the y-coefficients by c_1 and c_2. The determinant

$$\begin{vmatrix} c_1 & b_1 \\ c_2 & b_2 \end{vmatrix}, \text{ which we call } D_x,$$

is the numerator of x and is obtained from D by replacing the x-coefficients by c_1 and c_2.

Example 3. Solve, using Cramer's Rule: $3x - 2y = 7$
$$3x + 2y = 9$$

$$D = \begin{vmatrix} 3 & -2 \\ 2 & 2 \end{vmatrix} = 3 \cdot 2 - 3(-2) = 6 + 6 = 12$$

$$D_x = \begin{vmatrix} 7 & -2 \\ 9 & 2 \end{vmatrix} = 7 \cdot 2 - 9(-2) = 14 + 18 = 32$$

$$D_y = \begin{vmatrix} 3 & 7 \\ 3 & 9 \end{vmatrix} = 3 \cdot 9 - 3 \cdot 7 = 27 - 21 = 6$$

Then

$$x = \frac{D_x}{D} = \frac{32}{12}, \text{ or } \frac{8}{3} \qquad y = \frac{D_y}{D} = \frac{6}{12}, \text{ or } \frac{1}{2}$$

The solution is $\left(\frac{8}{3}, \frac{1}{2}\right)$.

TRY THIS ➡

Solve, using Cramer's Rule.

5. $20x - 15y = 75$
$x + 3y = 0$ **(3, −1)**

The quotients in Cramer's Rule make sense only if the denominator determinant D is not 0. If $D = 0$, then one of two things happens.
1. If $D = 0$, and D_x and D_y are also 0, then the system is dependent (has many solutions).
2. If $D = 0$, and at least one of D_x or D_y is not 0, then the system is inconsistent (has no solution).

TRY THIS ➡️

Solve, using Cramer's Rule.

6. $2x - y = 6$
   $3x + 4y = 4$ $(\frac{28}{11}, -\frac{10}{11})$

Exercise Set 18-3

■ Evaluate. (*See Examples 1 and 2.*)

1. $\begin{vmatrix} 2 & 7 \\ 1 & 5 \end{vmatrix}$ 3

2. $\begin{vmatrix} 3 & 2 \\ 2 & -3 \end{vmatrix}$ −13

3. $\begin{vmatrix} 6 & -9 \\ 2 & 3 \end{vmatrix}$ 36

4. $\begin{vmatrix} 3 & 2 \\ -7 & 5 \end{vmatrix}$ 29

5. $\begin{vmatrix} 1.3 & 2.7 \\ 4.2 & 0.8 \end{vmatrix}$ −10.3

6. $\begin{vmatrix} 2.4 & 1.6 \\ 0.9 & 1.8 \end{vmatrix}$ 2.88

7. $\begin{vmatrix} -7 & -7 \\ 3 & 3 \end{vmatrix}$ 0

8. $\begin{vmatrix} 8 & -1 \\ 8 & -1 \end{vmatrix}$ 0

■ Solve, using Cramer's Rule. (*See Example 3.*)

9. $-2x + 4y = 3$ $(-\frac{25}{2}, -\frac{11}{2})$
   $3x - 7y = 1$

10. $5x - 4y = -3$ $(\frac{9}{19}, \frac{51}{38})$
    $7x + 2y = 6$

11. $3x - 4y = 6$ (2, 0)
    $5x + 9y = 10$

12. $5x + 8y = 1$ (−3, 2)
    $3x + 7y = 5$

13. $2x - 2y = 2$ (−4, −5)
    $6x - 5y = 1$

14. $5x - 6y = 8$ (4, 2)
    $2x - 5y = -2$

Use Quiz 32 after lesson 18—3.

Calculator Exercises

Solve, using Cramer's Rule.

15. $2.35x - 3.18y = 4.82$
    $1.92x + 6.77y = -3.87$

16. $0.0375x + 0.912y = -1.003$
    $463x - 801y = 946$

15. (0.9232208, −0.8334588) 16. (0.1312178, −1.1051761)

Challenge Exercises

17. Evaluate: $\begin{vmatrix} x & 4 \\ x & x^2 \end{vmatrix}$ $x^3 - 4x$

18. Solve: $\sqrt{3}x + \pi y = -5$ $(\frac{15 - 4\pi}{-3\sqrt{3} - \pi^2}, \frac{4\sqrt{3} + 5\pi}{-3\sqrt{3} - \pi^2})$
    $\pi x - 3y = 4$

18-4 Determinants and Three Equations

After finishing Lesson 18-4, you should be able to
■ evaluate determinants of third order.
■■ solve systems of three equations in three variables using Cramer's Rule.

▌ Determinants of Third Order

We now define third order determinants.

DEFINITION
The *determinant* of a matrix with three rows and three columns is defined as follows:

$$\begin{vmatrix} a_1 & b_1 & c_1 \\ a_2 & b_2 & c_2 \\ a_3 & b_3 & c_3 \end{vmatrix} = a_1 \cdot \begin{vmatrix} b_2 & c_2 \\ b_3 & c_3 \end{vmatrix} - a_2 \cdot \begin{vmatrix} b_1 & c_1 \\ b_3 & c_3 \end{vmatrix} + a_3 \cdot \begin{vmatrix} b_1 & c_1 \\ b_2 & c_2 \end{vmatrix}$$

The second order determinants on the right can be found by crossing out the row and column in which the a-coefficient occurs. Thus for a_2, we cross out the rows and columns shown:

$$\begin{vmatrix} a_1 & b_1 & c_1 \\ a_2 & b_2 & c_2 \\ a_3 & b_3 & c_3 \end{vmatrix}$$

Example 1. Evaluate.

$$\begin{vmatrix} -1 & 0 & 1 \\ -5 & 1 & -1 \\ 4 & 8 & 1 \end{vmatrix} = -1 \cdot \begin{vmatrix} 1 & -1 \\ 8 & 1 \end{vmatrix} - (-5) \cdot \begin{vmatrix} 0 & 1 \\ 8 & 1 \end{vmatrix} + 4 \cdot \begin{vmatrix} 0 & 1 \\ 1 & -1 \end{vmatrix}$$

$$= -1(1 + 8) + 5(-8) + 4(-1)$$
$$= -9 - 40 - 4$$
$$= -53$$

TRY THIS ▐▬▬▬▬▬▬▬▶

Answers. 1. −6 2. 93 3. 4

Evaluate.

1. $\begin{vmatrix} 2 & -1 & 1 \\ 1 & 2 & -1 \\ 3 & 4 & -3 \end{vmatrix}$

2. $\begin{vmatrix} 3 & 2 & 2 \\ -2 & 1 & 4 \\ 4 & -3 & 3 \end{vmatrix}$

3. $\begin{vmatrix} 2 & 0 & 2 \\ 0 & 2 & 0 \\ 1 & 0 & 2 \end{vmatrix}$

∎ Solving by Determinants

THEOREM 18-2 (Cramer's Rule)

If the system $a_1x + b_1y + c_1z = d_1$
$$a_2x + b_2y + c_2z = d_2$$
$$a_3x + b_3y + c_3z = d_3$$

has exactly one solution, it is given by

$$x = \frac{D_x}{D}, \; y = \frac{D_y}{D}, \; z = \frac{D_z}{D},$$

where

$$D = \begin{vmatrix} a_1 & b_1 & c_1 \\ a_2 & b_2 & c_2 \\ a_3 & b_3 & c_3 \end{vmatrix}, \; D_x = \begin{vmatrix} d_1 & b_1 & c_1 \\ d_2 & b_2 & c_2 \\ d_3 & b_3 & c_3 \end{vmatrix}, \; D_y = \begin{vmatrix} a_1 & d_1 & c_1 \\ a_2 & d_2 & c_2 \\ a_3 & d_3 & c_3 \end{vmatrix}, \; D_z = \begin{vmatrix} a_1 & b_1 & d_1 \\ a_2 & b_2 & d_2 \\ a_3 & b_3 & d_3 \end{vmatrix}.$$

We obtain the determinant D_x in the numerator of x from D by replacing the x coefficients by d_1, d_2, and d_3. A similar thing happens with D_y and D_z. We have thus extended *Cramer's Rule* to solve systems of three equations in three variables. As before, when $D = 0$, Cramer's rule cannot be used. If $D = 0$, and D_x, D_y, and D_z are 0, the system is dependent (has an infinite number of solutions). If $D = 0$ and one of D_x, D_y, or D_z, is not zero, then the system is inconsistent (has no solution).

Example 2. Solve, using Cramer's rule: $x - 3y + 7z = 13$
$$x + y + z = 1$$
$$x - 2y + 3z = 4$$

We find the appropriate determinants and evaluate.

$$D = \begin{vmatrix} 1 & -3 & 7 \\ 1 & 1 & 1 \\ 1 & -2 & 3 \end{vmatrix} = -10, \; D_x = \begin{vmatrix} 13 & -3 & 7 \\ 1 & 1 & 1 \\ 4 & -2 & 3 \end{vmatrix} = 20,$$

$$D_y = \begin{vmatrix} 1 & 13 & 7 \\ 1 & 1 & 1 \\ 1 & 4 & 3 \end{vmatrix} = -6, \; D_z = \begin{vmatrix} 1 & -3 & 13 \\ 1 & 1 & 1 \\ 1 & -2 & 4 \end{vmatrix} = -24.$$

Then

$$x = \frac{D_x}{D} = \frac{20}{-10} = -2, \; y = \frac{D_y}{D} = \frac{-6}{-10} = \frac{3}{5}, \; z = \frac{D_z}{D} = \frac{-24}{-10} = \frac{12}{5}.$$

The solution is $(-2, \frac{3}{5}, \frac{12}{5})$.

In practice it is actually not necessary to evaluate D_z, since, if we have the solutions for x and y, we could substitute in one of the equations and find z. We know $x = -2$ and $y = \frac{3}{5}$ in Example 2; so by using the second equation $-2 + \frac{3}{5} + z = 1$, we find $z = \frac{12}{5}$.

TRY THIS ➡

4. Solve, using Cramer's Rule.

$$x - 3y - 7z = 6$$
$$2x + 3y + z = 9 \qquad (1, 3, -2)$$
$$4x + y = 7$$

Exercise Set 18-4

■ Evaluate. (*See Example 1.*)

1. $\begin{vmatrix} 0 & 2 & 0 \\ 3 & -1 & 1 \\ 1 & -2 & 2 \end{vmatrix}$ -10

2. $\begin{vmatrix} 3 & 0 & -2 \\ 5 & 1 & 2 \\ 2 & 0 & -1 \end{vmatrix}$ 1

3. $\begin{vmatrix} -1 & -2 & -3 \\ 3 & 4 & 2 \\ 0 & 1 & 2 \end{vmatrix}$ -3

4. $\begin{vmatrix} 1 & 2 & 2 \\ 2 & 1 & 0 \\ 3 & 3 & 1 \end{vmatrix}$ 3

5. $\begin{vmatrix} 3 & 2 & 2 \\ -2 & 1 & 4 \\ 4 & -3 & 3 \end{vmatrix}$ 93

6. $\begin{vmatrix} 2 & -1 & 1 \\ 1 & 2 & -1 \\ 3 & 4 & -3 \end{vmatrix}$ -6

■■ Solve, using Cramer's Rule. (*See Example 2.*)

7. $3x + 2y - z = 4$
$3x - 2y + z = 5$ $\left(\frac{3}{2}, \frac{13}{14}, \frac{33}{14}\right)$
$4x - 5y - z = -1$

8. $3x - y + 2z = 1$
$x - y + 2z = 3$ $\left(-1, -\frac{6}{7}, \frac{11}{7}\right)$
$-2x + 3y + z = 1$

9. $2x - 3y + 5z = 27$
$x + 2y - z = -4$ $(2, -1, 4)$
$5x - y + 4z = 27$

10. $x - y + 2z = -3$
$x + 2y + 3z = 4$ $(-3, 2, 1)$
$2x + y + z = -3$

11. $r - 2s + 3t = 6$
$2r - s - t = -3$ $(1, 2, 3)$
$r + s + t = 6$

12. $a - 3c = 6$
$b + 2c = 2$ $(3, 4, -1)$
$7a - 3b - 5c = 14$

Challenge Exercises

13. Evaluate: $\begin{vmatrix} 1 & x & y \\ 1 & x & y \\ 1 & 1 & 1 \end{vmatrix}$

14. Verify: $\begin{vmatrix} 1 & x & x^2 \\ 1 & y & y^2 \\ 1 & z & z^2 \end{vmatrix} = (x - y)(y - z)(z - x)$

13. 0   14. $\begin{vmatrix} 1 & x & x^2 \\ 1 & y & y^2 \\ 1 & z & z^2 \end{vmatrix} = (yz^2 - zy^2) - (xz^2 - zx^2) + (xy^2 - yx^2) = yz^2 - zy^2 - xz^2 + zx^2 + xy^2$

$-yx^2$; $(x - y)(y - z)(z - x) = xyz - xz^2 - y^2z + yz^2 - x^2y + x^2z + xy^2 - xzy = yz^2 - zy^2$
$- xz^2 + zx^2 + xy^2 - yx^2$

18-5 Operations on Matrices

After finishing Lesson 18-5, you should be able to
- **I** find the dimensions of a matrix.
- **II** add matrices of the same dimensions.
- **III** add a matrix and a zero matrix of the same dimensions.
- **IIII** subtract matrices of the same dimensions.
- **IIIII** find the additive inverse of a matrix, and subtract matrices by adding an additive inverse.

I Dimensions of a Matrix

A matrix of m rows and n columns is called a matrix with *dimensions* $m \times n$ (read "m by n").

Examples. Find the dimensions of each matrix.

1. $\begin{bmatrix} 2 & -3 & 4 \\ -1 & \frac{1}{2} & \pi \end{bmatrix}$ **2.** $\begin{bmatrix} -3 & 8 & 9 \\ \pi & -2 & 5 \\ -6 & 7 & 8 \end{bmatrix}$ **3.** $\begin{bmatrix} 10 \\ -7 \end{bmatrix}$ **4.** $[-3 \quad 4]$

2×3 matrix 3×3 matrix 2×1 matrix 1×2 matrix

TRY THIS ➡

II Matrix Addition

DEFINITION
To *add* matrices, we add the corresponding members. The matrices must have the same dimensions.

Examples. Add.

5. $\begin{bmatrix} -5 & 0 \\ 4 & \frac{1}{2} \end{bmatrix} + \begin{bmatrix} 6 & -3 \\ 2 & 3 \end{bmatrix} = \begin{bmatrix} -5+6 & 0-3 \\ 4+2 & \frac{1}{2}+3 \end{bmatrix} = \begin{bmatrix} 1 & -3 \\ 6 & 3\frac{1}{2} \end{bmatrix}.$

6. $\begin{bmatrix} 1 & 3 & 2 \\ -1 & 5 & 4 \\ 6 & 0 & 1 \end{bmatrix} + \begin{bmatrix} -1 & -2 & 1 \\ 1 & -2 & 2 \\ -3 & 1 & 0 \end{bmatrix} = \begin{bmatrix} 0 & 1 & 3 \\ 0 & 3 & 6 \\ 3 & 1 & 1 \end{bmatrix}$

Addition of matrices is both commutative and associative.

THEOREM 18-3
For any matrices of the same dimensions, **A, B,** and **C,**
$\mathbf{A} + \mathbf{B} = \mathbf{B} + \mathbf{A}, \mathbf{A} + (\mathbf{B} + \mathbf{C}) = (\mathbf{A} + \mathbf{B}) + \mathbf{C}.$

Find the dimensions of each matrix.

1. $\begin{bmatrix} -3 & 5 \\ 4 & \frac{1}{4} \\ -\pi & 0 \end{bmatrix}$ 3×2

2. $\begin{bmatrix} -3 & 0 \\ 0 & 3 \end{bmatrix}$ 2×2

3. $\begin{bmatrix} 1 & 2 & 3 \\ 0 & 1 & 8 \\ 0 & 0 & 1 \end{bmatrix}$ 3×3

4. $[\pi \quad \sqrt{2}]$ 1×2

5. $\begin{bmatrix} -5 \\ \pi \end{bmatrix}$ 2×1

6. $[-3]$ 1×1

TRY THIS ➡

Answers.   7. a) $\begin{bmatrix} -2 & -6 \\ 13 & 0 \end{bmatrix}$ b) $\begin{bmatrix} -2 & -6 \\ 13 & 0 \end{bmatrix}$

7. Let $\mathbf{A} = \begin{bmatrix} 4 & -1 \\ 6 & -3 \end{bmatrix}$ and $\mathbf{B} = \begin{bmatrix} -6 & -5 \\ 7 & 3 \end{bmatrix}$

a) Find $\mathbf{A} + \mathbf{B}$.

b) Find $\mathbf{B} + \mathbf{A}$.

ⅠⅠⅠ Zero Matrices

DEFINITION

A *zero matrix* is a matrix all of whose elements are 0.

Example 7. Add.

$$\begin{bmatrix} 2 & -1 & 3 \\ 1 & 0 & -1 \end{bmatrix} + \begin{bmatrix} 0 & 0 & 0 \\ 0 & 0 & 0 \end{bmatrix} = \begin{bmatrix} 2 & -1 & 3 \\ 1 & 0 & -1 \end{bmatrix}$$

A zero matrix is denoted by **O**.

TRY THIS ▬▶

It follows that a zero matrix is an additive identity.

THEOREM 18-4

For any matrices $\mathbf{A}$ and $\mathbf{O}$ of the same dimensions, $\mathbf{A} + \mathbf{O} = \mathbf{A}$

8. Let $\mathbf{A} = \begin{bmatrix} 4 & -3 \\ 5 & 8 \end{bmatrix}$

and $\mathbf{O} = \begin{bmatrix} 0 & 0 \\ 0 & 0 \end{bmatrix}$

a) Find $\mathbf{A} + \mathbf{O}$.

b) Find $\mathbf{O} + \mathbf{A}$.

Answers.   8. a) $\begin{bmatrix} 4 & -3 \\ 5 & 8 \end{bmatrix}$

b) $\begin{bmatrix} 4 & -3 \\ 5 & 8 \end{bmatrix}$

ⅠⅠⅠⅠ Subtraction

The definition of subtraction is the same for matrices as it is for numbers.

DEFINITION

The matrix $\mathbf{A} - \mathbf{B}$ is the matrix which when added to $\mathbf{B}$ gives $\mathbf{A}$.

Answers.   9. $\begin{bmatrix} -1 & 4 & -7 \\ -2 & -4 & 8 \end{bmatrix}$

10. $\begin{bmatrix} -6 & 6 \\ 1 & -4 \\ -7 & 5 \end{bmatrix}$

THEOREM 18-5

To subtract matrices of the same dimensions we can subtract the corresponding elements.

Subtract.

9. $\begin{bmatrix} 1 & 3 & -2 \\ 4 & 0 & 5 \end{bmatrix} - \begin{bmatrix} 2 & -1 & 5 \\ 6 & 4 & -3 \end{bmatrix}$

10. $\begin{bmatrix} 1 & 2 \\ 4 & 1 \\ -5 & 4 \end{bmatrix} - \begin{bmatrix} 7 & -4 \\ 3 & 5 \\ 2 & -1 \end{bmatrix}$

Example 8. Subtract.

$$\begin{bmatrix} 1 & 2 \\ -2 & 0 \\ -3 & -1 \end{bmatrix} - \begin{bmatrix} 1 & -1 \\ 1 & 3 \\ 2 & 3 \end{bmatrix} = \begin{bmatrix} 0 & 3 \\ -3 & -3 \\ -5 & -4 \end{bmatrix}$$

TRY THIS ▬▶

▮▮▮▮▮ Additive Inverses and Subtraction

Additive inverses are defined for matrices the same way as for numbers.

DEFINITION
Two matrices are additive inverses of each other if their sum is a zero matrix.

THEOREM 18-6
The additive inverse of a matrix can be found by replacing each element by its additive inverse.

Example 9. Find the additive inverse of $\begin{bmatrix} -3 & 4 & 0 \\ 2 & 6 & 4 \\ -1 & 5 & -5 \end{bmatrix}$.

The additive inverse is $\begin{bmatrix} 3 & -4 & 0 \\ -2 & -6 & -4 \\ 1 & -5 & 5 \end{bmatrix}$.

TRY THIS ➡

Find the additive inverse.

11. $\begin{bmatrix} 2 & -1 & 5 \\ 6 & 4 & -3 \end{bmatrix}$

The additive inverse of **A** is denoted $-$**A**.

With numbers, we can subtract by adding an additive inverse. This is also true of matrices.

THEOREM 18-7
For any matrices **A** and **B** of the same dimensions,
A $-$ **B** $=$ **A** $+ (-$**B**$)$.

Example 10. Subtract, by adding an additive inverse.

$$\begin{bmatrix} 3 & -1 \\ -2 & 4 \end{bmatrix} - \begin{bmatrix} 2 & 1 \\ 3 & -2 \end{bmatrix} = \begin{bmatrix} 3 & -1 \\ -2 & 4 \end{bmatrix} + \begin{bmatrix} -2 & -1 \\ -3 & 2 \end{bmatrix}$$

$$\quad \textbf{A} \quad - \quad \textbf{B} \quad = \quad \textbf{A} \quad + \quad (-\textbf{B})$$

$$= \begin{bmatrix} 1 & -2 \\ -5 & 6 \end{bmatrix}$$

TRY THIS ➡

12. Let $\textbf{A} = \begin{bmatrix} 1 & 2 \\ 4 & 1 \\ -5 & 4 \end{bmatrix}$

and $\textbf{B} = \begin{bmatrix} 7 & -4 \\ 3 & 5 \\ 2 & -1 \end{bmatrix}$.

Subtract, by adding an additive inverse.
a) **A** $-$ **B**
b) **B** $-$ **A**

Answers.
11. $\begin{bmatrix} -2 & 1 & -5 \\ -6 & -4 & 3 \end{bmatrix}$
12. a) $\begin{bmatrix} -6 & 6 \\ 1 & -4 \\ -7 & 5 \end{bmatrix}$
b) $\begin{bmatrix} 6 & -6 \\ -1 & 4 \\ 7 & -5 \end{bmatrix}$

Exercise Set 18-5

For Exercises 1–36, let

$$\mathbf{A} = \begin{bmatrix} 1 & 2 \\ 4 & -3 \end{bmatrix}, \mathbf{B} = \begin{bmatrix} -3 & -5 \\ 2 & -1 \end{bmatrix}, \mathbf{C} = \begin{bmatrix} 1 & -1 \\ -1 & 1 \end{bmatrix}, \mathbf{D} = \begin{bmatrix} 1 & 1 \\ 1 & 1 \end{bmatrix}, \mathbf{E} = \begin{bmatrix} 1 & 3 \\ 2 & 6 \end{bmatrix},$$

$$\mathbf{F} = \begin{bmatrix} 3 & 3 \\ -1 & -1 \end{bmatrix}, \mathbf{G} = \begin{bmatrix} 1 & 0 & -2 \\ 0 & -1 & 3 \\ 3 & -2 & 4 \end{bmatrix}, \mathbf{H} = \begin{bmatrix} -1 & -2 & 5 \\ 1 & 0 & -1 \\ -2 & -3 & 1 \end{bmatrix}, \mathbf{M} = \begin{bmatrix} -4 & 5 & -2 \\ 1 & 0 & -4 \\ -2 & -3 & -5 \end{bmatrix},$$

$$\mathbf{O} = \begin{bmatrix} 0 & 0 \\ 0 & 0 \end{bmatrix}, \mathbf{P} = \begin{bmatrix} -2 & 3 & 4 \\ 8 & 0 & -1 \end{bmatrix}, \mathbf{Q} = \begin{bmatrix} -3 & -3 & 7 \\ -5 & 2 & 1 \end{bmatrix}, \mathbf{R} = \begin{bmatrix} -1 & 0 & 0 \\ 0 & 2 & 0 \end{bmatrix}$$

▮ Find the dimensions of each matrix. (*See Examples 1–4.*)

   1. **A** 2 × 2   2. **G** 3 × 3

   3. **Q** 2 × 3   4. **O** 2 × 2

▮▮ Add. (*See Examples 5 and 6.*)   See answer section

   5. **A** + **B**   6. **B** + **C**

   7. **D** + **F**   8. **E** + **F**

   9. **P** + **Q**   10. **R** + **P**

  11. **H** + **G**   12. **M** + **H**

▮▮▮ Add. (*See Example 7.*)   See answer section

  13. **A** + **O**   14. **O** + **B**

  15. **O** + **C**   16. **D** + **C**

▮▮▮▮ Subtract. (*See Example 8.*)   See answer section

  17. **A** − **B**   18. **C** − **B**

  19. **F** − **D**   20. **E** − **F**

  21. **H** − **M**   22. **G** − **H**

  23. **Q** − **P**   24. **R** − **Q**

▮▮▮▮▮ Find the additive inverse of each matrix. (*See Example 9.*)   See answer section

  25. −**D**   26. −**Q**

  27. −**E**   28. −**M**

Subtract by adding an additive inverse. (*See Example 10.*)   See answer section

  29. **D** − **C**   30. **C** − **E**

  31. **M** − **H**   32. **H** − **G**

  33. **P** − **Q**   34. **R** − **P**

  35. **O** − **F**   36. **O** − **A**

18-6 *Multiplying Matrices and Numbers*

After finishing Lesson 18-6, you should be able to
  I   find the scalar product of a number k and a matrix **A**.
  II   find the product of a row matrix and a column matrix.
  III   find the product **AB** of a matrix **A** and a matrix **B**, where the number of columns in **A** is the same as the number of rows in **B**.

I Scalar Products

We define a kind of product of a matrix and a number.

DEFINITION

The (*scalar*) product of a number k and a matrix **A** is the matrix, denoted k**A**, obtained by multiplying each number in **A** by the number k.

Examples. Let $\mathbf{A} = \begin{bmatrix} -3 & 0 \\ 4 & x \end{bmatrix}$. Find these scalar products.

1. $3\mathbf{A} = 3\begin{bmatrix} -3 & 0 \\ 4 & x \end{bmatrix} = \begin{bmatrix} -9 & 0 \\ 12 & 3x \end{bmatrix}$

2. $(-1)\mathbf{A} = -1\begin{bmatrix} -3 & 0 \\ 4 & x \end{bmatrix} = \begin{bmatrix} 3 & 0 \\ -4 & -x \end{bmatrix}$

TRY THIS

Find these scalar products.

1. $5\begin{bmatrix} 1 & -2 & x \\ 4 & y & 1 \\ 0 & -5 & x^2 \end{bmatrix}$

2. $t\begin{bmatrix} 1 & -1 & 4 & x \\ y & 3 & -2 & y \\ 1 & 4 & -5 & t \end{bmatrix}$

Answers.
1. $\begin{bmatrix} 5 & -10 & 5x \\ 20 & 5y & 5 \\ 0 & -25 & 5x^2 \end{bmatrix}$

2. $\begin{bmatrix} t & -t & 4t & tx \\ ty & 3t & -2t & ty \\ t & 4t & -5t & t^2 \end{bmatrix}$

II Product of a Row Matrix and a Column Matrix

We do not multiply two matrices by multiplying their corresponding members. The motivation for defining matrix products comes from equations. Let us begin by considering one equation,

$$3x + 2y - 2z = 4.$$

We will write the coefficients on the left side in a 1×3 matrix (a *row* matrix) and the variables in a 3×1 matrix (a *column* matrix). The 4 on the right is written in a 1×1 matrix.

$$[3 \quad 2 \quad -2]\begin{bmatrix} x \\ y \\ z \end{bmatrix} = [4]$$

We can return to our original equation by multiplying the members of the row matrix by those of the column matrix, and adding.

$$[3 \quad 2 \quad -2]\begin{bmatrix} x \\ y \\ z \end{bmatrix} = [3x + 2y - 2z] = [4]$$

We define multiplication accordingly.

DEFINITION
The *product* **AB** of a row matrix **A**, $[a_1 \ a_2 \ \cdots \ a_n]$, and a column matrix
B, $\begin{bmatrix} b_1 \\ b_2 \\ \vdots \\ b_n \end{bmatrix}$, is a 1×1 matrix whose member is $[a_1 b_1 + a_2 b_2 + \cdots + a_n b_n]$.

Example 3. Multiply.

$$[3 \quad 2 \quad -1]\begin{bmatrix} 1 \\ -2 \\ 3 \end{bmatrix} = [3 \cdot 1 + 2 \cdot (-2) + (-1) \cdot 3]$$

$$= [-4]$$

TRY THIS

Multiply.

3.
$$[4 \quad -2 \quad 3]\begin{bmatrix} 2 \\ 3 \\ -5 \end{bmatrix}$$

4.
$$[-2 \quad 1]\begin{bmatrix} x \\ y \end{bmatrix}$$

Answers. 3. $[-13]$ 4. $[-2x + y]$

ııı Products of Matrices

In the following example, we multiply each row of the matrix on the left by the column matrix.

Example 4. Multiply.

$$\begin{bmatrix} 3 & 1 & -1 \\ 1 & 2 & 2 \\ -1 & 0 & 5 \\ 4 & 1 & 2 \end{bmatrix}\begin{bmatrix} 1 \\ 2 \\ 4 \end{bmatrix} = \begin{bmatrix} 3 \cdot 1 + 1 \cdot 2 + (-1) \cdot 4 \\ 1 \cdot 1 + 2 \cdot 2 + 2 \cdot 4 \\ -1 \cdot 1 + 0 \cdot 2 + 5 \cdot 4 \\ 4 \cdot 1 + 1 \cdot 2 + 2 \cdot 4 \end{bmatrix} = \begin{bmatrix} 1 \\ 13 \\ 19 \\ 14 \end{bmatrix}$$

TRY THIS

5. Multiply.
$$\begin{bmatrix} 1 & 4 & 2 \\ -1 & 6 & 3 \\ 3 & 2 & -1 \\ 5 & 0 & 2 \end{bmatrix}\begin{bmatrix} 2 \\ 1 \\ 3 \end{bmatrix}$$

Answer. 5. $\begin{bmatrix} 12 \\ 13 \\ 5 \\ 16 \end{bmatrix}$

In all of the examples so far, the second matrix had only one column. If the second matrix has more than one column, we treat it in the same way when multiplying that we treated the single column. The product matrix will have as many columns as the second matrix.

Example 5. Multiply (compare with Example 4).

$$\begin{bmatrix} 3 & 1 & -1 \\ 1 & 2 & 2 \\ -1 & 0 & 5 \\ 4 & 1 & 2 \end{bmatrix} \begin{bmatrix} 1 & 0 \\ 2 & 1 \\ 4 & 3 \end{bmatrix} = \begin{bmatrix} 3\cdot 1 + 1\cdot 2 + (-1)\cdot 4 & 3\cdot 0 + 1\cdot 1 + (-1)3 \\ 1\cdot 1 + 2\cdot 2 + 2\cdot 4 & 1\cdot 0 + 2\cdot 1 + 2\cdot 3 \\ -1\cdot 1 + 0\cdot 2 + 5\cdot 4 & -1\cdot 0 + 0\cdot 1 + 5\cdot 3 \\ 4\cdot 1 + 1\cdot 2 + 2\cdot 4 & 4\cdot 0 + 1\cdot 1 + 2\cdot 3 \end{bmatrix} = \begin{bmatrix} 1 & -2 \\ 13 & 8 \\ 19 & 15 \\ 14 & 7 \end{bmatrix}$$

  A   **B**   *Same as in Example 4*   *The rows of **A** multiplied by the second column of **B***

TRY THIS ▬▬➤

If matrix **A** has *n* columns and matrix **B** has *n* rows, then we can compute the product **AB**, regardless of the other dimensions. The product will have as many rows as **A** and as many columns as **B**.

> 6. Multiply.
>
> $$\begin{bmatrix} 1 & 4 & 2 \\ -1 & 6 & 3 \\ 3 & 2 & -1 \\ 5 & 0 & 2 \end{bmatrix} \begin{bmatrix} 2 & -4 \\ 1 & 0 \\ 3 & 5 \end{bmatrix}$$

Exercise Set 18-6

For Exercises 1–28, let $\mathbf{A} = \begin{bmatrix} 1 & 2 \\ 4 & 3 \end{bmatrix}$, $\mathbf{B} = \begin{bmatrix} -3 & 5 \\ 2 & -1 \end{bmatrix}$,

Answer. 6. $\begin{bmatrix} 12 & 6 \\ 13 & 19 \\ 5 & -17 \\ 16 & -10 \end{bmatrix}$

$\mathbf{C} = \begin{bmatrix} 1 & -1 \\ -1 & 1 \end{bmatrix}$, $\mathbf{D} = \begin{bmatrix} 1 & 1 \\ 1 & 1 \end{bmatrix}$, $\mathbf{E} = \begin{bmatrix} 1 & 3 \\ 2 & 6 \end{bmatrix}$, $\mathbf{F} = \begin{bmatrix} 3 & 3 \\ -1 & -1 \end{bmatrix}$, $\mathbf{I} = \begin{bmatrix} 1 & 0 \\ 0 & 1 \end{bmatrix}$,

$\mathbf{G} = \begin{bmatrix} 1 & 0 & -2 \\ 0 & -1 & 3 \\ 3 & 2 & 4 \end{bmatrix}$, $\mathbf{H} = \begin{bmatrix} -1 & -2 & 5 \\ 1 & 0 & -1 \\ 2 & -3 & 1 \end{bmatrix}$, $\mathbf{Z} = \begin{bmatrix} -2 & 9 & 6 \\ -3 & 3 & 4 \\ 2 & -2 & 1 \end{bmatrix}$,

$\mathbf{J} = [-2 \quad 3 \quad -4]$, $\mathbf{K} = [8 \quad -1]$, $\mathbf{L} = [-1 \quad -2 \quad -3 \quad 4]$,

$\mathbf{M} = \begin{bmatrix} -2 \\ -4 \\ 7 \end{bmatrix}$, $\mathbf{N} = \begin{bmatrix} 8 \\ -6 \\ \frac{1}{2} \end{bmatrix}$, $\mathbf{P} = \begin{bmatrix} -3 \\ -2 \end{bmatrix}$, $\mathbf{Q} = \begin{bmatrix} 10 \\ -4 \\ 5 \\ 2 \end{bmatrix}$

▮ Multiply. (*See Examples 1 and 2.*)

1. $(-2)\mathbf{A}$
2. $(-5)\mathbf{B}$
3. $14\mathbf{C}$
4. $12\mathbf{D}$
5. $t\mathbf{E}$ *See answer section*
6. $p\mathbf{F}$
7. $(-1)\mathbf{Z}$
8. $(-1)\mathbf{H}$

▮▮ Multiply. (*See Example 3.*)

9. $\mathbf{KP}$
10. $\mathbf{JM}$
11. $\mathbf{JN}$
12. $\mathbf{LQ}$

▌▌▌ Multiply, if possible. (*See Examples 4 and 5.*)   See answer section

13. **AB**   14. **BC**

15. **CD**   16. **EF**

17. **JG**   18. **KF**

19. **JZ**   20. **FP**

21. **FI**   22. **IB**

23. **GH**   24. **HG**

25. **AP**   26. **KC**

27. **HA**   28. **CG**   Use Quiz 33 after lesson 18–6.

Challenge Exercises   See answer section

29. Let $\mathbf{A} = \begin{bmatrix} -1 & 0 \\ 2 & 1 \end{bmatrix}$ and $\mathbf{B} = \begin{bmatrix} 1 & -1 \\ 0 & 2 \end{bmatrix}$.

   a) Show that $(\mathbf{A} + \mathbf{B})(\mathbf{A} - \mathbf{B}) \neq \mathbf{A}^2 - \mathbf{B}^2$, where $\mathbf{A}^2 = \mathbf{AA}$ and $\mathbf{B}^2 = \mathbf{BB}$.

   b) Show that $(\mathbf{A} + \mathbf{B})(\mathbf{A} + \mathbf{B}) \neq \mathbf{A}^2 + 2\mathbf{AB} + \mathbf{B}^2$.

Let $\mathbf{A} = \begin{bmatrix} a & c \\ b & d \end{bmatrix}$, $\mathbf{B} = \begin{bmatrix} e & g \\ f & h \end{bmatrix}$, and $\mathbf{I} = \begin{bmatrix} 1 & 0 \\ 0 & 1 \end{bmatrix}$.

Prove.

30. $k(\mathbf{A} + \mathbf{B}) = k\mathbf{A} + k\mathbf{B}$ 31. $(-1)\mathbf{A} = -\mathbf{A}$

32. $(k + m)\mathbf{A} = k\mathbf{A} + m\mathbf{A}$ 33. Find **AI** and **IA**.

34. What can you conclude about matrix **I**?

CONSUMER NOTE: Interest on Savings

The formula $A = P(1 + r)^t$ applies when interest is compounded once a year. Usually, interest is compounded more often. It may be paid semi-annually, quarterly, or monthly.

   The more often interest is compounded, the faster savings grow. Once interest is compounded, it is added to the savings. Then interest is paid on both the original savings and the interest.

   Interest on savings is compounded at different rates. Savings institutions often advertise their interest rates. A consumer may shop for interest by asking several questions. How much interest will a certain amount of savings earn in a certain time? When does the interest period start? When may withdrawals be made without losing interest?

CHAPTER 18 REVIEW

Review the material in the chapter. Then see how you have done by trying these review exercises. If you miss an exercise, restudy the indicated lesson.

Solve, using matrices.

18-1   1. $x - 3y = 0$
            $5x - y = -14$ $(-3, -1)$

18-2   2. $x + 5y + 3z = 4$
            $3x - 2y + 4z = 21$ $(-1, -2, 5)$
            $2x + 3y - z = -13$

18-3   3.   Evaluate: $\begin{vmatrix} 2 & -3 \\ 2 & 5 \end{vmatrix}$ 16

18-3   4.   Solve, using Cramer's Rule.
            $5x - 2y = 19$ $(3, -2)$
            $7x + 3y = 15$

18-4   5.   Evaluate: $\begin{vmatrix} 2 & -1 & 1 \\ 1 & -2 & 3 \\ 4 & 1 & 2 \end{vmatrix}$ -15

18-4   6.   Solve, using Cramer's Rule.
            $2x - y + z = -1$ $(-1, 2, 3)$
            $x - 2y + 3z = 4$
            $4x + y + 2z = 4$

Let $\mathbf{A} = \begin{bmatrix} 1 & 2 & -1 \\ 2 & 0 & 1 \\ -2 & 1 & 0 \end{bmatrix}$

and $\mathbf{B} = \begin{bmatrix} 0 & 4 & 2 \\ -1 & 2 & 0 \\ 0 & 2 & 1 \end{bmatrix}$.

Find.

18-5   7. $\mathbf{A} + \mathbf{B}$ 8. $\mathbf{A} - \mathbf{B}$
18-6   9. $3\mathbf{B}$ 10. $\mathbf{AB}$

7. $\begin{bmatrix} 1 & 6 & 1 \\ 1 & 2 & 1 \\ -2 & 3 & 1 \end{bmatrix}$ 8. $\begin{bmatrix} 1 & -2 & -3 \\ 3 & -2 & 1 \\ -2 & -1 & -1 \end{bmatrix}$ 9. $\begin{bmatrix} 3 & 6 & -3 \\ 6 & 0 & 3 \\ -6 & 3 & 0 \end{bmatrix}$ 10. $\begin{bmatrix} -2 & 6 & 1 \\ 0 & 10 & 5 \\ -1 & -6 & -4 \end{bmatrix}$

CHAPTER 18 TEST

Solve, using matrices.

1. $x + 2y = 5$ $(1, 2)$
     $2x - 5y = -8$

2. $3x + 4y + 2z = 3$ $(-3, 4, -2)$
     $5x - 2y - 13z = 3$
     $4x + 3y - 3z = 6$

3.   Evaluate: $\begin{vmatrix} 1 & 2 \\ 2 & -5 \end{vmatrix}$ -9

4.   Solve, using Cramer's Rule.
     $2x + 3y = 2$ $(-5, 4)$
     $5x - y = -29$

5.   Evaluate: $\begin{vmatrix} 3 & 4 & 2 \\ 5 & -2 & 0 \\ 4 & 3 & -3 \end{vmatrix}$ 124

6.   Solve, using Cramer's Rule.
     $3x + 2y + 2z = 3$
     $2x - 4y + z = 0$ $(2, \frac{1}{2}, -2)$
     $x + 2y - z = 5$

Let $\mathbf{A} = \begin{bmatrix} 1 & 1 & 3 \\ 0 & 2 & -1 \\ 2 & -1 & 0 \end{bmatrix}$

and $\mathbf{B} = \begin{bmatrix} -1 & 0 & 2 \\ 1 & -2 & 0 \\ 0 & 1 & -3 \end{bmatrix}$.

Find.

7. $\mathbf{B} + \mathbf{A}$ 8. $\mathbf{A} - \mathbf{B}$
9. $-2\mathbf{B}$ 10. $\mathbf{AB}$

7. $\begin{bmatrix} 0 & 1 & 5 \\ 1 & 0 & -1 \\ 2 & 0 & -3 \end{bmatrix}$ 8. $\begin{bmatrix} 2 & 1 & 1 \\ -1 & 4 & -1 \\ 2 & -2 & 3 \end{bmatrix}$ 9. $\begin{bmatrix} 2 & 0 & -4 \\ -2 & 4 & 0 \\ 0 & -2 & 6 \end{bmatrix}$ 10. $\begin{bmatrix} 0 & 1 & -7 \\ 2 & -5 & 3 \\ -3 & 2 & 4 \end{bmatrix}$

Ready for Combinatorial Algebra and Probability?

1-7   1.   Evaluate n^r when $n = 5$ and $r = 3$.   125

1-7   2.   Evaluate $n(n - 1)(n - 2)$ when $n = 5$.   60

6-4   3.   Multiply: $(a + b)^2$. $a^2 + 2ab + b^2$

6-3   4.   Multiply $a + b$ and $a^2 + 2ab + b^2$. $a^3 + 3a^2b + 3ab^2 + b^3$

1-8   5.   Simplify: $(5x)^3$. $125x^3$

1-8   6.   Simplify: $(-2y)^4$. $16y^4$

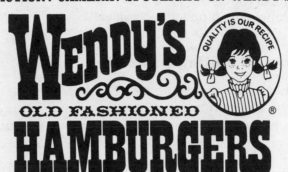

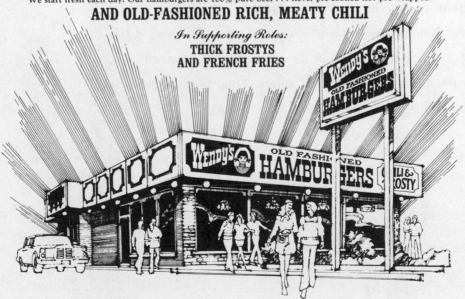

How did they figure out how many ways they can fix hamburgers?

19-1 Combinatorial Algebra: Permutations

After finishing Lesson 19-1, you should be able to
I   use the Fundamental Counting Principle to determine the total number of ways a compound event may occur.
II   find the total number of permutations of a set of *n* objects, by applying the formula $_nP_n = n!$
III   express a factorial as a product and evaluate.

I The Fundamental Counting Principle

We shall develop means of determining the number of ways a set of objects can be arranged or combined, the number of ways certain objects can be chosen, or the number of ways a succession of events can occur. The study of such things is called *combinatorial algebra*.

Example 1. How many 3-letter code symbols can be formed with the letters *A*, *B*, and *C* without repetition?

Consider placing letters in these frames   ☐☐☐

We can select any of the ☐3☐ letters for the first letter in the symbol. Once this letter has been selected, the second is selected from the remaining ☐2☐ letters. Then the third is already determined since there is only ☐1☐ letter left.

$$A \big\langle {{B - C} \atop {C - B}}$$
$$B \big\langle {{A - C} \atop {C - A}}$$
$$C \big\langle {{A - B} \atop {B - A}}$$

There are $3 \cdot 2 \cdot 1$ possibilities. Thus the symbols are

ABC, ACB, BAC,
BCA, CAB, CBA.

In the preceding example, a selection was made. Let us call this an *event*. When several of them occur we say that the event is *compound*. The following principle concerns compound events.

THEOREM 19-1 (Fundamental Counting Principle)

In a compound event in which the first event may occur independently in n_1 ways, the second may occur independently in n_2 ways, and so on, and the kth event may occur independently in n_k ways, the total number of ways the compound event may occur is $n_1 \cdot n_2 \cdot n_3 \cdots n_k$.

Example 2. How many 3-letter code symbols can be formed with the letters A, B, and C with repetition?

There are 3 choices for the first letter, and since we allow repetition, 3 choices for the second, and 3 for the third. Thus by the Fundamental Counting Principle there are $3 \cdot 3 \cdot 3$, or 27, choices.

Example 3. A family is redecorating their living room. They will choose one of 3 paint colors, one of 4 carpets, and one of 2 drapery fabrics. How many possible arrangements can they make for the living room?

There are 3 choices for the paint, 4 choices for the carpet, and 2 choices for the drapes. Thus, by the Fundamental Counting Principle, there are $3 \cdot 4 \cdot 2$, or 24, choices.

TRY THIS

1. How many 3-digit numbers can be named using all the digits 5, 6, 7 without repetition? with repetition? **6, 27**

2. A man is planning a date. He will first put on one of 4 suits, then call one of 2 girl friends, and then select one of 5 restaurants. How many possible arrangements can he make for his date (assuming the girls will accept)? **40**

3. In how many ways can 5 different cars be parked in a row in a parking lot? **120**

▪ Permutations

A *permutation* of a set of n objects is an ordered arrangement of the objects. Consider, for example, a set of 4 objects $\{A, B, C, D\}$. Here are some ordered arrangements of these objects.

     ABDC   DBAC   ADBC
     BACD   CBDA   DCAB

To find the number of ordered arrangements of the set we select a first one; there are 4 choices. Then we select a second one; there are 3 choices. Then we select a third one; there are 2 choices. Finally there is 1 choice for the last selection. Thus by the Fundamental Counting Principle, there are $4 \cdot 3 \cdot 2 \cdot 1$, or 24, permutations of a set of 4 objects.

TRY THIS →

> 4. How many permutations are there of a set of 5 objects? Consider a set $\{A, B, C, D, E\}$. **120**

We can generalize this to a set of n objects. We have n choices for the first selection, $n - 1$ for the second, $n - 2$ for the third, and so on. For the nth selection there is only one choice.

THEOREM 19-2

The total number of permutations of a set of n objects, denoted ${}_nP_n$, is given by ${}_nP_n = n(n-1)(n-2)\cdots 3\cdot 2\cdot 1$.

Examples. Find the following.

4. ${}_4P_4 = 4\cdot 3\cdot 2\cdot 1 = 24$

5. ${}_7P_7 = 7\cdot 6\cdot 5\cdot 4\cdot 3\cdot 2\cdot 1 = 5040$

TRY THIS →

> Evaluate.
>
> 5. ${}_3P_3$
> 6. ${}_5P_5$
> 7. ${}_6P_6$

Answers. 5. 6 6. 120 7. 720

Example 6. How many different ways can 5 paintings be lined up on the wall of an art gallery?

By Theorem 19-2, there are ${}_5P_5$ ways.

$$
\begin{aligned}
{}_5P_5 &= 5\cdot 4\cdot 3\cdot 2\cdot 1\\
&= 120
\end{aligned}
$$

TRY THIS →

> 8. In how many different ways can 4 horses be lined up for a race? **24**
> 9. In how many different ways can 6 people line up at a ticket window? **720**
> 10. In how many ways can the 9 players of a baseball team be put into batting order, if the pitcher bats last? **40,320**

III Factorial Notation

Products such as $5\cdot 4\cdot 3\cdot 2\cdot 1$ are used so often that it is convenient to adopt a notation for them. For the product $5\cdot 4\cdot 3\cdot 2\cdot 1$ we write 5!, read "5-factorial."

DEFINITION

$n! = n(n-1)(n-2)\cdots 3\cdot 2\cdot 1.$

Examples.

7. $7! = 7\cdot 6\cdot 5\cdot 4\cdot 3\cdot 2\cdot 1 = 5040$

8. $3! = \qquad 3\cdot 2\cdot 1 = \quad 6$

9. $1! = \qquad\qquad 1 = \quad 1$

TRY THIS ━━━━━━━━━━━━━▶

Answers.   11. 362,880   12. 24

Evaluate.

11.   9!

12.   4!

We also define 0! to be 1. We do this so that certain formulas and theorems can be stated concisely.

We can now simplify the formula of Theorem 19-2.

$$_nP_n = n!$$

TRY THIS ━━━━━━━▶

13.   Using factorial notation only, represent the number of permutations of 18 objects.   18!

Note that $8! = 8 \cdot 7!$ We can see this as follows.

$$8! = 8 \cdot 7 \cdot 6 \cdot 5 \cdot 4 \cdot 3 \cdot 2 \cdot 1 = 8 \cdot (7 \cdot 6 \cdot 5 \cdot 4 \cdot 3 \cdot 2 \cdot 1)$$
$$= 8 \cdot 7!$$

Generalizing gives us the following theorem.

THEOREM 19-3

For any natural number n,

$$n! = n(n - 1)!$$

TRY THIS ━━━━━━━▶

Represent each in the form $n(n - 1)!$

14.   10!   10 · 9!

15.   20!   20 · 19!

By using Theorem 19-3 repeatedly, we can further manipulate factorial notation.

Example 10.   Rewrite 7! with a factor of 5!

$$7! = 7 \cdot 6 \cdot 5!$$

Example 11.   Rewrite 12! with a factor of 7!

$$12! = 12 \cdot 11 \cdot 10 \cdot 9 \cdot 8 \cdot 7!$$

TRY THIS ━━━━━━━▶

16.   Rewrite 11! with a factor of 8!   11 · 10 · 9 · 8!

17.   Rewrite 17! with a factor of 12! 17 · 16 · 15 · 14 · 13 · 12!

Exercise Set 19-1

■ (*See Examples 1–3.*)

1. How many 4-letter code symbols can be formed with the letters *P, D, Q, X* without repetition? with repetition?   24, 256

2. How many 5-digit numbers can be formed using all the digits 0, 1, 2, 3, 4 without repetition? with repetition?   120, 3125

3. How many ways can 6 bicycles be parked in a row?   720

4. How many ways can 7 different cards be laid out on a table in a row?   5040

5. A woman is going out for the evening. She will put on one of 6 pantsuits, one pair out of 8 pairs of shoes, and go to one of 7 restaurants. In how many ways can this be done?   336

6. A man is going out for the evening. He will put on one of 7 suits, one pair out of 4 pairs of shoes, and go to one of 10 restaurants. In how many ways can this be done?   280

■■ Evaluate. (*See Examples 4 and 5.*)

7. $_6P_6$ 720

8. $_5P_5$ 120

9. $_4P_4$ 24

10. $_2P_2$ 2

(*See Example 6.*)

11. How many ways can 7 people line up in a row?   5040

12. How many ways can 8 motorcycles be parked in a row?   40,320

13. How many permutations are there of the set $\{R, S, T, U, V, W\}$?   720

14. How many permutations are there of the set $\{M, N, O, P, Q, R, S\}$?   5040

15. The owner of a business hires 8 secretaries, one for each of 8 department managers. How many different assignments of the secretaries are possible?   40,320

16. An ice cream store has 9 different flavors of ice cream and room under the counter for 9 cartons of ice cream lined up in a row. How many different ways can the ice cream be arranged under the counter?   362,880

■■■ Evaluate. (*See Examples 7–9.*)

17. 5!   120

18. 6!   720

19. 1!   1

20. 0!   1

Represent each in the form $n(n − 1)!$ (*See page 569.*)

21. 9!   9 · 8!

22. 13!   13 · 12!

23. a!   a · (a − 1)!

24. m!   m · (m − 1)!

(*See Examples 10 and 11.*)

25. Rewrite 27! with a factor of 22!
    27 · 26 · 25 · 24 · 23 · 22!

26. Rewrite 13! with a factor of 5!
    13 · 12 · 11 · 10 · 9 · 8 · 7 · 6 · 5!

19-2 Permutations, n Objects r at a Time

After finishing Lesson 19-2, you should be able to

▮ apply the formula $_nP_r = \dfrac{n!}{(n-r)!}$ to find the number of permutations of n objects taken r at a time.

▮▮ apply the expression n^r to find the number of distinct arrangements of n objects taken r at a time with replacement, or with repetition.

▮ Permutations of *n* Objects Taken *r* at a Time

Consider a set of 6 objects. In how many ways can we construct an ordered subset having three members? We can select the first object in 6 ways. There are then 5 choices for the second and then 4 choices for the third. By the Fundamental Counting Principle, there are then $6 \cdot 5 \cdot 4$ ways to construct the subset. In other words, there are $6 \cdot 5 \cdot 4$ permutations of a set of 6 objects taken three at a time. Note that $6 \cdot 5 \cdot 4$ is equal to $\dfrac{6 \cdot 5 \cdot 4 \cdot 3!}{3!}$,

or $\dfrac{6!}{3!}$. We adopt the following notation.

$_nP_r$ denotes the number of permutations of a set of n objects, taken r at a time.

Generalizing the above result gives us a theorem.

THEOREM 19-4

The number of permutations of a set of n objects taken r at a time is given by

$$_nP_r = \frac{n!}{(n-r)!}.$$

Examples. Compute.

1. $_6P_4 = \dfrac{6!}{(6-4)!}$ *By Theorem 19-4*

$= \dfrac{6!}{2!}$

$= \dfrac{6 \cdot 5 \cdot 4 \cdot 3 \cdot 2!}{2!}$ *By Theorem 19-3*

$= 6 \cdot 5 \cdot 4 \cdot 3$ *Simplifying*

$= 360$ *Multiplying*

2. $_5P_2 = \dfrac{5!}{(5-2)!}$ *By Theorem 19-4*

$= \dfrac{5!}{3!}$

$= \dfrac{5 \cdot 4 \cdot 3!}{3!}$ *By Theorem 19-3*

$= 5 \cdot 4$

$= 20$

TRY THIS ▬▬▬▬▬▶

Answers.   1. 210   2. 5040   3. 56   4. 55,440

Example 3.   How many ways can letters of the set
$\{A, B, C, D, E, F, G\}$ be arranged to form code symbols
of **a)** 7 letters? **b)** 5 letters? **c)** 2 letters?

a) $_7P_7 = 7 \cdot 6 \cdot 5 \cdot 4 \cdot 3 \cdot 2 \cdot 1 = 5040$

b) $_7P_5 = 7 \cdot 6 \cdot 5 \cdot 4 \cdot 3 \qquad = 2520$

c) $_7P_2 = 7 \cdot 6 \qquad\qquad\qquad = \quad 42$

Example 4.   A baseball manager arranges the
batting order as follows: The 4 infielders will bat
first, then the outfielders, catcher, and pitcher will
follow, not necessarily in that order. How many
batting orders are possible?

The infielders can bat in 4! different ways; the rest
in 5! different ways. Then by the Fundamental
Counting Principle we have $_4P_4 \cdot {}_5P_5 = 4! \cdot 5!$, or
2880, possible batting orders.

TRY THIS ▬▬▬▬▬▶

Answers.   5. 95,040   6. 151,200   7. 2880

▮▮ Repeated Use of the Same Object

For an arrangement of objects to be a permutation,
we can't repeat any of the objects. Sometimes we
want to be able to repeat, so we have another theorem.

Example 5.   How many 5-letter code symbols can be formed
with the letters A, B, C, and D if we allow repeated use of the
same letter? We have five spaces:

We can select the first in 4 ways, the second in 4
ways, and so on. Thus there are 4^5, or 1024,
arrangements. Generalizing gives us a theorem.

THEOREM 19-5

The number of arrangements of n objects taken r at a
time, with repetition, is n^r.

TRY THIS ▬▬▬▬▬▶

Compute.

1. $_7P_3$ 2. $_{10}P_4$
3. $_8P_2$ 4. $_{11}P_5$

---

5.   In how many ways can a
5-player starting unit be
selected from a basketball
squad of 12 members and
arranged in a straight line?

6.   A teacher wants to write a
6-item test from a pool of
10 questions. In how many
ways can this be done?

7.   How many 7-digit numbers
can be named, without re-
petition, using the digits 2,
3, 4, 5, 6, 7, and 8 if the
even digits come first?

---

8.   How many 5-letter code
symbols can be formed
by repeated use of the
letters of the alphabet?
Just find an expression.
Do not evaluate. 26^5

Example 6. A standard deck of cards has 52 different cards. How many 3-card ordered arrangements can be made by selecting the 3 cards **a)** without replacement? **b)** with replacement?

a) The case 'without replacement' is the number of permutations of 52 things taken 3 at a time.

$$_{52}P_3 = 52 \cdot 51 \cdot 50 = 132,600 \quad \textit{By Theorem 19-4}$$

b) The case 'with replacement' is the number of arrangements of 52 objects taken 3 at a time, with repetition.

$$52 \cdot 52 \cdot 52 = 52^3 = 140,608 \quad \textit{By Theorem 19-5}$$

Thus there are 140,608 possible ordered arrangements.

TRY THIS ▬▬▶

9. How many 2-card ordered arrangements can be made by selecting 2 cards from a deck of 52
   a) without replacement?
   b) with replacement?
   a) 2652 b) 2704

Exercise Set 19-2

∎ Evaluate. (*See Examples 1 and 2.*)
1. $_4P_3$ 24
3. $_{10}P_7$ 604,800
5. $_{20}P_2$ 380
7. $_8P_3$ 336

2. $_7P_5$ 2520
4. $_{10}P_3$ 720
6. $_{30}P_2$ 870
8. $_7P_4$ 840

(*See Examples 3 and 4.*)
9. How many ways can the letters of the set $\{M, N, O, P, Q\}$ be arranged to form code symbols of 4 letters? 3 letters? 120, 60
11. How many ways can 4 people be assigned to 6 offices? 360

10. How many ways can the letters of the set $\{P, D, Q, W, T, Z\}$ be arranged to form code symbols of 3 letters? 5 letters? 120, 720
12. How many ways can 3 people be assigned to 5 offices? 60

∎∎ (*See Examples 5 and 6.*)
13. How many 4-number license plates can be made using the digits 0, 1, 2, 3, 4, 5 if repetitions are allowed? not allowed? 1296, 360
15. A teacher wants to write a 4-item test from a pool of 12 questions. In how many ways can this be done? 11,880
17. As in Exercise 13, but the even digits must come first. 648, 180
19. As in Exercise 13, but the license number must be even. 648, 180

14. How many 5-number license plates can be made using the digits 1, 2, 3, 4, 5, 6, 7 if repetitions are allowed? not allowed? 16,807, 2520
16. A teacher wants to write a 5-item test from a pool of 8 questions. In how many ways can this be done? 6720
18. As in Exercise 14, but the odd digits must come first. 9604, 1440
20. As in Exercise 14, but the license number must be odd. 9604, 1440

19-3 Combinatorial Algebra: Combinations

After finishing Lesson 19-3, you should be able to

■ apply the formula $_nC_r = \begin{pmatrix} n \\ r \end{pmatrix}$ to find the number of combinations of a set of *n* objects taken *r* at a time.

■ Permutations of a set are ordered subsets. Unordered subsets are called *combinations*.

Example 1. How many combinations are there of the set {A, B, C, D} taken 3 at a time?

The combinations are the subsets

    {A, B, C}   {B, C, D}   {A, C, D}   {A, B, D}

Note that the set {A, B, C} is the same as the set {B, A, C} since they contain the same objects.

TRY THIS ➡

1. Consider the set {A, B, C, D}. How many combinations are there taken
   a) 4 at a time? **1**
   b) 3 at a time? **4**
   c) 2 at a time? **6**
   d) 1 at a time? **4**
   e) 0 at a time? **1**

DEFINITION

The number of combinations of a set of *n* objects taken *r* at a time, denoted $_nC_r$, is the number of subsets that contain *r* objects.

A general formula for $_nC_r$ is given in the next theorem. First we define some convenient symbolism.

DEFINITION

$\begin{pmatrix} n \\ r \end{pmatrix}$ is defined to mean $\dfrac{n!}{r!(n-r)!}$.

The notation $\begin{pmatrix} n \\ r \end{pmatrix}$ is read "*n* over *r*," or (for reasons we see later) "binomial coefficient *n* over *r*."

Examples. Evaluate.

2. $\begin{pmatrix} 5 \\ 2 \end{pmatrix} = \dfrac{5!}{2!(5-2)!}$ *By definition of* $\begin{pmatrix} 5 \\ 2 \end{pmatrix}$

    $= \dfrac{5!}{2!3!}$

    $= \dfrac{5 \cdot 4 \cdot 3!}{2!3!}$ *By Theorem 19-3*

    $= 10$

3. $\dbinom{7}{4} = \dfrac{7!}{4!(7-4)!} = \dfrac{7!}{4!3!} = \dfrac{7 \cdot 6 \cdot 5 \cdot 4!}{3!4!} = \dfrac{7 \cdot 6 \cdot 5}{3 \cdot 2 \cdot 1} = 35$

TRY THIS ━━━━━▶

Answers. 2. 45   3. 45

Evaluate.

2. $\dbinom{10}{8}$

3. $\dbinom{10}{2}$

THEOREM 19-6

The number of combinations of a set of *n* objects taken *r* at a time is given by $_nC_r = \dbinom{n}{r}$.

TRY THIS ━━━━━▶

Answers. 4. 21   5. 21

Evaluate.

4. $_7C_5$

5. $_7C_2$

Example 4. For a sociological study 4 people are chosen at random from a group of 10 people. How many ways can this be done?

No order is implied here so the number of ways 4 people can be selected is $_{10}C_4$.

$$_{10}C_4 = \dbinom{10}{4} \quad \textit{By Theorem 19-6}$$

$$= \frac{10!}{4!6!}$$

$$= \frac{10 \cdot 9 \cdot 8 \cdot 7 \cdot 6!}{4!6!}$$

$$= \frac{10 \cdot 9 \cdot 8 \cdot 7}{4 \cdot 3 \cdot 2 \cdot 1}$$

$$= 210$$

TRY THIS ━━━━━▶

6. How many ways can a 5-player starting unit be selected from a 12-member basketball squad? **792**

Example 5. How many committees can be formed from a set of 5 governors and 7 senators if each committee contains 3 governors and 4 senators?

The 3 governors can be selected in $_5C_3$ ways and the 4 senators can be selected in $_7C_4$ ways. Using the Fundamental Counting Principle, it follows that the number of committees will be

$$_5C_3 \cdot {_7C_4} = 10 \cdot 35 = 350.$$

TRY THIS ➡

Example 6. *Wendy's Hamburgers,* a national firm, advertises "We Fix Hamburgers 256 Ways!" This is accomplished using various *combinations* of catsup, onion, mustard, pickle, mayonnaise, relish, tomato, or lettuce. Of course, one can also have a plain hamburger. Use combination notation to show the number of possible hamburgers. Do not evaluate. (We will show an easy way in Lesson 19-4.)

> 7. A committee is to be chosen from 12 men and 8 women and is to consist of 3 men and 2 women. How many ways can this committee be formed? **6160**

There are 8 basic seasonings. Each way of fixing a hamburger is a combination, or subset, of these seasonings. There are $\binom{8}{0}$ subsets with 0 seasonings, $\binom{8}{1}$ subsets with 1 seasoning, $\binom{8}{2}$ subsets with 2 seasonings, and so on, up to $\binom{8}{8}$ subsets with 8 seasonings. Thus the total number of combinations, or subsets, is

$$\binom{8}{0} + \binom{8}{1} + \binom{8}{2} + \cdots + \binom{8}{8}.$$

TRY THIS ➡

> 8. Wendy's excludes cheese from the possibilities. Including cheese as a possibility, use combination notation to show the number of ways Wendy's could fix hamburgers. $\binom{9}{0} + \binom{9}{1} + \binom{9}{2} + \ldots + \binom{9}{9}$ or 512

Exercise Set 19-3

▮ Evaluate. (*See Examples 2 and 3.*)

1. $_9C_5$ **126**
2. $_{14}C_2$ **91**
3. $\binom{50}{2}$ **1225**
4. $\binom{40}{3}$ **9880**
5. $\binom{12}{8}$ **495**
6. $\binom{14}{9}$ **2002**
7. $_nC_3$ $\frac{n(n-1)(n-2)}{6}$
8. $_nC_2$ $\frac{n(n-1)}{2}$

(*See Examples 4–6.*)

9. There are 23 students in a club. How many ways can 4 officers be selected? **8855**

10. On a test a student is to select 6 out of 10 questions, without regard to order. How many ways can this be done? **210**

11. How many basketball games can be played in a 9-team league if each team plays all other teams twice? 72

12. How many basketball games can be played in a 10-team league if each team plays all other teams twice? 90

13. How many lines are determined by 8 points, no three of which are collinear? How many triangles are determined by the same points if no four are coplanar? 28, 56

14. How many lines are determined by 7 points, no three of which are collinear? How many triangles are determine by the same points if no four are coplanar? 21, 35

15. Of the first 10 questions on a test, a student must answer 7. On the second 5 questions, 3 must be answered. In how many ways can this be done? 1200

16. Of the first 8 questions on a test, a student must answer 6. On the second 4 questions, 3 must be answered. In how many ways can this be done? 112

17. Suppose the Senate of the United States consisted of 58 Democrats and 42 Republicans. How many committees consisting of 6 Democrats and 4 Republicans could be formed? You do not need to simplify the expression. $\binom{58}{6} \cdot \binom{42}{4}$

18. Suppose the Senate of the United States consisted of 63 Republicans and 37 Democrats. How many committees consisting of 8 Republicans and 12 Democrats could be formed? You need not simplify the expression. $\binom{63}{8} \cdot \binom{37}{12}$

19. How many 5-card poker hands consisting of 3 aces and 2 cards that are not aces are possible with a 52-card deck? See p. 583 for a description of a 52-card deck. 4512

20. How many 5-card poker hands consisting of 2 kings and 3 cards that are not kings are possible with a 52-card deck? 103,776

Challenge Exercises

21. How many line segments are determined by the 5 vertices of a pentagon? Of these, how many are diagonals?

22. How many line segments are determined by the n vertices of an n-agon? Of these, how many are diagonals?

Solve for n.

23. $\binom{n+1}{3} = 2 \cdot \binom{n}{2}$

24. $\binom{n}{n-2} = 6$

25. $\binom{n+2}{4} = 6 \cdot \binom{n}{2}$

26. $\binom{n}{3} = 2 \cdot \binom{n-1}{2}$

27. Prove that $\binom{n}{r} = \binom{n}{n-r}$.

28. How many ways can 2 people be chosen from 3 men and 4 women such that at least one is a woman?

21. 10, 5 22. $\binom{n}{2}$, $\binom{n}{2} - n$ 23. 5 24. 4
25. 7 26. 6 27. By definition $\binom{n}{r} = \frac{n!}{r!(n-r)!}$.
Also by definition $\binom{n}{n-r} = \frac{n!}{(n-r)![n-(n-r)]!}$
$= \frac{n!}{(n-r)!r!} = \frac{n!}{r!(n-r)!}$ $\therefore \binom{n}{r} = \binom{n}{n-r}$ 28. 18

19-4 The Binomial Theorem

After finishing Lesson 19-4, you should be able to
■ find the *r*th term of the binomial expansion of $(a + b)^n$.
■■ use the Binomial Theorem to expand expressions like $(x^2 + 3y)^9$.
■■■ determine the number of subsets of a finite set.

Consider the following expanded powers of $(a + b)^n$, where $a + b$ is any binomial. Look for patterns.

$$(a + b)^0 = \qquad\qquad\qquad 1$$
$$(a + b)^1 = \qquad\qquad\qquad a + b$$
$$(a + b)^2 = \qquad\qquad\quad a^2 + 2ab + b^2$$
$$(a + b)^3 = \qquad\quad a^3 + 3a^2b + 3ab^2 + b^3$$
$$(a + b)^4 = \quad a^4 + 4a^3b + 6a^2b^2 + 4ab^3 + b^4$$
$$(a + b)^5 = a^5 + 5a^4b + 10a^3b^2 + 10a^2b^3 + 5ab^4 + b^5$$

Note that each expansion is a polynomial. It is also a series, though not arithmetic or geometric. There are some patterns to be noted.

1. In each term, the sum of the exponents is *n*.
2. The exponents of *a* start with *n* and decrease. The last term has no factor of *a*. The first term has no factor of *b*. The exponents of *b* start in the second term with 1 and increase to *n*.
3. There is one more term than the degree of the polynomial.
4. If *a* and *b* are positive, all the terms are positive. If *b* is negative, its odd powers are negative, so the terms would alternate from positive to negative.

All that remains is finding a way to determine the coefficients. The next theorem shows how to do this.

THEOREM 19-7 (The Binomial Theorem)
For any binomial $(a + b)$ and any natural number *n*,

$$(a + b)^n = \binom{n}{0}a^n + \binom{n}{1}a^{n-1}b + \binom{n}{2}a^{n-2}b^2 + \cdots + \binom{n}{n}b^n.$$

The statement of Theorem 19-7 in sigma notation is as follows.

$$(a + b)^n = \sum_{r=0}^{n} \binom{n}{r}a^{n-r}b^r$$

Because of this theorem $\binom{n}{r}$ is called a *binomial coefficient*.

▮ Finding the *r*th Term

Look at the theorem. We see that the $(r + 1)$st term is $\binom{n}{r} a^{n-r} b^r$.

That is, the 1st term is $\binom{n}{0} a^{n-0} b^0$, the 2nd term is $\binom{n}{1} a^{n-1} b^1$, the

3rd term is $\binom{n}{2} a^{n-2} b^2$, the 8th term is $\binom{n}{7} a^{n-7} b^7$, and so on.

Example 1. Find the 7th term of $(4x - y^2)^9$.

We let $r = 6$, $n = 9$, $a = 4x$, and $b = -y^2$ in the formula

$\binom{n}{r} a^{n-r} b^r$. Then

$$\binom{9}{6}(4x)^3(-y^2)^6 = \frac{9!}{6!3!}(4x)^3(-y^2)^6$$

$$= \frac{9 \cdot 8 \cdot 7 \cdot 6!}{3! \cdot 6!}(64x^3y^{12})$$

$$= 5376x^3y^{12}.$$

TRY THIS ▬▬▬▶

> 1. Find the 4th term of
> $(x - 3)^8$. $-1512x^5$
> 2. Find the 6th term of
> $(y^2 + 2)^{10}$. $8064y^{10}$

▮▮ Binomial Expansion

Let us now find an expansion.

Example 2. Expand $(x^2 - 2y)^5$.

Note that $a = x^2$, $b = -2y$, and $n = 5$. Then using the binomial theorem we have

$$(x^2 - 2y)^5 = \binom{5}{0}(x^2)^5 + \binom{5}{1}(x^2)^4(-2y) + \binom{5}{2}(x^2)^3(-2y)^2 +$$

$$\binom{5}{3}(x^2)^2(-2y)^3 + \binom{5}{4}x^2(-2y)^4 + \binom{5}{5}(-2y)^5$$

$$= \frac{5!}{0!5!}x^{10} + \frac{5!}{1!4!}x^8(-2y) + \frac{5!}{2!3!}x^6(-2y)^2 +$$

$$\frac{5!}{3!2!}x^4(-2y)^3 + \frac{5!}{4!1!}x^2(-2y)^4 + \frac{5!}{5!0!}(-2y)^5$$

$$= x^{10} - 10x^8y + 40x^6y^2 - 80x^4y^3 + 80x^2y^4 - 32y^5.$$

TRY THIS ▬▬▬▶

> Expand.
>
> 3. $(x^2 - 1)^5$
>
> 4. $\left(2x + \dfrac{1}{y}\right)^4$

Answers.   3. $x^{10} - 5x^8 + 10x^6 - 10x^4 + 5x^2 - 1$ 4. $16x^4 + 32\dfrac{x^3}{y}$
$+ 24\dfrac{x^2}{y^2} + 8\dfrac{x}{y^3} + \dfrac{1}{y^4}$

A Proof of Theorem 19-7

Consider the nth power of a binomial $(a + b)$

$$(a + b)^n = \underbrace{(a + b)(a + b)(a + b)(a + b) \cdots (a + b)}_{n \text{ factors}}$$

When we multiply, we will find all possible products of a's and b's. For example, when we multiply all the first terms we will get n factors of a, or a^n. Thus the first term in the expansion is a^n. The binomial coefficient $\binom{n}{0}$ is 1; this establishes that the first term mentioned in the theorem is correct.

To get a term such as the $a^{n-r}b^r$ term, we will take a's from $n - r$ factors and b's from r factors. Thus we take n objects, $n - r$ of them a's and r of them b's. The number of ways we can do this is

$$\frac{n!}{(n - r)!r!}.$$

This is $\binom{n}{r}$. Thus the $a^{n-r}b^r$ term in the expansion has the coefficient $\binom{n}{r}$.

⦙⦙⦙ Subsets

Suppose a set has n objects. The number of subsets containing r members is $\binom{n}{r}$, by Theorem 19-6. The total number of subsets of a set is the number with 0 elements, plus the number with 1 element, plus the number with two elements, and so on. The total number of subsets of a set with n members is

$$\binom{n}{0} + \binom{n}{1} + \binom{n}{2} + \cdots + \binom{n}{n}.$$

Now let us expand $(1 + 1)^n$.

$$(1 + 1)^n = \binom{n}{0} + \binom{n}{1} + \binom{n}{2} + \cdots + \binom{n}{n}$$

Thus the total number of subsets is $(1 + 1)^n$ or 2^n. We have proved the following theorem.

THEOREM 19-8

The total number of subsets of a set with n members is 2^n.

Example 3. How many subsets are in the set $\{A, B, C, D, E\}$?

The set has 5 members, so the number of subsets is 2^5, or 32.

Example 4. *Wendy's Hamburgers* makes hamburgers 256 ways using combinations of 8 seasonings. Show why.

The total number of combinations is

$$\binom{8}{0} + \binom{8}{1} + \cdots + \binom{8}{8} = 2^8$$
$$= 256.$$

TRY THIS

> 5. How many subsets are there of the set of all states of the United States? 2^{50}
> 6. Including cheese as a possibility, Wendy's makes hamburgers using combinations of 9 seasonings. How many different ways is this? 2^9 or 512

Exercise Set 19-4

❙ Find the indicated term of the binomial expression. (*See Example 1.*)

1. 3rd, $(a + b)^6$ $15a^4b^2$
2. 6th, $(x + y)^7$ $21x^2y^5$
3. 12th, $(a - 2)^{14}$ $-745{,}472a^3$
4. 11th, $(x - 3)^{12}$ $3{,}897{,}234x^2$
5. 5th, $(2x^3 - \sqrt{y})^8$ $1120x^{12}y^2$
6. 4th, $\left(\dfrac{1}{b^2} + \dfrac{b}{3}\right)^7$ $\dfrac{35}{27}\dfrac{1}{b^5}$
7. Middle, $(2u - 3v^2)^{10}$ $-1{,}959{,}552u^5v^{10}$
8. Middle two, $(\sqrt{x} + \sqrt{3})^5$ $30x\sqrt{x}, 30x\sqrt{3}$

❙❙ Expand. (*See Example 2.*)

9. $(m + n)^5$ $m^5 + 5m^4n + 10m^3n^2 + 10m^2n^3 + 5mn^4 + n^5$
10. $(a - b)^4$ $a^4 - 4a^3b + 6a^2b^2 - 4ab^3 + b^4$
11. $(x^2 - 3y)^5$ $x^{10} - 15x^8y + 90x^6y^2 - 270x^4y^3 + 405x^2y^4 - 243y^5$
12. $(3c - d)^6$ $729c^6 - 1458c^5d + 1215c^4d^2 - 540c^3d^3 + 135c^2d^4 - 18cd^5 + d^6$
13. $(x^{-2} + x^2)^4$ $x^{-8} + 4x^{-4} + 6 + 4x^4 + x^8$
14. $\left(\dfrac{1}{\sqrt{x}} - \sqrt{x}\right)^6$ $\dfrac{1}{x^3} - \dfrac{6}{x^2} + \dfrac{15}{x} - 20 + 15x - 6x^2 + x^3$
15. $(1 - 1)^n$ $\binom{n}{0} - \binom{n}{1} + \binom{n}{2} - \binom{n}{3} + \ldots + \binom{n}{n}(-1)^n$
16. $(1 + 3)^n$ $\binom{n}{0} + \binom{n}{1}3 + \binom{n}{2}9 + \binom{n}{3}27 + \ldots + \binom{n}{n}3^n$
17. $(\sqrt{2} + 1)^6 - (\sqrt{2} - 1)^6$ $140\sqrt{2}$
18. $(1 - \sqrt{2})^4 + (1 + \sqrt{2})^4$ 34
19. $(\sqrt{2} - i)^4$, where $i^2 = -1$ $-7 - 4i\sqrt{2}$
20. $(1 + i)^6$, where $i^2 = -1$ $-8i$

❙❙❙ Determine the number of subsets. (*See Examples 3 and 4.*)

21. Of a set of 7 members   128
22. Of a set of 6 members   64
23. Of the set of letters of the English alphabet, which contains 26 letters 2^{26}
24. Of the set of letters of the Greek alphabet, which contains 24 letters 2^{24}

19-5 Probability

After finishing Lesson 19-5, you should be able to
▮ compute the probability of a simple event, using Principle *P*.

We say that when a coin is tossed the chances that it will fall heads are 1 out of 2, or that the *probability* that it will fall heads is $\frac{1}{2}$. Of course this does not mean that if a coin is tossed ten times it will fall heads exactly five times. If the coin is tossed a great number of times, however, it will fall heads very nearly half of them.

▮Experimental and Theoretical Probability

If we toss a coin a large number of times, say 1000, and count the number of heads, we can determine the probability. If there are 503 heads we would calculate the probability to be

$$\frac{503}{1000} \text{ or } 0.503.$$

This is an *experimental* determination of the probability.

If we consider a coin and reason that it is just as likely to fall heads as tails we would calculate the probability to be $\frac{1}{2}$. This is a *theoretical* determination of probability.

You might ask "What is the *true* probability?" In fact there is none. Experimentally we can determine probabilities within certain limits. These may or may not agree with what we obtain theoretically. In this chapter we consider only theoretically determined probability, and will make a definition accordingly. We use the notation $P(E)$ for the probability of an event E.

DEFINITION (Principle *P*)

The probability of an event E that can occur m ways out of n equally likely outcomes is given by $P(E) = \dfrac{m}{n}$.

Example 1. A die (plural, dice) is a cube with 6 faces, each containing a number of dots from 1 to 6. What is the probability of rolling a 3?

The *event* is rolling a 3. It can occur in only one way. The number of possible outcomes is 6. By Principle *P*,

$$P(3) = \frac{1}{6}.$$

Example 2. What is the probability of rolling an even number on a die?

The event P(even) can occur in 3 ways (getting a 2, 4, or 6). The number of possible outcomes is 6. By Principle P,

$$P(\text{even}) = \frac{3}{6}$$

$$= \frac{1}{2}.$$

TRY THIS ➡

1. What is the probability of rolling a prime number on a die? $\frac{1}{2}$

Many examples involve a standard deck of playing cards, described as follows:

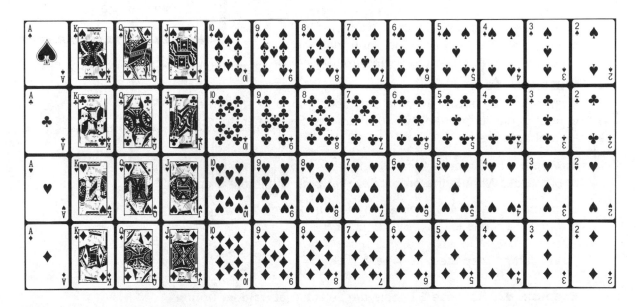

Example 3. What is the probability of drawing an ace from a well-shuffled deck of 52 cards?

An ace can be drawn in 4 ways. There are 52 equally likely outcomes (cards in the deck). By Principle P,

$$P(\text{drawing an ace}) = \frac{4}{52}, \text{ or } \frac{1}{13}.$$

Example 4.   Suppose we select, without looking, one marble from a bag containing 3 red marbles and 4 green marbles. What is the probability of selecting a red marble?

A red marble can be selected in 3 ways. There are 7 equally likely ways of selecting a marble. By Principle P, P(selecting a red marble) $= \dfrac{3}{7}$.

TRY THIS ➡️

2. Suppose we draw a card from a well-shuffled deck of 52 cards. What is the probability of drawing
    a) a king?
    b) a spade?
    c) a black card?
    d) a jack or a queen?
3. Suppose we select, without looking, one marble from a bag containing 5 red marbles and 6 green marbles. What is the probability of selecting a green marble?

We can use Principle P only when outcomes are equally likely. We could reason that the probability that a thumbtack will land point up is $\frac{1}{2}$ because there are just two ways for it to land: 🖈 🖈. But these are not equally likely. If the point of the tack is very long, like a nail, it would almost always land on its side. If the point is short, so that it looks like a coin, it should land point up about half the time. The next theorem follows at once from Principle P.

Answers.   2. a) $\frac{1}{13}$ b) $\frac{1}{4}$ c) $\frac{1}{2}$ d) $\frac{2}{13}$ 3. $\frac{6}{11}$

THEOREM 19-9

The probability of any event is a number from 0 to 1. If an event cannot occur its probability is 0. If an event is certain to occur its probability is 1.

Example 5.   Suppose 2 cards are drawn from a well-shuffled deck of 52 cards. What is the probability that both of them are spades?

13 of the 52 cards are spades, so the number m of ways of drawing 2 spades is $_{13}C_2$. By Principle P,

$$P(\text{getting 2 spades}) = \frac{m}{n} = \frac{_{13}C_2}{_{52}C_2} = \frac{78}{1326} = \frac{1}{17}.$$

Example 6.   Suppose 2 people are selected at random from a group that consists of 6 men and 4 women. What is the probability that both of them are women?

The number of ways of selecting 2 women from a group of 4 is $_4C_2$. The number of ways of selecting 2 people from a group of 10 is $_{10}C_2$. Thus the probability of selecting 2 women from the group of 10 is P, where $P = \dfrac{_4C_2}{_{10}C_2} = \dfrac{6}{45} = \dfrac{2}{15}$.

Example 7. Suppose 3 people are selected at random from a group that consists of 6 men and 4 women. What is the probability that 1 man and 2 women are selected?

One man can be selected in $_6C_1$ ways, and 2 women can be selected in $_4C_2$ ways. By the Fundamental Counting Principle the number of ways of selecting 1 man and 2 women is $_6C_1 \cdot _4C_2$. The number of ways of selecting 3 people from a group of 10 is $_{10}C_3$. Thus the probability is

$$\frac{_6C_1 \cdot _4C_2}{_{10}C_3}, \text{ or } \frac{3}{10}.$$

TRY THIS

Answers. 4. $\frac{11}{850}$ 5. $\frac{15}{91}$ 6. $\frac{6}{13}$

Example 8. What is the probability of getting a total of 8 on a roll of a pair of dice? (Assume the dice are different, say one red and one green.)

On each die there are 6 possible outcomes. There are $6 \cdot 6$, or 36, possible outcomes for the pair. The outcome set (the set of all possible outcomes) is shown below.

4. Suppose 3 cards are drawn from a well-shuffled deck of 52 cards. What is the probability that all three of them are spades?

5. Suppose 2 people are selected at random from a group which consists of 8 men and 6 women. What is the probability that both of them are women?

6. Suppose 3 people are selected at random from a group which consists of 8 men and 6 women. What is the probability that 2 men and 1 woman are selected?

Red die

6	(1, 6)	(2, 6)	(3, 6)	(4, 6)	(5, 6)	(6, 6)
5	(1, 5)	(2, 5)	(3, 5)	(4, 5)	(5, 5)	(6, 5)
4	(1, 4)	(2, 4)	(3, 4)	(4, 4)	(5, 4)	(6, 4)
3	(1, 3)	(2, 3)	(3, 3)	(4, 3)	(5, 3)	(6, 3)
2	(1, 2)	(2, 2)	(3, 2)	(4, 2)	(5, 2)	(6, 2)
1	(1, 1)	(2, 1)	(3, 1)	(4, 1)	(5, 1)	(6, 1)

    1   2   3   4   5   6 Green die

The pairs that total 8 are as shown. There are 5 ways of getting a total of 8, so the probability is $\frac{5}{36}$.

TRY THIS

7. What is the probability of getting a total of 7 on a roll of a pair of dice? $\frac{1}{6}$

Exercise Set 19-5

Use Quiz 34 after lesson 19—5.

▮ Suppose we draw a card from a well-shuffled deck of 52 cards. (*See Examples 1–3.*) What is the probability of drawing

1. a heart? $\frac{1}{4}$

2. a queen? $\frac{1}{13}$

3. a 4? $\frac{1}{13}$

4. a club? $\frac{1}{4}$

5. a black card? $\frac{1}{2}$

6. a red card? $\frac{1}{2}$

7. a 9 or a king? $\frac{2}{13}$

8. an ace or a deuce? $\frac{2}{13}$

Suppose we select, without looking, one marble from a bag containing 4 red marbles and 10 green marbles. (*See Example 4.*) What is the probability of selecting

9. a red marble? $\frac{2}{7}$

10. a green marble? $\frac{5}{7}$

11. a purple marble? 0

12. a white marble? 0

Suppose 4 cards are drawn from a well-shuffled deck of 52 cards. (*See Example 5.*) What is the probability that

13. all 4 are spades? $\frac{11}{4165}$

14. all 4 are hearts? $\frac{11}{4165}$

(*See Examples 6–8.*)

15. If marbles are drawn at random all at once from a bag containing 8 white marbles and 6 black marbles, what is the probability that 2 will be white and 2 will be black? $\frac{60}{143}$

16. From a group of 8 men and 7 women, a committee of 4 is chosen. What is the probability that 2 men and 2 women will be chosen? $\frac{28}{65}$

17. What is the probability of getting a total of 6 on a roll of a pair of dice? $\frac{5}{36}$

18. What is the probability of getting a total of 3 on a roll of a pair of dice? $\frac{1}{18}$

19. What is the probability of getting snake eyes (a total of 2) on a roll of a pair of dice? $\frac{1}{36}$

20. What is the probability of getting box-cars (a total of 12) on a roll of a pair of dice? $\frac{1}{36}$

21. From a bag containing 5 nickels, 8 dimes, and 7 quarters, 5 coins are drawn at random all at once. What is the probability of getting 2 nickels, 2 dimes, and 1 quarter? $\frac{245}{1938}$

22. From a bag containing 6 nickels, 10 dimes, and 4 quarters, 6 coins are drawn at random all at once. What is the probability of getting 3 nickels, 2 dimes, and 1 quarter? $\frac{30}{323}$

COMPUTER NOTE: Computers Go into Business

Beginning in the 1950s, electronic computers entered the world of business. Now they are an established part of that world. They prepare paychecks, keep track of sales and inventory, and calculate costs and profits.

CHAPTER 19 REVIEW

Review the material in the chapter. Then see how you have done by trying these review exercises. If you miss an exercise, restudy the indicated lesson.

19-1   1.   Evaluate 8!   40,320
19-1   2.   How many different displays are possible using 9 signal flags in a row?   362,880
19-2   3.   Evaluate $_6P_3$.   120
19-2   4.   The Greek alphabet contains 24 letters. How many different 3-letter code names can be formed, without repetition?   12,144
19-3   5.   Evaluate $\binom{10}{3}$.   120
19-3   6.   How many different 3-card hands are possible from a 52-card deck? (Do not consider order.)   22,100
19-4   7.   Find the 12th term of $(a + x)^{18}$. Do *not* multiply out the factorials in the binomial coefficient. $\binom{18}{11}a^7x^{11}$
19-4   8.   Expand: $(m + n)^7$. $m^7 + 7m^6n + 21m^5n^2 + 35m^4n^3 + 35m^3n^4 + 21m^2n^5 + 7mn^6 + n^7$
19-5   9.   A bag contains 4 white balls, 3 blue balls, and 7 red balls. A ball is drawn at random. What is the probability that it is red? $\frac{1}{2}$

CHAPTER 19 TEST

1.   Evaluate $_5P_5$.   120
2.   How many ways can 6 books be arranged on a shelf?   720
3.   Evaluate $_4P_2$.   12
4.   How many ways can the letters of the set $\{D, E, F, G, H\}$ be arranged to form code symbols of 3 letters, without repetition?   60
5.   Evaluate $_8C_3$.   56
6.   The winner of a contest can choose any 8 of 15 prizes. How many different selections can he make?   6435
7.   Find the 4th term of $(a + x)^{12}$. $220a^9x^3$
8.   Expand: $(x^2 + 3y)^4$. $x^8 + 12x^6y + 54x^4y^2 + 108x^2y^3 + 81y^4$
9.   From a deck of 52 cards 1 card is drawn. What is the probability that it is a club? $\frac{1}{4}$

Use Cumulative Test 5 after Cumulative Review below.

CUMULATIVE REVIEW FOR CHAPTERS 16–19

16-1 1. Graph: $y = (\frac{1}{5})^x$. Curve through $(-1, 5)$, $(0, 1)$, $(1, \frac{1}{5})$

16-2 2. Graph: $y = \log_2(x + 1)$. Curve through $(-\frac{1}{2}, -1)$, $(0, 0)$, $(1, 1)$, $(3, 2)$, $(7, 3)$

16-2 3. Convert $10^{0.4771} = 3$ to a logarithmic equation. $0.4771 = \log_{10} 3$

16-2 4. Convert $\log_5 25 = 2$ to an exponential equation. $5^2 = 25$

16-2 Solve.

5. $\log_4 x = 3$ 6. $\log_x 64 = 3$ 7. $\log_{10} 10{,}000 = x$

5. 64   6. 4   7. 4

16-2 Simplify.

8. $7^{\log_7 10}$ 9. $\log_p p^a$ 8. 10   9. a

16-3 10. Express $\frac{1}{2} \log_a x + 3 \log_a y - 2 \log x$ as a single logarithm. $\log_a \frac{\sqrt{x}y^3}{x^2}$

16-3 11. Given $\log_{10} 3 = 0.477$ and $\log_{10} 10 = 1$, find $\log_{10} 90$. 1.954

Use Table 2 to find each of the following.

16-4 12. log 0.00134 7.1271 − 10

16-4 13. antilog 2.6294 426

16-5 14. Use logarithms to calculate: $\dfrac{70.7 \times (10.6)^2}{18.6 \times \sqrt{276}}$. 25.71

16-6 15. Find log 4518 using interpolation. 3.6549

Solve.

16-7 16. $4^{3x+5} = 16$ −1

16-7 17. $\log(x + 9) - \log x = 1$ 1

16-8 18. An earthquake has a magnitude of 7 on the Richter scale. What is its intensity? 10^7 times I_0

17-1 19. Find the first four terms, the 10th term, and the 15th term for the sequence $a_n = n + \dfrac{1}{n}$. $2, 2\frac{1}{2}, 3\frac{1}{3}, 4\frac{1}{4}; 10\frac{1}{10}; 15\frac{1}{15}$

17-2 20. Write sigma notation for $\frac{1}{3} + \frac{1}{9} + \frac{1}{27} + \frac{1}{81}$. $\sum\limits_{k=1}^{4} \frac{1}{3^k}$

17-3 21. Find the 17th term of the arithmetic sequence 7, 4, 1, . . . −41

17-4 22. Find the sum of the odd numbers from 1 to 99, inclusive. 2500

17-5 23. Find the common ratio for the geometric sequence 12, $-4, \frac{4}{3}, -\frac{4}{9}, \ldots$ $-\frac{1}{3}$

17-5 24. Find the 5th term of the geometric sequence 2, −10, 50, . . . 1250

17-6 25. Find the sum of the geometric series $\sum\limits_{k=1}^{7} 4^k$. 21,844

17-7 26. Find the sum of the geometric series $\frac{8}{3} + \frac{4}{3} + \frac{2}{3} + \cdots$ $\frac{16}{3}$

17-7 27. Find fractional notation for $5.15\overline{15}$. $\frac{170}{33}$

Solve, using matrices.

18-1   28. $2x + y = 7$ $(\frac{39}{11}, -\frac{1}{11})$
           $x - 5y = 4$

18-2   29. $p + q + r = 1$
           $p + 2q + 3r = 4$ $(1, -3, 3)$
           $p + 3q + 7r = 13$

18-3   30.   Evaluate: $\begin{vmatrix} 3 & 2 \\ -7 & 5 \end{vmatrix}$.   29

18-3   31.   Solve, using Cramer's Rule: $2x - 2y = 2$ $(-4, -5)$
                                       $6x - 5y = 1$

18-4   32.   Evaluate: $\begin{vmatrix} -1 & -2 & -3 \\ 3 & 4 & 2 \\ 0 & 1 & 2 \end{vmatrix}$. -3

18-4   33.   Solve, using Cramer's Rule: $3x - y + 2z = 1$
                                       $x - y + 2z = 3$ $(-1, -\frac{6}{7}, \frac{11}{7})$
                                      $-2x + 3y + z = 1$

18-5   34.   Add: $\begin{bmatrix} 1 & 3 \\ 2 & 6 \end{bmatrix} + \begin{bmatrix} 3 & 3 \\ -1 & -1 \end{bmatrix}$. $\begin{bmatrix} 4 & 6 \\ 1 & 5 \end{bmatrix}$

18-5   35.   Subtract: $\begin{bmatrix} -1 & 0 & 0 \\ 0 & 2 & 0 \end{bmatrix} - \begin{bmatrix} -3 & -3 & 7 \\ -5 & 2 & 1 \end{bmatrix}$. $\begin{bmatrix} 2 & 3 & -7 \\ 5 & 0 & -1 \end{bmatrix}$

Multiply, if possible.

18-6   36. $-5 \begin{bmatrix} -3 & 5 \\ 2 & -1 \end{bmatrix}$ 37. $[8 \quad -1] \begin{bmatrix} 3 & 3 \\ -1 & -1 \end{bmatrix}$

       38. $\begin{bmatrix} 3 & 3 \\ -1 & -1 \end{bmatrix} \begin{bmatrix} -3 \\ -2 \end{bmatrix}$ 36. $\begin{bmatrix} 15 & -25 \\ -10 & 5 \end{bmatrix}$ 37. $[25 \quad 25]$ 38. $\begin{bmatrix} -15 \\ 5 \end{bmatrix}$

19-1   39.   In how many ways can 8 motorcycles be parked in a row?   40,320

19-1   40.   Evaluate 6!.   720

19-2   41.   Evaluate $_8P_3$.   336

19-2   42.   How many 5-digit license plates can be made using the digits 1, 2, 3, 4, 5, 6, 7 if repetitions are allowed? not allowed?   16,807; 2520

19-3   43.   There are 23 students in a club. How many ways can 4 officers be selected?   8855

19-4   44.   Expand: $(x^2 - 3y)^5$. $x^{10} - 15x^8y + 90x^6y^2 - 270x^4y^3 + 405x^2y^4 - 243y^5$

19-4   45.   Determine the number of subsets of a set of 6 members.   64

19-5   46.   What is the probability of getting a total of 6 on a roll of a pair of dice? $\frac{5}{36}$

Ready for Trigonometric Functions?

8-1   1.   List the domain and range for $\{(6, 3), (8, 2), (7, 1)\}$.

Domain: $\{6, 8, 7\}$; range: $\{3, 2, 1\}$

8-5   Given $f(x) = 2x^2 + 1$ find

    2. $f(3)$ 19   3. $f(-2)$.   9

Here is a graph of $y = 2|x|$.
By translating this graph, sketch:

8-7   4. $y = 2|x| - 1$
    5. $y = -4 + 2|x|$.

By transforming $y = 2|x|$, sketch:

8-8   6. $y = 3|x|$
    7. $y = -\frac{1}{2}|x|$.

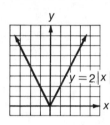

4. Ray from (0, −1) through (−1, 1), (−2, 3) and also ray from (0, −1) through (1, 1), (2, 3)   5. Ray from (0, −4) through (−1, −2), (−2, 0) and also ray from (0, −4) through (1, −2), (2, 0)   6. Ray from (0, 0) through (−1, 3), (−2, 6) and also ray from (0, 0) through (1, 3), (2, 6)   7. Ray from (0, 0) through (−2, −1), (−4, −2) and also ray from (0, 0) through (2, −1), (4, −2)

8-9   8.   Show that $f(x) = x^3 - x$ is odd. $f(-x) = (-x)^3 - (-x) = -x^3 + x = -(x^3 - x) = -f(x)$

8-9   9.   Show that $g(x) = 2x^2 - x^4$ is even. $g(-x) = 2(-x)^2 - (-x)^4 = 2x^2 - x^4 = g(x)$

Factor completely.

7-6   10. $24a^2 - 96b^2$ $24(a - 2b)(a + 2b)$

7-6   11. $3x^3y - 15x^2y^2 + 18xy^3$ $3xy(x - 3y)(x - 2y)$

Multiply and simplify where possible.

6-3   12. $x^2(6 + xy - 2y^2)$ $6x^2 + x^3y - 2x^2y^2$

6-3   13. $(3t + 2)(t - 4)$ $3t^2 - 10t - 8$

9-1   14. $\dfrac{(a^2 - 4)}{-2a - 6} \cdot \dfrac{a + 3}{a - 2}$ $\frac{a + 2}{2}$

Add or subtract and simplify.

9-3   15. $\dfrac{4}{-x} + \dfrac{6}{x}$ $\frac{2}{x}$ 16. $\dfrac{5cd}{4c^2 - 1} - \dfrac{c - d}{2c + 1}$ $\frac{-2c^2 + 7dc + c - d}{(2c - 1)(2c + 1)}$

Solve.

12-2   17. $a^2 + a - 12 = 0$ 3, −4   18. $6y^2 + 20y = 16$ $\frac{2}{3}$, −4

12-3   19. $1 + \dfrac{3}{x^2} = \dfrac{1}{x}$ $\frac{1 \pm i\sqrt{11}}{2}$ 20. $2x + x(x - 1) = 1$ $\frac{-1 \pm \sqrt{5}}{2}$

16-6   Find each of the following using interpolation.

    21.   log 37.27   1.5713   22.   antilog 3.8449   6997

Chapter 20
Trigonometric Functions

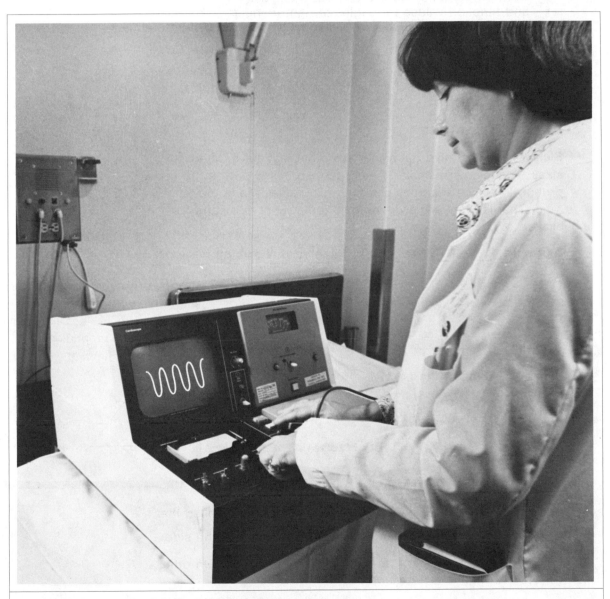

The graph displayed on the medical testing device illustrates one kind of trigonometric function.

20-1 Triangles

After finishing Lesson 20-1, you should be able to
- **I** write proportions based on similar triangles.
- **II** find function values for angles of right triangles.
- **III** use trigonometric functions to find missing parts of right triangles.

We consider an important class of functions, the trigonometric functions. They are based on certain properties of triangles.

I Similar Triangles

Similar triangles have the same shape but may have different sizes. Triangles are similar if their corresponding angles are congruent. In similar triangles corresponding sides are in the same ratio. That is, they are proportional. The symbol $\sim$ means "is similar to."

Example 1. $\triangle ABC \sim \triangle A'B'C'$. Write several true proportions.

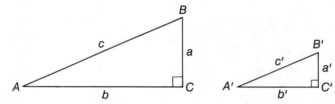

These are some of the possible proportions.

$$\frac{a}{a'} = \frac{b}{b'} \qquad \frac{c}{c'} = \frac{b}{b'} \qquad \frac{a}{a'} = \frac{c}{c'}$$

TRY THIS ➡

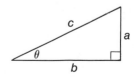

1. $\triangle PQR \sim \triangle GHK$. Write three proportions.

Answers may vary.

II Trigonometric Ratios

In a right triangle the side opposite the right angle is called the hypotenuse. In the right triangle shown, the ratio $\frac{a}{c}$ of the side *opposite* θ to the hypotenuse depends on the size of θ. In other words, this ratio is a *function* of θ.

This function is called the *sine* function. There are other such ratios, or functions, defined as follows.

Function	Abbreviation for function value	Defining ratio
sine	sin (θ) or sin θ	$\dfrac{\text{side opposite } \theta}{\text{hypotenuse}}$
cosine	cos (θ) or cos θ	$\dfrac{\text{side adjacent } \theta}{\text{hypotenuse}}$
tangent	tan (θ) or tan θ	$\dfrac{\text{side opposite } \theta}{\text{side adjacent } \theta}$

Note that the function values depend only on the size of the angle, not the size of the triangle.

Example 2. In this triangle find sin θ, cos θ, and tan θ.

$$\sin \theta = \frac{\text{side opposite } \theta}{\text{hypotenuse}} = \frac{3}{5}$$

$$\cos \theta = \frac{\text{side adjacent } \theta}{\text{hypotenuse}} = \frac{4}{5}$$

$$\tan \theta = \frac{\text{side opposite } \theta}{\text{side adjacent } \theta} = \frac{3}{4}$$

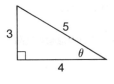

TRY THIS ➡

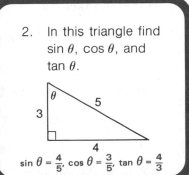

2. In this triangle find sin θ, cos θ, and tan θ.

$\sin \theta = \frac{4}{5}$, $\cos \theta = \frac{3}{5}$, $\tan \theta = \frac{4}{3}$

▥ Solving Triangle Problems

Values for the trigonometric functions are given in tables. We use them to find lengths of segments or measures of angles without measuring them directly.

Example 3. Terry stands on level ground, 200 meters from the base of a TV tower. She finds she must look up at an angle of 26.5° to see the top of the tower. How tall is the tower?

From a diagram we see that a right triangle is formed. We plan to use the tangent function. From the definition of the tangent function, we have

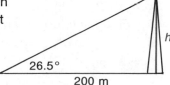

$$\frac{h}{200} = \tan 26.5°.$$

Then $h = 200 \tan 26.5°$. We find, from a table, that $\tan 26.5° = 0.4986$, approximately. Thus

$$h = 200 \times 0.4986 = 99.72 \text{ m}.$$

Example 4. A kite flies at a height of 30 m when 65 m of string is out. Assuming that the string is in a straight line, what is the angle that it makes with the ground?

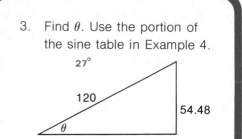

Because we know the length of the side opposite θ and the hypotenuse, we plan to use the sine function. A portion of a sine table is given below.

sin 26.5° = 0.4462	sin 28.5° = 0.4772
sin 27° = 0.4540	sin 29° = 0.4848
sin 27.5° = 0.4617	sin 29.5° = 0.4924
sin 28° = 0.4695	sin 30° = 0.5000

From the definition of the sine function, we have

$$\frac{30}{65} = \sin \theta \approx 0.4615.$$

From the table, we find that θ is about 27.5°.

TRY THIS

3. Find θ. Use the portion of the sine table in Example 4.

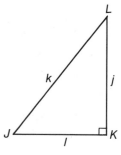

Exercise Set 20-1

▮ Write three proportions for each pair of similar triangles. (*See Example 1.*)

1.   Answers may vary.

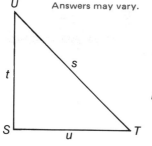

2.   Answers may vary.

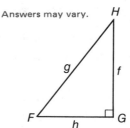

▮▮ Find the indicated function values for each of the following triangles. (*See Example 2.*)

3. Find sin θ, cos θ, and tan θ.

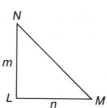

$\sin \theta = \frac{7}{25}$, $\cos \theta = \frac{24}{25}$, $\tan \theta = \frac{7}{24}$

4. Find sin θ, cos θ, and tan θ.

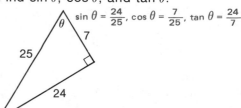

$\sin \theta = \frac{24}{25}$, $\cos \theta = \frac{7}{25}$, $\tan \theta = \frac{24}{7}$

5. Find $\sin \theta$, $\cos \theta$, and $\tan \theta$.

$\sin \theta = \frac{5}{13}$, $\cos \theta = \frac{12}{13}$, $\tan \theta = \frac{5}{12}$

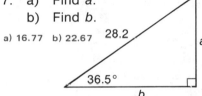

6. Find $\sin \theta$, $\cos \theta$, and $\tan \theta$.

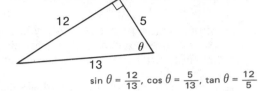

$\sin \theta = \frac{12}{13}$, $\cos \theta = \frac{5}{13}$, $\tan \theta = \frac{12}{5}$

■■■ Use the following function values. (*See Examples 3 and 4.*)

$\sin 36° = 0.5878$	$\cos 36° = 0.8090$	$\tan 36° = 0.7265$
$\sin 36.5° = 0.5948$	$\cos 36.5° = 0.8039$	$\tan 36.5° = 0.7400$
$\sin 37° = 0.6018$	$\cos 37° = 0.7986$	$\tan 37° = 0.7536$
$\sin 37.5° = 0.6088$	$\cos 37.5° = 0.7934$	$\tan 37.5° = 0.7673$
$\sin 38° = 0.6157$	$\cos 38° = 0.7880$	$\tan 38° = 0.7813$

7. a) Find a.
   b) Find b.

   a) 16.77 b) 22.67

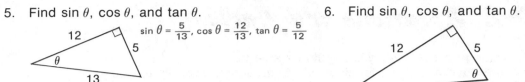

8. a) Find a.
   b) Find b.

   a) 15.64 b) 20.02

9. a) Find a.
   b) Find c.

   a) 36.49 b) 45.99

10. a) Find a.
    b) Find c.

    a) 49.55 b) 61.25

11. Find θ.

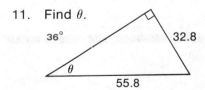

12. Find θ.

20-2 *Rotations and Angles*

After finishing Lesson 20-2, you should be able to
▮ tell the quadrant of the terminal side of an angle, given its measure.
▮▮ convert from degree to radian measure and conversely.

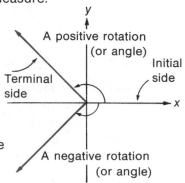

Consider a rotating ray, with its endpoint at the origin of an *xy*-plane. The ray starts in position along the positive half of the *x*-axis. Counterclockwise rotations will be called positive. Clockwise rotations will be called negative. Note that the rotating ray and the positive half of the *x*-axis form an angle. Thus we often speak of "rotations" and "angles" interchangeably. The rotating ray is often called the *terminal side* of the angle, and the positive half of the *x*-axis is called the *initial side*.

▮ Measures of Rotations or Angles

The measure of an angle, or rotation, may be given in degrees. For example, a complete revolution has a measure of 360°, half a revolution has a measure of 180°, and so on. We also speak of an *angle* of 90° or 720°, or −240°, and so on. An angle between 0° and 90° has its terminal side in the first quadrant. An angle between 90° and 180° has its terminal side in the second quadrant. An angle between 0° and −90° has its terminal side in the fourth quadrant, and so on.

Examples. In which quadrant does the terminal side of each angle lie?

1. 53°   First quadrant
2. 253°   Third quadrant
3. −126°   Third quadrant
4. −373°   Fourth quadrant

TRY THIS ▬▬▶

In which quadrant does the terminal side of each angle lie?

1. 47°   2. 212°
3. −43°   4. −135°
5. 365°   6. 740°
1. First   2. Third   3. Fourth
4. Third   5. First   6. First

▮▮ Radian Measure

A circle with a radius of length 1 is called a *unit circle*. The distance around this circle from the initial side of an angle to the terminal side can be used as a measure of the rotation. The unit of measure is called a *radian*.

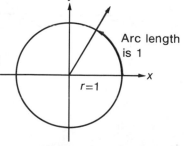

Arc length is 1

r = 1

1 Radian

A rotation of 360° (1 revolution) thus has a measure of 2π radians. Half a revolution is a rotation of 180°, or π radians. A quarter revolution is a rotation of 90°, or $\frac{\pi}{2}$ radians, and so on. To convert between degrees and radians we can use the notion of "multiplying by one." Note the following:

$$\frac{1 \text{ revolution}}{1 \text{ revolution}} = 1 = \frac{2\pi \text{ radians}}{360 \text{ degrees}} = \frac{\pi \text{ radians}}{180 \text{ degrees}}$$

Also

$$\frac{180 \text{ degrees}}{\pi \text{ radians}} = 1.$$

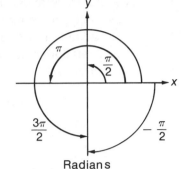

Radians

When a rotation is given in radians, the word "radians" is optional and often omitted. Thus if no unit is given for a rotation, it is understood to be in radians.

Example 5. Convert 60° to radians.

$$60° = 60° \cdot \frac{\pi \text{ radians}}{180°} \qquad \textit{Multiplying by 1}$$

$$= \frac{60°}{180°} \pi \text{ radians}$$

$$= \frac{\pi}{3} \text{ radians, or } \frac{\pi}{3}$$

Using 3.14 for π, we find that $\frac{\pi}{3}$ is about 1.05.

TRY THIS ➡

Convert to radian measure. Give answers in terms of π. Then give each answer using 3.14 for π.

7. 225° $\frac{5\pi}{4}$, 3.93
8. 300° $\frac{5\pi}{3}$, 5.23
9. −315° $-\frac{7\pi}{4}$, −5.50

Example 6. Convert $\frac{3\pi}{4}$ radians to degrees.

$$\frac{3\pi}{4} \text{ radians} = \frac{3\pi}{4} \text{ radians} \cdot \frac{180°}{\pi \text{ radians}} \qquad \textit{Multiplying by 1}$$

$$= \frac{3\pi}{4\pi} \cdot 180$$

$$= 135°$$

TRY THIS ➡

Convert to degree measure.

10. $\frac{4\pi}{3}$ 11. $\frac{5\pi}{2}$ 12. $-\frac{4\pi}{5}$

10. 240°   11. 450°   12. −144°

The diagrams at the right show unit circles marked in both radians and degrees. These relationships should be memorized.

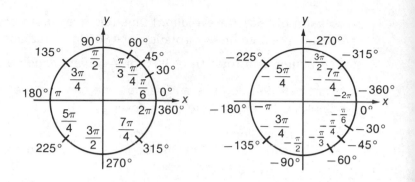

Exercise Set 20-2

▌For angles of the following measures, state in which quadrant the terminal side lies. (*See Examples 1–4.*)

1. 34° First
2. 320° Fourth
3. −120° Third
4. −175° Third
5. 60° First
6. −135° Third
7. 495° Second
8. 855° Second

▌▌Convert to radian measure. Give answers in terms of π. Then give each answer using 3.14 for π. (*See Example 5.*)

9. 30° $\frac{\pi}{6}$, 0.52
10. 15° $\frac{\pi}{12}$, 0.26
11. 100° $\frac{5\pi}{9}$, 1.74
12. 200° $\frac{10\pi}{9}$, 3.49
13. 75° $\frac{5\pi}{12}$, 1.31
14. 105° $\frac{7\pi}{12}$, 1.83
15. 120° $\frac{2\pi}{3}$, 2.09
16. 240° $\frac{4\pi}{3}$, 4.19
17. −320° $-\frac{16\pi}{6}$, −5.58
18. −250° $-\frac{25\pi}{18}$, −4.36
19. −85° $-\frac{17\pi}{36}$, −1.48
20. −175° $-\frac{35\pi}{36}$, −3.05

Convert to degree measure. (*See Example 6.*)

21. 1 radian $(\frac{180}{\pi})° \approx 57.3°$
22. 2 radians $(\frac{360}{\pi})° \approx 114.6°$
23. 8π 1440°
24. -12π −2160°
25. $\frac{3}{4}\pi$ 135°
26. $\frac{5}{4}\pi$ 225°

Calculator Exercises

27. 0.2095π 28. 0.0707222π 29. 1.1922222π 30. 0.4103888π 31. 74.694267° 32. 134.54140° 33. 2172.0382° 34. 401.56050° 35. 1477.08° 36. −2543.4° 37. 135.576° 38. −216.9° 39. $\frac{5}{24}\pi$ or 37.5°

Convert to radian measure. Leave answers in terms of π.

27. 37.71° 28. 12.73° 29. 214.6° 30. 73.87°

Convert these radian measures to degree measure.

31. 1.303 32. 2.347 33. 37.89 34. 7.005
35. 8.206π 36. −14.13π 37. 0.7532π 38. −1.205π

39. What is the angle between the hands of a clock at 7:45?

20-3 *Trigonometric Functions of Angles*

After finishing Lesson 20-3, you should be able to
▮ find the sin, cos, and tan of an angle or rotation.
▮▮ find the values of the six trigonometric functions of an angle or rotation.
▮▮▮ find the function values for any angle whose terminal side makes an angle of 30°, 45°, or 60° with the *x*-axis.

▮ The Sine, Cosine, and Tangent Functions

We can use angles or rotations to extend the idea of trigonometric functions. Consider a circle of radius *r* as shown at the right. Each rotation θ determines a point *R* on the circle. Consider $\triangle OMR$. All trigonometric function values can be considered ratios of sides of triangles, placed as shown. A triangle placed that way is said to be *in standard position*. The point *R* can be anywhere on the circle of radius *r*. Its coordinates may be positive, negative, or zero, depending on its location. The length of the radius (hypotenuse of the triangle) is always considered positive. Then, regardless of the position of point *R*, we have

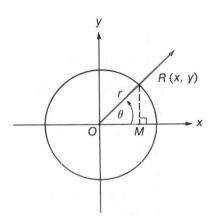

$$\sin \theta = \frac{y}{r} \left(\frac{\text{second coordinate}}{\text{radius}} \right).$$

The figures at the right show *R* in quadrants II and III. In quadrant II *y* and *r* are both positive, so $\sin \theta$ is positive. In quadrant III *y* is negative (and *r* is positive) so $\sin \theta$ is negative.

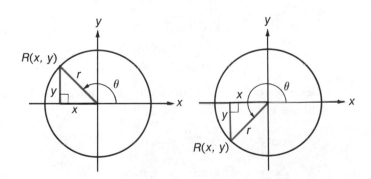

The values of the cosine and tangent functions are as follows.

$$\cos \theta = \frac{x}{r} \left(\frac{\text{first coordinate}}{\text{radius}} \right)$$

$$\tan \theta = \frac{y}{x} \left(\frac{\text{second coordinate}}{\text{first coordinate}} \right)$$

Example 1. Find the sine, cosine, and tangent of the angle shown.

$$\sin \theta = \frac{y}{r} = \frac{4}{5} = 0.8$$

$$\cos \theta = \frac{x}{r} = \frac{-3}{5} = -0.6$$

$$\tan \theta = \frac{y}{x} = \frac{4}{-3} \approx -1.33$$

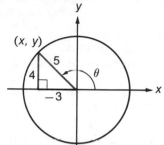

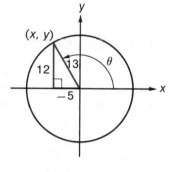

1. Find the sine, cosine, and tangent of the angle shown.

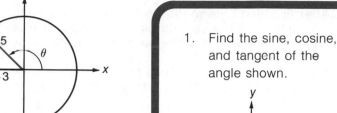

TRY THIS

Answers. 1. $\sin \theta = \frac{12}{13} \approx 0.923$, $\cos \theta = -\frac{-5}{13} \approx -0.385$, $\tan \theta = \frac{12}{-5} = -2.4$

▮▮ Reciprocal Functions

We can define three new trigonometric functions by taking the reciprocals of the previously defined functions.

DEFINITION

The *cotangent, secant,* and *cosecant* functions are the respective reciprocals of the tangent, cosine, and sine functions.

$$\cot \theta = \frac{x}{y} \left(\frac{\text{first coordinate}}{\text{second coordinate}} \right)$$

$$\sec \theta = \frac{r}{x} \left(\frac{\text{radius}}{\text{first coordinate}} \right)$$

$$\csc \theta = \frac{r}{y} \left(\frac{\text{radius}}{\text{second coordinate}} \right)$$

Example 2. Find the cotangent, secant, and cosecant of the angle shown in Example 1.

$$\cot \theta = \frac{x}{y} = \frac{-3}{4} = -0.75$$

$$\sec \theta = \frac{r}{x} = \frac{5}{-3} \approx -1.67$$

$$\csc \theta = \frac{r}{y} = \frac{5}{4} = 1.25$$

2. Find the cotangent, secant, and cosecant of the angle shown in margin Exercise 1.

TRY THIS

Answers. 2. $\cot \theta = \frac{-5}{12} \approx -0.417$, $\sec \theta = \frac{13}{-5} = -2.6$, $\csc = \frac{13}{12} \approx 1.08$

Notice the signs of the function values in each quadrant. Suppose a rotation θ determines any point on a circle in the first quadrant. Since both coordinates are positive there, the function values for all the circular functions will be positive.

Example 3. Give the signs of the six trigonometric functions for an angle in the second quadrant.

In the second quadrant, the first coordinate is negative and the second coordinate is positive. Thus the sine function has positive values and the cosine has negative values. The secant, being the reciprocal of the cosine, also has negative values, and the cosecant, being the reciprocal of the sine, has positive values. The tangent and cotangent both have negative values in the second quadrant.

TRY THIS

3. Give the signs of the six trigonometric functions for an angle in the third quadrant.

The figure below shows the quadrants in which the function values are positive.

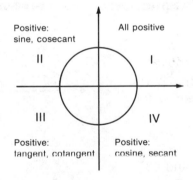

Positive:
sine, cosecant

All positive

II

I

III

IV

Positive:
tangent, cotangent

Positive:
cosine, secant

Answer.   3. The sine, cosine, secant, and cosecant functions all have negative values. The tangent and cotangent functions have positive values.

Ⅲ Special Angles and Reference Angles

Our knowledge of triangles enables us to determine function values for certain angles. First recall the Pythagorean theorem. It says that in any right triangle $a^2 + b^2 = c^2$, where c is the length of the hypotenuse.

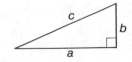

   In a 45° right triangle the legs are the same length. Let us consider such a triangle whose legs have length 1. Then its hypotenuse has length c given by

$$1^2 + 1^2 = c^2, \quad \text{or} \quad c^2 = 2, \quad \text{or} \quad c = \sqrt{2}.$$

Such a triangle is shown below. From this diagram we can easily determine the function values for 45° or $\frac{\pi}{4}$:

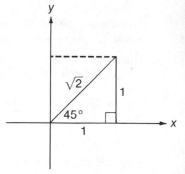

$$\sin 45° = \frac{1}{\sqrt{2}} = \frac{\sqrt{2}}{2} \qquad \cot 45° = \frac{1}{1} = 1$$

$$\cos 45° = \frac{1}{\sqrt{2}} = \frac{\sqrt{2}}{2} \qquad \sec 45° = \frac{\sqrt{2}}{1} = \sqrt{2}$$

$$\tan 45° = \frac{1}{1} = 1 \qquad \csc 45° = \frac{\sqrt{2}}{1} = \sqrt{2}$$

The three function values on the left should be memorized. The others are their reciprocals and can be found easily.

Example 4. Find a decimal approximation for sin 45°. Use 1.414 for $\sqrt{2}$.

$$\sin 45° = \frac{\sqrt{2}}{2} \approx \frac{1.414}{2} \approx 0.707$$

TRY THIS ➡

4. Find decimal approximations for cos 45°, sec 45°, and csc 45°. Use 1.414 for $\sqrt{2}$.

Answers. 4. cos 45° ≈ 0.707, sec 45° ≈ 1.414, csc 45° ≈ 1.414

Next we consider an equilateral triangle, each of whose sides has length 2. If we take half of it as shown, we obtain a right triangle having a hypotenuse of length 2 and a leg of length 1. The other leg has length a, given by the Pythagorean theorem as follows:

$$a^2 + 1^2 = 2^2, \quad \text{or} \quad a^2 = 3, \quad \text{or} \quad a = \sqrt{3}.$$

The acute angles of this triangle have measures of 30° and 60°. We can now determine function values for 30° and 60°. The function values for 30° are as follows:

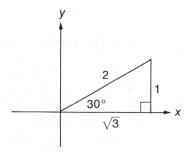

$$\sin 30° = \frac{1}{2} \qquad \cot 30° = \sqrt{3}$$

$$\cos 30° = \frac{\sqrt{3}}{2} \qquad \sec 30° = \frac{2}{\sqrt{3}} = \frac{2\sqrt{3}}{3}$$

$$\tan 30° = \frac{1}{\sqrt{3}} = \frac{\sqrt{3}}{3} \qquad \csc 30° = 2$$

We can now determine the function values for 60°, or $\frac{\pi}{3}$, by repositioning the 30°–60° triangle.

$$\sin 60° = \frac{\sqrt{3}}{2} \qquad \cot 60° = \frac{\sqrt{3}}{3}$$

$$\cos 60° = \frac{1}{2} \qquad \sec 60° = 2$$

$$\tan 60° = \sqrt{3} \qquad \csc 60° = \frac{2\sqrt{3}}{3}$$

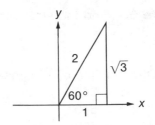

Example 5. Find a decimal approximation for $\cos 30°$. Use 1.732 for $\sqrt{3}$.

$$\cos 30° = \frac{\sqrt{3}}{2} \approx \frac{1.732}{2} \approx 0.866$$

TRY THIS

> Find decimal approximations for the following. Use 1.732 for $\sqrt{3}$.
>
> 5. $\tan 30°$ 0.576
> 6. $\sec 30°$ 1.15
> 7. $\sin 60°$ 0.864
> 8. $\cot 60°$ 0.576
> 9. $\csc 60°$ 1.15

The sine, cosine, and tangent function values for 30° and 60° should also be memorized. Note that the others are their reciprocals.

We can now determine the trigonometric function values for any angle whose terminal side makes a 30°, 45°, or 60° angle with the x-axis. Consider, for example, an angle of 150°, or $\frac{5\pi}{6}$. The terminal side makes a 30° angle with the x-axis. As the next diagram shows, triangle *ONR* is congruent to triangle *ON'R'*. Hence the ratios of the sides of the two triangles are the same except perhaps for sign.

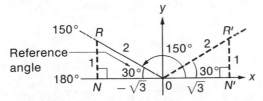

We could determine the function values directly from triangle *ONR*, but this is not necessary. If we remember that the sine is positive in quadrant II and that the cosine and tangent are negative, we can simply use the values for 30°, prefixing the appropriate sign. The triangle *ONR* is called a *reference* triangle and its acute angle at the origin is called a *reference* angle.

In general, to find the function values of an angle, we find them for the reference angle and prefix the appropriate sign.

Example 6. Find the sine, cosine, and tangent of 600°, or $\frac{10\pi}{3}$.

We find the multiple of 180° nearest 600°:

$$180° \times 2 = 360°$$
$$180° \times 3 = 540°$$
$$180° \times 4 = 720°$$

The nearest multiple is 540°. The difference between 600° and 540° is 60°. This gives us the reference angle.

We recall that $\sin 60° = \frac{\sqrt{3}}{2}$, $\cos 60° = \frac{1}{2}$, and $\tan 60° = \sqrt{3}$.

We also recall that the sine and cosine are negative in the third quadrant, and that the tangent is positive. Hence we have

$$\sin 600° = -\frac{\sqrt{3}}{2},$$
$$\cos 600° = -\frac{1}{2},$$
$$\tan 600° = \sqrt{3}$$

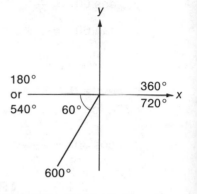

TRY THIS ▆▆▆➤

Draw reference angles. Find the sine, cosine, and tangent of each angle.

10. 330°

11. −510°

12. $\frac{23\pi}{6}$

Answers.   10. $\sin 330° = -\frac{1}{2}$, $\cos 330° = \frac{\sqrt{3}}{2}$, $\tan 330° = -\frac{\sqrt{3}}{3}$

11. $\sin(-510°) = -\frac{1}{2}$, $\cos(-510°) = -\frac{\sqrt{3}}{2}$, $\tan(-510°) = \frac{\sqrt{3}}{3}$

Exercise Set 20-3 12. $\sin \frac{23\pi}{6} = -\frac{1}{2}$, $\cos \frac{23\pi}{6} = \frac{\sqrt{3}}{2}$, $\tan \frac{23\pi}{6} = -\frac{\sqrt{3}}{3}$

❚Find the sin, cos, and tan function values for the angle θ shown. (*See Example 1.*)

1.

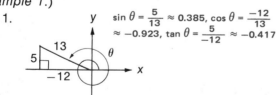

$\sin \theta = \frac{5}{13} \approx 0.385$, $\cos \theta = \frac{-12}{13}$ ≈ -0.923, $\tan \theta = \frac{5}{-12} \approx -0.417$

2.

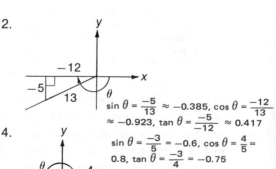

$\sin \theta = \frac{-5}{13} \approx -0.385$, $\cos \theta = \frac{-12}{13}$ ≈ -0.923, $\tan \theta = \frac{-5}{-12} \approx 0.417$

3.

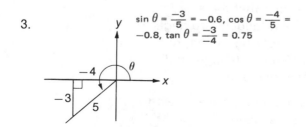

$\sin \theta = \frac{-3}{5} = -0.6$, $\cos \theta = \frac{-4}{5} = -0.8$, $\tan \theta = \frac{-3}{-4} = 0.75$

4.

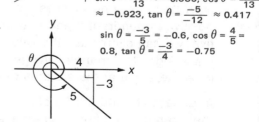

$\sin \theta = \frac{-3}{5} = -0.6$, $\cos \theta = \frac{4}{5} = 0.8$, $\tan \theta = \frac{-3}{4} = -0.75$

▮▮ Find the cot, sec, and csc function values for the angle θ shown. (*See Example 2.*)

5.
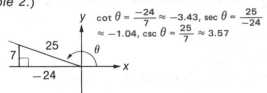
$\cot \theta = \frac{-24}{7} \approx -3.43$, $\sec \theta = \frac{25}{-24}$
≈ -1.04, $\csc \theta = \frac{25}{7} \approx 3.57$

6.
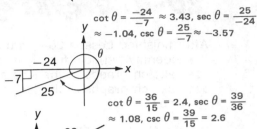
$\cot \theta = \frac{-24}{-7} \approx 3.43$, $\sec \theta = \frac{25}{-24}$
≈ -1.04, $\csc \theta = \frac{25}{-7} \approx -3.57$

7.
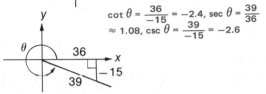
$\cot \theta = \frac{36}{-15} = -2.4$, $\sec \theta = \frac{39}{36}$
≈ 1.08, $\csc \theta = \frac{39}{-15} = -2.6$

8.
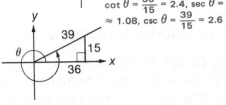
$\cot \theta = \frac{36}{15} = 2.4$, $\sec \theta = \frac{39}{36}$
≈ 1.08, $\csc \theta = \frac{39}{15} = 2.6$

Find the six trigonometric function values for the angle θ shown. (*See Example 3.*)

9.
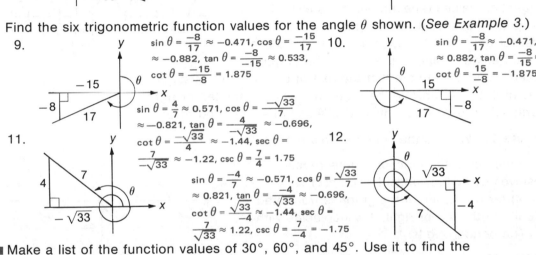
$\sin \theta = \frac{-8}{17} \approx -0.471$, $\cos \theta = \frac{-15}{17}$
≈ -0.882, $\tan \theta = \frac{-8}{-15} \approx 0.533$,
$\cot \theta = \frac{-15}{-8} = 1.875$

10.
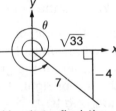
$\sin \theta = \frac{-8}{17} \approx -0.471$, $\cos \theta = \frac{15}{17}$
≈ 0.882, $\tan \theta = \frac{-8}{15} \approx -0.533$,
$\cot \theta = \frac{15}{-8} = -1.875$

$\sin \theta = \frac{4}{7} \approx 0.571$, $\cos \theta = \frac{-\sqrt{33}}{7}$
≈ -0.821, $\tan \theta = \frac{4}{-\sqrt{33}} \approx -0.696$,
$\cot \theta = \frac{-\sqrt{33}}{4} \approx -1.44$, $\sec \theta =$
$\frac{7}{-\sqrt{33}} \approx -1.22$, $\csc \theta = \frac{7}{4} = 1.75$

11.
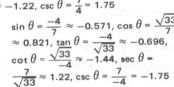

12.

$\sin \theta = \frac{-4}{7} \approx -0.571$, $\cos \theta = \frac{\sqrt{33}}{7}$
≈ 0.821, $\tan \theta = \frac{-4}{\sqrt{33}} \approx -0.696$,
$\cot \theta = \frac{\sqrt{33}}{-4} \approx -1.44$, $\sec \theta =$
$\frac{7}{\sqrt{33}} \approx 1.22$, $\csc \theta = \frac{7}{-4} = -1.75$

▮▮▮ Make a list of the function values of 30°, 60°, and 45°. Use it to find the following, if they exist. Use reference angles. (*See Example 6.*)

13. $\cos 180°$ -1
14. $\sin 360°$ 0
15. $\sec 720°$ 1
16. $\csc 720°$ Undefined
17. $\sin 150°$ $\frac{1}{2}$
18. $\cos 150°$ $-\frac{\sqrt{3}}{2}$
19. $\sec 315°$ $\sqrt{2}$
20. $\csc 315°$ $-\sqrt{2}$
21. $\sin(-210°)$ $\frac{1}{2}$
22. $\cos(-210°)$ $-\frac{\sqrt{3}}{2}$
23. $\sin \frac{11\pi}{4}$ $\frac{\sqrt{2}}{2}$
24. $\cos \frac{11\pi}{4}$ $-\frac{\sqrt{2}}{2}$
25. $\tan 90°$ Undefined
26. $\cot 180°$ Undefined
27. $\sin(-270°)$ 1
28. $\cos 270°$ 0
29. $\tan 240°$ $\sqrt{3}$
30. $\cot 240°$ $\frac{\sqrt{3}}{3}$
31. $\tan(-315°)$ 1
32. $\cot(-315°)$ 1
33. $\tan 210°$ $\frac{\sqrt{3}}{3}$
34. $\cot 210°$ $\sqrt{3}$
35. $\tan \frac{11\pi}{6}$ $-\frac{\sqrt{3}}{3}$
36. $\cot \frac{11\pi}{6}$ $-\sqrt{3}$

20-4 Graphs of Trigonometric Functions

After finishing Lesson 20-4, you should be able to
- **I**   identify periodic functions from their graphs.
- **II**   sketch graphs of the sine and cosine functions.
- **III**   sketch graphs of the tangent, cotangent, secant, and cosecant functions.

I Periodic Functions

Certain functions with a repeating pattern are
called *periodic*. The function shown is periodic.
The function values repeat themselves every two
units as we move from left to right. In other
words, for any x, we have $f(x) = f(x + 2)$. To see
this another way, think of the part of the graph
between 0 and 2 and note that the rest of the graph consists of
copies of it. If we translate the graph two units to the left or right,
the original graph will be obtained. We say f has a period of 2.

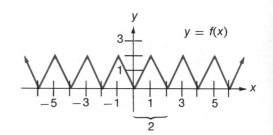

Example 1.   What is the period of this function?

In the function g, the function values repeat
themselves every four units. Hence $g(x) =$
$g(x + 4)$ for any x, and if the graph is translated
four units to the left or right, it will coincide with
itself. The period of g is 4.

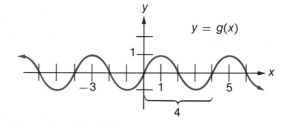

DEFINITION

If a function f has the property that $f(x + p) = f(x)$ for all x in
the domain, where p is a constant, then f is said to be *periodic*.
The smallest positive number p (if there is one) for which
$f(x + p) = f(x)$ for all x is called the *period* of the function.

TRY THIS

1.   What is the period of this function?

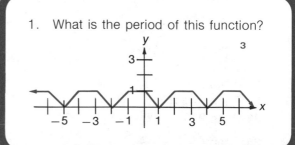

II The Sine and Cosine Functions

We can graph trigonometric functions. We
use the horizontal axis for angle or rotation sizes and the vertical axis for function
values.

Here is a graph of the sine function. Function values increase to a maximum of 1 at $\frac{\pi}{2}$, then decrease to 0 at π, decrease further to -1 at $\frac{3}{2}\pi$, then increase to 0 at 2π, and so on.

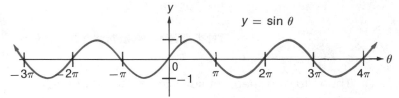

Example 2. Is the sine function periodic? If so, what is its period? Is the sine function even? odd?

From the graph of the sine function, certain properties are apparent.

> The sine function is periodic, with period 2π.
> It is an odd function, by symmetry with respect to the origin.
> Thus we know that $\sin(-s) = -\sin s$ for all real numbers s.

TRY THIS ➡

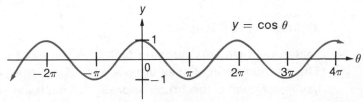

2. What is the domain of the sine function?
3. What is the range of the sine function?

Answers. 2. The set of all real numbers 3. The set of all real numbers from -1 to 1, inclusive.

The following theorem summarizes some properties of the sine function.

THEOREM 20-1

$\sin\theta = \sin(\theta + 2k\pi)$, k any integer
$\sin(-\theta) = -\sin\theta$

The *amplitude* of a periodic function is half the difference between its maximum and minimum function values. It is always positive. The maximum value of the sine function can be seen to be 1, either from the graph or the unit circle, while the minimum value is -1. Thus the amplitude of the sine function is 1.

Here is a graph of the cosine function.

Example 3. Is the cosine function even? odd? What is its domain? What is its range?

From the graph of the cosine function, we notice certain properties.

> The cosine function is an even function, by symmetry with respect to the y-axis. Thus we know that $\cos(-s) = \cos s$ for all real numbers s.
> The domain is the set of all real numbers.
> The range is the set of all real numbers from -1 to 1 inclusive. Thus the amplitude is 1.

TRY THIS ━━━━▶

The following theorem summarizes some properties of the cosine function.

THEOREM 20-2
$\cos \theta = \cos (\theta + 2k\pi)$, *k* any integer
$\cos (-\theta) = \cos \theta$

ⅲ Graphs of the Other Functions

Not every notation, or angle, has a tangent. For example, the

tangent ratio for $\frac{\pi}{2}$ would be $\dfrac{\sin \frac{\pi}{2}}{\cos \frac{\pi}{2}}$, or $\dfrac{1}{0}$. But division by 0 is

not defined, and so $\tan \frac{\pi}{2}$

is meaningless. Here is a
graph of the tangent function. We use *x* instead of *θ*.
The variable *x* represents
any real number.
   Note that the function
value is 0 when *x* = 0, and
the values increase as *x*

increases toward $\frac{\pi}{2}$. As we

approach $\frac{\pi}{2}$ the tangent

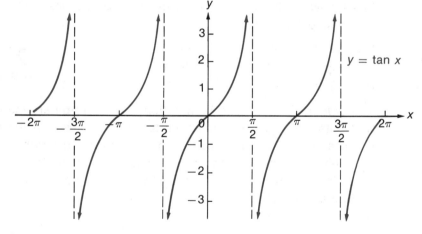

values become very large. In fact, they increase without bound.
The dashed vertical lines are not part of the graph. They are
asymptotes, and the graph approaches each asymptote closely.

Example 4.   Is the tangent function periodic? If so, what is its
period? What is its domain? What is its range?

The tangent function is periodic, with a period of π.

Its domain is the set of all real numbers except $\frac{\pi}{2} + k\pi$, *k* an integer.

Its range is the set of all real numbers.

TRY THIS ━━━━━━▶

5. Is the tangent function even? odd? **Odd**

The cotangent function is also not defined for all rotations or angles. For instance,

$$\cot \pi = \frac{\cot \pi}{\sin \pi} = \frac{1}{0},$$

which involves division by 0. Here is a graph of the cotangent function.

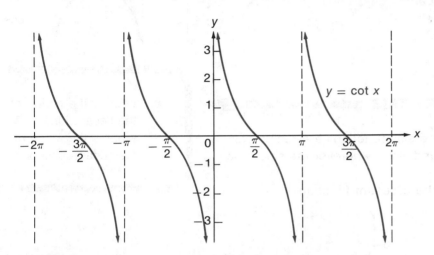

Example 5. What is the domain of the cotangent function? What is its range?

The domain of the cotangent function is the set of all real numbers except $k\pi$, k any integer. Its range is the set of all real numbers.

TRY THIS ━━━━━━▶

6. Is the cotangent function periodic? If so, what is its period? **Yes, π**
7. Is the cotangent function even? odd? **Odd**

The secant and cosine functions are reciprocals. For example,

$$\sec 0 = \frac{1}{\cos 0} = \frac{1}{1} = 1.$$

This function will be undefined for those numbers for which $\cos x = 0$.

Here is a graph of the secant function. The co-sine graph is dotted in for reference, since these functions are reciprocals.

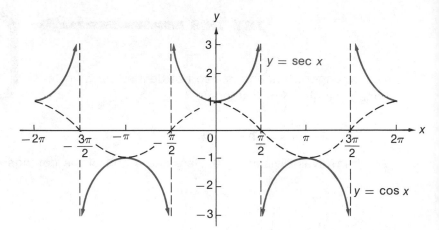

Example 6. What is the domain of the secant function?

The domain of the secant function is the set of all real numbers except

$\frac{\pi}{2} + k\pi$, k an integer.

TRY THIS ➡

8. What is the period of the secant function?
9. What is the range of the secant function?

Since the cosecant and sine functions are reciprocals, the cosecant will be undefined wherever the sine function is 0.

Here is a graph of the cosecant function.

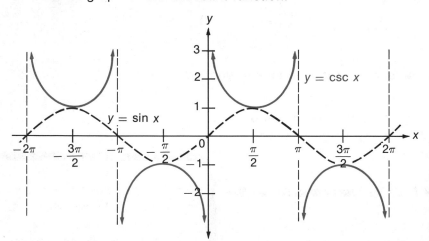

10. What is the period of the cosecant function?
11. What is the domain of the cosecant function?
12. What is the range of the cosecant function?

The sine graph is dotted in for reference, since these functions are reciprocals.

TRY THIS ➡

Exercise Set 20-4

▮ Which of the following functions are periodic? (*See Example 1.*)

1. 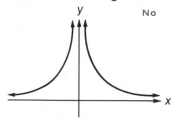 No

2. 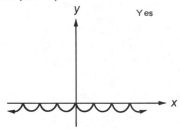 Yes

3. 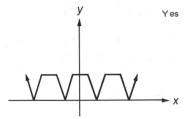 Yes

4. 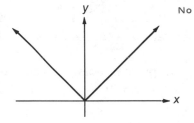 No

5. 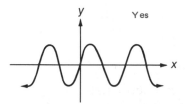 Yes

6. 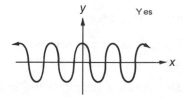 Yes

7. What is the period of this function?

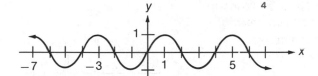

4

8. What is the period of this function?

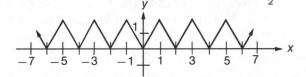

2

▮▮ Make graphs of the sine and cosine functions. (*See Examples 2 and 3.*)

9. a) Sketch a graph of $y = \sin x$.
    b) By reflecting the graph in a) across the y-axis, sketch a graph of $y = \sin (-x)$.
    c) By reflecting the graph in a) across the x-axis, sketch a graph of $y = -\sin x$.
    d) How do the graphs in b) and c) compare?   See answer section

10. a) Sketch a graph of $y = \cos x$.
    b) By reflecting the graph in a) across the y-axis, sketch a graph of $y = \cos(-x)$.
    c) By reflecting the graph in a) across the x-axis, sketch a graph of $y = -\cos x$.
    d) How do the graphs in b) and c) compare?

▌▌▌ Here is a table of approximate values of functions. Use the table, plus your knowledge of the properties of the functions, to make graphs. (*See Examples 4–6.*)

	$\dfrac{\pi}{16}$	$\dfrac{\pi}{8}$	$\dfrac{\pi}{6}$	$\dfrac{\pi}{4}$	$\dfrac{\pi}{3}$	$\dfrac{3}{8}\pi$	$\dfrac{7}{16}\pi$	$-\dfrac{\pi}{16}$	$-\dfrac{\pi}{8}$	$-\dfrac{\pi}{6}$	$-\dfrac{\pi}{4}$
Tan	0.2	0.4	0.6	1	1.7	2.4	4.9	−0.2	−0.4	−0.6	−1
Cot	4.9	2.4	1.7	1	0.6	0.4	0.2	−4.9	−2.4	−1.7	−1
Sec	1.02	1.1	1.2	1.4	2	2.6	5.0	1.02	1.1	1.2	1.4
Csc	5.0	2.6	2	1.4	1.2	1.08	1.02	−5.0	−2.6	−2	−1.4

11. Graph the tangent function between -2π and 2π.

12. Graph the cotangent function between -2π and 2π.

13. Graph the secant function between -2π and 2π. 11.–14. See text pages 608–610 for graphs.

14. Graph the cosecant function between -2π and 2π.

Challenge Exercises

Verify the following properties.

15. $\sec(-x) = \sec x$ 16. $\csc(-x) = -\csc x$ See answer section

17. Construct a graph of the sine function by copying the coordinate axes on other paper. Then, from the unit circle shown here, transfer vertical distances with a compass.

18. Construct a graph of the cosine function. Follow the instructions for Exercise 17, but transfer *horizontal* distances from the unit circle with a compass.

17. and 18. See text page 607 for graphs.

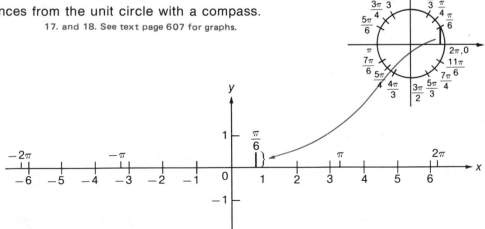

20-5 Relations Among Trigonometric Functions

After finishing Lesson 20-5, you should be able to
- **I** derive variations of the Pythagorean identities.
- **II** derive variations of the cofunction identities.
- **III** write trigonometric identities in terms of degrees.
- **IIII** given the function values for an acute angle, find the function values for its complement.

We have already seen some of the important relations that exist among the six trigonometric functions. There are certain other relations, called *identities*. An identity is an equation that holds for all sensible replacements for the variables. We use the sign $\equiv$ to indicate that an equation is an identity.

▮ Quotient and Pythagorean Identities

The tangent and cotangent functions can be expressed in terms of the sine and cosine functions.

THEOREM 20-3   (The Quotient Identities)

$$\tan \theta \equiv \frac{\sin \theta}{\cos \theta}, \cos \theta \neq 0$$

$$\cot \theta \equiv \frac{\cos \theta}{\sin \theta}, \sin \theta \neq 0$$

Example 1. Derive an identity that gives $\sin \theta$ in terms of $\tan \theta$ and $\cos \theta$.

By Theorem 20-3 we have $\tan \theta \equiv \dfrac{\sin \theta}{\cos \theta}$. Solving for $\sin \theta$ we

have $\sin \theta \equiv \tan \theta \cdot \cos \theta$.

TRY THIS ➡

> 1.   Derive an identity that gives $\cos \theta$ in terms of $\sin \theta$ and $\cot \theta$.
>

The unit circle has an equation

$$x^2 + y^2 = 1.$$

For any point on the unit circle, the coordinates x and y satisfy this equation. Suppose a rotation θ determines a point T on the unit circle, with coordinates (x, y). Since $\cos \theta = x$ and $\sin \theta = y$, we obtain the identity

$$\sin^2 \theta + \cos^2 \theta \equiv 1$$

by substituting in the equation of the unit circle.

When exponents are used with the trigonometric functions, we write $\sin^2 \theta$ instead of $(\sin \theta)^2$. This identity relates the sine and cosine of any angle. It is an important identity, known as one of the *Pythagorean* identities. Now we will divide the above identity by $\sin^2 \theta$.

$$\frac{\sin^2 \theta}{\sin^2 \theta} + \frac{\cos^2 \theta}{\sin^2 \theta} \equiv \frac{1}{\sin^2 \theta}.$$

Since the cosecant is the reciprocal of the sine, this simplifies to

$$1 + \cot^2 \theta \equiv \csc^2 \theta.$$

This relation is valid for any rotation θ for which $\sin^2 \theta \neq 0$, since we divided by $\sin^2 \theta$.

The third Pythagorean identity, obtained by dividing the first by $\cos^2 \theta$, is

$$1 + \tan^2 \theta \equiv \sec^2 \theta.$$

The Pythagorean identities should be memorized.

THEOREM 20-4   (The Pythagorean Identities)

$\sin^2 \theta + \cos^2 \theta \equiv 1$
$1 + \cot^2 \theta \equiv \csc^2 \theta$
$1 + \tan^2 \theta \equiv \sec^2 \theta$

Example 2.   Derive identities that give $\cos^2 \theta$ and $\cos \theta$ in terms of $\sin \theta$.

$$\sin^2 \theta + \cos^2 \theta \equiv 1$$
$$\cos^2 \theta \equiv 1 - \sin^2 \theta \qquad \textit{Solving for } \cos^2 \theta$$
$$|\cos \theta| \equiv \sqrt{1 - \sin^2 \theta} \qquad \textit{Taking the principal square root}$$
$$\cos \theta \equiv \pm \sqrt{1 - \sin^2 \theta}$$

The sign must be determined by the quadrant in which the terminal side of θ lies.

TRY THIS ➡

2. Derive an identity for $\sin^2 \theta$ in terms of $\cos \theta$.
3. Derive an identity for $\sin \theta$ in terms of $\cos \theta$.

Answers.   2. $\sin^2 \theta \equiv 1 - \cos^2 \theta$ 3. $\sin \theta \equiv \pm \sqrt{1 - \cos^2 \theta}$

Example 3.   Obtain identities from
$1 + \cot^2 \theta \equiv \csc^2 \theta$.

We obtain:

$$\csc^2 \theta - \cot^2 \theta \equiv 1 \qquad \text{and} \qquad \cot^2 \theta \equiv \csc^2 \theta - 1$$

TRY THIS ━━━━━▶

4. From the identity
$1 + \tan^2\theta \equiv \sec^2\theta$, derive
two other identities.
$\sec^2\theta - \tan^2\theta \equiv 1$, $\tan^2\theta \equiv \sec^2\theta - 1$

∎ The Cofunction Identities

The sine and cosine are called cofunctions of each other. Another class of identities gives functions in terms of their cofunctions.

Example 4. Consider this graph.
The graph of $y = \sin\theta$ has been translated to the left a distance of $\frac{\pi}{2}$, to obtain the graph of $y = \sin\left(\theta + \frac{\pi}{2}\right)$. The latter is also a graph of the cosine function. Thus we obtain the identity $\sin\left(\theta + \frac{\pi}{2}\right) \equiv \cos\theta$.

TRY THIS ━━━━━▶

By means similar to those above, we obtain the identity $\cos\left(\theta - \frac{\pi}{2}\right) \equiv \sin\theta$.

If the graph of $y = \sin\theta$ is translated to the right a distance of $\frac{\pi}{2}$, we obtain the graph of $y = \sin\left(\theta - \frac{\pi}{2}\right)$. The latter is a reflection of the cosine function across the *x*-axis. In other words, it is a graph of $y = -\cos\theta$. We thus obtain the following identity:

$$\sin\left(\theta - \frac{\pi}{2}\right) \equiv -\cos\theta.$$

By means similar to those above, we obtain the identity

$$\cos\left(\theta + \frac{\pi}{2}\right) \equiv -\sin\theta.$$

5. a) Graph $y = \cos\theta$.
   b) Translate to obtain a graph of
      $y = \cos\left(\theta - \frac{\pi}{2}\right)$.
   c) Graph $y = \sin\theta$.
   d) How do the graphs of
      b) and c) compare?
   e) Write the identity thus
      established.

a), b), c) See answer section
d) Same e) $\cos\left(\theta - \frac{\pi}{2}\right) \equiv \sin\theta$

We now consider function values at $\frac{\pi}{2} - \theta$. Since the sine function is odd, we know that

$$\sin\left(\frac{\pi}{2} - \theta\right) \equiv \sin\left[-\left(\theta - \frac{\pi}{2}\right)\right] \equiv -\sin\left(\theta - \frac{\pi}{2}\right).$$

Now consider the identity already established,

$$\sin\left(\theta - \frac{\pi}{2}\right) \equiv -\cos\theta.$$

This is equivalent to

$$-\sin\left(\theta - \frac{\pi}{2}\right) \equiv \cos\theta. \qquad \textit{Multiplying by } -1$$

We now have the following identity:

$$\sin\left(\frac{\pi}{2} - \theta\right) \equiv \cos\theta. \qquad \textit{Theorem 20-1}$$

Similarly, we can establish the identity $\cos\left(\frac{\pi}{2} - \theta\right) \equiv \sin\theta$.

The following theorem summarizes the cofunction identities.

THEOREM 20-5   (The Cofunction Identities)

$$\sin\left(\theta + \frac{\pi}{2}\right) \equiv \cos\theta \qquad \cos\left(\theta + \frac{\pi}{2}\right) \equiv -\sin\theta$$

$$\sin\left(\theta - \frac{\pi}{2}\right) \equiv -\cos\theta \qquad \cos\left(\theta - \frac{\pi}{2}\right) \equiv \sin\theta$$

$$\sin\left(\frac{\pi}{2} - \theta\right) \equiv \cos\theta \qquad \cos\left(\frac{\pi}{2} - \theta\right) \equiv \sin\theta$$

These should be learned. Identities relating the tangent and cotangent cofunctions and the secant and cosecant cofunctions can be obtained from these.

Example 5.   Find an identity for $\sec\left(\theta + \frac{\pi}{2}\right)$.

$$\sec\left(\theta + \frac{\pi}{2}\right) \equiv \frac{1}{\cos\left(\theta + \frac{\pi}{2}\right)} \qquad \textit{Definition of sec}$$

$$\equiv \frac{1}{-\sin\theta} \qquad \textit{Theorem 20-5 (cofunction identity)}$$

$$\equiv -\csc\theta \qquad \textit{Definition of csc}$$

TRY THIS ➡

6.   Find an identity for $\csc\left(\theta + \frac{\pi}{2}\right)$.

$\csc\left(\theta + \frac{\pi}{2}\right) \equiv \sec\theta$

Example 6. Find an identity for $\tan\left(\theta + \dfrac{\pi}{2}\right)$.

$$\tan\left(\theta + \frac{\pi}{2}\right) \equiv \frac{\sin\left(\theta + \dfrac{\pi}{2}\right)}{\cos\left(\theta + \dfrac{\pi}{2}\right)} \qquad \textit{Theorem 20-3 (quotient identity)}$$

$$\equiv \frac{\cos\theta}{-\sin\theta} \qquad \textit{Theorem 20-5 (cofunction identity)}$$

$$\equiv -\cot\theta \qquad \textit{Theorem 20-3 (quotient identity)}$$

TRY THIS ➡

> 7. Find an identity for
> $\cot\left(\theta + \dfrac{\pi}{2}\right)$.
>
> $\cot\left(\theta + \dfrac{\pi}{2}\right) \equiv -\tan\theta$

ⅠⅠⅠ Identities and Degrees

All trigonometric identities hold whether we express the rotation in radians or degrees. When we use degrees, some of them of course look a little different.

Example 7. Rewrite $\sin\left(\theta + \dfrac{\pi}{2}\right) \equiv \cos\theta$ in terms of degrees.

This identity becomes $\sin(\theta + 90°) \equiv \cos\theta$.

TRY THIS ➡

> Rewrite the following identities in terms of degrees.
>
> 8. $\cos\left(\dfrac{\pi}{2} - \theta\right) \equiv \sin\theta$
>
> 9. $\sin\left(\theta - \dfrac{\pi}{2}\right) \equiv -\cos\theta$
>
> 8. $\cos(90° - \theta) \equiv \sin\theta$
> 9. $\sin(\theta - 90°) \equiv -\cos\theta$

ⅠⅠⅠⅠ Cofunctions and Complements

Recall that $\sin(90° - \theta) \equiv \cos\theta$. If θ is less than 90°, then $90° - \theta$ is its complement. Thus the sine of an acute angle is the cosine of its complement. A similar thing is true for all of the trigonometric functions. That is, a function value for an acute angle is the cofunction of its complement. The complete list of these relations is as follows.

$$\sin\theta \equiv \cos(90° - \theta) \qquad \cos\theta \equiv \sin(90° - \theta)$$
$$\tan\theta \equiv \cot(90° - \theta) \qquad \cot\theta \equiv \tan(90° - \theta)$$
$$\sec\theta \equiv \csc(90° - \theta) \qquad \csc\theta \equiv \sec(90° - \theta)$$

Example 8. Use the following. Find the six function values for 72°.

$$\sin 18° = 0.3090 \qquad \cos 18° = 0.9511$$
$$\tan 18° = 0.3249 \qquad \cot 18° = 3.078$$
$$\sec 18° = 1.051 \qquad \csc 18° = 3.236$$

Since 72° and 18° are complements, we have
sin 72° = cos 18°, etc., and the function values
are as follows.

sin 72° = 0.9511	cos 72° = 0.3090
tan 72° = 3.078	cot 72° = 0.3249
sec 72° = 3.236	csc 72° = 1.051

TRY THIS ➡

Answer. 10. sin 15° = 0.2588, cos 15° = 0.9659, tan 15° = 0.2679, cot 15° =
3.732, sec 15° = 1.035, csc 15° = 3.864

10. Use the following.
sin 75° = 0.9659
cos 75° = 0.2588
tan 75° = 3.732
cot 75° = 0.2679
sec 75° = 3.864
csc 75° = 1.035
Find the function values for
the complement of 75°.

Exercise Set 20-5

See answer section

■ Derive the following. (*See Examples 1–3.*)

1. An identity for csc θ in terms of cot θ
2. An identity for tan θ in terms of sec θ
3. An identity for cot θ in terms of csc θ
4. An identity for sec θ in terms of tan θ

■■ Find identities for the following. (*See Examples 4–6.*)

5. $\tan\left(\theta - \dfrac{\pi}{2}\right)$ $\tan(\theta - \frac{\pi}{2}) \equiv -\cot\theta$
6. $\cot\left(\theta - \dfrac{\pi}{2}\right)$ $\cot(\theta - \frac{\pi}{2}) \equiv -\tan\theta$
7. $\sec\left(\dfrac{\pi}{2} - \theta\right)$ $\sec(\frac{\pi}{2} - \theta) \equiv \csc\theta$
8. $\csc\left(\dfrac{\pi}{2} - \theta\right)$ $\csc(\frac{\pi}{2} - \theta) \equiv \sec\theta$

■■■ Rewrite the identity in terms of degrees. (*See Example 7.*)

9. $\sin(\theta \pm \pi) \equiv -\sin\theta$ $\sin(\theta \pm 180°) \equiv -\sin\theta$
10. $\cos\left(\theta \pm \dfrac{\pi}{2}\right) \equiv -\cos\theta$ $\cos(\theta \pm 90°) \equiv -\cos\theta$
11. $\sin\theta \equiv \sin(\theta + 2k\pi)$ $\sin\theta \equiv \sin[\theta + 2k(180°)]$
12. $\cos\theta \equiv \cos(\theta + 2k\pi)$ $\cos\theta \equiv \cos[\theta + 2k(180°)]$
13. $\sin\left(\dfrac{\pi}{2} + \theta\right) \equiv \cos\theta$ $\sin(90° - \theta) \equiv \cos\theta$
14. $\cos\left(\theta + \dfrac{\pi}{2}\right) \equiv -\sin\theta$ $\cos(\theta + 90°) \equiv -\sin\theta$

■■■■ Use the given function values to find the six function values of the complement angle. (*See Example 8.*)   See answer section

15. sin 65° = 0.9063   cos 65° = 0.4226
    tan 65° = 2.145   cot 65° = 0.4663
    sec 65° = 2.366   csc 65° = 1.103
16. sin 32° = 0.5299   cos 32° = 0.8480
    tan 32° = 0.6249   cot 32° = 1.600
    sec 32° = 1.179   csc 32° = 1.887
17. sin 52° = 0.7880   cos 52° = 0.6157
    tan 52° = 1.280   cot 52° = 0.7813
    sec 52° = 1.624   csc 52° = 1.269
18. sin 27° = 0.4540   cos 27° = 0.8910
    tan 27° = 0.5095   cot 27° = 1.963
    sec 27° = 1.122   csc 27° = 2.203

Challenge Exercises

19. $\sin\theta \equiv \cos(\frac{\pi}{2} - \theta)$, $\cos\theta \equiv \sin(\frac{\pi}{2} - \theta)$, $\tan\theta \equiv \cot(\frac{\pi}{2} - \theta)$, $\cot\theta \equiv \tan(\frac{\pi}{2} - \theta)$, $\sec\theta \equiv$
$\csc(\frac{\pi}{2} - \theta)$, $\csc\theta \equiv \sec(\frac{\pi}{2} - \theta)$ 20. The function of an angle is equal to the cofunction of
its complement.

19. For the six trigonometric functions, list the cofunction identities involving $\dfrac{\pi}{2} - \theta$.

20. Describe the pattern you see in Exercise 19.

20-6 More Graphs

After finishing Lesson 20-6, you should be able to
I   sketch graphs of $y = A \sin \theta$ and $y = A \cos \theta$ and determine the amplitude of the function.
II   sketch graphs of $y = \sin B\theta$ and $y = \cos B\theta$ and determine the period of the function.
III   sketch graphs of $y = A \sin B\theta$ and $y = A \cos B\theta$ and determine the amplitude and period of the function.

We shall consider graphs of some variations of the sine and cosine function. In particular, we are interested in the following:

$$y = A \sin (B\theta) \quad \text{and} \quad y = A \cos (B\theta),$$

where A and B are constants. These constants have the effect of stretching or shrinking the basic graphs and thus cause changes in their amplitudes and periods.

▮Change of Amplitude

The constant A in $y = A \sin \theta$ causes a vertical stretching or shrinking of the graph and thus a change in the amplitude.

Example 1.   Sketch a graph of $y = 2 \sin \theta$. What is the amplitude?

The function $y = 2 \sin \theta$ is equivalent to $\dfrac{y}{2} = \sin \theta$. The graph is

a vertical stretching of the graph of $y = \sin \theta$. The amplitude of this function is 2. That is, $A = 2$.

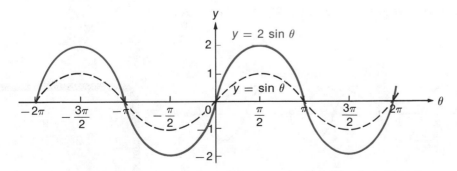

If the constant A in $y = A \sin x$ is negative, there will also be a reflection across the x-axis. If the absolute value of A is less than 1, then there will be a vertical shrinking. The amplitude will be $|A|$.

Answer.   1. Cosine curve with amplitude 2 through $(-2\pi, 2)$, $(-3\pi/2, 0)$,
$(-\pi, -2)$, $(-\pi/2, 0)$, $(0, 2)$, $(\pi/2, 0)$, $(\pi, -2)$, $(3\pi/2, 0)$, $(2\pi, 2)$

Example 2. Sketch a graph of $y = -\frac{1}{2} \sin \theta$. What
is the amplitude?

The graph of $y = -\frac{1}{2} \sin \theta$ is a vertical shrinking and a reflec-
tion of the graph of $y = \sin \theta$. The amplitude is $\frac{1}{2}$. ($|A| = \frac{1}{2}$.)

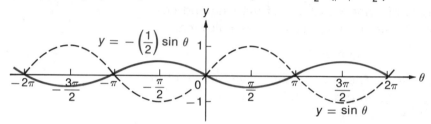

TRY THIS ▬▬▬▬➤

Answer.   2. Cosine curve with amplitude 1/2 through $(-2\pi, -1/2)$,
$(-3\pi/2, 0)$, $(-\pi, 1/2)$, $(-\pi/2, 0)$, $(0, -1/2)$, $(\pi/2, 0)$, $(\pi, 1/2)$, $(3\pi/2, 0)$,
$(2\pi, -1/2)$

▪ Change of Period

The constant B in $y = \sin B\theta$ causes a horizontal
stretching or shrinking of the graph and thus a
change in the period.

Example 3. Sketch a graph of $y = \sin 2\theta$. What is the period?

The function $y = \sin 2\theta$ is equivalent to $y = \sin \frac{\theta}{\frac{1}{2}}$. The graph is

a horizontal shrinking of the graph of $y = \sin \theta$. The period of
this function is π.

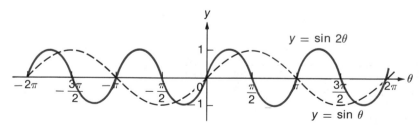

Answer.   3. Cosine curve with period π through $(-2\pi, 1)$, $(-3\pi/2, -1)$,
$(-\pi, 1)$, $(-\pi/2, -1)$, $(0, 1)$, $(\pi/2, -1)$, $(\pi, 1)$, $(3\pi/2, -1)$, $(2\pi, 1)$

If $|B| > 1$, there will be a horizontal shrink. If $|B| < 1$, there will be a horizontal stretch. If B is negative, there will also be a reflection across the y-axis. The period will be $\dfrac{2\pi}{|B|}$.

Example 4. Sketch a graph of $y = \sin\left(-\tfrac{1}{2}\theta\right)$. What is the period?

The graph of $y = \sin\left(-\tfrac{1}{2}\theta\right)$ is a horizontal stretching of the graph of $y = \sin\theta$. It is also a reflection. The period is $\dfrac{2\pi}{\left|-\tfrac{1}{2}\right|}$, or 4π.

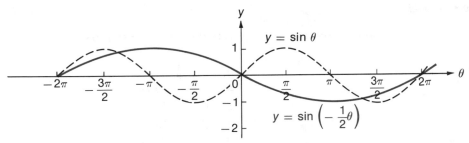

Answer.   4. Cosine curve with period 4π through $(-2\pi, -1)$, $(-\pi, 0)$, $(0, 1)$, $(\pi, 0)$, $(2\pi, -1)$

TRY THIS

4. Sketch a graph of $y = \cos\left(-\tfrac{1}{2}\theta\right)$. What is the period?

ⅢChange of Amplitude and Period

The constants A and B in $y = A \sin B\theta$ cause both a vertical and a horizontal stretching or shrinking of the graph.

Example 5. Sketch a graph of $y = 3 \sin (2\theta)$. What is the amplitude and period?

The function $y = 3 \sin (2\theta)$ is equivalent to $\dfrac{y}{3} = \sin\dfrac{\theta}{\tfrac{1}{2}}$. The graph is a vertical stretching and a horizontal shrinking of the graph of $y = \sin\theta$. This function has an amplitude of 3 and a period of π.

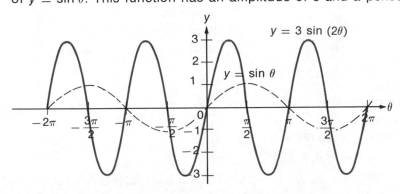

TRY THIS ▬▬▶

5. Sketch a graph of $y = 3\cos(2\theta)$. What is the amplitude and period?

Exercise Set 20-6   See answer section

∎ Sketch graphs of these functions. Determine the amplitude. (*See Examples 1 and 2.*)

1. $y = \frac{1}{2}\sin\theta$
2. $y = \frac{1}{2}\cos\theta$
3. $y = 3\sin\theta$
4. $y = 3\cos\theta$
5. $y = -\frac{1}{3}\sin\theta$
6. $y = -\frac{1}{3}\cos\theta$
7. $y = 4\sin\theta$
8. $y = 4\cos\theta$
9. $y = -2\sin\theta$
10. $y = -2\cos\theta$

∎∎ Sketch graphs of these functions. Determine the period. (*See Examples 3 and 4.*)

11. $y = \sin 3\theta$
12. $y = \cos 3\theta$
13. $y = \sin\frac{1}{2}\theta$
14. $y = \cos\frac{1}{2}\theta$
15. $y = \sin\left(-\frac{1}{3}\theta\right)$
16. $y = \cos\left(-\frac{1}{3}\theta\right)$
17. $y = \sin(-2\theta)$
18. $y = \cos(-2\theta)$
19. $y = \sin(-3\theta)$
20. $y = \cos(-3\theta)$

∎∎∎ Sketch graphs of these functions. Determine the amplitude and the period. (*See Example 5.*)

21. $y = 2\sin(2\theta)$
22. $y = 2\cos(2\theta)$
23. $y = \frac{1}{2}\sin(2\theta)$
24. $y = \frac{1}{2}\cos(2\theta)$
25. $y = -2\sin\left(\frac{1}{2}\theta\right)$
26. $y = -2\cos\left(\frac{1}{2}\theta\right)$
27. $y = \frac{1}{2}\sin(-2\theta)$
28. $y = \frac{1}{2}\cos(-2\theta)$
29. $y = -\frac{1}{2}\sin(-2\theta)$
30. $y = -\frac{1}{2}\cos(-2\theta)$

Challenge Exercises   See answer section

Sketch graphs of these functions.

31. $y = \cos(2\theta - \pi)$
32. $y = \sin(2\theta + \pi)$
33. $y = 2 + \sin\theta$
34. $y = -3 + \cos\theta$

20-7 Tables of Trigonometric Functions

After finishing Lesson 20-7, you should be able to
I find function values from a table.
II find function values of acute angles, interpolating if necessary.
III find function values for angles of any size.

I Using a Table

By use of certain formulas, tables of values for the trigonometric functions have been constructed. Table 3 at the back of the book is such a table. A portion of it is shown below. This table gives the function values for angles from 0° to 90° only. Values for other angles can always be determined from these, since any angle has an acute reference angle.

Degrees	Radians	Sin	Cos	Tan	Cot	Sec	Csc		
36° 00'	0.6283	0.5878	0.8090	0.7265	1.376	1.236	1.701	0.9425	54° 00'
10	312	901	073	310	368	239	695	396	50
20	341	925	056	355	360	241	688	367	40
30	0.6370	0.5948	0.8039	0.7400	1.351	1.244	1.681	0.9338	30
40	400	972	021	445	343	247	675	308	20
50	429	995	004	490	335	249	668	279	10
37° 00'	0.6458	0.6018	0.7986	0.7536	1.327	1.252	1.662	0.9250	53° 00'
10	487	041	969	581	319	255	655	221	50
20	516	065	951	627	311	258	649	192	40
30	0.6545	0.6088	0.7934	0.7673	1.303	1.260	1.643	0.9163	30
40	574	111	916	720	295	263	636	134	20
50	603	134	898	766	288	266	630	105	10
38° 00'	0.6632	0.6157	0.7880	0.7813	1.280	1.269	1.624	0.9076	52° 00'
10	661	180	862	860	272	272	618	047	50
20	690	202	844	907	265	275	612	0.9018	40
30	0.6720	0.6225	0.7826	0.7954	1.257	1.278	1.606	0.8988	30
40	749	248	808	0.8002	250	281	601	959	20
50	778	271	790	050	242	284	595	930	10
30	0.7418	0.6756	0.7373	0.9163	1.091	1.356	1.480	0.8290	30
40	447	777	353	217	085	360	476	261	20
50	476	799	333	271	079	364	471	232	10
43° 00'	0.7505	0.6820	0.7314	0.9325	1.072	1.367	1.466	0.8203	47° 00'
10	534	841	294	380	066	371	462	174	50
20	563	862	274	435	060	375	457	145	40
30	0.7592	0.6884	0.7254	0.9490	1.054	1.379	1.453	0.8116	30
40	621	905	234	545	048	382	448	087	20
50	650	926	214	601	042	386	444	058	10
44° 00'	0.7679	0.6947	0.7193	0.9657	1.036	1.390	1.440	0.8029	46° 00'
10	709	967	173	713	030	394	435	999	50
20	738	988	153	770	024	398	431	970	40
30	0.7767	0.7009	0.7133	0.9827	1.018	1.402	1.427	0.7941	30
40	796	030	112	884	012	406	423	912	20
50	825	050	092	942	006	410	418	883	10
45° 00'	0.7854	0.7071	0.7071	1.000	1.000	1.414	1.414	0.7854	45° 00'
		Cos	Sin	Cot	Tan	Csc	Sec	Radians	Degrees

The headings on the left of Table 3 range from 0° to 45° only. Thus the table may seem to be only half of what it should be. Function values from 45° to 90° are found by using the cofunction values of their complements. For angles from 45° to 90° the headings on the right are used, together with the headings at the bottom. For example, sin 37° is found to be 0.6018 using the top and left headings. The cosine of 53° (the complement of 37°) is found also to be 0.6018, using the bottom and right headings.

Example 1. Find cos 37°20′.

We find 37°20′ in the left column and then *cos* at the top. At the intersection of this row and column we find the entry we seek:

cos 37°20′ = 0.7951.

TRY THIS ▬▬▶

Use Table 3 to find the following.

1. sin 15°20′ **0.2644**
2. cot 64°50′ **0.4699**

Example 2. Find cot 0.9192.

Since no degree symbol is given, we know that the angle is in radians. Because the angle is greater than 45° or $\frac{\pi}{4}$ radians, we will use the headings on the right to find 0.9192. Next we find *cot* at the bottom. At the intersection of this row and column we find the entry we seek:

cot 0.9192 = 0.7627.

TRY THIS ▬▬▶

Use Table 3 to find the following.

3. cos 0.4451 **0.9026**
4. tan 0.8319 **1.098**

▮▮ Interpolation

The process of linear interpolation can be applied to tables of any function. In particular, we can use it with tables of the trigonometric functions.

Example 3. Find tan 27°43′.

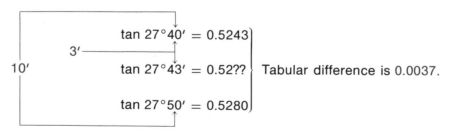

$$\left. \begin{array}{l} \text{tan } 27°40′ = 0.5243 \\ \text{tan } 27°43′ = 0.52?? \\ \text{tan } 27°50′ = 0.5280 \end{array} \right\}$$ Tabular difference is 0.0037.

Because 43′ is $\frac{3}{10}$ of the way from 40′ to 50′, we take $\frac{3}{10}$ of 0.0037, the tabular difference. This is 0.0011. Thus

tan 27°43′ = 0.5243 + 0.0011, or 0.5254.

To interpolate where a function is decreasing there is a slight difference as the next example shows.

Example 4. Find cot 29°44′.

$$\text{cot } 29°40' = 1.756$$

4'

10'

$$\text{cot } 29°44' = 1.7??$$ Tabular difference is 0.012.

$$\text{cot } 29°51' = 1.744$$

We take 0.4 of the tabular difference, 0.012, and obtain 0.0048, or 0.005. Because the cotangent function is *decreasing* in the interval (0°, 90°), we *subtract* 0.005 from 1.756. Thus cot 29°44' = 1.751.

TRY THIS ➡

Use Table 3 for the following.
5. Find sin 38°47'. **0.6264**
6. Find cot 27°45'. **1.900**

Once the process of interpolation is understood, it will not be necessary to write as much as we did in the examples above. After a bit of practice, you will find that interpolation is rather easy, and you can accomplish some of the steps without writing. Let us look at an example of using the tables in reverse, that is, given a function value, to find the measure of an angle.

Example 5. Given tan B = 0.3727, find B (between 0° and 90°).

$$\text{tan } 20°20' = 0.3706$$

10' $$\text{tan } B \quad = 0.3727$$ — 0.0021   Tabular difference is 0.0033.

$$\text{tan } 20°30' = 0.3739$$

We find that B is $\frac{21}{33}$ or $\frac{7}{11}$ of the way from 20°20' to 20°30'. The tabular difference is 10', so we take $\frac{7}{11}$ of 10' and obtain 6'. Thus B = 20°26'.

TRY THIS ➡

7. Given sin θ = 0.3624, find θ. **21°15'**
8. Given cot θ = 1.614, find θ. **31°47'**

ⅲ Function Values for Angles of Any Size

Table 3 gives function values for angles from 0° to 90°. To find the function value for any other angle, we first find the reference angle, which is the angle that the terminal side makes with the *x*-axis. We then look up the function values for the reference angle in the table and use the appropriate sign, depending on the quadrant in which the terminal side lies.

Example 6. Find sin 285°40′.

We first find the reference angle. To do this we find the multiple of 180° that is nearest 285°40′. The multiples of 180° are 180°, 360°, and so on. Now 285°40′ is nearest 360°. We subtract to find the reference angle.

$$\begin{array}{r} 360° = 359°60′ \\ -285°40′ \\ \hline 74°20′ \end{array}$$

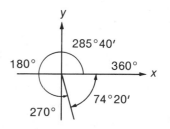

Now we find that sin 74°20′ = 0.9628. The terminal side is in quadrant IV, where the sine is negative. Hence

sin 285°40′ = −0.9628.

TRY THIS ➡

Use Table 3 for the following.
9. Find cos 563°20′. −0.9182
10. Find cos (−729°50′.
                         0.9853

Exercise Set 20-7

▌ Use Table 3 to find the following. (*See Examples 1 and 2.*)

1. sin 13°20′ 0.2306
2. sin 41°40′ 0.6648
3. cos 56°30′ 0.5519
4. cos 71°50′ 0.3118
5. tan 28°40′ 0.5467
6. tan 57°10′ 1.550
7. csc 62°30′ 1.127
8. csc 70°10′ 1.063
9. tan 0.3956 0.4176
10. tan 0.7010 0.8441
11. cos 0.9134 0.6111
12. cot 1.0443 0.5812

▌▌ Use Table 3 to find the following. (*See Examples 3 and 4.*)

13. sin 28°31′ 0.4775
14. sin 36°42′ 0.5977
15. cos 53°55′ 0.5889
16. cos 80°33′ 0.1642
17. tan 24°12′ 0.4494
18. cot 54°18′ 0.7186
19. cos 75.15° 0.2563
20. cos 81.91° 0.1407
21. sin 17.43° 0.2995
22. sin 38.72° 0.6255

For each of the following, find θ in degrees and minutes between 0° and 90°. (*See Example 5.*)

23. sin θ = 0.2368 13°42′
24. sin θ = 0.3864 22°44′
25. cos θ = 0.3749 67°59′
26. cos θ = 0.3538 69°17′
27. cos θ = 0.6348 50°36′
28. cos θ = 0.9678 14°34′

▌▌▌ Use Table 3 to find the following. (*See Example 6.*)

29. sin 307°10′ −0.7969
30. sin 336°30′ 0.6383
31. cos 410°20′ −0.3987
32. cos 456°40′ −0.1161

20-8 Algebraic Manipulations

After finishing Lesson 20-8, you should be able to
▌ compute with and simplify expressions containing trigonometric expressions.
▌▌ solve equations containing trigonometric expressions.

Trigonometric expressions such as sin 2θ or tan $(x - \pi)$ represent numbers, just as algebraic expressions represent numbers. Thus we can work with trigonometric expressions in much the same way as we work with purely algebraic expressions.

▌Computing and Simplifying

Example 1.   Multiply and simplify cos y (tan y − sec y).

$$\cos y\, (\tan y - \sec y) = \cos y \tan y - \cos y \sec y \quad \textit{Multiplying}$$
$$= \cos y \,\frac{\sin y}{\cos y} - \cos y \,\frac{1}{\cos y} \quad \textit{Simplifying}$$
$$= \sin y - 1$$

In Example 1 we used certain identities to accomplish simplification. There is no general rule for doing this, but it is often helpful to put everything in terms of sines and cosines, as we did in Example 1.

TRY THIS ══════▶

1.   Multiply and simplify
sin x (cot x + csc x).
cos x + 1

Example 2.   Factor and simplify $\sin^2 x \cos^2 x + \cos^4 x$.

$$\sin^2 x \cos^2 x + \cos^4 x = \cos^2 x\, (\sin^2 x + \cos^2 x) \quad \textit{Factoring}$$
$$= \cos^2 x\, (1) \quad \textit{Substituting 1 for } \sin^2 x + \cos^2 x$$
$$= \cos^2 x$$

Example 3.   Factor and simplify $\tan x + \cos \left(\frac{\pi}{2} - x\right)$.

$$\tan x + \cos \left(\frac{\pi}{2} - x\right) = \tan x + \sin x \quad \textit{Using an identity for } \cos \left(\frac{\pi}{2} - x\right)$$
$$= \frac{\sin x}{\cos x} + \sin x \quad \textit{Using an identity for } \tan x$$
$$= \sin x \left(\frac{1}{\cos x} + 1\right) \quad \textit{Factoring}$$
$$= \sin x\, (\sec x + 1)$$

TRY THIS ➤

Example 4.   Simplify $\dfrac{\sin x - \sin x \cos x}{\sin x + \sin x \tan x}$.

$$\dfrac{\sin x - \sin x \cos x}{\sin x + \sin x \tan x} = \dfrac{\sin x\,(1 - \cos x)}{\sin x\,(1 + \tan x)} \quad \text{Factoring}$$

$$= \dfrac{1 - \cos x}{1 + \tan x} \quad \text{Simplifying}$$

> Factor and simplify.
>
> 2. $\sin^3 \theta + \sin \theta \cos^2 \theta$
> 3. $\cot x - \sin\left(\dfrac{\pi}{2} - x\right)$
>
> **2.** $\sin \theta$ **3.** $\cos x\,(\csc x - 1)$

TRY THIS ➤

> 4.   Simplify. $\dfrac{1 + \sin x}{1 - \cot x}$
>
> $\dfrac{\cos x + \sin x \cos x}{\cos x - \cos x \cot x}$

‖ Solving Equations

Example 5.   Solve for $\tan x$: $\tan^2 x + \tan x = 56$.

$$\tan^2 x + \tan x - 56 = 0 \qquad \text{Rewriting as a quadratic equation}$$
$$(\tan x + 8)(\tan x - 7) = 0 \qquad \text{Factoring}$$

$$\tan x + 8 = 0 \qquad \text{or} \qquad \tan x - 7 = 0$$
$$\tan x = -8 \qquad \text{or} \qquad \tan x = 7$$

TRY THIS ➤

> 5.   Solve for $\cot x$.
> $$\cot^2 x + \cot x = 12$$
> $\cot x = -4$ or $\cot x = 3$

Example 6.   Solve for $\sec x$: $\sec^2 x - \frac{3}{4}\sec x = \frac{1}{2}$.

$$\sec^2 x - \tfrac{3}{4}\sec x - \tfrac{1}{2} = 0.$$

We now use the quadratic formula, and obtain

$$\sec x = \dfrac{\frac{3}{4} \pm \sqrt{\frac{9}{16} - 4 \cdot 1 \cdot \left(-\frac{1}{2}\right)}}{2} = \dfrac{\frac{3}{4} \pm \sqrt{\frac{41}{16}}}{2}$$

$$= \dfrac{\frac{3}{4} \pm \frac{\sqrt{41}}{4}}{2} = \dfrac{3 \pm \sqrt{41}}{8}$$

> 6.   Solve for $\cos \theta$.
> $$\cos^2 \theta - \tfrac{1}{4}\cos \theta = \tfrac{3}{2}$$
> $\cos \theta = \dfrac{1 \pm \sqrt{97}}{8}$

TRY THIS ➤

Exercise Set 20-8

‖ Multiply and simplify. (*See Example 1.*)

1. $(\sin x - \cos x)(\sin x + \cos x)$ $\sin^2 x - \cos^2 x$

2. $(\tan \theta - \cot \theta)(\tan \theta + \cot \theta)$ $\tan^2 \theta - \cot^2 \theta$

3. $\tan x\,(\cos x - \csc x)$ $\sin x - \sec x$

4. $\cot x\,(\sin x + \sec x)$ $\cos x + \csc x$

5. $\cos \theta \sin \theta\,(\sec \theta + \csc \theta\ )$ $\sin \theta + \cos \theta$

6. $\tan y \sin y\,(\cot y - \csc y)$ $\sin y - \tan y$

Use Quiz 36 after lesson 20—8.

7. $(\sin x + \cos x)(\csc x - \sec x)$ $\cot x - \tan x$

8. $(\sin x + \cos x)(\sec x + \csc x)$ $\tan x + \cot x + 2$

9. $(\sin y - \cos y)^2$ $1 - 2\sin y \cos y$

10. $(\sin \theta + \cos \theta)^2$ $1 + 2\sin \theta \cos \theta$

11. $(1 + \tan \theta)^2$ $\sec^2 \theta + 2\tan \theta$

12. $(1 + \cot x)^2$ $\csc^2 x + 2\cot x$

Factor and simplify. (*See Examples 2 and 3.*)

13. $\sin x \cos x + \cos^2 x$ $\cos x(\sin x + \cos x)$

14. $\sec \theta \csc x - \csc^2 \theta$ $\csc x(\sec x - \csc x)$

15. $\sin^2 y - \cos^2 y$ $(\sin y - \cos y)(\sin y + \cos y)$

16. $\tan^2 y - \cot^2 y$ $(\tan y - \cot y)(\tan y + \cot y)$

17. $\tan x + \sin (\pi - x)$ $\tan x + \sin x$

18. $\cot \theta - \cos (\pi - \theta)$ $\cot \theta + \cos \theta$

19. $\sin^4 \theta - \cos^4 \theta$ $(\sin \theta - \cos \theta)(\sin \theta + \cos \theta)$

20. $\tan^4 x - \sec^4 x$ $-(\tan^2 x + \sec^2 x)$

21. $3 \cot^2 y + 6 \cot y + 3$ $3(\cot y + 1)^2$

22. $4 \sin^2 y + 8 \sin y + 4$ $4(\sin y + 1)^2$

23. $\csc^4 \theta + 4 \csc^2 \theta - 5$ $(\csc^2 \theta + 5)(\cot^2 \theta)$

24. $\tan^4 x - 2 \tan^2 x - 3$ $(\tan^2 x - 3)(\sec^2 x)$

Simplify. (*See Example 4.*)

25. $\dfrac{\sin^2 x \cos x}{\cos^2 x \sin x}$ $\tan x$

26. $\dfrac{\cos^2 x \sin x}{\sin^2 x \cos x}$ $\cot x$

27. $\dfrac{4 \sin \theta \cos^3 \theta}{18 \sin^2 \theta \cos \theta}$ $\frac{2}{9}\cos \theta \cot \theta$

28. $\dfrac{30 \sin^3 x \cos x}{6 \cos^2 x \sin x}$ $5\tan x \sin x$

29. $\dfrac{\cos^2 x - 2 \cos x + 1}{\cos x - 1}$ $\cos x - 1$

30. $\dfrac{\sin^2 x + 2 \sin x + 1}{\sin x + 1}$ $\sin x + 1$

31. $\dfrac{\cos^2 x - 1}{\cos x - 1}$ $\cos x + 1$

32. $\dfrac{\sin^2 \theta - 1}{\sin \theta + 1}$ $\sin \theta - 1$

■■ Solve for the indicated trigonometric expression. (*See Examples 5 and 6.*)

33. $\tan^2 x + 4 \tan x = 21$, for $\tan x$

34. $\sec^2 \theta - 7 \sec \theta = -10$, for $\sec \theta$

35. $8 \sin^2 \theta - 2 \sin \theta = 3$, for $\sin \theta$

36. $6 \cos^2 x + 17 \cos x = -5$, for $\cos x$

37. $\cot^2 x + 9 \cot x - 10 = 0$, for $\cot x$

38. $\csc^2 \theta + 3 \csc \theta - 10 = 0$, for $\csc \theta$

39. $\sin^2 \theta + \cos \left(\theta + \dfrac{\pi}{2} \right) = 6$, for $\sin \theta$

40. $2 \cos^2 \left(x - \dfrac{\pi}{2} \right) - 3 \cos \left(x - \dfrac{\pi}{2} \right) - 2 = 0$, for $\sin x$

41. $\tan^2 \theta - 6 \tan \theta = 4$, for $\tan \theta$

42. $2 \csc^2 x - 3 \csc x - 4 = 0$, for $\csc x$

See answer section

COMPUTER NOTE: World War II and Computers

Until World War II, computing devices were mostly mechanical. They relied on gears and other machine parts to operate. During the war, the first all-electronic computers were built. One was ENIAC (Electronic Numerical Integrator and Calculator), built secretly at the University of Pennsylvania. Later it was moved to Aberdeen, Maryland, where it was used to calculate the paths of artillery shells.

Chapter 20 Review

Review the material in the chapter. Then see how you have done by trying these review exercises. If you miss an exercise, restudy the indicated lesson.

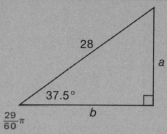

20-1   1.   Given $\sin 37.5° = 0.6088$ and $\cos 37.5° = 0.7934$ find a and b.   a = 17.05, b = 22.22

20-2   2.   Convert $87°$ to radian measure. Leave in terms of π. $\frac{29}{60}\pi$

20-3   3.   Convert $\frac{3\pi}{2}$ to degrees.   270°

20-3   4.   Find the six trigonometric function values for the angle θ shown.   See answer section

20-3   5.   Complete the following table.

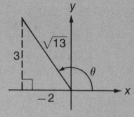

θ	30°	45°	60°
$\sin \theta$			
$\tan \theta$			

$\frac{1}{2}, \frac{\sqrt{2}}{2}, \frac{\sqrt{3}}{2}$
$\frac{\sqrt{3}}{3}, 1, \sqrt{3}$

20-3   6.   Find the following exactly. Do *not* use the table.   a) $\frac{\sqrt{2}}{2}$ b) 1
           a) $\sin 495°$ b) $\tan (-315°)$

20-4   7.   Sketch a graph of the cosine function.   See text page 607.

20-4   8.   Sketch a graph of the tangent function.   See text page 608.

20-5   9.   Express $\tan \theta$ in terms of $\sec \theta$. $\tan \theta \equiv \pm \sqrt{\sec^2 \theta - 1}$

20-5   Find cofunction identities for each expression.

10. $\cos \left(\theta + \frac{\pi}{2}\right)$ 11. $\sin \left(x - \frac{\pi}{2}\right)$ 10. $\cos (\theta + \frac{\pi}{2}) \equiv -\sin \theta$ 11. $\sin (x - \frac{\pi}{2}) \equiv -\cos x$

20-5   12.   Find an identity for $\tan \left(\theta - \frac{\pi}{2}\right)$. $\tan (\theta - \frac{\pi}{2}) \equiv -\cot \theta$

20-5   13.   Use the following.
           $\sin 24° = 0.4067$ $\cos 24° = 0.9135$
           $\tan 24° = 0.4452$ $\cot 24° = 2.246$ sin 66° = 0.9135, cos 66° = 0.4067, tan 66° = 2.246,
           $\sec 24° = 1.095$ $\csc 24° = 2.459$ cot 66° = 0.4452, sec 66° = 2.459, csc 66° = 1.095
           Find the six function values for $66°$.

20-6   14.   Sketch a graph of $y = 3 \cos \theta$. What is the amplitude of the function?   See answer section

20-6   15.   Sketch a graph of $y = \sin 2\theta$. What is the period of the function?   See answer section

20-7   Use Table 3 to find the following.   16. 6.827   17. 0.5147   18. 16°10′   19. 39°
           16. $\cot 8°20'$ 17. $\tan 27°14'$
           18. $\cot \theta = 3.450, 0 < \theta < 90°$. Find θ.
           19. $\sin \theta = 0.6293, 0 < \theta < 90°$. Find θ.

20-8   20.   Simplify $\cos \theta (\tan \theta + \cot \theta)$.   csc θ

20-8   21.   Solve $3 \tan^2 \theta - 2 \tan \theta - 2 = 0$ for $\tan \theta$. $\frac{1 \pm \sqrt{7}}{3}$

Chapter 20 Test

1. Given $\sin 36.5° = 0.5948$ and $\cos 36.5° = 0.8039$ find a
   and b.   a = 19.03, b = 25.72

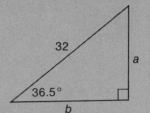

2. Convert $64°$ to radian measure. Leave in terms of π. $\frac{16}{45}\pi$

3. Convert $\frac{5\pi}{6}$ to degrees.   150°

4. Find the six trigonometric function values for the angle θ.

5. Complete the following table.
      $\sin\theta = -\frac{1}{2}$, $\cos\theta = -\frac{\sqrt3}{2}$, $\tan\theta = \frac{\sqrt3}{3}$, $\cot\theta$
      $= \sqrt3$, $\sec\theta = -\frac{2\sqrt3}{3}$, $\csc\theta = -2$

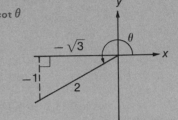

θ	30°	45°	60°
$\cos\theta$				$\frac{\sqrt3}{2}, \frac{\sqrt2}{2}, \frac{1}{2}$
$\cot\theta$				$\sqrt3, 1, \frac{\sqrt3}{3}$

6. Find the following exactly. Do not use the table.   a) $-\frac{1}{2}$ b) $-\sqrt2$
   a) $\sin -150°$ b) $\csc 315°$

7. Sketch a graph of the sine function.   See text page 607.

8. Sketch a graph of the cotangent function.   See text page 609.

9. Express $\cot\theta$ in terms of $\csc\theta$. $\cot\theta \equiv \pm\sqrt{\csc^2\theta - 1}$

Find cofunction identities for each expression.

10. $\sin\left(\theta + \frac{\pi}{2}\right)$ 11. $\cos\left(\frac{\pi}{2} - x\right)$ 10. $\sin(\theta + \frac{\pi}{2}) \equiv \cos\theta$ 11. $\cos(\frac{\pi}{2} - x) \equiv \sin x$

12. Find an identity for $\cot\left(\theta + \frac{\pi}{2}\right)$. $\cot(\theta + \frac{\pi}{2}) \equiv -\tan\theta$

13. Use the following.
    $\sin 54° = 0.8090$ $\cos 54° = 0.5878$ sin 36° = 0.5878, cos 36° = 0.8090, tan 36° = 0.7265,
    $\tan 54° = 1.376$ $\cot 54° - 0.7265$ cot 36° = 1.376, sec 36° = 1.236, csc 36° = 1.701
    $\sec 54° = 1.701$ $\csc 54° = 1.236$
    Find the six function values for $36°$.

14. Sketch a graph of $y = 2\sin\theta$. What is the amplitude of the
    function?   See answer section

15. Sketch a graph of $y = \sin\frac{1}{2}\theta$. What is the period of the
    function?   See answer section

Use Table 3 to find the following.

16. $\sec 17°40'$ 17. $\cot 34°16'$ 16. 1.049   17. 1.468

18. $\sin\theta = 0.5878$, $0 < \theta < 90°$. Find θ.   36°

19. $\cos\theta = 0.8027$, $0 < \theta < 90°$. Find θ.   36°37'

20. Simplify $\dfrac{\csc\theta(\sin^2\theta + \cos^2\theta\tan\theta)}{\sin\theta + \cos\theta}$.   1

21. Solve $6\sec^2\theta - 5\sec\theta - 2 = 0$ for $\sec\theta$. $\frac{5 \pm \sqrt{73}}{12}$

Ready for Trigonometric Identities and Equations?

Solve.

7-7   1. $a^2 - 11a + 24 = 0$ 3, 8   2. $2b^2 - 3b = 5$ $\frac{5}{2}$, −1

Multiply and simplify where possible.

10-3   3. $\sqrt{x^2 - a} \cdot \sqrt{x^2 + a}$ $\sqrt{x^4 - a^2}$ 4. $\sqrt[5]{8g^2h} \cdot \sqrt[5]{4g^3h^2}$ $2g\sqrt[5]{h^3}$

20-8   5. $\sin y \, (\csc y - \cot y)$ $1 - \cos y$ 6. $\tan \theta \cdot \cos \theta \cdot \csc \theta$ 1

Simplify.

10-2   7. $\sqrt{(-81)^2}$ 81   8. $\sqrt{(9c)^2}$ 9|c|

10-7   Simplify by rationalizing the denominators.

9. $\dfrac{\sqrt[3]{4m}}{\sqrt[3]{5n}}$ $\dfrac{\sqrt[3]{100mn^2}}{5|n|}$ 10. $\dfrac{5\sqrt{5} - 2\sqrt{3}}{2\sqrt{3} - 3\sqrt{5}}$ $\dfrac{63 + 4\sqrt{15}}{-33}$

Find $f^{-1}(x)$.

8-6   11. $f(x) = 3x - 2$ $f^{-1}(x) = \frac{x+2}{3}$ 12. $f(x) = 2 + \sqrt{x + 3}$ $f^{-1}(x) = x^2 - 4x + 1$

Find the absolute value of each complex number.

11-4   13. $|-a + bi|$ $\sqrt{a^2 + b^2}$ 14. $|5 - 12i|$ 13

20-1   15. Find $\sin \theta$, $\cos \theta$, and $\tan \theta$
       for the triangle to the right.

$\sin \theta = \frac{8}{17}$, $\cos \theta = \frac{15}{17}$, $\tan \theta = \frac{8}{15}$

20-2   Convert:

16. 40° to radians $\frac{2\pi}{9}$

17. $\dfrac{6\pi}{5}$ radians to degrees.   216°

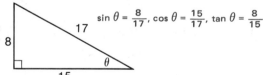

18. $\sin 300° = -\frac{\sqrt{3}}{2}$, $\cos 300° = \frac{1}{2}$,

20-3   18. List all function values for 300°.

20-4   19. Sketch graphs of the sine and cosine functions.

20-5   20. List the Pythagorean identities.

$\tan 300° = -\sqrt{3}$, $\cot 300° = -\frac{\sqrt{3}}{3}$

$\sec 300° = 2$, $\csc 300° = -\frac{2\sqrt{3}}{3}$

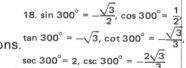

19. See text page 607.   20. See text page 614.

20-7   Find:

21. $\cos 15°30'$ 0.9636   22. $\sec 1.2828$ 3.521

23. $\tan 87°17'$ 21.07   24. $\sin 182°10'$ −0.0378

20-8   25. Solve for $\sin \theta$:

$6 \sin^2 \theta + \sin \theta - 2 = 0$ $\sin \theta = \frac{1}{2}$ or $\sin \theta = -\frac{2}{3}$

Chapter 21
Trigonometric Identities and Equations

Observers in a balloon can use trigonometry to calculate distances on the ground.

21-1 Sum and Difference Identities

After finishing Lesson 21-1, you should be able to
- ▌ use the cosine sum and difference identities to simplify trigonometric expressions.
- ▌▌ use the sine and tangent sum and difference identities to simplify trigonometric expressions.

We will now consider some important identities involving sums or differences of angles or rotations.

▌Cosines of Sums or Differences

A basic identity that can be proved is

$$\cos(\alpha - \beta) \equiv \cos\alpha\cos\beta + \sin\alpha\sin\beta.$$

Example 1.   Simplify $\cos\left(\dfrac{3\pi}{4} - \dfrac{\pi}{3}\right)$.

$$\cos\left(\frac{3\pi}{4} - \frac{\pi}{3}\right) = \cos\frac{3\pi}{4}\cos\frac{\pi}{3} + \sin\frac{3\pi}{4}\sin\frac{\pi}{3}$$

$$= -\frac{\sqrt{2}}{2}\cdot\frac{1}{2} + \frac{\sqrt{2}}{2}\cdot\frac{\sqrt{3}}{2}$$

$$= \frac{\sqrt{2}}{4}(\sqrt{3} - 1) \ \text{ or } \ \frac{\sqrt{6} - \sqrt{2}}{4}$$

TRY THIS ➡

> 1.   Simplify $\cos\left(\dfrac{\pi}{2} - \dfrac{\pi}{6}\right)$.
> $\frac{1}{2}$

Example 2.   Find $\cos 15°$.

$$\cos 15° = \cos(45° - 30°) \quad \textit{Writing 15° in terms of angles with known functions}$$

$$= \cos 45°\cos 30° + \sin 45°\sin 30°$$

$$= \frac{\sqrt{2}}{2}\cdot\frac{\sqrt{3}}{2} + \frac{\sqrt{2}}{2}\cdot\frac{1}{2}$$

$$= \frac{\sqrt{2}}{4}(\sqrt{3} + 1), \text{ or } \frac{\sqrt{6} + \sqrt{2}}{4}$$

TRY THIS ➡

> 2.   Find $\cos 105°$ as $\cos(150° - 45°)$.
> $\frac{\sqrt{2} - \sqrt{6}}{4}$

Example 3. Simplify $\sin\left(-\dfrac{5\pi}{2}\right)\sin\dfrac{\pi}{2}+\cos\dfrac{\pi}{2}\cos\left(-\dfrac{5\pi}{2}\right)$.

This is equal to $\cos\dfrac{\pi}{2}\cos\left(-\dfrac{5\pi}{2}\right)+\sin\dfrac{\pi}{2}\sin\left(-\dfrac{5\pi}{2}\right)$.

By the given identity, we can simplify this to

$\cos\left[\dfrac{\pi}{2}-\left(-\dfrac{5\pi}{2}\right)\right]$, or $\cos\dfrac{6\pi}{2}$, or $\cos 3\pi$, which is -1.

TRY THIS

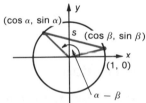

Simplify. 3. $\cos\dfrac{7\pi}{12}$ 4. $\cos 25°$

3. $\sin\dfrac{\pi}{3}\sin\left(-\dfrac{\pi}{4}\right)+$

   $\cos\left(-\dfrac{\pi}{4}\right)\cos\dfrac{\pi}{3}$

4. $\cos 37°\cos 12°+$

   $\sin 12°\sin 37°$

A Proof of the Cosine Identity

We have seen that $\cos(\alpha-\beta)=\cos\alpha\cos\beta+\sin\alpha\sin\beta$. Let us see how this identity is developed.

Suppose angles α and β have coordinates as shown.

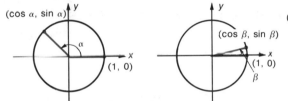

The figure on the right shows these angles on the same coordinate axes. Notice that the size of the angle between them is $\alpha-\beta$. We use the distance formula to write an expression for the length s.

$s^2=(\cos\alpha-\cos\beta)^2+(\sin\alpha-\sin\beta)^2$
$=(\cos^2\alpha-2\cos\alpha\cos\beta+\cos^2\beta)+(\sin^2\alpha-2\sin\alpha\sin\beta+\sin^2\beta)$
$=(1-2\cos\alpha\cos\beta)+(1-2\sin\alpha\sin\beta)$
$=2-2(\cos\alpha\cos\beta+\sin\alpha\sin\beta)$

Now imagine that the unit circle above is rotated so that $(\cos\beta,\sin\beta)$ is at $(1,0)$. The length s has not changed.

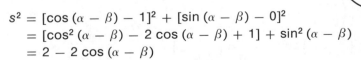

$s^2=[\cos(\alpha-\beta)-1]^2+[\sin(\alpha-\beta)-0]^2$
$=[\cos^2(\alpha-\beta)-2\cos(\alpha-\beta)+1]+\sin^2(\alpha-\beta)$
$=2-2\cos(\alpha-\beta)$

Equating our two expressions for s^2, we obtain

$2-2\cos(\alpha-\beta)=2-2(\cos\alpha\cos\beta+\sin\alpha\sin\beta),$
$\cos(\alpha-\beta)=\cos\alpha\cos\beta+\sin\alpha\sin\beta.$

Next let us consider $\cos(\alpha + \beta)$. This is equal to $\cos[\alpha - (-\beta)]$, and by the identity above, we have

$$\cos(\alpha + \beta) \equiv \cos \alpha \cos(-\beta) + \sin \alpha \sin(-\beta).$$

But $\cos(-\beta) \equiv \cos \beta$ and $\sin(-\beta) \equiv -\sin \beta$, so the identity we seek is the following.

$$\cos(\alpha + \beta) \equiv \cos \alpha \cos \beta - \sin \alpha \sin \beta$$

Example 4.   Find $\cos 105°$.

$$\begin{aligned}
\cos 105° &= \cos(60° + 45°) \\
&= \cos 60° \cos 45° - \sin 60° \sin 45° \\
&= \frac{1}{2} \cdot \frac{\sqrt{2}}{2} - \frac{\sqrt{3}}{2} \cdot \frac{\sqrt{2}}{2} \\
&= \frac{\sqrt{2} - \sqrt{6}}{4}
\end{aligned}$$

TRY THIS ━━━▶

5.   Find $\cos 75°$ as $\cos(30° + 45°)$.
$\frac{\sqrt{6} - \sqrt{2}}{4}$

▮ Other Formulas

To develop an identity for the sine of a sum, we recall that

$$\sin \theta \equiv \cos\left(\frac{\pi}{2} - \theta\right).$$

In this identity we shall substitute $\alpha + \beta$ for θ, obtaining

$$\sin(\alpha + \beta) \equiv \cos\left[\frac{\pi}{2} - (\alpha + \beta)\right].$$

We can now use the identity for the cosine of a difference. We get

$$\begin{aligned}
\sin(\alpha + \beta) &\equiv \cos\left[\frac{\pi}{2} - (\alpha + \beta)\right], \\
&\equiv \cos\left[\left(\frac{\pi}{2} - \alpha\right) - \beta\right], \\
&\equiv \cos\left(\frac{\pi}{2} - \alpha\right)\cos \beta + \sin\left(\frac{\pi}{2} - \alpha\right)\sin \beta, \\
&\equiv \sin \alpha \cos \beta + \cos \alpha \sin \beta.
\end{aligned}$$

Thus the identity we seek is

$$\sin(\alpha + \beta) \equiv \sin \alpha \cos \beta + \cos \alpha \sin \beta.$$

Example 5. Simplify $\sin \left(\frac{5\pi}{4} + \frac{\pi}{3} \right)$.

$$\sin \left(\frac{5\pi}{4} + \frac{\pi}{3} \right) = \sin \frac{5\pi}{4} \cos \frac{\pi}{3} + \cos \frac{5\pi}{4} \sin \frac{\pi}{3}$$

$$= -\frac{\sqrt{2}}{2} \cdot \frac{1}{2} + \left(-\frac{\sqrt{2}}{2} \right) \frac{\sqrt{3}}{2}$$

$$= \frac{-\sqrt{2}}{4} - \frac{\sqrt{6}}{4}$$

$$= \frac{-\sqrt{2} - \sqrt{6}}{4}$$

TRY THIS

6. Simplify $\sin \left(\frac{\pi}{4} + \frac{\pi}{3} \right)$.
$\frac{\sqrt{2} + \sqrt{6}}{4}$

To find a formula for the sine of a difference, we can use the identity just derived, substituting $-\beta$ for β. We obtain

$$\sin (\alpha - \beta) \equiv \sin \alpha \cos \beta - \cos \alpha \sin \beta.$$

A formula for the tangent of a sum can be derived as follows, using identities already established:

$$\tan (\alpha + \beta) \equiv \frac{\sin (\alpha + \beta)}{\cos (\alpha + \beta)}$$

$$\equiv \frac{\sin \alpha \cos \beta + \cos \alpha \sin \beta}{\cos \alpha \cos \beta - \sin \alpha \sin \beta} \cdot \frac{\dfrac{1}{\cos \alpha \cos \beta}}{\dfrac{1}{\cos \alpha \cos \beta}}$$

$$\equiv \frac{\dfrac{\sin \alpha \cos \beta}{\cos \alpha \cos \beta} + \dfrac{\cos \alpha \sin \beta}{\cos \alpha \cos \beta}}{\dfrac{\cos \alpha \cos \beta}{\cos \alpha \cos \beta} - \dfrac{\sin \alpha \sin \beta}{\cos \alpha \cos \beta}}$$

$$\equiv \frac{\dfrac{\sin \alpha}{\cos \alpha} + \dfrac{\sin \beta}{\cos \beta}}{1 - \dfrac{\sin \alpha \sin \beta}{\cos \alpha \cos \beta}}$$

$$\equiv \frac{\tan \alpha + \tan \beta}{1 - \tan \alpha \tan \beta}$$

Similarly, a formula for the tangent of a difference can be established. The following theorem summarizes the sum and difference formulas. These should be memorized.

THEOREM 21-1

$\cos(\alpha - \beta) \equiv \cos\alpha\cos\beta + \sin\alpha\sin\beta$

$\cos(\alpha + \beta) \equiv \cos\alpha\cos\beta - \sin\alpha\sin\beta$

$\sin(\alpha - \beta) \equiv \sin\alpha\cos\beta - \cos\alpha\sin\beta$

$\sin(\alpha + \beta) \equiv \sin\alpha\cos\beta + \cos\alpha\sin\beta$

$\tan(\alpha - \beta) \equiv \dfrac{\tan\alpha - \tan\beta}{1 + \tan\alpha\tan\beta}$

$\tan(\alpha + \beta) \equiv \dfrac{\tan\alpha + \tan\beta}{1 - \tan\alpha\tan\beta}$

The identities involving sines and tangents can be used in the same way as those involving cosines in the earlier examples.

Example 6. Find tan 15°.

$$\tan 15° = \tan(45° - 30°)$$
$$= \frac{\tan 45° - \tan 30°}{1 + \tan 45° \tan 30°}$$
$$= \frac{1 - \sqrt{\frac{3}{3}}}{1 + \sqrt{\frac{3}{3}}} = \frac{3 - \sqrt{3}}{3 + \sqrt{3}} = 2 - \sqrt{3}$$

Example 7. Simplify $\sin\dfrac{\pi}{3}\cos\pi + \sin\pi\cos\dfrac{\pi}{3}$.

This is equal to $\sin\dfrac{\pi}{3}\cos\pi + \cos\dfrac{\pi}{3}\sin\pi$. Thus by the

fourth identity in the list above, we can simplify to

$$\sin\left(\frac{\pi}{3} + \pi\right) \text{ or } \sin\frac{4\pi}{3} \text{ or } -\frac{\sqrt{3}}{2}.$$

TRY THIS

7. Find tan 75° as tan(45° + 30°). $2 + \sqrt{3}$

8. Simplify $\sin\dfrac{\pi}{2}\cos\dfrac{\pi}{3} - \sin\dfrac{\pi}{3}\cos\dfrac{\pi}{2}$. $\sin\dfrac{\pi}{6}$ or $\dfrac{1}{2}$

Exercise Set 21-1

▪ Use the cosine sum and difference identities to simplify the following. (*See Examples 1 and 3.*)

1. $\cos(A - B)$ $\cos A \cos B + \sin A \sin B$
2. $\cos(A + B)$ $\cos A \cos B - \sin A \sin B$
3. $\cos(45° + 30°)$ $\dfrac{\sqrt{6} - \sqrt{2}}{4}$
4. $\cos(45° - 30°)$ $\dfrac{\sqrt{6} + \sqrt{2}}{4}$
5. $\cos(45° + 60°)$ $\dfrac{\sqrt{2} - \sqrt{6}}{4}$
6. $\cos(60° - 45°)$ $\dfrac{\sqrt{2} + \sqrt{6}}{4}$
7. $\cos\left(\dfrac{\pi}{4} + \dfrac{\pi}{3}\right)$ $\dfrac{\sqrt{2} - \sqrt{6}}{4}$
8. $\cos\left(\dfrac{\pi}{4} - \dfrac{\pi}{3}\right)$ $\dfrac{\sqrt{2} + \sqrt{6}}{4}$
9. $\cos A \cos B + \sin A \sin B$ $\cos(A - B)$
10. $\cos A \cos B - \sin A \sin B$ $\cos(A + B)$
11. $\cos(\alpha + \beta) + \cos(\alpha - \beta)$ $2\cos\alpha\cos\beta$
12. $\cos(\alpha + \beta) - \cos(\alpha - \beta)$ $-2\sin\alpha\sin\beta$

Use the cosine sum and difference identities to find the following. (*See Examples 2 and 4.*)

13. $\cos 165°$ $\quad \dfrac{-\sqrt{2}-\sqrt{6}}{4}$

14. $\cos 195°$ $\quad \dfrac{-\sqrt{6}-\sqrt{2}}{4}$

15. $\cos 135°$ $\quad -\dfrac{\sqrt{2}}{2}$

16. $\cos 225°$ $\quad -\dfrac{\sqrt{2}}{2}$

■ Use the other sum and difference identities to simplify the following. (*See Examples 5 and 7.*)

17. $\sin (P + Q)$ $\quad \sin P \cos Q + \cos P \sin Q$

18. $\sin (P - Q)$ $\quad \sin P \cos Q - \cos P \sin Q$

19. $\tan (P - Q)$ $\quad \dfrac{\tan P - \tan Q}{1 + \tan P \tan Q}$

20. $\tan (P + Q)$ $\quad \dfrac{\tan P + \tan Q}{1 - \tan P \tan Q}$

21. $\sin (45° + 60°)$ $\quad \dfrac{\sqrt{2}+\sqrt{6}}{4}$

22. $\sin (45° - 30°)$ $\quad \dfrac{\sqrt{6}-\sqrt{2}}{4}$

23. $\tan (45° + 30°)$ $\quad 2 + \sqrt{3}$

24. $\tan (45° - 30°)$ $\quad 2 - \sqrt{3}$

25. $\sin P \cos Q + \sin Q \cos P$ $\quad \sin (P + Q)$

26. $\cos Q \sin P - \cos P \sin Q$ $\quad \sin (P - Q)$

27. $\dfrac{\tan A - \tan B}{1 + \tan A \tan B}$ $\quad \tan (A - B)$

28. $\dfrac{\tan A + \tan B}{1 - \tan A \tan B}$ $\quad \tan (A + B)$

29. $\dfrac{\tan 20° + \tan 32°}{1 - \tan 20° \tan 32°}$ $\quad \tan 52°$

30. $\dfrac{\tan 35° - \tan 12°}{1 + \tan 35° \tan 12°}$ $\quad \tan 23°$

31. $\sin (\alpha + \beta) + \sin (\alpha - \beta)$ $\quad 2 \sin \alpha \cos \beta$

32. $\sin (\alpha + \beta) - \sin (\alpha - \beta)$ $\quad 2 \cos \alpha \sin \beta$

Use the sum and difference formulas to find the following. (*See Example 6.*)

33. $\sin 15°$ $\quad \dfrac{\sqrt{6}-\sqrt{2}}{4}$

34. $\sin 105°$ $\quad \dfrac{\sqrt{6}+\sqrt{2}}{4}$

35. $\sin 135°$ $\quad \dfrac{\sqrt{2}}{2}$

36. $\sin 150°$ $\quad \dfrac{1}{2}$

37. $\tan 75°$ $\quad 2 + \sqrt{3}$

38. $\tan 105°$ $\quad -2 - \sqrt{3}$

Calculator Exercises

Given that $\sin \theta = 0.6249$ and $\cos \phi = 0.1102$, and that θ and ϕ are both first-quadrant angles, find the following.

39. $\sin (\theta + \phi)$ $\quad 0.8448$

40. $\cos (\theta + \phi)$ $\quad -0.5351$

Challenge Exercises

41. Find an identity for $\sin 2\theta$. [Hint: $2\theta = \theta + \theta$.] $\quad \sin 2\theta \equiv 2 \sin \theta \cos \theta$

42. Find an identity for $\cos 2\theta$. [Hint: $2\theta = \theta + \theta$.] $\quad \cos 2\theta \equiv \cos^2 \theta - \sin^2 \theta$

43. Derive an identity for $\cot (\alpha + \beta)$ in terms of $\cot \alpha$ and $\cot \beta$. $\quad \cot (\alpha + \beta) \equiv \dfrac{\cot \alpha \cot \beta - 1}{\cot \beta + \cot \alpha}$

44. Derive an identity for $\cot (\alpha - \beta)$ in terms of $\cot \alpha$ and $\cot \beta$. $\quad \cot (\alpha - \beta) \equiv \dfrac{\cot \alpha \cot \beta + 1}{\cot \beta - \cot \alpha}$

The cofunction identities can be derived from the sum and difference formulas. Derive identities for the following.

45. $\sin \left(\dfrac{\pi}{2} - x \right)$ $\quad \begin{aligned}\sin (\tfrac{\pi}{2} - x) &\equiv \sin \tfrac{\pi}{2} \cos x - \cos \tfrac{\pi}{2} \sin x \\ &\equiv 1 \cdot \cos x - 0 \cdot \sin x \equiv \cos x\end{aligned}$

46. $\cos \left(\dfrac{\pi}{2} - x \right)$ $\quad \begin{aligned}\cos (\tfrac{\pi}{2} - x) &\equiv \cos \tfrac{\pi}{2} \cos x + \sin \tfrac{\pi}{2} \sin x \\ &\equiv 0 \cdot \cos x + 1 \cdot \sin x \equiv \sin x\end{aligned}$

47. Find $\sin 45° + \sin 30°$ and compare with $\sin 75°$. (Use Table 3.)

48. Find $\cos 45° - \cos 30°$ and compare with $\cos 15°$. (Use Table 3.)

49. Find a formula for $\sin (\sin x + \sin y)$.

50. Find a formula for $\cos (\cos x + \cos y)$.

47. $\sin 45° + \sin 30° = 1.2071$, $\sin 75° = 0.9659$ 48. $\cos 45° - \cos 30° = -0.1589$, $\cos 15° = 0.9659$ 49. $\sin (\sin x + \sin y) \equiv$ $\sin (\sin x) \cos (\sin y) + \cos (\sin x) \sin (\sin y)$ 50. $\cos (\cos x + \cos y) \equiv \cos (\cos x) \cos (\cos y) - \sin (\cos x) \sin (\cos y)$

21-2 Half-Angle and Double-Angle Identities

After finishing Lesson 21-2, you should be able to
■ use the double-angle identities to find function values of twice an angle when one function value is known for that angle.
■■ use the half-angle identities to find the function values of half an angle when one function value is known for that angle.

Two important classes of trigonometric identities are known as the double-angle identities and the half-angle identities.

∎Double-Angle Identities

To develop these identities we shall use the sum formulas from the preceding lesson. We first develop a formula for $\sin 2\theta$. We shall consider a number θ and substitute it for both α and β in the identity for $\sin (\alpha + \beta)$.

$$\sin 2\theta \equiv \sin (\theta + \theta)$$
$$\equiv \sin \theta \cos \theta + \cos \theta \sin \theta$$
$$\equiv 2 \sin \theta \cos \theta$$

The identity we seek is

$$\sin 2\theta \equiv 2 \sin \theta \cos \theta.$$

Example 1. If $\sin \theta = \frac{3}{8}$ and θ is in the first quadrant, what is $\sin 2\theta$?

From the diagram, we see that $\cos \theta = \dfrac{\sqrt{55}}{8}$. Thus

$$\sin 2\theta = 2 \sin \theta \cos \theta = 2 \cdot \frac{3}{8} \cdot \frac{\sqrt{55}}{8} = \frac{3\sqrt{55}}{32}.$$

TRY THIS ➡

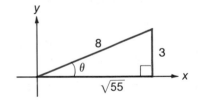

1. If $\sin \theta = \frac{3}{5}$ and θ is in the first quadrant, what is $\sin 2\theta$? $\frac{24}{25}$

Double-angle identities for the cosine and tangent functions can be derived in much the same way as the identity above.

$$\cos (\alpha + \beta) \equiv \cos \alpha \cos \beta - \sin \alpha \sin \beta$$
$$\cos 2\theta \equiv \cos (\theta + \theta)$$
$$\equiv \cos \theta \cos \theta - \sin \theta \sin \theta$$
$$\equiv \cos^2 \theta - \sin^2 \theta$$

So $\cos 2\theta \equiv \cos^2 \theta - \sin^2 \theta$.

Now we derive an identity for $\tan 2\theta$.

$$\tan(\alpha + \beta) \equiv \frac{\tan \alpha + \tan \beta}{1 - \tan \alpha \tan \beta}$$

$$\tan 2\theta \equiv \tan(\theta + \theta)$$

$$\equiv \frac{\tan \theta + \tan \theta}{1 - \tan \theta \tan \theta}$$

$$\equiv \frac{2 \tan \theta}{1 - \tan^2 \theta}$$

So $\tan 2\theta \equiv \dfrac{2 \tan \theta}{1 - \tan^2 \theta}$

Example 2. Given that $\tan \theta = -\frac{3}{4}$ and θ is in the second quadrant, find $\sin 2\theta$, $\cos 2\theta$, $\tan 2\theta$, and the quadrant in which 2θ lies.

By drawing a diagram as shown, we find that $\sin \theta = \frac{3}{5}$ and $\cos \theta = -\frac{4}{5}$.

$$\sin 2\theta = 2 \sin \theta \cos \theta = 2 \cdot \tfrac{3}{5} \cdot (-\tfrac{4}{5}) = -\tfrac{24}{25}$$

$$\cos 2\theta = \cos^2 \theta - \sin^2 \theta = (-\tfrac{4}{5})^2 \quad (\tfrac{3}{5})^2 = \tfrac{16}{25} \quad \tfrac{9}{25} = \tfrac{7}{25}$$

$$\tan 2\theta = \frac{2 \tan \theta}{1 - \tan^2 \theta} = \frac{2 \cdot (-\tfrac{3}{4})}{1 - (-\tfrac{3}{4})^2} = \frac{-\tfrac{3}{2}}{1 - \tfrac{9}{16}} = -\tfrac{24}{7}$$

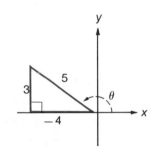

Since $\sin 2\theta$ is negative and $\cos 2\theta$ is positive, we know that 2θ is in Quadrant IV. Note that $\tan 2\theta$ could have been found more easily in this case by dividing the values of $\sin 2\theta$ and $\cos 2\theta$.

TRY THIS ➡

> 2. Given that $\cos \theta = -\frac{5}{13}$ with θ in the third quadrant. Find $\sin 2\theta$, $\cos 2\theta$, and $\tan 2\theta$. Also, determine the quadrant in which 2θ lies.

Two other useful identities for $\cos 2\theta$ can easily be derived as follows.

Answer.   2. $\sin 2\theta = \dfrac{120}{169}$, $\cos 2\theta = -\dfrac{119}{169}$, $\tan 2\theta = -\dfrac{120}{119}$, Quadrant II

$$\cos 2\theta \equiv \cos^2 \theta - \sin^2 \theta$$

$$\equiv (1 - \sin^2 \theta) - \sin^2 \theta \qquad \text{Using } \sin^2 \theta + \cos^2 \theta \equiv 1$$

$$\equiv 1 - 2 \sin^2 \theta$$

$$\cos 2\theta \equiv \cos^2 \theta - \sin^2 \theta$$

$$\equiv \cos^2 \theta - (1 - \cos^2 \theta) \qquad \text{Using } \sin^2 \theta + \cos^2 \theta \equiv 1$$

$$\equiv 2 \cos^2 \theta - 1$$

Solving these two identities for $\sin^2 \theta$ and $\cos^2 \theta$, respectively, we obtain two more identities that are often useful. The following theorem summarizes the double-angle identities. They should be memorized.

THEOREM 21-2

$$\sin 2\theta \equiv 2 \sin \theta \cos \theta$$

$$\cos 2\theta \equiv \cos^2 \theta - \sin^2 \theta$$
$$\cos 2\theta \equiv 1 - 2 \sin^2 \theta$$
$$\cos 2\theta \equiv 2 \cos^2 \theta - 1$$

$$\tan 2\theta \equiv \frac{2 \tan \theta}{1 - \tan^2 \theta}$$

$$\sin^2 \theta \equiv \frac{1 - \cos 2\theta}{2}$$

$$\cos^2 \theta \equiv \frac{1 + \cos 2\theta}{2}$$

By dividing the last two identities, it is easy to derive the following useful identity.

$$\tan^2 \theta \equiv \frac{1 - \cos 2\theta}{1 + \cos 2\theta}$$

From the basic identities (in the lists to be memorized), others can be obtained.

Example 3. Find a formula for $\sin 3\theta$ in terms of function values of θ.

$$\sin 3\theta \equiv \sin (2\theta + \theta)$$
$$\equiv \sin 2\theta \cos \theta + \cos 2\theta \sin \theta$$
$$\equiv (2 \sin \theta \cos \theta) \cos \theta + (2 \cos^2 \theta - 1) \sin \theta$$
$$\equiv 2 \sin \theta \cos^2 \theta + 2 \sin \theta \cos^2 \theta - \sin \theta$$
$$\equiv 4 \sin \theta \cos^2 \theta - \sin \theta$$

TRY THIS

3. Find a formula for $\cos 3\theta$ in terms of function values of θ.

Answer.   3. $\cos^3 \theta - 3\sin^2 \theta \cos \theta$, $\cos \theta - 4\sin^2 \theta \cos \theta$ or $2\cos^3 \theta - \cos \theta$ $-2\sin^2 \theta \cos \theta$

‖ Half-Angle Identities

To develop these identities, we use previously developed ones. Consider

$$\sin^2 \theta \equiv \frac{1 - \cos 2\theta}{2}.$$

Note that the right side of this identity is in terms of 2θ. Letting $2\theta = \phi$ we have $\theta = \frac{\phi}{2}$. Taking the square roots gives

$$\left| \sin \frac{\phi}{2} \right| \equiv \sqrt{\frac{1 - \cos \phi}{2}}.$$

Similarly for cosine and tangent, by taking square roots and re-placing θ by $\dfrac{\phi}{2}$ we have the following.

$$\left|\cos\frac{\phi}{2}\right| \equiv \sqrt{\frac{1+\cos\phi}{2}} \qquad \left|\tan\frac{\phi}{2}\right| \equiv \sqrt{\frac{1-\cos\phi}{1+\cos\phi}}$$

We can eliminate the absolute value signs by introducing $\pm$ signs with the understanding that we use $+$ or $-$ depending on the quadrant in which the angle lies. We thus obtain the formulas summarized in the following theorem. They should be memorized.

THEOREM 21-3

$$\sin\frac{\phi}{2} \equiv \pm\sqrt{\frac{1-\cos\phi}{2}} \qquad \cos\frac{\phi}{2} \equiv \pm\sqrt{\frac{1+\cos\phi}{2}} \qquad \tan\frac{\phi}{2} \equiv \pm\sqrt{\frac{1-\cos\phi}{1+\cos\phi}}$$

Example 5. Find $\sin 15°$.

$$\begin{aligned}
\sin 15° &= \sin\frac{30°}{2}\\
&= \pm\sqrt{\frac{1-\cos 30°}{2}}\\
&= \pm\sqrt{\frac{1-\left(\frac{\sqrt{3}}{2}\right)}{2}}\\
&= \pm\sqrt{\frac{2-\sqrt{3}}{4}}\\
&= \frac{\sqrt{2-\sqrt{3}}}{2}
\end{aligned}$$

The expression is positive, because $15°$ is in the first quadrant.

TRY THIS ➡

4. Find $\cos 15°$.
$$\frac{\sqrt{2+\sqrt{3}}}{2}$$

Two other formulas for $\tan\dfrac{\phi}{2}$ can be obtained.

THEOREM 21-4

$$\tan\frac{\phi}{2} \equiv \frac{\sin\phi}{1+\cos\phi} \qquad \tan\frac{\phi}{2} \equiv \frac{1-\cos\phi}{\sin\phi}$$

These formulas give the correct sign of $\tan\left(\dfrac{\phi}{2}\right)$ directly.

Example 5. Find $\tan 45°$.

$$\tan 45° = \tan \frac{90°}{2} = \frac{\sin 90°}{1 + \cos 90°} = \frac{1}{1 + 0} = 1$$

TRY THIS ➤

5. Find $\tan \frac{\pi}{8}$. Hint: $\frac{\pi}{8} = \left(\frac{1}{2}\right)\left(\frac{\pi}{4}\right)$.
$$\sqrt{2} - 1$$

Exercise Set 21-2

▮ Find $\sin 2\theta$, $\cos 2\theta$, $\tan 2\theta$, and the quadrant in which 2θ lies. (*See Examples 1 and 2.*) See answer section

1. $\sin \theta = \frac{4}{5}$ (θ in quadrant I)
2. $\sin \theta = \frac{5}{13}$ (θ in quadrant I)
3. $\cos \theta = -\frac{4}{5}$ (θ in quadrant III)
4. $\cos \theta = -\frac{3}{5}$ (θ in quadrant III)
5. $\tan \theta = \frac{4}{3}$ (θ in quadrant III)
6. $\tan \theta = \frac{3}{4}$ (θ in quadrant III)

Find these formulas. (*See Examples 3 and 4.*) See answer section

7. Find a formula for $\sin 4\theta$ in terms of function values of θ.
8. Find a formula for $\cos 4\theta$ in terms of function values of θ.
9. Find a formula for $\sin^4 \theta$ in terms of function values of θ or 2θ or 4θ, raised only to the first power.
10. Find a formula for $\cos^4 \theta$ in terms of function values of θ or 2θ or 4θ, raised only to the first power.

▮▮ Find the following without using tables. (*See Examples 5 and 6.*)

11. $\sin 75°$ [Hint: $75 = \frac{150}{2}$.] $\frac{\sqrt{2 + \sqrt{3}}}{2}$
12. $\cos 75°$ $\frac{\sqrt{2 - \sqrt{3}}}{2}$
13. $\tan 75°$ $2 + \sqrt{3}$
14. $\tan 67.5°$ [Hint: $67.5 = \frac{135}{2}$.] $\sqrt{2} + 1$
15. $\sin \frac{5\pi}{8}$ $\frac{\sqrt{2 + \sqrt{2}}}{2}$
16. $\cos \frac{5\pi}{8}$ $-\frac{\sqrt{2 - \sqrt{2}}}{2}$
17. $\sin \frac{3\pi}{8}$ $\frac{\sqrt{2 + \sqrt{2}}}{2}$
18. $\cos \frac{3\pi}{8}$ $\frac{\sqrt{2 - \sqrt{2}}}{2}$

Challenge Exercises 19. cos x 20. cos x 21. sin x 22. sin 4θ 23. cos x 24. cos 2x 25. 1 26. 1 27. 1
28. 8 29. 32 30. sin 2x 31. sin 2x cos 2x

Simplify.

19. $1 - 2 \sin^2 \frac{x}{2}$
20. $2 \cos^2 \frac{x}{2} - 1$
21. $2 \sin \frac{x}{2} \cos \frac{x}{2}$
22. $2 \sin 2x \cos 2x$
23. $\cos^2 \frac{x}{2} - \sin^2 \frac{x}{2}$
24. $2 \sin^2 \frac{x}{2} + \cos x$
25. $\cos^4 x - \sin^4 x$
26. $(\sin x + \cos x)^2 - \sin 2x$
27. $(\sin x - \cos x)^2 + \sin 2x$
28. $(-4 \cos x \sin x + 2 \cos 2x)^2 + (2 \cos 2x + 4 \sin x \cos x)^2$
29. $(-4 \cos 2x + 8 \cos x \sin x)^2 + (8 \sin x \cos x + 4 \cos 2x)^2$
30. $2 \sin x \cos^3 x + 2 \sin^3 x \cos x$
31. $2 \sin x \cos^3 x - 2 \sin^3 x \cos x$

21-3 Proving Identities

After finishing Lesson 21-3, you should be able to
▮ prove trigonometric identities.

▮ Many trigonometric identities can be proved from the identities you have already learned. These include the basic identities, the Pythagorean and cofunction identities, as well as the sum and difference formulas of Theorem 21-1, the double-angle formulas of Theorem 21-2, and the half-angle formulas of Theorems 21-3 and 21-4.

None of these formulas involves the cotangent, secant, and cosecant because these functions are reciprocals of the sine, cosine, and tangent, and can easily be derived from them.

In proving other identities, it is usually helpful to express all function values in terms of sines and cosines. *It is most important* in proving an identity to work with only one side at a time. The idea is to simplify each side separately until the same expression is obtained in the two cases.

Example 1. Prove the following identity.

$$\tan^2 x - \sin^2 x \equiv \sin^2 x \tan^2 x$$

$\dfrac{\sin^2 x}{\cos^2 x} - \sin^2 x$	$\sin^2 x\,\dfrac{\sin^2 x}{\cos^2 x}$
$\dfrac{\sin^2 x - \sin^2 x\,\cos^2 x}{\cos^2 x}$	
$\dfrac{\sin^2 x(1 - \cos^2 x)}{\cos^2 x}$	
$\dfrac{\sin^2 x\,\sin^2 x}{\cos^2 x}$	

Answer.
1.
$\cot^2 x - \cos^2 x$	$\cos^2 x\,\cot^2 x$
$\dfrac{\cos^2 x}{\sin^2 x} - \cos^2 x$	$\cos^2 x\,\dfrac{\cos^2 x}{\sin^2 x}$
$\dfrac{\cos^2 x - \cos^2 x\,\sin^2 x}{\sin^2 x}$	
$\dfrac{\cos^2 x\,(1 - \sin^2 x)}{\sin^2 x}$	
$\dfrac{\cos^2 x\,\cos^2 x}{\sin^2 x}$	

TRY THIS

Prove the following identity:

1. $\cot^2 x - \cos^2 x \equiv \cos^2 x \cot^2 x$.

Example 2. Prove the following identity.

$$\frac{\sin 2\theta}{\sin \theta} - \frac{\cos 2\theta}{\cos \theta} \equiv \sec \theta$$

$\dfrac{2 \sin \theta \cos \theta}{\sin \theta} - \dfrac{\cos^2\theta - \sin^2\theta}{\cos \theta}$	$\dfrac{1}{\cos \theta}$
$\dfrac{2 \cos^2\theta - \cos^2\theta + \sin^2\theta}{\cos \theta}$	
$\dfrac{\cos^2\theta + \sin^2\theta}{\cos \theta}$	
$\dfrac{1}{\cos \theta}$	

Answer. 2.

$\dfrac{\sin 2\theta + \sin \theta}{\cos 2\theta + \cos \theta + 1}$	$\tan \theta$
$\dfrac{2\sin \theta \cos \theta + \sin \theta}{2\cos^2 \theta + \cos \theta}$	$\dfrac{\sin \theta}{\cos \theta}$
$\dfrac{\sin \theta \,(2\cos \theta + 1)}{\cos \theta \,(2\cos \theta + 1)}$	
$\dfrac{\sin \theta}{\cos \theta}$	

Note how the double-angle formulas are used in the above proof.

TRY THIS

2. Prove the following identity.

$$\frac{\sin 2\theta + \sin \theta}{\cos 2\theta + \cos \theta + 1} \equiv \tan \theta$$

Exercise Set 21-3

▌Prove the identities. (*See Examples 1 and 2.*) See answer section

1. $\csc x - \cos x \cot x \equiv \sin x$

2. $\sec x - \sin x \tan x \equiv \cos x$

3. $\dfrac{1 + \cos \theta}{\sin \theta} + \dfrac{\sin \theta}{\cos \theta} \equiv \dfrac{\cos \theta + 1}{\sin \theta \cos \theta}$

4. $\dfrac{1}{\sin \theta \cos \theta} - \dfrac{\cos}{\sin \theta} \equiv \dfrac{\sin \theta \cos \theta}{1 - \sin^2 \theta}$

5. $\dfrac{1 - \sin x}{\cos x} \equiv \dfrac{\cos x}{1 + \sin x}$

6. $\dfrac{1 - \cos x}{\sin x} \equiv \dfrac{\sin x}{1 + \cos x}$

7. $\dfrac{1 + \tan \theta}{1 + \cot \theta} \equiv \dfrac{\sec \theta}{\csc \theta}$

8. $\dfrac{\cot \theta - 1}{1 - \tan \theta} \equiv \dfrac{\csc \theta}{\sec \theta}$

9. $\dfrac{\sin x + \cos x}{\sec x + \csc x} \equiv \dfrac{\sin x}{\sec x}$

10. $\dfrac{\sin x - \cos x}{\sec x - \csc x} \equiv \dfrac{\cos x}{\csc x}$

11. $\dfrac{1 + \tan \theta}{1 - \tan \theta} + \dfrac{1 + \cot \theta}{1 - \cot \theta} \equiv 0$

12. $\dfrac{\cos^2 \theta + \cot \theta}{\cos^2 \theta - \cot \theta} \equiv \dfrac{\cos^2 \theta \tan \theta + 1}{\cos^2 \theta \tan \theta - 1}$

13. $\dfrac{1 + \cos 2\theta}{\sin 2\theta} \equiv \cot \theta$

14. $\dfrac{2 \tan \theta}{1 + \tan^2 \theta} \equiv \sin 2\theta$

15. $\sec 2\theta \equiv \dfrac{\sec^2 \theta}{2 - \sec^2 \theta}$

16. $\cot 2\theta \equiv \dfrac{\cot^2 \theta - 1}{2 \cot \theta}$

17. $\dfrac{\sin (\alpha + \beta)}{\cos \alpha \cos \beta} \equiv \tan \alpha + \tan \beta$

18. $\dfrac{\cos (\alpha - \beta)}{\cos \alpha \sin \beta} \equiv \tan \alpha + \cot \beta$

19. $1 - \cos 5\theta \cos 3\theta - \sin 5\theta \sin 3\theta \equiv 2 \sin^2 \theta$

20. $2 \sin \theta \cos^3 \theta + 2 \sin^3 \theta \cos \theta \equiv \sin 2\theta$

21. $\dfrac{\tan \theta + \sin \theta}{2 \tan \theta} \equiv \cos^2 \dfrac{\theta}{2}$

22. $\dfrac{\tan \theta - \sin \theta}{2 \tan \theta} \equiv \sin^2 \dfrac{\theta}{2}$

23. $\cos^4 x - \sin^4 x \equiv \cos 2x$

24. $\dfrac{\cos^4 x - \sin^4 x}{1 - \tan^4 x} \equiv \cos^4 x$

25. $\dfrac{\tan 3\theta - \tan \theta}{1 + \tan 3\theta \tan \theta} \equiv \dfrac{2 \tan \theta}{1 - \tan^2 \theta}$

26. $\left(\dfrac{1 + \tan \theta}{1 - \tan \theta}\right)^2 \equiv \dfrac{1 + \sin 2\theta}{1 - \sin 2\theta}$

27. $\dfrac{\cos^3 x - \sin^3 x}{\cos x - \sin x} \equiv \dfrac{2 + \sin 2x}{2}$

28. $\dfrac{\sin^3 t + \cos^3 t}{\sin t + \cos t} \equiv \dfrac{2 - \sin 2t}{2}$

29. $\sin(\alpha + \beta)\sin(\alpha - \beta) \equiv \sin^2 \alpha - \sin^2 \beta$

30. $\cos(\alpha + \beta)\cos(\alpha - \beta) \equiv \cos^2 \alpha - \sin^2 \beta$

31. $\cos(\alpha + \beta) + \cos(\alpha - \beta) \equiv 2 \cos \alpha \cos \beta$

32. $\sin(\alpha + \beta) + \sin(\alpha - \beta) \equiv 2 \sin \alpha \cos \beta$

Challenge Exercises

33. $\begin{bmatrix} \cos x & \sin x \\ -\sin x & \cos x \end{bmatrix} = \cos^2 x + \sin^2 x = 1$, $\begin{bmatrix} \cos x & -\sin x \\ \sin x & \cos x \end{bmatrix} = \cos^2 x + \sin^2 x = 1$

34. $\begin{bmatrix} \cos x & \sin x \\ -\sin x & \cos x \end{bmatrix}$

$\begin{bmatrix} \cos y & \sin y \\ -\sin y & \cos y \end{bmatrix} = \begin{bmatrix} \cos x \cos y - \sin x \sin y & \cos x \sin y + \sin x \cos y \\ -\sin x \cos y - \cos x \sin y & -\sin x \sin y + \cos x \cos y \end{bmatrix} = \begin{bmatrix} \cos(x + y) & \sin(x + y) \\ -\sin(x + y) & \cos(x + y) \end{bmatrix}$

33. Show that

$$\begin{vmatrix} \cos x & \sin x \\ -\sin x & \cos x \end{vmatrix} = \begin{vmatrix} \cos x & -\sin x \\ \sin x & \cos x \end{vmatrix}.$$

34. Show that

$$\begin{bmatrix} \cos x & \sin x \\ -\sin x & \cos x \end{bmatrix}\begin{bmatrix} \cos y & \sin y \\ -\sin y & \cos y \end{bmatrix} = \begin{bmatrix} \cos(x + y) & \sin(x + y) \\ -\sin(x + y) & \cos(x + y) \end{bmatrix}.$$

HISTORICAL NOTE: The First Stadium

Today a stadium is a place where sports events take place. In ancient Greece and Rome, a stadium was a unit of linear measure. It equaled about 185 meters.

According to legend, the first stadium was paced off by the mythical Greek hero Hercules. This stadium was used to mark the site of the first Olympic games. Later stadia were shorter. The mathematician Pythagoras reasoned that he could tell the height of Hercules by comparing the length of the Olympic stadium with the length of an ordinary stadium.

Pythagoras's reasoning went like this: Hercules paced off the first stadium. An ordinary person used the same number of steps to pace off a shorter stadium. So the ratio of the lengths of the stadia equals the ratio of the paces. The ratio of heights must be about the same. If the ratio of the Olympic stadium to a shorter stadium is 5/4, for instance, the height of Hercules must be about 5/4 the height of an ordinary man.

21-4 Inverses of the Trigonometric Functions

After finishing Lesson 21-4, you should be able to
▮   find all values of arcsin a, arccos a, and arctan a, in degrees and in radians, given a number a.
▮▮   find principal values of the inverses of the trigonometric functions.

▮ Finding Inverse Values

To obtain the inverse of any relation we interchange the first and second members of each ordered pair in the relation. If a relation is defined by an equation, say in x and y, interchanging x and y produces an equation of the inverse relation. The graphs of a relation and its inverse are reflections of each other across the line $y = x$.

Let us consider the inverse of the sine function, $y = \sin x$. The inverse may be denoted several ways, as follows.

$$x = \sin y \qquad y = \sin^{-1} x \qquad y = \arcsin x$$

Thus $\sin^{-1} x$ is a number whose sine is x. The notation $\sin^{-1} x$ is not exponential notation. It does *not* mean $\dfrac{1}{\sin x}$. Either of the latter two kinds of notation above can be read "the inverse sine of x" or "the arc sine of x" or "the number (or angle) whose sine is x." Notation is chosen similarly for the inverses of the other trigonometric functions: $\cos^{-1} x$ or $\arccos x$, $\tan^{-1} x$ or $\arctan x$, and so on.

Example 1.   Graph $y = \sin^{-1} x$ and $y = \tan^{-1} x$.

These graphs are shown at the right. Note how they compare with the graphs of the sine function and tangent function. Note that these relations are not functions.

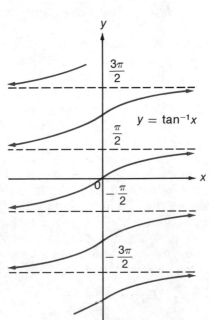

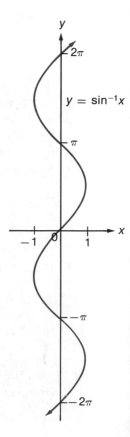

TRY THIS

1. Sketch a graph of $y = \cos^{-1} x$. Is this relation a function?
2. Sketch a graph of $y = \cot^{-1} x$. Is this relation a function?

Answers.　1. Not a function　2. Not a function

We can find inverse values using either a graph or a unit circle. In practice the unit circle is easier to use.

Example 2.　Find all values of arcsin $\frac{1}{2}$ using a graph.

On the graph of $y = $ arcsin x, we draw a vertical line at $x = \frac{1}{2}$. It intersects the graph at points whose y-value is arcsin $\frac{1}{2}$. Some of the numbers whose sine is $\frac{1}{2}$ are seen to be $\dfrac{\pi}{6}$, $\dfrac{5\pi}{6}$, $\dfrac{-7\pi}{6}$, and

so on. From the graph we can see that $\dfrac{\pi}{6}$ plus

any multiple of 2π is such a number. Also $\dfrac{5\pi}{6}$ plus

any multiple of 2π is such a number. The complete set of values is given by $\dfrac{\pi}{6} + 2k\pi$, k an in-

teger, and $\dfrac{5\pi}{6} + 2k\pi$, k an integer.

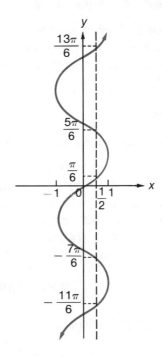

Example 3.　Find all values of arcsin $\frac{1}{2}$ using a unit circle.

On the unit circle there are two points at which the sine is $\frac{1}{2}$. The rotation for the point in the first quadrant is $\dfrac{\pi}{6}$ plus any multiple of 2π. The rota-

tion for the point in the second quadrant is $\dfrac{5\pi}{6}$

plus any multiple of 2π. Hence we obtain all values of arcsin $\frac{1}{2}$ as follows:

$$\frac{\pi}{6} + 2k\pi \text{ and } \frac{5\pi}{6} + 2k\pi, k \text{ an integer.}$$

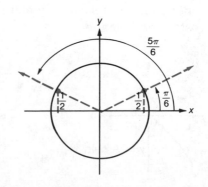

Example 4. Find all values of arctan 1.

We find the two points on the unit circle at which the tangent is 1. These points are opposite ends of a diameter. Hence the arc lengths differ by π.

Thus we have for all values of arctan 1, $\dfrac{\pi}{4} + k\pi$, k an integer.

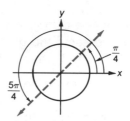

Example 5. Find, in degrees, all values of $\cos^{-1}(-0.9397)$.

From Table 3 we find that the angle whose cosine is 0.9397 is 20°. This is the reference angle. We sketch this on a unit circle to find the two points where the cosine is -0.9397. The angles are 160° and 200°, plus any multiple of 360°. Thus the values of $\cos^{-1}(-0.9397)$ are $160° + k \cdot 360°$ and $200° + k \cdot 360°$, where k is any integer.

TRY THIS ➡

▪ Principal Values

The inverses of the trigonometric functions are not themselves functions. However, if we restrict the ranges of these relations, we can obtain functions. The following graphs show how this restriction is made.

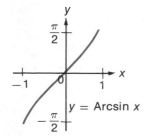

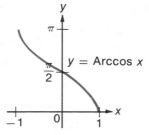

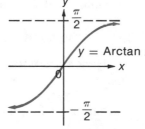

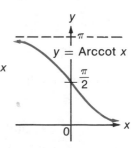

These relations with their ranges so restricted are functions, and the values in these restricted ranges are called *principal values*. To denote principal values we shall capitalize, as follows: Arcsin x, Sin^{-1} x, Arccos x, Cos^{-1} x, and so on. Thus whereas arcsin $(\frac{1}{2})$ represents an infinite set of numbers, Arcsin $(\frac{1}{2})$ represents the single number $\frac{\pi}{6}$.

Note that for the function $y = $ Arcsin x the range is the interval $\left[-\frac{\pi}{2}, \frac{\pi}{2}\right]$. For the function $y = $ Arctan x the range is $\left(-\frac{\pi}{2}, \frac{\pi}{2}\right)$. For the function $y = $ Arccos x the range is $[0, \pi]$, and for $y = $ Arccot x the range is $(0, \pi)$. The diagrams below show where principal values are found on the unit circle.

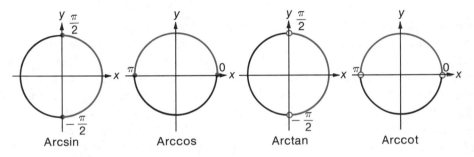

| Arcsin | Arccos | Arctan | Arccot |

Example 6. Find Arcsin $\dfrac{\sqrt{2}}{2}$ and Cos$^{-1}\left(-\dfrac{1}{2}\right)$.

In the restricted range as shown in the figure, the only number whose sine is $\dfrac{\sqrt{2}}{2}$ is $\dfrac{\pi}{4}$. Hence Arcsin $\dfrac{\sqrt{2}}{2} = \dfrac{\pi}{4}$.

The only number whose cosine is $-\dfrac{1}{2}$ in the restricted range is $\dfrac{2\pi}{3}$. Hence Cos$^{-1}\left(-\dfrac{1}{2}\right) = \dfrac{2\pi}{3}$.

TRY THIS ⟹

Find the following.

7. Arcsin $\dfrac{\sqrt{3}}{2}$ $\frac{\pi}{3}$

8. Cos$^{-1}\left(-\dfrac{\sqrt{2}}{2}\right)$ $\frac{3\pi}{4}$

9. Arccot (-1) $\frac{3\pi}{4}$

10. Tan$^{-1}(-1)$ $-\frac{\pi}{4}$

Exercise Set 21-4

▌Find all values of the following without using tables. (*See Examples 3 and 4.*)

1. arcsin $\dfrac{\sqrt{2}}{2}$ $\frac{\pi}{4} + 2k\pi, \frac{3\pi}{4} + 2k\pi$

2. arcsin $\dfrac{\sqrt{3}}{2}$ $\frac{\pi}{3} + 2k\pi, \frac{2\pi}{3} + 2k\pi$

3. cos$^{-1} \dfrac{\sqrt{2}}{2}$ $\frac{\pi}{4} + 2k\pi, \frac{7\pi}{4} + 2k\pi$

4. cos$^{-1} \dfrac{\sqrt{3}}{2}$ $\frac{\pi}{6} + 2k\pi, \frac{11\pi}{6} + 2k\pi$

Use Quiz 37 after lesson 21–4.

5. $\sin^{-1}\left(-\dfrac{\sqrt{2}}{2}\right)$ $\frac{5\pi}{4} + 2k\pi, \frac{7\pi}{4} + 2k\pi$

6. $\sin^{-1}\left(-\dfrac{\sqrt{3}}{2}\right)$ $\frac{4\pi}{3} + 2k\pi, \frac{5\pi}{3} + 2k\pi$

7. $\arccos\left(-\dfrac{\sqrt{2}}{2}\right)$ $\frac{3\pi}{4} + 2k\pi, \frac{5\pi}{4} + 2k\pi$

8. $\arccos\left(-\dfrac{\sqrt{3}}{2}\right)$ $\frac{5\pi}{6} + 2k\pi, \frac{7\pi}{6} + 2k\pi$

9. $\arctan \sqrt{3}$ $\frac{\pi}{3} + k\pi$

10. $\arctan \dfrac{\sqrt{3}}{3}$ $\frac{\pi}{6} + k\pi$

11. $\cot^{-1} 1$ $\frac{\pi}{4} + k\pi$

12. $\cot^{-1} \sqrt{3}$ $\frac{\pi}{6} + k\pi$

13. $\arctan\left(-\dfrac{\sqrt{3}}{3}\right)$ $\frac{5\pi}{6} + k\pi$

14. $\arctan\left(-\sqrt{3}\right)$ $\frac{2\pi}{3} + k\pi$

15. $\text{arccot}\,(-1)$ $\frac{3\pi}{4} + k\pi$

16. $\text{arccot}\,(-\sqrt{3})$ $\frac{5\pi}{6} + k\pi$

17. $\text{arcsec}\,1$ $2k\pi$

18. $\text{arcsec}\,2$ $\frac{\pi}{3} + 2k\pi, \frac{5\pi}{3} + 2k\pi$

19. $\csc^{-1} 1$ $\frac{\pi}{2} + 2k\pi$

20. $\csc^{-1} 2$ $\frac{\pi}{6} + 2k\pi, \frac{5\pi}{6} + 2k\pi$

Use tables to find, in degrees, all values of the following. (*See Example 5.*)

21. $\arcsin 0.3907$ $23° + k360°, 157° + k360°$
22. $\arcsin 0.9613$ $74° + k360°, 106° + k360°$
23. $\sin^{-1} 0.6293$ $39° + k360°, 141° + k360°$
24. $\sin^{-1} 0.8746$ $61° + k360°, 119° + k360°$
25. $\arccos 0.7990$ $36°58' + k360°, 323°02' + k360°$
26. $\arccos 0.9265$ $22°6' + k360°, 337°54' + k360°$
27. $\cos^{-1} 0.9310$ $21°25' + k360°, 338°35' + k360°$
28. $\cos^{-1} 0.2735$ $74°8' + k360°, 285°52' + k360°$
29. $\tan^{-1} 0.3673$ $20°10' + k180°$
30. $\tan^{-1} 1.091$ $47°30' + k180°$
31. $\cot^{-1} 1.265$ $38°20' + k180°$
32. $\cot^{-1} 0.4770$ $64°30' + k180°$
33. $\sec^{-1} 1.167$ $31° + k360°, 329° + k360°$
34. $\sec^{-1} 1.440$ $46° + k360°, 314° + k360°$
35. $\text{arccsc}\,6.277$ $9°10' + k360°, 170°50' + k360°$
36. $\text{arccsc}\,1.111$ $64°10' + k360°, 115°50' + k360°$

■■ Find the following without using tables. (*See Example 6.*)

37. $\text{Arccos}\left(-\dfrac{\sqrt{3}}{2}\right)$ $\frac{5\pi}{6}$

38. $\text{Arcsin}\,\dfrac{1}{2}$ $\frac{\pi}{6}$

39. $\text{Cos}^{-1}\dfrac{1}{2}$ $\frac{\pi}{3}$

40. $\text{Cos}^{-1}\dfrac{\sqrt{2}}{2}$ $\frac{\pi}{4}$

41. $\text{Sin}^{-1}\left(-\dfrac{\sqrt{3}}{2}\right)$ $-\frac{\pi}{3}$

42. $\text{Sin}^{-1}\left(-\dfrac{1}{2}\right)$ $-\frac{\pi}{6}$

43. $\text{Tan}^{-1}\left(-\dfrac{\sqrt{3}}{3}\right)$ $-\frac{\pi}{6}$

44. $\text{Tan}^{-1}\,(-\sqrt{3})$ $-\frac{\pi}{3}$

45. $\text{Arccot}\left(-\dfrac{\sqrt{3}}{3}\right)$ $\frac{2\pi}{3}$

46. $\text{Arccot}\,(-\sqrt{3})$ $\frac{5\pi}{6}$

Find the following, in degrees, using tables.

47. $\text{Arcsin}\,0.2334$ $13°30'$
48. $\text{Arcsin}\,0.4514$ $26°50'$
49. $\text{Sin}^{-1}\,(-0.6361)$ $-39°30'$
50. $\text{Sin}^{-1}\,(-0.8192)$ $-55°$
51. $\text{Arccos}\,(-0.8897)$ $152°50'$
52. $\text{Arccos}\,(-0.2924)$ $107°$
53. $\text{Tan}^{-1}\,(-0.4074)$ $-22°10'$
54. $\text{Tan}^{-1}\,(-0.2401)$ $-13°30'$
55. $\text{Cot}^{-1}\,(-5.396)$ $169°30'$
56. $\text{Cot}^{-1}\,(-1.319)$ $142°50'$

21-5 Trigonometric Equations

After finishing Lesson 21-5, you should be able to
▌ solve simple trigonometric equations.
▌▌ solve trigonometric equations requiring the use of identities.

▌Solving Simple Equations

When an equation contains a trigonometric expression with a variable such as sin x, it is called a *trigonometric equation*. To solve such an equation, we find all replacements for the variable that make the equation true.

Example 1. Solve $2 \sin x = 1$.

We first solve for sin x: $\sin x = \frac{1}{2}$.

Now we note that the solutions are those angles having a sine of $\frac{1}{2}$. We look for them. The unit circle is helpful. There are just two points on it for which the sine is $\frac{1}{2}$, as shown. They are the points for $\frac{\pi}{6}$ and $\frac{5\pi}{6}$. These angles, plus any multiple of 2π, are the solutions

$$\frac{\pi}{6} + 2k\pi \quad \text{and} \quad \frac{5\pi}{6} + 2k\pi, \text{ where } k \text{ is any integer.}$$

In degrees, the solutions are $30° + k \cdot 360°$ and $150° + k \cdot 360°$, where k is any integer.

Example 2. Solve $4 \cos^2 x = 1$.
$$\cos^2 x = \tfrac{1}{4},$$
$$|\cos x| = \tfrac{1}{2}, \qquad \textit{Taking principal square roots}$$
$$\cos x = \pm\tfrac{1}{2}.$$

Now we use the unit circle to find those numbers having a cosine of $\pm\frac{1}{2}$. The solutions are $\frac{\pi}{3}, \frac{2\pi}{3}, \frac{4\pi}{3}, \frac{5\pi}{3}$, plus any multiple of 2π.

In solving trigonometric equations, it is usually sufficient to find just the solutions from 0 to 2π. We then remember that any multiple of 2π may be added to obtain all the solutions.

1. Find all solutions from 0 to 2π. Give answers both in degrees and radians.
    $4 \sin^2 x = 1$

TRY THIS ➤

Answer.

The following example illustrates that when we look for solutions from 0 to 2π we must be cautious.

Example 3. Find the solutions of $2 \sin 2x = 1$ from 0 to 2π.

We first solve for $\sin 2x$: $\sin 2x = \frac{1}{2}$.

Points on the unit circle for which $\sin 2x = \frac{1}{2}$ are $\frac{\pi}{6}$ and $\frac{5\pi}{6}$.

However, since x is to run from 0 to 2π, $2x$ must run from 0 to 4π. These other values of $2x$ are $\frac{13\pi}{6}$ and $\frac{17\pi}{6}$. Thus the desired values of x from 0 to 2π are half of these. Therefore,

$$x = \frac{\pi}{12}, \frac{5\pi}{12}, \frac{13\pi}{12}, \frac{17\pi}{12}.$$

TRY THIS ➡️

2. Find all solutions from 0 to 2π. Leave answers in terms of π. $\frac{\pi}{6}, \frac{5\pi}{6}$,

$2 \cos 2x = 1$ $\frac{7\pi}{6}, \frac{11\pi}{6}$

In solving trigonometric equations, we often apply some algebra before working with the trigonometric part. In the next examples, we begin by factoring.

Example 4. Solve $8 \cos^2 \theta - 2 \cos \theta = 1$.

$$8 \cos^2 \theta - 2 \cos \theta - 1 = 0 \qquad \textit{Getting 0 on one side}$$
$$(4 \cos \theta + 1)(2 \cos \theta - 1) = 0 \qquad \textit{Factoring}$$

$$4 \cos \theta + 1 = 0 \qquad \text{or} \qquad 2 \cos \theta - 1 = 0 \qquad \textit{Principle of zero products}$$
$$\cos \theta = -\tfrac{1}{4} \qquad \text{or} \qquad \cos \theta = \tfrac{1}{2}$$
$$= -0.25$$

From the table we find that for $\cos \theta = -0.25$, $\theta = 104°30'$ or $255°30'$. For $\cos \theta = \frac{1}{2}$, $\theta = 60°$ or $300°$. The solutions from 0 to $360°$ are $104°30'$, $255°30'$, $60°$, and $300°$.

Example 5. Solve $2 \sin^2 \phi + \sin \phi = 0$.

$$\sin \phi\,(2 \sin \phi + 1) = 0 \qquad \textit{Factoring}$$

$$\sin \phi = 0 \qquad \text{or} \qquad 2 \sin \phi + 1 = 0 \qquad \textit{Principle of zero products}$$
$$\sin \phi = 0 \qquad \text{or} \qquad \sin \phi = -\tfrac{1}{2}$$
$$\phi = 0, \pi \qquad \text{or} \qquad \phi = \frac{7\pi}{6}, \frac{11\pi}{6}.$$

The solutions from 0 to 2π are $\mathbf{0}$, π, $\frac{7\pi}{6}$, and $\frac{11\pi}{6}$.

Answers.   3. $75°31'$, $284°29'$, $120°$, $240°$ 4. $\frac{\pi}{2}, \frac{3\pi}{2}, \frac{2\pi}{3}, \frac{4\pi}{3}$

Solve.

3. $8 \cos^2 \theta + 2 \cos \theta = 1$
4. $2 \cos^2 \phi + \cos \phi = 0$

TRY THIS ➡️

▪ Solving Equations Using Identities

When a trigonometric equation involves more than one function, we may use identities to put it in terms of a single function. This can usually be done in several ways as the following example and exercise show.

Example 6.   Solve the equation $\sin x + \cos x = 1$.

To express $\cos x$ in terms of $\sin x$, we use the identity $\sin^2 x + \cos^2 x = 1$. From this we obtain $\cos x = \pm \sqrt{1 - \sin^2 x}$.

$$\sin x \pm \sqrt{1 - \sin^2 x} = 1 \qquad \textit{Substituting}$$
$$\pm \sqrt{1 - \sin^2 x} = 1 - \sin x \qquad \textit{Getting the radical alone on one side}$$
$$1 - \sin^2 x = 1 - 2\sin x + \sin^2 x \qquad \textit{Squaring both sides}$$
$$-2\sin^2 x + 2\sin x = 0$$
$$-2\sin x\,(\sin x - 1) = 0 \qquad \textit{Factoring}$$

$$-2\sin x = 0 \quad \text{or} \quad \sin x - 1 = 0 \qquad \textit{Using the principle of zero products}$$
$$\sin x = 0 \quad \text{or} \quad \sin x = 1$$

The values of x from 0 to 2π satisfying these equations are

$$x = 0,\ x = \pi,\ \text{and}\ x = \frac{\pi}{2}.$$

Now we check these in the original equation. We find that π does not check but the other values do. Thus the solutions are 0 and $\frac{\pi}{2}$.

It is important to check in examples such as these. Values are often obtained that are not solutions of the original equation.

TRY THIS ➡

5.   Solve $\sin x + \cos x = 1$. Begin by squaring both sides. $0, \frac{\pi}{2}$

Example 7.   Solve $\cos 2x + \sin x = 1$.

$$1 - 2\sin^2 x + \sin x = 1 \qquad \textit{Using the identity } \cos 2x \equiv 1 - 2\sin^2 x$$
$$-2\sin^2 x + \sin x = 0$$
$$\sin x\,(1 - 2\sin x) = 0 \qquad \textit{Factoring}$$

$$\sin x = 0 \quad \text{or} \quad 1 - 2\sin x = 0 \qquad \textit{Principle of zero products}$$
$$\sin x = 0 \quad \text{or} \quad \sin x = \tfrac{1}{2}$$
$$x = 0, \pi \quad \text{or} \quad x = \frac{\pi}{6}, \frac{5\pi}{6}.$$

All values check. The solutions from 0 to 2π are 0, $\pi, \dfrac{\pi}{6}$, and $\dfrac{5\pi}{6}$.

TRY THIS ➡️

6. Solve $\sin 2x + \cos x = 0$.
$\dfrac{\pi}{2}, \dfrac{3\pi}{2}, \dfrac{7\pi}{6}, \dfrac{11\pi}{6}$

Exercise Set 21-5

▌Solve, finding all solutions. (*See Examples 1 and 2.*)

1. $\sin x = \dfrac{\sqrt{3}}{2}$ $\frac{\pi}{3}, \frac{2\pi}{3}$

2. $\cos x = \dfrac{\sqrt{3}}{2}$ $\frac{\pi}{6}, \frac{11\pi}{6}$

3. $\cos x = \dfrac{\sqrt{2}}{2}$ $\frac{\pi}{4}, \frac{7\pi}{4}$

4. $\tan x = \sqrt{3}$ $\frac{\pi}{3}, \frac{4\pi}{3}$

5. $\sin x = 0.3448$ $20°10', 159°50'$

6. $\cos x = 0.6406$ $50°10', 309°50'$

Solve, finding all solutions from 0 to 2π or 0° to 360°. (*See Examples 3–5.*)

7. $\cos x = -0.5495$ See answer section

8. $\sin x = -0.4279$

9. $2 \sin x + \sqrt{3} = 0$

10. $\sqrt{3} \tan x + 1 = 0$

11. $2 \tan x + 3 = 0$

12. $4 \sin x - 1 = 0$

13. $4 \sin^2 x - 1 = 0$

14. $2 \cos^2 x = 1$

15. $2 \sin^2 x + \sin x = 1$

16. $2 \cos^2 x + 3 \cos x = -1$

17. $\cos^2 x + 2 \cos x = 3$

18. $2 \sin^2 x - \sin x = 3$

19. $2 \sin^2 \theta + 7 \sin \theta = 4$

20. $2 \sin^2 \theta - 5 \sin \theta + 2 = 0$

21. $6 \cos^2 \phi + 5 \cos \phi + 1 = 0$

22. $2 \sin^2 \phi + \sin \phi - 1 = 0$

23. $\cos 2x \sin x + \sin x = 0$

24. $\sin 2x \cos x - \cos x = 0$

▌▌Find all solutions of the following equations from 0 to 2π. (*See Examples 6 and 7.*)   See answer section

25. $\tan x \sin x - \tan x = 0$

26. $2 \sin x \cos x + \sin x = 0$

27. $2 \sec x \tan x + 2 \sec x + \tan x + 1 = 0$

28. $2 \csc x \cos x - 4 \cos x - \csc x + 2 = 0$

29. $\sin 2x \sin x - \cos x = 0$

30. $\sin 2x \cos x - \sin x = 0$

31. $\sin 2x + 2 \sin x \cos x = 0$

32. $\cos 2x \sin x + \sin x = 0$

33. $\cos 2x \cos x + \sin 2x \sin x = 1$

34. $\sin 2x \sin x - \cos 2x \cos x = -\cos x$

35. $\sin 2x + 2 \sin x - \cos x - 1 = 0$

36. $\sin 2x + \sin x + 2 \cos x + 1 = 0$

37. $\sec^2 x = 4 \tan^2 x$

38. $\sec^2 x - 2 \tan^2 x = 0$

39. $\sec^2 x + 3 \tan x - 11 = 0$

40. $\tan^2 x + 4 = 2 \sec^2 x + \tan x$

41. $\cos (\pi - x) + \sin \left(x - \dfrac{\pi}{2}\right) = 1$

42. $\sin (\pi - x) + \cos \left(\dfrac{\pi}{2} - x\right) = 1$

43. $2 \cos x + 2 \sin x = \sqrt{6}$

44. $2 \cos x + 2 \sin x = \sqrt{2}$

45. $\sqrt{3} \cos x - \sin x = 1$

46. $\sqrt{2} \cos x - \sqrt{2} \sin x = 2$

21-6 Solving Right Triangles

After finishing Lesson 21-6, you should be able to
I solve triangles using three-digit precision.
II solve applied problems involving triangles.

The trigonometric functions are ratios of sides of triangles, as developed in Chapter 20. Triangles need not, however, be in standard position on a coordinate system, as in that chapter. In the right triangle shown here, the sine of angle A is $\frac{a}{c}$, the length of the side opposite A divided by the length of the hypotenuse. Similarly, $\cos A = \frac{b}{c}$, the length of the side adjacent to A divided by the length of the hypotenuse. The other trigonometric ratios can be considered in a similar manner.

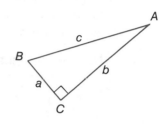

Example 1. In this triangle, find $\cos A$. Find $\tan B$.

$$\cos A = \frac{\text{adjacent}}{\text{hypotenuse}} = \frac{4}{5}$$

$$\tan B = \frac{\text{opposite}}{\text{adjacent}} = \frac{4}{3}$$

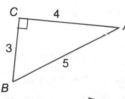

Answer. 1. $\sin B = \frac{5}{13}$, $\cos B = \frac{12}{13}$, $\tan B = \frac{5}{12}$, $\cot B = \frac{12}{5}$, $\sec B = \frac{13}{12}$, $\csc B = \frac{13}{5}$

TRY THIS ➡

1. Find the six trigonometric function values for angle B.

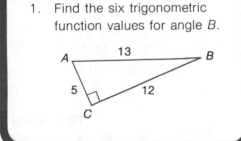

Solving Triangles

A triangle has three sides and three angles. When the measures of certain of these parts are known, it is possible to find the measures of the rest. Doing this is called *solving* a triangle. Solving triangles is important in many applications of trigonometry. In fact, such applications were the beginnings of trigonometry. The word *trigonometry* actually means "triangle measurement."

Example 2. Find the measures of the acute angles of this triangle.

$$\cot A = \frac{18.00}{7.000} = 2.571 \quad \textit{Correct to 4 digits}$$

$$A = 21°15' \quad \textit{From the table}$$

$$B = 90° - A$$

$$= 68°45'$$

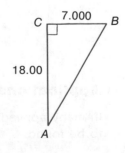

In Example 2 the tangent function could also have been used. Whenever an angle is to be found, we choose a function that involves the known sides.

The precision to which we can find an angle depends on how precisely we know the lengths of the sides. In Example 2 we determine the cotangent ratio to 4 digits, and this gives the angle measure to the nearest minute. The following table shows the precision in other cases.

Number of digits in ratio	Precision of angle measure
4	To nearest minute
3	To nearest ten minutes
2	To nearest degree

TRY THIS ➡

2. Find the measures of the acute angles of right triangle *ABC*, with $a = 4$ and $c = 7$. Use four-digit precision. A = 34°51', B = 55°09'

Example 3. Find the length *b* in right triangle *ABC* where $\angle A = 19°$ and $c = 70$.

The known side is the hypotenuse. The side we seek is adjacent to the known angle. Thus we shall use the cosine: $\cos A = \dfrac{b}{70}$.

$$b = 70 \cos A$$
$$= 70(\cos 19°)$$
$$= 70(0.9455)$$
$$= 66.19$$

TRY THIS ➡

3. Find the lengths *a* and *b* in right triangle *ABC*, where $\angle A = 35°$ to the nearest minute, and $c = 67.00$ to four-digit precision. Assume that angle *A* is given to the nearest minute, and length *AB* to four-digit precision. a = 38.43, b = 54.89

ıı Applications of Solving Triangles

In many applied problems, unknown parts of right triangles are to be found.

Example 4.   A device for measuring cloud height at night consists of a vertical beam of light, which makes a spot on a cloud. The spot is viewed from a point 135 m away. The angle of elevation is 67°40′. The angle between the horizontal and a line of sight is called an *angle of elevation*. It is called an *angle of depression* if the line of sight is below the horizontal. Find the height of the cloud.

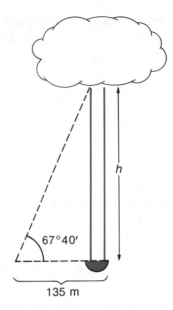

From the drawing we have

$$h = 135(\tan 67° \ 40′)$$
$$= 135(2.434)$$
$$= 329 \text{ m}$$

In the preceding example, it should be noted that distances are precise to three digits and the angle is precise to the nearest ten minutes.

TRY THIS

4.   The length of a guy wire to a pole is 12.6 m. It makes an angle of 71°20′ with the ground, which is horizontal. It is attached to the pole how high above the ground?   **11.9 m**

Example 5.   Two markers at ground level are viewed in one direction from an observation tower. The markers and the base of the tower are on a line and the observer's eye is 21.3 m above the ground. The angles of depression to the markers are 53°10′ and 27°50′. How far is one marker from the other?

From the drawing we see that the distance we seek is d, which is $d_1 - d_2$. From the right triangles in the drawing, we have

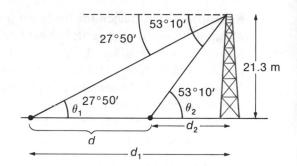

$$\frac{d_1}{21.3} = \cot \theta_1 \text{ and } \frac{d_2}{21.3} = \cot \theta_2.$$

Then $d_1 = 21.3 \cot 27°50'$ and $d_2 = 21.3 \cot 53°10'$.

$$\begin{aligned}
d &= d_1 - d_2 \\
&= 21.3 \cot 27°50' - 21.3 \cot 53°10' \\
&= 21.3(\cot 27°50' - \cot 53°10') \\
&= 21.3(1.894 - 0.7490) \\
&= 24.4 \text{ m}
\end{aligned}$$

TRY THIS ▬▬▬➤

In aerial navigation, directions are given in degrees, clockwise from north. Thus east is 90°, south is 180°, and so on. In some applications directions, or *bearings,* are given by reference to north or south using an acute angle. For example, N 40°W means 40° west of north and S 30° E means 30° east of south. Both these ideas appear in some of the exercises that follow.

5. From an airplane flying 2.4 km above level ground, one can see two towns directly to the east. The angles of depression to the towns are 5°10′ and 77°30′. How far apart are the towns, to the nearest kilometer? **26 km**

Exercise Set 21-6

▌ In Exercises 1–18, standard lettering for a right triangle will be used: A, B, and C are the angles, C being the right angle. The sides opposite A, B, and C are a, b, and c, respectively. Solve the triangles, using three-digit precision. (*See Examples 2 and 3.*)

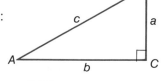

1. $A = 36°10'$, $a = 27.2$ See answer section
2. $A = 87°40'$, $a = 9.73$
3. $B = 12°40'$, $b = 98.1$
4. $B = 69°50'$, $b = 127$
5. $A = 17°20'$, $b = 13.6$
6. $A = 78°40'$, $b = 1340$
7. $B = 23°10'$, $a = 0.0345$
8. $B = 69°20'$, $a = 0.00488$
9. $A = 47°30'$, $c = 48.3$
10. $A = 88°50'$, $c = 3950$
11. $B = 82°20'$, $c = 0.982$
12. $B = 56°30'$, $c = 0.0447$
13. $a = 12.0$, $b = 18.0$
14. $a = 10.0$, $b = 20.0$
15. $a = 16.0$, $c = 20.0$
16. $a = 15.0$, $c = 45.0$
17. $b = 1.80$, $c = 4.00$
18. $b = 100$, $c = 450$

■ Solve. (*See Examples 4 and 5.*)

19. A guy wire to a pole makes an angle of 73°10′ with the level ground, and is 4.8 m from the pole at the ground. How far above the ground is the wire attached to the pole?   15.9 m

20. A kite string makes an angle of 31°40′ with the (level) ground and 148 m of string is out. How high is the kite?   77.7 m

21. A road rises 3 m per 100 horizontal m (it has a 3% grade). What angle does it make with the horizontal?   1°40′

22. A kite is 60 m high when 220 m of string is out. What angle does the kite make with the ground?   15°50′

23. What is the angle of elevation of the sun when a 2 m man casts a 3.1 m shadow?   32°50′

24. What is the angle of elevation of the sun when a 11.5 m mast casts a 6 m shadow?   62°30′

25. From a balloon 835 m high, a command post is seen with an angle of depression of 7°40′. How far is it from a point on the ground below the balloon to the command post?   6200 m

26. From a lighthouse 18 m above sea level, the angle of depression to a small boat is 11°20′. How far from the foot of the lighthouse is the boat?   89.8 m

27. An airplane travels at 120 km/h for 2 h in a direction of 243° from Chicago. At the end of this time, how far south of Chicago is the plane?   109 km

28. An airplane travels at 150 km/h for 2 h in a direction of 138° from Omaha. At the end of this time, how far east of Omaha is the plane?   201 km

29. Ship *A* is due west of a lighthouse. Ship *B* is 12 km south of ship *A*. From ship *B* the bearing to the lighthouse is N 63°20′E. How far is ship *A* from the lighthouse?   23.9 km

30. Lookout station *A* is 15 km west of station *B*. The bearing from *A* to a fire directly south of *B* is S 37°50′E. How far is the fire from *B*?   19.3 km

31. In one direction from a balloon 2 km high, the angles of depression to two towns in line with the balloon are 81°20′ and 13°40′. How far apart are the towns?   7.92 km

32. In one direction from a balloon   4670 km
1000 m high, the angles of depression to two artillery posts in line with the balloon are 11°50′ and 84°10′. How far apart are the artillery posts?

33. A weather balloon is directly west of two observing stations 10 km apart. The angles of elevation of the balloon from the two stations are 17°50′ and 78°10′. How high is the balloon?   3.45 km

34. From two points south of a hill on level ground and 325 m apart, the angles of elevation of the hill are 12°20′ and 82°40′. How high is the hill?   73.1 km

Challenge Exercises   35. Area of right △ABC = $\frac{1}{2}$ab (using standard lettering). $\frac{1}{4}c^2 \sin 2A = \frac{1}{4}(a^2 + b^2)2\sin A \cos A$
$= \frac{2}{4}(a^2 + b^2)\frac{a}{c}\frac{b}{c} = \frac{1}{2}c^2 \frac{ab}{c^2} = \frac{1}{2}ab$

35. Show that the area of a right triangle is $\frac{1}{4}c^2 \sin 2A$.

21-7 The Law of Sines

After finishing Lesson 21-7, you should be able to
I use the law of sines to solve any triangle, given a side and two angles.
II use the law of sines to solve triangles, given two sides and an angle opposite one of them, finding two solutions when they exist, and recognizing when a solution does not exist.

The trigonometric functions can be used to solve triangles that are not right triangles (oblique triangles). In order to solve oblique triangles we need to derive some properties, one of which is called the *law of sines*. We shall consider any oblique triangle. It may or may not have an obtuse angle. We will consider both cases, but the derivations are essentially the same.

The triangles are lettered in the standard way, with angles A, B, and C and the sides opposite them a, b, and c, respectively. The altitude from vertex C has length h. In either triangle we now have, from triangle ADC,

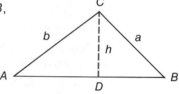

$$\frac{h}{b} = \sin A \quad \text{or} \quad h = b \sin A.$$

From triangle DBC above we have $\frac{h}{a} = \sin B$, or $h = a \sin B$.

Below we have $\frac{h}{a} = \sin (180° - B) = \sin B$. So in either kind of triangle we now have

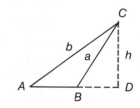

$$h = b \sin A \quad \text{and} \quad h = a \sin B.$$

Thus it follows that

$$b \sin A = a \sin B$$

$$\frac{a}{\sin A} = \frac{b}{\sin B} \qquad \textit{Dividing by sin A sin B}$$

There is no danger of dividing by 0 here because we are dealing with triangles whose angles are never 0° or 180°.

If we were to consider an altitude from vertex A in the triangles shown, the same argument would give us

$$\frac{b}{\sin B} = \frac{c}{\sin C}.$$

We combine these results to obtain the law of sines, which holds for right triangles as well as oblique triangles.

THEOREM 21-5

The law of sines. In any triangle ABC,

$$\frac{a}{\sin A} = \frac{b}{\sin B} = \frac{c}{\sin C}.$$

[The sides are proportional to the sines of the opposite angles.]

▪ Solving Triangles (AAS)

When two angles and a side of any triangle are known, the law of sines can be used to solve the triangle.

Example 1. In triangle ABC, $a = 4.56$, $A = 43°$, and $C = 57°$. Solve the triangle.

We first draw a sketch. We find B, as follows:

$$B = 180° - (43° + 57°),$$
$$= 80°.$$

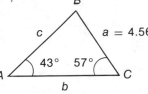

We can now find the other two sides, using the law of sines:

$$\frac{c}{\sin C} = \frac{a}{\sin A} \qquad\qquad \frac{b}{\sin B} = \frac{a}{\sin A}$$

$$c = \frac{a \sin C}{\sin A} \qquad\qquad b = \frac{a \sin B}{\sin A}$$

$$= \frac{4.56 \sin 57°}{\sin 43°} \qquad\qquad = \frac{4.56 \sin 80°}{0.6820}$$

$$= \frac{4.56 \times 0.8387}{0.6820} \qquad\qquad = \frac{4.56 \times 0.9848}{0.6820}$$

$$= 5.61, \qquad\qquad = 6.58$$

We have now found the unknown parts of the triangle, $B = 80°$, $c = 5.61$, and $b = 6.58$. A calculator or slide rule is of great help in doing calculations like this.

TRY THIS ➡

1. In $\triangle ABC$, $a = 6.53$, $A = 41°$, and $C = 52°$. Solve the triangle.

   $B = 87°$, $b = 9.94$, $c = 7.84$

▪▪ The Ambiguous Case (SSA)

When two sides of a triangle and an angle opposite one of them are known, the law of sines can be used to solve the triangle. However, there may be more than one solution. Thus this is known as the ambiguous case. Suppose a, b, and A are given. Then the various possibilities are as shown in the four cases below.

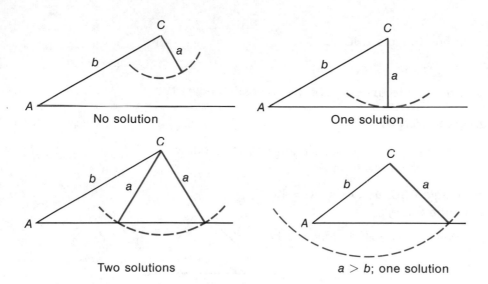

No solution

One solution

Two solutions

$a > b$; one solution

The following examples correspond to the four possibilities described above.

Example 2. In triangle ABC, $a = 15$, $b = 25$, and $A = 47°$. Solve the triangle.

We look for B:

$$\frac{a}{\sin A} = \frac{b}{\sin B}$$

Then

$$\sin B = \frac{b \sin A}{a} = \frac{25 \sin 47°}{15} = \frac{25 \times 0.7314}{15} = 1.219$$

Since there is no angle having a sine greater than 1, there is no solution.

Example 3. In triangle ABC, $a = 12$, $b = 5$, and $B = 24°38'$. Solve the triangle.

We look for A:

$$\frac{a}{\sin A} = \frac{b}{\sin B}$$

$$\sin A = \frac{a \sin B}{b} = \frac{12 \sin 24°38'}{5} = \frac{12 \times 0.4168}{5} = 1.000$$

$$A = 90°$$

Then $C = 90° - 24°38' = 65°22'$. Since $\frac{c}{a} = \cos B$,

$$c = a \cos B = 12 \times 0.9090 = 10.9.$$

Example 4.   In triangle ABC, $a = 20$, $b = 15$, and $B = 30°$. Solve the triangle.

We look for A:

$$\frac{a}{\sin A} = \frac{b}{\sin B}$$

$$\sin A = \frac{a \sin B}{b} = \frac{20 \sin 30°}{15} = \frac{20 \times 0.5}{15} = 0.667$$

There are two angles less than $180°$ having a sine of 0.6667. They are $42°$ and $138°$. This gives us two possible solutions.

Possible solution 1. We know that $A = 42°$. Then $C = 180° - (30° + 42°) = 108°$.

We now find c.

$$\frac{c}{\sin C} = \frac{b}{\sin B}$$

$$c = \frac{b \sin C}{\sin B} = \frac{15 \sin 108°}{\sin 30°} = \frac{15 \times 0.9511}{0.5} = 28.5$$

These parts make a triangle, as shown. Hence we have a solution.

Possible solution 2. $A = 138°$. Then $C = 12°$.
We now find c.

$$c = \frac{b \sin C}{\sin B} = \frac{15 \sin 12°}{\sin 30°} = \frac{15 \times 0.2079}{0.5} = 6.2$$

These parts make a triangle. Hence we have a second solution.

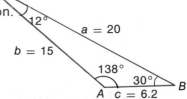

TRY THIS

2.   In triangle ABC, $a = 25$, $b = 20$ and $B = 33°$. Solve the triangle.

Example 5.   In triangle ABC, $a = 25$, $b = 10$, and $A = 42°$. Solve the triangle.

By the law of sines we find that $B = 15°30'$ or $B = 164°30'$. Since $a > b$, we know there is only one solution. If we had not noticed this, we could tell it now. An angle of $164°30'$ cannot be an angle of this triangle because it already has an angle of $42°$, and these two would total more than $180°$. Therefore,

$$C = 180° - (42° + 15°30') = 122°30'.$$

Using this value in the law of sines, we find $c = 31.5$.

TRY THIS

3. In triangle ABC, $b = 20$, $c = 10$, and $B = 38°$. Solve the triangle.

$C = 18°$, $A = 124°$, $a = 26.9$

Exercise Set 21-7   See answer section

▌Solve triangle ABC. (*See Example 1.*)

1. $A = 60°$, $B = 70°$, $b = 20$
2. $A = 48°$, $B = 62°$, $b = 35$
3. $A = 36°$, $B = 48°$, $a = 12$
4. $A = 40°$, $B = 60°$, $b = 100$
5. $A = 133°$, $B = 30°$, $b = 18$
6. $B = 120°$, $C = 30°$, $a = 16$
7. $B = 38°$, $C = 21°$, $b = 24$
8. $A = 131°$, $C = 23°$, $b = 10$
9. $A = 68°30'$, $C = 42°40'$, $c = 23.5$
10. $B = 118°20'$, $C = 45°40'$, $b = 42.1$

▌▌Solve triangle ABC. (*See Examples 2–5.*)

11. $B = 150°$, $a = 3$, $b = 7$
12. $A = 30°$, $a = 6$, $c = 9$
13. $C = 60°$, $a = 12$, $c = 30$
14. $B = 45°$, $a = 15$, $b = 17$
15. $A = 36°$, $a = 24$, $b = 34$
16. $C = 43°$, $c = 28$, $b = 27$
17. $A = 116°20'$, $a = 17.2$, $c = 13.5$
18. $A = 47°50'$, $a = 28.3$, $b = 18.2$
19. $C = 61°10'$, $c = 30.3$, $b = 24.2$
20. $B = 58°40'$, $a = 25.1$, $b = 32.6$

Challenge Exercises

21. A reconnaissance airplane leaves its airport on the East Coast of the United States and flies in a direction of 085°. Because of bad weather it returns to another airport 230 km to the north of its home base. For the return it flies in a direction of 283°. What was the total distance it flew?   1470 km
22. Lookout station B is 10.2 km east of station A. The bearing of a fire from A is S 10°40'W. The bearing of the fire from B is S 31°20'W. How far is the fire from A? from B?   24.7 km from A, 28.4 km from B
23. A boat leaves a lighthouse A and sails 5.1 km. At this time it is sighted from lighthouse B, 7.2 km west of A. The bearing of the boat from B is N 65°10'E. How far is the boat from B?   10.6 km or 2.4 km
24. An airplane leaves airport A and flies 200 km. At this time its bearing from airport B, 250 km to the west, is 120°. How far is the airplane from B?   373 km or 60.3 km

21-8 The Law of Cosines

After finishing Lesson 21-8, you should be able to
I   use the law of cosines, with the law of sines, to solve any triangle, given two sides and the included angle.
II use the law of cosines to solve any triangle, given three sides.

A second property of triangles important in solving oblique triangles is called the *law of cosines*. To derive this property we shall consider any triangle *ABC* placed on a coordinate system. We will place the origin at one of the vertices, say *C*, and the positive half of the *x*-axis along one of the sides, say *CB*. Then the coordinates of *B* are $(a, 0)$, and the coordinates of *A* are $(b \cos C, b \sin C)$. We will next use the distance formula to determine c^2.

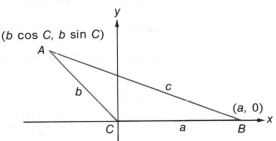

$$c^2 = (b \cos C - a)^2 + (b \sin C - 0)^2.$$
$$c^2 = b^2 \cos^2 C - 2ab \cos C + a^2 + b^2 \sin^2 C$$
$$c^2 = a^2 + b^2 (\sin^2 C + \cos^2 C) - 2ab \cos C$$
$$c^2 = a^2 + b^2 - 2ab \cos C$$

Had we placed the origin at one of the other vertices, we would have obtained

$$a^2 = b^2 + c^2 - 2bc \cos A \quad \text{or} \quad b^2 = a^2 + c^2 - 2ac \cos B.$$

This result can be summarized as follows.

THEOREM 21-6   (The law of cosines)
In any triangle *ABC*,

$$a^2 = b^2 + c^2 - 2bc \cos A,$$
$$b^2 = a^2 + c^2 - 2ac \cos B, \text{ and}$$
$$c^2 = a^2 + b^2 - 2ab \cos C.$$

(In any triangle, the square of a side is the sum of the squares of the other two sides, minus twice the product of those sides and the cosine of the included angle.)

Only one of the above formulas need be memorized. The other two can be obtained by a change of letters.

∎Solving Triangles (SAS)

When two sides of a triangle and the included angle are known, we can use the law of cosines to find the third side. The law of sines can then be used to finish solving the triangle.

Example 1. In triangle ABC, $a = 24$, $c = 32$, and $B = 115°$. Solve the triangle.

We first find the third side. From the law of cosines,

$$b^2 = a^2 + c^2 - 2ac \cos B$$
$$= 24^2 + 32^2 - 2 \cdot 24 \cdot 32(-0.4226)$$
$$= 2249$$
$$b = \sqrt{2249} \approx 47.4$$

Next, we use the law of sines to find a second angle.

$$\frac{a}{\sin A} = \frac{b}{\sin B}$$

$$\sin A = \frac{a \sin B}{b} = \frac{24 \sin 115°}{47.4} = \frac{24 \times 0.9063}{47.4} = 0.4589$$

$$A = 27°20'$$

The third angle is now easy to find.

$$C = 180° - (115° + 27°20') = 37°40'$$

TRY THIS

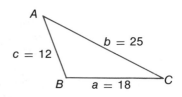

1. In triangle ABC, $b = 18$, $c = 28$, and $A = 122°$. Solve the triangle.

    $a = 40.5$, $B = 22°10'$, $C = 35°50'$

∎∎Solving Triangles (SSS)

When all three sides of a triangle are known, the law of cosines can be used to solve the triangle.

Example 2. In triangle ABC, $a = 18$, $b = 25$, and $c = 12$. Solve the triangle.

Let us first find angle B. We select the formula from the law of cosines that contains $\cos B$; in other words, $b^2 = a^2 + c^2 - 2ac \cos B$. We solve this for $\cos B$ and substitute.

$$\cos B = \frac{a^2 + c^2 - b^2}{2ac} = \frac{18^2 + 12^2 - 25^2}{2 \cdot 18 \cdot 12} = -0.3634$$

$$B = 111°20'$$

Similarly, we shall find angle A.

$$a^2 = b^2 + c^2 - 2bc \cos A$$
$$\cos A = \frac{b^2 + c^2 - a^2}{2bc}$$
$$= \frac{25^2 + 12^2 - 18^2}{2 \cdot 25 \cdot 12}$$
$$= 0.7417$$

Thus $A = 42°10'$.
Then $C = 180° - (111°20' + 42°10') = 26°30'$.

TRY THIS

> 2. In triangle ABC, $a = 25$, $b = 10$, and $c = 20$. Solve the triangle.
>
> A = 108°10', B = 22°20', C = 49°30'

Exercise Set 21-8   <small>See answer section</small>

▌Solve the triangles. (*See Example 1.*)

1. $C = 135°$, $a = 6$, $b = 7$
3. $A = 30°$, $b = 12$, $c = 24$
5. $A = 133°$, $b = 12$, $c = 15$
7. $B = 72°40'$, $c = 16$, $a = 78$

2. $A = 116°$, $b = 31$, $c = 25$
4. $C = 120°$, $a = 5$, $b = 8$
6. $C = 60°$, $a = 15$, $b = 12$
8. $A = 24°30'$, $b = 68$, $c = 14$

▌▌Solve the triangles. (*See Example 2.*)

9. $a = 2$, $b = 3$, $c = 4$
11. $a = 4$, $b = 6$, $c = 7$
13. $a = 12$, $b = 14$, $c = 20$
15. $a = 3.3$, $b = 2.7$, $c = 2.8$
17. $a = 2.2$, $b = 4.1$, $c = 2.4$

10. $a = 7$, $b = 9$, $c = 10$
12. $a = 7$, $b = 8$, $c = 10$
14. $a = 22$, $b = 22$, $c = 35$
16. $a = 16$, $b = 20$, $c = 32$
18. $a = 3.6$, $b = 6.2$, $c = 4.1$

Challenge Exercises

19. An airplane leaves an airport and flies west 147 km. It then flies 200 km in a direction of 220°. How far is it then from the airport and in what direction?   315 km, 240°50'

20. Two airplanes leave an airport at the same time. The first flies 150 km/h in a direction of 320°. The second flies 200 km/h in a direction of 200°. After 3 h, how far apart are the planes?   912 km

21-9 Polar Notation for Complex Numbers

After finishing Lesson 21-9, you should be able to
   I find polar notation when given rectangular notation for a complex number, and conversely.
   II use polar notation to multiply and divide complex numbers.
   III use DeMoivre's theorem to raise complex numbers to powers.
   IIII find the nth roots of a complex number.

In Chapter 11, we studied complex numbers. We now use our knowledge of trigonometry to develop polar notation for complex numbers.

   Consider any complex number $a + bi$. Recall that the length r of the segment from the origin to $a + bi$ is $\sqrt{a^2 + b^2}$. This distance r is called the absolute value of $a + bi$.

   Suppose that the segment makes an angle θ with the real axis. As the next diagram shows,

$$a = r \cos \theta \quad \text{and} \quad b = r \sin \theta.$$

Thus

$$a + bi = r \cos \theta + ir \sin \theta$$
$$= r (\cos \theta + i \sin \theta).$$

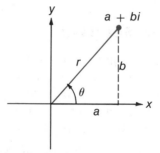

This is polar notation for $a + bi$. The angle θ is called the *argument*.

DEFINITION

Polar notation for the complex number $a + bi$ is $r (\cos \theta + i \sin \theta)$, where r is the absolute value and θ is the argument. This is sometimes shortened to r cis θ.

Polar notation for complex numbers is also called *trigonometric notation*.

I Change of Notation

To change from polar notation to rectangular notation $a + bi$, we recall that $a = r \cos \theta$ and $b = r \sin \theta$.

Example 1.   Write rectangular notation for $2 (\cos 120° + i \sin 120°)$.

$$a = 2 \cos 120° = -1$$
$$b = 2 \sin 120° = \sqrt{3}$$

Thus $2 (\cos 120° + i \sin 120°) = -1 + i\sqrt{3}$

TRY THIS ━━━▶

To change from rectangular notation to polar nota-tion, we remember that $r = \sqrt{a^2 + b^2}$ and θ is an angle for which $\sin \theta = \dfrac{b}{r}$ and $\cos \theta = \dfrac{a}{r}$.

Example 2. Find polar notation for $1 + i$.

We note that $a = 1$ and $b = 1$. Then

$$r = \sqrt{1^2 + 1^2} = \sqrt{2},$$

$$\sin \theta = \frac{1}{\sqrt{2}} \text{ and } \cos \theta = \frac{1}{\sqrt{2}}$$

Thus $\theta = \dfrac{\pi}{4}$, or $45°$, and we have

$$1 + i = \sqrt{2} \text{ cis } \frac{\pi}{4} \text{ or } 1 + i = \sqrt{2} \text{ cis } 45°.$$

> Write rectangular notation for the following. 1. $1 - i$ 2. $\sqrt{3} - i$
>
> 1. $\sqrt{2}(\cos 315° + i \sin 315°)$
>
> 2. $2\left(\cos - \dfrac{\pi}{6} + i \sin - \dfrac{\pi}{6}\right)$

> Write polar notation for the fol-lowing.
>
> 3. $1 - i$
> 4. $-3\sqrt{2} - 3\sqrt{2}i$

TRY THIS ━━━▶

Answers. 3. $\sqrt{2}$ cis $\dfrac{7\pi}{4}$ or $\sqrt{2}$ cis $315°$ 4. 6 cis $\dfrac{5\pi}{4}$ or 6 cis $225°$

In changing to polar notation, note that there are many angles satisfying the given conditions. We ordinarily choose the smallest positive angle.

▮ Multiplication and Polar Notation

Multiplication of complex numbers is somewhat easier to do with polar notation than with rectangular notation. We simply multiply the absolute values and add the arguments.

THEOREM 21-7
For any complex numbers r_1 cis θ_1 and r_2 cis θ_2,

$$(r_1 \text{ cis } \theta_1)(r_2 \text{ cis } \theta_2) = r_1 \cdot r_2 \text{ cis } (\theta_1 + \theta_2).$$

To divide complex numbers we do the reverse of the above.

THEOREM 21-8
For any complex numbers r_1 cis θ_1 and r_2 cis θ_2, $(r_2 \neq 0)$,

$$\frac{r_1 \text{ cis } \theta_1}{r_2 \text{ cis } \theta_2} = \frac{r_1}{r_2} \text{ cis } (\theta_1 - \theta_2).$$

Example 3. Find the product of 3 cis 40° and 7 cis 20°.

$$3 \text{ cis } 40° \cdot 7 \text{ cis } 20° = 3 \cdot 7 \text{ cis } (40° + 20°)$$
$$= 21 \text{ cis } 60°$$

Example 4. Divide 2 cis π by 4 cis $\frac{\pi}{2}$.

$$\frac{2 \text{ cis } \pi}{4 \text{ cis } \frac{\pi}{2}} = \frac{2}{4} \text{ cis } \left(\pi - \frac{\pi}{2}\right) = \frac{1}{2} \text{ cis } \frac{\pi}{2}$$

TRY THIS

5. Multiply 5 cis 25° by
    4 cis 30°. **5. 20 cis 55°** **6. 2 cis $\frac{\pi}{4}$**
6. Divide 10 cis $\frac{\pi}{2}$ by 5 cis $\frac{\pi}{4}$.

ꟼꟼꟼ DeMoivre's Theorem

An important theorem about powers and roots of complex numbers is named for French mathematician DeMoivre (1667–1754). Let us consider a number r cis θ and its square.

$$(r \text{ cis } \theta)^2 = (r \text{ cis } \theta)(r \text{ cis } \theta)$$
$$= r \cdot r \text{ cis } (\theta + \theta)$$
$$= r^2 \text{ cis } 2\theta$$

Similarly, we see that $(r \text{ cis } \theta)^3 = r \cdot r \cdot r \text{ cis } (\theta + \theta + \theta) = r^3 \text{ cis } 3\theta$. The generalization of this is DeMoivre's theorem.

THEOREM 21-9 (DeMoivre's Theorem)
For any complex number r cis θ and any natural number n,
$(r \text{ cis } \theta)^n = r^n \text{ cis } n\theta$.

Example 5. Find $(1 + i)^9$.

We first find polar notation.

$$1 + i = \sqrt{2} \text{ cis } 45°$$

Then

$$(1 + i)^9 = (\sqrt{2} \text{ cis } 45°)^9$$
$$= (\sqrt{2})^9 \text{cis } 9 \cdot 45°$$
$$= 2^{\frac{9}{2}} \text{ cis } 405°$$
$$= 16\sqrt{2} \text{ cis } 45° \quad (405° \text{ has the same}$$
$$\text{terminal side as } 45°).$$

TRY THIS

7. Find $(1 - i)^{10}$
8. Find $(\sqrt{3} + i)^4$

Answers. 7. 32 cis 270° 8. 16 cis 120°

ΙΙΙΙ Roots of Complex Numbers

As we shall see, every nonzero complex number has two square roots, three cube roots, four fourth roots, and so on. In general a nonzero complex number has n different nth roots. These can be found by the formula which we now state and prove.

THEOREM 21-10

The nth roots of a complex number r cis θ are given by

$$r^{\frac{1}{n}} \text{ cis} \left(\frac{\theta}{n} + k \cdot \frac{360°}{n} \right), \text{ where } k = 0, 1, 2, \dots, n - 1.$$

We show that this formula gives us n different roots, using DeMoivre's theorem. We take the expression for the nth roots and raise it to the nth power, to show that we get r cis θ.

$$\left[r^{\frac{1}{n}} \text{ cis} \left(\frac{\theta}{n} + k \cdot \frac{360°}{n} \right) \right]^n = (r^{\frac{1}{n}})^n \text{ cis} \left(\frac{\theta}{n} \cdot n + k \cdot n \cdot \frac{360°}{n} \right)$$
$$= r \text{ cis } (\theta + k \cdot 360°) = r \text{ cis } \theta.$$

Thus we know that the formula gives us nth roots for any natural number k. Next we show that there are at least n different roots. To see this, consider substituting 0, 1, 2, and so on, for k. From 0 to $n - 1$ the angles obtained and their sines and cosines are all different. But when $k = n$ the cycle begins to repeat. There cannot be more than n different nth roots. This fact follows from the *Fundamental Theorem of Algebra,* considered in Chapter 11.

Example 6. Find the square roots of $2 + 2\sqrt{3}i$.

We first find polar notation.

$$2 + 2\sqrt{3}i = 4 \text{ cis } 60°.$$

Then

$$(4 \text{ cis } 60°)^{\frac{1}{2}} = 4^{\frac{1}{2}} \text{ cis} \left(\frac{60°}{2} + k \cdot \frac{360°}{2} \right), k = 0, 1,$$
$$= 2 \text{ cis} \left(30° + k \cdot \frac{360°}{2} \right), k = 0, 1.$$

Thus the roots are 2 cis 30° and 2 cis 210°, or

$$\sqrt{3} + i \quad \text{and} \quad -\sqrt{3} - i$$

TRY THIS

9. Find the square roots of $2i$.

Answer. $\sqrt{2}$ cis 45° and $\sqrt{2}$ cis 225°, or $1 + i$ and $-1 - i$

Example 7. Find the cube roots of 1. Locate them on a graph.

$$1 = 1 \text{ cis } 0°$$

$$(1 \text{ cis } 0°)^{\frac{1}{3}} = 1^{\frac{1}{3}} \text{ cis } \left(\frac{0°}{3} + k \cdot \frac{360°}{3} \right), \ k = 0, 1, 2$$

The roots are 1 cis 0°, 1 cis 120°, and 1 cis 240°, or

$$1, \ -\frac{1}{2} + \frac{\sqrt{3}}{2}i, \text{ and } -\frac{1}{2} - \frac{\sqrt{3}}{2}i.$$

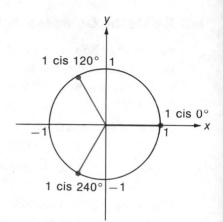

Note in the example that the graphs of the cube roots lie equally spaced about a circle. This is true of the *n*th roots of any complex number.

TRY THIS ➡

10. Find the cube roots of −1. Locate them on a graph.

Answer.   10. cis 60°, cis 180°, and cis 300°; or $\frac{1}{2} + \frac{\sqrt{3}}{2}$ i, −1 and $\frac{1}{2} - \frac{\sqrt{3}}{2}$ i

Exercise Set 21-9

▍Find rectangular notation. (*See Example 1.*)

1. 3 (cos 30° + *i* sin 30°) $\frac{3\sqrt{3}}{2} + \frac{3}{2}i$
2. 5 (cos 60° + *i* sin 60°) $\frac{5}{2} + \frac{5\sqrt{3}}{2}i$
3. 4 (cos 135° + *i* sin 135°) $-2\sqrt{2} + 2i\sqrt{2}$
4. 6 (cos 150° + *i* sin 150°) $-3\sqrt{3} + 3i$
5. 10 cis 270°   −10i
6. 12 cis 90°   12i
7. 5 cis (−45°) $\frac{5\sqrt{2}}{2} - \frac{5\sqrt{2}}{2}i$
8. 5 cis (−60°) $\frac{5}{2} - \frac{5\sqrt{3}}{2}i$
9. $\sqrt{8} \left(\cos \frac{\pi}{4} + i \sin \frac{\pi}{4} \right)$ 2 + 2i
10. $\sqrt{8} \left(\cos \frac{3\pi}{4} + i \sin \frac{3\pi}{4} \right)$ −2 + 2i
11. $4 \left(\cos \frac{\pi}{6} + i \sin \frac{\pi}{6} \right)$ $2\sqrt{3} + 2i$
12. $5 \left(\cos \frac{\pi}{3} + i \sin \frac{\pi}{3} \right)$ $\frac{5}{2} + \frac{5\sqrt{3}}{2}i$
13. $\sqrt{8} \text{ cis } \frac{5\pi}{4}$ −2 − 2i
14. $\sqrt{8} \text{ cis } \left(-\frac{\pi}{4} \right)$ 2 − 2i

Find polar notation. (*See Example 2.*)

15. 1 − *i* $\sqrt{2} \text{ cis } \frac{7\pi}{4}$ or $\sqrt{2}$ cis 315°
16. −1 − *i* $\sqrt{2} \text{ cis } \frac{5\pi}{4}$ or $\sqrt{2}$ cis 225°
17. $\sqrt{3}$ + *i*   2 cis $\frac{\pi}{6}$ or 2 cis 30°
18. $-\sqrt{3}$ + *i*   2 cis $\frac{5\pi}{6}$ or 2 cis 150°
19. $10\sqrt{3}$ − 10*i*   20 cis $\frac{11\pi}{6}$ or 20 cis 330°
20. $-10\sqrt{3}$ + 10*i*   20 cis $\frac{5\pi}{6}$ or 20 cis 150°
21. 2*i*   2 cis $\frac{\pi}{2}$ or 2 cis 90°
22. 3*i*   3 cis $\frac{\pi}{2}$ or 3 cis 90°
23. −5   5 cis π or 5 cis 180°
24. −10   10 cis π or 10 cis 180°
25. −4*i*   4 cis $\frac{3\pi}{2}$ or 4 cis 270°
26. −5*i*   5 cis $\frac{3\pi}{2}$ or 5 cis 270°

Use Quiz 38 after lesson 21–9.

▌▌ Convert to polar notation and then multiply or divide (*See Examples 3 and 4.*)

27. $(1 - i)(2 + 2i)$ 4 cis 0
28. $(\sqrt{3} + i)(1 + i)$ $2\sqrt{2}$ cis $\frac{5\pi}{12}$
29. $(10\sqrt{3} + 10i)(\sqrt{3} - i)$ 40 cis 0
30. $(1 + i\sqrt{3})(1 + i)$ $2\sqrt{2}$ cis $\frac{7\pi}{12}$
31. $(2\sqrt{3} + 2i)(2i)$ 8 cis $\frac{2\pi}{3}$
32. $(3\sqrt{3} - 3i)(2i)$ 12 cis $\frac{\pi}{3}$
33. $\dfrac{1 + i}{1 - i}$ cis $\frac{\pi}{2}$
34. $\dfrac{1 - i}{1 + i}$ cis $\frac{3\pi}{2}$
35. $\dfrac{-1 + i}{\sqrt{3} + i}$ $\frac{\sqrt{2}}{2}$ cis $\frac{7\pi}{12}$
36. $\dfrac{1 - i}{\sqrt{3} - i}$ $\frac{\sqrt{2}}{2}$ cis $\frac{23\pi}{12}$
37. $\dfrac{2\sqrt{3} - 2i}{1 + \sqrt{3}i}$ 2 cis $\frac{3\pi}{2}$
38. $\dfrac{3 - 3\sqrt{3}i}{\sqrt{3} - i}$ 3 cis $\frac{11\pi}{6}$

▌▌▌ Raise the number to the power. Give your answer in polar notation. (*See Example 5.*)

39. $\left(2 \text{ cis } \dfrac{\pi}{3}\right)^3$ 8 cis π or 8 cis 180°
40. $\left(3 \text{ cis } \dfrac{\pi}{2}\right)^4$ 81 cis 0 or 81 cis 0°
41. $\left(2 \text{ cis } \dfrac{\pi}{6}\right)^6$ 64 cis π or 64 cis 180°
42. $\left(2 \text{ cis } \dfrac{\pi}{5}\right)^5$ 32 cis π or 32 cis 180°
43. $(1 + i)^6$ 8 cis $\frac{3\pi}{2}$ or 8 cis 270°
44. $(1 - i)^6$ 8 cis $\frac{\pi}{2}$ or 8 cis 90°

Raise the number to the power. Give your answer in rectangular notation. (*See Example 5.*)

45. $(2 \text{ cis } 240°)^4$ $-8 - 8i\sqrt{3}$
46. $(2 \text{ cis } 120°)^4$ $-8 + 8i\sqrt{3}$
47. $(1 + \sqrt{3}i)^4$ $-8 - 8i\sqrt{3}$
48. $(-\sqrt{3} + i)^6$ -64
49. $\left(\dfrac{1}{\sqrt{2}} + \dfrac{1}{\sqrt{2}}i\right)^{10}$ i
50. $\left(\dfrac{1}{\sqrt{2}} - \dfrac{1}{\sqrt{2}}i\right)^{12}$ -1
51. $\left(\dfrac{\sqrt{3}}{2} + \dfrac{1}{2}i\right)^{12}$ 1
52. $\left(\dfrac{\sqrt{3}}{2} - \dfrac{1}{2}i\right)^{14}$ $\frac{1}{2} - \frac{\sqrt{3}}{2}i$

▌▌▌▌ Find the following. (*See Examples 6 and 7.*)   See answer section

53. Find square roots of $-1 + \sqrt{3}i$.
54. The square roots of $-\sqrt{3} - i$.
55. The cube roots of i.
56. The cube roots of $-i$.
57. The fourth roots of 16.
58. The fourth roots of -16.

Challenge Exercises
See answer section

59. Show that for any complex numbers z, w, $|z \cdot w| = |z| \cdot |w|$.
[*Hint:* Let $z = r_1 \text{ cis } \theta_1$ and $w = r_2 \text{ cis } \theta_2$.]
60. Show that for any complex number z and any nonzero complex number w, $\left|\dfrac{z}{w}\right| = \dfrac{|z|}{|w|}$.
61. Find the cube roots of 68.4321.
62. Find the cube roots of 456.86.

CHAPTER 21 REVIEW

Review the material in the chapter. Then see how you have done by trying these review exercises. If you miss an exercise, restudy the indicated lesson.

21-1   Use the sum and difference identities to write equivalent expressions. You need not simplify.

1. $\cos(x + y)$ $\cos x \cos y - \sin x \sin y$
2. $\tan(45° - 30°)$ $\dfrac{\tan 45° - \tan 30°}{1 + \tan 45° \tan 30°}$
3. $\cos 37° \cos 16° + \sin 27° \sin 16°$ $\cos(27° - 16°)$ or $\cos 11°$

21-2   Find $\sin 2\theta$, $\cos 2\theta$, $\tan 2\theta$, and the quadrant in which 2θ lies.

4. $\sin \theta = \frac{3}{5}$ (θ in Quadrant I) $\sin 2\theta = \frac{24}{25}$, $\cos 2\theta = \frac{7}{25}$, $\tan 2\theta = \frac{24}{7}$; θ in quadrant I
5. $\tan \theta = \frac{4}{3}$ (θ in Quadrant III) $\sin 2\theta = \frac{24}{25}$, $\cos 2\theta = -\frac{7}{25}$, $\tan 2\theta = -\frac{24}{7}$, θ in quadrant II

21-2   6. Find $\sin \dfrac{\pi}{8}$. $\dfrac{\sqrt{2 - \sqrt{2}}}{2}$

21-3   7. Prove the identity $\tan 2\theta \equiv \dfrac{2 \tan \theta}{1 - \tan^2 \theta}$.   See answer section

21-4   8. Find, in radians, all values of $\sin^{-1} \frac{1}{2}$. $\frac{\pi}{6} + 2k\pi$ and $\frac{5\pi}{6} + 2k\pi$

21-4   9. Use Table 3 to find in degrees all values of $\cot^{-1} 0.1584$. $81° + k180°$

20-4   10. Find $\text{Arcsin}\left(\dfrac{-\sqrt{2}}{2}\right)$. $-\frac{\pi}{4}$

21-5   11. Find the solutions of $\sin^2 x - 7 \sin x = 0$ from 0 to 2π. $0, \pi$

21-5   12. Find all solutions of $\sin 2x - \cos x = 0$ from 0 to 2π. $\frac{\pi}{6}, \frac{5\pi}{6}, \frac{\pi}{2}, \frac{3\pi}{2}$

21-6   Solve the triangles. Angle C is a right angle. Use three-digit precision.

13. $a = 7.3$, $c = 8.6$ $A = 58°10'$, $B = 31°50'$, $b = 4.54$
14. $a = 30.5$, $B = 51°10'$ $A = 38°50'$, $b = 37.9$, $c = 48.6$

21-6   15. One leg of a right triangle bears east. The hypotenuse is 734 m long and bears N 57°20'E. Find the perimeter.   1748 m

21-7   16. Solve $\triangle ABC$. $B = 118°20'$, $C = 27°40'$, $b = 0.974$. $A = 34°$, $a = 0.619$, $c = 0.514$
21-8   17. In $\triangle ABC$, $a = 3.7$, $c = 4.9$, $B = 135°$. Find b. $b = 7.96$
21-9   18. Find polar notation for $1 + i$. $\sqrt{2} \text{ cis } \frac{\pi}{4}$ or $\sqrt{2} \text{ cis } 45°$
21-9   19. Find rectangular notation for $2(\cos 135° + i \sin 135°)$. $-\sqrt{2} + \sqrt{2}i$
21-9   20. Find the product of $7 \text{ cis } 18°$ and $10 \text{ cis } 32°$. $70 \text{ cis } 50°$
21-9   21. Find the cube roots of $1 + i$. $\sqrt[6]{2} \text{ cis } 15°$, $\sqrt[6]{2} \text{ cis } 135°$, and $\sqrt[6]{2} \text{ cis } 255°$
21-9   22. Find $(2 \text{ cis } 120°)^3$ and give your answer in rectangular notation.   8

CHAPTER 21 TEST

Use the sum and difference identities to write equivalent expressions. You need not simplify.

1. $\sin(A - B)$ sin A cos B − cos A sin B
2. $\cos(45° + 60°)$ cos 45 cos 60 − sin 45 sin 60
3. $\sin\dfrac{\pi}{8}\cos\dfrac{\pi}{3} + \cos\dfrac{\pi}{8}\sin\dfrac{\pi}{3}$ $\sin(\frac{\pi}{8} + \frac{\pi}{3})$ or $\sin\frac{11\pi}{24}$

Find sin 2θ, cos 2θ, tan 2θ, and the quadrant in which 2θ lies.

4. $\cos\theta = \frac{4}{5}$ (θ in Quadrant I) $\sin 2\theta = \frac{24}{25}$, $\cos 2\theta = \frac{7}{25}$, $\tan 2\theta = \frac{24}{7}$, θ in quadrant I
5. $\tan\theta = -\frac{3}{4}$ (θ in Quadrant II) $\sin 2\theta = -\frac{24}{25}$, $\cos 2\theta = \frac{7}{25}$, $\tan 2\theta = -\frac{24}{7}$, θ in quadrant IV

6. Find $\sin\dfrac{7\pi}{8}$. $\dfrac{\sqrt{2-\sqrt{2}}}{2}$

7. Prove the identity $\tan\theta \equiv \dfrac{\sin 2\theta}{1 + \cos 2\theta}$.   See answer section
8. Find, in radians, all values of $\cos^{-1}\frac{1}{2}$. $\frac{\pi}{3} + 2k\pi$ and $\frac{5\pi}{3} + 2k\pi$
9. Use tables to find in degrees all values of $\sin^{-1} 0.9537$.   72°30′ + k360° and 107°30′ + k360°
10. Find Arccos $\left(\dfrac{\sqrt{3}}{2}\right)$. $\frac{\pi}{6}$
11. Find all solutions of $2\cos^2 x + 1 = -3\cos x$ from 0 to 2π. $\frac{2\pi}{3}, \frac{4\pi}{3}, \pi$
12. Find all solutions of $\cos^2 x = 1 + \sin^2 x$ from 0 to 2π.   0, π, 2π

Solve the triangles. Angle C is a right angle. Use three-digit precision.

13. $a = 9.2$, $c = 10.1$ A = 65°40′, B = 24°20′, b = 4.16
14. $a = 28.5$, $B = 49°10′$ A = 40°50′, b = 33.0, c = 43.6

15. One leg of a right triangle bears west. The hypotenuse is 692 m long and bears N 56°30′E. Find the perimeter.   1651 m
16. Solve $\triangle ABC$. $B = 117°10′$, $C = 26°50′$, $b = 0.963$.   A = 36°, a = 0.636, c = 0.489
17. In $\triangle ABC$, $a = 3.8$, $c = 4.6$, and $B = 132°$. Find b.   b = 7.68
18. Find polar notation for $1 - i$. $\sqrt{2}$ cis $\frac{7\pi}{4}$
19. Find rectangular notation for $3(\cos 120° + i\sin 120°)$. $-\frac{3}{2} + \frac{3\sqrt{3}}{2}i$
20. Find the product of 8 cis 24° and 12 cis 39°.   96 cis 63°
21. Find the cube roots of $1 - i$. $\sqrt[6]{2}$ cis 105°, $\sqrt[6]{2}$ cis 225°, and $\sqrt[6]{2}$ cis 345°
22. Find $(2 \text{ cis } 150°)^3$ and give your answer in rectangular notation.   8i

TABLE 1: *SQUARES AND SQUARE ROOTS*

N	N^2	$\sqrt{N}$	N	N^2	$\sqrt{N}$
1	1	1	51	2,601	7.141
2	4	1.414	52	2,704	7.211
3	9	1.732	53	2,809	7.280
4	16	2	54	2,916	7.348
5	25	2.236	55	3,025	7.416
6	36	2.449	56	3,136	7.483
7	49	2.646	57	3,249	7.550
8	64	2.828	58	3,364	7.616
9	81	3	59	3,481	7.681
10	100	3.162	60	3,600	7.746
11	121	3.317	61	3,721	7.810
12	144	3.464	62	3,844	7.874
13	169	3.606	63	3,969	7.937
14	196	3.742	64	4,096	8
15	225	3.873	65	4,225	8.062
16	256	4	66	4,356	8.124
17	289	4.123	67	4,489	8.185
18	324	4.243	68	4,624	8.246
19	361	4.359	69	4,761	8.307
20	400	4.472	70	4,900	8.367
21	441	4.583	71	5,041	8.426
22	484	4.690	72	5,184	8.485
23	529	4.796	73	5,329	8.544
24	576	4.899	74	5,476	8.602
25	625	5	75	5,625	8.660
26	676	5.099	76	5,776	8.718
27	729	5.196	77	5,929	8.775
28	784	5.292	78	6,084	8.832
29	841	5.385	79	6,241	8.888
30	900	5.477	80	6,400	8.944
31	961	5.568	81	6,561	9
32	1,024	5.657	82	6,724	9.055
33	1,089	5.745	83	6,889	9.110
34	1,156	5.831	84	7,056	9.165
35	1,225	5.916	85	7,225	9.220
36	1,296	6	86	7,396	9.274
37	1,369	6.083	87	7,569	9.327
38	1,444	6.164	88	7,744	9.381
39	1,521	6.245	89	7,921	9.434
40	1,600	6.325	90	8,100	9.487
41	1,681	6.403	91	8,281	9.539
42	1,764	6.481	92	8,464	9.592
43	1,849	6.557	93	8,649	9.644
44	1,936	6.633	94	8,836	9.695
45	2,025	6.708	95	9,025	9.747
46	2,116	6.782	96	9,216	9.798
47	2,209	6.856	97	9,409	9.849
48	2,304	6.928	98	9,604	9.899
49	2,401	7	99	9,801	9.950
50	2,500	7.071	100	10,000	10

TABLE 2: *COMMON LOGARITHMS*

x	0	1	2	3	4	5	6	7	8	9
1.0	.0000	.0043	.0086	.0128	.0170	.0212	.0253	.0294	.0334	.0374
1.1	.0414	.0453	.0492	.0531	.0569	.0607	.0645	.0682	.0719	.0755
1.2	.0792	.0828	.0864	.0899	.0934	.0969	.1004	.1038	.1072	.1106
1.3	.1139	.1173	.1206	.1239	.1271	.1303	.1335	.1367	.1399	.1430
1.4	.1461	.1492	.1523	.1553	.1584	.1614	.1644	.1673	.1703	.1732
1.5	.1761	.1790	.1818	.1847	.1875	.1903	.1931	.1959	.1987	.2014
1.6	.2041	.2068	.2095	.2122	.2148	.2175	.2201	.2227	.2253	.2279
1.7	.2304	.2330	.2355	.2380	.2405	.2430	.2455	.2480	.2504	.2529
1.8	.2553	.2577	.2601	.2625	.2648	.2672	.2695	.2718	.2742	.2765
1.9	.2788	.2810	.2833	.2856	.2878	.2900	.2923	.2945	.2967	.2989
2.0	.3010	.3032	.3054	.3075	.3096	.3118	.3139	.3160	.3181	.3201
2.1	.3222	.3243	.3263	.3284	.3304	.3324	.3345	.3365	.3385	.3404
2.2	.3424	.3444	.3464	.3483	.3502	.3522	.3541	.3560	.3579	.3598
2.3	.3617	.3636	.3655	.3674	.3692	.3711	.3729	.3747	.3766	.3784
2.4	.3802	.3820	.3838	.3856	.3874	.3892	.3909	.3927	.3945	.3962
2.5	.3979	.3997	.4014	.4031	.4048	.4065	.4082	.4099	.4116	.4133
2.6	.4150	.4166	.4183	.4200	.4216	.4232	.4249	.4265	.4281	.4298
2.7	.4314	.4330	.4346	.4362	.4378	.4393	.4409	.4425	.4440	.4456
2.8	.4472	.4487	.4502	.4518	.4533	.4548	.4564	.4579	.4594	.4609
2.9	.4624	.4639	.4654	.4669	.4683	.4698	.4713	.4728	.4742	.4757
3.0	.4771	.4786	.4800	.4814	.4829	.4843	.4857	.4871	.4886	.4900
3.1	.4914	.4928	.4942	.4955	.4969	.4983	.4997	.5011	.5024	.5038
3.2	.5051	.5065	.5079	.5092	.5105	.5119	.5132	.5145	.5159	.5172
3.3	.5185	.5198	.5211	.5224	.5237	.5250	.5263	.5276	.5289	.5307
3.4	.5315	.5328	.5340	.5353	.5366	.5378	.5391	.5403	.5416	.5428
3.5	.5441	.5453	.5465	.5478	.5490	.5502	.5514	.5527	.5539	.5551
3.6	.5563	.5575	.5587	.5599	.5611	.5623	.5635	.5647	.5658	.5670
3.7	.5682	.5694	.5705	.5717	.5729	.5740	.5752	.5763	.5775	.5786
3.8	.5798	.5809	.5821	.5832	.5843	.5855	.5866	.5877	.5888	.5899
3.9	.5911	.5922	.5933	.5944	.5955	.5966	.5977	.5988	.5999	.6010
4.0	.6021	.6031	.6042	.6053	.6064	.6075	.6085	.6096	.6107	.6117
4.1	.6128	.6138	.6149	.6160	.6170	.6180	.6191	.6201	.6212	.6222
4.2	.6232	.6243	.6253	.6263	.6274	.6284	.6294	.6304	.6314	.6325
4.3	.6335	.6345	.6355	.6365	.6375	.6385	.6395	.6405	.6415	.6425
4.4	.6435	.6444	.6454	.6464	.6474	.6484	.6493	.6503	.6513	.6522
4.5	.6532	.6542	.6551	.6561	.6571	.6580	.6590	.6599	.6609	.6618
4.6	.6628	.6637	.6646	.6656	.6665	.6675	.6684	.6693	.6702	.6712
4.7	.6721	.6730	.6739	.6749	.6758	.6767	.6776	.6785	.6794	.6803
4.8	.6812	.6821	.6830	.6839	.6848	.6857	.6866	.6875	.6884	.6893
4.9	.6902	.6911	.6920	.6928	.6937	.6946	.6955	.6964	.6972	.6981
5.0	.6990	.6998	.7007	.7016	.7024	.7033	.7042	.7050	.7059	.7067
5.1	.7076	.7084	.7093	.7101	.7110	.7118	.7126	.7135	.7143	.7152
5.2	.7160	.7168	.7177	.7185	.7193	.7202	.7210	.7218	.7226	.7235
5.3	.7243	.7251	.7259	.7267	.7275	.7284	.7292	.7300	.7308	.7316
5.4	.7324	.7332	.7340	.7348	.7356	.7364	.7372	.7380	.7388	.7396

x	0	1	2	3	4	5	6	7	8	9
5.5	.7404	.7412	.7419	.7427	.7435	.7443	.7451	.7459	.7466	.7474
5.6	.7482	.7490	.7497	.7505	.7513	.7520	.7528	.7536	.7543	.7551
5.7	.7559	.7566	.7574	.7582	.7589	.7597	.7604	.7612	.7619	.7627
5.8	.7634	.7642	.7649	.7657	.7664	.7672	.7679	.7686	.7694	.7701
5.9	.7709	.7716	.7723	.7731	.7738	.7745	.7752	.7760	.7767	.7774
6.0	.7782	.7789	.7796	.7803	.7810	.7818	.7825	.7832	.7839	.7846
6.1	.7853	.7860	.7868	.7875	.7882	.7889	.7896	.7903	.7910	.7917
6.2	.7924	.7931	.7938	.7945	.7952	.7959	.7966	.7973	.7980	.7987
6.3	.7993	.8000	.8007	.8014	.8021	.8028	.8035	.8041	.8048	.8055
6.4	.8062	.8069	.8075	.8082	.8089	.8096	.8102	.8109	.8116	.8122
6.5	.8129	.8136	.8142	.8149	.8156	.8162	.8169	.8176	.8182	.8189
6.6	.8195	.8202	.8209	.8215	.8222	.8228	.8235	.8241	.8248	.8254
6.7	.8261	.8267	.8274	.8280	.8287	.8293	.8299	.8306	.8312	.8319
6.8	.8325	.8331	.8338	.8344	.8351	.8357	.8363	.8370	.8376	.8382
6.9	.8388	.8395	.8401	.8407	.8414	.8420	.8426	.8432	.8439	.8445
7.0	.8451	.8457	.8463	.8470	.8476	.8482	.8488	.8494	.8500	.8506
7.1	.8513	.8519	.8525	.8531	.8537	.8543	.8549	.8555	.8561	.8567
7.2	.8573	.8579	.8585	.8591	.8597	.8603	.8609	.8615	.8621	.8627
7.3	.8633	.8639	.8645	.8651	.8657	.8663	.8669	.8675	.8681	.8686
7.4	.8692	.8698	.8704	.8710	.8716	.8722	.8727	.8733	.8739	.8745
7.5	.8751	.8756	.8762	.8768	.8774	.8779	.8785	.8791	.8797	.8802
7.6	.8808	.8814	.8820	.8825	.8831	.8837	.8842	.8848	.8854	.8859
7.7	.8865	.8871	.8876	.8882	.8887	.8893	.8899	.8904	.8910	.8915
7.8	.8921	.8927	.8932	.8938	.8943	.8949	.8954	.8960	.8965	.8971
7.9	.8976	.8982	.8987	.8993	.8998	.9004	.9009	.9015	.9020	.9025
8.0	.9031	.9036	.9042	.9047	.9053	.9058	.9063	.9069	.9074	.9079
8.1	.9085	.9090	.9096	.9101	.9106	.9112	.9117	.9122	.9128	.9133
8.2	.9138	.9143	.9149	.9154	.9159	.9165	.9170	.9175	.9180	.9186
8.3	.9191	.9196	.9201	.9206	.9212	.9217	.9222	.9227	.9232	.9238
8.4	.9243	.9248	.9253	.9258	.9263	.9269	.9274	.9279	.9284	.9289
8.5	.9294	.9299	.9304	.9309	.9315	.9320	.9325	.9330	.9335	.9340
8.6	.9345	.9350	.9555	.9360	.9365	.9370	.9375	.9380	.9385	.9390
8.7	.9395	.9400	.9405	.9410	.9415	.9420	.9425	.9430	.9435	.9440
8.8	.9445	.9450	.9455	.9460	.9465	.9469	.9474	.9479	.9484	.9489
8.9	.9494	.9499	.9504	.9509	.9513	.9518	.9523	.9528	.9533	.9538
9.0	.9542	.9547	.9552	.9557	.9562	.9566	.9571	.9576	.9581	.9586
9.1	.9590	.9595	.9600	.9605	.9609	.9614	.9619	.9624	.9628	.9633
9.2	.9638	.9643	.9647	.9652	.9657	.9661	.9666	.9671	.9675	.9680
9.3	.9685	.9689	.9694	.9699	.9703	.9708	.9713	.9717	.9722	.9727
9.4	.9731	.9736	.9741	.9745	.9750	.9754	.9759	.9763	.9768	.9773
9.5	.9777	.9782	.9786	.9791	.9795	.9800	.9805	.9809	.9814	.9818
9.6	.9823	.9827	.9832	.9836	.9841	.9845	.9850	.9854	.9859	.9863
9.7	.9868	.9872	.9877	.9881	.9886	.9890	.9894	.9899	.9903	.9908
9.8	.9912	.9917	.9921	.9926	.9930	.9934	.9939	.9943	.9948	.9952
9.9	.9956	.9961	.9965	.9969	.9974	.9978	.9983	.9987	.9991	.9996

TABLE 3. *VALUES OF TRIGONOMETRIC FUNCTIONS*

Degrees	Radians	Sin	Cos	Tan	Cot	Sec	Csc		
0° 00′	0.0000	0.0000	1.0000	0.0000	—	1.000	—	1.5708	90° 00′
10	029	029	000	029	343.8	000	343.8	679	50
20	058	058	000	058	171.9	000	171.9	650	40
30	0.0087	0.0087	1.0000	0.0087	114.6	1.000	114.6	1.5621	30
40	116	116	0.9999	116	85.94	000	85.95	592	20
50	145	145	999	145	68.75	000	68.76	563	10
1° 00′	0.0175	0.0175	0.9998	0.0175	57.29	1.000	57.30	1.5533	89° 00′
10	204	204	998	204	49.10	000	49.11	504	50
20	233	233	997	233	42.96	000	42.98	475	40
30	0.0262	0.0262	0.9997	0.0262	38.19	1.000	38.20	1.5446	30
40	291	291	996	291	34.37	000	34.38	417	20
50	320	320	995	320	31.24	001	31.26	388	10
2° 00′	0.0349	0.0349	0.9994	0.0349	28.64	1.001	28.65	1.5359	88° 00′
10	378	378	993	378	26.43	001	26.45	330	50
20	407	407	992	407	24.54	001	24.56	301	40
30	0.0436	0.0436	0.9990	0.0437	22.90	1.001	22.93	1.5272	30
40	465	465	989	466	21.47	001	21.49	243	20
50	495	494	988	495	20.21	001	20.23	213	10
3° 00′	0.0524	0.0523	0.9986	0.0524	19.08	1.001	19.11	1.5184	87° 00′
10	553	552	985	553	18.07	002	18.10	155	50
20	582	581	983	582	17.17	002	17.20	126	40
30	0.0611	0.0610	0.9981	0.0612	16.35	1.002	16.38	1.5097	30
40	640	640	980	641	15.60	002	15.64	068	20
50	669	669	978	670	14.92	002	14.96	039	10
4° 00′	0.0698	0.0698	0.9976	0.0699	14.30	1.002	14.34	1.5010	86° 00′
10	727	727	974	729	13.73	003	13.76	981	50
20	756	756	971	758	13.20	003	13.23	952	40
30	0.0785	0.0785	0.9969	0.0787	12.71	1.003	12.75	1.4923	30
40	814	814	967	816	12.25	003	12.29	893	20
50	844	843	964	846	11.83	004	11.87	864	10
5° 00′	0.0873	0.0872	0.9962	0.0875	11.43	1.004	11.47	1.4835	85° 00′
10	902	901	959	904	11.06	004	11.10	806	50
20	931	929	957	934	10.71	004	10.76	777	40
30	0.0960	0.0958	0.9954	0.0963	10.39	1.005	10.43	1.4748	30
40	989	987	951	992	10.08	005	10.13	719	20
50	0.1018	0.1016	948	0.1022	9.788	005	9.839	690	10
6° 00′	0.1047	0.1045	0.9945	0.1051	95.14	1.006	9.567	1.4661	84° 00′
10	076	074	942	080	9.255	006	9.309	632	50
20	105	103	939	110	9.010	006	9.065	603	40
30	0.1134	0.1132	0.9936	0.1139	8.777	1.006	8.834	1.4573	30
40	164	161	932	169	8.556	007	8.614	544	20
50	193	190	929	198	8.345	007	8.405	515	10
7° 00′	0.1222	0.1219	0.9925	0.1228	8.144	1.008	8.206	1.4486	83° 00′
10	251	248	922	257	7.953	008	8.016	457	50
20	280	276	918	287	7.770	008	7.834	428	40
30	0.1309	0.1305	0.9914	0.1317	7.596	1.009	7.661	1.4399	30
40	338	334	911	346	7.429	009	7.496	370	20
50	367	363	907	376	7.269	009	7.337	341	10
8° 00′	0.1396	0.1392	0.9903	0.1405	7.115	1.010	7.185	1.4312	82° 00′
10	425	421	899	435	6.968	010	7.040	283	50
20	454	449	894	465	6.827	011	6.900	254	40
30	0.1484	0.1478	0.9890	0.1495	6.691	1.011	6.765	1.4224	30
40	513	507	886	524	6.561	012	6.636	195	20
50	542	536	881	554	6.435	012	6.512	166	10
9° 00′	0.1571	0.1564	0.9877	0.1584	6.314	1.012	6.392	1.4137	81° 00′
		Cos	Sin	Cot	Tan	Csc	Sec	Radians	Degrees

Degrees	Radians	Sin	Cos	Tan	Cot	Sec	Csc		
9° 00′	0.1571	0.1564	0.9877	0.1584	6.314	1.012	6.392	1.4137	81° 00′
10	600	593	872	614	197	013	277	108	50
20	629	622	868	644	084	013	166	079	40
30	0.1658	0.1650	0.9863	0.1673	5.976	1.014	6.059	1.4050	30
40	687	679	858	703	871	014	5.955	1.4021	20
50	716	708	853	733	769	015	855	992	10
10° 00′	0.1745	0.1736	0.9848	0.1763	5.671	1.015	5.759	1.3963	80° 00′
10	774	765	843	793	576	016	665	934	50
20	804	794	838	823	485	016	575	904	40
30	0.1833	0.1822	0.9833	0.1853	5.396	1.017	5.487	1.3875	30
40	862	851	827	883	309	018	403	846	20
50	891	880	822	914	226	018	320	817	10
11° 00′	0.1920	0.1908	0.9816	0.1944	5.145	1.019	5.241	1.3788	79° 00′
10	949	937	811	974	066	019	164	759	50
20	978	965	805	0.2004	4.989	020	089	730	40
30	0.2007	0.1994	0.9799	0.2035	4.915	1.020	5.016	1.3701	30
40	036	0.2022	793	065	843	021	4.945	672	20
50	065	051	787	095	773	022	876	643	10
12° 00′	0.2094	0.2079	0.9781	0.2126	4.705	1.022	4.810	1.3614	78° 00′
10	123	108	775	156	638	023	745	584	50
20	153	136	769	186	574	024	682	555	40
30	0.2182	0.2164	0.9763	0.2217	4.511	1.024	4.620	1.3526	30
40	211	193	757	247	449	025	560	497	20
50	240	221	750	278	390	026	502	468	10
13° 00′	0.2269	0.2250	0.9744	0.2309	4.331	1.026	4.445	1.3439	77° 00′
10	298	278	737	339	275	027	390	410	50
20	327	306	730	370	219	028	336	381	40
30	0.2356	0.2334	0.9724	0.2401	4.165	1.028	4.284	1.3352	30
40	385	363	717	432	113	029	232	323	20
50	414	391	710	462	061	030	182	294	10
14° 00′	0.2443	0.2419	0.9703	0.2493	4.011	1.031	4.134	1.3265	76° 00′
10	473	447	696	524	3.962	031	086	235	50
20	502	476	689	555	914	032	039	206	40
30	0.2531	0.2504	0.9681	0.2586	3.867	1.033	3.994	1.3177	30
40	560	532	674	617	821	034	950	148	20
50	589	560	667	648	776	034	906	119	10
15° 00′	0.2618	0.2588	0.9659	0.2679	3.732	1.035	3.864	1.3090	75° 00′
10	647	616	652	711	689	036	822	061	50
20	676	644	644	742	647	037	782	032	40
30	0.2705	0.2672	0.9636	0.2773	3.606	1.038	3.742	1.3003	30
40	734	700	628	805	566	039	703	974	20
50	763	728	621	836	526	039	665	945	10
16° 00′	0.2793	0.2756	0.9613	0.2867	3.487	1.040	3.628	1.2915	74° 00′
10	822	784	605	899	450	041	592	886	50
20	851	812	596	931	412	042	556	857	40
30	0.2880	0.2840	0.9588	0.2962	3.376	1.043	3.521	1.2828	30
40	909	868	580	994	340	044	487	799	20
50	938	896	572	0.3026	305	045	453	770	10
17° 00′	0.2967	0.2924	0.9563	0.3057	3.271	1.046	3.420	1.2741	73° 00′
10	996	952	555	089	237	047	388	712	50
20	0.3025	979	546	121	204	048	356	683	40
30	0.3054	0.3007	0.9537	0.3153	3.172	1.049	3.326	1.2654	30
40	083	035	528	185	140	049	295	625	20
50	113	062	520	217	108	050	265	595	10
18° 00′	0.3142	0.3090	0.9511	0.3249	3.078	1.051	3.236	1.2566	72° 00′
		Cos	Sin	Cot	Tan	Csc	Sec	Radians	Degrees

Degrees	Radians	Sin	Cos	Tan	Cot	Sec	Csc		
18° 00′	0.3142	0.3090	0.9511	0.3249	3.078	1.051	3.236	1.2566	72° 00′
10	171	118	502	281	047	052	207	537	50
20	200	145	492	314	018	053	179	508	40
30	0.3229	0.3173	0.9483	0.3346	2.989	1.054	3.152	1.2479	30
40	258	201	474	378	960	056	124	450	20
50	287	228	465	411	932	057	098	421	10
19° 00′	0.3316	0.3256	0.9455	0.3443	2.904	1.058	3.072	1.2392	71° 00′
10	345	283	446	476	877	059	046	363	50
20	374	311	436	508	850	060	021	334	40
30	0.3403	0.3338	0.9426	0.3541	2.824	1.061	2.996	1.2305	30
40	432	365	417	574	798	062	971	275	20
50	462	393	407	607	773	063	947	246	10
20° 00′	0.3491	0.3420	0.9397	0.3640	2.747	1.064	2.924	1.2217	70° 00′
10	520	448	387	673	723	065	901	188	50
20	549	475	377	706	699	066	878	159	40
30	0.3578	0.3502	0.9367	0.3739	2.675	1.068	2.855	1.2130	30
40	607	529	356	772	651	069	833	101	20
50	636	557	346	805	628	070	812	072	10
21° 00′	0.3665	0.3584	0.9336	0.3839	2.605	1.071	2.790	1.2043	69° 00′
10	694	611	325	872	583	072	769	1.2014	50
20	723	638	315	906	560	074	749	985	40
30	0.3752	0.3665	0.9304	0.3939	2.539	1.075	2.729	1.1956	30
40	782	692	293	973	517	076	709	926	20
50	811	719	283	0.4006	496	077	689	897	10
22° 00′	0.3840	0.3746	0.9272	0.4040	2.475	1.079	2.669	1.1868	68° 00′
10	869	773	261	074	455	080	650	839	50
20	898	800	250	108	434	081	632	810	40
30	0.3927	0.3827	0.9239	0.4142	2.414	1.082	2.613	1.1781	30
40	956	854	228	176	394	084	595	752	20
50	985	881	216	210	375	085	577	723	10
23° 00′	0.4014	0.3907	0.9205	0.4245	2.356	1.086	2.559	1.1694	67° 00′
10	043	934	194	279	337	088	542	665	50
20	072	961	182	314	318	089	525	636	40
30	0.4102	0.3987	0.9171	0.4348	2.300	1.090	2.508	1.1606	30
40	131	0.4014	159	383	282	092	491	577	20
50	160	041	147	417	264	093	475	548	10
24° 00′	0.4189	0.4067	0.9135	0.4452	2.246	1.095	2.459	1.1519	66° 00′
10	218	094	124	487	229	096	443	490	50
20	247	120	112	522	211	097	427	461	40
30	0.4276	0.4147	0.9100	0.4557	2.194	1.099	2.411	1.1432	30
40	305	173	088	592	177	100	396	403	20
50	334	200	075	628	161	102	381	374	10
25° 00′	0.4363	0.4226	0.9063	0.4663	2.145	1.103	2.366	1.1345	65° 00′
10	392	253	051	699	128	105	352	316	50
20	422	279	038	734	112	106	337	286	40
30	0.4451	0.4305	0.9026	0.4770	2.097	1.108	2.323	1.1257	30
40	480	331	013	806	081	109	309	228	20
50	509	358	001	841	066	111	295	199	10
26° 00′	0.4538	0.4384	0.8988	0.4877	2.050	1.113	2.281	1.1170	64° 00′
10	567	410	975	913	035	114	268	141	50
20	596	436	962	950	020	116	254	112	40
30	0.4625	0.4462	0.8949	0.4986	2.006	1.117	2.241	1.1083	30
40	654	488	936	0.5022	1.991	119	228	054	20
50	683	514	923	059	977	121	215	1.1025	10
27° 00′	0.4712	0.4540	0.8910	0.5095	1.963	1.122	2.203	1.0996	63° 00′
		Cos	Sin	Cot	Tan	Csc	Sec	Radians	Degrees

Degrees	Radians	Sin	Cos	Tan	Cot	Sec	Csc		
27° 00′	0.4712	0.4540	0.8910	0.5095	1.963	1.122	2.203	1.0996	63° 00′
10	741	566	897	132	949	124	190	966	50
20	771	592	884	169	935	126	178	937	40
30	0.4800	0.4617	0.8870	0.5206	1.921	1.127	2.166	1.0908	30
40	829	643	857	243	907	129	154	879	20
50	858	669	843	280	894	131	142	850	10
28° 00′	0.4887	0.4695	0.8829	0.5317	1.881	1.133	2.130	1.0821	62° 00′
10	916	720	816	354	868	134	118	792	50
20	945	746	802	392	855	136	107	763	40
30	0.4974	0.4772	0.8788	0.5430	1.842	1.138	2.096	1.0734	30
40	0.5003	797	774	467	829	140	085	705	20
50	032	823	760	505	816	142	074	676	10
29° 00′	0.5061	0.4848	0.8746	0.5543	1.804	1.1143	2.063	1.0647	61° 00′
10	091	874	732	581	792	145	052	617	50
20	120	899	718	619	780	147	041	588	40
30	0.5149	0.4924	0.8704	0.5658	1.767	1.149	2.031	1.0559	30
40	178	950	689	696	756	151	020	530	20
50	207	975	675	735	744	153	010	501	10
30° 00′	0.5236	0.5000	0.8660	0.5774	1.732	1.155	2.000	1.0472	60° 00′
10	265	025	646	812	720	157	1.990	443	50
20	294	050	631	851	709	159	980	414	40
30	0.5323	0.5075	0.8616	0.5890	1.698	1.161	1.970	1.0385	30
40	352	100	601	930	686	163	961	356	20
50	381	125	587	969	675	165	951	327	10
31° 00′	0.5411	0.5150	0.8572	0.6009	1.664	1.167	1.942	1.0297	59° 00′
10	440	175	557	048	653	169	932	268	50
20	469	200	542	088	643	171	923	239	40
30	0.5498	0.5225	0.8526	0.6128	1.632	1.173	1.914	1.0210	30
40	527	250	511	168	621	175	905	181	20
50	556	275	496	208	611	177	896	152	10
32° 00′	0.5585	0.5299	0.8480	0.6249	1.600	1.179	1.887	1.0123	58° 00′
10	614	324	465	289	590	181	878	094	50
20	643	348	450	330	580	184	870	065	40
30	0.5672	0.5373	0.8434	0.6371	1.570	1.186	1.861	1.0036	30
40	701	398	418	412	560	188	853	1.0007	20
50	730	422	403	453	550	190	844	977	10
33° 00′	0.5760	0.5446	0.8387	0.6494	1.540	1.192	1.836	0.9948	57° 00′
10	789	471	371	536	530	195	828	919	50
20	818	495	355	577	520	197	820	890	40
30	0.5847	0.5519	0.8339	0.6619	1.511	1.199	1.812	0.9861	30
40	876	544	323	661	501	202	804	832	20
50	905	568	307	703	1.492	204	796	803	10
34° 00′	0.5934	0.5592	0.8290	0.6745	1.483	1.206	1.788	0.9774	56° 00′
10	963	616	274	787	473	209	781	745	50
20	992	640	258	830	464	211	773	716	40
30	0.6021	0.5664	0.8241	0.6873	1.455	1.213	1.766	0.9687	30
40	050	688	225	916	446	216	758	657	20
50	080	712	208	959	437	218	751	628	10
35° 00′	0.6109	0.5736	0.8192	0.7002	1.428	1.221	1.743	0.9599	55° 00′
10	138	760	175	046	419	223	736	570	50
20	167	783	158	089	411	226	729	541	40
30	0.6196	0.5807	0.8141	0.7133	1.402	1.228	1.722	0.9512	30
40	225	831	124	177	393	231	715	483	20
50	254	854	107	221	385	233	708	454	10
36° 00′	0.6283	0.5878	0.8090	0.7265	1.376	1.236	1.701	0.9425	54° 00′
		Cos	Sin	Cot	Tan	Csc	Sec	Radians	Degrees

Degrees	Radians	Sin	Cos	Tan	Cot	Sec	Csc		
36° 00′	0.6283	0.5878	0.8090	0.7265	1.376	1.236	1.701	0.9425	54° 00′
10	312	901	073	310	368	239	695	396	50
20	341	925	056	355	360	241	688	367	40
30	0.6370	0.5948	0.8039	0.7400	1.351	1.244	1.681	0.9338	30
40	400	972	021	445	343	247	675	308	20
50	429	995	004	490	335	249	668	279	10
37° 00′	0.6458	0.6018	0.7986	0.7536	1.327	1.252	1.662	0.9250	53° 00′
10	487	041	969	581	319	255	655	221	50
20	516	065	951	627	311	258	649	192	40
30	0.6545	0.6088	0.7934	0.7673	1.303	1.260	1.643	0.9163	30
40	574	111	916	720	295	263	636	134	20
50	603	134	898	766	288	266	630	105	10
38° 00′	0.6632	0.6157	0.7880	0.7813	1.280	1.269	1.624	0.9076	52° 00′
10	661	180	862	860	272	272	618	047	50
20	690	202	844	907	265	275	612	0.9018	40
30	0.6720	0.6225	0.7826	0.7954	1.257	1.278	1.606	0.8988	30
40	749	248	808	0.8002	250	281	601	959	20
50	778	271	790	050	242	284	595	930	10
39° 00′	0.6807	0.6293	0.7771	0.8098	1.235	1.287	1.589	0.8901	51° 00′
10	836	316	753	146	228	290	583	872	50
20	865	338	735	195	220	293	578	843	40
30	0.6894	0.6361	0.7716	0.8243	1.213	1.296	1.572	0.8814	30
40	923	383	698	292	206	299	567	785	20
50	952	406	679	342	199	302	561	756	10
40° 00′	0.6981	0.6428	0.7660	0.8391	1.192	1.305	1.556	0.8727	50° 00′
10	0.7010	450	642	441	185	309	550	698	50
20	039	472	623	491	178	312	545	668	40
30	0.7069	0.6494	0.7604	0.8541	1.171	1.315	1.540	0.8639	30
40	098	517	585	591	164	318	535	610	20
50	127	539	566	642	157	322	529	581	10
41° 00′	0.7156	0.6561	0.7547	0.8693	1.150	1.325	1.524	0.8552	49° 00′
10	185	583	528	744	144	328	519	523	50
20	214	604	509	796	137	332	514	494	40
30	0.7243	0.6626	0.7490	0.8847	1.130	1.335	1.509	0.8465	30
40	272	648	470	899	124	339	504	436	20
50	301	670	451	952	117	342	499	407	10
42° 00′	0.7330	0.6691	0.7431	0.9004	1.111	1.346	1.494	0.8378	48° 00′
10	359	713	412	057	104	349	490	348	50
20	389	734	392	110	098	353	485	319	40
30	0.7418	0.6756	0.7373	0.9163	1.091	1.356	1.480	0.8290	30
40	447	777	353	217	085	360	476	261	20
50	476	799	333	271	079	364	471	232	10
43° 00′	0.7505	0.6820	0.7314	0.9325	1.072	1.367	1.466	0.8203	47° 00′
10	534	841	294	380	066	371	462	174	50
20	563	862	274	435	060	375	457	145	40
30	0.7592	0.6884	0.7254	0.9490	1.054	1.379	1.453	0.8116	30
40	621	905	234	545	048	382	448	087	20
50	650	926	214	601	042	386	444	058	10
44° 00′	0.7679	0.6947	0.7193	0.9657	1.036	1.390	1.440	0.8029	46° 00′
10	709	967	173	713	030	394	435	999	50
20	738	988	153	770	024	398	431	970	40
30	0.7767	0.7009	0.7133	0.9827	1.018	1.402	1.427	0.7941	30
40	796	030	112	884	012	406	423	912	20
50	825	050	092	942	006	410	418	883	10
45° 00′	0.7854	0.7071	0.7071	1.000	1.000	1.414	1.414	0.7854	45° 00′
		Cos	Sin	Cot	Tan	Csc	Sec	Radians	Degrees

Glossary

absolute value The absolute value of a number is its distance from 0 on the number line.

addition principle For equations: If an equation $a = b$ is true, then $a + c = b + c$ is true for any number c. For inequalities: If any number is added on both sides of a true inequality we get another true inequality.

additive identity Zero is the additive identity for addition.

additive inverse If the sum of two numbers is 0, they are additive inverses of each other.

amplitude In the graph of a periodic function, the amplitude is the maximum displacement from a central position.

angle of depression The angle from the horizontal downward to a line of sight.

angle of elevation The angle from the horizontal upward to a line of sight.

antilogarithm As a function, the inverse of a logarithm function. $\text{Antilog}_b x = b^x$

arithmetic sequence A sequence is arithmetic if each term can be obtained from the preceeding one by adding a constant, or the difference between successive terms is a constant.

associative laws Addition: For any numbers a, b, and c, $a + (b + c) = (a + b) + c$. Multiplication: $(a \cdot b) \cdot c = a \cdot (b \cdot c)$.

asymptote A line is an asymptote to a curve if the curve gets very close to the line as the distance from the origin increases.

base In exponential notation n^x, n is the base. In logarithmic notation, $\log_b x$, b is the base.

binomial coefficient The binomial coefficient $\binom{n}{a}$ means $\dfrac{n!}{a!(n-a)!}$.

binomial theorem A theorem that tells how to expand a power of a binomial.

cartesian coordinates When axes are placed on a plane at right angles so that ordered pairs of numbers are matched with the points of the plane we say we have a cartesian coordinate system.

cartesian product (of sets) The cartesian product of sets A and B, denoted $A \times B$, is the set of all ordered pairs with first member from A and second member from B.

characteristic (of logarithm) The integer part of a base 10 logarithm.

coefficient In any term, the coefficient is the number that is multiplied by the variable.

combination A combination of r objects of a set is a subset containing r objects.

common logarithm A base 10 logarithm.

commutative laws Addition: For any numbers a and b, $a + b = b + a$. Multiplication: $a \cdot b = b \cdot a$.

completing the square Adding one or more terms to an expression to make it the square of a binomial.

complex fractional expression A fractional expression that has fractional expressions within it.

complex number The sum of a real and an imaginary number.

compound event An event that is considered to be made up of two or more events.

conditional sentence An if-then sentence.

conjugate The conjugate of the complex number $a + bi$ is $a - bi$.

conjunction An expression formed by connecting two or more sentences with the word *and*.

consistent system A system of equations or inequalities having a solution.

constant term A term with no variable.

constant of variation Whenever a situation gives rise to a relation $y = kx$, where x and y are variables, k is the constant of variation.

converse The converse of a sentence "if a, then b," is "if b, then a."

Cramer's rule A rule for solving systems of equations using determinants.

degree The degree of a term is its exponent (or the number of times a variable occurs as a factor). The degree of a polynomial is the greatest degree of any of its terms.

dependent system A system of n equations is dependent if it is equivalent to a system of fewer than n of them.

direct variation A relation between variables x and y in which their relationship can be expressed by an equation $y = kx$, where k is a constant.

discriminant For a quadratic equation $ax^2 + bx + c = 0$, the expression $b^2 - 4ac$ is called the discriminant.

disjunction An expression formed by connecting two or more sentences with the word *or*.

distance formula A formula giving the distance between any two points.

distributive laws Multiplication over addition: For any numbers a, b, and c, $(a + b) \cdot c = a \cdot c + b \cdot c$. Multiplication over subtraction: For any numbers a, b, and c, $(a - b) \cdot c = a \cdot c - b \cdot c$.

domain SEE *function*.

ellipse A set of all points P in a plane such that the sum of the distances from P to two fixed points F_1 and F_2 is constant.

equivalent expressions Expressions that represent the same number for all sensible replacements of the variables.

even function If $f(a) = f(-a)$ for all a in the domain of a function, then that function is even.

exponent In exponential notation n^x, x is the exponent.

factor When two or more numbers (or expressions) are multiplied, each of the numbers is a factor of the product.

factor theorem If a number a, when substituted into a polynomial, makes the expression zero, then $x - a$ is a factor of the polynomial.

focus Ellipses, hyperbolas, and parabolas have associated with them a point called a focus or points called *foci* (plural).

function A correspondence or rule that assigns to each member of one set (called the *domain*) exactly one member of some set (called the *range*).

fundamental counting principle If an event can occur in n_1 ways, another in n_2 ways, then the combined event can occur in $n_1 \cdot n_2$ ways.

fundamental theorem of algebra Any polynomial of degree n greater than 1, with complex number coefficients, can be factored into n linear factors.

geometric sequence A sequence in which successive terms have a common ratio.

hyperbola A set of all points P in a plane such that the absolute value of the difference of the distances from P to two fixed points F_1 and F_2 is constant.

identity An equation which is true for all sensible replacements of the variables.

image Under a transformation, the point corresponding to a given point.

imaginary number The square root of a negative number.

inconsistent system A system of equations or inequalities having no solution.

inequality A sentence formed by placing $>$, $<$, $\geq$, $\leq$, or $\neq$ between two expressions.

integer Any natural number, the additive inverse of a natural number, or zero.

intercept In the graph of an equation in two variables, the point where the graph crosses an axis.

interpolation A process by which function values can be determined between other values in a table.

inverse of a function The relation obtained by interchanging the first and second members of all ordered pairs in the relation.

inverse variation A relation between two variables, x and y, in which $y = \dfrac{k}{x}$, $x \neq 0$, and k is a constant.

irrational number A number that cannot be named by fractional notation $\dfrac{a}{b}$, where a and b are integers.

line of symmetry In any figure, a line that divides the figure so that if it is folded on the line the two halves will match.

linear equation An equation in which the variables occur to the first power only.

linear function A function that can be described by a linear equation.

linear programming A kind of mathematics in which maximum and minimum values of certain functions can be found.

logarithmic function The inverse of an exponential function.

mantissa The portion of a base 10 logarithm between 0 and 1.

matrix A rectangular array.

monomial A polynomial with just one term.

multiplication principle For equations: If an equation $a = b$ is true, then $a \cdot c = b \cdot c$ is true for any number c. For inequalities: If we multiply on both sides of a true inequality by a positive number, we get another true inequality. If we multiply by a negative number, the inequality sign must be reversed to get another true inequality.

multiplicative identity The number 1 is the multiplicative identity.

multiplicative inverse SEE *reciprocal*.

nonsensible replacement A replacement for a variable for which an expression does not name any number.

odd function If $f(a) = -f(-a)$ for all a in the domain of a function, then that function is odd.

parabola A set of all points in a plane equidistant from a fixed line and a fixed point.

period The smallest horizontal distance needed for a graph to complete a cycle.

permutation A permutation of a set is an ordered arrangement of that set, without repetition.

polynomial An expression
$a_n x^n + a_{n-1} x^{n-1} + \cdots a_1 x + a_0$.

principle of zero products An equation with 0 on one side and with a factorization on the other can be solved by finding those numbers that make the factors 0.

quadrant The x and y axes divide the plane into four regions, called quadrants.

quadratic equation An equation in which the term of highest degree has degree two.

quadratic formula A formula for finding the solutions of a quadratic equation.

quadratic function A function that can be described by a quadratic equation.

radian A measure of angles. There are 2π radians in a circle.

radical The symbol $\sqrt{}$ is called a radical.

radicand The expression under a radical.

range SEE *function*.

rational number Any number of ordinary arithmetic or the additive inverse of any number of ordinary arithmetic.

rationalizing a denominator Simplifying a radical expression so that there are no radicals in the denominator and only whole numbers or variables in the radicand.

real number There is a real number for every point of the number line.

reciprocal Two expressions are reciprocals if their product is 1. A reciprocal is also called a *multiplicative inverse*.

reference angle The smallest angle that the terminal side of an angle makes with the x-axis.

reflection A transformation in which points are reflected across a line.

relation Any set of ordered pairs.

root of a polynomial Any number which makes the polynomial zero.

slope of a line A number that tells how steeply the line slants.

synthetic division A method of division of a polynomial by a binomial $x - a$, in which the variables are not written.

transformation A function from a set to itself.

translation A geometric transformation in which all points are moved in the same direction, the same distance.

trinomial square An expression with three terms that is the square of a binomial.

zero (of a polynomial) A number, which when substituted into a polynomial, makes it zero.

Index

Additional Answers

CHAPTER 1 ANSWERS

Exercise Set 1–3, page 14

9. Commutative law, addition   10. Commutative law, addition   11. Associative law, addition   12. Associative law, addition   13. Associative law, addition   14. Associative law, addition   15. Commutative law, addition   16. Commutative law, addition

Exercise Set 1–4, page 19

19. Associative law, addition   20. Commutative law, multiplication   21. Commutative law, addition   22. Associative law, multiplication

Chapter 1 Review, page 44

14. Commutative law, addition   15. Associative law, addition   16. Associative law, multiplication   17. Distributive law, multiplication over addition

Chapter 1 Test, page 45

14. Commutative law, addition   15. Associative law, addition   16. Associative law, multiplication   17. Distributive law, multiplication over addition

CHAPTER 2 ANSWERS

Exercise Set 2–1, page 51

1. The equation, $91 + 4 = 7 - 9$, says that $91 + 4$ and $7 - 9$ name the same number.   2. The equation, $18 \times 4 = 144 \div 2$, says that 18×4 and $144 \div 2$ name the same number.

CHAPTER 3 ANSWERS

TRY THIS, pages 66, 69

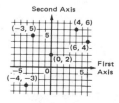

12. Line through $(0, -1)$ and $(2, 3)$ 13. Line through $(2, -1)$ and $(-1, 2)$

Exercise Set 3–1, page 70

Odd Exercises 1–15   Even Exercises 2–16

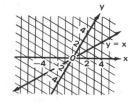

31. Line through $(3, 3)$ and $(-3, -3)$ 32. Line through $(-3, 3)$ and $(3, -3)$ 33. Line through $(1, -3)$ and $(-1, 3)$ 34. Line through $(1, 3)$ and $(-1, -3)$ 35. Line through $(0, 2)$ and $(-2, 0)$ 36. Line through $(2, 0)$ and $(0, -2)$ 37. Line through $(0, 1)$ and $(-1, -2)$ 38. Line through $(1, 1)$ and $(0, -1)$ 39. Line through $(1, -3)$ and $(0, 1)$ 40. Line through $(1, -1)$ and $(0, 2)$ 41. Line through $(3, 4)$ and $(-1, -2)$ 42. Line through $(2, 1)$ and $(-1, -1)$ 43. Line through $(5, 0)$ and $(0, 2)$ 44. Line through $(1, 1)$ and $(-2, 2)$ 45. Line through $(2, 0)$ and $(0, -3)$ 46. Line through $(3, 0)$ and $(0, -4)$ 47. Line through $(0, 2)$ and $(-4, 0)$ 48. Line through $(6, 0)$ and $(0, -2)$

51.   52.

TRY THIS, pages 73, 74, 75

9. Line through $(2, 1)$ and $(-4, -1)$ 10. Line through $(3, 0)$ and $(0, -2)$ 11. Line through $(3, 0)$ and $(0, -2)$ 12. Line through $(7, 0)$ and $(0, 4)$ 13. Line through $(2, 0)$ and $(0, 9)$ 14. Vertical line through $(4, 0)$ 15. Horizontal line through $(0, -3)$ 16. x-axis

Exercise Set 3–2, page 76

21. Line through $(4, 0)$ and $(0, 2)$ 22. Line through $(9, 0)$ and $(0, 3)$ 23. Line through $(-8, 0)$ and $(0, 2)$ 24. Line through $(-6, 0)$ and $(0, 3)$ 25. Line through $(2, 0)$ and $(0, 8)$ 26. Line through $(2, 0)$ and $(0, 6)$ 27. Line through $(1, 3)$ and $(-1, -1)$ 28. Line through $(0, 3)$ and $(-2, -1)$ 29. Line through $(1, 3)$ and $(-1, -3)$ 30. Line through $(1, 4)$ and $(-1, -4)$ 31. Line through $(6, 0)$ and $(0, 3)$

32. Line through (5, 0) and (0, 4)

43. Line through (2, 0) and (0, −2)   44. Line through (4, 0) and (0, −4)   45. Line through ($\frac{1}{3}$, 0) and (0, −1)

46. Line through ($\frac{4}{3}$, 0) and (0, −4)   47. Line through (4, 0) and (0, −5)   48. Line through (5, 0) and (0, −3)

49. Line through (−1, 0) and (0, −5)   50. Line through (−1, 0) and (0, −2)   51. Line through (7, 0) and (0, 2)

52. Line through (4, 0) and (0, 2)   53. Vertical line through (2, 0)   54. Vertical line through (4, 0)   55. Horizontal line through (0, −6)   56. Horizontal line through (0, −3)

57. Vertical line through (−5, 0)   58. Vertical line through (−3, 0)   59. Horizontal line through (0, 7)   60. Horizontal line through (0, 5)

Exercise Set 3–3, page 81

35.

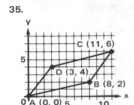

36.

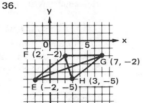

Exercise Set 3–5, page 89

21. The side which contains (3, 4) and (6, 9) has slope $\frac{5}{3}$. The side which contains (−2, 7) and (3, 4) has slope $-\frac{3}{5}$. Since $\frac{5}{3} \cdot (-\frac{3}{5}) = -1$, these two sides are perpendicular.

Chapter 3 Review, page 94

2. Line through (2, 3) and (−1, −3)

5. Line through (−2, 0) and (0, 5)   6. Vertical line through (9, 0)   7. Horizontal line through (0, −2)

Chapter 3 Test, page 95

2. Line through (1, 3) and (−2, −3)

5. Line through (−4, 0) and (0, 3)   6. Vertical line through (−3, 0)   7. Horizontal line through (0, 4)

CHAPTER 4 ANSWERS

TRY THIS, page 101

3. Line through (0, 1) and (−2, −3) and line through (0, 1) and (1, −2)   4. Line through (3, 3) and (0, 0) and line through (3, 3) and (4, 0)

Exercise Set 4–1, page 102

9. Line through (3, 1) and (0, 4) and line through (3, 1) and (0, −2)   10. Line through (4, 1) and (0, −3) and line

through (4, 1) and (0, 5)   11. Line through (3, 2) and (0, −4) and line through (3, 2) and (2, −3)   12. Line through (2, −1) and (0, 5) and line through (2, −1) and (0, −2)   13. Line through (1, −5) and (3, 3) and line through (1, −5) and (4, −4)   14. Line through (3, $\frac{3}{2}$) and (0, 3) and line through (3, $\frac{3}{2}$) and (0, −3)   15. Line through (2, 1) and (0, −1) and line through (2, 1) and (0, 5)

16. Line through (−3, −2) and (0, 1) and line through (−3, −2) and (3, 2)   17. Line through ($\frac{5}{2}$, −2) and (0, 3) and line through ($\frac{5}{2}$, −2) and (5, 3)   18. Line through (7, 2) and (3, 4) and line through (7, 2) and (2, −3)   19. Line through (3, −2) and (−3, 0) and line through (3, −2) and (0, −6)   20. Line through (4, 0) and (−4, 2) and line through (4, 0) and (0, −2)

Chapter 4 Review, page 124

1. Line through (4, −1) and (0, 3) and line through (4, −1) and (0, −5)   2. Line through (−1, 3) and (3, 1) and line through (−1, 3) and (−2, 0)

Chapter 4 Test, page 125

1. Line through (3, −1) and (0, 2) and line through (3, −1) and (0, −4)   2. Line through (2, 3) and (−2, −4) and line through (2, 3) and (3, −2)

CHAPTER 5 ANSWERS

TRY THIS, page 131

3. All points left of −2   4. All points left of, and including, −2   5. All points right of 3   6. All points left of, and including, 3

Exercise Set 5–1, page 133

1. All points left of, and including, 4   2. All points left of, and including, −1   3. All points right of 5   4. All points right of 3   5. All points left of 10   6. All points left of −4   7. All points right of, and including, −5   8. All points right of, and including, −1   9. All points left of 0   10. All points left of −8

TRY THIS, pages 134, 135

1. All points between −1 and 4, including −1   2. All points between −1 and 4, including 4   3. All points between −1 and 4, including −1 and 4

6. All points left of, and including, −2 and all points right of 2   7. All points left of −2 and all points right of, and including, 2   8. All points left of, and including −2, and all points right of, and including, 2

Exercise Set 5–2, page 138

1. All points between −2 and 4   2. All points between −2 and 4, including 4   3. All points between −2 and 4, includ-

ing −2   4. All points between −2 and 4, including −2 and 4   5. All points between 1 and 6   6. All points between 0 and 3, including 0 and 3   7. All points between −7 and −3, including −7 and −3   8. All points between −9 and −5, including −9

17. All points left of −1 and all points right of 2   18. All points left of −2 and all points right of 0   19. All points left of, and including, −3 and all points right of 1   20. All points left of, and including, −1 and all points right of 3   21. All points left of −8 and all points right of −2   22. All points left of, and including, −10 and all points right of, and including, −5   23. All points left of 1 and all points right of, and including, 5   24. All points left of, and including, 3 and all points right of, and including, 9   25. $x < -9$ or $x > -5$ 26. $x < -13$ or $x > -5$ 27. $x \leqslant 5$ or $x \geqslant 11$ 28. $x \leqslant 5$ or $x \geqslant 9$ 29. $x < 4$ or $x > 15$ 30. $x < -4$ or $x > 16$

TRY THIS, pages 144, 145, 146

2. All points above line through (3, 3) and (0, 0)   3. All points left of and including line through (2, 1) and (0, −5)   4. All points above line through (5, 0) and (0, −2)   5. All points below line through (2, 0) and (0, −3)   6. All points below and including line through (3, 0) and (0, 2)   7. All points left of and including vertical line through (−1, 0)   8. All points right of vertical line through (2, 0)   9. All points above horizontal line through (0, −2)   10. All points between horizontal line through (0, 1) and horizontal line through (0, 3), including both lines   11. All points between vertical line through (−4, 0) and vertical line through (1, 0), including line through (−4, 0)

Exercise Set 5—4, page 147

1. All points above line through (1, 2) and (−1, −2)   2. All points above line through (1, 3) and (−1, −3)   3. All points below and including line through (2, 3) and (−2, −1)   4. All points below and including line through (0, 3) and (−3, 0)   5. All points above line through (0, 2) and (−2, 0)   6. All points above line through (0, 4) and (−4, 0)   7. All points below and including line through (2, 0) and (0, −2)   8. All points below line through (3, 0) and (0, −3)   9. All points above line through (3, 2) and (0, −1)   10. All points above and including line through (2, 0) and (0, −2)   11. All points below line through (4, 0) and (0, 4)   12. All points below and including line through (5, 0) and (0, 5)   13. All points below line through (8, 0) and (0, −8)   14. All points below and including line through (3, 0) and (0, −3)   15. All points below and including line through (4, 0) and (0, 3)   16. All points below line through (3, 0) and (0, 2)   17. All points below line through (3, 0) and (0, 7)   18. All points above and including line through (4, 0) and (0, 5)   19. All points above line through (−3, 0) and (0, 3)   20. All points below and including line through (−4, 0) and (0, 2)   21. All points left of vertical line through (−4, 0)   22. All points right of and including vertical line through (1, 0)   23. All points above and including horizontal line through (0, 5)   24. All points below

horizontal line through (0, 2)   25. All points right of and including y-axis   26. All points above and including x-axis   27. All points between horizontal line through (0, −1) and horizontal line through (0, −4)   28. All points between horizontal line through (0, 3) and horizontal line through (0, −2)   29. All points between vertical line through (3, 0) and vertical line through (−3, 0), including both lines   30. All points between vertical line through (4, 0) and vertical line through (−4, 0), including both lines   31. All points above ray through (0, 0) and (2, 2) and also above ray through (0, 0) and (−2, 2)   32. All points below, and including, ray through (0, 0) and (2, 2) and also below, and including, ray through (0, 0) and (−2, 2)   33. All points above ray through (0, 3) and (2, 5) and also above ray through (0, 3) and (−2, 5)   34. Square with vertices (0, 2), (2, 0), (0, −2), (−2, 0)   35. All points outside square with vertices (0, 2), (2, 0), (0, −2), (−2, 0)   36. All points inside square with vertices (0, 2), (2, 0), (0, −2), (−2, 0)

TRY THIS, pages 149, 150

1. All points above line through (3, 3) and (0, 0) and also below line through (2, −3) and (0, 1)   2. All points above horizontal line through (0, 3) and also right of vertical line through (−3, 0)   3. All points inside, and including, polygon with vertices $(\frac{1}{2}, 3)$, (5, 3), (5, 1), (3, 1), (0, 2)

Exercise Set 5—5, page 150

1. All points above line through (3, 0) and (0, 3) and also below line through (3, 3) and (0, 0)   2. All points above line through (3, 3) and (0, 0) and also below line through (3, −2) and (0, 1)   3. All points above, and including, line through (3, 3) and (0, 0) and also below line through (4, 0) and (0, 4)   4. All points above, and including, line through (3, 3) and (0, 0) and also below line through (2, 0) and (0, 2)   5. All points above, and including, horizontal line through (0, 2) and also right of vertical line through (1, 0)   6. All points below, and including, horizontal line through (0, −2) and also right of vertical line through (2, 0)   7. All points above, and including, line through (2, −4) and (0, 2) and also left of vertical line through (3, 0)   8. All points below, and including, line through (2, −1) and (0, 3) and also right of vertical line through (−2, 0)   9. All points above, and including, line through (−3, 0) and (0, 3) and also above, and including, horizontal line through (0, −2)   10. All points above, and including, line through (2, 0) and (0, 2) and also below, and including, horizontal line through (0, 4)   11. All points above, and including, line through (2, 0) and (0, −2) and also below, and including, line through (3, −2) and (0, 1)   12. All points above, and including, line through (4, 0) and (0, −4) and also below, and including, line through (3, 0) and (0, 3)   13. All points between line through (1, 3) and (−1, −1) and line through (0, 3) and (−2, −1)   14. All points between line through (1, −1) and (0, 2) and line through (1, −3) and (0, 0)   15. All points above, and including, line through (1, 2) and (0, −1) and also below, and including, line through (0, 1) and (−2, 0)   16. All points above, and including, line

through (3, 2) and (1, −1) and also above, and including, line through (3, 2) and (0, 3)   17. All points inside and including quadrilateral with vertices (0, 0), (0, 6), (4, 4) and (6, 0)   18. All points inside, and including, quadrilateral with vertices (0, 0), (0, 4), $(\frac{40}{11}, \frac{24}{11})$ and (5, 0)   19. All points inside, and including, parallelogram with vertices $(1, \frac{9}{4})$, $(1, \frac{25}{6})$, $(3, \frac{5}{2})$ and $(3, \frac{3}{4})$ 20. All points inside, and including, parallelogram with vertices $(\frac{1}{2}, 6)$, $(\frac{3}{2}, 8)$, $(\frac{5}{2}, 8)$ and $(\frac{3}{2}, 6)$

TRY THIS, page 152

1. Max. of F is 120 when x = 3 and y = 3; min. of F is 34 when x = 1 and y = 0.   2. Max. of G is 45 when x = 6 and y = 0; min. of G is 12 when x = 0 and y = 3.

Exercise Set 5–6, page 154

5. 8 of A and 10 of B to maximize score at 102.   6. 5 of A and 15 of B to maximize score at 425.   7. $7000 at Bank X and $15,000 at Bank Y to maximize income at $1395.   8. $22,000 in corporate bonds and $18,000 in municipal bonds to maximize income at $3110.

Chapter 5 Review, page 156

1. All points right of −1   2. All points left of, and including, 4

5. All points between −3 and 2   6. All points left of −2 and right of 5

17. All points above line through (−2, 0) and (0, 2)
18. All points below, and including, line through (5, 0) and (0, −3)   19. All points above line through (3, 3) and (0, 0) and also below, and including, line through (−1, 0) and (0, −2)   20. All points above, and including, horizontal line through (0, 2) and also left of, and including, vertical line through (−5, 0)   21. All points inside, and including, quadrilateral with vertices (0, 0), (0, 5), (6, 2) and (8, 0)

Chapter 5 Test, page 157

1. All points right of −2   2. All points left of, and including, 5

5. All points between −2 and 4   6. All points left of −3 and right of 4

17. All points below line through (3, 0) and (0, 3)   18. All points below, and including, line through (6, 0) and (0, 9)   19. All points above, and including, line through (1, 2) and (0, 0) and also below line through (1, 2) and (3, 0)   20. All points below, and including, horizontal line through (0, 3) and also right of, and including, vertical line through (−5, 0)   21. All points inside, and including, quadrilateral with vertices (2, 0), (2, 4), (6, 2) and (8, 0)

CHAPTER 6 ANSWERS

Exercise Set 6–1, page 164

1. $8x^2 + (−2x) + (−5)$ 2. $9y^3 + (−3y^2) + 6$ 3. $18xy + (−8x^3) + (−y) + 50$ 4. $24y^3 + (−9y^2) + (−y) + (−21)$ 5. $4xy + (−5xy^2) + 6x^2y + (−7x^2y^2)$ 6. $8ab + (−9ab^3) + 11a^3b + (−12a^2b^2)$ 7. $2x^5 + (−7x^4) + (−6x^3) + 3x^2 + (−8x) + (−9)$ 8. $5y^5 + (−9y^4) + (−8y^3) + (−3y^2) + 9y + (−11)$ 9. $5x^3, 7x^2, −3x, −9; 5, 7, −3, −9$ 10. $8y^3, −9y^2, 12y, 11; 8, −9, 12, 11$ 11. $−3xyz, 7x^2y^2, −5xy^2z, 4xyz^2; −3, 7, −5, 4$ 12. $−9abc, 19a^2bc, −8ab^2c, 12abc^2; −9, 19, −8, 12$

Exercise Set 6–2, page 169

25. $13x − 6$ 26. $13y + 5$ 27. $−4x^2 − 3x + 13$ 28. $−13y^2 + 2y + 11$ 29. $2a − 4b + 3c$ 30. $4x − 10y + 4z$ 31. $−2x^2 + 6x$ 32. $5y^2 + 6y + 3y^3$ 33. $−4a^2 + 8ab − 5b^2$ 34. $−3y^2 − 6yz − 12z^2$ 35. $−2x^2 − 17x + 5$ 36. $−4a^2 − 11a + 4$ 37. $6y^3 − 7y^2 + 8y − 2$ 38. $6x^4 − 8x^2 + 9x − 4$ 39. $6a − 5b − 2c + 4d$ 40. $8x − 6y + 4z + 2w$ 41. $−0.01x^3 − 0.11x^2 + 0.02x + 5$ 42. $0.06y^4 + 0.032y^3 − 0.94y^2 + 0.93$ 43. $x^4 − x^2 − 1$ 44. $y^5 − 6y^4 + \frac{2}{3}y^3$

Exercise Set 6–3, page 172

39. $x^3 − 64$ 40. $y^3 + 3y^2 − 20$ 41. $y^3 + 27$ 42. $x^3 − 2x^2 + 8x + 32$ 43. $x^4 − x^3 + x^2 − 3x + 2$ 44. $y^4 + y^3 − 27y^2 − 4y + 56$ 45. $−6x^5 + 12x^4 − 7x^3 − 22x^2 + 39x − 27$ 46. $−8x^5 + 2x^4 + 2x^3 − 7x^2 + 16x − 5$ 47. $x^3 + y^3$ 48. $a^3 − b^3$ 49. $3a^4 + 12a^3 − 16a^2 − 4a + 5$ 50. $5x^4 + 40x^3 − 37x^2 − 16x + 14$ 51. $2m^5 + 10m^4 − 14m^3 − 3m^2 − 15m + 21$ 52. $3t^5 − 12t^4 + 24t^3 − 5t^2 + 20t − 40$ 53. $8x^3 + 26x^2y + 37xy^2 + 28y^3$ 54. $40p^3 + 109p^2q + 128pq^2 + 63q^3$

CHAPTER 8 ANSWERS

Ready for, page 212

1.

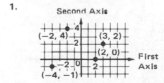

TRY THIS, page 217

6.

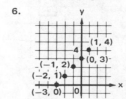

7.

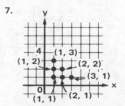

Exercise Set 8–1, page 217

1. {(−1, 0), (−1, 1), (−1, 2), (0, 1), (0, 2), (1, 2)}
2. {(2, 1), (2, 0), (2, −1), (1, 0), (1, −1), (0, −1)}
3. {(−1, −1), (−1, 0), (−1, 1), (−1, 2), (0, 0), (0, 1), (0, 2), (1, 1), (1, 2), (2, 2)} 4. {(2, 2), (2, 1), (2, 0), (2, −1), (1, 1), (1, 0), (1, −1), (0, 0), (0, −1), (−1, −1)}
5. {(−1, −1), (0, 0), (1, 1), (2, 2)} 6. {(−1, 0), (−1, 1), (−1, 2), (0, −1), (0, 1), (0, 2), (1, −1), (1, 0), (1, 2), (2, −1), (2, 0), (2, 1)} 7. {(0, a), (0, b), (0, c), (2, a), (2, b), (2, c), (4, a), (4, b), (4, c), (5, a), (5, b), (5, c)} 8. {(1, d), (1, e), (1, f), (3, d), (3, e), (3, f), (5, d), (5, e), (5, f), (9, d), (9, e), (9, f)} 9. {(x, 1), (x, 2), (y, 1), (y, 2), (z, 1), (z, 2)}
10. {(5, a), (5, z), (7, a), (7, z), (10, a), (10, z)}
11. {(−1, −1), (−1, 0), (−1, 1), (−1, 2), (0, −1), (0, 0), (0, 1), (0, 2), (1, −1), (1, 0), (1, 1), (1, 2), (2, −1), (2, 0), (2, 1), (2, 2)} 12. {(−1, −1), (−1, 1), (−1, 3), (−1, 5), (1, −1), (1, 1), (1, 3), (1, 5), (3, −1), (3, 1), (3, 3), (3, 5), (5, −1), (5, 1), (5, 3), (5, 5)}

21. 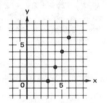 22.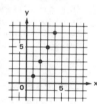

23. 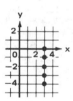 24.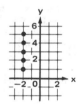

25. 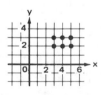 26.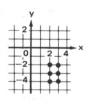

27.   28.

TRY THIS, pages 218, 219

1. Line through (1, 3) and (−2, −3) 2. All points above, and including, parabola through (−2, 3), (−1, 0), (0, −1), (1, 0) and (2, 3)

Exercise Set 8–2, page 219

1. Line through (0, 1) and (−1, −3) 2. Line through (1, 1) and (−1, −3) 3. All points above, and including parabola through (−2, 6), (−1, 3), (0, 2), (1, 3), (2, 6) 4. All points above, and including, parabola through (−2, 2), (−1, −1), (0, −2), (1, −1), (2, 2) 5. Parabola through (6, 2), (3, 1), (2, 0), (3, −1), (6, −2) 6. Parabola through (2, 2), (−1, 1), (−2, 0), (−1, −1), (2, −2) 7. Line through (3, 0) and (0, −8) 8. Line through (10, 0) and (0, −5) 9. Line through (−4, 0) and (0, 3) 10. Line through (5, 0) and (0, −4) 11. Horizontal line through (0, −2) 12. Horizontal line through (0, 6) 13. Vertical line through (3, 0) 14. Vertical line through (−7, 0) 15. Line through $(\frac{1}{2}, 2)$, (1, 1), $(2, \frac{1}{2})$ and line through $(-2, -\frac{1}{2})$, (−1, −1), $(-\frac{1}{2}, -2)$
16. Line through $(-\frac{1}{2}, 2)$, (−1, 1), $(-2, \frac{1}{2})$ and line through $(2, -\frac{1}{2})$, (1, −1), $(\frac{1}{2}, -2)$ 17. Parabola through (−1, 10.388), (0, 2.168), (1, 0.368), (2, 4.988) 18. Parabola through (−1, −2.612), (0, 1.444), (1, 3.39), (2, 3.226), (3, 0.952), (4, −3.432) 19. Ray from (−1, 0) through (2, 3); ray from (−1, 0) through (−4, 3) 20. Ray from (1, 0) through (4, 3); ray from (1, 0) through (−2, 3)
21. Parabola through (−2, 8), (−1, 1), (0, 0), (1, 1), (2, 8) 22. Curve beginning at (0, 0) through (1, 1), (4, 2), (9, 3)

TRY THIS, pages 221, 223

2. 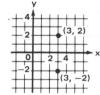 3.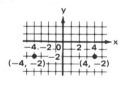

Exercise Set 8–3, page 224

7. 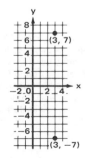 8.

9.

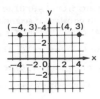

10.

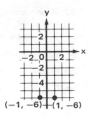

49.

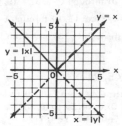

50.

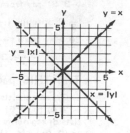

TRY THIS, page 226

2.

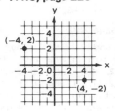

Exercise Set 8—5, page 236

23.

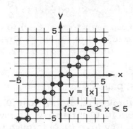

Exercise Set 8—4, page 229

7.

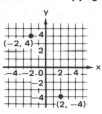

8.

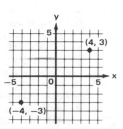

TRY THIS, pages 241, 242

1. Ray from (0, −1) through (2, 1); ray from (0, −1) through through (−2, 1)   **2.** Ray from (0, 4) through (2, 6); ray from (0, 4) through (−2, 6)   **3.** Ray from (−3, 0) through (0, 3); ray from (−3, 0) through (−6, 3)   **4.** Ray from (1, 0) through (4, 3); ray from (1, 0) through (−2, 3)

Exercise Set 8—7, page 243

1. Ray from (0, 2) through (2, 4); ray from (0, 2) through (−2, 4)   **2.** Ray from (0, 3) through (2, 5); ray from (0, 3) through (−2, 5)   **3.** Ray from (0, −2) through (2, 0); ray from (0, −2) through (−2, 0)   **4.** Ray from (0, −3) through (3, 0); ray from (0, −3) through (−3, 0)   **5.** Ray from (0, 5) through (2, 7); ray from (0, 5) through (−2, 7)   **6.** Ray from (0, 6) through (2, 8); ray from (0, 6) through (−2, 8)   **7.** Ray from (0, −4) through (4, 0); ray from (0, −4) through through (−4, 0)   **8.** Ray from (0, −5) through (5, 0); ray from (0, −5) through (−5, 0)   **9.** Ray from $(0, \frac{1}{2})$ through $(3, \frac{7}{2})$; ray from $(0, \frac{1}{2})$ through $(-3, \frac{7}{2})$ **10.** Ray from $(0, \frac{3}{4})$ through $(2, \frac{11}{4})$; ray from $(0, \frac{3}{4})$ through $(-2, \frac{11}{4})$ **11.** Ray from (3, 0) through (6, 3); ray from (3, 0) through (0, 3)   **12.** Ray from (2, 0) through (5, 3); ray from (2, 0) through (−1, 3)   **13.** Ray from (−2, 0) through (1, 3); ray from (−2, 0) through (−5, 3)   **14.** Ray from (−4, 0) through (−1, 3); ray from (−4, 0) through (−7, 3)   **15.** Ray from (4, 0) through (7, 3); ray from (4, 0) through (1, 3)   **16.** Ray from (5, 0) through (8, 3); ray from (5, 0) through (2, 3)   **17.** Ray from (−5, 0) through (−2, 3); ray from (−5, 0) through (−8, 3)   **18.** Ray from (−6, 0) through

9.

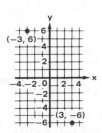

10.

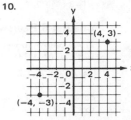

47.

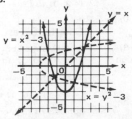

48.

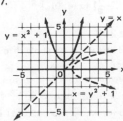

$(-3, 3)$; ray from $(-6, 0)$ through $(-9, 3)$ **19.** Ray from $(\frac{1}{2}, 0)$ through $(\frac{7}{2}, 3)$; ray from $(\frac{1}{2}, 0)$ through $(-\frac{5}{2}, 3)$ **20.** Ray from $(-\frac{3}{4}, 0)$ through $(\frac{9}{4}, 3)$; ray from $(-\frac{3}{4}, 0)$ through $(-\frac{15}{4}, 3)$

TRY THIS, pages 245, 247

1. Graph consists of segments from $(-6, 0)$ to $(-4, 6)$ to $(-2, 0)$ to $(0, 6)$ to $(2, 0)$ to $(4, 6)$ to $(6, 0)$ **2.** Graph consists of segments from $(-6, 0)$ to $(-4, 1)$ to $(-2, 0)$ to $(0, 1)$ to $(2, 0)$ to $(4, 1)$ to $(6, 0)$ **3.** Graph consists of segments from $(-6, 0)$ to $(-4, -1)$ to $(-2, 0)$ to $(-1, -1)$ to $(2, 0)$ to $(4, -1)$ to $(6, 0)$ **4.** Graph consists of segments from $(-2, 0)$ to $(-\frac{3}{2}, 2)$ to $(-\frac{1}{2}, -2)$ to $(\frac{1}{2}, 2)$ to $(\frac{3}{2}, -2)$ to $(2, 0)$
5. Graph consists of segments from $(-8, 0)$ to $(-6, 2)$ to $(-2, -2)$ to $(2, 2)$ to $(6, -2)$ to $(8, 0)$ **6.** Graph consists of segments from $(-8, 0)$ to $(-6, -2)$ to $(-2, 2)$ to $(2, -2)$ to $(6, 2)$ to $(8, 0)$

Exercise Set 8–8, page 247

1. Ray from $(0, 0)$ through $(2, 8)$; ray from $(0, 0)$ through $(-2, 8)$ **2.** Ray from $(0, 0)$ through $(2, 6)$; ray from $(0, 0)$ through $(-2, 6)$ **3.** Ray from $(0, 0)$ through $(2, 10)$; ray from $(0, 0)$ through $(-2, 10)$ **4.** Ray from $(0, 0)$ through $(2, 12)$; ray from $(0, 0)$ through $(-2, 12)$ **5.** Ray from $(0, 0)$ through $(4, 1)$; ray from $(0, 0)$ through $(-4, 1)$ **6.** Ray from $(0, 0)$ through $(3, 1)$; ray from $(0, 0)$ through $(-3, 1)$ **7.** Ray from $(0, 0)$ through $(2, -6)$; ray from $(0, 0)$ through $(-2, -6)$ **8.** Ray from $(0, 0)$ through $(2, -8)$; ray from $(0, 0)$ through $(-2, -8)$ **9.** Ray from $(0, 0)$ through $(4, -1)$; ray from $(0, 0)$ through $(-4, -1)$ **10.** Ray from $(0, 0)$ through $(6, -2)$; ray from $(0, 0)$ through $(-6, -2)$ **11.** Graph consists of segments from $(-4, 0)$ to $(0, 12)$ to $(2, -12)$ to $(3, 0)$ **12.** Graph consists of segments from $(-4, 0)$ to $(0, 8)$ to $(2, -8)$ to $(3, 0)$ **13.** Graph consists of segments from $(-4, 0)$ to $(0, -8)$ to $(2, 8)$ to $(3, 0)$ **14.** Graph consists of segments from $(-4, 0)$ to $(0, -12)$ to $(2, 12)$ to $(3, 0)$ **15.** Graph consists of segments from $(-4, 0)$ to $(0, 16)$ to $(2, -16)$ to $(3, 0)$ **16.** Graph consists of segments from $(-4, 0)$ to $(0, 20)$ to $(2, -20)$ to $(3, 0)$ **17.** Graph consists of segments from $(-4, 0)$ to $(0, 2)$ to $(2, -2)$ to $(3, 0)$ **18.** Graph consists of segments from $(-4, 0)$ to $(0, \frac{4}{3})$ to $(2, -\frac{4}{3})$ to $(3, 0)$
19. Graph consists of segments from $(-4, 0)$ to $(0, -2)$ to $(2, 2)$ to $(3, 0)$ **20.** Graph consists of segments from $(-4, 0)$ to $(0, -\frac{4}{3})$ to $(2, \frac{4}{3})$ to $(3, 0)$ **21.** Ray from $(0, 0)$ through $(4, 8)$; ray from $(0, 0)$ through $(-4, 8)$ **22.** Ray from $(0, 0)$ through $(2, 6)$; ray from $(0, 0)$ through $(-2, 6)$ **23.** Ray from $(0, 0)$ through $(4, 2)$; ray from $(0, 0)$ through $(-4, 2)$ **24.** Ray from $(0, 0)$ through $(6, 2)$; ray from $(0, 0)$ through $(-6, 2)$ **25.** Graph consists of segments from $(-\frac{4}{3}, 0)$ to $(0, 4)$ to $(\frac{2}{3}, -4)$ to $(1, 0)$ **26.** Graph consists of segments from $(-2, 0)$ to $(0, 4)$ to $(1, -4)$ to $(\frac{3}{2}, 0)$

27. Graph consists of segments from $(-8, 0)$ to $(0, 4)$ to $(4, -4)$ to $(6, 0)$ **28.** Graph consists of segments from $(-12, 0)$ to $(0, 4)$ to $(6, -4)$ to $(9, 0)$ **29.** Graph consists of segments from $(-\frac{3}{2}, 0)$ to $(-1, -4)$ to $(0, 4)$ to $(2, 0)$ **30.** Graph consists of segments from $(-1, 0)$ to $(-\frac{2}{3}, -4)$ to $(0, 4)$ to $(\frac{4}{3}, 0)$ **31.** Graph consists of segments from $(-6, 0)$ to $(-4, -4)$ to $(0, 4)$ to $(8, 0)$ **32.** Graph consists of segments from $(-9, 0)$ to $(-6, -4)$ to $(0, 4)$ to $(12, 0)$

TRY THIS, page 248

1. Line through $(0, -3)$ and $(-3, 3)$

Exercise Set 8–9, page 250

1. Line through $(3, 0)$ and $(0, -3)$ **2.** Line through $(-5, 0)$ and $(0, 5)$ **3.** Line through $(3, 3)$ and $(0, -3)$ **4.** Line through $(0, 4)$ and $(-2, -2)$ **5.** Line through $(1, -1)$ and $(0, 2)$ **6.** Line through $(1, -4)$ and $(0, 1)$ **7.** Line through $(2, 2)$ and $(-2, 0)$ **8.** Line through $(0, 3)$ and $(-6, 0)$ **9.** $f(-x) = 2(-x)^4 + 4(-x)^2 = 2x^4 + 4x^2 = f(x)$ **10.** $f(-x) = 5(-x)^2 + 3(-x)^4 = 5x^2 + 3x^4 = f(x)$ **11.** $f(-x) = |2(-x)| = |-2x| = |2x| = f(x)$ **12.** $f(-x) = |3(-x)| = |-3x| = |3x| = f(x)$ **13.** $f(-x) = 3(-x)^4 - 4(-x)^6 = 3x^4 - 4x^6 = f(x)$ **14.** $f(-x) = 5(-x)^8 - 3(-x)^2 = 5x^8 - 3x^2 = f(x)$ **15.** $g(-x) = 4(-x)^3 - (-x) = -4x^3 + x$; $-g(x) = -(4x^3 - x) = -4x^3 + x$ **16.** $f(-x) = -3(-x)^3 + 2(-x) = 3x^3 - 2x$; $-f(x) = -(-3x^3 + 2x) = 3x^3 - 2x$ **17.** $h(-x) = 2(-x) + 5(-x)^3 = -2x - 5x^3$; $-h(x) = -(2x + 5x^3) = -2x - 5x^3$ **18.** $h(-x) = 4(-x)^3 - 5(-x) = -4x^3 + 5x$; $-h(x) = -(4x^3 - 5x) = -4x^3 + 5x$ **19.** $f(-x) = 4(-x) = -4x$; $-f(x) = -(4x) = -4x$ **20.** $f(-x) = -4(-x) = 4x$; $-f(x) = -(-4x) = 4x$ **21.** $f(-x) = (-x)^5 + (-x)^3 + (-x) = -x^5 - x^3 - x$; $-f(x) = -(x^5 + x^3 + x) = -x^5 - x^3 - x$ **22.** $f(-x) = -3(-x)^5 - 2(-x)^3 - (-x) = 3x^5 + 2x^3 + x$; $-f(x) = -(-3x^5 - 2x^3 - x) = 3x^5 + 2x^3 + x$

Chapter 8 Review, page 252

2. All points above, and including, parabola through $(-2, 5)$, $(-1, 2)$, $(0, 1)$, $(1, 2)$, $(2, 5)$

18. Graph consists of segments from $(-4, 2)$ to $(-3, 1)$ to $(-2, 1)$ to $(0, -2)$ to $(2, 1)$ to $(3, 1)$ to $(4, 2)$ **19.** Graph consists of segments from $(-3, 0)$ to $(-2, -1)$ to $(-1, -1)$ to $(1, -4)$ to $(3, -1)$ to $(4, -1)$ to $(5, 0)$ **20.** Graph consists of segments from $(-4, 0)$ to $(-3, -\frac{1}{2})$ to $(-2, -\frac{1}{2})$ to $(-2, 0)$ to $(2, -\frac{1}{2})$ to $(3, -\frac{1}{2})$ to $(4, 0)$

Chapter 8 Test, page 253

2. All points above, and including, parabola through $(-2, 7)$, $(-1, 4)$, $(0, 3)$, $(1, 4)$, $(2, 7)$

18. Graph consists of segments from $(-3, 0)$ to $(-2, \frac{1}{2})$ to $(-1, \frac{1}{2})$ to $(0, 1)$ to $(1, \frac{1}{2})$ to $(2, \frac{1}{2})$ to $(3, 0)$ **19.** Graph consists of segments from $(-3, -2)$ to $(-2, -1)$ to $(-1, -1)$ to $(0, 0)$ to $(1, -1)$ to $(2, -1)$ to $(3, -2)$ **20.** Graph consists of segments from $(-2, 0)$ to $(-1, 1)$ to $(0, 1)$ to $(1, 2)$ to $(2, 1)$ to $(3, 1)$ to $(4, 0)$

CHAPTER 9 ANSWERS

Exercise Set 9–2, page 265

1. 140 2. 234 3. 504 4. 840 5. $24x^3$ 6. $24y^3$
7. $12x^2y$ 8. $36r^2s^3$ 9. $30a^3b^2$ 10. $90x^3y^3$ 11. $(a + b)$
$(a - b)$ 12. $(x - 4)(x + 4)$ 13. $6(y - 2)$ or $6(2 - y)$
14. $10(y - 1)$ or $10(1 - y)$ 15. $3(y + 3)(y - 3)$ 16. b
$(a + b)(a - b)$ 17. $5(y - 3)(y - 3)$ 18. $4(x - 4)(x - 4)$
19. $(a + 1)(a - 1)(a - 1)$ 20. $(x - 2)(x + 2)(x + 2)$
21. $(x + 2)(x - 2)$ or $(x + 2)(2 - x)$ 22. $(y + 3)(y - 3)$ or
$(y + 3)(3 - y)$ 23. $(x + 5)(x + 5)(x - 3)$ 24. $(y + 4)$
$(y + 4)(y - 7)$ 25. $(2r + 3)(r - 4)(3r - 1)$ 26. $(3x + 2)$
$(x - 2)(4x + 3)$ 27. $(2x + 1)(x - 3)(x - 3)(x - 1)$
28. $(3x - 2)(x + 2)(2x + 3)(x - 2)(x - 2)$

CHAPTER 11 ANSWERS

TRY THIS, page 351

1. $(3i)^2 + 9 = 9i^2 + 9 = -9 + 9 = 0$; $(-3i)^2 + 9 = 9i^2 + 9 = -9 + 9 = 0$ 2. $(1 + i)^2 - 2(1 + i) + 2 = 1 + 2i + i^2 - 2 - 2i + 2 = 0$ 3. $(1 - i)^2 + 2(1 - i) + 1 = 1 - 2i + i^2 + 2 - 2i + 1 = 3 - 4i$; Therefore $(1 - i)$ is not a solution of $x^2 + 2x + 1 = 0$.

TRY THIS, page 355

1.
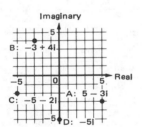

Exercise Set 11–4, page 356

1.
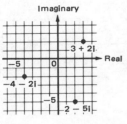

2.
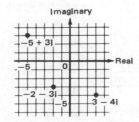

3.
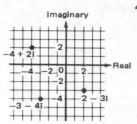

4.
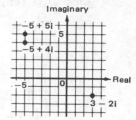

5.
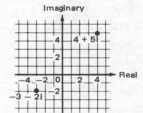

6.
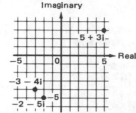

17. Let $z = a + bi$. $|z| = |a + bi| = \sqrt{a^2 + b^2}$. Then $-z = -(a + bi) = -a - bi$. $|-z| = |-a - bi| = \sqrt{(-a)^2 + (-b)^2} = \sqrt{a^2 + b^2}$ $\therefore |z| = |-z|$ 18. Let $z = a + bi$. $|z| = |a + bi| = \sqrt{a^2 + b^2}$ The conjugate of z is $a - bi$. $|a - bi| = \sqrt{a^2 + (-b)^2} = \sqrt{a^2 + b^2}$. $\therefore |a + bi| = |a - bi|$ 19. $(ac - bd) + (ad + bc)i$
20. $\dfrac{ac + bd}{c^2 + d^2} + \dfrac{bc - ad}{c^2 + d^2} i$ 21. Let $z = a + bi$ and $w = c + di$.
Then $|z \cdot w| = |(ac - bd) + (ad + bc)i| = \sqrt{(ac - bd)^2 + (ad + bc)^2} = \sqrt{a^2c^2 + b^2d^2 + a^2d^2 + b^2c^2}$.
$|z| \cdot |w| = \sqrt{a^2 + b^2} \sqrt{c^2 + d^2} = \sqrt{a^2c^2 + a^2d^2 + b^2c^2 + b^2d^2}$. $\therefore |z \cdot w| = |z| \cdot |w|$
22. $\left|\dfrac{z}{w}\right| = \dfrac{a + bi}{c + di} = \dfrac{ac + bd}{c^2 + d^2} + \dfrac{bc - ad}{c^2 + d^2} i =$

$$\sqrt{\left(\dfrac{ac + bd}{c^2 + d^2}\right)^2 + \left(\dfrac{bc - ad}{c^2 + d^2}\right)^2} = \dfrac{\sqrt{a^2b^2 + b^2d^2 + b^2c^2 + a^2d^2}}{c^2 + d^2}.$$

$$\dfrac{|z|}{|w|} = \dfrac{\sqrt{a^2 + b^2}}{\sqrt{c^2 + d^2}} = \dfrac{\sqrt{a^2 + b^2}}{\sqrt{c^2 + d^2}} \cdot \dfrac{\sqrt{c^2 + d^2}}{\sqrt{c^2 + d^2}} =$$

$$\dfrac{\sqrt{a^2c^2 + a^2d^2 + b^2c^2 + b^2d^2}}{c^2 + d^2} \qquad \therefore \left|\dfrac{z}{w}\right| = \dfrac{|z|}{|w|}$$

Chapter 11 Review, page 362

13.
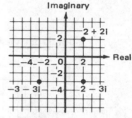

Chapter 11 Test, page 363

13.

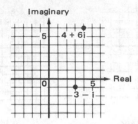

Cumulative Review, page 365

44.

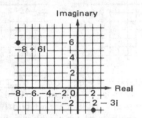

CHAPTER 12 ANSWERS

Exercise Set 12–3, page 378

60. $ax^2 + bx + c = 0$; $x^2 + \frac{b}{a}x + \frac{c}{a} = 0$; $x^2 + \frac{b}{a}x = -\frac{c}{a}$; $x^2 + \frac{b}{a}x + (\frac{b}{2a})^2 = -\frac{c}{a} + (\frac{b}{2a})^2$; $x^2 + \frac{b}{a}x + \frac{b^2}{4a^2} = -\frac{c}{a} + \frac{b^2}{4a^2}$; $(x + \frac{b}{2a})^2 = -\frac{4ac}{4a^2} + \frac{b^2}{4a^2}$; $(x + \frac{b}{2a})^2 = \frac{b^2 - 4ac}{4a^2}$; $x + \frac{b}{2a} = \frac{\pm\sqrt{b^2 - 4ac}}{2a}$; $x = -\frac{b}{2a} \pm \frac{\sqrt{b^2 - 4ac}}{2a}$; $x = \frac{-b \pm \sqrt{b^2 - 4ac}}{2a}$

62. a) The solutions of $cx^2 + bx + a = 0$ are $\frac{-b \pm \sqrt{b^2 - 4ac}}{2c}$

The reciprocals of these are $\frac{2c}{-b \pm \sqrt{b^2 - 4ac}}$. Multiply

$\frac{2c}{-b + \sqrt{b^2 - 4ac}}$ by $\frac{-b - \sqrt{b^2 - 4ac}}{-b - \sqrt{b^2 - 4ac}}$ and multiply

$\frac{2c}{-b - \sqrt{b^2 - 4ac}}$ by $\frac{-b + \sqrt{b^2 - 4ac}}{-b + \sqrt{b^2 - 4ac}}$. The results are

$\frac{-b - \sqrt{b^2 - 4ac}}{2a}$ and $\frac{-b + \sqrt{b^2 - 4ac}}{2a}$ which are the solu-

tions to $ax^2 + bx + c = 0$. b) The solutions of $ax^2 + bx + c = 0$ are $\frac{-b \pm \sqrt{b^2 - 4ac}}{2a}$. The solutions of $ax^2 - bx + c = 0$

are $\frac{b \pm \sqrt{b^2 - 4ac}}{2a}$. Since $\frac{-b + \sqrt{b^2 - 4ac}}{2a} + \frac{b - \sqrt{b^2 - 4ac}}{2a}$

$= 0$ and $\frac{-b - \sqrt{b^2 - 4ac}}{2a} + \frac{b + \sqrt{b^2 - 4ac}}{2a} = 0$, the solutions

to $ax^2 + bx + c = 0$ are additive inverses of the solutions to $ax^2 - bx + c = 0$.

Exercise Set 12–4, page 380

17. a) $k < \frac{9}{4}$ b) $k = \frac{9}{4}$ c) $k > \frac{9}{4}$ 18. a) $k < \frac{1}{4}$ b) $k = \frac{1}{4}$ c) $k > \frac{1}{4}$ 19. a) $k < 4$ b) $k = 4$ c) $k > 4$ 20. a) $k < 1$ b) $k = 1$ c) $k > 1$ 21. a) $k < \frac{5}{4}$ b) $k = \frac{5}{4}$ c) $k > \frac{5}{4}$ 22. a) $k > \frac{11}{3}$ b) $k = \frac{11}{3}$ c) $k < \frac{11}{3}$ 23. Given $a^2x + bx + c = 0$, $a \neq 0$, a, b, c $\in$ rationals, $b^2 - 4ac > 0$ and $b^2 - 4ac = d^2$ where $d \in$ rationals. $\therefore x = \frac{-b \pm \sqrt{b^2 - 4ac}}{2a} = \frac{-b \pm d}{2a}$

By the closure properties in rationals both $\frac{-b + d}{2a}$ and $\frac{-b - d}{2a}$ are rational 24. a) Two rational solutions b) Two real (not rational) solutions 25. Given $ax^2 + bx + c = 0$ with rational coefficients. Let $a = \frac{m}{n}$, $b = \frac{m'}{n'}$, and $c = \frac{m''}{n''}$ where m, n, m', n', m'', n'' are integers. $\therefore \frac{m}{n}x^2 + \frac{m'}{n'}x + \frac{m''}{n''} = 0$. Multiply this quadratic equation by (nn'n'') the LCM of the denominators. The result is n'n''mx^2 + nn''m'x + nn'm'' = 0. Since integers are closed with respect to multiplication n'n''m, nn''m', and nn'm'' represent integer coefficients. 26. a) If $b^2 - 4ac = 0$, then $x = \frac{-b \pm \sqrt{b^2 - 4ac}}{2a}$ $= \frac{-b \pm \sqrt{0}}{2a} = \frac{-b}{2a}$. Since both a and b are real, $\frac{-b}{2a}$ is real by the closure properties and $ax^2 + bx + c = 0$ has one real solution. b) If a, b, and c $\in$ reals and $b^2 - 4ac > 0$, then $\sqrt{b^2 - 4ac}$ represents a positive real number (let $\sqrt{b^2 - 4ac}$ $= d$). Thus $x = \frac{-b \pm \sqrt{b^2 - 4ac}}{2a} = \frac{-b \pm d}{2a}$. By the closure properties in the reals both $\frac{-b + d}{2a}$ and $\frac{-b - d}{2a}$ are real. Since $\frac{-b + d}{2a} \neq \frac{-b - d}{2a}$, there exists two real solutions. c) If $b^2 - 4ac < 0$, then $\sqrt{b^2 - 4ac}$ represents an imaginary number. The two solutions, $x = \frac{-b \pm \sqrt{b^2 - 4ac}}{2a}$ are both complex and can be written as $-\frac{b}{2a} + \frac{1}{2a}\sqrt{b^2 - 4ac}$ and $-\frac{b}{2a} - \frac{1}{2a}\sqrt{b^2 - 4ac}$. By definition they are complex conjugates of each other.

Exercise Set 12–5, page 383

13. $2x^2 + 10x + 1 = 0$ 14. $4x^2 + 4\pi x + 1 = 0$ 15. $x^2 - \sqrt{3}x + 8 = 0$ 16. $x^2 - 5x - \sqrt{2} = 0$

45. The solutions of $ax^2 + bx + c = 0$ are $x = \frac{-b \pm \sqrt{b^2 - 4ac}}{2a}$.

$\frac{-b + \sqrt{b^2 - 4ac}}{2a} + \frac{-b - \sqrt{b^2 - 4ac}}{2a} = \frac{-2b}{2a} = -\frac{b}{a}$.

$\frac{-b + \sqrt{b^2 - 4ac}}{2a} \cdot \frac{-b - \sqrt{b^2 - 4ac}}{2a} = \frac{(-b)^2 - (\sqrt{b^2 - 4ac})^2}{4a^2}$

$= \frac{b^2 - b^2 + 4ac}{4a^2} = \frac{4ac}{4a^2} = \frac{c}{a}$.

CHAPTER 13 ANSWERS

TRY THIS, pages 396, 397, 399

1. a) Parabola through $(-1, 3)$, $(0, 0)$, $(1, 3)$ 2. a) Parabola through $(-4, -4)$, $(0, 0)$, $(4, -4)$ 3. a) Parabola through $(-1, 3)$, $(0, 0)$, $(1, 3)$ b) Parabola through $(1, 3)$, $(2, 0)$, $(3, 3)$ 4. a) Parabola through $(-1, -3)$, $(0, 0)$, $(1, -3)$ b) Parabola through $(-3, -3)$, $(-2, 0)$, $(-1, -3)$

Exercise Set 13—1, page 399

1. a) Parabola through $(-2, 4)$, $(0, 0)$, $(2, 4)$ b) $(0, 0)$ c) $x = 0$ 2. a) Parabola through $(-2, -4)$, $(0, 0)$, $(2, 4)$ b) $(0, 0)$ c) $x = 0$ 3. a) Parabola through $(-1, -4)$, $(0, 0)$ $(1, -4)$ b) $(0, 0)$ c) $x = 0$ 4. a) Parabola through $(-1, 2)$, $(0, 0)$, $(1, 2)$ b) $(0, 0)$ c) $x = 0$ 5. a) Parabola through $(1, 4)$, $(3, 0)$, $(5, 4)$ b) $(3, 0)$ c) $x = 3$ 6. a) Parabola through $(5, 4)$ $(7, 0)$, $(9, 4)$ b) $(7, 0)$ c) $x = 7$
7. a) Parabola through $(2, 2)$, $(3, 0)$, $(4, 2)$ b) $(3, 0)$ c) $x = 3$ 8. a) Parabola through $(6, -4)$, $(7, 0)$, $(9, 4)$ b) $(7, 0)$ c) $x = 7$ 9. a) Parabola through $(-10, -2)$, $(-9, 0)$, $(-8, -2)$ b) $(-9, 0)$ c) $x = -9$ 10. a) Parabola through $(-8, 2)$, $(-7, 0)$, $(-6, 2)$ b) $(-7, 0)$ c) $x = -7$
11. a) Parabola through $(0, 3)$, $(1, 0)$, $(2, 3)$ b) $(1, 0)$ c) $x = 1$ 12. a) Parabola through $(1, -4)$, $(2, 0)$, $(3, -4)$ b) $(2, 0)$ c) $x = 2$ 13. a) Parabola through $(-\frac{3}{2}, -2)$, $(-\frac{1}{2}, 0)$, $(\frac{1}{2}, -2)$ b) $(-\frac{1}{2}, 0)$ c) $x = -\frac{1}{2}$ 14. a) Parabola through $(0, -\frac{3}{4})$, $(\frac{1}{2}, 0)$, $(1, -\frac{3}{4})$ b) $(\frac{1}{2}, 0)$ c) $x = 0$

15. All points below, and including, parabola through $(-2, 4)$, $(0, 0)$, $(2, 4)$ 16. All points above parabola through $(-2, 4)$, $(0, 0)$, $(2, 4)$ 17. All points above parabola through $(-1, 2)$, $(0, 0)$, $(1, 2)$ 18. All points below, and including, parabola through $(-1, 2)$, $(0, 0)$, $(1, 2)$ 19. All points below parabola through $(-2, -4)$, $(0, 0)$, $(2, -4)$ 20. All points above, and including, parabola through $(-2, -4)$, $(0, 0)$, $(2, -4)$

TRY THIS, page 401

1. a) Parabola through $(1, 7)$, $(2, 4)$, $(3, 7)$ 2. a) Parabola through $(-3, -4)$, $(-2, -1)$, $(-1, -4)$

Exercise Set 13—2, page 402

1. a) Parabola through $(1, 5)$, $(3, 1)$, $(5, 5)$ b) $(3, 1)$ c) $x = 3$ d) min. $= 1$ 2. a) Parabola through $(-4, 1)$, $(-2, -3)$, $(0, 1)$ b) $(-2, -3)$ c) $x = -2$ d) min. $= -3$ 3. a) Parabola through $(-3, 2)$, $(-1, -2)$, $(1, 2)$ b) $(-1, -2)$ c) $x = -1$ d) min. $= -2$ 4. a) Parabola through $(-1, 6)$, $(1, 2)$, $(3, 6)$ b) $(1, 2)$ c) $x = 1$ d) min. $= 2$ 5. a) Parabola through $(0, -1)$, $(1, -3)$, $(2, -1)$ b) $(1, -3)$ c) $x = 1$ d) min. $= -3$ 6. a) Parabola through $(-2, 6)$, $(-1, 4)$, $(0, 6)$ b) $(-1, 4)$ c) $x = -1$ d) min. $= 4$ 7. a) Parabola through $(-5, -2)$, $(-4, 1)$, $(-3, -2)$ b) $(-4, 1)$ c) $x = -4$ d) max. $= 1$ 8. a) Parabola through $(4, -5)$, $(5, -3)$, $(6, -5)$ b) $(5, -3)$ c) $x = 5$ d) max. $= -3$ 9. a) $(9, 5)$ b) $x = 9$ c) Min. $= 5$ 10. a) $(-5, -8)$ b) $x = -5$ c) Min. $= -8$

11. a) $(-\frac{1}{4}, -13)$ b) $x = -\frac{1}{4}$ c) Min. $= -13$ 12. a) $(\frac{1}{4}, 19)$ b) $x = \frac{1}{4}$ c) Min. $= 19$ 13. a) $(10, -20)$ b) $x = 10$ c) Max. $= -20$ 14. a) $(-12, 23)$ b) $x = -12$ c) Max. $= 23$ 15. a) $(-4.58, 65\pi)$ b) $x = -4.58$ c) Min. $= 65\pi$ 16. a) $(38.2, -\sqrt{34})$ b) $x = 38.2$ c) Min. $= -\sqrt{34}$

Exercise Set 13—3, page 405

1. a) $f(x) = (x - 1)^2 - 4$ b) $(1, -4)$, $x = 1$, min. $= -4$ 2. a) $f(x) = (x + 1)^2 - 6$ b) $(-1, -6)$, $x = -1$, min. $= -6$ 3. a) $f(x) = -(x - 2)^2 + 10$ b) $(2, 10)$, $x = 2$, max. $= 10$ 4. a) $f(x) = -(x + 2)^2 + 7$ b) $(-2, 7)$, $x = -2$, max. $= 7$
5. a) $f(x) = (x + \frac{3}{2})^2 - \frac{49}{4}$ b) $(-\frac{3}{2}, -\frac{49}{4})$, $x = -\frac{3}{2}$, min. $= -\frac{49}{4}$ 6. a) $f(x) = (x + \frac{5}{2})^2 - \frac{9}{4}$ b) $(-\frac{5}{2}, -\frac{9}{4})$, $x = -\frac{5}{2}$, min. $= -\frac{9}{4}$ 7. a) $f(x) = (x - \frac{9}{2})^2 - \frac{81}{4}$ b) $(\frac{9}{2}, -\frac{81}{4})$, $x = \frac{9}{2}$, min. $= -\frac{81}{4}$ 8. a) $f(x) = (x + \frac{1}{2})^2 - \frac{1}{4}$ b) $(-\frac{1}{2}, -\frac{1}{4})$, $x = -\frac{1}{2}$, min. $= -\frac{1}{4}$ 9. a) $f(x) = 3(x - 4)^2 + 2$ b) $(4, 2)$, $x = 4$, min. $= 2$ 10. a) $f(x) = 4(x + 1)^2 - 7$ b) $(-1, -7)$, $x = -1$, min. $= -7$ 11. a) $f(x) = \frac{3}{4}(x + 6)^2 - 27$ b) $(-6, -27)$, $x = -6$, min. $= -27$ 12. a) $f(x) = \frac{3}{2}(x - 1)^2 - \frac{3}{2}$ b) $(1, -\frac{3}{2})$, $x = 1$, min. $= -\frac{3}{2}$ 13. a) $f(x) = -2(x - \frac{1}{2})^2 + \frac{3}{2}$ b) $(\frac{1}{2}, \frac{3}{2})$, $x = \frac{1}{2}$, max. $= \frac{3}{2}$ 14. a) $f(x) = -2(x + \frac{1}{2})^2 + \frac{7}{2}$ b) $(-\frac{1}{2}, \frac{7}{2})$, $x = -\frac{1}{2}$, max. $= \frac{7}{2}$

Exercise Set 13—4, page 408

13. All points below parabola through $(0, -1)$, $(2, -5)$, $(4, -1)$ 14. All points above, and including, parabola through $(-4, 0)$, $(-\frac{3}{2}, -\frac{25}{4})$, $(1, 0)$ 15. All points above parabola through $(-2, 2)$, $(-1, -1)$, $(0, 2)$ 16. All points above parabola through $(-2, -2)$, $(-1, -4)$, $(0, -2)$

Chapter 13 Review, page 420

1. Parabola through $(-2, -8)$, $(0, 0)$, $(2, -8)$ 2. Parabola through $(-3, -8)$, $(0, 0)$, $(3, 8)$ 3. Parabola through $(-3, -5)$, $(-1, 3)$, $(1, -5)$

Chapter 13 Test, page 421

1. Parabola through $(-2, 8)$, $(0, 0)$, $(2, 8)$ 2. Parabola through $(3, 8)$, $(5, 0)$, $(7, 8)$ 3. Parabola through $(3, 4)$, $(5, -4)$, $(7, 4)$

CHAPTER 14 ANSWERS

Exercise Set 14—1, page 427

23. Let (a, c) and (b, c) be two points on a horizontal line. Then $d = \sqrt{(a - b)^2 + (c - c)^2} = \sqrt{(a - b)^2} = |a - b|$. Let (c, a) and (c, b) be two points on a vertical line. Then $d = \sqrt{(c - c)^2 + (a - b)^2} = \sqrt{(a - b)^2} = |a - b|$.   24. Let P_1

(x_1, y_1) and $P_2(x_2, y_2)$ be the endpoints of a segment and M be the point $(\frac{x_1 + x_2}{2}, \frac{y_1 + y_2}{2})$. If the $d(P_1 M) = d(MP_2)$ $= \frac{1}{2}d(P_1 P_2)$, then M is the midpoint of $P_1 P_2$. $d(P_1 M) =$

$$\sqrt{(\frac{x_1 + x_2}{2} - x_1)^2 + (\frac{y_1 + y_2}{2} - y_1)^2} =$$

$\frac{1}{2}\sqrt{(x_2 - x_1)^2 + (y_2 - y_1)^2}$. $d(MP_2) =$

$$\sqrt{(x_2 - \frac{x_1 + x_2}{2})^2 + (y_2 - \frac{y_1 + y_2}{2})^2} =$$

$\frac{1}{2}\sqrt{(x_2 - x_1)^2 + (y_2 - y_1)^2}$. $d(P_1 P_2) =$

$\sqrt{(x_2 - x_1)^2 + (y_2 - y_1)^2}$. $\therefore$ M is the midpoint of $P_1 P_2$.

TRY THIS, page 430

6. Circle with center $(-1, 3)$, radius 2

Exercise Set 14–2, page 431

5. Circle with center $(-1, -3)$, radius 2   6. Circle with center $(2, -3)$, radius 1

23. The equation of the circle is $b^2 + c^2 = a^2$. The slope of AB is $\frac{c}{b + a}$, and the slope of BC is $\frac{c}{b - a}$. $\frac{c}{b + a} \cdot \frac{c}{b - a}$ $= \frac{c^2}{b^2 - a^2} = \frac{c^2}{-(a^2 - b^2)} = \frac{c^2}{-(c^2)} = -1$. Since the product of the slopes is -1, lines AB and BC are perpendicular. $\therefore \angle ABC$ is a right angle.

TRY THIS, pages 433, 434, 435

1. Vertices: $(-3, 0)$, $(3, 0)$, $(0, 1)$, $(0, -1)$; foci: $(-2\sqrt{2}, 0)$, $(2\sqrt{2}, 0)$ 2. Vertices: $(-3, 0)$, $(3, 0)$, $(0, 5)$, $(0, -5)$; foci: $(0, 4)$, $(0, -4)$ 3. Vertices: $(-\sqrt{2}, 0)$, $(\sqrt{2}, 0)$, $(0, 2)$, $(0, -2)$; foci: $(0, \sqrt{2})$, $(0, -\sqrt{2})$ 4. Center: $(-3, 2)$; vertices: $(-\frac{16}{5}, 2)$, $(-\frac{14}{5}, 2)$, $(-3, \frac{7}{3})$, $(-3, \frac{5}{3})$; foci: $(-3, \frac{34}{15})$, $(-3, \frac{26}{15})$ 5. Center: $(2, -3)$; vertices: $(\frac{5}{3}, -3)$, $(\frac{7}{3}, -3)$, $(2, -\frac{14}{5})$, $(2, -\frac{16}{5})$; foci: $(\frac{34}{15}, -3)$, $(\frac{26}{15}, -3)$

Exercise Set 14–3, page 435

1. Center: $(0, 0)$; vertices: $(-2, 0)$, $(2, 0)$, $(0, 1)$, $(0, -1)$; foci: $(-\sqrt{3}, 0)$, $(\sqrt{3}, 0)$ 2. Center: $(0, 0)$; vertices: $(-1, 0)$, $(1, 0)$, $(0, 2)$, $(0, -2)$; foci: $(0, \sqrt{3})$, $(0, -\sqrt{3})$ 3. Center: $(1, 2)$; vertices: $(-1, 2)$, $(3, 2)$, $(1, 3)$, $(1, 1)$; foci: $(1 - \sqrt{3}, 2)$, $(1 + \sqrt{3}, 2)$ 4. Center: $(1, 2)$; vertices: $(0, 2)$, $(2, 2)$, $(1, 4)$, $(1, 0)$; foci: $(1, 2 + \sqrt{3})$, $(1, 2 - \sqrt{3})$ 5. Center: $(-3, 2)$; vertices: $(-8, 2)$, $(2, 2)$, $(-3, 6)$, $(-3, -2)$; foci: $(-6, 2)$, $(0, 2)$ 6. Center: $(2, -3)$; vertices: $(-3, -3)$, $(7, -3)$, $(2, 1)$, $(2, -7)$; foci: $(-1, -3)$, $(5, -3)$ 7. Center: $(0, 0)$; vertices: $(-3, 0)$, $(3, 0)$, $(0, 4)$, $(0, -4)$; foci: $(0, \sqrt{7})$, $(0, -\sqrt{7})$ 8. Center: $(0, 0)$; vertices: $(-4, 0)$, $(4, 0)$, $(0, 3)$, $(0, -3)$; foci: $(-\sqrt{7}, 0)$, $(\sqrt{7}, 0)$ 9. Center: $(-2, 1)$; vertices: $(-10, 1)$, $(6, 1)$, $(-2, 1 + 4\sqrt{3})$, $(-2, 1 - 4\sqrt{3})$; foci: $(-6, 1)$, $(2, 1)$ 10. Center: $(5, 5)$; vertices: $(5 - 4\sqrt{3}, 5)$, $(5 + 4\sqrt{3}, 5)$, $(5, 13)$, $(5, -3)$; foci: $(5, 9)$, $(5, 1)$ 11. Center: $(0, 0)$; vertices: $(-\sqrt{3}, 0)$, $(\sqrt{3}, 0)$, $(0, \sqrt{2})$, $(0, -\sqrt{2})$;

foci: $(-1, 0)$, $(1, 0)$ 12. Center: $(0, 0)$; vertices: $(-\sqrt{7}, 0)$, $(\sqrt{7}, 0)$, $(0, \sqrt{5})$, $(0, -\sqrt{5})$; foci: $(-\sqrt{2}, 0)$, $(\sqrt{2}, 0)$ 13. Center: $(0, 0)$; vertices: $(-\frac{1}{2}, 0)$, $(\frac{1}{2}, 0)$, $(0, \frac{1}{3})$, $(0, -\frac{1}{3})$; foci: $(\frac{\sqrt{5}}{6}, 0)$, $(-\frac{\sqrt{5}}{6}, 0)$ 14. Center: $(0, 0)$; vertices: $(-\frac{1}{5}, 0)$, $(\frac{1}{5}, 0)$, $(0, \frac{1}{4})$, $(0, -\frac{1}{4})$; foci: $(0, \frac{3}{20})$, $(0, -\frac{3}{20})$ 15. Center: $(2, -1)$; vertices: $(-1, -1)$, $(5, -1)$, $(2, 1)$, $(2, -3)$; foci: $(2 - \sqrt{5}, -1)$, $(2 + \sqrt{5}, -1)$ 16. Center: $(5, -2)$; vertices: $(3, -2)$, $(7, -2)$, $(5, -2 + \sqrt{2})$, $(5, -2 - \sqrt{2})$; foci: $(5 - \sqrt{2}, -2)$, $(5 + \sqrt{2}, -2)$ 17. Center: $(1, 1)$; vertices: $(0, 1)$, $(2, 1)$, $(1, 3)$, $(1, -1)$; foci: $(1, 1 + \sqrt{3})$, $(1, 1 - \sqrt{3})$ 18. Center: $(-3, 1)$; vertices: $(-5, 1)$, $(-1, 1)$, $(-3, 4)$, $(-3, -2)$; foci: $(-3, 1 + \sqrt{5})$, $(-3, 1 - \sqrt{5})$

TRY THIS, pages 437, 438, 439, 440

1. Vertices: $(-3, 0)$, $(3, 0)$; foci: $(-\sqrt{13}, 0)$, $(\sqrt{13}, 0)$; asymptotes: $y = \frac{2}{3}x$, $y = -\frac{2}{3}x$ 2. Vertices: $(-4, 0)$, $(4, 0)$; foci: $(-4\sqrt{2}, 0)$, $(4\sqrt{2}, 0)$; asymptotes: $y = x$, $y = -x$ 3. Vertices: $(0, 5)$, $(0, -5)$; foci: $(0, \sqrt{34})$, $(0, -\sqrt{34})$; asymptotes: $y = \frac{5}{3}x$, $y = -\frac{5}{3}x$ 4. Vertices: $(0, 5)$, $(0, -5)$; foci: $(0, 5\sqrt{2})$, $(0, -5\sqrt{2})$; asymptotes: $y = x$, $y = -x$ 5. Center: $(1, -2)$; vertices: $(-4, -2)$, $(6, -2)$; foci: $(1 - \sqrt{29}, -2)$, $(1 + \sqrt{29}, -2)$; asymptotes: $y + 2 = \frac{2}{5}(x - 1)$, $y + 2 = -\frac{2}{5}(x - 1)$ 6. Center: $(-1, 2)$; vertices: $(-1, 5)$, $(-1, -1)$; foci: $(-1, 7)$, $(-1, -3)$; asymptotes: $y - 2 = \frac{3}{4}(x + 1)$, $y - 2 = -\frac{3}{4}(x + 1)$ 7. Hyperbola with x-axis and y-axis as asymptotes; one branch through $(1, 3)$, $(\sqrt{3}, \sqrt{3})$, $(3, 1)$; one branch through $(-3, -1)$ $(-\sqrt{3}, -\sqrt{3})$, $(-1, -3)$ 8. Hyperbola with x-axis and y-axis as asymptotes; one branch through $(-2, \frac{1}{2})$, $(-1, 1)$, $(-\frac{1}{2}, 2)$; one branch through $(\frac{1}{2}, -2)$, $(1, -1)$, $(2, -\frac{1}{2})$

Exercise Set 14–4, page 440

1. Center: $(0, 0)$; vertices: $(3, 0)$, $(-3, 0)$; foci: $(\sqrt{10}, 0)$, $(-\sqrt{10}, 0)$; asymptotes: $y = \frac{1}{3}x$, $y = -\frac{1}{3}x$ 2. Center: $(0, 0)$; vertices: $(1, 0)$, $(-1, 0)$; foci: $(\sqrt{10}, 0)$, $(-\sqrt{10}, 0)$; asymptotes: $y = 3x$, $y = -3x$ 3. Center: $(2, -5)$; vertices: $(5, -5)$, $(-1, -5)$; foci: $(2, +\sqrt{10}, -5)$, $(2 - \sqrt{10}, -5)$; asymptotes: $y + 5 = \frac{1}{3}(x - 2)$, $y + 5 = -\frac{1}{3}(x - 2)$ 4. Center: $(2, -5)$; vertices: $(3, -5)$, $(1, -5)$; foci: $(2 + \sqrt{10}, -5)$, $(2 - \sqrt{10}, -5)$; asymptotes: $y + 5 = 3(x - 2)$, $y + 5 = -3(x - 2)$ 5. Center: $(-1, -3)$; vertices: $(-1, -1)$, $(-1, -5)$; foci: $(-1, -3 + 2\sqrt{5})$, $(-1, -3 - 2\sqrt{5})$; asymptotes: $y + 3 = \frac{1}{2}(x + 1)$, $y + 3 = -\frac{1}{2}(x + 1)$ 6. Center: $(-1, -3)$; vertices: $(-1, 2)$, $(-1, -8)$; foci: $(-1, -3 + \sqrt{41})$, $(-1, -3 - \sqrt{41})$; asymptotes: $y + 3 = \frac{5}{4}(x + 1)$, $y + 3 = -\frac{5}{4}(x + 1)$ 7. Center: $(0, 0)$; vertices: $(2, 0)$, $(-2, 0)$; foci: $(\sqrt{5}, 0)$, $(-\sqrt{5}, 0)$;

asymptotes: $y = \frac{1}{2}x$, $y = -\frac{1}{2}x$ 8. Center: (0, 0); vertices: (1, 0), (−1, 0); foci: ($\sqrt{5}$, 0), (−$\sqrt{5}$, 0); asymptotes: $y = 2x$, $y = -2x$ 9. Center: (0, 0); vertices: ($\sqrt{2}$, 0), (−$\sqrt{2}$, 0); foci: (2, 0), (−2, 0); asymptotes: $y = x$, $y = -x$ 10. Center: (0, 0); vertices: ($\sqrt{3}$, 0), (−$\sqrt{3}$, 0); foci: ($\sqrt{6}$, 0), (−$\sqrt{6}$, 0); asymptotes: $y = x$, $y = -x$ 11. Center: (1, −2); vertices: (2, −2), (0, −2); foci: $(1 + \sqrt{2}, -2)$, $(1 - \sqrt{2}, -2)$; asymptotes: $y + 2 = x - 1$, $y + 2 = -(x - 1)$ 12. Center: (−1, −2); vertices: (0, −2), (−2, −2); foci: $(-1 + \sqrt{5}, -2)$, $(-1 - \sqrt{5}, -2)$; asymptotes: $y + 2 = 2(x + 1)$, $y + 2 = -2(x + 1)$ 13. Center: $(\frac{1}{3}, 3)$; vertices: $(\frac{4}{3}, 3)$, $(-\frac{2}{3}, 3)$; foci: $(\frac{1}{3} + \sqrt{37}, 3)$, $(\frac{1}{3} - \sqrt{37}, 3)$; asymptotes: $y - 3 = 6(x - \frac{1}{3})$, $y - 3 = -6(x - \frac{1}{3})$ 14. Center: (−3, 1); vertices: (−1, 1), (−5, 1); foci: $(-3 + \sqrt{13}, 1)$, $(-3 - \sqrt{13}, 1)$; asymptotes: $y - 1 = \frac{3}{2}(x + 3)$, $y - 1 = -\frac{3}{2}(x + 3)$ 15. Hyperbola with x-axis and y-axis as asymptotes; one branch through $(\frac{1}{2}, 2)$, (1, 1), $(2, \frac{1}{2})$; one branch through $(-2, -\frac{1}{2})$, (−1, −1), $(-\frac{1}{2}, -2)$ 16. Hyperbola with x-axis and y-axis as asymptotes; one branch through (−1, 4), (−2, 2), (−4, 1); one branch through (4, −1), (2, −2), (1, −4)   17. Hyperbola with x-axis and y-axis as asymptotes; one branch through (−4, 2), (−$\sqrt{8}$, $\sqrt{8}$), (−2, 4); one branch through (4, −2), ($\sqrt{8}$, −$\sqrt{8}$), (2, −4)   18. Hyperbola with x-axis and y-axis as asymptotes; one branch through $(\frac{1}{2}, 4)$, (1, 2), (2, 1), $(4, \frac{1}{2})$; one branch through $(-4, -\frac{1}{2})$, (−2, −1), (−1, −2), $(-\frac{1}{2}, -4)$

TRY THIS, pages 441, 442, 443

1. Parabola through (−1, 2), (0, 0), (1, 2); vertex: (0, 0); focus: $(0, \frac{1}{8})$; directrix: $y = -\frac{1}{8}$ 2. Parabola through (4, 2), (0, 0), (−4, 2); vertex: (0, 0); focus: (0, 2); directrix: $y = -2$ 3. Parabola through (−2, −4), (0, 0), (2, −4); vertex: (0, 0); focus: $(0, -\frac{1}{4})$; directrix: $y = -\frac{1}{4}$ 4. Parabola through $(-\frac{3}{2}, 3)$, (0, 0), $(-\frac{3}{2}, -3)$; vertex: (0, 0); focus: $(-\frac{3}{2}, 0)$; directrix: $x = \frac{3}{2}$ 5. Parabola through (−3, 0), $(-1, -\frac{1}{2})$, (1, 0); vertex: $(-1, -\frac{1}{2})$; focus: $(-1, \frac{3}{2})$; directrix: $y = -\frac{5}{2}$ 6. Parabola through (−2, 3), (2, −1), (−2, −5); vertex: (2, −1); focus: (1, −1); directrix: $x = 3$

Exercise Set 14–5, page 444

1. Parabola through (−4, 2), (0, 0), (4, 2); vertex: (0, 0); focus: (0, 2); directrix: $y = -2$ 2. Parabola through (−4, 1), (0, 0), (4, 1); vertex: (0, 0); focus: (0, 4); directrix: $y = -4$ 3. Parabola through $(-\frac{3}{2}, 3)$, (0, 0), $(-\frac{3}{2}, -3)$;

vertex: (0, 0); focus: $(-\frac{3}{2}, 0)$; directrix: $x = \frac{3}{2}$ 4. Parabola through (−2, 2), (0, 0), (−2, −2); vertex: (0, 0); focus: $(-\frac{1}{2}, 0)$; directrix: $x = \frac{1}{2}$ 5. Parabola through (−4, 4), (0, 0), (4, 4); vertex: (0, 0); focus: (0, 1); directrix: $y = -1$ 6. Parabola through (−4, 4), (0, 0), (−4, −4); vertex: (0, 0); focus: (−1, 0); directrix: $x = 1$ 7. Parabola through (−1, 4), (0, 0), (1, 4); vertex: (0, 0); focus: $(0, \frac{1}{16})$; directrix: $y = -\frac{1}{16}$ 8. Parabola through (−2, 2), (0, 0), (2, 2); vertex: (0, 0); focus: $(0, \frac{1}{2})$; directrix: $y = -\frac{1}{2}$ 9. Parabola through $(-5, -\frac{1}{2})$, (−2, 1), $(1, -\frac{1}{2})$; vertex: (−2, 1); focus: $(-2, -\frac{1}{2})$; directrix: $y = \frac{5}{2}$ 10. Parabola through (−7, 13), (−2, 3), (−7, −7); vertex: (−2, 3); focus: (−7, 3); directrix: $x = 3$ 11. Parabola through (−3, −5), (0, 0), (1, −5); vertex: (−1, −3); focus: $(-1, -\frac{7}{2})$; directrix: $y = -\frac{5}{2}$ 12. Parabola through (8, −2), (7, −3), (8, −4); vertex: (7, −3); focus: $(\frac{29}{4}, -3)$; directrix: $x = \frac{27}{4}$ 13. Parabola through (−2, 2), (0, −2), (2, 2); vertex: (0, −2); focus: $(0, -\frac{7}{4})$; directrix: $y = -\frac{5}{2}$ 14. Parabola through (0, 0), (2, −2), (4, 2); vertex: $(2, -2)$; focus: $(2, -\frac{3}{2})$; directrix: $y = -\frac{5}{2}$ 15. Parabola through (−4, 3), (−2, −1), (0, 3); vertex: (−2, −1); focus: $(-2, -\frac{3}{4})$; directrix: $y = -\frac{5}{4}$ 16. Parabola through (−5, 5), (−3, 1), (−1, 5); vertex: (−3, 1); focus: $(-3, \frac{5}{4})$; directrix: $y = \frac{3}{4}$ 17. Parabola through (8, 2), $(\frac{23}{4}, \frac{1}{2})$, (8, −1); vertex: $(\frac{23}{4}, \frac{1}{2})$; focus: $(6, \frac{1}{2})$; directrix: $x = \frac{11}{2}$ 18. Parabola through (−2, 1), $(-\frac{17}{4}, -\frac{1}{2})$, (−2, −2); vertex: $(-\frac{17}{4}, -\frac{1}{2})$; focus: $(-4, -\frac{1}{2})$; directrix: $x = -\frac{9}{2}$

Exercise Set 14–6, page 447

19. $A = L \cdot W$, $P = 2L + 2W$; $P = 2(\frac{A}{W}) + 2W$, $PW = 2A + 2W^2$, $O = 2W^2 - PW + 2A$, $W = \frac{P \pm \sqrt{P^2 - 16A}}{4} = \frac{1}{4}(P - \sqrt{P^2 - 16A})$; $P = 2L + 2(\frac{A}{L})$, $PL = 2L^2 + 2A$, $O = 2L^2 - PL + 2A$, $L = \frac{P \pm \sqrt{P^2 - 16A}}{4} = \frac{1}{4}(P + \sqrt{P^2 - 16A})$

Chapter 14 Review, page 452

5. Center: (2, −1); vertices: (−3, −1), (7, 1), (2, 3), (2, −5); foci: (−1, −1), (5, −1)   6. Center: $(-2, \frac{1}{4})$; vertices: $(0, \frac{1}{4})$, $(-4, \frac{1}{4})$; foci: $(-2 + \sqrt{6}, \frac{1}{4})$, $(-2 - \sqrt{6}, \frac{1}{4})$; asymptotes: $y - \frac{1}{4} = \frac{\sqrt{2}}{2}(x + 2)$, $y - \frac{1}{4} = -\frac{\sqrt{2}}{2}(x + 2)$ 7. Parabola through

$(-3, 6)$, $(0, 0)$, $(-3, -6)$; vertex: $(0, 0)$; focus: $(-3, 0)$; directrix: $x = 3$

Chapter 14 Test, page 453

5. Center: $(-2, 1)$; vertices: $(-6, 1)$, $(2, 1)$, $(-2, 4)$, $(-2, -2)$; foci: $(-2 - \sqrt{7}, 1)$, $(-2 + \sqrt{7}, 1)$ 6. Center: $(0, 0)$; vertices: $(\sqrt{6}, 0)$, $(-\sqrt{6}, 0)$; foci: $(\sqrt{22}, 0)$, $(-\sqrt{22}, 0)$; asymptotes: $y = \frac{\sqrt{6}}{3}x$, $y = -\frac{\sqrt{6}}{3}x$ 7. Parabola through $(-4, \frac{1}{2})$, $(-1, 2)$, $(4, \frac{1}{2})$; vertex: $(-1, 2)$; focus: $(-1, \frac{1}{2})$; directrix: $y = \frac{7}{2}$

CHAPTER 15 ANSWERS

Exercise Set 15–1, page 458

5. a) Yes b) No c) No   6. a) No b) No c) No
7. a) Yes b) Yes c) No   8. a) No b) Yes c) No

Exercise Set 15–3, page 465

1. Q: $x^2 - 9x + 5$, R: -7 2. Q: $x^2 - 5x + 3$, R: 9 3. Q: $2x^3 + 13x^2 + 39x + 118$, R: 342 4. Q: $2x^3 - 8x^2 + 29x - 115$, R: 453 5. Q: $x^2 - 4x + 8$, R: -24 6. Q: $x^2 + 2x + 1$, R: 12 7. Q: $x^2 - 3x + 9$, R: 0 8. Q: $x^2 + 3x + 9$, R: 0 9. Q: $x^3 + x^2 + x + 1$, R: 0 10. Q: $x^4 - 2x^3 + 4x^2 - 8x + 16$, R: 0 11. Q: $2x^3 + x^2 + \frac{7}{2}x + \frac{7}{4}$, R: $-\frac{1}{8}$ 12. Q: $3x^3 + \frac{3}{4}x^2 - \frac{29}{16}x - \frac{29}{64}$, R: $\frac{483}{256}$ 13. Q: $x^3 + 2x^2 + 4x + 8$, R: 0 14. Q: $x^5 - x^4 + x^3 - x^2 + x - 1$, R: 2 15. Q: $x^2 - ix + i + 1$, R: $4 + i$ 16. Q: $x^2 + 2ix - 4i + 2$, R: $-6 - 2i$

21. Yes, No   22. Yes, No   23. No, No   24. No, No
25. Yes, Yes, Yes   26. Yes, Yes, Yes

Exercise Set 15–4, page 470

1. -3(multiplicity 2), 1(multiplicity 1)   2. -2(multiplicity 1), π(multiplicity 5)   3. 3(multiplicity 2), -4(multiplicity 3), 0(multiplicity 4)   4. 0(multiplicity 3), 1(multiplicity 2), -4(multiplicity 1)   5. 3(multiplicity 2), 2(multiplicity 2)   6. 2(multiplicity 2), -1(multiplicity 2)

Exercise Set 15–5, page 474

23.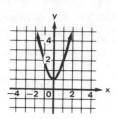

24.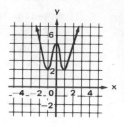

25.

26.

Cumulative Review, page 478

15. Parabola through $(-2, -6)$, $(-1, -2)$, $(0, -6)$; vertex: $(-1, -2)$; line of symmetry: $x = -1$; max. $= -2$ 16. Vertex: $(\frac{1}{4}, 19)$; line of symmetry: $x = \frac{1}{4}$; min. $= 19$ 17. $f(x) = 3(x - 4)^4 + 2$; vertex: $(4, 2)$; line of symmetry: $x = 4$; min. $= 2$

27. Center: $(-1, -3)$; vertices: $(-1, 2)$, $(-1, 8)$; foci: $(-1, -3 + \sqrt{41})$, $(-1, -3 - \sqrt{41})$; asymptotes: $y + 3 = \frac{5}{4}(x + 1)$, $y + 3 = -\frac{5}{4}(x + 1)$ 28. Hyperbola with x-axis and y-axis as asymptotes; one branch through $(-1, 4)$, $(-2, 2)$, $(-4, 1)$; one branch through $(4, -1)$, $(2, -2)$, $(1, -4)$ 29. Parabola through $(-4, 4)$, $(0, 0)$, $(-4, -4)$; vertex: $(0, 0)$; focus: $(-1, 0)$; directrix: $x = 1$

CHAPTER 16 ANSWERS

TRY THIS, page 483

1. b) Curve through $(-3, \frac{1}{27})$, $(-2, \frac{1}{9})$, $(-1, \frac{1}{3})$, $(0, 1)$, $(1, 3)$, $(2, 9)$ 2. Curve through $(-2, 9)$, $(-1, 3)$, $(0, 1)$, $(1, \frac{1}{3})$, $(2, \frac{1}{9})$

Exercise Set 16–1, page 484

1. Curve through $(-2, \frac{1}{4})$, $(-1, \frac{1}{2})$, $(0, 1)$, $(1, 2)$, $(2, 4)$, $(3, 9)$ 2. Curve through $(-2, \frac{1}{9})$, $(-1, \frac{1}{3})$, $(0, 1)$, $(1, 3)$, $(2, 9)$ 3. Curve through $(-1, \frac{1}{5})$, $(0, 1)$, $(1, 5)$ 4. Curve through $(-1, \frac{1}{6})$, $(0, 1)$, $(1, 6)$ 5. Curve through $(-1, 4)$, $(0, 1)$, $(1, \frac{1}{4})$ 6. Curve through $(-1, 5)$, $(0, 1)$, $(1, \frac{1}{5})$ 7. Curve through $(-2, 6.25)$, $(-1, 2.5)$, $(0, 1)$, $(1, 0.4)$ 8. Curve through $(-1, 3.3)$, $(0, 1)$, $(1, 0.3)$ 9. Curve through $(-1, \frac{1}{4})$, $(0, \frac{1}{2})$, $(1, 1)$, $(2, 2)$, $(3, 4)$ 10. Curve through $(-2, \frac{1}{3})$, $(-1, 1)$, $(0, 3)$, $(1, 9)$ 11. Curve through $(-3, \frac{1}{5})$, $(-2, 1)$, $(-1, 5)$ 12. Curve through $(1, \frac{1}{6})$, $(2, 1)$, $(3, 6)$ 13. Curve through $(-2, 0.1826283)$, $(-1, 0.4273504)$, $(0, 1)$, $(1, 2.34)$, $(2, 5.4756)$ 14. Curve through $(-2, 3.0995834)$, $(-1, 1.7605633)$, $(0, 1)$, $(1, 0.568)$, $(2, 0.322624)$ 15. Curve through $(0, 1)$, $(-1, 3)$, $(-2, 9)$ and curve through $(0, 1)$, $(1, 3)$, $(2, 9)$ 16. Curve through

(1, 1), (0, 2), (−1, 4), (−2, 8) and curve through (1, 1), (2, 2), (3, 4), (4, 8)   17. Curve through (0, 2), (−1, $\frac{10}{3}$), (−2, $\frac{82}{9}$) and curve through (0, 2), (1, $\frac{10}{3}$), (2, $\frac{82}{9}$)   18. Curve through through (0, 2), (−1, $\frac{5}{2}$), (−2, $\frac{17}{4}$), (−3, $\frac{65}{8}$) and curve through (0, 2), (1, $\frac{5}{2}$), (2, $\frac{17}{4}$), (3, $\frac{65}{8}$)

TRY THIS, page 486

1. Curve through ($\frac{1}{4}$, −1), (1, 0), (4, 1), (16, 2)

Exercise Set 16–2, page 489

1. Curve through ($\frac{1}{2}$, −1), (1, 0), (4, 2), (8, 3)   2. Curve through ($\frac{1}{3}$, −1), (1, 0), (3, 1), (9, 2)   3. Curve through (−$\frac{1}{2}$, −1), (0, 0), (1, 1), (3, 2), (7, 3)   4. Curve through ($\frac{7}{3}$, −1), (3, 0), (5, 1), (11, 2)

49. Curve through (−8, 3), (−4, 2), (−2, 1), (−1, 0), (−$\frac{1}{2}$, −1); curve through ($\frac{1}{2}$, −1), (1, 0), (2, 1), (4, 2), (8, 3)
50. Curve through (−9, 2), (−3, 1), (−1, 0), ($\frac{1}{3}$, −1); curve through ($\frac{1}{3}$, −1), (1, 0), (3, 1), (9, 2)

Chapter 16 Review, page 514

1. Curve through (−1, $\frac{1}{5}$), (0, 1), (1, 5)   2. Curve through ($\frac{1}{5}$, −1), (1, 0), (5, 1)

Chapter 16 Test, page 515

1. Curve through (−1, $\frac{1}{3}$), (0, 1), (1, 3), (2, 9)   2. Curve through ($\frac{1}{3}$, −1), (1, 0), (3, 1), (9, 2)

CHAPTER 18 ANSWERS

Exercise Set 18–5, page 558

5. $\begin{bmatrix} -2 & -3 \\ 6 & -4 \end{bmatrix}$ 6. $\begin{bmatrix} -2 & -6 \\ 1 & 0 \end{bmatrix}$ 7. $\begin{bmatrix} 4 & 4 \\ 0 & 0 \end{bmatrix}$ 8. $\begin{bmatrix} 4 & 6 \\ 1 & 5 \end{bmatrix}$
9. $\begin{bmatrix} -5 & 0 & 11 \\ 3 & 2 & 0 \end{bmatrix}$ 10. $\begin{bmatrix} -3 & 3 & 4 \\ 8 & 2 & -1 \end{bmatrix}$ 11. $\begin{bmatrix} 0 & -2 & 3 \\ 1 & -1 & 2 \\ 1 & -5 & 5 \end{bmatrix}$
12. $\begin{bmatrix} -5 & 3 & 3 \\ 2 & 0 & -5 \\ -4 & -6 & -4 \end{bmatrix}$ 13. $\begin{bmatrix} 1 & 2 \\ 4 & -3 \end{bmatrix}$ 14. $\begin{bmatrix} -3 & -5 \\ 2 & -1 \end{bmatrix}$
15. $\begin{bmatrix} 1 & -1 \\ -1 & 1 \end{bmatrix}$ 16. $\begin{bmatrix} 1 & 1 \\ 1 & 1 \end{bmatrix}$ 17. $\begin{bmatrix} 4 & 7 \\ 2 & -2 \end{bmatrix}$ 18. $\begin{bmatrix} 4 & 4 \\ -3 & 2 \end{bmatrix}$
19. $\begin{bmatrix} 2 & 2 \\ -2 & -2 \end{bmatrix}$ 20. $\begin{bmatrix} -2 & 0 \\ 3 & 7 \end{bmatrix}$ 21. $\begin{bmatrix} 3 & -7 & 7 \\ 0 & 0 & 3 \\ 0 & 0 & 6 \end{bmatrix}$

22. $\begin{bmatrix} 2 & 2 & -7 \\ -1 & -1 & 4 \\ 5 & 1 & 3 \end{bmatrix}$ 23. $\begin{bmatrix} -1 & -6 & 3 \\ -13 & 2 & 2 \end{bmatrix}$ 24. $\begin{bmatrix} 2 & 3 & -7 \\ 5 & 0 & -1 \end{bmatrix}$
25. $\begin{bmatrix} -1 & -1 \\ -1 & -1 \end{bmatrix}$ 26. $\begin{bmatrix} 3 & 3 & -7 \\ 5 & -2 & -1 \end{bmatrix}$ 27. $\begin{bmatrix} -1 & -3 \\ -2 & -6 \end{bmatrix}$
28. $\begin{bmatrix} 4 & -5 & 2 \\ -1 & 0 & 4 \\ 2 & 3 & 5 \end{bmatrix}$ 29. $\begin{bmatrix} 0 & 2 \\ 2 & 0 \end{bmatrix}$ 30. $\begin{bmatrix} 0 & -4 \\ -3 & -5 \end{bmatrix}$
31. $\begin{bmatrix} -3 & 7 & -7 \\ 0 & 0 & -3 \\ 0 & 0 & -6 \end{bmatrix}$ 32. $\begin{bmatrix} -2 & -2 & 7 \\ 1 & 1 & -4 \\ -5 & -1 & -3 \end{bmatrix}$ 33. $\begin{bmatrix} 1 & 6 & -3 \\ 13 & -2 & -2 \end{bmatrix}$
34. $\begin{bmatrix} 1 & -3 & -4 \\ -8 & 2 & 1 \end{bmatrix}$ 35. $\begin{bmatrix} -3 & -3 \\ 1 & 1 \end{bmatrix}$ 36. $\begin{bmatrix} -1 & -2 \\ -4 & 3 \end{bmatrix}$

Exercise Set 18–6, page 561

1. $\begin{bmatrix} -2 & -4 \\ -8 & -6 \end{bmatrix}$ 2. $\begin{bmatrix} 15 & -25 \\ -10 & 5 \end{bmatrix}$ 3. $\begin{bmatrix} 14 & -14 \\ -14 & 14 \end{bmatrix}$ 4. $\begin{bmatrix} 12 & 12 \\ 12 & 12 \end{bmatrix}$
5. $\begin{bmatrix} t & 3t \\ 2t & 6t \end{bmatrix}$ 6. $\begin{bmatrix} 3p & 3p \\ -p & -p \end{bmatrix}$ 7. $\begin{bmatrix} 2 & -9 & -6 \\ 3 & -3 & -4 \\ -2 & 2 & -1 \end{bmatrix}$
8. $\begin{bmatrix} 1 & 2 & -5 \\ -1 & 0 & 1 \\ -2 & 3 & -1 \end{bmatrix}$ 9. $[-22]$ 10. $[-36]$ 11. $[-36]$
12. $[-9]$ 13. $\begin{bmatrix} 1 & 3 \\ -6 & 17 \end{bmatrix}$ 14. $\begin{bmatrix} -8 & 8 \\ 3 & -3 \end{bmatrix}$ 15. $\begin{bmatrix} 0 & 0 \\ 0 & 0 \end{bmatrix}$
16. $\begin{bmatrix} 0 & 0 \\ 0 & 0 \end{bmatrix}$ 17. $[-14 \ -11 \ -3]$ 18. $[25 \ 25]$
19. $[-13 \ -1 \ -4]$ 20. $\begin{bmatrix} -15 \\ 5 \end{bmatrix}$ 21. $\begin{bmatrix} 3 & 3 \\ -1 & -1 \end{bmatrix}$
22. $\begin{bmatrix} -3 & 5 \\ 2 & -1 \end{bmatrix}$ 23. $\begin{bmatrix} -5 & 4 & 3 \\ 5 & -9 & 4 \\ 7 & -18 & 17 \end{bmatrix}$ 24. $\begin{bmatrix} 14 & 12 & 16 \\ -2 & -2 & -6 \\ 5 & 5 & -9 \end{bmatrix}$
25. $\begin{bmatrix} -7 \\ -18 \end{bmatrix}$ 26. $[9 \ -9]$ 27. Not possible 28. Not possible 29. a) $(A + B)(A - B) = \begin{bmatrix} 0 & -1 \\ 2 & 3 \end{bmatrix}\begin{bmatrix} -2 & 1 \\ 2 & -1 \end{bmatrix} = \begin{bmatrix} -2 & 1 \\ 2 & -1 \end{bmatrix}$, $A^2 - B^2 = \begin{bmatrix} 1 & 0 \\ 0 & 1 \end{bmatrix} - \begin{bmatrix} 1 & -3 \\ 1 & 4 \end{bmatrix} = \begin{bmatrix} 0 & 3 \\ -1 & -3 \end{bmatrix}$
b) $(A + B)(A + B) = \begin{bmatrix} 0 & -1 \\ 2 & 3 \end{bmatrix}\begin{bmatrix} 0 & -1 \\ 2 & 3 \end{bmatrix} = \begin{bmatrix} -2 & -3 \\ 6 & 7 \end{bmatrix}$, $A^2 + 2AB + B^2 = \begin{bmatrix} 1 & 0 \\ 0 & 1 \end{bmatrix} + 2\begin{bmatrix} -1 & 1 \\ 2 & 0 \end{bmatrix} + \begin{bmatrix} 1 & -3 \\ 1 & 4 \end{bmatrix} = \begin{bmatrix} 0 & -1 \\ 5 & 5 \end{bmatrix}$
30. $k(A + B) = k\begin{bmatrix} a + e & c + g \\ b + f & d + h \end{bmatrix} = \begin{bmatrix} ka + ke & kc + kg \\ kb + kf & kd + kh \end{bmatrix}$, $kA + kB = \begin{bmatrix} ka & kc \\ kb & kd \end{bmatrix} + \begin{bmatrix} ke & kg \\ kf & kh \end{bmatrix} = \begin{bmatrix} ka + ke & kc + kg \\ kb + kf & kd + kh \end{bmatrix}$, 31. $(-1)A = (-1)\begin{bmatrix} -1 & 0 \\ 2 & 1 \end{bmatrix} = \begin{bmatrix} 1 & 0 \\ -2 & -1 \end{bmatrix}$, $-A = -\begin{bmatrix} -1 & 0 \\ 2 & 1 \end{bmatrix} = \begin{bmatrix} 1 & 0 \\ -2 & -1 \end{bmatrix}$
32. $(k + m)A = (k + m)\begin{bmatrix} -1 & 0 \\ 2 & 1 \end{bmatrix} = \begin{bmatrix} -(k + m) & 0 \\ 2(k + m) & k + m \end{bmatrix} = \begin{bmatrix} -k + (-m) & 0 \\ 2k + 2m & k + m \end{bmatrix}$, $kA + mA = k\begin{bmatrix} -1 & 0 \\ 2 & 1 \end{bmatrix} + m\begin{bmatrix} -1 & 0 \\ 2 & 1 \end{bmatrix} = \begin{bmatrix} -k & 0 \\ 2k & k \end{bmatrix} + \begin{bmatrix} -m & 0 \\ 2m & m \end{bmatrix} = \begin{bmatrix} -k + (-m) & 0 \\ 2k + 2m & k + m \end{bmatrix}$ 33. $AI = \begin{bmatrix} a & c \\ b & d \end{bmatrix}$, $IA = \begin{bmatrix} a & c \\ b & d \end{bmatrix}$ 34. Matrix I is a 2 X 2 identity matrix with respect to matrix multiplication

CHAPTER 20 ANSWERS

Exercise Set 20–4, page 611

9.

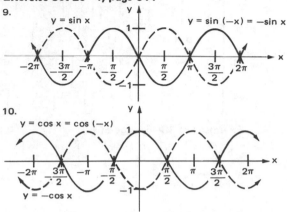

10.

15. The cosine function is even. Since cos (−x) = cos x, then $\frac{1}{\cos(-x)} = \frac{1}{\cos x}$. Since the secant function is the reciprocal of the cosine function, sec (−x) = $\frac{1}{\cos(-x)}$ and sec x = $\frac{1}{\cos x}$. By substitution sec (−x) = sec x. Therefore the secant function is also even. 16. The sine function is odd. Since sin (−x) = −sin x, then $\frac{1}{\sin(-x)} = -\frac{1}{\sin x}$. Since the cosecant function is the reciprocal of the sine function, csc (−x) = $\frac{1}{\sin(-x)}$ and −csc x = $-\frac{1}{\sin x}$. By substitution csc (−x) = −csc x. Therefore the cosecant function is also odd.

TRY THIS, page 615

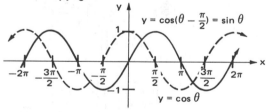

Exercise Set 20–5, page 618

1. $\csc \theta \equiv \pm\sqrt{1 + \cot^2 \theta}$ 2. $\tan \theta \equiv \pm\sqrt{\sec^2 \theta - 1}$
3. $\cot \theta \equiv \pm\sqrt{\csc^2 \theta - 1}$ 4. $\sec \theta \equiv \pm\sqrt{1 + \tan^2 \theta}$

15. sin 25° = 0.4226, cos 25° = 0.9063, tan 25° = 0.4663, cot 25° = 2.145, sec 25° = 1.103, csc 25° = 2.366   16. sin 58° = 0.8480, cos 58° = 0.5299, tan 58° = 1.600, cot 58° = 0.6249, sec 58° = 1.887, csc 58° = 1.179   17. sin 38° = 0.6157, cos 38° = 0.7880, tan 38° = 0.7813, cot 38° = 1.280, sec 38° = 1.269, csc 38° = 1.624   18. sin 63° = 0.8910, cos 63° = 0.4540, tan 63° = 1.963, cot 63° = 0.5095, sec 63° = 2.203, csc 63° = 1.122

Exercise Set 20–6, page 622

1. Sine curve with amplitude 1/2 through (−2π, 0), (−3π/2, 1/2), (−π, 0), (−π/2, −1/2), (0, 0), (π/2, 1/2), (π, 0), (3π/2, −1/2), (2π, 0)   2. Cosine curve with amplitude 1/2 through (−2π, 1/2), (−3π/2, 0), (−π, −1/2), (−π/2, 0), (0, 1/2), (π/2, 0), (π, −1/2), (3π/2, 0), (2π, 1/2)   3. Sine curve with amplitude 3 through (−2π, 0), (−3π/2, 3), (−π, 0), (−π/2, −3), (0, 0), (π/2, 3), (π, 0), (3π/2, −3), (2π, 0)   4. Cosine curve with amplitude 3 through (−2π, 3), (−3π/2, 0), (−π, −3), (−π/2, 0), (0, 3), (π/2, 0), (π, −3), (3π/2, 0), (2π, 3)   5. Sine curve with amplitude 1/3 through (−2π, 0), (−3π/2, −1/3), (−π, 0), (−π/2, 1/3), (0, 0), (π/2, −1/3), (π, 0), (3π/2, 1/3), (2π, 0)   6. Cosine curve with amplitude 1/3 through (−2π, −1/3), (−3π/2, 0), (−π, 1/3), (−π/2, 0), (0, −1/3), (π/2, 0), (π, 1/3), (3π/2, 0), (2π, −1/3)   7. Sine curve with amplitude 4 through (−2π, 0), (−3π/2, 4), (−π, 0), (−π/2, −4), (0, 0), (π/2, 4), (π, 0), (3π/2, −4), (2π, 0)   8. Cosine curve with amplitude 4 through (−2π, 4), (−3π/2, 0), (−π, −4), (−π/2, 0), (0, 4), (π/2, 0), (π, −4), (3π/2, 0), (2π, 4)   9. Sine curve with amplitude 2 through (−2π, 0), (−3π/2, −2), (−π, 0), (−π/2, 2), (0, 0), (π/2, −2), (π, 0), (3π/2, 2), (2π, 0)   10. Cosine curve with amplitude 2 through (−2π, −2), (−3π/2, 0), (−π, 2), (−π/2, 0), (0, −2), (π/2, 0), (π, 2), (3π/2, 0), (2π, −2)   11. Sine curve with period 2π/3 through (−2π, 0), (−11π/6, 1), (−3π/2, −1), (−7π/6, 1), (−5π/6, −1), (−π/2, 1), (−π/6, −1), (0, 0), (π/6, 1), (π/2, −1), (5π/6, 1), (7π/6, −1), (3π/2, 1), (11π/6, −1), (2π, 0)   12. Cosine curve with period 2π/3 through (−2π, 1), (−5π/3, −1), (−4π/3, 1), (−π, −1), (−2π/3, 1), (−π/3, −1), (0, 1), (π/3, −1), (2π/3, 1), (π, −1), (4π/3, 1), (5π/3, −1), (2π, 1)   13. Sine curve with period 4π through (−2π, 0), ((−π, −1), (0, 0), (π, 1), (2π, 0)   14. Cosine curve with period 4π through (−2π, −1), (−π, 0), (0, 1), (π, 0), (2π, −1)   15. Sine curve with period 6π through (−3π, 0), (−3π/2, 1), (0, 0), (3π/2, −1), (3π, 0)   16. Cosine curve with period 6π through (−3π, −1), (−3π/2, 0), (0, 1), (3π/2, 0), (3π, −1)   17. Sine curve with period π through (−2π, 0), (−7π/4, −1), (−5π/4, 1), (−3π/4, −1), (−π/4, 1), (π/4, −1), (3π/4, 1), (5π/4, −1), (7π/4, 1), (2π, 0)   18. Cosine curve with period π through (−2π, 1), (−3π/2, −1), (−π, 1), (−π/2, −1), (0, 1), (π/2, −1), (π, 1), (3π/2, −1), (2π, 1)   19. Sine curve with period 2π/3 through (−2π, 0), (−11π/6, −1), (−3π/2, 1), (−7π/6, −1), (−5π/6, 1), (−π/2, −1), (−π/6, 1), (0, 0), (π/6, −1), (π/2, 1), (5π/6, −1), (7π/6, 1), (3π/2, −1), (11π/6, 1), (2π, 0)   20. Cosine curve with period 2π/3 through (−2π, 1), (−5π/3, −1), (−4π/3, 1), (−π, −1), (−2π/3, 1), (−π/3, −1), (0, 1), (π/3, −1), (2π/3, 1), (π, −1), (4π/3, 1), (5π/3, −1), (2π, 1)   21. Sine curve with amplitude 2, period π, through (−2π, 0), (−7π/4, 2), (−5π/4, −2), (−3π/4, 2), (−π/4, −2), (0, 0), (π/4, 2), (3π/4, −2), (5π/4, 2), (7π/2, −2), (2π, 0)   22. Cosine curve with amplitude 2, period π, through (−2π, 2), (−3π/2, −2), (−π, 2), (−π/2, −2), (0, 2), (π/2, −2), (π, 2), (3π/2, −2), (2π, 2)   23. Sine curve with amplitude 1/2, period π, through (−2π, 0), (−7π/4, 1/2), (−5π/4, −1/2),

$(-3\pi/4, 1/2)$, $(-\pi/4, -1/2)$, $(0, 0)$, $(\pi/4, 1/2)$, $(3\pi/4, -1/2)$, $(5\pi/4, 1/2)$, $(7\pi/4, -1/2)$, $(2\pi, 0)$ 24. Cosine curve with amplitude 1/2, period π, through $(-2\pi, 1/2)$, $(-3\pi/2, -1/2)$, $(-\pi, 1/2)$, $(-\pi/2, -1/2)$, $(0, 1/2)$, $(\pi/2, -1/2)$, $(\pi, 1/2)$, $(3\pi/2, -1/2)$, $(2\pi, 1/2)$ 25. Sine curve with amplitude 2, period 4π, through $(-2\pi, 0)$, $(-\pi, 2)$, $(0, 0)$, $(\pi, -2)$, $(2\pi, 0)$ 26. Cosine curve with amplitude 2, period 4π, through $(-2\pi, 2)$, $(-\pi, 0)$, $(0, -2)$, $(\pi, 0)$, $(2\pi, 2)$ 27. Sine curve with amplitude 1/2, period π, through $(-2\pi, 0)$, $(-7\pi/4, -1/2)$, $(-5\pi/4, 1/2)$, $(-3\pi/4, -1/2)$, $(-\pi/4, 1/2)$, $(0, 0)$, $(\pi/4, -1/2)$, $(3\pi/4, 1/2)$, $(5\pi/4, -1/2)$, $(7\pi/4, 1/2)$, $(2\pi, 0)$ 28. Cosine curve with amplitude 1/2, period π, through $(-2\pi, 1/2)$, $(-3\pi/2, -1/2)$, $(-\pi, 1/2)$, $(-\pi/2, -1/2)$, $(0, 1/2)$, $(\pi/2, -1/2)$, $(\pi, 1/2)$, $(3\pi/2, -1/2)$, $(2\pi, 1/2)$ 29. Sine curve with amplitude 1/2, period π, through $(-2\pi, 0)$, $(-7\pi/4, 1/2)$, $(-5\pi/4, -1/2)$, $(-3\pi/4, 1/2)$, $(-\pi/4, -1/2)$, $(0, 0)$, $(\pi/4, 1/2)$, $(3\pi/4, -1/2)$, $(5\pi/4, 1/2)$, $(7\pi/4, -1/2)$, $(2\pi, 0)$ 30. Cosine curve with amplitude 1/2, period π, through $(-2\pi, -1/2)$, $(-3\pi/2, 1/2)$, $(-\pi, -1/2)$, $(-\pi/2, 1/2)$, $(0, -1/2)$, $(\pi/2, 1/2)$, $(\pi, -1/2)$, $(3\pi/2, 1/2)$, $(2\pi, -1/2)$

31. Cosine curve through $(-2\pi, -1)$, $(-3\pi/2, 1)$, $(-\pi, -1)$, $(-\pi/2, 1)$, $(0, -1)$, $(\pi/2, 1)$, $(\pi, -1)$, $(3\pi/2, 1)$, $(2\pi, -1)$ 32. Sine curve through $(-2\pi, 0)$, $(-7\pi/4, -1)$, $(-5\pi/4, 1)$, $(-3\pi/4, -1)$, $(-\pi/4, 1)$, $(0, 0)$, $(\pi/4, -1)$, $(3\pi/4, 1)$, $(5\pi/4, -1)$, $(7\pi/4, 1)$, $(2\pi, 0)$ 33. Sine curve through $(-2\pi, 2)$, $(-3\pi/2, 3)$, $(-\pi, 2)$, $(-\pi/2, 1)$, $(0, 2)$, $(\pi/2, 3)$, $(\pi, 2)$, $(3\pi/2, 1)$, $(2\pi, 2)$ 34. Cosine curve through $(-2\pi, -2)$, $(-3\pi/2, -3)$, $(-\pi, -4)$, $(-\pi/2, -3)$, $(0, -2)$, $(\pi/2, -3)$, $(\pi, -4)$, $(3\pi/2, -3)$, $(2\pi, -2)$

Exercise Set 20–8, page 629

33. $\tan x = -7$ or $\tan x = 3$ 34. $\sec \theta = 5$ or $\sec \theta = 2$
35. $\sin \theta = \frac{3}{4}$ or $\sin \theta = -\frac{1}{2}$ 36. $\cos x = -\frac{1}{3}$ or $\cos x = -\frac{5}{2}$
37. $\cot x = -10$ or $\cot x = 1$ 38. $\csc \theta = -5$ or $\csc \theta = 2$
39. $\sin \theta = 3$ or $\sin \theta = -2$ 40. $\sin x = -\frac{1}{2}$ or $\sin x = 2$
41. $\tan \theta = 3 \pm \sqrt{13}$ 42. $\csc x = \frac{3 \pm \sqrt{41}}{4}$

Chapter 20 Review, page 630

4. $\sin \theta = \frac{3\sqrt{13}}{13}$, $\cos \theta = -\frac{2\sqrt{13}}{13}$, $\tan \theta = -\frac{3}{2}$, $\cot \theta = -\frac{2}{3}$, $\sec \theta = -\frac{\sqrt{13}}{2}$, $\csc \theta = \frac{\sqrt{13}}{3}$

14. Cosine curve with amplitude 3 through $(-2\pi, 3)$, $(-3\pi/2, 0)$, $(-\pi, -3)$, $(-\pi/2, 0)$, $(0, 3)$, $(\pi/2, 0)$, $(\pi, -3)$, $(3\pi/2, 0)$, $(2\pi, 3)$ 15. Sine curve with period π through $(-2\pi, 0)$, $(-7\pi/4, 1)$, $(-5\pi/4, -1)$, $(-3\pi/4, 1)$, $(-\pi/4, -1)$, $(0, 0)$, $(\pi/4, 1)$, $(3\pi/4, -1)$, $(5\pi/4, 1)$, $(7\pi/4, -1)$, $(2\pi, 0)$

Chapter 20 Test, page 631

14. Sine curve with amplitude 2 through $(-2\pi, 0)$, $(-3\pi/2, 2)$, $(-\pi, 0)$, $(-\pi/2, -2)$, $(0, 0)$, $(\pi/2, 2)$, $(\pi, 0)$, $(3\pi/2, -2)$, $(2\pi, 0)$ 15. Sine curve with period 4π through $(-2\pi, 0)$, $(-\pi, -1)$, $(0, 0)$, $(\pi, 1)$, $(2\pi, 0)$

CHAPTER 21 ANSWERS

Exercise Set 21–2, page 644

1. $\sin 2\theta = \frac{24}{25}$, $\cos 2\theta = -\frac{7}{25}$, $\tan 2\theta = -\frac{24}{7}$, Quadrant II
2. $\sin 2\theta = \frac{120}{169}$, $\cos 2\theta = \frac{119}{169}$, $\tan 2\theta = \frac{120}{119}$, Quadrant I
3. $\sin 2\theta = \frac{24}{25}$, $\cos 2\theta = \frac{7}{25}$, $\tan 2\theta = \frac{24}{7}$, Quadrant I
4. $\sin 2\theta = \frac{24}{25}$, $\cos 2\theta = -\frac{7}{25}$, $\tan 2\theta = -\frac{24}{7}$, Quadrant II
5. $\sin 2\theta = \frac{24}{25}$, $\cos 2\theta = -\frac{7}{25}$, $\tan 2\theta = -\frac{24}{7}$, Quadrant II
6. $\sin 2\theta = \frac{24}{25}$, $\cos 2\theta = \frac{7}{25}$, $\tan 2\theta = \frac{24}{7}$, Quadrant I

7. $4 \sin \theta \cos^2 \theta - 4 \sin^3 \theta \cos \theta$, $4 \sin \theta \cos \theta - 8 \sin^3 \theta \cos \theta$ or $8 \sin \theta \cos^3 \theta - 4 \sin \theta \cos \theta$ 8. $\cos^4 \theta - 6 \cos^2 \theta \sin^2 \theta + \sin^4 \theta$, $1 - 4 \sin^2 \theta + 4 \sin^4 \theta - 4 \sin^2 \theta \cos^2 \theta$ or $4 \cos^4 \theta - 4 \cos^2 \theta + 1 - 4 \sin^2 \theta \cos^2 \theta$
9. $\dfrac{3 - 4 \cos 2\theta + \cos 4\theta}{8}$ 10. $\dfrac{3 + 4 \cos 2\theta + \cos 4\theta}{8}$

Exercise Set 21–3, page 646

1. $\csc x - \cos x \cot x$ | $\sin x$ 2. $\sec x - \sin x \tan x$ | $\cos x$

$\dfrac{1}{\sin x} - \cos x \dfrac{\cos x}{\sin x}$ | $\sin x$ | $\dfrac{1}{\cos x} - \sin x \dfrac{\sin x}{\cos x}$ | $\cos x$

$\dfrac{1 - \cos^2 x}{\sin x}$ | | $\dfrac{1 - \sin^2 x}{\cos x}$

$\dfrac{\sin^2 x}{\sin x}$ | | $\dfrac{\cos^2 x}{\cos x}$

$\sin x$ | | $\cos x$

3. $\dfrac{1 + \cos \theta}{\sin \theta} + \dfrac{\sin \theta}{\cos \theta}$ | $\dfrac{\cos \theta + 1}{\sin \theta \cos \theta}$

$\dfrac{1 + \cos \theta}{\sin \theta} \cdot \dfrac{\cos \theta}{\cos \theta} + \dfrac{\sin \theta}{\cos \theta} \cdot \dfrac{\sin \theta}{\sin \theta}$ | $\dfrac{\cos \theta + 1}{\sin \theta \cos \theta}$

$\dfrac{\cos \theta + \cos^2 \theta + \sin^2 \theta}{\sin \theta \cos \theta}$

$\dfrac{\cos \theta + 1}{\sin \theta \cos \theta}$

4. $\dfrac{1}{\sin \theta \cos \theta} - \dfrac{\cos \theta}{\sin \theta}$ | $\dfrac{\sin \theta \cos \theta}{1 - \sin^2 \theta}$

$\dfrac{1}{\sin \theta \cos \theta} - \dfrac{\cos \theta}{\sin \theta} \cdot \dfrac{\cos \theta}{\cos \theta}$ | $\dfrac{\sin \theta \cos \theta}{\cos^2 \theta}$

$\dfrac{1 - \cos^2 \theta}{\sin \theta \cos \theta}$ | $\dfrac{\sin \theta}{\cos \theta}$

$\dfrac{\sin^2 \theta}{\sin \theta \cos \theta}$

$\dfrac{\sin \theta}{\cos \theta}$

5. $\dfrac{1 - \sin x}{\cos x}$ | $\dfrac{\cos x}{1 + \sin x}$

$\dfrac{1 - \sin x}{\cos x} \cdot \dfrac{\cos x}{\cos x}$ | $\dfrac{\cos x}{1 + \sin x} \cdot \dfrac{1 - \sin x}{1 - \sin x}$

$\dfrac{\cos x - \sin x \cos x}{\cos^2 x}$ | $\dfrac{\cos x - \cos x \sin x}{1 - \sin^2 x}$

| $\dfrac{\cos x - \sin x \cos x}{\cos^2 x}$

CHAPTER 20

Answers for TRY THIS

20–1 1. Answers may vary. 2. $\sin \theta = \frac{4}{5}$, $\cos \theta = \frac{3}{5}$, $\tan \theta = \frac{4}{3}$ 3. $27°$

20–2 1. First 2. Third 3. Fourth 4. Third 5. First 6. First 7. $\frac{5\pi}{4}$, 3.93 8. $\frac{5\pi}{3}$, 5.23 9. $-\frac{7\pi}{4}$, −5.50 10. $240°$ 11. $450°$ 12. $-144°$

20–3 1. $\sin \theta = \frac{12}{13} \approx 0.923$, $\cos \theta = \frac{-5}{13} \approx -0.385$, $\tan \theta = \frac{12}{-5} = -2.4$ 2. $\cot \theta = \frac{5}{-12} \approx -0.417$, $\sec \theta = \frac{13}{-5} = -2.6$, $\csc \theta = \frac{13}{12} \approx 1.08$ 3. The sine, cosine, secant, and cosecant functions all have negative values. The tangent and cotangent functions have positive values. 4. $\cos 45° \approx 0.707$, $\sec 45° \approx 1.414$, $\csc 45° \approx 1.414$ 5. 0.576 6. 1.15 7. 0.864 8. 0.576 9. 1.15 10. $\sin 330° = -\frac{1}{2}$, $\cos 330° = \frac{\sqrt{3}}{2}$, $\tan 330° = -\frac{\sqrt{3}}{3}$ 11. $\sin (-510°) = -\frac{1}{2}$, $\cos (-510°) = -\frac{\sqrt{3}}{2}$, $\tan (-510°) = \frac{\sqrt{3}}{3}$ 12. $\sin \frac{23\pi}{6} = -\frac{1}{2}$, $\cos \frac{23\pi}{6} = \frac{\sqrt{3}}{2}$, $\tan \frac{23\pi}{6} = -\frac{\sqrt{3}}{3}$

20–4 1. 3 2. The set of all real numbers. 3. The set of all real numbers from −1 to 1, inclusive. 4. Yes, 2π 5. Odd 6. Yes, π 7. Odd 8. 2π 9. All real numbers 1 and greater in addition to all real numbers −1 and less. 10. 2π 11. Set of all real numbers except $k\pi$, k an integer. 12. All real numbers 1 and greater in addition to all real numbers −1 and less.

20–5 1. $\cos \theta \equiv \sin \theta \cot \theta$ 2. $\sin^2 \theta \equiv 1 - \cos^2 \theta$ 3. $\sin \theta \equiv \pm\sqrt{1 - \cos^2 \theta}$ 4. $\sec^2 \theta - \tan^2 \theta \equiv 1$, $\tan^2 \theta \equiv \sec^2 \theta - 1$ 5. d) Same e) $\cos (\theta - \frac{\pi}{2}) \equiv \sin \theta$ 6. $\csc (\theta + \frac{\pi}{2}) \equiv \sec \theta$ 7. $\cot (\theta + \frac{\pi}{2}) \equiv -\tan \theta$ 8. $\cos (90° - \theta) \equiv \sin \theta$ 9. $\sin (\theta - 90°) \equiv -\cos \theta$ 10. $\sin 15° = 0.2588$, $\cos 15° = 0.9659$, $\tan 15° = 0.2679$, $\cot 15° = 3.732$, $\sec 15° = 1.035$, $\csc 15° = 3.864$

20–6 1. Cosine curve with amplitude 2 through $(-2\pi, 2)$, $(-3\pi/2, 0)$, $(-\pi, -2)$, $(-\pi/2, 0)$, $(0, 2)$, $(\pi/2, 0)$, $(\pi, -2)$, $(3\pi/2, 0)$, $(2\pi, 2)$ 2. Cosine curve with amplitude 1/2 through $(-2\pi, -1/2)$, $(-3\pi/2, 0)$, $(-\pi, 1/2)$, $(-\pi/2, 0)$, $(0, -1/2)$, $(\pi/2, 0)$, $(\pi, 1/2)$, $(3\pi/2, 0)$, $(2\pi, -1/2)$ 3. Cosine curve with period π through $(-2\pi, 1)$, $(-3\pi/2, -1)$, $(-\pi, 1)$, $(-\pi/2, -1)$, $(0, 1)$, $(\pi/2, -1)$, $(\pi, 1)$, $(3\pi/2, -1)$, $(2\pi, 1)$ 4. Cosine curve with period 4π through $(-2\pi, -1)$, $(-\pi, 0)$, $(0, 1)$, $(\pi, 0)$, $(2\pi, -1)$ 5. Cosine curve with amplitude 3, period π, through $(-2\pi, 3)$, $(-3\pi/2, -3)$, $(-\pi, 3)$, $(-\pi/2, -3)$, $(0, 3)$, $(\pi/2, -3)$, $(\pi, 3)$, $(3\pi/2, -3)$, $(2\pi, 3)$

20–7 1. 0.2644 2. 0.4699 3. 0.9026 4. 1.098 5. 0.6264 6. 1.900 7. $21°15'$ 8. $31°47'$ 9. −0.9182 10. 0.9853

20–8 1. $\cos x + 1$ 2. $\sin \theta$ 3. $\cos x (\csc x - 1)$ 4. $\frac{1 + \sin x}{1 - \cot x}$ 5. $\cot x = -4$ or $\cot x = 3$ 6. $\cos \theta = \frac{1 \pm \sqrt{97}}{8}$

Exercise Set 20–1, page 594

1. Answers may vary. 3. $\sin \theta = \frac{7}{25}$, $\cos \theta = \frac{24}{25}$, $\tan \theta = \frac{7}{24}$ 5. $\sin \theta = \frac{5}{13}$, $\cos \theta = \frac{12}{13}$, $\tan \theta = \frac{5}{12}$ 7. a) 16.77 b) 22.67 9. a) 36.49 b) 45.99 11. $36°$

Exercise Set 20–2, page 598

1. First 3. Third 5. First 7. Second 9. $\frac{\pi}{6}$, 0.52 11. $\frac{5\pi}{9}$, 1.74 13. $\frac{5\pi}{12}$, 1.31 15. $\frac{2\pi}{3}$, 2.09 17. $-\frac{16\pi}{9}$, −5.58 19. $-\frac{17\pi}{36}$, −1.48 21. $(\frac{180}{\pi})° \approx 57.3°$ 23. $1440°$ 25. $135°$ 27. 0.2095π 29. 1.1922222π

Exercise Set 20–3, page 604

1. $\sin \theta = \frac{5}{13} \approx 0.385$, $\cos \theta = \frac{-12}{13} \approx -0.923$, $\tan \theta = \frac{5}{-12} \approx -0.417$ 3. $\sin \theta = \frac{-3}{5} = -0.6$, $\cos \theta = \frac{-4}{5} = -0.8$, $\tan \theta = \frac{-3}{-4} = 0.75$ 5. $\cot \theta = \frac{-24}{7} \approx -3.43$, $\sec \theta = \frac{25}{-24} \approx -1.04$, $\csc \theta = \frac{25}{7} \approx 3.57$ 7. $\cot \theta = \frac{36}{-15} = -2.4$, $\sec \theta = \frac{39}{36} \approx 1.08$, $\csc \theta = \frac{39}{-15} = -2.6$ 9. $\sin \theta = \frac{-8}{17} \approx -0.471$, $\cos \theta = \frac{-15}{17} \approx -0.882$, $\tan \theta = \frac{-8}{-15} \approx 0.533$, $\cot \theta = \frac{-15}{-8} = 1.875$, $\sec \theta = \frac{17}{-15} \approx -1.13$, $\csc \theta = \frac{17}{-8} = -2.125$ 11. $\sin \theta = \frac{4}{7} \approx 0.571$, $\cos \theta = \frac{-\sqrt{33}}{7} \approx -0.821$, $\tan \theta = \frac{4}{-\sqrt{33}} \approx -0.696$, $\cot \theta = \frac{-\sqrt{33}}{4} \approx -1.44$, $\sec \theta = \frac{7}{-\sqrt{33}} \approx -1.22$, $\csc \theta = \frac{7}{4} = 1.75$ 13. −1 15. 1 17. $\frac{1}{2}$ 19. $\sqrt{2}$ 21. $\frac{1}{2}$ 23. $\frac{\sqrt{2}}{2}$ 25. Undefined 27. 1 29. $\sqrt{3}$ 31. 1 33. $\frac{\sqrt{3}}{3}$ 36. $-\frac{\sqrt{3}}{3}$

Exercise Set 20–4, page 611

1. No 3. Yes 5. Yes 7. 4 11.–13. See text pages 608–610 for graphs.

Exercise Set 20–5, page 618

1. $\csc \theta \equiv \pm\sqrt{1 + \cot^2 \theta}$ 3. $\cot \theta \equiv \pm\sqrt{\csc^2 \theta - 1}$ 5. $\tan (\theta - \frac{\pi}{2}) \equiv -\cot \theta$ 7. $\sec (\frac{\pi}{2} - \theta) \equiv \csc \theta$ 9. $\sin (\theta \pm 180°) \equiv -\sin \theta$ 11. $\sin \theta \equiv \sin [\theta + 2k(180°)]$ 13. $\sin (90° - \theta) \equiv \cos \theta$ 15. $\sin 25° = 0.4226$, $\cos 25° = 0.9063$, $\tan 25° = 0.4663$, $\cot 25° = 2.145$, $\sec 25° = 1.103$, $\csc 25° = 2.366$ 17. $\sin 38° = 0.6157$, $\cos 38° = 0.7880$, $\tan 38° = 0.7813$, $\cot 38° = 1.280$, $\sec 38° = 1.269$, $\csc 38° = 1.624$

Exercise Set 20–6, page 622

1. Sine curve with amplitude 1/2 through $(-2\pi, 0)$, $(-3\pi/2, 1/2)$, $(-\pi, 0)$, $(-\pi/2, -1/2)$, $(0, 0)$, $(\pi/2, 1/2)$, $(\pi, 0)$, $(3\pi/2, -1/2)$, $(2\pi, 0)$ 3. Sine curve with amplitude 3 through $(-2\pi, 0)$, $(-3\pi/2, 3)$, $(-\pi, 0)$, $(-\pi/2, -3)$, $(0, 0)$, $(\pi/2, 3)$, $(\pi, 0)$, $(3\pi/2, -3)$, $(2\pi, 0)$ 5. Sine curve with amplitude 1/3 through $(-2\pi, 0)$, $(-3\pi/2, -1/3)$, $(-\pi, 0)$, $(-\pi/2, 1/3)$, $(0, 0)$, $(\pi/2, -1/3)$, $(\pi, 0)$, $(3\pi/2, 1/3)$, $(2\pi, 0)$ 7. Sine curve with amplitude 4 through $(-2\pi, 0)$, $(-3\pi/2, 4)$, $(-\pi, 0)$, $(-\pi/2, -4)$, $(0, 0)$, $(\pi/2, 4)$, $(\pi, 0)$, $(3\pi/2, -4)$,

18. $\dfrac{\cos(\alpha - \beta)}{\cos \alpha \sin \beta}$ | $\tan \alpha + \cot \beta$

$\dfrac{\cos \alpha \cos \beta + \sin \alpha \sin \beta}{\cos \alpha \sin \beta}$ | $\dfrac{\sin \alpha}{\cos \alpha} + \dfrac{\cos \beta}{\sin \beta}$

$\dfrac{\sin \alpha \sin \beta + \cos \alpha \cos \beta}{\cos \alpha \sin \beta}$ | $\dfrac{\sin \alpha \sin \beta + \cos \alpha \cos \beta}{\cos \alpha \sin \beta}$

19. $1 - \cos 5\theta \cos 3\theta - \sin 5\theta \sin 3\theta$ | $2\sin^2 \theta$

$1 - (\cos 5\theta \cos 3\theta + \sin 5\theta \sin 3\theta)$ | $2 \cdot \dfrac{1 - \cos 2\theta}{2}$

$1 - \cos(5\theta - 3\theta)$

$1 - \cos 2\theta$ | $1 - \cos 2\theta$

20. $2\sin \theta \cos^3 \theta + 2\sin^3 \theta \cos \theta$ | $\sin 2\theta$

$2\sin \cos \theta (\cos^2 \theta + \sin^2 \theta)$ | $2\sin \theta \cos \theta$

$2\sin \theta \cos \theta (1)$

$2\sin \theta \cos \theta$

21. $\dfrac{\tan \theta + \sin \theta}{2\tan \theta}$ | $\cos^2 \dfrac{\theta}{2}$

$\dfrac{\dfrac{\sin \theta}{\cos \theta} + \sin \theta}{2\dfrac{\sin \theta}{\cos \theta}}$ | $\dfrac{1 + \cos \theta}{2}$

$\dfrac{\dfrac{\sin \theta + \sin \theta \cos \theta}{\cos \theta}}{2\dfrac{\sin \theta}{\cos \theta}}$

$\dfrac{\sin \theta + \sin \theta \cos \theta}{2\sin \theta}$

$\dfrac{1 + \cos \theta}{2}$

22. $\dfrac{\tan \theta - \sin \theta}{2\tan \theta}$ | $\sin^2 \dfrac{\theta}{2}$

$\dfrac{\dfrac{\sin \theta}{\cos \theta} - \sin \theta}{2\dfrac{\sin \theta}{\cos \theta}}$ | $\dfrac{1 - \cos \theta}{2}$

$\dfrac{\dfrac{\sin \theta - \sin \theta \cos \theta}{\cos \theta}}{2\dfrac{\sin \theta}{\cos \theta}}$

$\dfrac{1 - \cos \theta}{2}$

23. $\dfrac{\cos^4 x - \sin^4 x}{(\cos^2 x - \sin^2 x)(\cos^2 x + \sin^2 x)}$ | $\dfrac{\cos 2x}{\cos^2 x - \sin^2 x}$

$\cos^2 x - \sin^2 x$

24. $\dfrac{\cos^4 x - \sin^4 x}{1 - \tan^4 x}$ | $\cos^4 x$

$\dfrac{\cos^4 x - \sin^4 x}{1 - \dfrac{\sin^4 x}{\cos^4 x}}$ | $\cos^4 x$

$\dfrac{\cos^4 x - \sin^4 x}{\dfrac{\cos^4 x - \sin^4 x}{\cos^4 x}}$

$\cos^4 x$

25. $\dfrac{\tan 3\theta - \tan \theta}{1 + \tan 3\theta \tan \theta}$ | $\dfrac{2\tan \theta}{1 - \tan^2 \theta}$

$\tan(3\theta - \theta)$ | $\tan 2\theta$

$\tan 2\theta$

26. $\left(\dfrac{1 + \tan \theta}{1 - \tan \theta}\right)^2$ | $\dfrac{1 + \sin 2\theta}{1 - \sin 2\theta}$

$\left(\dfrac{\sin \theta + \cos \theta}{\sin \theta - \cos \theta}\right)^2$ | $\dfrac{1 + \sin 2\theta}{1 - \sin 2\theta}$

$\dfrac{\sin^2 \theta + 2\sin \theta \cos \theta + \cos^2 \theta}{\sin^2 \theta - 2\sin \theta \cos \theta + \cos^2 \theta}$

$\dfrac{1 + \sin 2\theta}{1 - \sin 2\theta}$

27. $\dfrac{\cos^3 x - \sin^3 x}{\cos x - \sin x}$ | $\dfrac{2 + \sin 2x}{2}$

$\dfrac{(\cos x - \sin x)(\cos^2 x + \cos x \sin x + \sin^2 x)}{\cos x - \sin x}$ | $\dfrac{2 + 2\sin x \cos x}{2}$

$1 + \sin x \cos x$ | $1 + \sin x \cos x$

28. $\dfrac{\sin^3 t + \cos^3 t}{\sin t + \cos t}$ | $\dfrac{2 - \sin 2t}{2}$

$\dfrac{(\sin t + \cos t)(\sin^2 t - \sin t \cos t + \cos^2 t)}{\sin t + \cos t}$ | $\dfrac{2 - 2\sin t \cos t}{2}$

$1 - \sin t \cos t$ | $1 - \sin t \cos t$

29. $\sin(\alpha + \beta)\sin(\alpha - \beta)$

$(\sin \alpha \cos \beta + \cos \alpha \sin \beta)(\sin \alpha \cos \beta - \cos \alpha \sin \beta)$

$\sin^2 \alpha \cos^2 \beta - \cos^2 \alpha \sin^2 \beta$

$\sin^2 \alpha (1 - \sin^2 \beta) - (1 - \sin^2 \alpha)(\sin^2 \beta)$

$\sin^2 \alpha - \sin^2 \alpha \sin^2 \beta - \sin^2 \beta + \sin^2 \alpha \sin^2 \beta$

$\sin^2 \alpha - \sin^2 \beta$

30. $\cos(\alpha + \beta)\cos(\alpha - \beta)$

$(\cos \alpha \cos \beta - \sin \alpha \sin \beta)(\cos \alpha \cos \beta + \sin \alpha \sin \beta)$

$\cos^2 \alpha \cos^2 \beta - \sin^2 \alpha \sin^2 \beta$

$\cos^2 \alpha (1 - \sin^2 \beta) - (1 - \cos^2 \alpha)\sin^2 \beta$

$\cos^2 \alpha - \cos^2 \alpha \sin^2 \beta - \sin^2 \beta + \cos^2 \alpha \sin^2 \beta$

$\cos^2 \alpha - \sin^2 \beta$

31. $\cos(\alpha + \beta) + \cos(\alpha - \beta)$

$(\cos \alpha \cos \beta - \sin \alpha \sin \beta) + (\cos \alpha \cos \beta + \sin \alpha \sin \beta)$

$2\cos \alpha \cos \beta$

32. $\sin(\alpha + \beta) + \sin(\alpha - \beta)$

$(\sin \alpha \cos \beta + \cos \alpha \sin \beta) + (\sin \alpha \cos \beta - \cos \alpha \sin \beta)$

$2\sin \alpha \cos \beta$

Exercise Set 21–5, page 656

7. $123°20'$, $236°40'$ 8. $205°20'$, $334°40'$ 9. $\dfrac{4\pi}{3}$, $\dfrac{5\pi}{3}$

10. $\dfrac{5\pi}{6}$, $\dfrac{11\pi}{6}$ 11. $123°41'$, $303°41'$ 12. $14°29'$, $165°31'$

13. $\dfrac{\pi}{6}$, $\dfrac{5\pi}{6}$, $\dfrac{7\pi}{6}$, $\dfrac{11\pi}{6}$ 14. $\dfrac{\pi}{4}$, $\dfrac{3\pi}{4}$, $\dfrac{5\pi}{4}$, $\dfrac{7\pi}{4}$ 15. $\dfrac{\pi}{6}$, $\dfrac{5\pi}{6}$, $\dfrac{3\pi}{2}$

16. $\dfrac{2\pi}{3}$, π, $\dfrac{4\pi}{3}$ 17. 0 18. $\dfrac{3\pi}{2}$ 19. $\dfrac{\pi}{6}$, $\dfrac{5\pi}{6}$ 20. $\dfrac{\pi}{6}$, $\dfrac{5\pi}{6}$

21. $109°28'$, $120°$, $240°$, $250°32'$ 22. $\dfrac{\pi}{6}$, $\dfrac{5\pi}{6}$, $\dfrac{3\pi}{2}$ 23. 0,

$\dfrac{\pi}{2}$, π, $\dfrac{3\pi}{2}$ 24. $\dfrac{\pi}{4}$, $\dfrac{\pi}{2}$, $\dfrac{5\pi}{4}$, $\dfrac{3\pi}{2}$ 25. 0, π 26. 0, $\dfrac{2\pi}{3}$, π, $\dfrac{4\pi}{3}$

27. $\dfrac{3\pi}{4}$, $\dfrac{7\pi}{4}$ 28. $\dfrac{\pi}{6}$, $\dfrac{\pi}{3}$, $\dfrac{5\pi}{6}$, $\dfrac{5\pi}{3}$ 29. $\dfrac{\pi}{4}$, $\dfrac{\pi}{2}$, $\dfrac{3\pi}{4}$, $\dfrac{5\pi}{4}$, $\dfrac{3\pi}{2}$, $\dfrac{7\pi}{4}$

30. 0, $\dfrac{\pi}{4}$, $\dfrac{3\pi}{4}$, π, $\dfrac{5\pi}{4}$, $\dfrac{7\pi}{4}$ 31. 0, $\dfrac{\pi}{2}$, π, $\dfrac{3\pi}{2}$ 32. 0, $\dfrac{\pi}{2}$, π, $\dfrac{3\pi}{2}$

33. 0 34. 0, $\dfrac{\pi}{2}$, π, $\dfrac{3\pi}{2}$ 35. $\dfrac{\pi}{6}$, $\dfrac{5\pi}{6}$, π 36. $\dfrac{2\pi}{3}$, $\dfrac{4\pi}{3}$, $\dfrac{3\pi}{2}$

37. $\dfrac{\pi}{6}$, $\dfrac{5\pi}{6}$, $\dfrac{7\pi}{6}$, $\dfrac{11\pi}{6}$ 38. $\dfrac{\pi}{4}$, $\dfrac{3\pi}{4}$, $\dfrac{5\pi}{4}$, $\dfrac{7\pi}{4}$ 39. $63°26'$,

$243°26', 101°19', 281°19'$ 40. $45°, 225°, 116°34', 296°34'$ 41. $\frac{2\pi}{3}, \frac{4\pi}{3}$ 42. $\frac{\pi}{6}, \frac{5\pi}{6}$ 43. $\frac{\pi}{12}, \frac{5\pi}{12}$ 44. $\frac{7\pi}{12}, \frac{23\pi}{12}$ 45. $\frac{\pi}{6}, \frac{3\pi}{2}$ 46. $\frac{7\pi}{4}$

Exercise Set 21–6, page 660

1. $B = 53°50', b = 37.2, c = 46.1$ 2. $B = 2°20', b = 0.396, c = 9.74$ 3. $A = 77°20', a = 436, c = 447$ 4. $A = 20°10', a = 46.6, c = 135$ 5. $B = 72°40', a = 4.24, c = 14.3$ 6. $B = 11°20', a = 6690, c = 6820$ 7. $A = 66°50', b = 0.0148, c = 0.0375$ 8. $A = 20°40', b = 0.0129, c = 0.0138$ 9. $B = 42°30', a = 35.6, b = 32.6$ 10. $B = 1°10', a = 3950, b = 80.6$ 11. $A = 7°40', a = 0.131, b = 0.973$ 12. $A = 33°30', a = 0.247, b = 0.0373$ 13. $A = 33°40', B = 56°20', c = 21.6$ 14. $A = 26°30', B = 63°30', c = 22.4$ 15. $A = 53°10', B = 36°50', b = 12.0$ 16. $A = 19°30', B = 70°30', b = 42.4$ 17. $A = 63°20', B = 26°40', a = 3.57$ 18. $A = 77°10', B = 12°50', a = 439$

Exercise Set 21–7, page 666

1. $C = 50°, a = 18.4, c = 16.3$ 2. $C = 70°, a = 29.5, c = 37.3$ 3. $C = 96°, b = 15.1, c = 20.3$ 4. $C = 80°, a = 74.2, c = 114$ 5. $C = 17°, a = 26.3, c = 10.5$ 6. $A = 30°, b = 27.7, c = 16.0$ 7. $A = 121°, a = 33.4, c = 14.0$ 8. $B = 26°, a = 17.2, c = 8.91$ 9. $B = 68°50', a = 32.3, b = 32.3$ 10. $A = 16°, a = 13.2, c = 34.2$ 11. $A = 12°20', C = 17°40', c = 4.25$ 12. $C = 48°40', B = 101°20', b = 11.8$ or $C = 131°20', B = 18°40', b = 3.84$ 13. $A = 20°16', B = 99°44', b = 34.19$ 14. $A = 38°36', C = 96°24', c = 23.88$ 15. $B = 56°20', C = 87°40', c = 40.8$ or $B = 123°40', C = 20°20', c = 14.2$ 16. $B = 41°10', A = 95°50', a = 40.8$ 17. $C = 44°40', B = 19°, b = 6.25$ 18. $B = 28°30', C = 103°40', c = 37.1$ 19. $B = 44°20', A = 74°30', a = 33.3$ 20. $A = 41°10', C = 80°10', c = 37.6$

Exercise Set 21–8, page 669

1. $c = 12.0, A = 20°40', B = 24°20'$ 2. $a = 47.6, B = 35°50', C = 28°10'$ 3. $a = 14.9, B = 23°40', C = 126°20'$ 4. $c = 11.4, A = 22°20', B = 37°40'$ 5. $a = 24.8, B = 20°40', C = 26°20'$ 6. $c = 13.7, A = 71°30', B = 48°30'$ 7. $b = 74.8, A = 95°30', C = 11°50'$ 8. $a = 55.6, B = 149°30', C = 6°$ 9. $A = 29°, B = 46°30', C = 104°30'$ 10. $A = 42°50', B = 61°, C = 76°10'$ 11. $A = 34°50', B = 58°50', C = 86°20'$ 12. $A = 44°, B = 52°40', C = 83°20'$ 13. $A = 36°10', B = 43°30', C = 100°20'$ 14. $A = 37°20', B = 37°20', C = 105°20'$ 15. $A = 73°40', B = 51°50', C = 54°30'$ 16. $A = 24°10', B = 30°40', C = 125°10'$ 17. $A = 25°40', B = 126°, C = 28°20'$ 18. $A = 33°40', B = 107°, C = 39°20'$

Exercise Set 21–9, page 674

53. $\sqrt{2}$ cis $60°$ and $\sqrt{2}$ cis $240°$ or $\sqrt{2}$ cis $\frac{\pi}{3}$ and $\sqrt{2}$ cis $\frac{4\pi}{3}$

54. $\sqrt{2}$ cis $105°$ and $\sqrt{2}$ cis $285°$ or $\sqrt{2}$ cis $\frac{7\pi}{12}$ and $\sqrt{2}$ cis $\frac{19\pi}{12}$ 55. cis $30°$, cos $150°$, and cis $270°$ or cis $\frac{\pi}{6}$, cis $\frac{5\pi}{6}$,

and cis $\frac{3\pi}{2}$ 56. cis $90°$, cis $210°$, and cis $330°$ or cis $\frac{\pi}{2}$, cis $\frac{7\pi}{6}$, and cis $\frac{11\pi}{6}$ 57. 2 cis $0°$, 2 cis $90°$, 2 cis $180°$, and 2 cis $270°$ or 2 cis 0, 2 cis $\frac{\pi}{2}$, 2 cis π, and 2 cis $\frac{3\pi}{2}$ 58. 2 cis $45°$, 2 cis $135°$, 2 cis $225°$, and 2 cis $315°$ or 2 cis $\frac{\pi}{4}$, 2 cis $\frac{3\pi}{4}$, 2 cis $\frac{5\pi}{4}$, and 2 cis $\frac{7\pi}{4}$ 59. $|z \cdot w| = |r_1 r_2$ cis $(\theta_1 + \theta_2)| = |r_1 r_2 \cos(\theta_1 + \theta_2) + r_1 r_2$ i sin $(\theta_1 + \theta_2)|$
$= \sqrt{r_1{}^2 r_2{}^2 \cos^2(\theta_1 + \theta_2) + r_1{}^2 r_2{}^2 \sin^2(\theta_1 + \theta_2)}$
$= \sqrt{r_1{}^2 r_2{}^2} = r_1 r_2$. $|z| \cdot |w| = |r_1$ cis $\theta_1| \cdot |r_2$ cis $\theta_2| = |r_1 \cos\theta_1 + r_1$ i sin $\theta_1| \cdot |r_2 \cos\theta_2 + r_2$ i sin $\theta_2| = \sqrt{r_1{}^2 \cos^2\theta_1 + r_1{}^2 \sin^2\theta_1} \cdot \sqrt{r_2{}^2 \cos^2\theta_2 + r_2{}^2 \sin^2\theta_2}$
$= \sqrt{r_1{}^2} \cdot \sqrt{r_2{}^2} = r_1 r_2$ 60. $\left|\frac{z}{w}\right| = \left|\frac{r_1}{r_2}$ cis $(\theta_1 - \theta_2)\right| = \left|\frac{r_1}{r_2} \cos(\theta_1 - \theta_2) - \frac{r_1}{r_2}$ i sin $(\theta_1 - \theta_2)\right| = \sqrt{\frac{r_1{}^2}{r_2{}^2} \cos^2(\theta_1 - \theta_2) + \frac{r_1{}^2}{r_2{}^2} \sin^2(\theta_1 - \theta_2)} = \sqrt{\frac{r_1{}^2}{r_2{}^2}} = \frac{r_1}{r_2}$. $\frac{|z|}{|w|} = \frac{|r_1 \text{ cis } \theta_1|}{|r_2 \text{ cis } \theta_2|} = \frac{|r_1 \cos\theta_1 + r_1 \text{ i sin } \theta_1|}{|r_2 \cos\theta_2 + r_2 \text{ i sin } \theta_2|} = \frac{\sqrt{r_1{}^2 \cos^2\theta_1 + r_1{}^2 \sin^2\theta_1}}{\sqrt{r_2{}^2 \cos^2\theta_2 + r_2{}^2 \sin^2\theta_2}} = \frac{\sqrt{r_1{}^2}}{\sqrt{r_2{}^2}} = \frac{r_1}{r_2}$ 61. $\sqrt[3]{68.4321}$, $\sqrt[3]{68.4321}$ cis $120°$, $\sqrt[3]{68.4321}$ cis $240°$ 62. $\sqrt[3]{456.86}$, $\sqrt[3]{456.86}$ cis $120°$, $\sqrt[3]{456.86}$ cis $240°$

Chapter 21 Review, page 676

7.

$\tan 2\theta$	$\frac{2\tan\theta}{1 - \tan^2\theta}$
$\tan(\theta + \theta)$	$\frac{2\tan\theta}{1 - \tan^2\theta}$
$\frac{\tan\theta + \tan\theta}{1 - \tan\theta\tan\theta}$	
$\frac{2\tan\theta}{1 - \tan^2\theta}$	

Chapter 21 Test, page 677

7.

$\tan\theta$	$\frac{\sin 2\theta}{1 + \cos 2\theta}$
$\tan\theta$	$\frac{2\sin\theta\cos\theta}{1 + (2\cos^2\theta - 1)}$
	$\frac{2\sin\theta\cos\theta}{2\cos^2\theta}$
	$\frac{\sin\theta}{\cos\theta}$
	$\tan\theta$